TEXAS STATE DIRECTORY

THE COMPREHENSIVE GUIDE TO THE DECISION-MAKERS IN TEXAS GOVERNMENT

Austin, Texas
2018

$49.95

Published by
Texas State Directory Press, Inc.
P.O. Box 12186
Austin, Texas 78711
512/477-5698
Toll Free 800/388-8075
FAX: 512/473-2447
www.txdirectory.com
Email: tsdpress@txdirectory.com

PREFACE

In today's age of Internet and cell phone apps, some turn to one of these digital sources and ignore traditional print media. Information is obtained in quick bursts and one has to search many sites to make the bits and pieces fit together. Contrary to that movement, the TEXAS STATE DIRECTORY remains the quickest and most accurate source for information for all forms of Texas government. For our clients that prefer the Internet or demand their information right up-to-the-minute, we suggest you supplement your purchase of the Directory with an online subscription to TEXAS STATE DIRECTORY ONLINE. Our goal is to make it easy for you to stay informed with the most current information available. You can order any of our products or online services securely online at www.txdirectory.com/catalog.

The first edition of the Texas State Directory was published in 1935 and it was updated bi-annually until 1979. The decision to publish annually was made due to the changing nature of and growing interest in Texas government. In 1981 we added the TEXAS LEGISLATIVE HANDBOOK, a pocket guide to the Legislature, and in 1983 we added the TEXAS LEGISLATIVE GUIDE, which gives Texans an inside look at the way the Texas Legislature functions. In 2004, we launched TEXAS STATE DIRECTORY ONLINE, which has all of the features of the printed Directory, but is updated daily. Our product line now contains the best reference sources for politically active and concerned Texans. Additionally mailing lists for individual offices are available and can be created and downloaded at http://lists.txdirectory.com.

The TEXAS STATE DIRECTORY remains the only true "almanac" of Texas government and the most comprehensive guide available to Texas decision-makers. Each year, thousands of new faces appear in Texas political offices and on state boards and commissions. The 61st (2018) edition contains over 3,000 changes from our 2017 book.

The TEXAS STATE DIRECTORY contains five principal sections, with appropriate subdivisions: 1) The State Section, with subsections devoted to the Executive Branch, the Legislative Branch, the Judicial Branch, and a compendium of Agencies, Boards and Commissions; 2) The County Section, with data concerning each of Texas' 254 counties and their public officials; 3) The City Section, with information about each incorporated municipality and their public officials; 4) The Federal Section, with listings of Texas' United States Senators, Representatives, and the Fifth Circuit Court of Appeals and 5) The Reference Section, including the Democratic and Republican Party officials, legislative reference tools, Capitol maps, and other information of general interest.

Contrary to the way many conduct their business these days, we still consider this a people-oriented, personal contact business, and our thanks go to all who provided updates to us in a timely and professional manner. As we begin our 83rd year of serving Texans, we look forward to serving you through this new edition of the TEXAS STATE DIRECTORY, as well as our other publications and services.

Julie Sayers, Publisher
Janet Miller, Marketing Director
Deena Zimmerhanzel, Business Manager
Scott P. Sayers, Jr., Consultant

CONTENTS

STATE

SECTION

STATE SECTION

The State Section of the TEXAS STATE DIRECTORY is designed as a comprehensive guide to every branch of state government and the elected and appointed officials in charge of each. The principal subdivisions of this section are: The Executive Branch; The Legislative Branch; The Judicial Branch; and Agencies, Boards, and Commissions. These reflect the three branches of government and the unique importance in Texas state government of the various agencies and Governor-appointed, citizen-controlled boards and commissions.

Within each of the major subsections there are further breakdowns presenting detailed information in the following order:

EXECUTIVE BRANCH
Governor's Office
Secretary of State
Executive Agencies

LEGISLATIVE BRANCH

Senate
Lieutenant Governor (President of the Texas Senate) and staff
Members of the Senate (including biographical information)
Seniority Leaders
Senators' Capitol Office and Telephone Numbers
Senate Standing Committees
Current Senate District Map
Senate Seating Chart
Senators and Representatives by District

House of Representatives
Speaker of the House of Representatives and staff
State Representatives (including biographical information)
Representatives' Capitol Office and Telephone Numbers
House of Representatives Standing Committees
House of Representatives Seating Chart
Current House of Representatives District Map
House Members in Order of Seniority
County Delegations
Agencies, Boards and Commissions relating to the Legislature

JUDICIAL BRANCH
Supreme Court of Texas
Texas Court of Criminal Appeals
Texas Court of Appeals
District Judges by Districts
Criminal District Courts
District Attorneys by County
Administrative Judicial Regions
Agencies, Boards and Commissions relating to the Judiciary

AGENCIES, BOARDS AND COMMISSIONS
Listed alphabetically under specific reference word, as:
Agriculture, Texas Department of

EXECUTIVE
BRANCH

GOVERNOR'S OFFICE

P.O. Box 12428, Austin 78711 - State Capitol Bldg., 1100 Congress, Room 2S.1
Austin 78701 • 512/463-2000 • 800/843-5789 • *FAX: 512/463-1849*
www.gov.texas.gov • Agency # 301

GREG ABBOTT(R) - 48th Governor of Texas, 12-31-2018

Spouse: Cecilia

Born November 13, 1957 in Wichita Falls, Texas; Raised in Duncanville, Texas. B.B.A. Finance-University of Texas at Austin, 1981; J.D.-Vanderbilt University Law School, 1984. Practiced law with Butler & Binion-Houston, 1984-92. Judge 129th State District Court in Houston, 1992-96; Named "Trial Judge of the Year" by the Texas Association of Civil Trial and Appellate Specialists. Texas Supreme Court Justice, 1996-2001. Named "Jurist of the Year" by Texas Review of Law & Politics and Appellate Specialists; and "Appellate Judge of the Year" from the Texas Chapter of the American Board of Trial Advocates. 50th Attorney General of Texas, December 2002-2014; Texas' longest-serving Attorney General. Governor of Texas, January 1, 2015 to present.

Governor of Texas	The Honorable Greg Abbott	512/463-2000
EXECUTIVE OFFICE		**FAX: 512/463-5571**
Chief of Staff	Luis Saenz	(512) 463-1762
Deputy Chief of Staff &		
Communications Director	Matt Hirsch	(512) 463-1762
Deputy Chief of Staff	David Whitley	(512) 463-1762
Counselor and COO	Reed Clay	(512) 463-1762
Senior Advisor for Fiscal Affairs	Tommy Williams	(512) 463-1762
Senior Advisor and Policy Director	John Colyandro	(512) 463-1762
Senior Advisor for State Operations	Steven Albright	(512) 463-1762
Executive Aide	Jim Dwyer	(512) 936-0832
Executive Assistant	Morgan Stewart	(512) 463-1762
SCHEDULING		**FAX: (512) 475-2349**
Director	Kim Snyder	(512) 463-7210
OFFICE OF THE FIRST LADY		**FAX: (512) 475-2598**
Senior Advisor to the Governor		
for the Office of the First Lady	Lauren Clay	(512) 475-2324
Senior Advisor to the First Lady	Chelsea Holden	(512) 475-2324
ADMINISTRATION		**FAX: (512) 463-8464**
Director	Jordan Hale	(512) 463-2000
APPOINTMENTS		**FAX: (512) 475-2576**
Director	Peggy Venable	(512) 463-1828
LEGISLATIVE		**FAX: (512) 475-2211**
Director	Walter Fisher	(512) 463-1830
BUDGET		**FAX: (512) 463-1975**
Director	Sarah Hicks	(512) 475-2171
COMMUNICATIONS		**FAX: (512) 463-1847**
Director	Matt Hirsch	(512) 463-1826
FINANCIAL SERVICES		**FAX: (512) 463-4114**
Director	Theresa Boland	(512) 936-0166

Governor's Office Cont.

POLICY   FAX: (512) 463-1975
Director   John Colyandro ....(512) 463-1762

GENERAL COUNSEL   FAX: (512) 463-1932
General Counsel   Andrew Oldham ....(512) 463-1788

INTERNAL AUDIT   FAX: (512) 475-2598
Director   Rene Valadez ....(512) 936-2601

CONSTITUENT COMMUNICATION   FAX: (512) 463-1849
Director   Greg Davidson ....(512) 463-1800

CRIMINAL JUSTICE GRANTS   FAX: (512) 475-3155
Director   Camille Cain ....(512) 463-1919

HOMELAND SECURITY GRANTS   FAX: (512) 463-3155
Director   Aimee Snoddy ....(512) 463-1919

ECONOMIC DEVELOPMENT & TOURISM   FAX: (512) 936-0303
Director   Bryan Daniel ....(512) 936-0101

BUSINESS AND COMMUNITY DEVELOPMENT   FAX: (512) 936-0303
Director   Nicole Ryf ....(512) 936-0483

TEXAS TOURISM   FAX: (512) 936-0450
Director   Brad Smyth ....(512) 936-0100

MILITARY PREPAREDNESS   FAX: (512) 475-0108
Director   Keith Graf ....(512) 936-0100

GOVERNOR'S COMMISSION FOR WOMEN
Director   Position Vacant ....(512) 936-0101

GOVERNOR'S CENTER FOR MANAGEMENT & DEVELOPMENT
Director   Joyce Sparks ....(512) 475-8100

GOVERNOR'S COMMITTEE ON PEOPLE WITH DISABILITIES   FAX: (512) 463-5745
Director   Ron Lucey ....(512) 463-5739

TEXAS FILM COMMISSION   FAX: (512) 463-4114
Director   Position Vacant ....(512) 463-9200

TEXAS MUSIC OFFICE   FAX: (512) 463-4114
Director   Brendon Anthony ....(512) 463-6666

TEXAS WORKFORCE INVESTMENT COUNCIL   FAX: (512) 936-8118
Director   Lee Rector ....(512) 936-8100

OFFICE OF STATE-FEDERAL RELATIONS   FAX: (512) 463-1975
Program Director   Jerry Strickland ....(512) 463-4375

SECRETARY OF STATE

P.O. Box 12697, Austin 78711-2697 - State Capitol, Room 1E.8, Austin 78701
512/463-5770 • *FAX: 512/475-2761*
www.sos.state.tx.us • Agency # 307

Tenure - Term of Appointing Governor

ROLANDO PABLOS (R) – 111th Secretary of State

Spouse: Dr. Laura San Martin

Secretary Pablos has a long history of public service including numerous local, state and federal appointments. He recently served as commissioner on two state regulatory agencies: the Public Utility Commission of Texas and the Texas Racing Commission.

He was the founding CEO of the El Paso-based Borderplex Alliance. As a bi-national economic development organization, Borderplex helped promote prosperity on both sides of the US-Mexico border.

Secretary Pablos also served as Honorary Consul to Spain, working to ensure the formation and development of business and diplomatic relationships.

After obtaining a bachelor's degree in biology from St. Mary's University, Secretary Pablos earned a master's degree in business administration from the University of Texas at San Antonio and a master's degree in hospitality management from the University of Houston. He earned a law degree from St. Mary's University School of Law. Secretary of State, February 2017 to present.

Secretary of State	Rolando Pablos	512/463-5770
Deputy Secretary of State	Coby Shorter, III	512/463-5770

EXECUTIVE DIVISION

General Counsel	Lindsey Aston	(512) 463-5770
Executive Assistant/Scheduler	Linda Payne	(512) 463-5702
Special Assistant	Anthony Giuliani	(512) 463-5770
Assistant Secretary of State for Mexican and Border Affairs	Avdiel Huerta	(512) 463-5770
Director of Border Affairs	Enriqueta Caballero	(956) 969-9075
Director of Communications	Sam Taylor	(512) 463-9981
Director of Protocol	Cammy Jones	(512) 463-5268

BUSINESS & PUBLIC FILINGS DIVISION
James E. Rudder Building
1019 Brazos Street
Austin, TX 78701

Division Director	Carmen Flores	(512) 463-5588
Deputy Director	Mike Powell	(512) 463-9856
Dir. of Government Filings	Robert Sumners	(512) 463-5562
Authentications/Notaries Public	Sandy Slaughter	(512) 463-5730
Texas Register	Jill Ledbetter	(512) 475-9623
Service of Process	Venita Okpegbue	(512) 463-6653

Secretary of State Cont.

ELECTIONS DIVISION
James E. Rudder Building
1019 Brazos Street
Austin, TX 78701

Division Director	Keith Ingram	(512) 463-9871
General Law	Position Vacant	(512) 475-2821
Voter Registration	Betsy Schonhoff	(512) 463-5653
Elections Funds Management	Dan Glotzer	(512) 463-9861
Elections Administration	Position Vacant	(512) 463-3204

ADMINISTRATIVE SERVICES DIVISION
James E. Rudder Building
1019 Brazos Street
Austin, TX 78701

Division Director	Vincent Houston	(512) 463-5593
Director of Financial Mgmt.	Louis Ng	(512) 463-5594
Human Resources	Dara Stone	(512) 463-5592
Operating Support	Shuford Scott	(512) 463-5607

INFORMATION TECHNOLOGY
James E. Rudder Building
1019 Brazos Street
Austin, TX 78701

Division Director	W. Scott Brandt	(512) 463-5640

The secretary of state serves as the state's chief elections officer, the governor's liaison on border and Mexican affairs, and Texas' chief protocol officer for state and international matters. The Secretary of State's Office also serves as the formal repository for official and business records, publishes government rules and regulations, keeps the state seal and attests to the governor's signature on official documents.

DISABILITIES, GOVERNOR'S COMMITTEE ON PEOPLE WITH*

P.O. Box 12428, Austin 78711-2428 • 512/463-5739 • 7-1-1• *FAX: 512/463-5745*
www.gov.texas.gov/disabilities

Aaron W. Bangor Ph.D	Chair, Austin, 2-1-18
Ellen M. Bauman	Board Member, Joshua, 2-1-19
Nancy M. Clemmer	Board Member, Austin, 2-1-18
Elizabeth Dickey	Board Member, Austin, 2-1-19
Heather C. Griffith-Dhanjal	Board Member, Fort Worth, 2-1-18
Archer Hadley	Board Member, Austin, 2-1-19
Saul Herrera	Board Member, Midland, 2-1-19
Faye Kuo, J.D.	Board Member, San Antonio, 2-1-18
Richard Martinez	Board Member, San Antonio, 2-1-18
Linda Millstone	Board Member, Austin, 2-1-19
Dylan Rafaty	Board Member, Plano, 2-1-19
Marco Trevino	Board Member, Edinburg, 2-1-18

STAFF:

Executive Director	Ronald Lucey . . . . .512/463-5742 / *Fax: 512/463-5745*

*Subject to the Texas Sunset Act; will be reviewed in 2027.

FILM COMMISSION, TEXAS

P.O. Box 12428, Austin 78711-2428 • 512/463-9200 • *FAX: 512/463-4114*
www.gov.texas.gov/film

STAFF:

Director	Position Vacant
Office Manager	Katie Kelly
Senior Production Consultant	Lindsey Ashley
Production Consultant	Ali Nichols
Production and Community Relations Specialist	Kim LeBlanc
Production Assistant	Position Vacant
Animation & Video Game Liaison	Position Vacant
Incentive Program Manager	Stephanie Whallon
Production Incentives Specialist	Michelle Habecker
Production Incentives Specialist	Tara Khanna
Senior Marketing Coordinator	Minh Vu
Marketing Coordinator	Taylor Hertsenberg

GOVERNOR'S COMMISSION FOR WOMEN
1100 San Jacinto Blvd., Rm. 1.212
P.O. Box 12428, Austin 78711-2428 • 512/475-2615 • *FAX: 512/463-1832*
www.gov.texas.gov/women

15 Members - 2 Years

Catherine Susser	Chair, Corpus Christi, 12-31-17
Estela Avery	Commissioner, Fredericksburg, 12-31-17
Tina Yturria Buford	Commissioner, Harlingen, 12-31-17
Jennifer Chiang	Commissioner, Sugar Land, 12-31-17
Starr Corbin	Commissioner, Georgetown, 12-31-17
Debbie Gustafson	Commissioner, Wichita Falls, 12-31-17
Karen Harris	Commissioner, Lakehills, 12-31-17
Amy Henderson	Commissioner, Amarillo, 12-31-17
Nancy Ann Hunt	Commissioner, Dallas, 12-31-17
Karen Manning	Commissioner, Houston, 12-31-17
Imelda Navarro	Commissioner, Laredo, 12-31-17
Rienke Radler	Commissioner, Fort Worth, 12-31-17
Jinous Ruhani	Commissioner, Austin, 12-31-17
Laura Koenig Young	Commissioner, Tyler, 12-31-17
Vacant	

STAFF:

Executive Director	Position Vacant. . . . . . . 512/475-2615 / *Fax: 512/463-1832*

MUSIC OFFICE, TEXAS
1100 San Jacinto, Suite 3.418, P.O. Box 12428, Austin 78711-2428
512/463-6666 • *FAX: 512/463-4114*
www.texasmusicoffice.com

STAFF:

Director	Brendon Anthony	512/463-6666
Digital Media Specialist	Marc Fort	512/463-6666
Program Specialist	Stephen Ray	512/463-6666

TEXAS MILITARY DEPARTMENT
P.O. Box 5218, Camp Mabry, Austin 78763-5218
512/782-5001 • *FAX: 512/782-5578*
www.tmd.texas.gov • Agency # 401

3 Members - 2 Years

Major General John F. Nichols	Adjutant General of Texas, Austin, 1-31-18	512/782-5006
Brigadier General Dawn Ferrell	Deputy Adjutant General for Air, Wichita Falls	512/782-5007
Brigadier General Tracy Norris	Deputy Adjutant General for Army, Austin	512/782-5007

STAFF:

Texas State Guard	Vacant Position	512/782-5255
Chief of Staff to the Adjutant General	Colonel Gregory Chaney	512/782-5022
Director of Government Affairs	Major Malcolm Warbrick	512/782-5531
Public Affairs Officer	Lieutenant Colonel Travis Walters	512/782-5620
General Counsel	Lieutenant Colonel Sonya Batchelor	512/782-5057
Executive Director	Mr. Bill Wilson	512/782-5688

The adjutant general is commander of the Texas Military Forces and subordinate only to the governor in matters pertaining to its three branches, the Texas Army National Guard, Texas Air National Guard and Texas State Guard.

---

* Subject to the Texas Sunset Act; will be reviewed in 2019.

TEXAS MILITARY PREPAREDNESS COMMISSION (TMPC)
Office of the Governor, P.O. Box 12428, Austin 78711 • 512/475-1475
gov.texas.gov/organization/military

Major General Kevin Pottinger, USAF (Ret.)	Chair, Keller, 2-1-21
Carol A. Bonds	Commissioner, San Angelo, 2-1-19
Garry Bradford	Commissioner, Corpus Christi, 2-1-21
Darrell Coleman	Commissioner, 2-1-19
Tom Duncavage	Commissioner, League City, 2-1-23
Woody Gilliland	Commissioner, Abilene, 2-1-23
Dennis L. Lewis	Commissioner, Texarkana, 2-1-21
Kenneth Sheets	Commissioner, Mesquite, 2-1-21
William Shine	Commissioner, Harker Heights, 2-1-19
Annie L. Sobel, M.D.	Commissioner, Lubbock, 2-1-23
Shannalea Taylor	Commissioner, Del Rio, 2-1-21
A. F. "Tom" Thomas	Commissioner, El Paso, 2-1-23
James Whitmore	Commissioner, New Braunfels, 2-1-23
Sen. Donna Campbell, M.D.	Ex Officio Member, Texas State Senator
Rep. Roland Gutierrez	Ex Officio Member, Texas House Representative
Major General John F. Nichols	Ex Officio Member, Austin, Adjutant General of Texas

STAFF:

Director	Keith Graf . . . . .512/475-1475 / *Fax: 512/936-0080*
Program Manager	Alexandra Taylor . . . . . . .512/936-0100 / *Fax: 512/936-0080*

Established in 2003 by the 78th Texas Legislature and placed in the Governor's Office of Economic Development and Tourism in 2009, the Texas Military Preparedness Commission's (TMPC) goal is to preserve, protect, expand, and attract new military missions, assets, and installations. Additionally, the TMPC encourages defense-related businesses to expand or relocate in Texas.

WORKFORCE INVESTMENT COUNCIL, TEXAS*
1100 San Jacinto, Suite 1.100, Austin 78701
512/936-8100 *FAX: 512/936-8118*
gov.texas.gov/organization/twic

19 Members - 6 Years

Wes Jurey	Chair, Arlington, 9-1-19
Sharla Hotchkiss	Vice Chair, Midland, 9-1-17
Mark Barberena	Board Member, Fort Worth, 9-1-19
Robert Cross	Board Member, Houston, 9-1-15
Mark Dunn	Board Member, Lufkin, 9-1-19
Dr. Carmen Olivas Graham	Board Member, El Paso, 9-1-17
Thomas Halbouty	Board Member, Southlake, 9-1-19
Richard Hatfield	Board Member, Austin, 9-1-15
Robert Hawkins	Board Member, Bellmead, 9-1-17
Larry Jeffus	Board Member, Garland, 9-1-15
Paul Jones	Board Member, Austin, 9-1-17
Dr. Richard Rhodes	Board Member, Austin, 9-1-19
Joyce Delores Taylor	Board Member, Houston, 9-1-15
Vacant	Board Member
Bryan Daniel	Ex Officio Member, Executive Director, Economic Dev.
Mike Morath	Ex Officio Member, Commissioner, TX Education Agency
Dr. Raymund Paredes	Ex Officio Member, Commissioner, TX Higher Ed. Coord. Bd.
Charles Smith	Ex Officio Member, Exec. Comm., TX Health and Human Svcs. Comm.
Larry Temple	Ex Officio Member, Executive Director, TX Workforce Comm.

STAFF:

Director	Lee Rector	512/936-8102
Deputy Director	Raul Ortiz	512/936-8103
Program Specialist	Kaki Leyens	512/936-8108
Executive Assistant	Denise Curtis	512/936-8107
Program Specialist	Anne Dorsey	512/936-8106
Planner	Kristin McEntyre	512/936-8113
Research Specialist	David Mass	512/936-8111
Editor	Leslie McCormick	512/936-8105

*Subject to the Texas Sunset Act; will be reviewed in 2027.

LEGISLATIVE BRANCH

A COMPLETE GUIDE TO THE 85TH LEGISLATURE

THE HANDBOOK CONTAINS:
- *PHOTOS OF TEXAS LEGISLATORS*
- *PARTY AFFILIATION*
- *OFFICE LOCATION & PHONE NUMBERS*
- *DISTRICT REPRESENTATION*
- *COMMITTEE ASSIGNMENTS*
- *SEATING CHARTS*
- *CAPITOL COMPLEX MAP*
- *GOVERNOR'S STAFF*

ORDER FROM TEXAS STATE DIRECTORY PRESS:
WWW.TXDIRECTORY.COM
GROUP DISCOUNTS AVAILABLE

LIEUTENANT GOVERNOR'S OFFICE
The Capitol, Room 2E.13, P.O. Box 12068, Austin 78711-2068 • 512/463-0001
FAX: 512/936-6700 • www.senate.state.tx.us

DAN PATRICK (R) - 42nd Lieutenant Governor of Texas.
President of the Senate.
Spouse: Jan

B.A.-University of Maryland, 1972. A native of Baltimore, Dan has been a Texan since joining Houston CBS affiliate KHOU TV in 1979. In 1988 he launched talk radio KSEV. Twice elected to the Texas Senate from District 7 in Houston and Northwest Harris County, Mr. Patrick served as Chairman of the Education Committee during the 83rd Legislative Session.

Lieutenant Governor of Texas, January 2015-present.

LIEUTENANT GOVERNOR'S STAFF
Chief of Staff	Logan Spence	512/463-0001
Senior Advisor	Sherry Sylvester	512/463-0001
Legislative Coordinator	Colby Beuck	512/463-0001
Scheduler	Cylynda Caviness	512/463-0001
Press Secretary	Alejandro Garcia	512/463-0715
Parliamentarian	Karina Casari Davis	512/463-0248
Budget Director	Mike Morrissey	512/463-0079
Policy Director	John Gibbs	512/463-2525
General Counsel	Darrell Davila	512/463-0295

SENATE STAFF
Secretary of the Senate	Patsy Spaw	512/463-0100
Administrative Assistant	Nanci Longoria	512/463-0100
Sergeant-at-Arms	Rick DeLeon	512/463-0200
Journal Clerk	Polly Emerson	512/463-0050
Calendar Clerk	Tracy Ortiz	512/463-0060
Enrolling Clerk	Patience Worrel	512/463-0321
Media Services	Jill Turetsky	512/463-0300
Committee Coordinator	Scott Caffey	512/463-0070
Doorkeeper	Austin Osborn	512/463-0100

Additional Numbers:

Auditor	512/463-0404	Senate Payroll	512/463-0444
Bill Distribution	512/463-0252	Senate Purchasing	512/463-0222
Capitol Info./Guide Service	512/463-0063	Senate Research	512/463-0087
Human Resources	512/463-0400	Staff Services	512/463-0430
Post Office	512/463-0303	Support Services	512/463-0333
Publications/Printing	512/463-0080		

Information relating to Senators is listed in the following form:

NAME (Spouse), Party, Hometown **Capitol Telephone**
Profession, Education, Birthdate. Legislative Experience:
H - Dates of tenure in the Texas House; S - tenure in Texas Senate
District Business Address and Telephone; *FAX Number*
District Number and Counties Represented
Standing Committee Assignments

Senator's Capitol Office and Telephone Numbers
Committee Membership
Current Senate District Map and Seating Chart
Senators by District

The Mailing Address for all Senators in Austin is:

> P.O. Box 12068
> Austin, Texas 78711-2068

Email address
for all Senators: firstname.lastname@senate.texas.gov
Example: jane.nelson@senate.texas.gov

TEXAS STATE SENATORS

PAUL BETTENCOURT (Susan), R-Houston   **512/463-0107**

CEO Bettencourt Tax Advisors, LLC. BS, Engineering- Texas A&M
  University. 10-20-1958. S-2015-present.
11451 Katy Freeway, Suite 209, Houston 77079 • 713/464-0282
  Fax: 713/461-0108

Dist. 7 - Harris (20%)

Government Reform-C; Intergovernmental Relations-VC; Education;
  Finance; Higher Education

‡BRIAN BIRDWELL (Mel), R-Granbury   **512/463-0122**

Retired Military. 11-3-1961. S-2010-present.
900 Austin Avenue, Suite 500, Waco 76701 • 254/772-6225
  Fax: 254/776-2843

Dist. 22 - Bosque, Ellis, Falls, Hill, Hood, Johnson, McLennan,
  Navarro, Somervell, Tarrant (5%)

Nominations-C; Criminal Justice; Finance; State Affairs

‡DAWN BUCKINGHAM, M.D. (Ed), R-Lakeway   **512/463-0124**

Ophthalmologist. BS, University of Texas at Austin Magna cum Laude;
  MD-UT Medical Branch at Galveston. 2-21-1968. S-2017 to present.
819 Water St., Ste. 125, Kerrville 78028 • 830/257-0350
  Fax: 830/257-0424

Dist. 24 - Bandera, Bell, Blanco, Brown, Burnet, Callahan, Comanche,
  Coryell, Gillespie, Hamilton, Kerr, Lampasas, Llano, Mills, San Saba,
  Taylor (70%), Travis (5%)

Health & Human Services; Higher Education; Nominations;
  Veteran Affairs & Border Security

KONNI BURTON (Phil), R-Colleyville   **512/463-0110**

Consultant. BBA, Marketing-University of North Texas.
  4-15-1963. S-2015-present.
933 West Weatherford Street, Suite 203, Fort Worth 76102
  817/882-8157; *Fax: 817/882-8539*

Dist. 10 - Tarrant (46%)

Administration-VC; Criminal Justice; Health & Human Services;
  Natural Resources & Economic Development

TEXAS STATE SENATORS

DONNA CAMPBELL, M.D. (Stan), R-New Braunfels **512/463-0125**

Physician. BS-Central State University; MN-Texas Woman's Univ.;
  MD-Texas Tech Health Science Center. 9-17-1954. S-2013-present.
1902 E. Common St., New Braunfels 78130 • 830/626-0065

Dist. 25 - Bexar (24%), Comal, Guadalupe (62%), Hays (69%),
  Kendall, Travis (7%)

Veteran Affairs & Border Security-C; Business & Commerce;
  Education; Intergovernmental Relations

‡BRANDON CREIGHTON, R-Conroe   **512/463-0104**

Attorney/Real Estate Developer. BA, Government-UT at Austin;
  JD-Oklahoma City University School of Law. 8-5-1970.
  H-2007-2014; S-2014-present.
2829 Technology Forest, Ste. 240, The Woodlands 77381
  281/292-4128; *Fax: 281/292-6253*

Dist. 4 - Chambers, Galveston (1%), Harris (3%), Jefferson,
  Montgomery (86%)

Business & Commerce-VC; Agriculture, Water & Rural Affairs;
  Criminal Justice; Government Reform; State Affairs; Transportation

CRAIG ESTES (Jennifer), R-Wichita Falls   **512/463-0130**

Businessman, Retired. BS, Business Admin.-Oral Roberts University;
  Harvard Business School. 8-20-1953. S-2001-present.
2525 Kell Blvd., Suite 302, Wichita Falls 76308 • 940/689-0191

Dist. 30 - Archer, Clay, Collin (15%), Cooke, Denton (17%), Erath,
  Grayson, Jack, Montague, Palo Pinto, Parker, Wichita, Wise, Young

Natural Resources & Economic Development-C;
  Business & Commerce; Nominations; State Affairs

‡ SYLVIA R. GARCIA, D-Houston   **512/463-0106**

Attorney. BA, Social Work-Texas Woman's University;
  JD-Thurgood Marshall School of Law at Texas Southern University.
  9-6-1950. S-2013-present.
13301 East Freeway, Houston 77015 • 713/453-5100
  Fax: 713/453-8800

Dist. 6 - Harris (20%)

Criminal Justice; Intergovernmental Relations;
  Natural Resources & Economic Development; Transportation

‡ Term expires 2021, all others 2019
( ) Spouse   **www.txdirectory.com/online/txsenate**

TEXAS STATE SENATORS

BOB HALL (Kay), R-Edgewood   **512/463-0102**
BS Engineering-The Citadel, The Military College of South Carolina
  1964; Officer, US Air Force. 3-5-1942. S-2015-present.
6537 Horizon Road, Suite B-1, Rockwall 75032 • 972/722-3131
  Fax: 972/722-3132

Dist. 2 - Dallas (17%), Delta, Fannin, Hopkins, Hunt, Kaufman,
  Rains, Rockwall, Van Zandt

Transportation-VC; Agriculture, Water & Rural Affairs; Education;
  Veteran Affairs & Border Security

KELLY G. HANCOCK (Robin), R-N. Richland Hills   **512/463-0109**
Independent Business Owner. BBA-Baylor University. 12-2-1963.
  H-2007-2013; S-2013-present.
9121 Belshire Drive, Suite 200, North Richland Hills 76182
  817/514-3804; *Fax: 817/514-3806*

Dist. 9 - Dallas (9%), Tarrant (34%)

Business & Commerce-C; Finance; Government Reform;
  Natural Resources & Economic Development; Transportation

‡**JUAN "CHUY" HINOJOSA**, D-McAllen   **512/463-0120**
Attorney. BS-Pan American University; JD-Georgetown University.
  3-7-1946. H-1981-91; 1997-2002; S-2002-present.
612 Nolana, Suite 410-B, McAllen 78504 • 956/972-1841
  Fax: 956/664-0602

Dist. 20 - Brooks, Hidalgo (58%), Jim Wells, Nueces (99%)

Finance-VC; Agriculture, Water & Rural Affairs;
  Natural Resources & Economic Development; Transportation

DON HUFFINES (Mary Catherine), R-Dallas   **512/463-0116**
Real Estate Developer, Huffines Communities. BBA, Finance-Univ. of
  Texas at Austin, 1981. 4-26-1958. S-2015-present.
8222 Douglas Avenue, Suite 675, Dallas 75225 • 214/239-6131

Dist. 16 - Dallas (34%)

Veteran Affairs & Border Security-VC; Administration;
  Education; Intergovernmental Relations;
  Natural Resources & Economic Development

‡ Term expires 2021, all others 2019
( ) Spouse
www.txdirectory.com/online/txsenate

TEXAS STATE SENATORS

JOAN HUFFMAN (Keith), R-Houston   **512/463-0117**

Attorney. BA-Louisiana State University-1979; JD-South Texas
  School of Law-1984. 8-17-1956. S-2009-present.
P.O. Box 541774, Houston 77254 • 281/980-3500

Dist. 17 - Brazoria (31%), Fort Bend (32%), Harris (13%)

State Affairs-C; Criminal Justice-VC; Finance

‡BRYAN HUGHES, R-Mineola   **512/463-0101**

Attorney. BBA-University of Texas at Tyler, 1992;
  JD-Baylor University School of Law, 1995. 7-21-1969.
  H-2003-2017; S- 2017-present.
100 Independence Place, Suite 301, Tyler 75703 • 903/581-1776

Dist. 1 - Bowie, Camp, Cass, Franklin, Gregg, Harrison, Lamar,
  Marion, Morris, Panola, Red River, Rusk, Smith, Titus, Upshur,
  Wood

State Affairs-VC; Administration; Criminal Justice; Education

‡LOIS W. KOLKHORST (Jim), R-Brenham   **512/463-0118**

Business Owner/Investor. BS-Texas Christian University. 11-4-1964.
  H-2001-2014; S-2014-present.
5606 N. Navarro, #300X, Victoria 77904 • 361/573-7300

Dist. 18 - Aransas, Austin, Burleson, Calhoun, Colorado, De Witt,
  Fayette, Fort Bend (49%), Goliad, Gonzales, Harris (1%), Jackson,
  Lavaca, Lee, Matagorda, Nueces (1%), Refugio, Victoria, Waller,
  Washington, Wharton

Administration-C; Agriculture, Water & Rural Affairs; Finance;
  Health & Human Services; Transportation

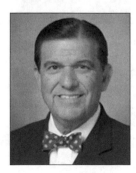

‡EDDIE LUCIO, JR. (Minnie), D-Brownsville   **512/463-0127**

Advertising Executive. BS-Pan American University. 1-20-1946.
  H-1986-90; S-1991-present.
7 North Park Plaza, Brownsville 78521 • 956/548-0227
  Fax: 956/548-0440

Dist. 27 - Cameron, Hidalgo (42%), Kenedy, Kleberg, Willacy

Intergovernmental Relations-C; Education-VC; Government Reform;
  State Affairs; Veteran Affairs & Border Security

‡ Term expires 2021, all others 2019
( ) Spouse

TEXAS STATE SENATORS

‡JOSÉ MENÉNDEZ (Nicole), D-San Antonio   **512/463-0126**

VP, Director of Multicultural Markets. BA, BBA-Southern Methodist
  University. 3-11-1969. H-2015-present.
4522 Fredericksburg Road, A-3, San Antonio 78201 • 210/733-6604

Dist. 26 - Bexar (47%)

Criminal Justice; Higher Education; Intergovernmental Relations;
  Nominations

‡BORRIS L. MILES (Cydonii), D-Houston   **512/463-0113**

Insurance and Real Estate Developer. BS, Criminal Justice-
  Sam Houston State University. 10-29-1965.
  H-2007-2009, 2011-2017; S-2017-present.
5302 Almeda Road, Suite A, Houston 77004 • 713/665-8322
  Fax: 713/665-0009

Dist. 13 - Fort Bend (19%), Harris (17%)

Agriculture, Water & Rural Affairs; Health & Human Services;
  Natural Resources & Economic Development; Nominations

‡JANE NELSON (J. Michael), R-Flower Mound   **512/463-0112**

Businesswoman. BS-University of North Texas. 10-5-1951.
  S-1993-present.
1225 South Main St., Suite 100, Grapevine 76051 • 817/424-3446
  Fax: 817/488-6648

Dist. 12 - Denton (83%), Tarrant (15%)

Finance-C; State Affairs

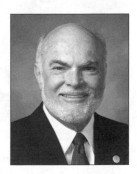

ROBERT NICHOLS (Donna), R-Jacksonville   **512/463-0103**

Engineer. BS, Engineering-Lamar University, 1968. 11-25-1944.
  S-2007-present.
329 Neches St., Jacksonville 75766 • 903/589-3003; *Fax: 903/589-0203*

Dist. 3 - Anderson, Angelina, Cherokee, Hardin, Henderson, Houston,
  Jasper, Liberty, Montgomery (14%), Nacogdoches, Newton, Orange,
  Polk, Sabine, San Augustine, San Jacinto, Shelby, Trinity, Tyler

Transportation-C; Administration; Business & Commerce; Finance

TEXAS STATE SENATORS

‡ **CHARLES PERRY** (Jacklyn), R-Lubbock   **512/463-0128**

CPA, Land Developer. BBA Accounting/Management/Information Syst.-
Texas Tech University, 1984. 3-9-1962. H-2001-2014;
S-2014-present.
11003 Quaker Avenue, #101, Lubbock 79424 • 806/783-9934

Dist. 28 - Baylor, Borden, Childress, Coke, Coleman, Concho, Cottle, Crane,
Crosby, Dawson, Dickens, Eastland, Fisher, Floyd, Foard, Garza, Hale,
Hardeman, Haskell, Hockley, Irion, Jones, Kent, Kimble, King, Knox,
Lamb, Lubbock, Lynn, Mason, McCulloch, Menard, Mitchell, Motley,
Nolan, Reagan, Runnels, Schleicher, Scurry, Shackelford, Stephens,
Sterling, Stonewall, Sutton, Taylor (30%), Terry, Throckmorton,
Tom Green, Upton, Ward, Wilbarger

Agriculture, Water & Rural Affairs-C; Criminal Justice;
Government Reform; Health & Human Services; Transportation

‡**JOSÉ R. RODRÌGUEZ** (Carmen), D-El Paso   **512/463-0129**

Former El Paso County Attorney. BA, Government-Pan American
University, 1971; JD-National Law Center at George Washington
University, 1974. 3-1-1948. S-2011-present.
100 N. Ochoa St., Ste. A, El Paso 79901 • 915/351-3500
Fax: 915/351-3579

Dist. 29 - Culberson, El Paso, Hudspeth, Jeff Davis, Presidio

Agriculture, Water & Rural Affairs-VC;
Natural Resources & Economic Development; Transportation;
Veteran Affairs & Border Security

CHARLES SCHWERTNER, M.D. (Belinda), R-Georgetown
          512/463-0105

Orthopedic Surgeon. BS, Pharmacy-University of Texas at Austin;
MD-UT Medical Branch. 5-29-1970. H-2011-2013; S-2013-present.
3000 Briarcrest Drive, Suite 202, Bryan 77802 • 979/776-0222
Fax: 979/776-0220

Dist. 5 - Brazos, Freestone, Grimes, Leon, Limestone, Madison,
Milam, Robertson, Walker, Williamson

Health & Human Services-C; Business & Commerce; Finance;
State Affairs

‡ Term expires 2021, all others 2019
( ) Spouse

TEXAS STATE SENATORS

KEL SELIGER (Nancy), R-Amarillo **512/463-0131**

Businessman. Dartmouth College. 6-16-1953. S-2004-present.
410 S. Taylor, Suite 1600; P.O. Box 9155, Amarillo 79105-9155
  806/374-8994; *Fax: 806/374-4607*

Dist. 31 - Andrews, Armstrong, Bailey, Briscoe, Carson, Castro, Cochran,
  Collingsworth, Dallam, Deaf Smith, Donley, Ector, Gaines, Glasscock,
  Gray, Hall, Hansford, Hartley, Hemphill, Howard, Hutchinson,
  Lipscomb, Loving, Martin, Midland, Moore, Ochiltree, Oldham, Parmer,
  Potter, Randall, Roberts, Sherman, Swisher, Wheeler, Winkler, Yoakum

Higher Education-C; Education; Finance;
  Natural Resources & Economic Development

‡LARRY TAYLOR (Kerri), R-Friendswood **512/463-0111**

Independent Insurance Agent. BBA-Baylor University, 1982.
  6-25-1960. H-2003-2013; S-2013-present.
6117 Broadway, Suite 122, Pearland 77581 • 281/485-9800
  Fax: 281/485-9804

Dist. 11 - Brazoria (69%), Galveston (99%), Harris (7%)

Education-C; Business & Commerce; Finance; Higher Education

VAN TAYLOR (Anne), R-Plano **512/463-0108**

Real Estate. BA-Harvard College, 1995; MBA-Harvard Business
  School. 8-1-1972. H-2010-2015; S-2015-2018.
6301 Preston Road, Ste. 700, Plano 75024 • 972/398-9416
  Fax: 972/398-9419

Dist. 8 - Collin (85%), Dallas (5%)

Education; Government Reform; Health & Human Services;
  Intergovernmental Relations; Natural Resources & Economic Dev.;
  Nominations

‡CARLOS I. URESTI (Lleanna), D-San Antonio **512/463-0119**

Attorney. BA-Saint Mary's University; JD-Saint Mary's Law School.
  9-12-1963. H-1997-2006; S-2006-present.
3315 Sidney Brooks Drive, Suite 100, San Antonio 78235
  210/932-2568 • 800/459-0119; *Fax: 210/932-2572*

Dist. 19 - Atascosa (98%), Bexar (29%), Brewster, Crockett, Dimmit,
  Edwards, Frio, Kinney, Maverick, Medina, Pecos, Real, Reeves,
  Terrell, Uvalde, Val Verde, Zavala

Health & Human Services-VC; Education; Finance;
  Government Reform; Veteran Affairs & Border Security

‡ Term expires 2021, all others 2019
( ) Spouse

TEXAS STATE SENATORS

KIRK WATSON (Liz), D-Austin   **512/463-0114**
Attorney. BS-Baylor University; JD-Baylor School of Law. 3-18-1958.
  S-2007-present.
P.O. Box 12068, Austin 78711-2068 • 512/463-0114
  Fax: 512/463-5949

Dist. 14 - Bastrop, Travis (74%)

Nominations-VC; Finance; Health & Human Services;
  Higher Education

ROYCE WEST (Carol), D-Dallas   **512/463-0123**
Attorney. BA, MA-University of Texas at Arlington;
  JD-University of Houston. 9-26-1952. S-1993-present.
5787 S. Hampton Road, Suite 385, Dallas 75232
  214/467-0123; *Fax: 214/467-0050*

Dist. 23 - Dallas (34%)

Higher Education-VC; Administration; Education; Finance

JOHN WHITMIRE, D-Houston   **512/463-0115**
Attorney. BA-University of Houston; JD-Bates College of Law.
  8-13-1949. H-1973-83; S-1983-present.
803 Yale, Houston 77007 • 713/864-8701; *Fax: 713/864-5287*

Dist. 15 - Harris (19%)

Criminal Justice-C; Business & Commerce; Finance

‡JUDITH ZAFFIRINI (Carlos), D-Laredo   **512/463-0121**
Communications Specialist & Former Educator.
  BS, MA, Ph.D.-University of Texas at Austin. 2-13-1946.
  S-1987-present.
1407 Washington Street, Laredo 78040-4411 • 956/722-2293
  Fax: 956/722-8586

Dist. 21 - Atascosa (2%), Bee, Bexar (1%), Caldwell, Duval,
  Guadalupe (38%), Hays (31%), Jim Hogg, Karnes, LaSalle,
  Live Oak, McMullen, San Patricio, Starr, Travis (14%), Webb,
  Wilson, Zapata

Natural Resources & Economic Development-VC; Administration;
  Business & Commerce; State Affairs

‡ Term expires 2021, all others 2019
( ) Spouse   **www.txdirectory.com/online/txsenate**

THE SENATE OF TEXAS
85th LEGISLATURE

The Honorable Dan Patrick, Lieutenant Governor
Capitol Building 2E.13 – 512/463-0001

SENATORS	OFFICE NO.	PHONE	FAX	ASSISTANT
Bettencourt, Paul	3E.16	512/463-0107	*463-8810*	Marc Salvato
Birdwell, Brian	E1.706	512/463-0122	*475-3729*	Ben Stratmann
Buckingham M.D., Dawn	GE.5	512/463-0124	*475-3732*	Travis Richmond
Burton, Konni	3E.2	512/463-0110	*475-3745*	Elliott Griffin
Campbell M.D., Donna	3E.8	512/463-0125		Jon Oliver
Creighton, Brandon	E1.606	512/463-0104	*463-6373*	Tara Garcia
Estes, Craig	3E.18	512/463-0130	*463-8874*	Noe Barrios
Garcia, Sylvia R.	3E.12	512/463-0106	*463-0346*	John Chapa-Gorczynski
Hall, Bob	E1.808	512/463-0102	*463-7202*	Amy Lane
Hancock, Kelly G.	1E.9	512/463-0109	*463-7003*	Adam Leggett
Hinojosa, Juan	3E.6	512/463-0120	*463-0229*	Luis Moreno
Huffines, Don	E1.608	512/463-0116	*463-3135*	Brent Connett
Huffman, Joan	1E.15	512/463-0117	*463-0639*	Wroe Jackson
Hughes, Bryan	GE.7	512/463-0101	*475-3751*	Cody Terry
Kolkhorst, Lois W.	GE.4	512/463-0118	*475-3736*	Chris Steinbach
Lucio Jr., Eddie	3S.5	512/463-0127	*463-0061*	Louie Sanchez
Menendez, Jose	E1.712	512/463-0126	*463-2114*	Tomas Larralde
Miles, Borris L.	3S.3	512/463-0113	*463-0006*	Rob Borja
Nelson, Jane	1E.5	512/463-0112	*463-0923*	Dave Nelson
Nichols, Robert	E1.704	512/463-0103	*463-1526*	Angus Lupton
Perry, Charles	E1.810	512/463-0128	*463-2424*	Matthew Dowling
Rodriguez, Jose R.	E1.610	512/463-0129	*463-7100*	Sushma Smith
Schwertner M.D., Charles	E1.806	512/463-0105	*463-5713*	Tom Holloway
Seliger, Kel	1E.12	512/463-0131	*475-3733*	Ginger Averitt
Taylor, Larry	3E.10	512/463-0111	*475-3727*	Cari Christman
Taylor, Van	E1.708	512/463-0108	*463-7579*	Lonnie Dietz
Uresti, Carlos I.	4E.2	512/463-0119	*463-1017*	Jason Hassay
Watson, Kirk	E1.804	512/463-0114	*463 5949*	Sarah Howard
West, Royce	1E.3	512/463-0123	*463-0299*	LaJuana D. Barton
Whitmire, John	1E.13	512/463-0115	*475-3737*	Lara Wendler
Zaffirini, Judith	1E.14	512/463-0121	*475-3738*	Jorge Ramirez

The last two digits of the telephone number are the same as the senator's district number.
Office numbers are listed in the following order: floor, wing and room number. Offices located in
the Capitol Extension will begin with the letter "E," the floor and then the room number.

SENIORITY LEADERS

MEMBER	NO. OF YEARS	NO. OF SESSIONS	
John Whitmire (D)	30	16	68th (1983)-84th Session
Judith Zaffirini (D)	28	14	70th (1987)-84th Session
Eddie Lucio Jr. (D)	26	13	72nd (1991)-84th Session
Jane Nelson (R)	24	12	73rd (1993)-84th Session
Royce West (D)	24	12	73rd (1993)-84th Session

SENATE STANDING COMMITTEES
85th REGULAR SESSION
The Honorable Dan Patrick, President of the Senate
The Honorable Kel Seliger, President Pro Tem

ADMINISTRATION
Clerk: Vanessa Cortez, E1.714, 512/463-0350

Lois W. Kolkhorst (R), Chair
Konni Burton (R), Vice Chair

Don Huffines (R)	Bryan Hughes (R)	Robert Nichols (R)
Royce West (D)	Judith Zaffirini (D)	

AGRICULTURE, WATER & RURAL AFFAIRS
Clerk: Lauren Murray, 335 Sam Houston Bldg., 512/463-0340

Charles Perry (R), Chair
José R. Rodríguez (D), Vice Chair

Brandon Creighton (R)	Bob Hall (R)	Juan "Chuy" Hinojosa (D)
Lois W. Kolkhorst (R)	Borris L. Miles (D)	

BUSINESS & COMMERCE
Clerk: Tatum Reagan, 370 Sam Houston Bldg., 512/463-0365

Kelly G. Hancock (R), Chair
Brandon Creighton (R), Vice Chair

Donna Campbell (R)	Craig Estes (R)	Robert Nichols (R)
Charles Schwertner (R)	Larry Taylor (R)	John Whitmire (D)
Judith Zaffirini (D)		

CRIMINAL JUSTICE
Clerk: Terra Tucker, 470 Sam Houston Bldg., 512/463-0345

John Whitmire (D), Chair
Joan Huffman (R), Vice Chair

Brian Birdwell (R)	Konni Burton (R)	Brandon Creighton (R)
Sylvia R. Garcia (D)	Bryan Hughes (R)	José Menéndez (D)
Charles Perry (R)		

EDUCATION
Clerk: Nicole Sunstrum, 440 Sam Houston Bldg., 512/463-0355

Larry Taylor (R), Chair
Eddie Lucio (D), Vice Chair

Paul Bettencourt (R)	Donna Campbell (R)	Bob Hall (R)
Don Huffines (R)	Bryan Hughes (R)	Kel Seliger (R)
Van Taylor (R)	Carlos I. Uresti (D)	Royce West (D)

FINANCE
Clerk: Stephanie Hoover, E1.038, 512/463-0370 / *Fax: 512/463-5752*

Jane Nelson (R), Chair
Juan "Chuy" Hinojosa (D), Vice Chair

Paul Bettencourt (R)	Brian Birdwell (R)	Kelly G. Hancock (R)
Joan Huffman (R)	Lois W. Kolkhorst (R)	Robert Nichols (R)
Charles Schwertner (R)	Kel Seliger (R)	Larry Taylor (R)
Carlos I. Uresti (D)	Kirk Watson (D)	Royce West (D)
John Whitmire (D)		

HEALTH & HUMAN SERVICES
Clerk: Luisa Venegoni, 420 Sam Houston Bldg., 512/463-0360

Charles Schwertner (R), Chair
Carlos I. Uresti (D), Vice Chair

Dawn Buckingham (R)	Konni Burton (R)	Lois W. Kolkhorst (R)
Borris L. Miles (D)	Charles Perry (R)	Van Taylor (R)
Kirk Watson (D)		

HIGHER EDUCATION
Clerk: Daniel Warner, 320 Sam Houston Bldg., 512/463-4788

Kel Seliger (R), Chair
Royce West (D), Vice Chair

Paul Bettencourt (R)	Dawn Buckingham (R)	José Menéndez (D)
Larry Taylor (R)	Kirk Watson (D)	

INTERGOVERNMENTAL RELATIONS
Clerk: Dilip Kanuga, 475 Sam Houston Bldg., 512/463-2527

Eddie Lucio (D), Chair
Paul Bettencourt (R), Vice Chair

Donna Campbell (R)	Sylvia R. Garcia (D)	Don Huffines (R)
José Menéndez (D)	Van Taylor (R)	

NATURAL RESOURCES & ECONOMIC DEVELOPMENT
Clerk: Paige McGhee, 325 Sam Houston Bldg., 512/463-0390

Craig Estes (R), Chair
Judith Zaffirini (D), Vice Chair

Konni Burton (R)	Sylvia R. Garcia (D)	Kelly G. Hancock (R)
Juan "Chuy" Hinojosa (D)	Don Huffines (R)	Borris L. Miles (D)
José R. Rodríguez (D)	Kel Seliger (R)	Van Taylor (R)

NOMINATIONS
Clerk: John Ryan Isaacson, E1.716, 512/463-2084

Brian Birdwell (R), Chair
Kirk Watson (D), Vice Chair

Dawn Buckingham (R)	Craig Estes (R)	José Menéndez (D)
Borris L. Miles (D)	Van Taylor (R)	

STATE AFFAIRS
Clerk: Addison Reagan, 380 Sam Houston Bldg., 512/463-0380

Joan Huffman (R), Chair
Bryan Hughes (R), Vice Chair

Brian Birdwell (R)	Brandon Creighton (R)	Craig Estes (R)
Eddie Lucio (D)	Jane Nelson (R)	Charles Schwertner (R)
Judith Zaffirini (D)		

TRANSPORTATION
Clerk: Amy Jeter, 450 Sam Houston Bldg., 512/463-0067

Robert Nichols (R), Chair
Bob Hall (R), Vice Chair

Brandon Creighton (R)	Sylvia R. Garcia (D)	Kelly G. Hancock (R)
Juan "Chuy" Hinojosa (D)	Lois W. Kolkhorst (R)	Charles Perry (R)
José R. Rodríguez (D)		

VETERAN AFFAIRS & BORDER SECURITY
Clerk: Carrie Smith, 345 Sam Houston Bldg., 512/463-2211

Donna Campbell (R), Chair
Don Huffines (R), Vice Chair

Dawn Buckingham (R)	Bob Hall (R)	Eddie Lucio (D)
José R. Rodríguez (D)	Carlos I. Uresti (D)	

GOVERNMENT REFORM, SELECT
Clerk: Stephanie Hoover, 3E.16, 512/463-0107

Paul Bettencourt (R), Chair

Brandon Creighton (R)	Kelly G. Hancock (R)	Eddie Lucio (D)
Charles Perry (R)	Van Taylor (R)	Carlos I. Uresti (D)

TEXAS SENATE DISTRICT MAP

State Senate Districts
85th Legislature
Plan S172

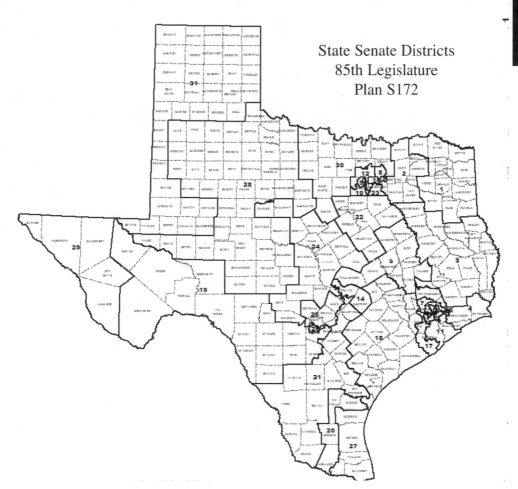

SENATE SEATING CHART
85th LEGISLATIVE SESSION

Press	**Lieutenant Governor** **The. Hon. Dan Patrick**	

Journal Clerk Polly Emerson	Secretary of the Senate Patsy Spaw	Calendar Clerk Tracy Ortiz

Lucio 27(D) Cameron	Burton 10(R) Tarrant	Buckingham 24(R) Travis	Hughes 1(R) Wood		Hall 2(R) Van Zandt	V. Taylor 8(R) Collin	Campbell 25(R) Comal	Watson 14(D) Travis
Huffines 16(R) Dallas	Menéndez 26(D) Bexar	Huffman 17 (R) Harris	Miles 13(D) Harris		Bettencourt 7(R) Harris	Creighton 4(R) Montgomery	L. Taylor 11(R) Galveston	Hancock 9(R) Tarrant
West 23(D) Dallas	Nichols 3(R) Cherokee	Uresti 19(D) Bexar	Schwertner 5(R) Williamson		Kolkhorst 18(R) Washington	Perry 28(R) Lubbock	Garcia 6(D) Harris	Rodríguez 29(D) El Paso
Whitmire 15(D) Harris	Nelson 12(R) Denton	Hinojosa 20(D) Hidalgo	Zaffirini 21(D) Webb		Seliger 31(R) Randall	Birdwell 22(R) Hood	Estes 30(R) Wichita	

Sergeant at Arms Rick DeLeon

85th LEGISLATURE, MEMBERS BY DISTRICT
TEXAS STATE SENATE

Dist. 1	Hughes (R)	Dist. 12	†Nelson (R)	Dist. 23	†West (D)
Dist. 2	†Hall (R)	Dist. 13	Miles (D)	Dist. 24	Buckingham (R)
Dist. 3	†Nichols (R)	Dist. 14	†Watson (D)	Dist. 25	†Campbell (R)
Dist. 4	†Creighton (R)	Dist. 15	†Whitmire (D)	Dist. 26	†Menéndez (D)
Dist. 5	†Schwertner (R)	Dist. 16	†Huffines (R)	Dist. 27	†Lucio (D)
Dist. 6	†Garcia (D)	Dist. 17	†Huffman (R)	Dist. 28	†Perry (R)
Dist. 7	†Bettencourt (R)	Dist. 18	†Kolkhorst (R)	Dist. 29	†Rodríguez (D)
Dist. 8	†Taylor, V. (R)	Dist. 19	†Uresti (D)	Dist. 30	†Estes (R)
Dist. 9	†Hancock (R)	Dist. 20	†Hinojosa (D)	Dist. 31	†Seliger (R)
Dist. 10	†Burton (R)	Dist. 21	†Zaffirini (D)		
Dist. 11	†Taylor, L. (R)	Dist. 22	†Birdwell (R)		

HOUSE OF REPRESENTATIVES

Dist. 1	†VanDeaver (R)	Dist. 27	†Reynolds (D)	Dist. 53	†Murr (R)
Dist. 2	†Flynn (R)	Dist. 28	†Zerwas (R)	Dist. 54	Cosper (R)
Dist. 3	†Bell (R)	Dist. 29	†E. Thompson (R)	Dist. 55	Shine (R)
Dist. 4	Gooden (R)	Dist. 30	†Morrison (R)	Dist. 56	†C. Anderson (R)
Dist. 5	Hefner (R)	Dist. 31	†Guillen (D)	Dist. 57	†Ashby (R)
Dist. 6	†Schaefer (R)	Dist. 32	†Hunter (R)	Dist. 58	†Burns (R)
Dist. 7	Dean (R)	Dist. 33	Holland (R)	Dist. 59	†Sheffield (R)
Dist. 8	†Cook (R)	Dist. 34	†Herrero (D)	Dist. 60	Lang (R)
Dist. 9	†Paddie (R)	Dist. 35	†Longoria (D)	Dist. 61	†P. King (R)
Dist. 10	†Wray (R)	Dist. 36	†Munoz (D)	Dist. 62	†Phillips (R)
Dist. 11	†Clardy (R)	Dist. 37	†Oliveira (D)	Dist. 63	†Parker (R)
Dist. 12	†Kacal (R)	Dist. 38	†Lucio (D)	Dist. 64	Stucky (R)
Dist. 13	†Schubert (R)	Dist. 39	†Martinez (D)	Dist. 65	†Simmons (R)
Dist. 14	†Raney (R)	Dist. 40	†Canales (D)	Dist. 66	†Shaheen (R)
Dist. 15	†Keough (R)	Dist. 41	†Guerra (D)	Dist. 67	†Leach (R)
Dist. 16	†Metcalf (R)	Dist. 42	†Raymond (D)	Dist. 68	†Springer (R)
Dist. 17	†Cyrier (R)	Dist. 43	†Lozano (R)	Dist. 69	†Frank (R)
Dist. 18	Bailes (R)	Dist. 44	†Kuempel (R)	Dist. 70	†Sanford (R)
Dist. 19	†White (R)	Dist. 45	†Isaac (R)	Dist. 71	Lambert (R)
Dist. 20	Wilson (R)	Dist. 46	†Dukes (D)	Dist. 72	†Darby (R)
Dist. 21	†Phelan (R)	Dist. 47	†Workman (R)	Dist. 73	Biedermann (R)
Dist. 22	†Deshotel (D)	Dist. 48	†Howard (D)	Dist. 74	†Nevarez (D)
Dist. 23	†Faircloth (R)	Dist. 49	†Hinojosa (D)	Dist. 75	†Gonzalez (D)
Dist. 24	†G. Bonnen (R)	Dist. 50	†Israel (D)	Dist. 76	†Blanco (D)
Dist. 25	†D. Bonnen (R)	Dist. 51	†E. Rodríguez (D)	Dist. 77	Ortega (D)
Dist. 26	†Miller (R)	Dist. 52	†Gonzales (R)	Dist. 78	†Moody (D)

[†] Incumbent
(D) Democrat
(R) Republican

Dist. 79 †Pickett (D)	Dist. 103 †Anchia (D)	Dist. 127 †Huberty (R)
Dist. 80 †T. King (D)	Dist. 104 †Alonzo (D)	Dist. 128 Cain (R)
Dist. 81 †Landgraf (R)	Dist. 105 †R. Anderson (R)	Dist. 129 †Paul (R)
Dist. 82 †Craddick (R)	Dist. 106 †Fallon (R)	Dist. 130 Oliverson (R)
Dist. 83 †Burrows (R)	Dist. 107 Neave (D)	Dist. 131 †Allen (D)
Dist. 84 †Frullo (R)	Dist. 108 †Meyer (R)	Dist. 132 †Schofield (R)
Dist. 85 †Stephenson (R)	Dist. 109 †Giddings (D)	Dist. 133 †Murphy (R)
Dist. 86 †Smithee (R)	Dist. 110 †Rose (D)	Dist. 134 †S. Davis (R)
Dist. 87 †Price (R)	Dist. 111 †Y. Davis (D)	Dist. 135 †Elkins (R)
Dist. 88 †K.King (R)	Dist. 112 †Button (R)	Dist. 136 †Dale (R)
Dist. 89 †Laubenberg (R)	Dist. 113 †Burkett (R)	Dist. 137 †Wu (D)
Dist. 90 †Romero (D)	Dist. 114 †Villalba (R)	Dist. 138 †Bohac (R)
Dist. 91 †Klick (R)	Dist. 115 †Rinaldi (R)	Dist. 139 †J. Johnson (D)
Dist. 92 †Stickland (R)	Dist. 116 Arévalo (D)	Dist. 140 †Walle (D)
Dist. 93 †Krause (R)	Dist. 117 Cortez (D)	Dist. 141 †S. Thompson (D)
Dist. 94 †Tinderholt (R)	Dist. 118 Uresti (D)	Dist. 142 †Dutton (D)
Dist. 95 †Collier (D)	Dist. 119 †Gutierrez (D)	Dist. 143 †Hernandez (D)
Dist. 96 †Zedler (R)	Dist. 120 Gervin-Hawkins (D)	Dist. 144 Perez (D)
Dist. 97 †Goldman (R)	Dist. 121 †Straus (R)	Dist. 145 †Alvarado (D)
Dist. 98 †Capriglione (R)	Dist. 122 †Larson (R)	Dist. 146 †Thierry (D)
Dist. 99 †Geren (R)	Dist. 123 †Bernal (D)	Dist. 147 †Coleman (D)
Dist. 100 †E. Johnson (D)	Dist. 124 †Minjarez (D)	Dist. 148 †Farrar (D)
Dist. 101 †Turner (D)	Dist. 125 †J. Rodríguez (D)	Dist. 149 Vo (D)
Dist. 102 †Koop (R)	Dist. 126 †Roberts (R)	Dist. 150 Swanson (R)

[†] Incumbent
(D) Democrat
(R) Republican

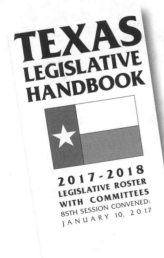

HOUSE OF REPRESENTATIVES
State Capitol, Room 2W.13; P.O. Box 2910, Austin 78768-2910 • 512/463-1000
www.house.texas.gov

JOE STRAUS III (R), Speaker of the House

Wife: Julie

Born September 1, 1959. Education: B.A.-Political Science, Vanderbilt University. Elected to the 79th Legislature on February 5, 2005. Served in the administration of President Ronald Reagan at what was then called the U.S. Customs Service. Served in the administration of President George H.W. Bush at the U.S. Department of Commerce. San Antonio native and fifth-generation Texan. Principal in an insurance, investments and executive benefits business. Former Chairman of the Republican Legislative Campaign Committee. Most recently elected Speaker by a 150-0 vote in January 2017.
Speaker of the House, 2009-present.

Speaker of the House	The Honorable Joe Straus III . . .512/463-1000	/ *Fax: 463-0675*

OFFICE OF THE SPEAKER

Scheduler	Tara Korstad 512/463-3000	/ *Fax: 463-0675*
Executive Assistant	Carolyn Scott 512/463-3000	/ *Fax: 463-0675*

EXECUTIVE OFFICES

Chief of Staff	Patricia Shipton 512/463-0056	/ *Fax: 463-0675*
Executive Assistant to the Chief of Staff	Jessica Hale Allen 512/463-0056	/ *Fax: 463-0675*
Director of Budget and Policy	Andrew Blifford 512/463-1100	/ *Fax: 463-0278*
Special Counsel and House Ethics Advisor	Frank Battle 512/463-1000	/ *Fax: 463-0278*
General Counsel	Jon Schnautz 512/463-0921	/ *Fax: 463-0675*
Communications Director	Jason Embry 512/463-0223	/ *Fax: 463-0675*
Policy Analyst Office	Staff Office 512/463-1100	/ *Fax: 463-0278*
Director of Appointments & Special Programs	Erin Daly Wilson 512/463-1000	/ *Fax: 463-0675*
District Director	Naomi Miller 210/828-4411	/ *Fax: 832-9994*

HOUSE BUSINESS OFFICE

Executive Director	Steven Adrian 512/463-0835	/ *Fax: 463-0747*
Accounting	Steven AdrianCochranCochran .512/463-0835	/ *Fax: 463-0747*
Payroll-Personnel	James Freeman 512/463-0865	/ *Fax: 463-8132*
Post Office	Vernon Green 512/463-0905	/ *Fax: 463-5896*
Property	Staff Office 512/463-0870	/ *Fax: 463-2792*
Purchasing & Supply	Dean Howard 512/463-8151	/ *Fax: 463-6337*
Reproduction	Scott Williams 512/463-0885	/ *Fax: 463-8139*
Photography	Monti Perkins 512/463-1392	/ *Fax: 463-0249*
Communications-Video/Audio	Mike Blackwell 512/463-0920	/ *Fax: 463-5729*
Special Services	Rebecca Ford 512/463-2488	/ *Fax: 463-5896*
House Research	Laura Hendrickson 512/463-0752	/ *Fax: 463-1962*
Chief Clerk	Robert Haney 512/463-0845	/ *Fax: 463-5896*
House Parliamentarian	Chris Griesel 512/463-2003	/ *Fax: 463-0153*
Journal Clerk	Jennifer Doran 512/463-0855	/ *Fax: 463-2111*
Voting Clerk	Scottie Hagen 512/463-0855	/ *Fax: 463-2111*
Committee Coordinator	Stacey Nicchio 512/463-0850	/ *Fax: 463-7547*
Sergeant-at-Arms	David Sauceda 512/463-0910	/ *Fax: 463-5896*

HOUSE MEMBERS BY DISTRICT - PAGE 43
Information concerning State Representatives is in the following form:

> **NAME** (Spouse), Party, Hometown   **Capitol Telephone**
> Profession, Education, Birthdate, Legislative Experience
> H–House of Representatives and Date of Tenure
> District Business Address and Telephone - *Fax Number*
> District Number and Counties Represented
> Senator(s) in District
> Committee Membership

Capitol Offices and Telephone Numbers
Committee Assignments
Seating Chart and District Map
House Seniority List
County Delegations, Senate and House

The Mailing Address for all Representatives in Austin is:
P.O. Box 2910
Austin, Texas 78768-2910
FAX: 512-463-5896

Email for Members:
firstname.lastname@house.texas.gov
Example: alma.allen@house.texas.gov

TEXAS HOUSE OF REPRESENTATIVES

ALMA A. ALLEN, D-Houston   **512/463-0744**

Educator. BS, M.Ed.-Texas Southern University;
  Ed.D.-University of Houston. 4-7-1939. H-2005-present.
10101 Fondren, #500, Houston 77096 • 713/776-0505
  Fax: 713/776-1490

Dist. 131 - Harris (4%)

Sens. Garcia, Huffman, Miles

Corrections-VC; Public Education

ROBERTO R. ALONZO (Sylvana), D-Dallas   **512/463-0408**

Attorney. BA-University of Texas at Austin; JD-Thurgood Marshall
  School of Law at Texas Southern University. 12-25-1956.
  H-1993-1997; H-2003-present.
312 W. 12th St., Suite A, Dallas 75208 • 214/942-7104; 866/449-5770;
  Fax: 214/942-8104

Dist. 104 - Dallas (7%)

Sens. Hancock, West

Pensions-VC; Calendars; Higher Education

( )Spouse

TEXAS HOUSE OF REPRESENTATIVES

CAROL ALVARADO, D-Houston   **512/463-0732**

Small Business Consultant. BA, MBA-University of Houston.
  10-26-1967. H-2009-present.
2900 Woodridge, Suite 305, Houston 77087 • 713/649-6563

Dist. 145 - Harris (4%)

Sens. Garcia, Miles, L. Taylor, Whitmire

Urban Affairs-C; Higher Education; Opioids & Substance Abuse,
  Select

RAFAEL ANCHIA (Marissa), D-Dallas   **512/463-0746**

Attorney. BA-Southern Methodist University; JD-Tulane Law.
  9-26-1968. H-2005-present.
1111 W. Mockingbird, Suite 1010, Dallas 75247 • 214/943-6081
  Fax: 214/920-9996

Dist. 103 - Dallas (7%)

Sens. Hancock, Huffines, West

International Trade & Intergovernmental Affairs-C; Pensions;
  State & Federal Power & Responsibility, Select

CHARLES "DOC" ANDERSON, R-Waco   **512/463-0135**

Veterinarian. DVM-Texas A&M University, 1981. 6-29-1945.
  H-2005-present.
900 Austin Ave., #804, Waco 76701 • 254/754-3892
  Fax: 254/754-1604

Dist. 56 - McLennan (70%)

Sen. Birdwell

Energy Resources-VC; Agriculture & Livestock

RODNEY ANDERSON (Heather), R-Grand Prairie   **512/463-0641**

Sr. VP, Alliant Natl. Title Insurance Co. BBA, Real Estate-
  The University of Texas at Arlington. 4-29-1968.
  H-2011-2013; 2015-present.
800 W. Airport Freeway, Suite 1100, Irving 75062 • 512/463-0641

Dist. 105 - Dallas (7%)

Sens. Hancock, Huffines, West

Elections; Insurance

( )Spouse

TEXAS HOUSE OF REPRESENTATIVES

DIANA ARÈVALO, D-San Antonio   **512/463-0616**

Executive Director. BBA-University of Texas at San Antonio;
  MBA-Our Lady of the Lake University. 10-27-1981. H-2017–present.
4522 Fredericksburg Road, #A-12-A, San Antonio 78201
  210/785-9114

Dist. 116 - Bexar (10%)

Sens. Menéndez, Uresti

Defense & Veterans' Affairs; Public Health; Rules & Resolutions

TRENT ASHBY (Nickie), R-Lufkin   **512/463-0508**

Angelina County Chairman, Citizens National Bank. BS, Agricultural
  Economics-Texas A&M University, 1996. 10-9-1972. H-2013-present.
2915 Atkinson Dr., Lufkin 75901 • 936/634-2762

Dist. 57 - Angelina, Houston, Leon, Madison, San Augustine, Trinity

Sens. Nichols, Schwertner

Appropriations; Calendars; Natural Resources

ERNEST BAILES (Courtney), R-Shepherd   **512/463-0570**

Self Employed. BA, Animal Science-Texas A&M University.
  4-13-1982. H-2017-present.
10501 Hwy. 150; P.O. Box 1116, Shepherd 77371 • 512/463-0570

Dist. 18 - Liberty, San Jacinto, Walker

Sens. Nichols, Schwertner

Economic & Small Business Development;
  Land & Resource Management; Rules & Resolutions

CECIL BELL, JR. (Jo Ann), R-Magnolia   **512/463-0650**

General Contractor. 5-17-1962. H-2013-present.
18230 FM 1488, Ste. 302, Magnolia 77354 • 281/259-3700
  Fax: 281/259-3706

Dist. 3 - Montgomery (27%), Waller

Sens. Creighton, Kolkhorst

Land & Resource Management-VC; Special Purpose Districts

( )Spouse

TEXAS HOUSE OF REPRESENTATIVES

DIEGO BERNAL (Elyse), D-San Antonio   **512/463-0532**

Attorney. MS, JD-University of Michigan. 10-19-1976.
  H-2015-present.
126 W. Rector St., Ste. 114, San Antonio 78216 • 210/308-9700
Dist. 123 - Bexar (10%)
Sens. Campbell, Menéndez
Public Education-VC; House Administration; Urban Affairs

KYLE BIEDERMANN (Barbi), R-Fredericksburg   **512/463-0325**

ACE Hardware Dealer. BS-University of South Florida. 4-30-1959.
  H-2017-present.
616 W. Main, Suite 101, Fredericksburg 78624 • 830/990-0185
Dist. 73 - Comal, Gillespie, Kendall
Sens. Buckingham, Campbell
County Affairs; Juvenile Justice & Family Issues

CÉSAR BLANCO, D-El Paso   **512/463-0622**

Consultant. BA, Political Science-University of Texas at El Paso.
  4-23-1976. H-2015-present.
9440 Viscount Blvd., Suite 205, El Paso 79925 • 915/599-9807
  Fax: 915/599-9776
Dist. 76 - El Paso (20%)
Sen. Rodríguez
Defense & Veterans' Affairs-VC; Land & Resource Management

DWAYNE BOHAC (Dawn), R-Houston   **512/463-0727**

Businessman. BBA, Marketing; BS, Political Science, Cum Laude-
  Texas A&M University, 1990. 9-4-1966. H-2003-present.
2600 Gessner, Suite 212, Houston 77080 • 713/460-2800
  Fax: 713/460-2822
Dist. 138 - Harris (4%)
Sens. Bettencourt, Huffman, Whitmire
Public Education; Ways & Means

( )Spouse

TEXAS HOUSE OF REPRESENTATIVES

DENNIS H. BONNEN (Kim), R-Angleton   **512/463-0564**

Banking. BA-Saint Edwards University. 3-3-1972. H-1997-present.
122 E. Myrtle St., Angleton 77515 • 979/848-1770; *Fax: 979/849-3169*
Dist. 25 - Brazoria (44%), Matagorda
Sens. Huffman, Kolkhorst, L. Taylor
Ways & Means-C; Culture, Recreation & Tourism

GREG BONNEN, M.D. (Kim), R-Friendswood   **512/463-0729**

Neurosurgeon. BS, Biochemistry-Texas A&M University;
   MD-University of Texas Medical Branch. 6-18-1966. H-2013-present.
174 Calder Road, Suite 116, League City 77573 • 281/338-0924
Dist. 24 - Galveston (56%)
Sen. L. Taylor
Appropriations; Energy Resources

CINDY BURKETT (Mike), R-Sunnyvale   **512/463-0464**

Real Estate Agent. BA, Political Science-Univ. of Texas at Arlington.
   8-13-1958. H-2011-present.
3200 Broadway, Suite 240, Garland 75043 • 972/278-7276
Dist. 113 - Dallas (7%)
Sens. Hall, Huffines
Redistricting-C; Local & Consent Calendars; Public Health;
   Transportation

DEWAYNE BURNS (Jennifer), R-Cleburne   **512/463-0538**

Investor, Farmer, Rancher. BS, Agriculture Services and Development-
   Tarleton State University. 6-22-1972. H-2015-present.
115 S. Main Street, Suite 202, Cleburne 76033 • 817/645-3685
   Fax: 817/645-3690
Dist. 58 - Bosque, Johnson
Sen. Birdwell
Homeland Security & Public Safety; Natural Resources;
   Rules & Resolutions

( )Spouse

TEXAS HOUSE OF REPRESENTATIVES

DUSTIN BURROWS (Elizabeth), R-Lubbock   **512/463-0542**

Attorney. BS-Rhodes College; JD-Texas Tech School of Law, 2001;
  MBA-Texas Tech University, 2004. 11-14-1978. H-2015-present.
5010 University Avenue, Ste. 300, Lubbock 79413 • 806/795-0635

Dist. 83 - Borden, Gaines, Lubbock (40%), Lynn, Mitchell, Scurry,
  Terry

Sens: Perry, Seliger

Agriculture & Livestock; Investments & Financial Services

ANGIE CHEN BUTTON (Darcy), R-Garland   **512/463-0486**

CPA, Marketing. BS, Accounting-National Taiwan University;
  MS, MA-UT Dallas. 2-9-1954. H-2009-present.
1201 International Parkway, Suite 130, Richardson 75081
  972/234-8980; *Fax: 972/470-0789*

Dist. 112 - Dallas (7%)

Sens. Hall, Huffines, V. Taylor

Economic & Small Business Development-C; Economic
  Competitiveness, Select; Higher Education

BRISCOE CAIN (Bergundi), R-Houston   **512/463-0733**

Attorney. BA-University of Houston; JD-South Texas College of Law.
  12-9-1984. H-2017-present.
P.O. Box 2910, Austin 78768-2910 • 512/463-0733

Dist. 128 - Harris (4%)

Sens. Creighton, Garcia, L. Taylor, Whitmire

Defense & Veterans' Affairs; Juvenile Justice & Family Issues

TERRY CANALES (Erica), D-Edinburg   **512/463-0426**

Attorney. JD-St. Mary's University. 1-1-1979. H-2013-present.
101 N. 10th Avenue, Suite B, Edinburg 78541 • 956/383-0860
  Fax: 956/383-4334

Dist. 40 - Hidalgo (22%)

Sens. Hinojosa, Lucio

Criminal Jurisprudence; Energy Resources

( )Spouse

TEXAS HOUSE OF REPRESENTATIVES

GIOVANNI CAPRIGLIONE (Elisa), R-Southlake   **512/463-0690**

Private Equity. BS, Physics-Worcester Polytechnic Institute;
MBA, Finance-Santa Clara University. 3-8-1973. H-2013-present.
1100 Bear Creek Parkway; P.O. Box 770, Keller 76244-0770
817/431-5339; *Fax: 817/431-9885*

Dist. 98 - Tarrant (9%)

Sens. Burton, Hancock, Nelson

S/C on Budget Transparency & Reform-C; Government
Transparency & Operation-VC; Appropriations;
General Investigating & Ethics; Local & Consent Calendars

TRAVIS CLARDY (Judy), R-Nacogdoches   **512/463-0592**

Attorney. BBA-Abilene Christian University; JD-Pepperdine University.
1-13-1962. H-2013-present.
202 E. Pilar, Room 310, Nacogdoches 75961 • 936/560-3982
Fax: 936/564-0051

Dist. 11 - Cherokee, Nacogdoches, Rusk

Sens. Hughes, Nichols

Local & Consent Calendars-VC; Energy Resources; Higher Education

GARNET COLEMAN (Angelique), D-Houston   **512/463-0524**

Business Consultant. BA-University of Saint Thomas. 9-8-1961.
H-1991-present.
5445 Almeda, Suite 501, Houston 77004 • 713/520-5355
Fax: 713/520-1860

Dist. 147 - Harris (4%)

Sens. Garcia, Miles, Whitmire

County Affairs-C; Public Health; Opioids & Substance Abuse, Select

NICOLE COLLIER (Gary), D-Fort Worth   **512/463-0716**

Attorney. BS, Political Science-University of Houston;
JD-Texas Wesleyan University School of Law. 9-12-1972.
H-2013-present.
101 S. Jennings, Suite 103A, Ft. Worth 76104 • 817/332-1180
Fax: 817/332-1183

Dist. 95 - Tarrant (9%)

Sens. Burton, Hancock

Business & Industry; Local & Consent Calendars; Public Health

( )Spouse

TEXAS HOUSE OF REPRESENTATIVES

BYRON C. COOK (Kay), R-Corsicana   **512/463-0730**

Businessman/Rancher. Navarro College. 4-8-1954. H-2003-present.
P.O. Box 2910, Austin 78768-2910 • 512/463-0730; *Fax: 512/463-2506*

Dist. 8 - Anderson, Freestone, Hill, Navarro

Sens. Birdwell, Nichols, Schwertner

State Affairs-C; **Economic Competitiveness, Select-C**; Calendars

PHILIP CORTEZ, D-San Antonio   **512/463-0269**

Public Relations Consultant. BA, Political Science; MPA-University of
    Texas at San Antonio. 7-7-1978. H-2013-2015, 2017-present.
2600 SW Military Dr. , Suite 211, San Antonio 78224
    210/923-3638; *Fax:210/923-3646*

Dist. 117 - Bexar (10%)

Sens. Campbell, Menéndez, Uresti

Public Health; Special Purpose Districts

SCOTT COSPER (Christy), R-Killeen   **512/463-0684**

Real Estate Developer. 11-8-1968. H-2017-present.
2916 Illinois Avenue, Killeen 76543 • 254/680-5568

Dist. 54 - Bell (48%), Lampasas

Sen. Buckingham

Appropriations; Special Purpose Districts

TOM CRADDICK (Nadine), R-Midland   **512/463-0500**

Business Dev. Rep. for Horizon Mud Co. BBA, MBA-Texas Tech Univ.
    9-19-1943. H-1969-present. Speaker of the Texas House 2003-2009.
    Speaker of the Texas House 2003-2009.
500 W. Texas, Suite 880, Midland 79701 • 432/682-3000
    Fax: 432/684-4864

Dist. 82 - Crane, Dawson, Martin, Midland, Upton

Sens. Perry, Seliger

Energy Resources; State Affairs

( )Spouse

TEXAS HOUSE OF REPRESENTATIVES

JOHN CYRIER (Rachelle), R-Lockhart   **512/463-0682**

President and CEO of Sabre Commercial. Texas A&M University, 1995.
  5-4-1973. H-2015-present.
1017 Main Street, Bastrop 78602 • 512/463-0682
Dist. 17 - Bastrop, Caldwell, Gonzales, Karnes, Lee

Sens. Kolkhorst, Watson, Zaffirini

Agriculture & Livestock; Environmental Regulation;
  House Administration

TONY DALE (Mary), R-Cedar Park   **512/463-0696**

Small Business Owner. BA, Political Science-Ohio State University.
  6-11-1969. H-2013-present.
P.O. Box 2910, Austin 78768-2910 • 512/463-0696; *Fax: 512/463-9333*
Dist. 136 - Williamson (39%)

Sen. Schwertner

Juvenile Justice & Family Issues-VC; Environmental Regulation

DREW DARBY (Clarisa), R-San Angelo   **512/463-0331**

Attorney/Businessman. BBA, Finance-University of Texas at Austin;
  JD-University of Texas School of Law, 1971. 2-22-1947.
  H-2007-present.
36 W. Beauregard, Suite 517; P.O. Box 3284, San Angelo 76902-3284
  325/658-7313; *Fax: 325/659-3762*
Dist. 72 - Coke, Concho, Glasscock, Howard, Irion, Reagan, Runnels,
  Sterling, Tom Green

Sens. Perry, Seliger

Energy Resources-C; **State & Federal Power & Responsibility,
  Select-C**; Redistricting; Ways & Means

SARAH DAVIS (Kent Adams), R-West University Place
                                        512/463-0389

Attorney. BS, Economics-Baylor University 1998;
  JD-University of Houston, 2001. 5-18-1976. H-2011-present.
6300 W. Loop South, Suite 140, Bellaire 77401 • 713/664-7095
Dist. 134 - Harris (4%)

Sens. Huffman, Miles, Whitmire

General Investigating & Ethics-C; Appropriations; Calendars;
  Corrections; Economic Competitiveness, Select

( )Spouse

TEXAS HOUSE OF REPRESENTATIVES

YVONNE DAVIS, D-Dallas   **512/463-0598**

Small Business Owner. BS-University of Houston. 2-4-1955.
  H-1993-present.
5787 S. Hampton Road, Suite 447, Dallas 75232 • 214/941-3895
  Fax: 214/941-6859

Dist. 111 - Dallas (7%)

Sens. Hancock, West

Ways & Means-VC; Transportation

JAY DEAN (Pokie), R-Longview   **512/463-0750**

Self Employed. BA-Louisiana State University. 3-5-1953.
  H-2017-present.
101 E. Methvin, Suite 103, Longview 75601 • 512/463-0750
  Fax: 512/463-9085

Dist. 7 - Gregg, Upshur

Sen. Hughes

Appropriations; Investments & Financial Services;
  Local & Consent Calendars; Opioids & Substance Abuse, Select

JOSEPH "JOE" DESHOTEL, D-Beaumont   **512/463-0662**

Attorney/Businessman. BS, Political Science-Lamar University;
  JD-TSU, Thurgood Marshall Law Center. 12-3-1951. H-1999-present.
One Plaza Square, Suite 203, Port Arthur 77642 • 409/724-0788
  Fax: 409/724-0750

Dist. 22 - Jefferson (64%)

Sen. Creighton

Texas Ports, Innovation & Infrastructure, Select-C;
  Economic & Small Business Development; Public Education

DAWNNA M. DUKES, D-Austin   **512/463-0506**

Consultant; Business Resource Planning & Marketing.
  BS, Psychology-Texas A&M University. 9-3-1963. H-1995-present.
P.O. Box 2910, Austin 78768 • 512/463-0506; *Fax: 512/463-7864*

Dist. 46 - Travis (16%)

Sen. Watson

Appropriations; International Trade & Intergovernmental Affairs

( )Spouse

TEXAS HOUSE OF REPRESENTATIVES

HAROLD V. DUTTON, JR., D-Houston **512/463-0510**

Attorney. BBA-Texas Southern University; JD-TSU Thurgood Marshall
School of Law. 2-17-1945. H-1985-present.
8799 North Loop East, Suite 200, Houston 77029 • 713/692-9192
  Fax: 713/692-6791

Dist. 142 - Harris (4%)

Sens. Creighton, Garcia, Miles, Whitmire

Juvenile Justice & Family Issues-C; Public Education

GARY ELKINS (Julie), R-Houston **512/463-0722**

Business Consultant. BS-Southwestern Assemblies of God University.
3-15-1955. H-1995-present.
9601 Jones Road, Suite 215, Houston 77065 • 832/912-8380
  Fax: 832/912-8879

Dist. 135 - Harris (4%)

Sens. Bettencourt, Whitmire

Government Transparency & Operation-C; Urban Affairs

WAYNE FAIRCLOTH (Cheryl), R-Galveston **512/463-0502**

Insurance Agent. BA-Sam Houston State University. 3-10-1953.
H-2015-present.
2121 Market Street, Suite 205, Galveston 77550 • 409/762-0304
  Fax: 409/762-0351

Dist. 23 - Chambers, Galveston (44%)

Sens. Creighton, L. Taylor

Culture, Recreation & Tourism-VC; Land & Resource Management;
  Rules & Resolutions; Texas Ports, Innovation & Infrastructure, Select

PAT FALLON (Susan), R-Frisco **512/463-0694**

Business Owner. University of Notre Dame, Government/International
Relations. 12-19-1967. H-2013-present.
100 W. Eldorado Pkwy., Little Elm 75068 • 469/362-0500
  Fax: 469/362-0540

Dist. 106 - Denton (24%)

Sens. Estes, Nelson

Culture, Recreation & Tourism; Elections

( )Spouse

TEXAS HOUSE OF REPRESENTATIVES

JESSICA FARRAR (Marco Sanchez), D-Houston   **512/463-0620**

Attorney at Law and Partner. BA, Architecture-University of Houston.
  JD-University of Texas School of Law. 11-16-1966. H-1995-present.
6515 Irvington, Houston 77022; P.O. Box 30099, Houston 77249-0099
  713/691-6912; *Fax: 713/691-3363*

Dist. 148 - Harris (4%)

Sens. Garcia, Miles, Whitmire

Judiciary & Civil Jurisprudence-VC; State Affairs

DAN FLYNN (Susan), R-Van   **512/463-0880**

Banker/Rancher. McCallum High School, Austin. 2-21-1943.
  H-2003-present.
P.O. Box 999, Canton 75103 • 903/567-0921; *Fax: 903/567-0923*

Dist. 2 - Hopkins, Hunt, Van Zandt

Sen. Hall

Pensions-C; Defense & Veterans' Affairs

JAMES FRANK (Alisha), R-Wichita Falls   **512/463-0534**

Owner, Sharp Iron Group and Transland. BS, Finance-Texas A&M
  University. 11-23-1966. H-2013-present.
1206 Hatton Road, Wichita Falls 76302 • 940/767-1700

Dist. 69 - Archer, Baylor, Clay, Foard, Knox, Wichita

Sens. Estes, Perry

Human Services-VC; Economic Competitiveness, Select;
  Local & Consent Calendars; Natural Resources

JOHN FRULLO (Patti), R-Lubbock   **512/463-0676**

Small Business Owner. BS, Accounting-University of Wyoming, 1984.
  8-27-1962. H-2010-present.
4601 50th Street, Suite 216, Lubbock 79414 • 806/763-2366

Dist. 84 - Lubbock (60%)

Sen. Perry

Culture, Recreation & Tourism-C;
  Licensing & Administrative Procedures

( )Spouse

TEXAS HOUSE OF REPRESENTATIVES

CHARLIE L. GEREN (Mindy), R-Fort Worth   **512/463-0610**

Restaurant Owner/Real Estate Broker/Rancher.
  BBA-Southern Methodist University. 10-22-1949. H-2001-present.
1011 Roberts Cut-Off, River Oaks 76114 • 817/738-8333
  Fax: 817/738-8362

Dist. 99 - Tarrant (9%)

Sens. Burton, Nelson

House Administration-C; Calendars;
  Licensing & Administrative Procedures; State Affairs

BARBARA GERVIN-HAWKINS, D-San Antonio   **512/463-0708**

Education. BA, Accounting-Eastern Michigan University, 1975.
  4-3-1954. H-2017-present.
403 S. WW White Rd., Suite 210, San Antonio 78219 • 210/333-0245

Dist. 120 - Bexar (10%)

Sens. Campbell, Menéndez, Uresti

Criminal Jurisprudence; Culture, Recreation & Tourism;
  Rules & Resolutions

HELEN GIDDINGS, D-Dallas   **512/463-0953**

Small Business Owner. University of Texas at Arlington. 4-21-1945.
  H-1993-present.
1510 N. Hampton Rd., Suite 340, DeSoto 75115 • 972/224-6795
  Fax: 972/228-6796

Dist. 109 - Dallas (7%)

Sens. Hall, West

State Affairs-VC; Appropriations; Calendars

CRAIG GOLDMAN (Auryn), R-Fort Worth   **512/463-0608**

Real Estate Investment. BA-University of Texas at Austin. 10-3-1968.
  H-2013-present.
4521 South Hulen St., Suite 208, Fort Worth 76109 • 817/920-5912
  Fax: 512/463-8342

Dist. 97 - Tarrant (9%)

Sens. Burton, Nelson

House Administration; Licensing & Administrative Procedures;
  Texas Ports, Innovation & Infrastructure, Select; Transportation

( )Spouse

TEXAS HOUSE OF REPRESENTATIVES

LARRY GONZALES (Marie), R-Round Rock　　**512/463-0670**

Business Owner Graphic Design Company. BA, Government-Univ. of Texas at Austin, 1993. 1-29-1970. H-2011-2019.
1801 E. Old Settlers Blvd., Ste. 125, Round Rock 78664 • 512/248-2558

Dist. 52 - Williamson (39%)

Sen. Schwertner

Appropriations; Government Transparency & Operation; Local & Consent Calendars; State & Federal Power & Responsibility, Select

MARY E. GONZÁLEZ, D-Clint　　**512/463-0613**

Izel Consulting. BA, History and Mexican American Studies- University of Texas at Austin; MLA, Social Justice-St. Edward's University. 10-30-1983. H-2013-present.
11200 Santos Sanchez, Socorro 79927 • 915/790-2299
Fax: 915/790-2144

Dist. 75 - El Paso (20%)

Sen. Rodríguez

Agriculture & Livestock-VC; Appropriations

LANCE GOODEN (Alexa), R-Terrell　　**512/463-0458**

Insurance Consultant. BBA, Finance, BA, Government-University of Texas at Austin. 12-1-1982. H-2011-2015: 2017-present.
P.O. Box 2910, Austin 78768-2910 • 512/463-0458

Dist. 4 - Henderson (83%), Kaufman

Sens. Hall, Nichols

Insurance; Public Education

R.D. "BOBBY" GUERRA (Leslie), D-McAllen　　**512/463-0578**

Attorney. BS-Pan American University; JD-Texas Southern University. 8-12-1953. H-2012-present.
10213 North 10th Street, Suite B, McAllen 78504 • 956/292-0407
Fax: 956/292-0418

Dist. 41 - Hidalgo (22%)

Sens. Hinojosa, Lucio

Energy Resources; Public Health

( )Spouse

TEXAS HOUSE OF REPRESENTATIVES

RYAN GUILLEN (Dalinda), D-Rio Grande City   **512/463-0416**

Investor. BS-Texas A&M University. 10-27-1977. H-2003-present.
100 N. FM 3167, Suite 212, Rio Grande City 78582 • 956/716-4838
Fax: 956/716-8219

Dist. 31 - Atascosa, Brooks, Duval, Jim Hogg, Kenedy, LaSalle,
Live Oak, McMullen, Starr, Willacy

Sens. Hinojosa, Lucio, Uresti, Zaffirini

Licensing & Administrative Procedures-VC; State Affairs

ROLAND GUTIERREZ (Sarah), D-San Antonio   **512/463-0452**

Attorney. BA, Political Science-UT San Antonio;
JD-St. Mary's School of Law. 9-1-1970. H-2008-present.
P.O. Box 2910, Austin 78768-2910 • 210/532-2758
Fax: 210/532-3830

Dist. 119 - Bexar (9%)

Sens. Campbell, Menéndez, Uresti

Defense & Veterans' Affairs-C; Judiciary & Civil Jurisprudence

COLE HEFNER (Kerri), R-Mount Pleasant   **512/463-0271**

Insurance Agent. 11-13-1980. H-2017-present.
115 W. 1st Street, Mount Pleasant 75455 • 512/463-0271
Fax: 512/463-1515

Dist. 5 - Camp, Morris, Rains, Smith (24%) Titus, Wood

Sens. Hall, Hughes

Criminal Jurisprudence; Pensions

ANA HERNANDEZ, D-Houston   **512/463-0614**

Attorney. BS, Political Science/Psychology-University of Houston;
JD-University of Texas at Austin. 8-25-1978. H-2005-present.
1233 Mercury Drive, Houston 77029 • 713/675-8596
Fax: 713/675-8599

Dist. 143 - Harris (4%)

Sens. Garcia, Whitmire

Judiciary & Civil Jurisprudence;
Licensing & Administrative Procedures; Redistricting

( )Spouse

TEXAS HOUSE OF REPRESENTATIVES

ABEL HERRERO (Matilda), D-Robstown   **512/463-0462**

Attorney. BA, Political Science-Texas A&M University;
  JD-The University of Texas at Austin. 10-29-1969.
  H-2005-2011; 2013-present.
606 North Carancahua, Suite 103A, Corpus Christi 78401-0690
  361/884-2277; *Fax: 361/884-6706*

Dist. 34 - Nueces (51%)

Sen. Hinojosa

Land & Resource Management-C;
  Licensing & Administrative Procedures

GINA HINOJOSA (John Donisi), D-Austin   **512/463-0668**

Attorney. BS, Government-The University of Texas;
  JD-George Washington Law School, 1999. H-2017-present.
P.O. Box 2910, Austin 78768-2910 • 512/463-0668; *Fax: 512/463-0957*

Dist. 49 - Travis (16%)

Sens. Watson, Zaffirini

Economic & Small Business Development;
  Homeland Security & Public Safety; House Administration

JUSTIN HOLLAND (Neely), R-Rockwall   **512/463-0484**

Real Estate. BA-Texas Tech University; MS-Texas A&M Commerce.
  3-15-1984. H-2017-present.
101 E. Rusk St., # 201, Rockwall 75087 • 972/722-7521
  Fax: 512/463-7834

Dist. 33 - Collin (12%), Rockwall

Sens. Estes, Hall, V. Taylor

Homeland Security & Public Safety; Investments & Financial Services

DONNA HOWARD (Derek), D-Austin   **512/463-0631**

Nursing. BS, Nursing, 1974; Masters in Health Education-UT at Austin,
  1977. 10-25-1951. H-2006-present.
P.O. Box 2910, Austin 78768-2910 • 512/463-0631; *Fax: 512/463-0901*

Dist. 48 - Travis (17%)

Sens. Campbell, Watson, Zaffirini

Calendars-VC; Appropriations; Higher Education;
  House Administration

( )Spouse

TEXAS HOUSE OF REPRESENTATIVES

DAN HUBERTY (Janet), R-Houston   **512/463-0520**

Sales Consultant. BBA-Cleveland State University;
  MBA-University of Phoenix. 6-21-1968. H-2011-present.
4501 Magnolia Cove, Suite 201, Kingwood 77345 • 281/360-9410
  Fax: 512/463-1606

Dist. 127 - Harris (4%)

Sens. Bettencourt, Creighton, Whitmire

Public Education-C; Pensions

TODD HUNTER (Alexis), R-Corpus Christi   **512/463-0672**

Attorney. BA-University of Kansas; JD-Southern Methodist Univ.
  8-26-1953. H-1989-1997; 2009-present.
15217 S.P.I.D., Suite 205, Corpus Christi 78418 • 361/949-4603
  Fax: 361/949-4634

Dist. 32 - Nueces (49%)

Sens. Hinojosa, Kolkhorst

Calendars-C; Criminal Jurisprudence-VC; County Affairs

JASON A. ISAAC (Carrie), R-Dripping Springs   **512/463-0647**

Small Business Owner. BBA-Stephen F. Austin University. 12-25-1971.
  H-2011-present.
P.O. Box 2910, Austin 78768-2910 • 512/463-0647; *Fax: 512/463-3573*

Dist. 45 - Blanco, Hays

Sens. Buckingham, Campbell, Zaffirini

Energy Resources; Urban Affairs

CELIA ISRAEL (Celinda Garza), D-Austin   **512/463-0821**

Realtor. BA-The University of Texas. 7-15-1964. H-2014-present.
P.O. Box 2910, Austin 78768-2910 • 512/463-0821; *Fax: 512/463-1199*

Dist. 50 - Travis (16%)

Sen. Watson

Elections-VC; Transportation

( )Spouse

TEXAS HOUSE OF REPRESENTATIVES

ERIC JOHNSON (Nakita), D-Dallas   **512/463-0586**

Attorney. BA-Harvard University; JD-University of Pennsylvania;
  MPA-Princeton University. 10-10-1975. H-2010-present.
8035 E. RL Thornton Freeway, Ste. 326, Dallas 75228
  214/565-5663

Dist. 100 - Dallas (7%)

Sens. Hall, West

Redistricting-VC; Investments & Financial Services;
  State & Federal Power & Responsibility, Select; Ways & Means

JARVIS D. JOHNSON, D-Houston   **512/463-0554**

Restaurant Owner. BS-Texas Southern University. 9-27-1971.
  H-2016-present.
6112 Wheatley St., Houston 77091 • 713/699-3043; *Fax: 713/699-3498*

Dist. 139 - Harris (4%)

Sens. Garcia, Whitmire

Homeland Security & Public Safety; Urban Affairs

KYLE J. KACAL (Marci), R-College Station   **512/463-0412**

Rancher. BA, Political Science-Texas A&M University; Ranch
  Management-Texas Christian University. 12-26-1969. H-2013-present.
3000 Briarcrest Dr., Suite 203, Bryan 77802 • 979/774-7276

Dist. 12 - Brazos (16%), Falls, Limestone, McLennan (30%), Robertson

Sens. Birdwell, Schwertner

Rules & Resolutions-VC; Calendars; Environmental Regulation;
  Natural Resources

MARK KEOUGH (Kimberly), R-The Woodlands   **512/463-0797**

Minister. BA-Cedarville University; M.Div.-Grace Theological;
  S.T.M.-Dallas Theological Seminary. 9-30-1953. H-2015-present.
25307 I-45 North, Suite 135, The Woodlands 77380 • 281/419-1090

Dist. 15 - Montgomery (37%)

Sen. Creighton

International Trade & Intergovernmental Affairs-VC; Human Services

( )Spouse

TEXAS HOUSE OF REPRESENTATIVES

KEN KING (Robin), R-Canadian   **512/463-0736**

Oil & Gas Service Executive. BS, Business Management. 12-28-1971.
  H-2013-present.
P.O. Box 507, Canadian 79014 • 806/323-8870

Dist. 88 - Armstrong, Bailey, Briscoe, Castro, Cochran, Donley, Gray,
  Hale, Hansford, Hemphill, Hockley, Lamb, Lipscomb, Ochiltree,
  Roberts, Swisher, Yoakum

Sens. Perry, Seliger

Calendars; Public Education;
  State & Federal Power & Responsibility, Select; State Affairs

PHIL S. KING (Terry), R-Weatherford   **512/463-0738**

Attorney. BA, MBA-Dallas Baptist University; JD-Texas Wesleyan.
  2-29-1956. H-1999-present.
2110 Fort Worth Hwy., Weatherford 76086 • 817/596-4796

Dist. 61 - Parker, Wise

Sen. Estes

Homeland Security & Public Safety-C; Energy Resources

TRACY O. KING (Cheryl), D-Uvalde   **512/463-0194**

Businessman. BS-Texas A&M University. 11-9-1960. H-1995-2003;
  H-2005-present.
1920 Palo Blanco, Laredo 78046 • 956/218-2798

Dist. 80 - Dimmit, Frio, Uvalde, Webb (36%), Zapata, Zavala

Sens. Uresti, Zaffirini

Agriculture & Livestock-C; Natural Resources;
  Texas Ports, Innovation & Infrastructure, Select

STEPHANIE KLICK (Don), R-Fort Worth   **512/463-0599**

Registered Nurse. BSN-Texas Christian University. 8-19-1956.
  H-2013-present.
6851 NE Loop 820, Suite 230, North Richland Hills 76180
  817/281-0079

Dist. 91 - Tarrant (9%)

Sens. Burton, Hancock

Human Services; Public Health

( )Spouse

TEXAS HOUSE OF REPRESENTATIVES

LINDA KOOP (Myron), R-Dallas   **512/463-0454**

Retired. BA-Colorado State University;
  MA-University of Texas at Dallas. 6-21-1950. H-2015-present.
300 North Coit Road, Ste. 330, Richardson 75080 • 972/479-0093

Dist. 102 - Dallas (7%)

Sens. Huffines, V. Taylor

Appropriations; Calendars; Public Education

MATT KRAUSE (Jennie), R-Fort Worth   **512/463-0562**

Attorney. BA-San Diego Christian University; JD-Liberty University.
  8-19-1980. H-2013-present.
6624 North Riverside Drive, Suite 330, Ft. Worth 76137
  817/847-4900; *Fax: 817/847-4902*

Dist. 93 - Tarrant (9%)

Sens. Burton, Hancock, Nelson

Culture, Recreation & Tourism; Land & Resource Management

JOHN KUEMPEL (Michelle), R-Seguin   **512/463-0602**

Salesman at CMC Steel. BS-University of Texas at Austin. 5-11-1970.
  H-2010-present.
523 E. Donegan, #102, Seguin 78155 • 830/379-8732

Dist. 44 - Guadalupe, Wilson

Sens. Campbell, Zaffirini

Licensing & Administrative Procedures-C; State Affairs

STAN LAMBERT (Debbie), R-Abilene   **512/463-0718**

Retired Banker. BBA-Abilene Christian University;
  MBA- Southern Methodist University. 12-21-1952. H-2017-present.
P.O. Box 2910, Austin 78768-2910 • 512/463-0718; *Fax: 512/463-0994*

Dist. 71 - Jones, Nolan, Taylor

Sens. Buckingham, Perry

Defense & Veterans' Affairs; Energy Resources

( )Spouse

TEXAS HOUSE OF REPRESENTATIVES

BROOKS LANDGRAF (Shelby), R-Odessa   **512/463-0546**

Attorney, Rancher. BS-Texas A&M University;
  JD-St. Mary's University. 3-15-1981. H-2015-present.
P.O. Box 2910, Austin 78768-2910 • 512/463-0546; *Fax: 512-463-8067*

Dist. 81 - Andrews, Ector, Ward, Winkler

Sens. Perry, Seliger

Energy Resources; Environmental Regulation;
  Local & Consent Calendars

MIKE LANG (Katie), R-Granbury   **512/463-0656**

Law Enforcement. BS-Texas Christian University. 8-29-1962.
  H-2017-present.
112 South Seaman St., Suite 302A, Eastland 76448 • 254/631-0528;
  Fax: 512/478-8805

Dist. 60 - Brown, Callahan, Coleman, Eastland, Hood, Palo Pinto,
  Shackelford, Stephens

Sens. Birdwell, Buckingham, Estes, Perry

Criminal Jurisprudence; Special Purpose Districts

LYLE LARSON, R-San Antonio   **512/463-0646**

Small Business Owner. BBA-Texas A&M University, 1981. 3-25-1959.
  H-2011-present.
2 Mecca Drive, San Antonio 78232 • 210/402-5402

Dist. 122 - Bexar (10%)

Sens. Campbell, Menéndez, Uresti

Natural Resources-C; Elections

JODIE LAUBENBERG (Bob), R-Parker   **512/463-0186**

State Representative. BA-University of Texas at Austin. 4-20-1957.
  H-2003-2019.
206 N. Murphy Road, Murphy 75094 • 972/424-6810

Dist. 89 - Collin (22%)

Sens. Estes, V. Taylor

Elections-C; Judiciary & Civil Jurisprudence

( )Spouse

TEXAS HOUSE OF REPRESENTATIVES

JEFF LEACH (Becky), R-Plano   **512/463-0544**

Attorney. BA-Baylor University; JD-Southern Methodist University,
  Dedman School of Law. 6-10-1982. H-2013-present.
777 E. 15th St., Ste. 202, Plano 75074 • 972/424-1419
  Fax: 972/424-1719

Dist. 67 - Collin (22%)

Sen. V. Taylor

Urban Affairs-VC; Economic & Small Business Development

OSCAR LONGORIA (Jennifer), D-Mission   **512/463-0645**

Attorney. BS, Communication Studies-The University of Texas at
  Austin, 2003; JD-The University of Texas School of Law.
  10-2-1981. H-2013-present.
1320 S. Main Street; P.O. Box 1029, Penitas 78576-1029
  956/580-6944; *Fax: 956/580-2233*

Dist. 35 - Cameron (17%), Hidalgo (13%)

Sens. Hinojosa, Lucio

Appropriations-VC; Investments & Financial Services;
  Local & Consent Calendars

J.M. LOZANO (Abby), R-Kingsville   **512/463-0463**

Restauranteur. BA, Government-University of Texas at Austin;
  MA-University of the Incarnate Word. 5-23-1980. H-2011-present.
1512-A Wildcat Dr., Ste. 106, Portland 78374 • 361/643-0063

Dist. 43 - Bee, Jim Wells, Kleberg, San Patricio

Sens. Hinojosa, Lucio, Zaffirini

Higher Education-C; Environmental Regulation

EDDIE LUCIO, III (Jaime), D-Brownsville   **512/463-0606**

Attorney. BBA-University of Texas at Austin; JD-University of Texas
  School of Law, 2005. 12-19-1978. H-2007-present.
1324 E. Madison, Brownsville 78520 • 956/542-2800
  Fax: 956/542-2889

Dist. 38 - Cameron (41%)

Sen. Lucio

Rules & Resolutions-C; Government Transparency & Operation;
  Natural Resources

( )Spouse

TEXAS HOUSE OF REPRESENTATIVES

ARMANDO A. "MANDO" MARTINEZ (Marisa), D-Weslaco
512/463-0530
Construction. BS-University of Texas Pan American. 1-6-1976.
  H-2005-present.
914 W. Pike Blvd., Weslaco 78596 • 956/447-9473; *Fax: 956/447-8683*
Dist. 39 - Hidalgo (22%)
Sen. Lucio
Transportation-VC; Culture, Recreation & Tourism; Redistricting

WILL METCALF (Megan), R-Conroe   **512/463-0726**

VP, Spirit Texas Bank. BS, Criminal Justice-Sam Houston State Univ.
  6-6-1964. H-2014-present.
1835 Spirit of Texas Way, Suite 100, Conroe 77301 • 936/539-0068
  Fax: 936/539-0066
Dist. 16 - Montgomery (37%)
Sens. Creighton, Nichols
Economic & Small Business Development;
  Homeland Security & Public Safety; Redistricting

MORGAN MEYER (Keana), R-Dallas   **512/463-0367**

Attorney. BS-Southern Methodist University, 1996; JD-Washington and
  Lee University Law School, 1999. 8-8-1974. H-2015-present.
P.O. Box 2910, Austin 78768-2910 • 512/463-0367; *Fax: 512/463-0078*
Dist. 108 - Dallas (7%)
Sens. Hall, Huffines, West
Public Education; State Affairs

RICK MILLER, R-Sugar Land   **512/463-0710**
Management Consultant. BS, Engineering- U. S. Naval Academy, 1968;
  MS National Resource Strategy- National Defense University.
  3-19-1945. H-2013-present.
1130 Industrial Blvd., Suite 126, Sugar Land 77478 • 281/980-0117
  Fax: 281/242-1073
Dist. 26 - Fort Bend (27%)
Sens. Huffman, Kolkhorst
Appropriations; Human Services

( )Spouse

TEXAS HOUSE OF REPRESENTATIVES

INA MINJAREZ (Leo Gomez), D-San Antonio   **512/463-0634**

Former Bexar County Prosecutor. BA, Govt. and English-Notre Dame;
  JD-St. Mary's Law School. 3-27-1975. H-2015-present.
1305 SW Loop 410, #218, San Antonio 78227 • 210/670-8211

Dist. 124 - Bexar (10%)

Sens. Menéndez, Uresti

Human Services; Local & Consent Calendars;
  Opioids & Substance Abuse, Select; Transportation

JOE MOODY (Adrianne), D-El Paso   **512/463-0728**

Attorney. BA-New Mexico State University; JD-Texas Tech University.
  1-9-1981. H-2009-2011; 2013-present.
5675 Woodrow Bean, Ste. 12, El Paso 79924 • 915/751-2700
  Fax: 915/751-2702

Dist. 78 - El Paso (20%)

Sen. Rodríguez

Criminal Jurisprudence-C; Economic Competitiveness, Select;
  General Investigating & Ethics-VC; Opioids & Substance Abuse,
  Select-VC;Juvenile Justice & Family Issues

GEANIE W. MORRISON (Jack), R-Victoria   **512/463-0456**

State Representative. Victoria College. 10-6-1950. H-1999-present.
1908 North Laurent, Suite 500; P.O. Box 4642, Victoria 77903-4642
  361/572-0196; *Fax: 361/576-0747*

Dist. 30 - Aransas, Calhoun, De Witt, Goliad, Refugio, Victoria

Sen. Kolkhorst

Transportation-C; Higher Education;
  Texas Ports, Innovation & Infrastructure, Select

SERGIO MUÑOZ, JR. (Maria Elena), D-Palmview   **512/463-0704**

Attorney. BBA-University of Texas at Austin;
  JD- Texas Southern University. 3-5-1982. H-2011-present.
121 E. Tom Landry, Mission 78572 • 956/584-8999
  Fax: 956/584-7555

Dist. 36 - Hidalgo (22%)

Sens. Hinojosa, Lucio

Insurance-VC; Appropriations

( )Spouse

TEXAS HOUSE OF REPRESENTATIVES

JIM MURPHY (Kathleen), R-Houston   **512/463-0514**

Commercial Real Estate. BA-University of Texas at Austin. 12-8-1957.
  H-2007-2009; 2011-present.
9525 Katy Freeway, Suite 215, Houston 77024 • 713/465-8800

Dist. 133 - Harris (4%)

Sens. Bettencourt, Huffman, Whitmire

Special Purpose Districts-C; Ways & Means

ANDREW MURR, R-Junction   **512/463-0536**

Attorney, Rancher. BS-Texas A&M University;
  JD-Texas Tech School of Law. 4-23-1977. H-2015-present.
715 Water St., Kerrville 78028 • 830/257-0432; *Fax: 512/463-1449*

Dist. 53 - Bandera, Crockett, Edwards, Kerr, Kimble, Llano, Mason,
  Medina, Menard, Real, Schleicher, Sutton

Sens. Buckingham, Perry, Uresti

State & Federal Power & Responsibility, Select-VC;
  Judiciary & Civil Jurisprudence; Local & Consent Calendars;
  Opioids & Substance Abuse, Select; Ways & Means

VICTORIA NEAVE, D-Dallas   **512/463-0244**

Attorney. BA, Government and Politics - Univ. of Texas at Dallas;
JD, Magna Cum Laude-Texas Southern University Thurgood Marshall
  School of Law. 12-29-1980. H-2017-present.
317 S. Galloway, #B, Mesquite 75149 • 512/463-0244
  Fax: 512/463-9967

Dist. 107 - Dallas (7%)

Sens. Hall, Huffines

County Affairs; Judiciary & Civil Jurisprudence

ALFONSO "PONCHO" NEVAREZ (Rossy), D-Eagle Pass
     512/463-0566

Attorney. BA-The University of Texas at Austin;
  JD-St. Mary's School of Law. 9-1-1972. H-2013-present.
1995 Williams St., Eagle Pass 78852 • 830/773-0860

Dist. 74 - Brewster, Culberson, Hudspeth, Jeff Davis, Kinney, Loving,
  Maverick, Pecos, Presidio, Reeves, Terrell, Val Verde

Sens. Rodríguez, Seliger, Uresti

Homeland Security & Public Safety-VC; Calendars;
  General Investigating & Ethics; Natural Resources; Opioids &
  Substance Abuse, Select

( )Spouse

TEXAS HOUSE OF REPRESENTATIVES

RENE O. OLIVEIRA, D-Brownsville   **512/463-0640**

Attorney. BS, JD-University of Texas at Austin. 3-14-1955.
  H-1981-87; H-1991-present.
855 W. Price Road, Suite 22, Brownsville 78520 • 956/542-1828
  Fax: 956/542-1618

Dist. 37 - Cameron (42%)

Sen. Lucio

Business & Industry-C; State Affairs;
  Economic Competitiveness, Select;
  Texas Ports, Innovation & Infrastructure, Select

TOM OLIVERSON, M.D. (Jennifer), R-Cypress   **512/463-0661**

Anesthesiologist. BS-Sam Houston State University;
  MD-Baylor College of Medicine. 6-8-1972. H-2017-present.
12345 Jones Rd., #221, Houston 77070 • 281/955-5152
  Fax: 512/463-4130

Dist. 130 - Harris (4%)

Sens. Bettencourt, Kolkhorst

House Administration; Insurance; Public Health

EVELINA ORTEGA (Mark), D-El Paso   **512/463-0638**

Attorney. BA, JD-The University of Texas at Austin. 8-18-1955.
  H-2017-present.
310 N. Mesa, Suite 519, El Paso 79901 • 915/351-4031

Dist. 77 - El Paso (20%)

Sen. Rodríguez

Economic & Small Business Development;
  International Trade & Intergovernmental Affairs;
  Texas Ports, Innovation & Infrastructure, Select

CHRIS PADDIE (Brooke), R-Marshall   **512/463-0556**

General Manager of KMHT Radio. BS-Texas A&M University.
  2-18-1974. H-2013-present.
102 W. Houston, Marshall 75670 • 903/935-1141; *Fax: 903/935-1142*

Dist. 9 - Cass, Harrison, Marion, Panola, Sabine, Shelby

Sens. Hughes, Nichols

Calendars; Licensing & Administrative Procedures;
  State & Federal Power & Responsibility, Select; State Affairs

( )Spouse

TEXAS HOUSE OF REPRESENTATIVES

TAN PARKER (Beth), R-Flower Mound   **512/463-0688**

Businessman. BA, Political Philosophy-University of Dallas;
MB-London School of Economics. 5-22-1971. H-2007-present.
800 Parker Square, Ste. 245, Flower Mound 75028 • 972/724-8477

Dist. 63 - Denton (25%)

Sen. Nelson

Investments & Financial Services-C; International Trade &
Intergovernmental Affairs; Redistricting

DENNIS PAUL (Eliza), R-Houston   **512/463-0734**

Engineer. BSCE, MSCE-University of Houston. 3-29-1961.
H-2015-present.
17225 El Camino Real, Suite 415, Houston 77058 • 281/488-8900

Dist. 129 - Harris (4%)

Sens. Garcia, L. Taylor

Texas Ports, Innovation & Infrastructure, Select-VC; Insurance;
Pensions; Rules & Resolutions

MARY ANN PEREZ, D-Houston   **512/463-0460**

Insurance Agent. BBA Cum Laude-Univ. of Houston-Downtown.
5-15-1962. H-2013-2015; 2017-present.
101 S. Richey St., Ste. F, Pasadena 77506 • 713/740-8153
Fax: 512/463-0763

Dist. 144 - Harris (4%)

Sens. Garcia, L. Taylor

Special Purpose Districts-VC; Appropriations

DADE PHELAN (Kim), R-Beaumont   **512/463-0706**

Real Estate Developer. BA-University of Texas. 9-18-1975.
H-2015-present.
P.O. Box 848, Nederland 77627-0848 • 409/745-2777

Dist. 21 - Jefferson (36%), Orange

Sens. Creighton, Nichols

Natural Resources-VC; Appropriations; Calendars;
Texas Ports, Innovation & Infrastructure, Select

( )Spouse

TEXAS HOUSE OF REPRESENTATIVES

LARRY PHILLIPS (Robin), R-Sherman   **512/463-0297**

Attorney. BBA-Baylor University; JD-University of Houston. 4-5-1966.
  H-2003-present.
421 N. Crockett, Sherman 75090 • 903/891-7297; *Fax: 903/870-0066*
Dist. 62 - Delta, Fannin, Grayson
Sens. Estes, Hall
Insurance-C; Transportation

JOSEPH C. "JOE" PICKETT (Shannon), D-El Paso   **512/463-0596**

State Representative. 12-6-1956. H-1995-present.
1790 Lee Trevino, Suite 307, El Paso 79936 • 915/590-4349
  Fax: 915/590-4726
Dist. 79 - El Paso (20%)
Sen. Rodríguez
Environmental Regulation-C; Transportation

FOUR PRICE (Karen), R-Amarillo   **512/463-0470**

Attorney. BBA, Finance-University of Texas at Austin;
  JD-St. Mary's School of Law. 10-8-1967. H-2011-present.
500 S. Taylor St., Ste. 506; P.O. Box 2848, Amarillo 79105-2848
  806/374-8787
Dist. 87 - Carson, Hutchinson, Moore, Potter, Sherman
Sen. Seliger
Opioids & Substance Abuse, Select-C; Public Health-C;
  General Investigating & Ethics; Natural Resources

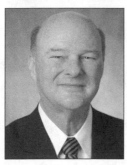

JOHN RANEY (Elizabeth), R-Bryan   **512/463-0698**

Small Business Owner. BBA, Marketing-Texas A&M University-1969.
  4-4-1947. H-2011-present.
4103 South Texas Ave., Suite 103, Bryan 77802 • 979/260-5040
  Fax: 979/260-5097
Dist. 14 - Brazos (84%)
Sen. Schwertner
Higher Education-VC; Appropriations; House Administration

( )Spouse

TEXAS HOUSE OF REPRESENTATIVES

RICHARD PEÑA RAYMOND (Michelle), D-Laredo

512/463-0558

Businessman. BA-University of Texas at Austin; JD-University of Texas
  School of Law. 10-27-1960. H-1993-99, 2001-present.
5702 McPherson, Ste. 16, Laredo 78041 • 956/753-7722
  Fax: 956/753-7729

Dist. 42 - Webb (64%)

Sen. Zaffirini

Human Services-C; Ways & Means

RON REYNOLDS (Jonita), D-Missouri City   **512/463-0494**

Attorney. BS, Public Affairs-Texas Southern University;
  JD-Texas Tech University School of Law. 9-18-1973. H-2011-present.
2440 Texas Parkway, Ste. 102, Missouri City 77489 • 281/208-3574
  Fax: 281/208-3696

Dist. 27 - Fort Bend (27%)

Sens. Huffman, Miles

Elections; Environmental Regulation

MATT RINALDI (Corley), R-Irving   **512/463-0468**

Attorney/Businessman. BBA-James Madison University;
  JD-Boston University School of Law, 2001. 4-11-1975.
  H-2015-present.
12300 Ford Rd., Suite B348, Farmers Branch 75234 • 972/247-8994

Dist. 115 - Dallas (7%)

Sen. Huffines

Agriculture & Livestock; Judiciary & Civil Jurisprudence

KEVIN ROBERTS (Hollie), R-Houston   **512/463-0496**

Businessman. BBA-Texas Tech University. 1-16-1966. H-2017-present.
6810 Cypress Creek Parkway, Houston 77069 • 281/444-1814
  Fax: 512/463-1507

Dist. 126 - Harris (4%)

Sens. Bettencourt, Whitmire

Appropriations; County Affairs;
  Opioids & Substance Abuse, Select; Texas Ports, Innovation &
  Infrastructure, Select

( )Spouse

TEXAS HOUSE OF REPRESENTATIVES

EDDIE RODRIGUEZ (Christine), D-Austin　　　**512/463-0674**

State Representative. BA-University of Texas at Austin. 7-1-1971.
　H-2003-present.
P.O. Box 2910, Austin 78768-2910 • 512/463-0674; *Fax: 512/463-0314*

Dist. 51 - Travis (17%)

Sens. Watson, Zaffirini

Environmental Regulation; Redistricting; State Affairs

JUSTIN RODRIGUEZ (Victoria), D-San Antonio　　**512/463-0669**

Attorney. BBA-University of the Incarnate Word; JD-University of
　Wisconsin Law School. 9-4-1974. H-2013-present.
6502 Bandera Road, Suite 104, San Antonio 78238 • 210/521-7100
　Fax: 210/521-7101

Dist. 125 - Bexar (10%)

Sens. Menéndez, Uresti

Appropriations; Pensions;
　Texas Ports, Innovation & Infrastructure, Select

RAMON ROMERO, JR., D-Fort Worth　　　**512/463-0740**

CEO. Tarrant County College. 11-13-1973. H-2015-present.
3663 Airport Freeway, Suite 102, Ft. Worth 76111
　817/924-6788; *Fax: 817/924-1997*

Dist. 90 - Tarrant (9%)

Sens. Burton, Hancock, Nelson

Business & Industry; Corrections; Rules & Resolutions

TONI ROSE, D-Dallas　　　**512/463-0664**

Consultant. BS, Criminal Justice-Paul Quinn College. 2-3-1968.
　H-2013-present.
3730 S. Lancaster Road, Ste. 140, Dallas 75216 • 214/371-3300
　Fax: 214/371-3304

Dist. 110 - Dallas (7%)

Sens. Hall, West

Appropriations; Calendars; Human Services; Opioids & Substance
　Abuse, Select

( )Spouse

TEXAS HOUSE OF REPRESENTATIVES

SCOTT SANFORD (Shelly), R-McKinney   **512/463-0356**

Minister. BBA-Baylor University. 10-3-1963. H-2013-present.
115 West Virginia St., Ste. 103, McKinney 75069 • 972/548-7500
 Fax: 972/548-7501

Dist. 70 - Collin (22%)

Sens. Estes, V. Tayor

Corrections; Insurance

MATT SCHAEFER (Jasilyn), R-Tyler   **512/463-0584**

Attorney. BA, Finance-Texas Tech University; JD-Texas Tech
 University School of Law. 2-11-1976. H-2013-present.
200 E. Ferguson, Ste. 506, Tyler 75702 • 903/592-0900
 Fax: 903/592-0902

Dist. 6 - Smith (76%)

Sen. Hughes

Corrections; Homeland Security & Public Safety

MIKE SCHOFIELD, R-Katy   **512/463-0528**

Attorney. BA, Political Science-Rutgers University;
 JD-Louisiana State University. 6-27-1964. H-2015-present.
1550 Foxlake Drive, Suite 120, Houston 77084 • 281/578-8484
 Fax: 512/463-7820

Dist. 132 - Harris (4%)

Sens. Bettencourt, Huffman, Kolkhorst

Judiciary & Civil Jurisprudence; Juvenile Justice & Family Issues

LEIGHTON SCHUBERT (Brittany), R-Caldwell   **512/463-0600**

Attorney. BA-Texas A&M University; JD-South Texas College of Law.
 7-14-1982. H-2015-present.
105 E. Main St., Suite 102A, Brenham 77833 • 974/421-9840
 Fax: 979/421-9862

Dist. 13 - Austin, Burleson, Colorado, Fayette, Grimes, Lavaca,
 Washington

Sens. Kolkhorst, Schwertner

Energy Resources; House Administration; Special Purpose Districts

( )Spouse

TEXAS HOUSE OF REPRESENTATIVES

MATT SHAHEEN (Robyn), R-Plano **512/463-0594**

Technology Executive. BS, Business Economics-Randolph Macon
  College; MA Liberal Arts-Southern Methodist University. 6-8-1965.
  H-2015-present.
5304 West Plano Parkway, Suite 2, Plano 75093 • 469/642-8708

Dist. 66 - Collin (22%)

Sen. V. Taylor

Government Transparency & Operation;
  International Trade & Intergovernmental Affairs

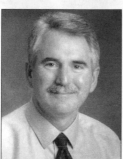

J.D. SHEFFIELD, D.O., R-Gatesville **512/463-0628**

Physician. BS-Howard Payne University; DO-University of North Texas
  Health Science Center. 8-13-1960. H-2013-present.
P.O. Box 704, Gatesville 76528-0704 • 254/679-9016

Dist. 59 - Comanche, Coryell, Erath, Hamilton, McCulloch, Mills,
  San Saba, Somervell

Sens. Birdwell, Buckingham, Estes, Perry

Public Health-VC; Appropriations; Opioids & Substance Abuse, Select;
  Rules & Resolutions

HUGH D. SHINE (Debbie), R-Temple **512/463-0630**

Investment Broker. BBA-Sam Houston State University;
  MBA-Baylor University. 7-27-1952. H-1986-1991; 2017-present.
4 South 1st St., Temple 76501 • 254/742-7616

Dist. 55 - Bell (52%)

Sen. Buckingham

Business & Industry-VC; General Investigating & Ethics;
  Ways & Means

RON SIMMONS (Lisa), R-Carrollton **512/463-0478**

Investment Advisor. BA-Dallas Baptist University. 9-21-1960.
  H-2013-present.
1029 Rosemeade Pkwy., Suite 108, Carrollton 75007 • 972/492-2080
  Fax: 972/492-7408

Dist. 65 - Denton (25%)

Sen. Nelson

Appropriations; Local & Consent Calendars; Transportation

( )Spouse

TEXAS HOUSE OF REPRESENTATIVES

JOHN T. SMITHEE (Becky), R-Amarillo   **512/463-0702**

Attorney. BBA-West Texas State University; JD-Texas Tech University.
   9-7-1951. H-1985-present.
320 S. Polk, LB 28, Amarillo 79101 • 806/372-3327; *Fax: 806/342-0327*
Dist. 86 - Dallam, Deaf Smith, Hartley, Oldham, Parmer, Randall
Sen. Seliger
Judiciary & Civil Jurisprudence-C; State Affairs

DREW SPRINGER, JR. (Lydia), R-Muenster   **512/463-0526**

Financial Services. BA, Accounting-University of North Texas.
   10-27-1966. H-2013-present.
406 East California Street, Gainesville 76240 • 940/580-1770
Dist. 68 - Childress, Collingsworth, Cooke, Cottle, Crosby, Dickens, Fisher,
   Floyd, Garza, Hall, Hardeman, Haskell, Jack, Kent, King, Montague,
   Motley, Stonewall, Throckmorton, Wheeler, Wilbarger, Young
Sens. Estes, Perry, Seliger
County Affairs-VC; Redistricting; Ways & Means

PHIL STEPHENSON, R-Wharton   **512/463-0604**

CPA. BBA, Accounting-Texas Tech University. 2-5-1945.
   H-2013-present.
1603 North Richmond Rd., Wharton 77488 • 979/532-1157
Dist. 85 - Fort Bend (18%), Jackson, Wharton
Sens. Huffman, Kolkhorst
Investments & Financial Services-VC; Ways & Means

JONATHAN STICKLAND (Krystal), R-Bedford   **512/463-0522**

Consultant. Tarrant County College and Parkland College. 9-4-1983.
   H-2013-present.
1600 Airport Freeway, Suite 334, Bedford 76022 • 817/283-5300
Dist. 92 - Tarrant (9%)
Sens. Burton, Hancock, Nelson
Business & Industry; County Affairs

( )Spouse

TEXAS HOUSE OF REPRESENTATIVES

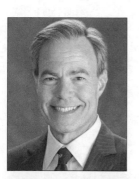

JOE STRAUS III (Julie), R-San Antonio   **512/463-1000**

Speaker of the House - 2009-present.

Insurance and Investments. BA, Political Science-Vanderbilt University. 9-1-1959. H-2005-present.
7373 Broadway, Suite 202-A, San Antonio 78209 • 210/828-4411
  Fax: 210/832-9994

Dist. 121 - Bexar (10%)

Sens. Campbell, Menéndez

LYNN STUCKY (Lori), R-Denton   **512/463-0582**

Veterinarian. BS, DVM-Kansas State University. 2-20-1958. H-2017-present.
400 West Oak Street, Suites 105 & 106, Denton 76201 • 512/463-0582
  Fax: 512/463-0471

Dist. 64 - Denton (25%)

Sens. Estes, Nelson

Agriculture & Livestock; Land & Resource Management

VALOREE SWANSON (Vern), R-Spring   **512/463-0572**

Business, Real Estate. BBA-Baylor University. 9-22-1957. H-2017-present.
23008 Northcrest, Spring 77389 • 281/257-4222; *Fax: 512/463-1908*

Dist. 150 - Harris (4%)

Sens. Bettencourt, Creighton

Elections; Human Services

SHAWN THIERRY, D-Houston   **512/463-0518**

Attorney. BA-Howard University; JD-Texas Southern. 8-6-1969. H-2017-present.
2616 S. Loop West, Ste. 635, Houston 77054 • 713/667-4146
  Fax:713/839-0934

Dist. 146 - Harris (4%)

Sens. Huffman, Miles

County Affairs; Juvenile Justice & Family Issues

( )Spouse

TEXAS HOUSE OF REPRESENTATIVES

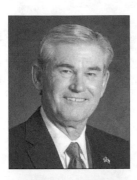

ED THOMPSON (Freddie), R-Pearland   **512/463-0707**

Insurance Agent. BBA, Finance-University of Houston. 11-24-1950.
  H-2013-present.
2341 N. Galveston Ave., Suite 120, Pearland 77581 • 281/485-6565

Dist. 29 - Brazoria (56%)

Sen. L. Taylor

Environmental Regulation-VC; Transportation

SENFRONIA THOMPSON, D-Houston   **512/463-0720**

Attorney. BS, Biology-Texas Southern University;
  MEd-Prairie View A&M University; JD-Texas Southern University;
  LLM-University of Houston Law Center. 1-1-1939. H-1973-present.
10527 Homestead Road, Houston 77016 • 713/633-3390
  Fax: 713/633-7830

Dist. 141 - Harris (4%)

Sens. Bettencourt, Garcia, Miles, Whitmire

Local & Consent Calendars-C; Econ. Competitiveness, Select-VP;
  Licensing & Admin. Procedures; State & Federal Power &
  Responsibility, Select; Transportation

TONY TINDERHOLT (Bethany), R-Arlington   **512/463-0624**

Retired. MA Educational Leadership-Touro College. 8-13-1970.
  H-2015-present.
4381 W. Green Oaks Blvd., Ste. 107, Arlington 76016 • 817/478-5000
  Fax: 512/463-8386

Dist. 94 - Tarrant (9%)

Sens. Birdwell, Burton, Hancock

Corrections; Government Transparency & Operation

CHRIS TURNER (Lisa), D-Grand Prairie   **512/463-0574**

Communications. BA, University of Texas at Austin. 10-10-1972.
  H-2009 to 2011; 2013-present.
320 Westway Place, Suite 501, Arlington 76018 • 817/459-2800
  Fax: 817/459-7900

Dist. 101 - Tarrant (9%)

Sens. Birdwell, Burton, Hancock

General Investigating & Ethics; Higher Education; Insurance;
  State & Federal Power & Responsibility, Select

( )Spouse

TEXAS HOUSE OF REPRESENTATIVES

TOMAS URESTI (Leslie), D-San Antonio   **512/463-0714**

Bond Officer. 9-17-1960. H-2017-present.
1114 SW Military Dr., Suite 103, San Antonio 78221 • 210/923-3870
  Fax: 512/463-1458

Dist. 118 - Bexar (10%)

Sens. Campbell, Uresti, Zaffirini

County Affairs; Government Transparency & Operation

GARY VANDEAVER (Pam), R-New Boston   **512/463-0692**

Retired Educator. BS, MS, EdD-East Texas State University. 9-25-1958.
  H-2015-present.
710 James Bowie Drive, New Boston 75570 • 903/628-0361

Dist. 1 - Bowie, Franklin, Lamar, Red River

Sen. Hughes

House Administration-VC; Appropriations; Opioids & Substance
  Abuse, Select; Public Education

JASON VILLALBA (Brooke), R-Dallas   **512/463-0576**

Attorney. BBA-Baylor University; JD-The Univ. of Texas at Austin.
  3-26-1971. H-2013-present.
10210 North Central Expressway, Suite 220, Dallas 75231
  214/363-8700; *Fax: 214/363-8701*

Dist. 114 - Dallas (7%)

Sen. Huffines

Business & Industry; Economic & Small Business Development

HUBERT VO (Kathy), D-Houston   **512/463-0568**

Businessman. BS, Mechanical Engineering-University of Houston.
  5-30-1956. H-2005-present.
7474 S. Kirkwood Avenue, Ste. 106, Houston 77072 • 281/988-0212

Dist. 149 - Harris (4%)

Sens. Huffman, Miles

Economic & Small Business Development-VC; House Administration;
  Insurance

( )Spouse

TEXAS HOUSE OF REPRESENTATIVES

ARMANDO L. WALLE (Debbie), D-Houston   **512/463-0924**

Law. BS, Political Science-University of Houston, 2004;
 JD-University of Houston School of Law, 2014. 3-7-1978.
 H-2009-present.
150 West Parker Road, Suite 700, Houston 77076 • 713/694-8620
 Fax: 713/694-8613

Dist. 140 - Harris (4%)

Sens. Garcia, Whitmire

Appropriations; Energy Resources

JAMES WHITE, R-Hillister   **512/463-0490**

Learning/Forestry Consultant. BS, Political Science; MEd-Prairie View
 A&M University; MS and PhD-Political Science-University of
 Houston. 7-16-1964. H-2011-present.
1001 W. Bluff; P.O. Box 395, Woodville 75979-0395 • 409/283-3700
 Fax: 409/283-3702

Dist. 19 - Hardin, Jasper, Newton, Polk, Tyler

Sen. Nichols

Corrections-C; International Trade & Intergovernmental Affairs;
 Opioids & Substance Abuse, Select

TERRY WILSON (Shannon), R-Marble Falls   **512/463-0309**

Retired US Army. BS-Texas A&M University. 8-28-1964.
 H-2017-present.
710 Main Street, Suite 242, Georgetown 78626 • 512/463-0309
 Fax: 512/463-0049

Dist. 20 - Burnet, Milam, Williamson (22%)

Sens. Buckingham, Schwertner

Criminal Jurisprudence; Defense & Veterans' Affairs

PAUL D. WORKMAN (Sherry), R-Austin   **512/463-0652**

Commercial Construction Consultant. BS-Building Construction-Texas
 A&M University, 1973. 11-8-1951. H-2011-present.
P.O. Box 2910, Austin 78768-2910 • 512/463-0652; *Fax: 512/463-0565*

Dist. 47 - Travis (17%)

Sens. Buckingham, Campbell, Watson

Business & Industry; Natural Resources

( )Spouse

TEXAS HOUSE OF REPRESENTATIVES

JOHN WRAY (Michele), R-Waxahachie   **512/463-0516**

Attorney. BS, Political Science-Texas A&M University, 1993;
  JD-University of Texas School of Law, 1996. H-2015-present.
133 Chieftain Drive, Suite 103, Waxahachie 75165 • 972/938-9392

Dist. 10 - Ellis, Henderson (17%)

Sens. Birdwell, Nichols

Homeland Security & Public Safety; Rules & Resolutions;
  Transportation

GENE WU (Miya Shay), D-Houston   **512/463-0492**

Attorney. BS-Texas A&M University; Masters of Public Policy-
  The University of Texas at Austin; JD-South Texas School of Law.
  3-23-1978. H-2013-present.
6500 Rookin St., Building C, Houston 77074 • 713/271-3900
  Fax: 713/271-3902

Dist. 137 - Harris (4%)

Sens. Huffman, Miles

Appropriations; Human Services

WILLIAM "BILL" ZEDLER (Ellen), R-Arlington   **512/463-0374**

Consultant. BBA, MBA-Sam Houston State University. 8-19-1943.
  H-2011-present.
5840 West Interstate 20, Suite 110, Arlington 76017 • 817/483-1885
  Fax: 817/478-1887

Dist. 96 - Tarrant (9%)

Sens. Birdwell, Burton

Public Health; Urban Affairs

JOHN ZERWAS, M.D. (Sylvia), R-Richmond   **512/463-0657**

Physician. BS-University of Houston; MD-Baylor College of Medicine.
  3-24-1955. H-2007-present.
22310 Grand Corner Dr., Ste. 110, Katy 77494 • 888/827-1560

Dist. 28 - Fort Bend (27%)

Sens. Huffman, Kolkhorst

Appropriations-C

( )Spouse

REPRESENTATIVES' OFFICE & TELEPHONE NUMBERS
85th LEGISLATURE

MEMBER	RM. NO.	PHONE 512/	FAX 512/	ASSISTANT
Allen, Alma A.	GW.5	463-0744	463-0761	Anneliese Vogel
Alonzo, Roberto R.	1N.12	463-0408	463-1817	Margarita Garza
Alvarado, Carol	GW.6	463-0732	463-4781	Alexander Hammond
Anchia, Rafael	1N.9	463-0746	463-5896	Liz Zornes
Anderson, Charles	GW.8	463-0135	463-0642	Tracy Morehead
Anderson, Rodney	E1.414	463-0641	463-0044	Pam Johnson
Arévalo, Diana	E2.304	463-0616	463-4873	Marc Hoskins
Ashby, Trent	E2.414	463-0508	463-5934	Judd Messer
Bailes, Ernest	E1.316	463-0570	463-0315	Nick Raymond
Bell Jr., Cecil	E2.708	463-0650	463-0575	Ariane Marion
Bernal, Diego	E1.220	463-0532	463-7675	Anita Fernandez
Biedermann, Kyle	E1.412	463-0325	463-6161	McKenzie Taylor
Blanco, César	E1.218	463-0622	463-0931	Josh Reyna
Bohac, Dwayne	GS.6	463-0727	463-0681	Travis Griffin
Bonnen, Dennis H.	1W.6	463-0564	463-8414	Shera Eichler
Bonnen M. D., Greg	E2.504	463-0729	463-5896	Brigitt Hartin
Burkett, Cindy	GN.10	463-0464	463-9295	John McCord
Burns, DeWayne	E1.322	463-0538	463-0897	Joy Davis
Burrows, Dustin	E2.710	463-0542	463-0671	Jeramy Kitchen
Button, Angie Chen	4N.5	463-0486	463-0793	Amanda Willard
Cain, Briscoe	E1.418	463-0733	463-1323	Brandon Waltens
Canales, Terry	E2.910	463-0426	463-0043	Curtis Smith
Capriglione, Giovanni	E2.610	463-0690		Amanda Calongne
Clardy, Travis	E2.908	463-0592	463-8792	Kelly Barnes
Coleman, Garnet	4N.10	463-0524	463-1260	Nicolas Kalla
Collier, Nicole	E2.318	463-0716	463-1516	Jacob Limon
Cook, Byron C.	GW.7	463-0730	463-2506	Toni Barcellona
Cortez, Philip	E2.714	463-0269	463-1096	Clarissa Rodriguez
Cosper, Scott	E2.816	463-0684	463-8987	Ryan Marquess
Craddick, Tom	1W.9	463-0500	463-7722	Kate Huddleston
Cyrier, John	E2.314	463-0682	463-9955	MeLissa Nemecek
Dale, Tony	E2.602	463-0696	463-9333	Greg Bentch
Darby, Drew	E1.308	463-0331	463-0517	Jason Modglin
Davis, Sarah	GW.4	463-0389	463-1374	Brigette Dechant
Davis, Yvonne	4N.9	463-0598	463-2297	Claude Spivey
Dean, Jay	E2.716	463-0750	463-9085	Daniel Mittnacht
Deshotel, Joseph	GW.12	463-0662	463-8381	Christian Manuel
Dukes, Dawnna M.	E2.302	463-0506	463-7864	Paul Theobald
Dutton Jr., Harold V.	3N.5	463-0510	463-8333	Tamoria Jones
Elkins, Gary	4N.3	463-0722	463-2331	Debra Clonts
Faircloth, Wayne	E2.812	463-0502	936-4260	Wesley Starnes
Fallon, Pat	E2.722	463-0694	463-1130	Shannan Sorrell

E1, E2 - Capitol Extension   www.txdirectory.com/online/txhouse

REPRESENTATIVES' OFFICE & TELEPHONE NUMBERS

MEMBER	RM. NO.	PHONE 512/	FAX 512/	ASSISTANT
Farrar, Jessica	1N.8	463-0620	463-0894	Ariana Campos
Flynn, Dan	1N.10	463-0880	463-2188	David Erinakes
Frank, James	E2.604	463-0534	463-8161	Jim Johnson
Frullo, John	4N.6	463-0676	463-0072	Matt Abel
Geren, Charlie L.	GW.15	463-0610	463-8310	Payton Spreen
Gervin-Hawkins, Barbara	E1.208	463-0708		J.D. Pedraza
Giddings, Helen	GW.11	463-0953	463-5887	Tamara Sadler
Goldman, Craig	E2.606	463-0608	463-8342	Amanda Robertson
Gonzales, Larry	E2.418	463-0670	463-1469	Chris Sanchez
González, Mary E.	E2.204	463-0613	463-1237	Joshua Carter
Gooden, Lance	E1.204	463-0458		Michael Paylor
Guerra, R. D.	E2.818	463-0578	463-1482	Anne Drescher
Guillen, Ryan	1W.3	463-0416	463-1012	Ben Wright
Gutierrez, Roland	GN.7	463-0452	463-1447	Margaret Frain Wallace
Hefner, Cole	E1.416	463-0271	463-1515	James Perryman
Hernandez, Ana	4S.3	463-0614	463-0612	Maria Delgado
Herrero, Abel	4S.6	463-0462	463-1705	Jesus Moreno
Hinojosa, Gina	E2.316	463-0668	463-0957	Doug Greco
Holland, Justin	E2.804	463-0484	463-7834	Robert A. Paulsen III
Howard, Donna	E1.504	463-0631	463-0901	Scott Daigle
Huberty, Dan	E2.408	463-0520	463-1606	Casey Christman
Hunter, Todd	1W.11	463-0672	463-2101	Angie Flores
Isaac, Jason A.	E1.320	463-0647	463-3573	Terry M. Franks
Israel, Celia	E2.212	463-0821	463-1199	Jennie Kennedy
Johnson, Eric	1N.7	463-0586	463-8147	Mary Elbanna
Johnson, Jarvis D.	E1.424	463-0554	463-8380	Richard Johnson III
Kacal, Kyle J.	E2.412	463-0412		Terra Willett
Keough, Mark	E2.402	463-0797	463-0898	Jason Millsaps
King, Ken	E2.410	463-0736	463-0211	Cheryl Lively
King, Phil S.	1N.5	463-0738	463-1957	Ashley Westenhover
King, Tracy O.	GW.16	463-0194	463-1220	Celina Overbo
Klick, Stephanie	E2.904	463-0599	463-0751	Bryan Shufelt
Koop, Linda	E1.406	463-0454	463-1121	Ryan Sparks
Krause, Matt	E2.214	463-0562	463-2053	Clayton Knippa
Kuempel, John	E2.422	463-0602	480-0391	Brittney Madden
Lambert, Stan	E2.820	463-0718	463-0994	Seth Juergens
Landgraf, Brooks	E1.312	463-0546	463-8067	
Lang, Mike	E1.410	463-0656	478-8805	James King
Larson, Lyle	E2.406	463-0646	463-0893	Lynlie Wallace
Laubenberg, Jodie	1W.4	463-0186		Suzanne Bowers
Leach, Jeff	GN.9	463-0544	463-9974	Lauren Young
Longoria, Oscar	E1.510	463-0645	463-0559	Lee Loya
Lozano, J.M.	GN.11	463-0463	463-1765	Matt Lamon

REPRESENTATIVES' OFFICE & TELEPHONE NUMBERS

MEMBER	RM. NO.	PHONE 512/	FAX 512/	ASSISTANT
Lucio III, Eddie	GN.8	463-0606	*463-0660*	Ruben O'Bell
Martinez, Armando A.	4N.4	463-0530	*463-0849*	Scott Jenkines
Metcalf, Will	E1.314	463-0726	*463-8428*	Zachary Stephenson
Meyer, Morgan	E1.318	463-0367	*463-0078*	Aaron Gibson
Miller, Rick	E2.822	463-0710	*463-0711*	Courtney Hjaltman
Minjarez, Ina	E2.312	463-0634	*463-7668*	Nar Dorrycott
Moody, Joe	E1.420	463-0728	*463-0397*	Ellic Sahualla
Morrison, Geanie W.	3S.2	463-0456	*463-0158*	Macgregor Stephenson
Munoz Jr., Sergio	4S.4	463-0704	*463-5364*	Loradel Mariano
Murphy, Jim	E1.506	463-0514	*463-8715*	Jason Briggs
Murr, Andrew	E1.306	463-0536	*463-1449*	Regan M. Ellmer
Neave, Victoria	E1.216	463-0244	*463-9967*	Katy Womble
Nevarez, Alfonso	E1.508	463-0566	*463-0220*	Obie Salinas
Oliveira, Rene O.	3N.6	463-0640	*463-8186*	J.J. Garza
Oliverson M.D., Tom	E2.720	463-0661	*463-4130*	Eiman Siddiqui
Ortega, Evelina	E2.704	463-0638	*463-8908*	Brooke Bennett
Paddie, Chris	E2.502	463-0556	*463-0611*	John Buxie
Parker, Tan	4S.2	463-0688		Patricia Robinson
Paul, Dennis	E2.814	463-0734	*463-0401*	Mitzi Stoute Faniola
Perez, Mary Ann	E1.212	463-0460	*463-0763*	David Gonzalez
Phelan, Dade	E1.324	463-0706	*463-1861*	Zach Johnson
Phillips, Larry	4N.7	463-0297	*463-1561*	Sara Hays
Pickett, Joseph C.	1W.5	463-0596	*463-6504*	Michael Breitinger
Price, Four	E2.902	463-0470	*463-8003*	Hal Talton
Raney, John	E2.808	463-0698	*463-5109*	Anna Hynes
Raymond, Richard Pena	1W.2	463-0558	*463-6296*	Kyle Mauro
Reynolds, Ron	E2.308	463-0494	*463-1403*	Jennifer Brader
Rinaldi, Matt	E2.508	463-0468	*463-1044*	Desiree Smith
Roberts, Kevin	E2.416	463-0496	*463-1507*	Ben Melson
Rodriguez, Eddie	4S.5	463-0674	*463-0314*	Summer Luciano
Rodriguez, Justin	E2.306	463-0669	*463-5074*	Ashlee Pena
Romero Jr., Ramon	E2.210	463-0740	*463-1075*	Michael Ramsey
Rose, Toni	E2.310	463-0664	*463-0476*	Daniel Clayton
Sanford, Scott	E2.322	463-0356	*463-0701*	Katherine Munal
Schaefer, Matt	E2.510	463-0584	*463-3217*	Alisha Jackson
Schofield, Mike	E1.402	463-0528	*463-7820*	Kenisha Schuster
Schubert, Leighton	E1.512	463-0600	*463-5240*	Cody Cazares
Shaheen, Matt	E2.208	463-0594	*463-1021*	Mikael Garcia
Sheffield D.O., J. D.	E2.810	463-0628	*463-3644*	Amanda Kit Tollett
Shine, Hugh D.	E2.806	463-0630	*463-0937*	Charlotte Blakemore
Simmons, Ron	E2.608	463-0478	*463-2089*	Zach Flores
Smithee, John T.	1W.10	463-0702	*476-7016*	Andrea Stingley
Springer Jr., Drew	E2.706	463-0526	*463-1011*	Jonathan Mathers

E1, E2 - Capitol Extension   www.txdirectory.com/online/txhouse

REPRESENTATIVES' OFFICE & TELEPHONE NUMBERS

MEMBER	RM. NO.	PHONE 512/	FAX 512/	ASSISTANT
Stephenson, Phil	E2.906	463-0604	*463-5244*	Matt Minor
Stickland, Jonathan	E1.404	463-0522		Tim Hardin
Straus III, Joe	2W.13	463-1000	*463-0675*	Patricia Shipton
Stucky, Lynn	E2.420	463-0582		Worth Farabee
Swanson, Valoree	E2.802	463-0572	*463-1908*	Mark Ramsey
Thierry, Shawn	E2.320	463-0518	*463-0941*	Jasmine Connor
Thompson, Ed	E2.506	463-0707	*463-8717*	Staci Rives
Thompson, Senfronia	3S.6	463-0720	*463-6306*	Milda Mora
Tinderholt, Tony	E1.422	463-0624	*463-8386*	Micah Cavanaugh
Turner, Chris	E1.408	463-0574	*463-1481*	Emily Amps
Uresti, Tomas	E2.712	463-0714	*463-1458*	Jack Andrews
VanDeaver, Gary	E1.310	463-0692	*463-0902*	Trish Conradt
Villalba, Jason	E2.404	463-0576	*463-7827*	Ashley Juergens
Vo, Hubert	4N.8	463-0568	*463-0548*	Mariam Balaparya
Walle, Armando L.	GW.18	463-0924	*463-1510*	Rahul Sreenivasan
White, James	GN.12	463-0490	*463-9059*	Saul L. Mendoza
Wilson, Terry	E2.702	463-0309	*463-0049*	Jeff Frazier II
Workman, Paul D.	E1.304	463-0652	*463-0565*	Don Barber
Wray, John	E1.302	463-0516	*463-1051*	Tabatha Vasquez
Wu, Gene	E2.718	463-0492	*463-1182*	Amy Bruno
Zedler, William	GS.2	463-0374	*463-0364*	Matthew Posey
Zerwas M.D., John	GW.17	463-0657		Nelda Hunter

HOUSE STANDING COMMITTEES
85TH REGULAR SESSION
The Honorable Joe Straus III, President of the House
The Honorable Dennis Bonnen, President Pro Tem

AGRICULTURE & LIVESTOCK
Clerk: Sam Bacarisse, E2.114, 512/463-0762

Tracy O. King (D), Chair
Mary E. González (D), Vice Chair

Charles "Doc" Anderson (R)	Dustin Burrows (R)	John Cyrier (R)
Matt Rinaldi (R)	Lynn Stucky (R)	

APPROPRIATIONS
Clerk: Nelda Hunter, E1.032, 512/463-1091

John Zerwas (R), Chair
Oscar Longoria (D), Vice Chair

Trent Ashby (R)	Greg Bonnen (R)	Giovanni Capriglione (R)
Scott Cosper (R)	Sarah Davis (R)	Jay Dean (R)
Dawnna M. Dukes (D)	Helen Giddings (D)	Larry Gonzales (R)
Mary E. González (D)	Donna Howard (D)	Linda Koop (R)
Rick Miller (R)	Sergio Muñoz (D)	Mary Ann Perez (D)
Dade Phelan (R)	John Raney (R)	Kevin Roberts (R)
Justin Rodriguez (D)	Toni Rose (D)	J. D. Sheffield (R)
Ron Simmons (R)	Gary VanDeaver (R)	Armando L. Walle (D)
Gene Wu (D)		

SUBCOMMITTEE ON BUDGET TRANSPARANCY & REFORM

Giovanni Capriglione (R), Chair
Donna Howard (D), Vice Chair

Kevin Roberts (R)	Ron Simmons (R)	Armando L. Walle (D)

SUBCOMMITTEE ON ARTICLE II
Clerk: Kyler Arnold, E1.032, 512/463-1091

Sarah Davis (R), Chair
Greg Bonnen (R), Vice Chair

Dawnna M. Dukes (D)	Sergio Muñoz (D)	Kevin Roberts (R)
J. D. Sheffield (R)	Gene Wu (D)	

SUBCOMMITTEE ON ARTICLE III
Clerk: Emily Howell, E1.032, 512/463-1091

Trent Ashby (R), Chair
Helen Giddings (D), Vice Chair

Mary E. González (D)	Donna Howard (D)	Linda Koop (R)
John Raney (R)	Gary VanDeaver (R)	

SUBCOMMITTEE ON ARTICLES I, IV& V
Clerk: Malika Te, E1.032, 512/463-1091

Oscar Longoria (D), Chair
Rick Miller (R), Vice Chair

Giovanni Capriglione (R)   Scott Cosper (R)   Toni Rose (D)

SUBCOMMITTEE ON ARTICLES VI, VII, & VIII
Clerk: Cameron Cocke, E1.032, 463-1091

Larry Gonzales (R), Chair
Armando L. Walle (D), Vice Chair

Jay Dean (R)	Mary Ann Perez (D)	Dade Phelan (R)
Justin Rodriguez (D)	Ron Simmons (R)	

BUSINESS & INDUSTRY
Clerk: Angelina Lopez, E2.128, 512/463-0766

René O. Oliveira (D), Chair
Hugh D. Shine (R), Vice Chair

Nicole Collier (D)	Ramon Romero (D)	Jonathan Stickland (R)
Jason Villalba (R)	Paul D. Workman (R)	

CALENDARS
Clerk: Paige Higerd, E2.148, 512/463-0758

Todd Hunter (R), Chair
Donna Howard (D), Vice Chair

Roberto R. Alonzo (D)	Trent Ashby (R)	Byron C. Cook (R)
Sarah Davis (R)	Charlie L. Geren (R)	Helen Giddings (D)
Kyle J. Kacal (R)	Ken King (R)	Linda Koop (R)
Alfonso "Poncho" Nevárez (D)	Chris Paddie (R)	Dade Phelan (R)
Toni Rose (D)		

CORRECTIONS
Clerk: Janis Reinken, E2.110, 463-0796

James White (R), Chair
Alma A. Allen (D), Vice Chair

Sarah Davis (R)	Ramon Romero (D)	Scott Sanford (R)
Matt Schaefer (R)	Tony Tinderholt (R)	

COUNTY AFFAIRS
Clerk: Kelsey Bernstein, E2.130, 512/463-0760

Garnet Coleman (D), Chair
Drew Springer (R), Vice Chair

Kyle Biedermann (R)	Todd Hunter (R)	Victoria Neave (D)
Kevin Roberts (R)	Jonathan Stickland (R)	Shawn Thierry (D)
Tomas Uresti (D)		

CRIMINAL JURISPRUDENCE
Clerk: Rachel Wetsel, E2.112, 512/463-0768

Joe Moody (D), Chair
Todd Hunter (R), Vice Chair

Terry Canales (D)	Barbara Gervin-Hawkins (D)	Cole Hefner (R)
Mike Lang (R)	Terry Wilson (R)	

CULTURE, RECREATION & TOURISM
Clerk: Jesse Sifuentez, E2.134, 512/463-1974

John Frullo (R), Chair
Wayne Faircloth (R), Vice Chair

Dennis H. Bonnen (R)	Pat Fallon (R)	Barbara Gervin-Hawkins (D)
Matt Krause (R)	Armando A. "Mando" Martinez (D)	

DEFENSE & VETERANS' AFFAIRS
Clerk: Margaret Wallace, E2.160, 512/463-1393

Roland Gutierrez (D), Chair
César Blanco (D), Vice Chair

Diana Arévalo (D)	Briscoe Cain (R)	Dan Flynn (R)
Stan Lambert (R)	Terry Wilson (R)	

ECONOMIC & SMALL BUSINESS DEVELOPMENT
Clerk: Victoria Smith, E2.118, 512/463-0069

Angie Chen Button (R), Chair
Hubert Vo (D), Vice Chair

Ernest Bailes (R)	Joseph "Joe" Deshotel (D)	Gina Hinojosa (D)
Jeff Leach (R)	Will Metcalf (R)	Evelina Ortega (D)
Jason Villalba (R)		

ELECTIONS
Clerk: Katharine Chambers, E2.144, 512/463-0772

Jodie Laubenberg (R), Chair
Celia Israel (D), Vice Chair

Rodney Anderson (R)	Pat Fallon (R)	Lyle Larson (R)
Ron Reynolds (D)	Valoree Swanson (R)	

ENERGY RESOURCES
Clerk: Link Browder, E2.162, 512/463-0774

Drew Darby (R), Chair
Charles "Doc" Anderson (R), Vice Chair

Greg Bonnen (R)	Terry Canales (D)	Travis Clardy (R)
Tom Craddick (R)	R. D. "Bobby" Guerra (D)	Jason A. Isaac (R)
Phil S. King (R)	Stan Lambert (R)	Brooks Landgraf (R)
Leighton Schubert (R)	Armando L. Walle (D)	

ENVIRONMENTAL REGULATION
Clerk: Julie Young, E2.154, 512/463-0776

Joseph C. "Joe" Pickett (D), Chair
Ed Thompson (R), Vice Chair

John Cyrier (R)	Tony Dale (R)	Kyle J. Kacal (R)
Brooks Landgraf (R)	J.M. Lozano (R)	Ron Reynolds (D)
Eddie Rodriguez (D)		

GENERAL INVESTIGATING & ETHICS
Clerk: Rocky Gage, E2.170, 512/463-0780

Sarah Davis (R), Chair
Joe Moody (D), Vice Chair

Giovanni Capriglione (R)	Alfonso "Poncho" Nevárez (D)	Four Price (R)
Hugh D. Shine (R)	Chris Turner (D)	

GOVERNMENT TRANSPARENCY & OPERATION
Clerk: Teri Avery, E2.206, 512/463-0903

Gary Elkins (R), Chair
Giovanni Capriglione (R), Vice Chair

Larry Gonzales (R)	Eddie Lucio (D)	Matt Shaheen (R)
Tony Tinderholt (R)	Tomas Uresti (D)	

HIGHER EDUCATION
Clerk: Grady Dahlberg, E2.106, 512/463-0782

J.M. Lozano (R), Chair
John Raney (R), Vice Chair

Roberto R. Alonzo (D)	Carol Alvarado (D)	Angie Chen Button (R)
Travis Clardy (R)	Donna Howard (D)	Geanie W. Morrison (R)
Chris Turner (D)		

HOMELAND SECURITY & PUBLIC SAFETY
Clerk: Jack Lenske, E2.146, 512/463-0133

Phil S. King (R), Chair
Alfonso "Poncho" Nevárez (D), Vice Chair

DeWayne Burns (R)	Gina Hinojosa (D)	Justin Holland (R)
Jarvis D. Johnson (D)	Will Metcalf (R)	Matt Schaefer (R)
John Wray (R)		

HOUSE ADMINISTRATION
Clerk: Buffy Crownover, E2.140, 512/463-0784

Charlie L. Geren (R), Chair
Gary VanDeaver (R), Vice Chair

Diego Bernal (D)	John Cyrier (R)	Craig Goldman (R)
Gina Hinojosa (D)	Donna Howard (D)	Tom Oliverson (R)
John Raney (R)	Leighton Schubert (R)	Hubert Vo (D)

HUMAN SERVICES
Clerk: Abbie Kamin, E2.152, 512/463-0786

Richard Peña Raymond (D), Chair
James Frank (R), Vice Chair

Mark Keough (R)	Stephanie Klick (R)	Rick Miller (R)
Ina Minjarez (D)	Toni Rose (D)	Valoree Swanson (R)
Gene Wu (D)		

INSURANCE
Clerk: Courtney Reid, E2.150, 512/463-0788

Larry Phillips (R), Chair
Sergio Muñoz (D), Vice Chair

Rodney Anderson (R)	Lance Gooden (R)	Tom Oliverson (R)
Dennis Paul (R)	Scott Sanford (R)	Chris Turner (D)
Hubert Vo (D)		

INTERNATIONAL TRADE & INTERGOVERNMENTAL AFFAIRS
Clerk: Jeff Madden, E2.158, 512/463-1211

Rafael Anchia (D), Chair
Mark Keough (R), Vice Chair

Dawnna M. Dukes (D)	Evelina Ortega (D)	Tan Parker (R)
Matt Shaheen (R)	James White (R)	

INVESTMENTS & FINANCIAL SERVICES
Clerk: Kory Curtis, E2.172, 512/463-0871

Tan Parker (R), Chair
Phil Stephenson (R), Vice Chair

Dustin Burrows (R)	Jay Dean (R)	Justin Holland (R)
Eric Johnson (D)	Oscar Longoria (D)	

JUDICIARY & CIVIL JURISPRUDENCE
Clerk: Beth Klunder, E2.120, 512/463-0790

John T. Smithee (R), Chair
Jessica Farrar (D), Vice Chair

Roland Gutierrez (D)	Ana Hernandez (D)	Jodie Laubenberg (R)
Andrew Murr (R)	Victoria Neave (D)	Matt Rinaldi (R)
Mike Schofield (R)		

JUVENILE JUSTICE & FAMILY ISSUES
Clerk: Tamoria Jones, E2.202, 512/463-0794

Harold V. Dutton (D), Chair
Tony Dale (R), Vice Chair

Kyle Biedermann (R)	Briscoe Cain (R)	Joe Moody (D)
Mike Schofield (R)	Shawn Thierry (D)	

LAND & RESOURCE MANAGEMENT
Clerk: Miguel Liscano, E2.136, 512/463-1623

Abel Herrero (D), Chair
Cecil Bell (R), Vice Chair

Ernest Bailes (R)   César Blanco (D)   Wayne Faircloth (R)
Matt Krause (R)   Lynn Stucky (R)

LICENSING & ADMINISTRATIVE PROCEDURES
Clerk: Brittney Madden, E2.156, 512/463-0798

John Kuempel (R), Chair
Ryan Guillen (D), Vice Chair

John Frullo (R)   Charlie L. Geren (R)   Craig Goldman (R)
Ana Hernandez (D)   Abel Herrero (D)   Chris Paddie (R)
Senfronia Thompson (D)

LOCAL & CONSENT CALENDARS
Clerk: Milda Mora, E2.166, 512/463-0800

Senfronia Thompson (D), Chair
Travis Clardy (R), Vice Chair

Cindy Burkett (R)   Giovanni Capriglione (R)   Nicole Collier (D)
Jay Dean (R)   James Frank (R)   Larry Gonzales (R)
Brooks Landgraf (R)   Oscar Longoria (D)   Ina Minjarez (D)
Andrew Murr (R)   Ron Simmons (R)

NATURAL RESOURCES
Clerk: Shannon Houston, E2.104, 512/463-0802

Lyle Larson (R), Chair
Dade Phelan (R), Vice Chair

Trent Ashby (R)   DeWayne Burns (R)   James Frank (R)
Kyle J. Kacal (R)   Tracy O. King (D)   Eddie Lucio (D)
Alfonso "Poncho" Nevárez (D) Four Price (R)   Paul D. Workman (R)

PENSIONS
Clerk: Kelli Linza, E2.164, 512/463-2054

Dan Flynn (R), Chair
Roberto R. Alonzo (D), Vice Chair

Rafael Anchia (D)	Cole Hefner (R)	Dan Huberty (R)
Dennis Paul (R)	Justin Rodriguez (D)	

PUBLIC EDUCATION
Clerk: Amy Peterson, E2.124, 512/463-0804

Dan Huberty (R), Chair
Diego Bernal (D), Vice Chair

Alma A. Allen (D)	Dwayne Bohac (R)	Joseph "Joe" Deshotel (D)
Harold V. Dutton (D)	Lance Gooden (R)	Ken King (R)
Linda Koop (R)	Morgan Meyer (R)	Gary VanDeaver (R)

PUBLIC HEALTH
Clerk: Sandra Talton, E2.1010, 512/463-0806

Four Price (R), Chair
J. D. Sheffield (R), Vice Chair

Diana Arévalo (D)	Cindy Burkett (R)	Garnet Coleman (D)
Nicole Collier (D)	Philip Cortez (D)	R. D. "Bobby" Guerra (D)
Stephanie Klick (R)	Tom Oliverson (R)	William "Bill" Zedler (R)

REDISTRICTING
Clerk: Fernando Trevino, E2.142, 512/463-9948

Cindy Burkett (R), Chair
Eric Johnson (D), Vice Chair

Drew Darby (R)	Ana Hernandez (D)	Armando A. Martinez (D)
Will Metcalf (R)	Tan Parker (R)	Eddie Rodriguez (D)
Drew Springer (R)		

RULES & RESOLUTIONS
Clerk: Sergio Cavazos, E2.138, 512/463-0812

Eddie Lucio (D), Chair
Kyle J. Kacal (R), Vice Chair

Diana Arévalo (D)	Ernest Bailes (R)	DeWayne Burns (R)
Wayne Faircloth (R)	Barbara Gervin-Hawkins (D)	Dennis Paul (R)
Ramon Romero (D)	J. D. Sheffield (R)	John Wray (R)

SPECIAL PURPOSE DISTRICTS
Clerk: Laurie McAnally, E2.1016, 512/463-0277

Jim Murphy (R), Chair
Mary Ann Perez (D), Vice Chair

Cecil Bell (R)	Philip Cortez (D)	Scott Cosper (R)
Mike Lang (R)	Leighton Schubert (R)	

STATE AFFAIRS
Clerk: Toni Barcellona, E2.108, 512/463-0814

Byron C. Cook (R), Chair
Helen Giddings (D), Vice Chair

Tom Craddick (R)	Jessica Farrar (D)	Charlie L. Geren (R)
Ryan Guillen (D)	Ken King (R)	John Kuempel (R)
Morgan Meyer (R)	René O. Oliveira (D)	Chris Paddie (R)
Eddie Rodriguez (D)	John T. Smithee (R)	

TRANSPORTATION
Clerk: Leigh Anne Lauderdale, E2.122, 512/463-0818

Geanie W. Morrison (R), Chair
Armando A. "Mando" Martinez (D), Vice Chair

Cindy Burkett (R)	Yvonne Davis (D)	Craig Goldman (R)
Celia Israel (D)	Ina Minjarez (D)	Larry Phillips (R)
Joseph C. "Joe" Pickett (D)	Ron Simmons (R)	Senfronia Thompson (D)
Ed Thompson (R)	John Wray (R)	

URBAN AFFAIRS
Clerk: Rudy England, E2.126, 512/463-9904

Carol Alvarado (D), Chair
Jeff Leach (R), Vice Chair

Diego Bernal (D)	Gary Elkins (R)	Jason A. Isaac (R)
Jarvis D. Johnson (D)	William "Bill" Zedler (R)	

WAYS & MEANS
Clerk: Stephen Bruno, E2.116, 512/463-0822

Dennis H. Bonnen (R), Chair
Yvonne Davis (D), Vice Chair

Dwayne Bohac (R)	Drew Darby (R)	Eric Johnson (D)
Jim Murphy (R)	Andrew Murr (R)	Richard Peña Raymond (D)
Hugh D. Shine (R)	Drew Springer (R)	Phil Stephenson (R)

STATE & FEDERAL POWER & RESPONSIBILITY, SELECT
Clerk: Laramie Stroud, 310 John H. Reagan Bldg., 512/463-8159

Drew Darby (R), Chair
Andrew Murr (R), Vice Chair

Rafael Anchia (D)	Larry Gonzales (R)	Eric Johnson (D)
Ken King (R)	Chris Paddie (R)	Senfronia Thompson (D)
Chris Turner (D)		

TEXAS PORTS, INNOVATION & INFRASTRUCTURE, SELECT
Clerk: Melissa Quevedo, E2.1006, 512/463-4546

Joseph "Joe" Deshotel (D), Chair
Dennis Paul (R), Vice Chair

Wayne Faircloth (R)	Craig Goldman (R)	Tracy O. King (D)
Geanie W. Morrison (R)	René O. Oliveira (D)	Evelina Ortega (D)
Dade Phelan (R)	Kevin Roberts (R)	Justin Rodriguez (D)

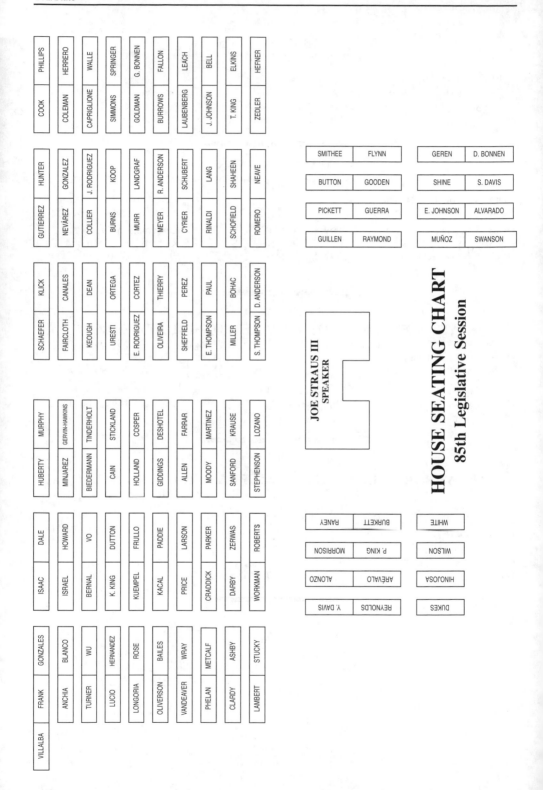

HOUSE SEATING CHART
85th Legislative Session

JOE STRAUS III
SPEAKER

HOUSE DISTRICT MAP

State House Districts
85th Legislature 2017-2018
Plan H309

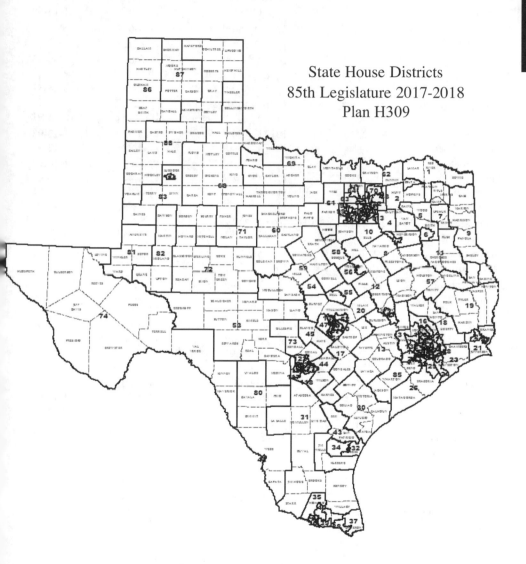

HOUSE MEMBERS IN ORDER OF SENIORITY
85th LEGISLATURE, 2017-2018

MEMBER	NO. OF YEARS	NO. OF SESSIONS	DATE OF ELECTION	OATH OF OFFICE
Craddick, Tom	48	24 61st-84th	11-5-68	1-14-69
Thompson, Senfronia	44	22 63rd-84th	11-5-62	1-9-73
Dutton, Jr., Harold	32	16 69th-84th	11-6-84	1-8-85
Smithee, John	32	16 69th-84th	11-6-84	1-8-85
Oliveira, René	31y/8m/14da	15 full 68th-69th, 72nd-84th		
		1 part 67th	4-21-81	4-28-81
Coleman, Garnet F.	25y/2m/25da	12 full 73rd-84th		
		1 part 72nd	10-15-91	10-18-91
Davis, Yvonne	24	12 73rd-84th	11-3-92	1-12-93
Giddings, Helen	24	12 73rd-84th	11-3-92	1-12-93
Dukes, Dawnna	22	11 74th-84th	11-8-94	1-10-95
Elkins, Gary	22	11 74th-84th	11-8-94	1-10-95
Farrar, Jessica	22	11 74th-84th	11-8-94	1-10-95
Pickett, Joe	22	11 74th-84th	11-8-94	1-10-95
Raymond, Richard Peña	21y/11m/21da	10 full 73rd-75th, $78th$-84th		
		1 part 77th	1-10-01	1-24-01
Bonnen, Dennis	20	10 75th-84th	11-5-96	1-14-97
King, Tracy	20	10 74th-$77th$, 79th-84th		
Alonzo, Roberto	18	9 73rd-$74th$, 78th-84th		
Deshotel, Joe	18	9 76th-84th	11-3-98	1-12-99
King, Phil	18	9 76th-84th	11-3-98	1-12-99
Morrison, Geanie	18	9 76th-84th	11-3-98	1-12-99
Geren, Charlie	16	8 77th-84th	11-7-00	1-09-01
Hunter, Todd	16	8 71st-74th, 81st-84th	11-4-09	1-13-09
Bohac, Dwayne	14	7 78th-84th	11-5-02	1-14-03
Cook, Byron	14	7 78th-84th	11-5-02	1-14-03
Flynn, Dan	14	7 78th-84th	11-5-02	1-14-03
Guillen, Ryan	14	7 78th-84th	11-5-02	1-14-03
Laubenberg, Jodie	14	7 78th-84th	11-5-02	1-14-03
Phillips, Larry	14	7 78th-84th	11-5-02	1-14-03
Rodriguez, Eddie	14	7 78th-84th	11-5-02	1-14-03
Allen, Alma	12	6 79th-84th	11-2-04	1-11-05
Anchia, Rafael	12	6 79th-84th	11-2-04	1-11-05
Anderson, Charles "Doc"	12	6 79th-84th	11-2-04	1-11-05
Martinez, Armando	12	6 79th-84th	11-2-04	1-11-05
Vo, Hubert	12	6 79th-84th	11-2-04	1-11-05
Zedler, Bill	12	6 78th-80th, 82nd-84th		
Straus, Joe	11y/10m/30da	5 full 1 part 79th-84th	2-5-05	2-10-05
Hernandez, Ana	11y/20da	5 full 1 part 79th-84th	12-10-05	12-20-05
Howard, Donna	10y/10m/7da	5 full 1 part 79th-84th	2-14-06	3-2-06

HOUSE MEMBERS IN ORDER OF SENIORITY (Cont.)

MEMBER	NO. OF YEARS	NO. OF SESSIONS	DATE OF ELECTION	OATH OF OFFICE
Darby, Drew	10	5 80th-84th	11-7-06	1-9-07
Herrero, Abel	10	5 79th - 81st, 83rd - 84th		
Lucio III, Eddie	10	5 80th-84th	11-7-06	1-9-07
Parker, Tan	10	5 80th-84th	11-7-06	1-9-07
Zerwas, John	10	5 80th-84th	11-7-06	1-9-07
Gutierrez, Roland	8yr 7m/30da	4 full 81st-84th 1 part 80th	5/13/08	5/14/08
Alvarado, Carol	8	4 81st-84th	11-4-08	1-13-09
Button, Angie Chen	8	4 81st-84th	11-4-08	1-13-09
Murphy, Jim	8	4 80th, 82nd - 84th		
Walle, Armando	8	4 81st-84th	11-4-08	1-13-09
Johnson, Eric	6y/8m/22da	3 full 82nd-84th 1 part 81st	4-19-10	4-20-10
Frullo, John	6y/1m/20da	3 full 82nd-84th 1 part 81st	11-2-10	11-22-10
John Kuempel	6y/12 da	3 full 82nd-84th 1 part 81st	12-14-10	12-30-10
Burkett, Cindy	6	3 82nd-84th	11-2-10	1-11-11
Davis, Sarah	6	3 82nd-84th	11-2-10	1-11-11
Gonzales, Larry	6	3 82nd-84th	11-2-10	1-11-11
Huberty, Dan	6	3 82nd-84th	11-2-10	1-11-11
Isaac, Jason	6	3 82nd-84th	11-2-10	1-11-11
Larson, Lyle	6	3 82nd-84th	11-2-10	1-11-11
Lozano, J.M.	6	3 82nd-84th	11-2-10	1-11-11
Moody, Joseph	6	3 81st, 83rd - 84th	11-2-10	1-11-11
Muñoz, Sergio	6	3 82nd-84th	11-2-10	1-11-11
Price, Four	6	3 82nd-84th	11-2-10	1-11-11
Reynolds, Ron	6	3 82nd-84th	11-2-10	1-11-11
Turner, Chris	6	3 81st, 83rd - 84th	11/6/12	1-8-13
White, James	6	3 82nd-84th	11-2-10	1-11-11
Workman, Paul	6	3 82nd-84th	11-2-10	1-11-11
Raney, John	5y/16da	2 full 83rd-84th 1 part 82nd	12-14-11	12-23-11
Guerra, R.D.	4y/3m/14da	2 full 83rd-84th 1 part 82nd	9-16-12	9-25-12
Shine, Hugh	4y/1m/30da	2 full 70th-71st 1 part 69th	11-4-86	11-14-86
Anderson, Rodney	4	2 82nd, 84th		
Ashby, Trent	4	2 83rd-84th		
Bell Jr., Cecil	4	2 83rd-84th		
Bonnen, Greg	4	2 83rd-84th		
Canales, Terry	4	2 83rd-84th		
Capriglione, Giovanni	4	2 83rd-84th		
Clardy, Travis	4	2 83rd-84th		

HOUSE MEMBERS IN ORDER OF SENIORITY (Cont.)

MEMBER	NO. OF YEARS	NO. OF SESSIONS	DATE OF ELECTION	OATH OF OFFICE
Collier, Nicole	4	2 83rd-84th		
Dale, Tony	4	2 83rd-84th		
Fallon, Pat	4	2 83rd-84th		
Frank, James	4	2 83rd-84th		
Goldman, Craig	4	2 83rd-84th		
Gooden, Lance	4	2 83rd-84th		
González, Mary	4	2 83rd-84th		
Kacal, Kyle	4	2 83rd-84th		
King, Ken	4	2 83rd-84th		
Klick, Stephanie	4	2 83rd-84th		
Krause, Matt	4	2 83rd-84th		
Leach, Jeff	4	2 83rd-84th		
Longoria, Oscar	4	2 83rd-84th		
Miller, Rick	4	2 83rd-84th		
Nevárez, Poncho	4	2 83rd-84th		
Paddie, Chris	4	2 83rd-84th		
Rodriguez, Justin	4	2 83rd-84th		
Rose, Toni	2	2 83rd-84th		
Sanford, Scott	4	2 83rd-84th		
Schaefer, Matt	4	2 83rd-84th		
Sheffield, J.D.	4	2 83rd-84th		
Simmons, Ron	4	2 83rd-84th		
Springer Jr., Drew	4	2 83rd-84th		
Stephenson, Phil	4	2 83rd-84th		
Stickland, Jonathan	4	2 83rd-84th		
Thompson, Ed	4	2 83rd-84th		
Villalba, Jason	4	2 83rd-84th		
Wu, Gene	4	2 83rd-84th		
Israel, Celia	2y/11m/1da	1 full 84th		
		1 part 83rd	1-28-14	2-12-14
Metcalf, Will	2y/1m/25da	1 full 84th		
		1 part 83rd	11-4-14	11-19-14
Blanco, César	2	1 84th		
Burns, DeWayne	2	1 84th		
Burrows, Dustin	2	1 84th		
Cortez, Philip	2	1 84th		
Faircloth, Wayne	2	1 84th		
Keough, Mark	2	1 84th		
Koop, Linda	2	1 84th		
Landgraf, Brooks	2	1 84th		
Meyer, Morgan	2	1 84th		
Murr, Andrew	2	1 84th		
Paul, Dennis	2	1 84th		
Phelan, Dade	2	1 84th		
Rinaldi, Matt	2	1 84th		
Romero, Jr., Ramon	2	1 84th		
Schofield, Mike	2	1 84th		
Shaheen, Matt	2	1 84th		
Tinderholt, Tony	2	1 84th		

HOUSE MEMBERS IN ORDER OF SENIORITY (Cont.)

MEMBER	NO. OF YEARS	NO. OF SESSIONS	DATE OF ELECTION	OATH OF OFFICE
VanDeaver, Gary	2	1 84th		
Wray, John	2	1 84th		
Bernal, Diego	1y/10m/7da	1 part 84th	2-17-15	3-3-15
Cyrier, John	1y/10m/7da	1 part 84th	2-17-15	3-3-15
Schubert, Leighton	1y/10m/7da	1 part 84th	2-17-15	3-3-15
Minjarez, Ina	1y/8m/11da	1 part 84th	4-21-15	4-30-15
Johnson, Jarvis	7m/22da	1 part 84th	5-7-16	5-19-16
Arévalo, Diana			11-8-16	1-10-17
Bailes, Ernest			11-8-16	1-10-17
Biedermann, Kyle			11-8-16	1-10-17
Cain, Briscoe			11-8-16	1-10-17
Cosper, Scott			11-8-16	1-10-17
Dean, James Jay			11-8-16	1-10-17
Gervin-Hawkins, Barbara			11-8-16	1-10-17
Hefner, Cole			11-8-16	1-10-17
Hinojosa, Gina			11-8-16	1-10-17
Holland, Justin			11-8-16	1-10-17
Lambert, Stan			11-8-16	1-10-17
Lang, Mike			11-8-16	1-10-17
Neave, Victoria			11-8-16	1-10-17
Oliverson, Tom			11-8-16	1-10-17
Ortega, Evelina			11-8-16	1-10-17
Roberts, Kevin			11-8-16	1-10-17
Stucky, Lynn			11-8-16	1-10-17
Swanson, Valoree			11-8-16	1-10-17
Thierry, Shawn			11-8-16	1-10-17
Uresti, Tomas			11-8-16	1-10-17
Wilson, Terry			11-8-16	1-10-17

COUNTY DELEGATIONS
85th LEGISLATURE 2017-2018

BEXAR COUNTY

Senators	District
Carlos Uresti *(D)*	19
Judith Zaffirini *(D)*	21
Donna Campbell *(R)*	25
José Menéndez *(D)*	26

Representatives	District
Diana Arévalo *(D)*	116
Philip Cortez *(D)*	117
Tomas Uresti *(D)*	118
Roland Gutierrez *(D)*	119
Barbara Gervin-Hawkins *(D)*	120
Joe Straus *(R)*	121
Lyle Larson *(R)*	122
Diego Bernal *(D)*	123
Ina Minjarez *(D)*	124
Justin Rodriguez *(D)*	125

BELL COUNTY

Senators	District
Dawn Buckingham *(R)*	24

Representatives	District
Scott Cosper *(R)*	54
Hugh Shine *(R)*	55

BRAZORIA COUNTY

Senators	District
Larry Taylor *(R)*	11
Joan Huffman *(R)*	17

Representatives	District
Dennis Bonnen *(R)*	25
Ed Thompson *(R)*	29

BRAZOS COUNTY

Senators	District
Charles Schwertner *(R)*	5

Representatives	District
Kyle Kacal *(R)*	12
John Raney *(R)*	14

CAMERON COUNTY

Senator	District
Eddie Lucio, Jr. *(D)*	27

Representatives	District
Oscar Longoria *(D)*	35
René Oliveira *(D)*	37
Eddie Lucio III *(D)*	38

COLLIN COUNTY

Senators	District
Van Taylor *(R)*	8
Craig Estes *(R)*	30

Representatives	District
Justin Holland *(R)*	33
Matt Shaheen *(R)*	66
Jeff Leach *(R)*	67
Scott Sanford *(R)*	70
Jodie Laubenberg *(R)*	89

DALLAS COUNTY

Senators	District
Bob Hall *(R)*	2
Van Taylor *(R)*	8
Kelly Hancock *(R)*	9
Don Huffines *(R)*	16
Royce West *(D)*	23

Representatives	District
Eric Johnson *(D)*	100
Linda Koop *(R)*	102
Rafael Anchia *(D)*	103
Roberto Alonzo *(D)*	104
Rodney Anderson *(R)*	105
Victoria Neave *(D)*	107
Morgan Meyer *(R)*	108
Helen Giddings *(D)*	109
Toni Rose *(D)*	110
Yvonne Davis *(D)*	111
Angie Chen Button *(R)*	112
Cindy Burkett *(R)*	113
Jason Villalba *(R)*	114
Matt Rinaldi *(R)*	115

DENTON COUNTY

Senators	District
Jane Nelson *(R)*	12
Craig Estes *(R)*	30

Representatives	District
Tan Parker *(R)*	63
Lynn Stucky *(R)*	64
Ron Simmons *(R)*	65
Pat Fallon *(R)*	106

EL PASO COUNTY

Senator	District
José Rodríguez *(D)*	29

Representatives	District
Mary González *(D)*	75
César Blanco *(D)*	76
Evelina Ortega *(D)*	77
Joe Moody *(D)*	78
Joseph Pickett *(D)*	79

FORT BEND COUNTY

Senators	District
Borris Miles *(D)*	13
Joan Huffman *(R)*	17
Lois Kolkhorst *(R)*	18

Representatives	District
Rick Miller *(R)*	26
Ron Reynolds *(D)*	27
John Zerwas *(R)*	28
Phil Stephenson *(R)*	85

GALVESTON COUNTY

Senator	District
Larry Taylor *(R)*	11

Representatives	District
Wayne Faircloth *(R)*	23
Greg Bonnen *(R)*	24

HARRIS COUNTY

Senators	District
Brandon Creighton *(R)*	4
Sylvia Garcia *(D)*	6
Paul Bettencourt *(R)*	7
Larry Taylor *(R)*	11
Borris Miles *(D)*	13
John Whitmire *(D)*	15
Joan Huffman *(R)*	17
Lois Kolkhorst *(R)*	18

Representatives	District
Kevin Roberts *(R)*	126
Dan Huberty *(R)*	127
Briscoe Cain *(R)*	128
Dennis Paul *(R)*	129
Tom Oliverson *(R)*	130
Alma Allen *(D)*	131
Mike Schofield *(R)*	132
Jim Murphy *(R)*	133
Sarah Davis *(R)*	134
Gary Elkins *(R)*	135
Gene Wu *(D)*	137
Dwayne Bohac *(R)*	138
Jarvis Johnson *(D)*	139
Armando L. Walle *(D)*	140
Senfronia Thompson *(D)*	141
Harold Dutton *(D)*	142
Ana E. Hernandez *(D)*	143
Mary Ann Perez *(D)*	144
Carol Alvarado *(D)*	145
Shawn Thierry *(D)*	146
Garnet Coleman *(D)*	147
Jessica Farrar *(D)*	148
Hubert Vo *(D)*	149
Valoree Swanson *(R)*	150

HIDALGO COUNTY

Senators	District
Juan Hinojosa *(D)*	20
Eddie Lucio, Jr. *(D)*	27

Representatives	District
Oscar Longoria *(D)*	35
Sergio Muñoz *(D)*	36
Armando Martinez *(D)*	39
Terry Canales *(D)*	40
Robert Guerra *(D)*	41

HENDERSON COUNTY

Senator	District
Robert Nichols *(R)*	3

Representatives	District
Lance Gooden *(R)*	4
John Wray *(R)*	10

JEFFERSON COUNTY

Senator	District
Brandon Creighton *(R)*	4

Representatives	District
Dade Phelan *(R)*	21
Joe Deshotel *(D)*	22

MONTGOMERY COUNTY

Senators	District
Robert Nichols *(R)*	3
Brandon Creighton *(R)*	4

Representatives	District
Cecil Bell *(R)*	3
Mark Keough *(R)*	15
Will Metcalf *(R)*	16

NUECES COUNTY

Senator	District
Juan Hinojosa *(D)*	20

Representatives	District
Todd Hunter *(R)*	32
Abel Herrero *(D)*	34

SMITH COUNTY

Senator	District
Bryan Hughes *(R)*	1

Representatives	District
Cole Hefner *(R)*	5
Matt Schaefer *(R)*	6

TARRANT COUNTY

Senators	District
Kelly Hancock *(R)*	9
Konni Burton *(R)*	10
Jane Nelson *(R)*	12
Brian Birdwell *(R)*	22

Representatives	District
Ramon Romero, Jr. *(D)*	90
Stephanie Klick *(R)*	91
Jonathan Stickland *(R)*	92
Matt Krause *(R)*	93
Tony Tinderholt *(R)*	94
Nicole Collier *(D)*	95
Bill Zedler *(R)*	96
Craig Goldman *(R)*	97
Giovanni Capriglione *(R)*	98
Charlie Geren *(R)*	99
Chris Turner *(D)*	101

TRAVIS COUNTY

Senators	District
Kirk Watson *(D)*	14
Judith Zaffirini *(D)*	21
Dawn Buckingham *(R)*	24
Donna Campbell *(R)*	25

Representatives	District
Dawnna Dukes *(D)*	46
Paul Workman *(R)*	47
Donna Howard *(D)*	48
Gina Hinojosa *(D)*	49
Cecelia Israel *(D)*	50
Eddie Rodriguez *(D)*	51

WEBB COUNTY

Senator	District
Judith Zaffirini *(D)*	21

Representatives	District
Richard Raymond *(R)*	42
Tracy O. King *(R)*	80

WILLIAMSON COUNTY

Senator	District
Charles Schwertner *(R)*	5

Representatives	District
Terry Wilson *(R)*	20
Larry Gonzales *(R)*	52
Tony Dale *(R)*	136

AUDITOR'S OFFICE, STATE

Robert E. Johnson Bldg., 1501 N. Congress, P.O. Box 12067, Austin 78711-2067
512/936-9500 • *FAX: 512/936-9400* • www.sao.texas.gov • Agency # 308

The Legislative Audit Committee:

The Honorable Dan Patrick	Joint Chair, Lieutenant Governor
The Honorable Joe Straus III	Joint Chair, Speaker of the House
The Honorable Jane Nelson	Member, Chair, Senate Finance Committee
The Honorable Robert Nichols	Member, Texas Senate
The Honorable John Zerwas, M.D.	Chair, House Appropriations Committee
The Honorable Dennis H. Bonnen	Chair, House Ways & Means Committee

Office of the Auditor:

State Auditor	Position Vacant	512/936-9500
First Assistant State Auditor	Lisa Collier	512/936-9300
Assistant State Auditor:	Position Vacant	
Assistant State Auditor	Verma Elliott	512/936-9611
Assistant State Auditor	Angelica Ramirez	512/936-9602

General Counsel:

General Counsel	Angie Welborn	512/936-9568

Audit Managers:

Audit Manager	Courtney Ambres-Wade	512/936-9613
Audit Manager	Becky Beachy	512/936-9484
Audit Manager	Michael Clayton	512/936-9465
Audit Manager	Hillary Eckford	512/936-9495
Audit Manager	Audrey O'Neill	512/936-9783
Audit Manager	Cesar Saldivar	512/936-9436
Audit Manager	Michael Simon	512/936-9480
Audit Manager	James Timberlake	512/936-9672
Audit Manager	John Young	512/936-9577

Professional Development:

Professional Dev. Manager	Jo Dale Guzman	512/936-9460

Investigations and Audit Support:

Investigations and Audit Support	Jennifer Wiederhold	512/936-9443

Risk Assessment and Legislative Coordination:

Risk Assessment Manager	Michael Stiernberg	512/936-9455

Quality Control:

Quality Control Manager	Brianna Pierce	512/936-9467

The State Auditor's Office (SAO) is the independent auditor for Texas state government. The SAO operates with oversight from the Legislative Audit Committee, a six-member permanent standing committee of the Texas Legislature, jointly chaired by the Lieutenant Governor and the Speaker of the House of Representatives. Other members of the committee include the Chair of the Senate Finance Committee, a Senator appointed by the Lieutenant Governor, the Chair of the House Appropriations Committee, and the Chair of the House Ways and Means Committee.

LEGISLATIVE BUDGET BOARD

Robert E. Johnson Office Building, 1501 N. Congress Avenue
P.O. Box 12666, Austin 78711-2666
512/463-1200 • *FAX: 512/475-2902* • www.lbb.state.tx.us • Agency # 104

10 Members

The Honorable Dan Patrick	Joint Chair, Houston
The Honorable Joe Straus III	Joint Chair, San Antonio
Rep. Drew Darby	Board Member, San Angelo
Sen. Kelly G. Hancock	Board Member, North Richland Hills
Sen. Joan Huffman	Board Member, Houston
Sen. Larry Taylor	Board Member, Friendswood
Rep. Dennis H. Bonnen	Chair, House Ways and Means Committee, Angleton
Sen. Jane Nelson	Chair, Senate Finance Committee, Flower Mound
Rep. John Zerwas, M.D.	Chair, House Appropriations Committee, Richmond
Vacant	Board Member

STAFF:

Director	Ursula Parks	512/463-1200
Assistant Director	Julie Ivie	512/463-1200
Assistant Director	Sarah Keyton	512/463-1200
Assistant Director	John McGeady	512/463-1200
Assistant Director	Paul Priest	512/463-1200
Communications Officer	RJ DeSilva	512/463-1200
Fiscal Project and Process Improvement Officer	Maria Hernandez	512/463-1200
Chief Legal Counsel	Amy Borgstedte	512/463-1200

Team Managers:

Agency Operations and Employee Services	Matt Medford	512/463-1200
Applied Research and Performance Audit	Garron Guszak	512/463-1200
Budget-Business and Economic Development	Emily Cormier	512/463-1200
Budget-Education-		
Public Education	Andy MacLaurin	512/463-1200
Higher Education	Demetrio Hernandez	512/463-1200
Budget		
General Government	Nora Velasco	512/463-1200
Health and Human Services	Elizabeth Prado	512/463-1200
Natural Res. and Judiciary	Mark Wiles	512/463-1200
Public Safety and Criminal Justice	Angela Isaack	512/463-1200
Network Operations	Allen Ambuhl	512/463/1200
Application Programming	Dmitry Rozinksky	512/463/1200
Contracts Oversight and Technology	Jacob Pugh	512/463-1200
Criminal Justice Data Analysis	Marialaura Molina	512/463-1200
Estimates and Revenue Analysis	Scott Dudley	512/463-1200
Federal Funds Analysis	Eduardo Rodriguez	512/463-1200
Performance Review-Agencies	Jeremiah Jarrell	512/463-1200
Performance Review-Schools	Lesli Cathey	512/463-1200
Publications and Production Svcs.	Wayne Pulver	512/463-1200

LEGISLATIVE COUNCIL, TEXAS

Robert E. Johnson Building, 1501 N. Congress Avenue
P.O. Box 12128, Austin 78711-2128 • 512/463-1155 • *FAX: 512/463-0157*
www.tlc.state.tx.us • Agency # 103

The Honorable Dan Patrick	Joint Chair, Houston
The Honorable Joe Straus III	Joint Chair, San Antonio
Sen. Dawn Buckingham, M.D.	TX Senator, Lakeway
Sen. Konni Burton	TX Senator, Colleyville
Sen. Sylvia R. Garcia	TX Senator, Houston
Sen. Bryan Hughes	TX Senator, Mineola
Sen. Charles Perry	TX Senator, Lubbock
Sen. Royce West	TX Senator, Dallas

STAFF:

Executive Director	Jeff Archer	.512/463-1155
General Counsel	Jon Heining	.512/463-1155
Assistant Executive Director	Kimberly Shields	.512/463-1155
Director, Legal Division	Mike Marshall	.512/463-1151
Chief Legal Editor	Michele Trepagnier	.512/463-1151
Director		
Research Division	Karen White	.512/463-1143
Information Systems Division	Mark Humphrey	.512/463-1160
Document Production Division	Janet Sullivan	.512/463-1155
Media Inquiries	Kimberly Shields	.512/463-1155

The Council consists of the Lieutenant Governor; the Speaker of the House of Representatives; six Senators appointed by the Lieutenant Governor; the Chairman of the House Administration Committee; and five other members of the House of Representatives appointed by the Speaker. The Lieutenant Governor and the Speaker are Joint Chairmen. Except for the Lieutenant Governor and the Speaker, each member serves a term beginning on the date of the member's appointment and ending with the convening of the first regular session that occurs after the date of appointment. The Lieutenant Governor and Speaker act as the council during a regular legislative session.

LEGISLATIVE REFERENCE LIBRARY

2N.3 State Capitol, 1100 Congress Ave., P.O. Box 12488, Austin 78711-2488
512/463-1252 • *FAX: 512/475-4626* • www.lrl.state.tx.us • Agency # 105

3 Ex-Officio Members; 3 Legislative Members

Term at the pleasure of the appointing official

he Honorable Dan Patrick	Lieutenant Governor, Houston
The Honorable Joe Straus III	Speaker of the House, San Antonio
Sen. Juan "Chuy" Hinojosa	TX Senator, McAllen
Sen. Charles Schwertner, M.D.	TX Senator, Georgetown
Rep. Alma A. Allen	TX House Representative, Houston
Rep. John Zerwas, M.D.	Chair, House Appropriations Committee, Richmond

STAFF:

Director	Mary Camp	.512/463-1252 / *Fax: 512/475-4626*

SUNSET ADVISORY COMMISSION

1501 North Congress, 6th Floor, P.O. Box 13066, Austin 78711-3066
512/463-1300 • *FAX: 512/463-0705*
www.sunset.texas.gov • Agency # 116

10 Legislative Members - 4 Years; 2 Public Members-2 Years

Sen. Brian Birdwell	Chair, Granbury, 9-1-21
Rep. Chris Paddie	Vice Chair, Marshall, 9-1-21
Sen. Dawn Buckingham, M.D.	TX Senator, Lakeway, 9-1-21
Sen. Bob Hall	TX Senator, Edgewood, 9-1-21
Sen. Robert Nichols	TX Senator, Jacksonville, 9-1-19
Sen. Kirk Watson	TX Senator, Austin, 9-1-19
Rep. Dan Flynn	TX House Representative, Van, 9-1-19
Rep. Stan Lambert	TX House Representative, Abilene, 9-1-21
Rep. Alfonso "Poncho" Nevárez	TX House Representative, Eagle Pass, 9-1-21
Rep. Senfronia Thompson	TX House Representative, Houston, 9-1-19
Emily Pataki	Senate Public Member, Cedar Park, 9-1-19
Ronald G. Steinhart	House Public Member, Dallas, 9-1-19

STAFF:

Director	Ken Levine . . . . .512/463-1300 / *Fax: 512/463-0705*
Deputy Director	Jennifer Jones . . . . . .512/463-1300 / *Fax: 512/463-0705*
General Counsel	Steven Ogle . . . . .512/463-1300 / *Fax: 512/463-0705*
Director of Business Operations	Anya Wiley . . . . .512/463-1300 / Fax: 512/463-0705
Business Manager	Cindy Womack . . . . .512/463-1300 / *Fax: 512/463-0705*
Office Manager	Janet Wood . . . . .512/463-1300 / *Fax: 512/463-0705*

The Texas Legislature created the Sunset Advisory Commission in 1977 to identify and eliminate waste, duplication, and inefficiency in government agencies. The Sunset Commission reviews the policies and programs of about 130 state agencies and questions the need for each agency; looks for duplication with other public services or programs; and recommends changes to improve each agency's operations and activities. The Commission seeks public input through hearings on every agency under Sunset review and recommends actions on each agency to the full Legislature. In most cases, agencies under Sunset review are automatically abolished unless legislation is enacted to continue them.

The 12-member Sunset Advisory Commission has five members of the Senate, five members of the House, and two public members, appointed by the lieutenant governor, and the speaker of the House, respectively. The chairmanship rotates between the Senate and the House every two years.

JUDICIAL
BRANCH

SUPREME COURT OF TEXAS

201 West 14th Street, Room 104 (78701), P.O. Box 12248, Austin 78711 • 512/463-1312
FAX: 512/463-1365 (Fax Filings Not Accepted) • www.txcourts.gov/supreme

STATE SECTION

9 Members - 6 Year staggered terms

NATHAN L. HECHT, Chief Justice (R) Place 1   512/463-1348

Sworn into office 10-1-13. Term expires 12-31-20
Born August 15, 1949. B.A. Yale University; J.D. Southern Methodist
University School of Law, 1974. Attorney with firm of Locke, Purnell, Boren,
Laney and Neely, 1976-81. District Judge, 95th Judicial District, 1981-86.
Justice, Fifth District Court of Appeals, 1986-1988. Nathan L. Hecht is the 27th
Chief Justice of the Supreme Court of Texas. He has been elected to the Court
six times, first in 1988 as a Justice, and most recently in 2014 as Chief Justice.
He is the longest-serving Member of the Court in Texas history and the senior
Texas appellate judge in active service.

PAUL W. GREEN, Justice (R) Place 5   512/463-1328

Sworn into office 1-1-05. Term expires 12-31-22
Born March 6, 1952. B.B.A. University of Texas at Austin, 1974;
J.D. St. Mary's University, 1977. Green McReynolds and Green in
San Antonio, 1977-1994; Justice, 4th Court of Appeals, 1995-2004.

PHIL JOHNSON, Justice (R) Place 8   512/463-1336

Appointed to the Supreme Court on 3-15-05. Term expires 12-31-20
Born October 24, 1944. B.A. Texas Tech University, 1965;
J.D. Texas Tech University School of Law, 1975. From 1965 until 1972 he
served in the U.S. Air Force as a pilot. He is a Vietnam veteran. Practiced law
with Crenshaw, Dupree & Milam, L.L.P., 1975-1998;
Justice, Seventh Court of Appeals 1999-2003;
Chief Justice, Seventh Court of Appeals, January 2003-March 2005.

EVA M. GUZMAN, Justice (R) Place 9   512/463-1340

Appointed by Governor Rick Perry and sworn into office 10-9-09.
Term expires 12-31-22
Born January 12, 1961. B.B.A. University of Houston; J.D. South Texas
College of Law; LL.M. from Duke University School of Law.Before taking
the bench, Justice Guzman enjoyed a successful 10-year career in Houston.
Judge Guzman served as an Associate Justice on the Texas Fourteenth Court
of Appeals.

( ) Party Affiliation

SUPREME COURT OF TEXAS

DEBRA H. LEHRMAN, Justice (R)   Place 3   512/463-1320

Appointed by Governor Rick Perry and sworn into office 1-1-11.
Term expires 12-31-22
Born November 16, 1956. Bachelor's degree and J.D. the University of
Texas. Judge Lehrman served as District Judge of the 360th District Court in
Fort Worth, Texas, and as a family law judge in Tarrant County for 22 years.

JEFFREY S. BOYD, Justice (R) Place 7   512/463-1332

Sworn into office 12-3-12. Term expires 12-31-20
Undergraduate degree Abilene Christian University; J.D., cum laude
Pepperdine University. Clerk for Judge Reavley on the Fifth Circuit U.S.
Court of Appeals, Attorney with Thompson & Knight 15 years. January 2011
joined Governor's Office as general counsel. Member of the Supreme Court
Advisory Committee since 2003.

JOHN P. DEVINE, Justice (R) Place 4   512/463-1316

Sworn into office 1-1-13. Term expires 12-31-18
BS Ball State University, 1980; J.D., South Texas College of Law, 1986.
Corporate positions with Shell Oil and Brown & Root. He served for seven
years as judge of the 190th state district court in Harris County and for nine
years as an appointed special judge for the Harris County justice of the peace
courts.

Jeffrey V. Brown, Justice (R) Place 6   512/463-3494

Appointed by Gov. Perry and sworn into office 10-3-13.
Term expires 12-31-18
Bachelors degree in English from the University of Texas and J.D. with hon-
ors from the University of Houston. Before becoming a judge, he practiced at
Baker Botts L.L.P. in Houston and from 2001-2007 was judge of the 55th
District Court. Since 2007 he had been a justice on Houston's 14th Court of
Appeals.

JIMMY BLACKLOCK, Justice (R) Place 2   512/463-1344

Sworn into office 1-2-18. Term expires 12-31-18.
Undergraduate degree-the University of Texas. Following graduation, he
attended Yale Law School where he was a member of the Federalist Society
and president of the Yale Law Republicans. Blacklock clerked for Judge Jerry
Smith on the 5th Circuit Court of Appeals. Blacklock served as Governor
Abbott's General Counsel after six years in the Texas Attorney General's
office, where he assisted on healthcare litigation, religious liberty and right to
life issues.

( ) Party Affiliation

SUPREME COURT OF TEXAS

STAFF:

Clerk of the Court	Blake A. Hawthorne	512/463-1312
Rules Attorney	Jaclyn Lynch	512/463-1353
General Counsel	Nina Hess Hsu	512/475-0938
Staff Attorney for Public Information	Osler McCarthy	512/463-1441
Executive Assistant	Nadine Schneider	512/463-1317

COURT OF CRIMINAL APPEALS

201 West 14th Street, Room 106 (78701), P.O. Box 12308, Austin 78711
512/463-1551; *FAX: 512-463-7061* • www.txcourts.gov/cca

9 Members - 6 Year staggered terms

Sharon Keller (R)
Presiding Judge
Term Began 1-1-01
Term Expires 12-31-18
512/463-1590

Mike E. Keasler (R)
Judge, Place 6
Term Began 1-1-99
Term Expires 12-31-22
512/463-1555

Barbara P. Hervey (R)
Judge, Place 7
Term Began 1-1-01
Term Expires 12-31-18
512/463-1575

Elsa Alcala (R)
Judge, Place 8
Term Began 3-20-11
Term Expires 12-31-18
512/463-1585

Robert (Bert) Richardson (R)
Judge, Place 3
Term Began 1-1-15
Term Expires 12-31-20
512/463-1565

Kevin P. Yeary (R)
Judge, Place 4
Term Began 1-1-15
Term Expires 12-31-20
512/463-1595

( ) Party Affiliation

COURT OF CRIMINAL APPEALS

David C. Newell (R)
Judge, Place 9
Term Began 10-1-15
Term Expires 12-31-20
512/463-1570

Mary Lou Keel (R)
Judge, Place 2
Term Began 1-1-17
Term Expires 12-31-22
512/463-1580

Scott Walker (R)
Judge, Place 5
Term Began 1-1-17
Term Expires 12-31-22
512/463-1560

STAFF:
Clerk of the Court
General Counsel
Chief Staff Attorney

( ) Party Affiliation

Deana Williamson
Sian Schilhab
Kathy Schneider

512/936-1640
512/463-1597
512/936-1627

COURT OF APPEALS

Justices are elected to 6 year terms

FIRST APPELLATE DISTRICT
301 Fannin
Houston, TX 77002-2066
713/274-2700

Chief Justice:	Sherry Radack (R)
Justices:	Laura Carter Higley (R)
	Terry Jennings (D)
	Evelyn Keyes (R)
	Jane N. Bland (R)
	Michael C. Massengale (R)
	Harvey G. Brown (R)
	Russell Lloyd (R)
	Jennifer Caughey (R)
Clerk of the Court:	Christopher A. Prine
Counties:	Austin, Brazoria, Chambers, Colorado, Fort Bend, Galveston, Grimes, Harris, Waller, Washington

SECOND APPELLATE DISTRICT
Tim Curry Criminal Justice Center
401 West Belknap, Suite 9000
Fort Worth, TX 76196
817/884-1900 • *Fax: 817/884-1932*

Chief Justice:	Bonnie Sudderth (R)
Justices:	Sue Walker (R)
	Bill Meier (R)
	Lee Gabriel (R)
	Elizabeth Kerr (R)
	Mark Pittman (R)
	J. Wade Birdwell (R)
Clerk of the Court:	Debra Spisak
Counties:	Archer, Clay, Cooke, Denton, Hood, Jack, Montague, Parker, Tarrant, Wichita, Wise, Young

THIRD APPELLATE DISTRICT
209 W. 14th St., Room 101
P.O. Box 12547
Austin, TX 78711-2547
512/463-1733 • *Fax: 512/463-1685*

Chief Justice:	Jeff L. Rose (R)
Justices:	David Puryear (R)
	Robert H. Pemberton (R)
	Melissa Goodwin (R)
	Scott Field (R)
	Cindy Olson Bourland (R)
Clerk of the Court:	Jeffrey D. Kyle
Counties:	Bastrop, Bell, Blanco, Burnet, Caldwell, Coke, Comal, Concho, Fayette, Hays, Irion, Lampasas, Lee, Llano, McCulloch, Milam, Mills, Runnels, San Saba, Schleicher, Sterling, Tom Green, Travis, Williamson

( ) Party Affiliation

COURT OF APPEALS

FOURTH APPELLATE DISTRICT
Cadena-Reeves Justice Center
300 Dolorosa, Suite 3200
San Antonio, TX 78205-3037
210/335-2635 • *Fax: 210/335-2762*

Chief Justice:	Sandee Bryan Marion (R)
Justices:	Karen Angelini (R)
	Marialyn Price Barnard (R)
	Rebeca C. Martinez (D)
	Patricia Alvarez (D)
	Luz Elena Chapa (D)
	Irene Rios (D)
Clerk of the Court:	Keith E. Hottle
Counties:	Atascosa, Bandera, Bexar, Brooks, Dimmit, Duval, Edwards, Frio, Gillespie, Guadalupe, Jim Hogg, Jim Wells, Karnes, Kendall, Kerr, Kimble, Kinney, La Salle, Mason, Maverick, McMullen, Medina, Menard, Real, Starr, Sutton, Uvalde, Val Verde, Webb, Wilson, Zapata, Zavala

FIFTH APPELLATE DISTRICT
George L. Allen Sr. Courts Bldg.
600 Commerce Street, Suite 200
Dallas, TX 75202-4658
214/712-3450 • *Fax: 214/745-1083*

Chief Justice:	Carolyn Wright (R)
Justices:	David L. Bridges (R)
	Molly Francis (R)
	Douglas S. Lang (R)
	Elizabeth Lang-Miers (R)
	Robert M. Fillmore (R)
	Lana R. Myers (R)
	David Evans (R)
	Ada Brown (R)
	Craig Stoddart (R)
	Bill Whitehill (R)
	David Schenck (R)
	Jason Boatright (R)
Clerk of the Court:	Lisa Matz
Counties:	Collin, Dallas, Grayson, Hunt, Kaufman, Rockwall

SIXTH APPELLATE DISTRICT
100 N. State Line Avenue, Suite 20
Texarkana, TX 75501
903/798-3046 • *Fax: 903/798-3034*

Chief Justice:	Josh R. Morriss (R)
Justices:	Bailey C. Moseley (R)
	Ralph K. Burgess (R)
Clerk of the Court:	Debbie Autrey
Counties:	Bowie, Camp, Cass, Delta, Fannin, Franklin, Gregg, Harrison, Hopkins, Hunt, Lamar, Marion, Morris, Panola, Red River, Rusk, Titus, Upshur, Wood

( ) Party Affiliation

COURT OF APPEALS

SEVENTH APPELLATE DISTRICT
501 S. Fillmore, Suite 2-A
P.O. Box 9540
Amarillo, TX 79105-9540
806/342-2650 • *Fax: 806/342-2675*

Chief Justice:	Brian Quinn (R)
Justices:	James T. Campbell (R)
	Patrick A. Pirtle (R)
	Judy Parker (R)
Clerk of the Court:	Vivian Long
Counties:	Armstrong, Bailey, Briscoe, Carson, Castro, Childress, Cochran, Collingsworth, Cottle, Crosby, Dallam, Deaf Smith, Dickens, Donley, Floyd, Foard, Garza, Gray, Hale, Hall, Hansford, Hardeman, Hartley, Hemphill, Hockley, Hutchinson, Kent, King, Lamb, Lipscomb, Lubbock, Lynn, Moore, Motley, Ochiltree, Oldham, Parmer, Potter, Randall, Roberts, Sherman, Swisher, Terry, Wheeler, Wilbarger, Yoakum

EIGHTH APPELLATE DISTRICT
500 E. San Antonio Ave., Suite 1203
El Paso, TX 79901-2408
915/546-2240 • *Fax: 915/546-2252*

Chief Justice:	Ann Crawford McClure (D)
Justices:	Yvonne Rodriguez (D)
	Gina Palafox (D)
Clerk of the Court:	Denise Pacheco
Counties:	Andrews, Brewster, Crane, Crockett, Culberson, El Paso, Hudspeth, Jeff Davis, Loving, Pecos, Presidio, Reagan, Reeves, Terrell, Upton, Ward, Winkler

NINTH APPELLATE DISTRICT
1001 Pearl Street, Suite 330
Beaumont, TX 77701
409/835-8402 • *Fax: 409/835-8497*

Chief Justice:	Steve McKeithen (R)
Justices:	Charles Kreger (R)
	Leanne Johnson (R)
	Hollis Horton (R)
Clerk of the Court:	Carol Anne Harley
Counties:	Hardin, Jasper, Jefferson, Liberty, Montgomery, Newton, Orange, Polk, San Jacinto, Tyler

TENTH APPELLATE DISTRICT
McLennan Co. Courthouse
501 Washington Avenue, Room 415
Waco, TX 76701-1373
254/757-5200 • *Fax: 254/757-2822*

Chief Justice:	Tom Gray (R)
Justices:	Rex D. Davis (R)
	Al Scoggins (R)
Clerk of the Court:	Sharri Roessler
Counties:	Bosque, Brazos, Burleson, Coryell, Ellis, Falls, Freestone, Hamilton, Hill, Johnson, Leon, Limestone, Madison, McLennan, Navarro, Robertson, Somervell, Walker

( ) Party Affiliation

COURT OF APPEALS

ELEVENTH APPELLATE DISTRICT
100 W. Main Street, Suite 300
P.O. Box 271
Eastland, TX 76448-0271
254/629-2638 • *Fax: 254/629-2191*

Chief Justice:	Jim R. Wright (R)
Justices:	John M. Bailey (R)
	Mike Willson (R)
Clerk of the Court:	Sherry Williamson
Counties:	Baylor, Borden, Brown, Callahan, Coleman, Comanche, Dawson, Eastland, Ector, Erath, Fisher, Gaines, Glasscock, Haskell, Howard, Jones, Knox, Martin, Midland, Mitchell, Nolan, Palo Pinto, Scurry, Shackelford, Stephens, Stonewall, Taylor, Throckmorton

TWELFTH APPELLATE DISTRICT
1517 W. Front Street, Suite 354
Tyler, TX 75702
903/593-8471 • *Fax: 903/593-2193*

Chief Justice:	James T. Worthen (R)
Justices:	Brian T. Hoyle (R)
	Greg Neeley (R)
Clerk of the Court:	Pam Estes
Counties:	Anderson, Angelina, Cherokee, Gregg, Henderson, Houston, Nacogdoches, Rains, Rusk, Sabine, San Augustine, Shelby, Smith, Trinity, Upshur, Van Zandt, Wood

THIRTEENTH APPELLATE DISTRICT

Nueces County Courthouse
901 Leopard, 10th Floor
Corpus Christi, TX 78401
Corpus: 361/888-0416 • *Fax: 361/888-0794*

Rio Grande Valley Office
100 E. Cano, 5th Floor
Edinburg, TX 78539
956/318-2405 • *Fax: 956/318-2403*

Chief Justice:	Rogelio Valdez (D)
Justices:	Nelda V. Rodriguez (D)
	Dori Contreras Garza (D)
	Gina M. Benavides (D)
	Nora Longoria (D)
	Leticia Hinojosa (D)
Clerk of the Court:	Dorian E. Ramirez
Counties:	Aransas, Bee, Calhoun, Cameron, De Witt, Goliad, Gonzales, Hidalgo, Jackson, Kenedy, Kleberg, Lavaca, Live Oak, Matagorda, Nueces, Refugio, San Patricio, Victoria, Wharton, Willacy

( ) Party Affiliation

COURT OF APPEALS

FOURTEENTH APPELLATE DISTRICT
301 Fannin, Suite 245
Houston, TX 77002
713/274-2800

Chief Justice:	Kem Thompson Frost (R)
Justices:	Bill J. Boyce (R)
	Tracy E. Christopher (R)
	Martha Hill Jamison (R)
	Brett Busby (R)
	John Donovan (R)
	Marc Brown (R)
	Kenneth Wise (R)
	Kevin Jewell (R)
Clerk of the Court:	Christopher A. Prine
Counties:	Austin, Brazoria, Chambers, Colorado, Fort Bend, Galveston, Grimes, Harris, Waller, Washington

STATE DISTRICT COURTS

DIST.	JUDGE	COUNTIES REPRESENTED (TERM OF OFFICE)	AC/PHONE #
1	Craig M. Mixson (R)	Jasper, Newton, Sabine, San Augustine (12-31-20)	409/384-3792
1-A	Delinda Gibbs-Walker (R)	Jasper, Newton (12-31-18)	409/384-9570
1A	Delinda Gibbs-Walker (R)	Tyler (12-31-18)	409/283-2162
2	Chris Day (R)	Cherokee (12-31-20)	903/683-2236
3	Mark A. Calhoon (R)	Anderson, Henderson, Houston (12-31-20)	903/723-7415
4	J. Clay Gossett (R)	Rusk (12-31-20)	903/657-0358
5	Bill Miller (R)	Bowie, Cass (12-31-20)	903/628-6783
6	Wes Tidwell (R)	Lamar, Red River (12-31-20)	903/737-2432
7	Kerry L. Russell (R)	Smith (12-31-20)	903/590-1643
8	Eddie Northcutt (R)	Delta, Franklin, Hopkins, Rains (12-31-20)	903/438-4022
9	Phil Grant (R)	Montgomery (12-31-20)	936/539-7866
10	Kerry Neves (R)	Galveston (12-31-20)	409/766-2230
11	Kristen B. Hawkins (D)	Harris (12-31-20)	832/927-2600
12	Donald L. Kraemer (R)	Grimes, Madison, Walker (12-31-20)	936/436-4915
13	James Lagomarsino (R)	Navarro (12-31-20)	903/654-3020
14	Eric V. Moye (D)	Dallas (12-31-20)	214/653-6000
15	Jim Fallon (R)	Grayson (12-31-20)	903/813-4303
16	Sherry Shipman (R)	Denton (12-31-20)	940/349-2310
17	Melody Wilkinson (R)	Tarrant (12-31-20)	817/884-1460
18	John Neill (R)	Johnson, Somervell (12-31-20)	817/556-6820
19	Ralph T. Strother (R)	McLennan (12-31-20)	254/757-5081
20	John W. Youngblood (R)	Milam (12-31-20)	254/697-7010
21	Carson Campbell (R)	Bastrop, Burleson, Lee, Washington (12-31-20)	512/581-4037
22	Bruce Boyer (R)	Caldwell, Comal, Hays (12-31-20)	512/398-1807
23	Ben Hardin (R)	Brazoria, Matagorda, Wharton (12-31-20)	979/864-1205
24	Jack W. Marr (R)	Calhoun, DeWitt, Goliad, Jackson, Refugio, Victoria (12-31-20)	361/575-3172
25	William D. Old, III (R)	Colorado, Gonzales, Guadalupe, Lavaca (12-31-20)	830/303-4188

( ) Party Affiliation

STATE DISTRICT COURTS

DIST.	JUDGE	COUNTIES REPRESENTED (TERM OF OFFICE)	AC/PHONE #
25A	Jessica R. Crawford (R)	Colorado, Gonzales, Guadalupe, Lavaca (12-31-20)	830/303-4188
26	Donna King (R)	Williamson (12-31-20)	512/943-1226
27	John Gauntt (R)	Bell, Lampasas (12-31-20)	254/933-5261
28	Nanette Hasette (D)	Nueces (12-31-20)	361/888-0506
29	Michael Moore (R)	Palo Pinto (12-31-20)	940/659-1274
30	Robert P. Brotherton (R)	Wichita (12-31-18)	940/766-8180
31	Steven R. Emmert (R)	Gray, Hemphill, Lipscomb, Roberts, Wheeler (12-31-18)	806/826-5501
32	Glen N. Harrison (R)	Fisher, Mitchell, Nolan (12-31-20)	325/235-3133
33	Allan Garrett (R)	Blanco, Burnet, Llano, San Saba (12-31-20)	512/756-5436
34	William E. Moody (D)	El Paso (12-31-20)	915/546-2101
35	Stephen Ellis (R)	Brown, Mills (12-31-20)	325/646-1987
36	Starr Bauer (R)	Aransas, Bee, Live Oak, McMullen, San Patricio (12-31-18)	361/364-9310
37	Michael E. Mery (D)	Bexar (12-31-20)	210/335-2515
38	Camile G. DuBose (R)	Medina, Real, Uvalde (12-31-20)	830/741-7146
39	Shane Hadaway (D)	Haskell, Kent, Stonewall, Throckmorton (12-31-18)	940/864-2661
40	Bob Carroll (R)	Ellis (12-31-18)	972/825-5060
41	Anna Perez (D)	El Paso (12-31-20)	915/546-2149
42	James Edison (R)	Callahan, Coleman, Taylor (12-31-20)	325/674-1314
43	Craig Towson (R)	Parker (12-31-20)	817/594-7343
44	Bonnie Lee Goldstein (D)	Dallas (12-31-18)	214/653-6996
45	Stephani Walsh (R)	Bexar (12-31-20)	210/335-2507
46	Dan Mike Bird (D)	Foard, Hardeman, Wilbarger (12-31-18)	940/552-7051
47	Daniel L. Schaap (R)	Armstrong, Potter, Randall (12-31-18)	806/379-2350
48	David L. Evans (R)	Tarrant (12-31-20)	817/884-2690
49	Joe Lopez (D)	Webb, Zapata (12-31-18)	956/523-4237
50	Bobby Burnett (R)	Baylor, Cottle, King, Knox (12-31-20)	940/889-6912
51	Barbara L. Walther (R)	Coke, Irion, Schleicher, Sterling, Tom Green (12-31-20)	325/659-6571
52	Trent D. Farrell (R)	Coryell (12-31-20)	254/865-5911
53	Scott Jenkins (D)	Travis (12-31-20)	512/854-9308
54	Matt Johnson (R)	McLennan (12-31-18)	254/757-5051
55	Jeff Shadwick (R)	Harris (12-31-18)	832/927-2650
56	Lonnie Cox (R)	Galveston (12-31-20)	409/766-2226
57	Antonia Arteaga (D)	Bexar (12-31-20)	210/335-2531
58	Kent Walston (D)	Jefferson (12-31-18)	409/835-8434
59	Rayburn Nall, Jr. (R)	Grayson (12-31-20)	903/813-4305
60	Justin Sanderson (D)	Jefferson (12-31-20)	409/835-8472
61	Fredericka Phillips (D)	Harris (12-31-20)	832/927-2625
62	Will Biard (R)	Delta, Franklin, Hopkins, Lamar (12-31-20)	903/737-2434
63	Enrique Fernandez (D)	Kinney, Terrell, Val Verde (12-31-20)	830/774-7523
64	Robert W. Kinkaid, Jr. (R)	Castro, Hale, Swisher (12-31-18)	806/291-5234
65	Yahara Lisa Gutierrez (D)	El Paso (12-31-20)	915/546-2102
66	A. Lee Harris (R)	Hill (12-31-18)	254/582-4045
67	Donald J. Cosby (R)	Tarrant (12-31-20)	817/884-1452
68	Martin Hoffman (D)	Dallas (12-31-18)	214/653-6510
69	Ron Enns (R)	Dallam, Hartley, Moore, Sherman (12-31-18)	806/935-2700
70	Denn Whalen (R)	Ector (12-31-18)	432/498-4270
71	Brad Morin (R)	Harrison (12-31-20)	903/935-8407
72	Ruben G. Reyes (R)	Crosby, Lubbock (12-31-20)	806/775-1023

( ) Party Affiliation

STATE DISTRICT COURTS

DIST.	JUDGE	COUNTIES REPRESENTED (TERM OF OFFICE)	AC/PHONE #
73	David A. Canales (D)	Bexar (12-31-20)	210/335-2523
74	Gary Coley (R)	McLennan (12-31-20)	254/757-5075
75	Mark Morefield (R)	Liberty (12-31-18)	936/336-4678
76	Kerry Woodson (R)	Camp, Morris, Titus (12-31-20)	903/577-6736
77	Patrick Simmons (R)	Freestone, Limestone (12-31-20)	254/729-3206
78	W. Bernard Fudge (R)	Wichita (12-31-20)	940/766-8182
79	Richard Terrell (D)	Brooks, Jim Wells (12-31-20)	361/668-5718
80	Larry Weiman (D)	Harris (12-31-20)	832/927-2680
81	Donna Rayes (D)	Atascosa, Frio, Karnes, La Salle, Wilson (12-31-18)	830/769-3572
82	Robert M. Stem (D)	Falls, Robertson (12-31-18)	254/883-1421
83	Robert Cadena (R)	Pecos, Terrell, Val Verde (12-31-18)	830/774-7654
84	Curtis W. Brancheau (R)	Hansford, Hutchinson, Ochiltree (12-31-20)	806/878-4022
85	Kyle Hawthorne (R)	Brazos (12-31-18)	979/361-4270
86	Casey Blair (R)	Kaufman (12-31-18)	972/932-0251
87	Deborah Oakes Evans (R)	Anderson, Freestone, Leon, Limestone (12-31-18)	903/723-7415
88	Earl Stover, III (R)	Hardin, Tyler (12-31-20)	409/246-5151
89	Charles M. Barnard (R)	Wichita (12-31-20)	940/766-8184
90	Stephen Bristow (R)	Stephens, Young (12-31-20)	940/549-0091
91	Steven R. Herod (R)	Eastland (12-31-20)	254/629-1797
92	Luis M. Singleterry (D)	Hidalgo (12-31-18)	956/318-2250
93	Rodolfo Delgado (D)	Hidalgo (12-31-20)	956/318-2255
94	Bobby Galvan (D)	Nueces (12-31-18)	361/888-0320
95	Ken Molberg (D)	Dallas (12-31-20)	214/653-6361
96	R.H. Wallace, Jr (R)	Tarrant (12-31-20)	817/884-1450
97	Jack McGaughey (R)	Archer, Clay, Montague (12-31-20)	940/894-2066
98	Rhonda Hurley (D)	Travis (12-31-20)	512/854-9384
99	William C. Sowder (R)	Lubbock (12-31-20)	806/775-1038
100	Stuart Messer (R)	Carson, Childress, Collingsworth, Donley, Hall (12-31-20)	806/874-0122
101	Staci Williams (D)	Dallas (12-31-18)	214/653-6937
102	Bobby Lockhart (R)	Bowie, Red River (12-31-18)	903/798-3527
103	Janet Leal (D)	Cameron (12-31-18)	956/544-0844
104	Lee Hamilton (R)	Taylor (12-31-20)	325/674-1313
105	Jack W. Pulcher (R)	Kenedy, Kleberg, Nueces (12-31-18)	361/595-0293
106	Carter T. Schildknecht (R)	Dawson, Gaines, Garza, Lynn (12-31-18)	806/872-3740
107	Benjamin Euresti, Jr. (D)	Cameron (12-31-18)	956/544-0845
108	Doug Woodburn (R)	Potter (12-31-20)	806/379-2355
109	Martin B. Muncy (R)	Andrews, Crane, Winkler (12-31-18)	432/524-1419
110	William P. Smith (R)	Briscoe, Dickens, Floyd, Motley (12-31-18)	806/983-3384
111	Monica Zapata Notzon (D)	Webb (12-31-18)	956/523-4230
112	Pete Gomez, Jr. (D)	Crockett, Pecos, Reagan, Sutton, Upton (12-31-18)	325/392-5225
113	Michael Landrum (R)	Harris (12-31-18)	832/927-2575
114	Christi Kennedy (R)	Smith (12-31-20)	903/590-1623
115	Lauren Parish (R)	Marion, Upshur (12-31-18)	903/843-2836
116	Tonya Parker (D)	Dallas (12-31-18)	214/653-6015
117	Sandra Watts (D)	Nueces (12-31-18)	361/888-0436
118	Timothy Yeats (R)	Glasscock, Howard, Martin (12-31-18)	432/264-2225
119	Ben Woodward (R)	Concho, Runnels, Tom Green (12-31-20)	325/659-6570
120	Maria Salas-Mendoza (D)	El Paso (12-31-18)	915/546-2103
121	John A. Didway (R)	Terry, Yoakum (12-31-20)	806/637-7742
122	John Ellisor (R)	Galveston (12-31-18)	409/766-2275

( ) Party Affiliation

STATE DISTRICT COURTS

DIST.	JUDGE	COUNTIES REPRESENTED (TERM OF OFFICE)	AC/PHONE #
123	LeAnn Kay Rafferty (R)	Panola, Shelby (12-31-20)	903/693-0315
124	F. Alfonso Charles (R)	Gregg (12-31-20)	903/236-1765
125	Kyle Carter (D)	Harris (12-31-20)	832/927-2550
126	Darlene Byrne (D)	Travis (12-31-20)	512/854-9313
127	R.K. Sandill (D)	Harris (12-31-20)	832/927-2525
128	Courtney Arkeen (R)	Orange (12-31-20)	409/882-7085
129	Michael Gomez (D)	Harris (12-31-20)	832/927-2500
130	Craig Estlinbaum (D)	Matagorda (12-31-20)	979/244-7635
131	Norma Gonzales (D)	Bexar (12-31-20)	210/335-2521
132	Ernie B. Armstrong (R)	Borden, Scurry (12-31-20)	325/573-5371
133	Jaclanel McFarland (D)	Harris (12-31-20)	832/927-2480
134	Dale B. Tillery (D)	Dallas (12-31-18)	214/653-6995
135	Kemper Stephen Williams (R)	Calhoun, DeWitt, Goliad, Jackson, Refugio, Victoria (12-31-20)	361/575-2412
136	Baylor Wortham (D)	Jefferson (12-31-20)	409/835-8481
137	John McClendon (R)	Lubbock (12-31-18)	806/775-1035
138	Arturo C. Nelson (D)	Cameron (12-31-20)	956/544-0877
139	Bobby Flores (D)	Hidalgo (12-31-20)	956/318-2260
140	Jim Bob Darnell (R)	Lubbock (12-31-20)	806/775-1032
141	John P. Chupp (R)	Tarrant (12-31-18)	817/884-1992
142	George "Jody" Gilles (R)	Midland (12-31-20)	432/688-4375
143	Mike Swanson (R)	Loving, Reeves, Ward (12-31-20)	432/943-2749
144	Lorina Rummel (R)	Bexar (12-31-18)	210/335-2511
145	Campbell Cox II (R)	Nacogdoches (12-31-20)	936/560-7799
146	Jack Jones (R)	Bell (12-31-20)	254/933-6737
147	Clifford A. Brown (D)	Travis (12-31-18)	512/854-9311
148	Guy Williams (D)	Nueces (12-31-18)	361/888-0333
149	Terri Tipton Holder (R)	Brazoria (12-31-18)	979/864-1261
150	Renee Yanta (R)	Bexar (12-31-18)	210/335-2533
151	Mike Engelhart (D)	Harris (12-31-20)	832/927-2455
152	Robert Schaffer (D)	Harris (12-31-20)	832/927-2425
153	Susan McCoy (R)	Tarrant (12-31-20)	817/884-2691
154	Felix Klein (R)	Lamb (12-31-18)	806/385-4222
155	Jeff Steinhauser (R)	Austin, Fayette (12-31-18)	979/968-8500
156	Patrick L. Flanigan (R)	Aransas, Bee, Live Oak, McMullen, San Patricio (12-31-18)	361/364-9310
157	Randall W. Wilson (R)	Harris (12-31-18)	832/927-2400
158	Steve Burgess (R)	Denton (12-31-18)	940/349-2320
159	Paul E. White (R)	Angelina (12-31-18)	936/639-3913
160	Jim Jordan (D)	Dallas (12-31-18)	214/653-7273
161	John W. Smith (R)	Ector (12-31-20)	432/498-4260
162	Maricela Moore (D)	Dallas (12-31-20)	214/653-7348
163	Dennis Powell (R)	Orange (12-31-20)	409/882-7090
164	Alexandra Smoots-Hogan (D)	Harris (12-31-20)	832/927-2380
165	Ursula A. Hall (D)	Harris (12-31-20)	832/927-2365
166	Laura Salinas (D)	Bexar (12-31-20)	210/335-2501
167	David Wahlberg (D)	Travis (12-31-20)	512/854-9310
168	Marcos Lizarraga (D)	El Paso (12-31-18)	915/546-2141
169	Gordon G. Adams (R)	Bell (12-31-18)	254/933-5265
170	Jim Meyer (R)	McLennan (12-31-18)	254/757-5045
171	Bonnie Rangel (D)	El Paso (12-31-18)	915/546-2100

( ) Party Affiliation

STATE DISTRICT COURTS

DIST.	JUDGE	COUNTIES REPRESENTED (TERM OF OFFICE)	AC/PHONE #
172	Donald J. Floyd (D)	Jefferson (12-31-18)	409/835-8485
173	Dan Moore (R)	Henderson (12-31-18)	903/675-6107
174	Hazel B. Jones (D)	Harris (12-31-20)	832/927-4200
175	Catherine Torres-Stahl (D)	Bexar (12-31-20)	210/335-2527
176	Nikita Harmon (D)	Harris (12-31-20)	832/927-4225
177	Robert Johnson (D)	Harris (12-31-20)	832/927-4250
178	Kelli Johnson (D)	Harris (12-31-20)	832/927-4275
179	Randy Roll (D)	Harris (12-31-20)	832/927-4100
180	Catherine V. Evans (R)	Harris (12-31-18)	832/927-4125
181	John B. Board (R)	Potter, Randall (12-31-18)	806/379-2360
182	Jeannine S. Barr (R)	Harris (12-31-18)	832/927-4150
183	Vanessa Velasquez (R)	Harris (12-31-18)	832/927-4175
184	Jan Krocker (R)	Harris (12-31-18)	832/927-3900
185	Susan Brown (R)	Harris (12-31-18)	832/927-3925
186	Jefferson Moore (R)	Bexar (12-31-18)	210/335-2505
187	Joey Contreras (R)	Bexar (12-31-18)	210/335-2517
188	David Brabham (R)	Gregg (12-31-18)	903/237-2588
189	William R. Burke, Jr. (R)	Harris (12-31-18)	832/927-2325
190	Debra Ibarra Mayfield (R)	Harris (12-31-18)	832/927-2300
191	Gena Slaughter (D)	Dallas (12-31-18)	214/653-6609
192	Craig Smith (D)	Dallas (12-31-18)	214/653-7709
193	Carl Ginsberg (D)	Dallas (12-31-18)	214/653-6998
194	Ernest White (D)	Dallas (12-31-18)	214/653-5802
195	Hector Garza (D)	Dallas (12-31-18)	214/653-5812
196	Andrew Bench (R)	Hunt (12-31-18)	903/408-4190
197	Migdalia Lopez (D)	Cameron, Willacy (12-31-18)	956/574-8150
198	Melvin Emerson (R)	Bandera, Kerr (12-31-18)	830/792-2290
199	Angela Tucker (R)	Collin (12-31-20)	972/548-4415
200	Gisela D. Triana (D)	Travis (12-31-20)	512/854-9306
201	Amy Clark Meachum (D)	Travis (12-31-18)	512/854-9305
202	John Tidwell (R)	Bowie (12-31-20)	903/628-6771
203	Teresa Hawthorne (D)	Dallas (12-31-18)	214/653-5822
204	Tammy Kemp (D)	Dallas (12-31-18)	214/653-5832
205	Francisco X. Dominguez (D)	Culberson, El Paso, Hudspeth (12-31-18)	915/546-2107
206	Rose Guerra Reyna (D)	Hidalgo (12-31-18)	956/318-2265
207	Jack H. Robison (R)	Caldwell, Comal, Hays (12-31-18)	512/398-1807
208	Denise Collins (R)	Harris (12-31-18)	832/927-3950
209	Michael T. McSpadden (R)	Harris (12-31-18)	832/927-3975
210	Gonzalo Garcia (D)	El Paso (12-31-18)	915/546-2130
211	Brody Shanklin (R)	Denton (12-31-18)	940/349-2330
212	Patricia V. Grady (R)	Galveston (12-31-18)	409/766-2266
213	Louis E. Sturns (R)	Tarrant (12-31-20)	817/884-1529
214	Inna Klein (R)	Nueces (12-31-20)	361/888-0463
215	Elaine H. Palmer (D)	Harris (12-31-20)	832/927-2203
216	Keith Williams (R)	Gillespie, Kerr (12-31-20)	830/792-2290
217	Robert K. Inselman (R)	Angelina (12-31-18)	936/637-0217
218	Russell Wilson (R)	Atascosa, Frio, Karnes, La Salle, Wilson (12-31-18)	830/769-3572
219	Scott J. Becker (R)	Collin (12-31-18)	972/548-4662
220	Phil Robertson (R)	Bosque, Comanche, Hamilton (12-31-18)	254/435-6626
221	Lisa Benge Michalk (R)	Montgomery (12-31-18)	936/539-7808
222	Roland Saul (R)	Deaf Smith, Oldham (12-31-18)	806/364-7222

( ) Party Affiliation

STATE DISTRICT COURTS

DIST.	JUDGE	COUNTIES REPRESENTED (TERM OF OFFICE)	AC/PHONE #
223	Phil Vanderpool (R)	Gray (12-31-18)	806/669-8014
224	Cathy Stryker (R)	Bexar (12-31-18)	210/335-2132
225	Peter Sakai (D)	Bexar (12-31-18)	210/335-2233
226	Sid L. Harle (R)	Bexar (12-31-18)	210/335-2446
227	Kevin M. O'Connell (R)	Bexar (12-31-18)	210/335-2304
228	Marc Carter (R)	Harris (12-31-18)	832/927-3800
229	Vacant	Duval, Jim Hogg, Starr	361/279-6233
230	Brad Hart (R)	Harris (12-31-18)	832/927-3825
231	Jesus Nevarez Jr. (R)	Tarrant (12-31-18)	817/884-3796
232	Kristin Guiney (R)	Harris (12-31-18)	832/927-3850
233	William W. Harris (R)	Tarrant (12-31-18)	817/884-1794
234	Wesley Ward (R)	Harris (12-31-18)	832/927-2234
235	Janelle M. Haverkamp (R)	Cooke (12-31-20)	940/668-5401
236	Tom Lowe (R)	Tarrant (12-31-18)	817/884-1709
237	Les Hatch (R)	Lubbock (12-31-18)	806/775-1027
238	Elizabeth Leonard (R)	Midland (12-31-18)	432/688-4380
239	Patrick Sebesta (R)	Brazoria (12-31-18)	979/864-1256
240	Chad Bridges (R)	Fort Bend (12-31-20)	281/341-8600
241	Jack M. Skeen, Jr. (R)	Smith (12-31-18)	903/590-1630
242	Lowell Hukill (R)	Castro, Hale, Swisher (12-31-18)	806/291-5254
243	Luis Aguilar (D)	El Paso (12-31-18)	915/546-2168
244	James Rush (R)	Ector (12-31-18)	432/498-4240
245	Roy L. Moore (R)	Harris (12-31-18)	713/274-1245
246	Charley Prine (R)	Harris (12-31-18)	713/274-4500
247	John Schmude (R)	Harris (12-31-18)	713/274-1274
248	Katherine Cabaniss (R)	Harris (12-31-18)	832/927-3875
249	Wayne Bridewell (R)	Johnson, Somervell (12-31-18)	817/556-6825
250	Karin Crump (D)	Travis (12-31-18)	512/854-9312
251	Anna Estevez (R)	Potter, Randall (12-31-18)	806/379-2365
252	Raquel West (D)	Jefferson (12-31-18)	409/835-8597
253	Chap B. Cain III (R)	Chambers, Liberty (12-31-18)	409/267-2750
254	Darlene Ewing (D)	Dallas (12-31-18)	214/653-6136
255	Kim Cooks (D)	Dallas (12-31-18)	214/653-6159
256	David Lopez (D)	Dallas (12-31-18)	214/653-6449
257	Judy Lynn Warne (R)	Harris (12-31-18)	713/274-4560
258	Earnest L. McClendon (R)	Polk, San Jacinto, Trinity (12-31-18)	936/327-6847
259	Brooks H. Hagler (D)	Jones, Shackelford (12-31-18)	325/823-2721
260	Buddie J. Hahn (R)	Orange (12-31-18)	409/882-7095
261	Lora Livingston (D)	Travis (12-31-18)	512/854-9309
262	Denise Bradley (R)	Harris (12-31-18)	832/927-3700
263	Jim Wallace (R)	Harris (12-31-18)	832/927-3725
264	Martha Jane Trudo (R)	Bell (12-31-18)	254/933-5245
265	Jennifer Bennett (D)	Dallas (12-31-18)	214/653-5842
266	Jason Cashon (R)	Erath (12-31-18)	254/965-1485
267	Robert E. Bell (R)	Calhoun, DeWitt, Goliad, Jackson, Refugio, Victoria (12-31-18)	361/578-1998
268	Brady G. Elliott (R)	Fort Bend (12-31-18)	281/341-8610
269	Daniel E. Hinde (R)	Harris (12-31-18)	832/927-2269
270	Brent Gamble (R)	Harris (12-31-18)	832/927-2270
271	Brock Smith (R)	Jack, Wise (12-31-18)	940/627-3200
272	Travis B. Bryan III (R)	Brazos (12-31-20)	979/361-4220

( ) Party Affiliation

STATE DISTRICT COURTS

DIST.	JUDGE	COUNTIES REPRESENTED (TERM OF OFFICE)	AC/PHONE #
273	Charles Mitchell (D)	Sabine, San Augustine, Shelby (12-31-18)	936/275-9634
274	Gary L. Steel (R)	Comal, Guadalupe, Hays (12-31-18)	830/221-1272
275	Juan R. Partida (D)	Hidalgo (12-31-18)	956/318-2270
276	Robert Rolston (D)	Camp, Marion, Morris, Titus (12-31-18)	903/577-6736
277	Stacey Mathews (R)	Williamson (12-31-18)	512/943-1277
278	Hal R. Ridley (R)	Leon, Madison, Walker (12-31-18)	903/536-1032
279	Randy Shelton (D)	Jefferson (12-31-18)	409/835-8655
280	Angelina D. A. Gooden (R)	Harris (12-31-18)	713/274-4680
281	Sylvia A. Matthews (R)	Harris (12-31-18)	832/927-2130
282	Amber Givens-Davis (D)	Dallas (12-31-18)	214/653-5852
283	Livia Francis (R)	Dallas (12-31-18)	214/653-5862
284	Cara Wood (R)	Montgomery (12-31-18)	936/539-7861
285	Richard Price (R)	Bexar (12-31-18)	210/335-2086
286	Jay M. "Pat" Phelan (R)	Cochran, Hockley (12-31-18)	806/894-8240
287	Gordon H. Green (D)	Bailey, Parmer (12-31-18)	806/272-5460
288	Solomon Casseb III (R)	Bexar (12-31-18)	210/335-2663
289	Daphne Previti Austin (R)	Bexar (12-31-18)	210/335-1185
290	Melisa Skinner (R)	Bexar (12-31-18)	210/335-2696
291	Stephanie Mitchell (D)	Dallas (12-31-18)	214/653-5872
292	Brandon Birmingham (D)	Dallas (12-31-18)	214/653-5882
293	Cynthia Muniz (D)	Dimmit, Maverick, Zavala (12-31-18)	830/758-1730
294	Teresa Drum (R)	Van Zandt (12-31-18)	903/567-4422
295	Caroline Baker (R)	Harris (12-31-18)	832/927-1375
296	John Roach, Jr. (R)	Collin (12-31-18)	972/548-4409
297	David Hagerman (R)	Tarrant (12-31-18)	817/884-1908
298	Emily G. Tobolowsky (D)	Dallas (12-31-18)	214/653-6781
299	Karen Sage (D)	Travis (12-31-18)	512/854-9442
300	Randall Hufstetler (R)	Brazoria (12-31-18)	979/864-1227
301	Mary Brown (D)	Dallas (12-31-18)	214/653-7407
302	Tena Callahan (D)	Dallas (12-31-18)	214/653-6189
303	Dennise Garcia (D)	Dallas (12-31-18)	214/653-7611
304	Andrea Martin (D)	Dallas (12-31-18)	214/698-4960
305	Cheryl Lee Shannon (D)	Dallas (12-31-18)	214/698-4924
306	Anne Darring (R)	Galveston (12-31-18)	409/766-2255
307	Tim Womack (R)	Gregg (12-31-18)	903/237-2534
308	James Lombardino (R)	Harris (12-31-18)	713/274-4600
309	Sheri Y. Dean (R)	Harris (12-31-18)	713/274-4520
310	Lisa Ann Millard (R)	Harris (12-31-18)	713/274-1310
311	Alicia Franklin (R)	Harris (12-31-18)	713/274-4580
312	David Farr (R)	Harris (12-31-18)	713/274-4540
313	Glenn Devlin (R)	Harris (12-31-18)	713/222-4900
314	John F. Phillips (R)	Harris (12-31-18)	713/222-4910
315	Michael H. Schneider, Jr. (R)	Harris (12-31-18)	713/222-4950
316	James Mosley (R)	Hutchinson (12-31-18)	806/878-4019
317	Larry Thorne (D)	Jefferson (12-31-18)	409/835-8588
318	David W. Lindemood (R)	Midland (12-31-18)	432/688-4390
319	David Stith (R)	Nueces (12-31-18)	361/888-0533
320	Don Emerson (R)	Potter (12-31-18)	806/379-2370
321	Carole Clark (R)	Smith (12-31-18)	903/590-1601
322	Nancy Berger (R)	Tarrant (12-31-18)	817/884-1427
323	Timothy A. Menikos (R)	Tarrant (12-31-18)	817/838-4600

( ) Party Affiliation

STATE DISTRICT COURTS

DIST.	JUDGE	COUNTIES REPRESENTED (TERM OF OFFICE)	AC/PHONE #
324	Jerome S. Hennigan (R)	Tarrant (12-31-18)	817/884-1432
325	Judith G. Wells (R)	Tarrant (12-31-18)	817/884-1537
326	Paul Rotenberry (R)	Taylor (12-31-18)	325/674-1325
327	Linda Chew (D)	El Paso (12-31-18)	915/546-2032
328	Ronald R. Pope (R)	Fort Bend (12-31-18)	281/341-4406
329	Randy M. Clapp (R)	Wharton (12-31-18)	979/532-1514
330	Andrea Plumlee (D)	Dallas (12-31-18)	214/653-7208
331	David Crain (D)	Travis (12-31-18)	512/854-9443
332	Mario E. Ramirez, Jr. (D)	Hidalgo (12-31-20)	956/318-2275
333	Daryl Moore (D)	Harris (12-31-20)	832/927-1800
334	Steven E. Kirkland (D)	Harris (12-31-20)	832/927-1825
335	Reva Towslee-Corbett (R)	Bastrop, Burleson, Lee, Washington (12-31-20)	979/567-2361
336	Laurine J. Blake (R)	Fannin (12-31-20)	903/583-2863
337	Herb Ritchie (D)	Harris (12-31-20)	832/755-7746
338	Ramona Franklin (D)	Harris (12-31-20)	832/927-3775
339	Maria T. Jackson (D)	Harris (12-31-20)	832/927-3650
340	Jay Weatherby (R)	Tom Green (12-31-20)	325/659-6569
341	Beckie Palomo (D)	Webb (12-31-20)	956/523-4325
342	Vacant	Tarrant	817/884-2710
343	Janna Whatley (R)	Aransas, Bee, Live Oak, McMullen, San Patricio (12-31-20)	361/364-9310
344	Randy McDonald (R)	Chambers (12-31-20)	409/267-2429
345	Jan Soifer (D)	Travis (12-31-20)	512/854-9374
346	Angie J. Barill (D)	El Paso (12-31-20)	915/546-2119
347	Missy Medary (R)	Nueces (12-31-20)	361/888-0593
348	Mike Wallach (R)	Tarrant (12-31-20)	817/884-2715
349	Pam Foster Fletcher (R)	Anderson, Houston (12-31-20)	903/723-7415
350	Thomas Wheeler (R)	Taylor (12-31-20)	325/674-1242
351	George Powell (D)	Harris (12-31-20)	832/927-3680
352	Josh Burgess (R)	Tarrant (12-31-18)	817/884-2730
353	Tim Sulak (D)	Travis (12-31-20)	512/854-9380
354	Kelli Aiken (R)	Hunt, Rains (12-31-20)	903/408-4194
355	Ralph H. Walton, Jr. (R)	Hood (12-31-18)	817/579-3233
356	Steven Thomas (R)	Hardin (12-31-20)	409/246-5155
357	Juan A. Magallanes (D)	Cameron (12-31-18)	956/548-9522
358	W. Stacy Trotter (R)	Ector (12-31-18)	432/498-4250
359	Kathleen A. Hamilton (R)	Montgomery (12-31-18)	936/539-7900
360	Patricia Baca Bennett (R)	Tarrant (12-31-20)	817/884-2708
361	Steve Smith (R)	Brazos (12-31-18)	979/361-4380
362	Bruce McFarling (R)	Denton (12-31-20)	940/349-2340
363	Tracy Holmes (D)	Dallas (12-31-18)	214/653-5892
364	Billy Eichman (R)	Lubbock (12-31-18)	806/775-1026
365	Amado Abascal (D)	Dimmit, Maverick, Zavala (12-31-18)	830/773-1151
366	Ray Wheless (R)	Collin (12-31-18)	972/548-4570
367	Margaret Barnes (R)	Denton (12-31-18)	940/349-2350
368	Rick J. Kennon (R)	Williamson (12-31-18)	512/943-1368
369	C. Michael Davis (R)	Anderson, Cherokee, Leon (12-31-18)	903/723-7415
370	Noe Gonzalez (D)	Hidalgo (12-31-18)	956/318-2280
371	Mollee Westfall (R)	Tarrant (12-31-18)	817/884-2985
372	Scott Wisch (R)	Tarrant (12-31-18)	817/884-2990

( ) Party Affiliation

STATE DISTRICT COURTS

DIST.	JUDGE	COUNTIES REPRESENTED (TERM OF OFFICE)	AC/PHONE #
377	Eli Garza (R)	Victoria (12-31-18)	361/578-8756
378	Joe Grubbs (R)	Ellis (12-31-20)	972/825-5014
379	Ron Rangel (D)	Bexar (12-31-20)	210/335-2911
380	Ben N. Smith (R)	Collin (12-31-20)	972/548-4762
381	Jose L. Garza (D)	Starr (12-31-20)	956/487-8665
382	Brett Hall (R)	Rockwall (12-31-20)	972/204-6610
383	Mike Herrera (D)	El Paso (12-31-20)	915/546-2132
384	Patrick M. Garcia (D)	El Paso (12-31-20)	915/546-2134
385	Robin Malone Darr (R)	Midland (12-31-18)	432/688-4385
386	Arcelia Trevino (D)	Bexar (12-31-20)	210/335-1150
387	Brenda Mullinix (R)	Fort Bend (12-31-20)	281/238-3290
388	Laura Strathmann (D)	El Paso (12-31-20)	915/543-3850
389	Letty Lopez (D)	Hidalgo (12-31-20)	956/318-2080
390	Julie H. Kocurek (D)	Travis (12-31-20)	512/854-4885
391	Brad Goodwin (R)	Tom Green (12-31-20)	325/659-6571
392	Scott McKee (R)	Henderson (12-31-20)	903/675-6110
393	Doug Robison (R)	Denton (12-31-20)	940/349-2360
394	Roy B. Ferguson (D)	Brewster, Culberson, Hudspeth, Jeff Davis, Presidio (12-31-20)	432/837-5831
395	Ryan D. Larson (R)	Williamson (12-31-20)	512/943-1395
396	George Gallagher (R)	Tarrant (12-31-20)	817/884-2768
397	Brian Keith Gary (R)	Grayson (12-31-18)	903/813-4311
398	Keno Vasquez (D)	Hidalgo (12-31-20)	956/318-2470
399	Frank J. Castro (D)	Bexar (12-31-20)	210/335-3667
400	Maggie Jaramillo (R)	Fort Bend (12-31-20)	281/341-4422
401	Mark J. Rusch (R)	Collin (12-31-20)	972/548-4241
402	Jeff Fletcher (R)	Wood (12-31-20)	903/763-2332
403	Brenda Kennedy (D)	Travis (12-31-18)	512/854-9808
404	Elia Cornejo Lopez (D)	Cameron (12-31-20)	956/544-0837
405	Michelle Slaughter (R)	Galveston (12-31-20)	409/765-2688
406	Oscar "O.J." Hale, Jr. (D)	Webb (12-31-20)	956/523-4954
407	Karen Pozza (D)	Bexar (12-31-20)	210/335-2462
408	Angelica Jimenez (D)	Bexar (12-31-20)	210/335-2831
409	Sam Medrano, Jr. (D)	El Paso (12-31-20)	915/834-8209
410	Jennifer Robin (R)	Montgomery (12-31-20)	936/539-7860
411	Kaycee Jones (R)	Polk, San Jacinto, Trinity (12-31-20)	936/327-6848
412	Edwin Denman (R)	Brazoria (12-31-18)	979/864-1915
413	William C. Bosworth, Jr. (R)	Johnson (12-31-20)	817/556-6040
414	Vicki Menard (R)	McLennan (12-31-18)	254/757-5053
415	Graham Quisenberry (R)	Parker (12-31-20)	817/598-6162
416	Andrea Thompson (R)	Collin (12-31-20)	972/548-4520
417	Cynthia Wheless (R)	Collin (12-31-18)	972/548-4658
418	Tracy A. Gilbert (R)	Montgomery (12-31-20)	936/538-3618
419	Orlinda Naranjo (D)	Travis (12-31-18)	512/854-4023
420	Edwin Allen Klein (R)	Nacogdoches (12-31-20)	936/560-7848
421	Chris Schneider (R)	Caldwell (12-31-20)	512/398-1807
422	B. Michael Chitty (R)	Kaufman (12-31-20)	972/932-0257
423	Chris Duggan (D)	Bastrop (12-31-20)	512/581-4037
424	Evan Stubbs (R)	Blanco, Burnet, Llano, San Saba (12-31-18)	512/764-5436
425	Betsy F. Lambeth (R)	Williamson (12-31-20)	512/943-3380

( ) Party Affiliation

STATE DISTRICT COURTS

DIST.	JUDGE	COUNTIES REPRESENTED (TERM OF OFFICE)	AC/PHONE #
426	Fancy H. Jezek (R)	Bell (12-31-20)	254/933-5246
427	Tamara Needles (D)	Travis (12-31-20)	512/854-3663
428	William R. Henry (R)	Hays (12-31-18)	512/393-7700
429	Jill R. Willis (R)	Collin (12-31-18)	972/547-5720
430	Israel Ramon (D)	Hidalgo (12-31-20)	956/318-2900
431	Jonathan Bailey (R)	Denton (12-31-20)	940/349-4370
432	Ruben Gonzalez, Jr. (R)	Tarrant (12-31-18)	817/884-2935
433	Dibrell "Dib" Waldrip (R)	Comal (12-31-20)	830/221-1270
434	James H. Shoemake (R)	Fort Bend (12-31-20)	281/633-7653
435	Patty Maginnis (R)	Montgomery (12-31-20)	936/538-3532
436	Lisa K. Jarrett (R)	Bexar (12-31-18)	210/335-1194
437	Lori I. Valenzuela (R)	Bexar (12-31-18)	210/335-2711
438	Rosie Alvarado (D)	Bexar (12-31-20)	210/335-0448
439	David Rakow (R)	Rockwall (12-31-20)	972/204-6630
440	Grant Kinsey (R)	Coryell (12-31-18)	254/865-5911
441	Rodney W. Satterwhite (R)	Midland (12-31-18)	432/688-4520
442	Tiffany Haertling (R)	Denton (12-31-20)	940/349-4380
443	Cindy Ermatinger (R)	Ellis (12-31-20)	972/825-5284
444	David A. Sanchez (D)	Cameron (12-31-20)	956/574-7035
445	Rene De Coss (R)	Cameron (12-31-20)	956/547-7070
446	Sara Kate Billingsley (R)	Ector (12-31-20)	432/498-4393
448	Sergio H. Enriquez (D)	El Paso (12-31-20)	915/543-3893
449	Renee Rodriguez-Betancourt (D)	Hidalgo (12-31-20)	956/381-0744
450	Brad Urrutia (D)	Travis (12-31-20)	512/854-2441
451	Bill Palmer Jr. (R)	Kendall (12-31-18)	830/249-9343
452	Robert Hofmann (R)	Edwards, Kimble, Mason, McCulloch, Menard (12-31-18)	325/347-0755
458	Kenneth S. Cannata	Fort Bend (12-31-18)	
459	Dustin Howell (R)	Travis (12-31-18)	
469	Piper McCraw (R)	Collin (12-31-20)	972/548-5660
470	Emily Miskel (R)	Collin (12-31-20)	972/548-5670
505	David Perwin (R)	Fort Bend (12-31-20)	281/238-3244
506	Andria Bender (R)	Grimes, Waller (12-31-18)	979/921-0921
507	Julia Maldonado (D)	Harris (12-31-20)	713/274-4620

CRIMINAL DISTRICT COURTS

Dallas	Criminal District Court 1	Robert Burns (D) (12-31-18)	214/653-5902
Dallas	Criminal District Court 2	Nancy Kennedy (D) (12-31-20)	214/653-5910
Dallas	Criminal District Court 3	Gracie Lewis (D) (12-31-20)	214/653-5922
Dallas	Criminal District Court 4	Dominique Collins (D) (12-31-20)	214/653-5932
Dallas	Criminal District Court 5	Carter Thompson (D) (12-31-18)	214/653-5942
Dallas	Criminal District Court 6	Jeanine Howard (D) (12-31-18)	972/739-3910
Dallas	Criminal District Court 7	Stephanie Fargo (R) (12-31-18)	972/739-3906
El Paso	Criminal District Court 1	Diane Navarette (D) (12-31-20)	915/546-8192
Jefferson	Criminal District Court 1	John B. Stevens (D) (12-31-18)	409/835-8432
Tarrant	Criminal District Court 1	Elizabeth Beach (R) (12-31-18)	817/884-1351
Tarrant	Criminal District Court 2	Wayne Francis Salvant (R) (12-31-20)	817/884-1347
Tarrant	Criminal District Court 3	Robb Catalano (R) (12-31-18)	817/884-1356
Tarrant	Criminal District Court 4	Mike Thomas (R) (12-31-18)	817/884-1362

( ) Party Affiliation

DISTRICT ATTORNEYS BY COUNTY

Anderson	Allyson Mitchell (R), Criminal DA	903/723-7400
Andrews	Tim Mason (R), Criminal DA	432/524-1405
Angelina	Joe Martin (R), 159th District	936/632-5090
Aransas	Kristen Barnebey (R), Criminal DA	361/790-0114
Archer	Casey Polhemus (R), 97th District	940/894-6211
Armstrong	Randall C. Sims (R), 47th District	806/379-2325
Atascosa	Audrey Gossett Louis (R), 81st District	830/393-2200
Austin	Travis Koehn (R), Criminal DA	979/865-5933
Bailey	Kathryn Gurley (R), 287th District	806/250-2050
Bandera	Scott Monroe (R), 198th District	830/315-2460
Bastrop	Bryan Goertz (R), Criminal DA	512/581-7125
Baylor	Jennifer A. Habert (R), 50th District	940/889-2852
Bee	Jose Aliseda (R), 156th District	361/358-1007
Bell	Henry L. Garza (R), 27th District	254/933-5215
Bexar	Nicholas LaHood (D), Criminal DA	210/335-2311
Blanco	Wiley B. "Sonny" McAfee (R), 33rd District	512/756-5449
Borden	Ben R. Smith (R), 132nd District	325/573-2462
Bosque	Adam Sibley (R), 220th District	254/435-2994
Bowie	Jerry Rochelle (R), Criminal DA	903/735-4800
Brazoria	Jeri Yenne (R), Criminal DA	979/864-1230
Brazos	Jarvis Parsons (R), 85th District	979/361-4320
Brewster	Sandy Wilson (R), 83rd District	432/336-3322
Briscoe	Wade Jackson (R), 110th District	806/983-2197
Brooks	Carlos O. Garcia (D), 79th District	361/325-5604
Brown	Micheal B. Murray (R), 35th District	325/646-0444
Burleson	Julie Renken (R), 21st District	979/567-2350
Burnet	Wiley B. "Sonny" McAfee (R), 33rd District	512/756-5449
Caldwell	Fred H. Weber (D), Criminal DA	512/398-1811
Calhoun	Dan Heard (D), Criminal DA	361/553-4422
Callahan	Shane Deel (R), Criminal DA	325/854-5810
Cameron	Luis V. Saenz (D), Criminal DA	956/544-0849
Camp	Charles C. Bailey (R), 76th District	903/577-6726
Carson	Luke Inman (R), 100th District	806/447-0055
Cass	Randal Lee (R), Criminal DA	903/756-7541
Castro	Shalyn Hamlin (R), Criminal DA	806/647-4445
Chambers	Cheryl Lieck (R), 344th District	409/267-2682
Cherokee	Elmer Beckworth (R), 2nd District	903/683-2573
Childress	Luke Inman (R), 100th District	806/447-0055
Clay	Casey Polhemus (R), 97th District	940/894-6211
Cochran	Christopher Dennis (R), 286th District	806/894-3130
Coke	Allison Palmer (R), 51st District	325/659-6583
Coleman	Heath Hemphill (R), 42nd District	325/625-1316
Collin	Greg Willis (R), Criminal DA	972/548-4323
Collingsworth	Luke Inman (R), 100th District	806/447-0055

( ) Party Affiliation

DISTRICT ATTORNEYS BY COUNTY

County	District Attorney
Colorado	Jay Johannes (R), Criminal DA 979/732-8203
Comal	Jennifer Anne Tharp (R), 22nd District 830/221-1301
Comanche	Adam Sibley (R), 220th District 254/435-2994
Concho	John Best (R), 119th District 325/653-1912
Cooke	John Warren (R), 235th District 940/668-5466
Coryell	Dustin Boyd (R), 52nd District 254/865-5911
Cottle	Jennifer A. Habert (R), 50th District 940/889-2852
Crane	Amanda Navarette (R), 109th District 432/586-6608
Crockett	Laurie K. English (R), 112nd District 325/392-2025
Crosby	Michael Sales (R), Criminal DA 806/675-2062
Culberson	Jaime Esparza (D), 34th District 915/546-2059
Dallam	David M. Green (R), 69th District 806/935-5654
Dallas	B Glasgow Glasgow (R), Criminal DA 214/653-3600
Dawson	Philip Mack Furlow (R), 106th District 806/872-2259
Deaf Smith	Jim English (R), Criminal DA 806/364-3700
Delta	Will Ramsay (R), 8th District 903/885-0641
Denton	Paul Johnson (R), Criminal DA 940/349-2600
DeWitt	Rob Lassmann (R), 24th District 361/275-2612
Dickens	Wade Jackson (R), 110th District 806/983-2197
Dimmit	Roberto Serna (D), 293rd District 830/773-9268
Donley	Luke Inman (R), 100th District 806/447-0055
Duval	Omar Escobar (D), 229th District 361/279-6220
Eastland	Russell D. Thomason (R), Criminal DA 254/629-2659
Ector	Robert N. Bland, IV (R), 70th District 432/498-4230
Edwards	Tonya S. Ahlschwede (R), 452nd District 325/347-8400
El Paso	Jaime Esparza (D), 34th District 915/546-2059
Ellis	Patrick Wilson (R), Criminal DA 972/825-5035
Erath	Alan Nash (R), 266th District 254/965-1462
Falls	Kathryn J. "Jodi" Gilliam (R), Criminal DA 254/883-1416
Fannin	Richard Glaser (R), Criminal DA 903/583-7448
Fayette	Peggy S. Supak (D), Criminal DA 979/968-8402
Fisher	Ricky Thompson (R), 32nd District 325/235-8639
Floyd	Wade Jackson (R), 110th District 806/983-2197
Foard	Staley Heatly (D), 46th District 940/553-3346
Fort Bend	John Healey, Jr. (R), Criminal DA 281/341-4460
Franklin	Will Ramsay (R), 8th District 903/885-0641
Freestone	Chris Martin (R), Criminal DA 903/389-3977
Frio	Audrey Gossett Louis (R), 81st District 830/393-2200
Gaines	Philip Mack Furlow (R), 106th District 806/872-2259
Galveston	Jack Roady (R), Criminal DA 409/766-2355
Garza	Philip Mack Furlow (R), 106th District 806/872-2259
Gillespie	Lucy Wilke (R), 216th District 830/896-4744
Glasscock	Hardy L. Wilkerson (R), Criminal DA 432/264-2220
Goliad	Rob Lassmann (R), 24th District 361/275-2612

( ) Party Affiliation

DISTRICT ATTORNEYS BY COUNTY

County	District Attorney	Phone
Gonzales	Paul Watkins (R), Criminal DA	830/672-6527
Gray	Franklin McDonough (R), 31st District	806/669-8035
Grayson	Joseph Brown (R), Criminal DA	903/813-4361
Gregg	Carl Dorrough (R), Criminal DA	903/236-8440
Grimes	Andria Bender (R), 278th District	936/873-2137
Guadalupe	David Willborn (R), Criminal DA	830/303-6130
Hale	Wally Hatch (R), 64th District	806/291-5241
Hall	Luke Inman (R), 100th District	806/447-0055
Hamilton	Adam Sibley (R), 220th District	254/435-2994
Hansford	Mark Snider (R), 84th District	806/878-4036
Hardeman	Staley Heatly (D), 46th District	940/553-3346
Hardin	David Sheffield (R), 88th District	409/246-5160
Harris	Kim Ogg (D), Criminal DA	713/755-5800
Harrison	Coke Solomon (R), Criminal DA	903/935-8408
Hartley	David M. Green (R), 69th District	806/935-5654
Haskell	Mike Fouts (D), 39th District	940/864-2072
Hays	Wes Mau (R), Criminal DA	512/393-7600
Hemphill	Franklin McDonough (R), 31st District	806/669-8035
Henderson	Mark W. Hall (R), 173rd District	903/675-6100
Hidalgo	Ricardo Rodriguez (D), Criminal DA	956/318-2300
Hill	Mark Pratt (R), 66th District	254/582-4070
Hockley	Christopher Dennis (R), 286th District	806/894-3130
Hood	Rob Christian (R), 355th District	817/579-3245
Hopkins	Will Ramsay (R), 8th District	903/885-0641
Houston	Donna Gordon Kaspar (R), 349th District	936/544-3255
Howard	Hardy L. Wilkerson (R), 118th District	432/264-2220
Hudspeth	Jaime Esparza (D), 34th District	915/546-2059
Hunt	Noble D. Walker, Jr. (R), 196th District	903/408-4180
Hutchinson	Mark Snider (R), 84th District	806/878-4036
Irion	Allison Palmer (R), 51st District	325/659-6583
Jack	Greg Lowery (R), 271st District	940/567-6261
Jackson	Pam Guenther (R), Criminal DA	361/782-7170
Jasper	Steve Hollis (D), Criminal DA	409/384-4362
Jeff Davis	Sandy Wilson (R), 83rd District	432/837-0990
Jefferson	Bob Wortham (D), Criminal DA	409/835-8550
Jim Hogg	Omar Escobar (D), 229th District	361/527-4056
Jim Wells	Carlos O. Garcia (D), 79th District	361/668-5716
Johnson	Dale Hanna (R), 18th District	817/556-6802
Jones	Joe Edd Boaz (R), 259th District	325/823-2742
Karnes	Audrey Gossett Louis (R), 81st District	830/393-2200
Kaufman	Erleigh Norville Wiley (R), Criminal DA	972/932-4331
Kendall	Nicole Bishop , 451st District	830/249-9343
Kenedy	John T. Hubert (R), 105th District	361/595-8544
Kent	Mike Fouts (D), 39th District	940/864-2072

( ) Party Affiliation

DISTRICT ATTORNEYS BY COUNTY

Kerr	Scott Monroe (R), 198th District	830/315-2460
Kerr	Lucy Wilke (R), 216th District	830/896-4744
Kimble	Tonya S. Ahlschwede (R), 452nd District	325/347-8400
King	Jennifer A. Habert (R), 50th District	940/889-2852
Kinney	Mike Bagley (R), Criminal DA	830/775-0505
Kleberg	John T. Hubert (R), 105th District	361/595-8545
Knox	Jennifer A. Habert (R), 50th District	940/889-2852
La Salle	Audrey Gossett Louis (R), 81st District	830/393-2200
Lamar	Gary Young (R), Criminal DA	903/737-2470
Lamb	Scott A. Say (R), Criminal DA	806/385-4222
Lampasas	John Greenwood (R), Criminal DA	512/556-8282
Lavaca	John Stuart Fryer (R), Criminal DA	361/798-4757
Lee	Martin Placke (R), Criminal DA	979/542-3233
Leon	Hope Knight (R), 369th District	903/536-7161
Liberty	Logan Pickett (R), 253rd District	936/336-4610
Limestone	Roy DeFriend (R), Criminal DA	254/729-3814
Lipscomb	Franklin McDonough (R), 31st District	806/669-8035
Live Oak	Jose Aliseda (R), 156th District	361/358-1007
Llano	Wiley B. "Sonny" McAfee (R), 33rd District	325/247-5755
Loving	Randall W. "Randy" Reynolds (D), 143rd District	432/445-2010
Lubbock	Matt D. Powell (R), Criminal DA	806/775-1100
Lynn	Philip Mack Furlow (R), 106th District	806/872-2259
Madison	Brian Risinger (R), Criminal DA	936/348-7049
Marion	Angela Smoak (R), Criminal DA	903/665-2611
Martin	Hardy L. Wilkerson (R), 118th District	432/264-2220
Mason	Tonya S. Ahlschwede (R), 452nd District	325/347-8400
Matagorda	Steven E. Reis (D), 23rd District	979/244-7657
Maverick	Roberto Serna (D), 293rd District	830/773-9268
McCulloch	Tonya S. Ahlschwede (R), 452nd District	325/347-8400
McLennan	Abel Reyna (R), Criminal DA	254/757-5084
McMullen	Jose Aliseda (R), 156th District	361/358-1007
Medina	Daniel J. Kindred (R), 38th District	830/741-6187
Menard	Tonya S. Ahlschwede (R), 452nd District	325/347-8400
Midland	Laura A. Nodolf (R), 142nd District	432/688-4411
Milam	Bill Torrey (R), Criminal DA	254/697-7013
Mills	Micheal B. Murray (R), 35th District	325/646-0444
Mitchell	Ricky Thompson (R), 32nd District	325/728-3457
Montague	Casey Polhemus (R), 97th District	940/894-6211
Montgomery	Brett W. Ligon (R), 9th District	936/539-7800
Moore	David M. Green (R), 69th District	806/935-5654
Morris	Steve Cowan (D), Criminal DA	903/645-2021
Motley	Wade Jackson (R), 110th District	806/983-2197
Nacogdoches	Nicole D. Lostracco (R), 145th District	936/560-7766
Navarro	R. Lowell Thompson (R), Criminal DA	903/654-3045

( ) Party Affiliation

DISTRICT ATTORNEYS BY COUNTY

County	District Attorney	Phone
Newton	Courtney Tracy Ponthier (R), Criminal DA	409/379-8600
Nolan	Ricky Thompson (R), 32nd District	325/235-8639
Nueces	Mark A. Gonzalez (D), 105th District	361/888-0410
Ochiltree	Jose N. Meraz (R), Criminal DA	806/435-8035
Oldham	Kent Birdsong (R), Criminal DA	806/267-2233
Orange	John D. Kimbrough (R), Criminal DA	409/883-6764
Palo Pinto	Kriste Burnett (R), 29th District	940/659-1251
Panola	Danny Buck Davidson (D), Criminal DA	903/693-0310
Parker	Donald Schnebly (R), 43rd District	817/598-6124
Parmer	Kathryn Gurley (R), 287th District	806/250-2050
Pecos	Sandy Wilson (R), 83rd District	432/336-3322
Pecos	Laurie K. English (R), 112nd District	432/336-6294
Polk	Lee Hon (R), Criminal DA	936/327-6868
Potter	Randall C. Sims (R), 47th District	806/379-2325
Presidio	Sandy Wilson (R), 83rd District	432/729-4452
Rains	Robert Vititow (R), Criminal DA	903/473-5000
Randall	James A. Farren (R), Criminal DA	806/468-5570
Reagan	Laurie K. English (R), 112nd District	325/392-2025
Real	Daniel J. Kindred (R), 38th District	830/278-2916
Red River	Val Varley (D), Criminal DA	903/427-2009
Reeves	Randall W. "Randy" Reynolds (D), 143rd District	432/445-2010
Refugio	Rob Lassmann (R), 24th District	361/275-2612
Roberts	Franklin McDonough (R), 31st District	806/669-8035
Robertson	W. Coty Siegert (R), Criminal DA	979/828-3205
Rockwall	Kenda Culpepper (R), Criminal DA	972/204-6800
Runnels	John Best (R), 119th District	325/653-1912
Rusk	Micheal Jimerson (R), Criminal DA	903/657-2265
Sabine	J. Kevin Dutton (R), 1st District	409/787-2901
San Augustine	J. Kevin Dutton (R), 1st District	936/275-9903
San Jacinto	Robert Trapp (R), Criminal DA	936/653-2601
San Patricio	Sam Smith (R), 36th District	361/364-9390
San Saba	Wiley B. "Sonny" McAfee (R), 33rd District	325/247-5755
Schleicher	Allison Palmer (R), 51st District	325/655-6116
Scurry	Ben R. Smith (R), 132nd District	325/573-2462
Shackelford	Joe Edd Boaz (R), 259th District	325/823-2742
Shelby	Stephen Shires (R), 123rd District	936/598-2489
Sherman	David M. Green (R), 69th District	806/935-5654
Smith	Matt Bingham III (R), Criminal DA	903/590-1721
Somervell	Dale Hanna (R), Criminal DA	817/556-6800
Starr	Omar Escobar (D), 229th District	956/716-4800
Stephens	Dee H. Peavy (R), 90th District	940/549-4132
Sterling	Allison Palmer (R), 51st District	325/659-6583
Stonewall	Mike Fouts (D), 39th District	940/864-2072
Sutton	Laurie K. English (R), 112nd District	325/392-2025

( ) Party Affiliation

DISTRICT ATTORNEYS BY COUNTY

County	District Attorney
Swisher	J. Michael Criswell (R), Criminal DA 806/995-3505
Tarrant	Sharen Wilson (R), Criminal DA 817/884-1400
Taylor	James Hicks (R), Criminal DA 325/674-1261
Terrell	Mike Bagley (R), 63rd District 830/775-0505
Terry	Jo'Shae Ferguson-Worley (R), Criminal DA 806/637-4984
Throckmorton	Mike Fouts (D), 39th District 940/864-2072
Titus	Charles C. Bailey (R), 76th District 903/577-6726
Tom Green	John Best (R), 119th District 325/659-6583
Tom Green	Allison Palmer (R), 51st District 325/659-6583
Travis	Margaret Moore (D), 53rd District 512/854-9400
Trinity	Bennie Schiro (R), 258th District 936/642-2401
Tyler	Lou Cloy (R), Criminal DA 409/283-8136
Upshur	Billy Byrd (R), Criminal DA 903/843-5513
Upton	Laurie K. English (R), 112nd District 432/336-6294
Uvalde	Daniel J. Kindred (R), 38th District 830/278-2916
Val Verde	Mike Bagley (R), 63rd District 830/774-7562
Van Zandt	Chris Martin (R), Criminal DA 903/567-4104
Victoria	Stephen B. Tyler (R), Criminal DA 361/575-0468
Walker	David Weeks (D), Criminal DA 936/435-2441
Waller	Elton Mathis (R), Criminal DA 979/826-7718
Ward	Randall W. "Randy" Reynolds (D), 143rd District 432/943-5038
Washington	Julie Renken (R), 21st District 979/277-6247
Webb	Isidro R. Alaniz (D), 49th District 956/523-4900
Wharton	Dawn Allison (R), 329th District 979/532-8051
Wheeler	Franklin McDonough (R), 31st District 806/669-8035
Wichita	Maureen Shelton (R), Criminal DA 940/766-8113
Wilbarger	Staley Heatly (D), 46th District 940/553-3346
Willacy	Annette C. Hinojosa (D), Criminal DA 956/689-2164
Williamson	Shawn Dick (R), 26th District 512/943-1234
Wilson	Audrey Gossett Louis (R), 81st District 830/393-2200
Winkler	Amanda Navarette (R), 109th District 432/586-3700
Wise	Greg Lowery (R), 271st District 940/627-5257
Wood	Jim Wheeler (R), Criminal DA 903/763-4515
Yoakum	Bill Helwig (R), Criminal DA 806/456-7491
Young	Dee H. Peavy (R), 90th District 940/549-4132
Zapata	Isidro R. Alaniz (D), 49th District 956/523-4900
Zavala	Roberto Serna (D), 293rd District 830/773-9268

( ) Party Affiliation

ADMINISTRATIVE JUDICIAL REGIONS

FIRST REGION

Presiding Judge: Mary Murphy, Justice, Ret., Fifth Court of Appeals
133 N. Riverfront L.B. 50
Dallas, TX 75207
214/653-2943 • *Fax: 214/653-2957*

Counties: Collin, Dallas, Ellis, Fannin, Grayson, Kaufman, Rockwall

SECOND REGION

Presiding Judge: Olen Underwood
301 N. Thompson, Suite 102
Conroe, TX 77301
936/538-8176 • *Fax: 936/538-8167*

Counties: Angelina, Bastrop, Brazos, Burleson, Chambers, Grimes, Hardin,
Jasper, Jefferson, Lee, Liberty, Madison, Montgomery, Newton,
Orange, Polk, San Jacinto, Trinity, Tyler, Walker, Waller, Washington

THIRD REGION

Presiding Judge: Billy Ray Stubblefield
405 MLK Blvd., Box 9
Georgetown, TX 78626
512/943-3777 • *Fax:943-3767*

Counties: Austin, Bell, Blanco, Bosque, Burnet, Caldwell, Colorado,
Comal, Comanche, Coryell, Falls, Fayette, Gonzales, Guadalupe,
Hamilton, Hays, Hill, Lampasas, Lavaca, Llano, McLennan,
Milam, Navarro, Robertson, San Saba, Travis, Williamson

FOURTH REGION

Presiding Judge:

Sid Harle
Bexar County Courthouse
100 Dolorosa, 5th Floor
San Antonio, TX 78205
210/335-3954 • *Fax: 210/335-3955*

Counties: Aransas, Atascosa, Bee, Bexar, Calhoun, De Witt, Dimmit, Frio,
Goliad, Jackson, Karnes, La Salle, Live Oak, Maverick, McMullen,
Refugio, San Patricio, Victoria, Webb, Wilson, Zapata, Zavala

FIFTH REGION

Presiding Judge: Missy Medary
200 North Almond St.
Alice, TX 78332
361/668-5766 • *Fax: 512/367-5788*

Counties: Brooks, Cameron, Duval, Hidalgo, Jim Hogg, Jim Wells, Kenedy,
Kleberg, Nueces, Starr, Willacy

SIXTH REGION

Presiding Judge: Stephen B. Ables
Kerr Co.Courthouse -700 Main Street, 2nd Floor
Kerrville, TX 78028
830/792-2290 • *Fax: 830/792-2294*

Counties: Bandera, Brewster, Crockett, Culberson, Edwards, ElPaso,
Gillespie, Hudspeth, Jeff Davis, Kendall, Kerr, Kimble, Kinney,
Mason, McCulloch, Medina, Menard, Pecos, Presidio, Reagan,
Real, Sutton, Terrell, Upton, Uvalde, Val Verde

SEVENTH REGION
Presiding Judge:

Dean Rucker
Midland County Courthouse
500 North Loraine St., Suite 502
Midland, TX 79701
432/688-4370 • *Fax: 432/688-4933*

Counties:

Andrews, Borden, Brown, Callahan, Coke, Coleman, Concho, Crane, Dawson, Ector, Fisher, Gaines, Garza, Glasscock, Haskell, Howard, Irion, Jones, Kent, Loving, Lynn, Martin, Midland, Mills, Mitchell, Nolan, Reeves, Runnels, Schleicher, Scurry, Shackelford, Sterling, Stonewall, Taylor, Throckmorton, Tom Green, Ward, Winkler

EIGHTH REGION
Presiding Judge:

David L. Evans
Tom Vandergriff Civil Courts Bldg.
100 North Calhoun St.
Fort Worth, TX 76196
817/884-1558 • *Fax: 817/884-1560*

Counties:

Archer, Clay, Cooke, Denton, Eastland, Erath, Hood, Jack, Johnson, Montague, Palo Pinto, Parker, Somervell, Stephens, Tarrant, Wichita, Wise, Young

NINTH REGION
Presiding Judge:

Kelly G. Moore, 121st Judicial District Court
500 West Main, Room 302W
Brownfield, TX 79316
806/637-1329 • *Fax: 806/637-8918*

Counties:

Armstrong, Bailey, Baylor, Briscoe, Carson, Castro, Childress, Cochran, Collingsworth, Cottle, Crosby, Dallam, Deaf Smith, Dickens, Donley, Floyd, Foard, Gray, Hale, Hall, Hansford, Hardeman, Hartley, Hemphill, Hockley, Hutchinson, King, Knox, Lamb, Lipscomb, Lubbock, Moore, Motley, Ochiltree, Oldham, Parmer, Potter, Randall, Roberts, Sherman, Swisher, Terry, Wheeler, Wilbarger, Yoakum

TENTH REGION
Presiding Judge:

Position Vacant

Counties:

Anderson, Bowie, Camp, Cass. Cherokee, Delta, Franklin, Freestone, Gregg, Harrison, Henderson, Hopkins, Houston, Hunt, Lamar, Leon, Limestone, Marion, Morris, Nacogdoches, Panola, Rains, Red River, Rusk, Sabine, San Augustine, Shelby, Smith, Titus, Upshur, Van Zandt, Wood

ELEVENTH REGION
Presiding Judge:

Position Vacant

Counties:

Brazoria, Fort Bend, Galveston, Harris, Matagorda, Wharton

BAR OF TEXAS, STATE*

Texas Law Center, 1414 Colorado, P.O. Box 12487, Austin 78711
512/427-1463 • 800/204-2222 • *FAX: 512/427-4100*
www.texasbar.com • Agency # 202

OFFICERS:

Chairman of the Board	Rehan Alimohammad
President	Tom Vick
Immediate Past President	Frank Stevenson
Immediate Past Chair of the Board	Jose Escobedo, Jr.
President-Elect	Joe K. Longley

Elected Directors - 3 Year Terms:

District 6, Place 3	Jerry C. Alexander
District 3	Christy Amuny
District 1	Micah Belden
District 16	H. Alan Carmichael
District 15	Jeff Chandler
District 70	Alison W. Colvin
District 9, Place 1	Leslie W. Dippel
District 4, Place 1	Laura Gibson
District 9, Place 3	Ann Greenberg
District 6	Sarah Clower Keathley
District 4, Place 2	Neil D. Kelly
District 6, Place 4	David C. Kent
District 17	Aldo R. Lopez
District 11	Robert E. McKnight, Jr.
District 7, Place 1	Gary Nickelson
District 9, Place 2	Christopher Oddo
District 14	Amie S. Peace
District 7, Place 2	Curtis Pritchard
District 8	Lisa S. Richardson
District 10, Place 2	Fidel Rodriguez, Jr.
District 4, Place 5	Scott Rothenberg
District 6, Place 5	Gregory W. Sampson
District 13	Scott Sherwood
District 10, Place 1	Rebecca Simmons
District 4, Place 4	Dinesh H. Singhal
District 6, Place 2	Scott Stolley
District 5	Andrew Tolchin
District 4, Place 6	K. Nicole Voyles
District 6, Place 1	Bradley C. Weber
District 4, Place 3	Michael Wynne

Public Member Directors:

Public Member	Michael Dokupil
Public Member	Estrella Escobar
Public Member	Jarrod T. Foerster
Public Member	Ricky G. Gonzalez, R.Ph.
Public Member	August W. Harris, III

State Bar of Texas Cont.

Minority Member Directors:
Minority Member	Rehan Alimohammad
Minority Member	Sylvia Borunda Firth
Minority Member	Angelica Hernandez
Minority Member	Rudolph K. Metayer

TYLA Members of the Board:
TYLA President	Baili Rhodes
TYLA President-Elect	Sally Pretorius
TYLA Immediate Past President	Sam Houston

Ex-Officio Members:
Executive Director	John Sirman .... .512/427-1500 / *Fax: 512/427-4108*
Legal Counsel	John Sirman .... .512/427-1711 / *Fax: 512/427-4211*
Chief Disciplinary Counsel	Linda Acevedo ...... .512/427-1330 / *Fax: 512/427-4167*
Assistant Deputy Director	Ray Cantu .... .512/427-1506 / *Fax: 512/427-4108*
Assistant Deputy Director	KaLyn Laney .... .512/427-1758 / *Fax: 512/427-4108*

Liaisons:
Court of Criminal Appeals Liaison	The Honorable Barbara P. Hervey
Supreme Court	The Honorable Phil Johnson
Out-of-State Lawyer Liaison	Timothy W. Mountz
Federal Judiciary Liaison	The Honorable Amos L. Mazzant III
Judicial Section Liaison	The Honorable Jennifer Rymell

Section Representatives to the Board Committee Members:
Medium-sized Sections	Erich M. Birch
Large-sized Sections	Wendy S. Burgower
Large-sized Sections	Elizabeth Copeland
Large-sized Sections	Philip Mack Furlow
Medium-sized Sections	Shelby Jean
Small-sized Sections	Audrey F. Moorehead

Staff Members:
Executive Director	John Sirman	.512/427-1500
Deputy Director	Pat Nester	.512/427-6822
Minority Affairs	Caren DesVignes	.512/427-1500
Officers & Directors	Candiss Held	.512/427-1500
Membership	Sandra Gavin	.512/427-1500
Texas Lawyers Care/ Pro Bono Information	Trish McAllister	.512/427-1500
External Affairs Officer	KaLyn Laney	.512/427-1758
Texas Young Lawyers Association	Tracy Brown	.512/427-1500
Texas Board of Legal Specialization	Gary McNeil	.512/427-1500
Chief Disciplinary Counsel	Linda Acevedo	.512/427-1330
State Bar College	Merianne Gaston	.512/427-1500
Chief Financial Officer	Cheryl Howell	.512/427-1500
Chief Information Officer	Brad Powell	.512/427-1500
Purchasing & Facilities	Paul Rogers	.512/427-1500
Lawyer Referral	Lisa Zvonek	.512/427-1500
MCLE	Nancy Smith	.512/427-1500
Texas Bar Foundation	Andrea Stone	.512/427-1500

1-800 NUMBERS:

Main Toll Free:	800/204-2222
Advertising Review:	800/566-4616
Attorney Occupation Tax:	800/583-8070
Barratry Hotline:	800/633-6630
Disaster Response Hotline:	800/504-7030
Grievance Information:	800/932-1900
Institutes and Seminars:	800/852-7371
Lawyer Referral Services:	800/252-9690
Lawyer's Ethics Hotline:	800/532-3947
TX Bd. of Legal Specialization:	800/204-2222
TX Equal Access to Justice:	800/252-3401
TX Judges' Assist. Program:	800/219-6474
TX Lawyers' Assist. Program:	800/343-8527
Texas Lawyers Care:	888/281-6511

46 members: including 3 SBOT officers, 30 elected directors, 6 public members, 4 minority directors, and 3 TYLA officers. The Executive Director, Chief Disciplinary Counsel, and SBOT Immediate Past Chair of the Board serve as ex-officio members. Also associated with the Board are 4 judicial liaisons and 1 out-of-state lawyer liaison.

*Subject to the Texas Sunset Act; will be reviewed in 2017.

COURT ADMINISTRATION, STATE OFFICE OF

Tom C. Clark State Courts Bldg., 205 W. 14th, 6th Floor
P.O. Box 12066, Austin 78711-2066 • 512/463-1625 • *FAX: 512/463-1648*
www.txcourts.gov • Agency # 212

STAFF:

Administrative Director	David Slayton	512/463-1625
Executive Assistant	Meredith Musick-Higgins	512/936-7554
Director of Public Affairs/		
Special Counsel	Megan LaVoie	512/463-1627
General Counsel	Maria Elena Ramon	512/463 1625
Assistant General Counsel	Scott Gibson	512/463-1461
Chief Financial Officer	Jennifer Henry	512/463-8872
Deputy Chief Financial Officer	Carol Harper	512/463-1631
Human Resources Officer	Charlotte Miller	512/463-1611
Director, Information Services	Casey Kennedy	512/463-1625
Deputy Director		
Information Services	Susan Chamberlain	512/463-8109
Director		
Research and Court Services	Scott Griffith	512/463-1625
Judicial Information Manager	Angela Garcia	512/936-1358
Court Services Manager	Amanda Stites	512/463-1643
Certification Division Director	Jeff Rinard	512/463-9750

The Office of Court Administration (OCA) is a unique state agency in the Judicial Branch that operates under the direction and supervision of the Supreme Court of Texas and the Chief Justice.

Our mission is to provide resources and information for the efficient administration of the Judicial Branch of Texas.

COURT REPORTERS CERTIFICATION
ADVISORY BOARD

205 W. 14th Street, Suite 600, P.O. Box 12066, Austin 78711-2066
512/475-4368 • *FAX: 512/463-1117*
www.txcourts.gov/jbcc/court-reporters-certification.aspx

7 Members - 6 Years

Members appointed by the Supreme Court

The Hon. William C. "Bill" Sowder	Chair, Lubbock, 2-1-21
Robin Cooksey	Board Member, Conroe, 2-1-21
Janice Eidd-Meadows	Board Member, Tyler, 2-1-21
Deborah K. Hamon	Board Member, Rockwall, 2-1-23
Molly Pela	Board Member, Houston, 2-1-19
Whitney Lehmberg Riley	Board Member, Boerne, 2-1-19
Kim Tindall	Board Member, San Antonio, 2-1-23

The Certification Division at the Office of Court Administration provides staff and support for the Advisory Board.

GUARDIANSHIP CERTIFICATION ADVISORY BOARD

205 W. 14th Street, Ste. 600, PO Box 12066, Austin 78711-2066
512/475-4368 • *FAX: 512/463-1117*
www.txcourts.gov/jbcc/guardianship-certification.aspx

5 Members - 6 Years

Members appointed by the Supreme Court

Jamie MacLean	Chair, Austin, 2-1-19
Jason S. Armstrong	Board Member, Lufkin, 2-1-19
The Honorable Gladys Burwell	Board Member, Friendswood, 2-1-19
Toni Rhodes Glover	Board Member, Fort Worth, 2-1-23
The Honorable Chris Wilmoth	Board Member, Dallas, 2-1-21

As of 09/01/2014, the duties and responsibilities of the Guardianship Certification Board were taken over by the Judicial Branch Certification Commission. The Certification Division at the Office of CourtAdministration provides staff and support for the Advisory Board.

JUDICIAL BRANCH CERTIFICATION COMMISSION*

205 W. 14th Street, Suite 600, P.O. Box 12066, Austin 78711-2066
512/475-4368 • *FAX: 512/463-1117*
www.txcourts.gov/jbcc

9 Members - 6 Years

5 Judges, 4 Public Members appointed by the Supreme Court

The Honorable Lee Hamilton	Chair, Abilene, 2-1-19
Velma Arellano	Commissioner, Edinburg, 2-1-21
Mark Blenden	Commissioner, Dallas, 2-1-23
Don D. Ford	Commissioner, Houston, 2-1-19
The Honorable Sid L. Harle	Commissioner, San Antonio, 2-1-23
The Honorable Migdalia Lopez	Commissioner, Brownsville, 2-1-23
Anne Murray Moore	Commissioner, Edinburg, 2-1-21
The Honorable Polly Spencer	Commissioner, San Antonio, 2-1-19
The Honorable Ben Woodward	Commissioner, San Angelo, 2-1-21

The Judicial Branch Certification Commission (JBCC) was established by the Texas Legislature, 83rd Regular Session, in Senate Bill 966. The nine member JBCC oversees certification, registration, licensing and regulation of court reporters and court reporting firms, guardians, process servers, and licensed court interpreters, and began operations on September 1, 2014. The Certification Division at the Office of Court Administration provides staff and support for the Commission.

*Subject to the Texas Sunset Act; will be reviewed in 2019.

STATE SECTION

JUDICIAL CONDUCT, STATE COMMISSION ON*

300 West 15th St., P.O. Box 12265, Austin 78711-2265
512/463-5533 • 877/228-5750 • *FAX: 512/463-0511*
www.scjc.texas.gov • Agency # 242

13 Members - 6 Years

The Honorable Douglas S. Lang	Chair, Dallas, 11-19-19
The Honorable Catherine N. Wylie	Vice-Chair, Houston, 11-19-21
The Honorable David C. Hall	Secretary Sweetwater, 11-19-21
The Honorable David Patronella	Judicial Member, Houston, 11-19-21
The Honorable Ruben G. Reyes	Judicial Member Lubbock, 11-19-23
The Honorable Tramer J. Woytek	Judicial Member, Hallettsville, 11-19-23
The Honorable Demetrius Bivins	Attorney Member, Houston, 11-19-19
The Honorable Ronald E. Bunch	Attorney Member, Waxahachie, 11-19-23
The Honorable Sujeeth B. Draksharam	Public Member, Sugarland, 11-19-21
The Honorable Valerie Ertz	Public Member, Dallas, 11-19-17
The Honorable Patti H. Johnson	Public Member, Canyon Lake, 11-19-17
The Honorable Darrick L. McGill	Public Member, Georgetown, 11-19-21
The Honorable David M. Russell	Public Member, Dripping Springs, 11-19-19

STAFF:

Executive Director	Eric Vinson . . . .(512) 463-5533 / (512) 463-0511
Deputy Director	Royce LeMoine
Deputy General Counsel	Jacqueline Habersham
Commission Counsels	Lorin Hayes
Commission Counsel	Joseph Unruh
Commission Counsel	Kelly Gier
Senior Investigator	Victor Hidalgo
Senior Investigator	Ron Bennett
Senior Investigator	Katherine Mitchell
Investigator	Crystal Lopez
Investigator	Michael Graham
Staff Services Officer	Kathryn Crabtree
Administrative Assistant	Connie Paredes
Administrative Assistant	Cherie Thomas

The State Commission on Judicial Conduct, is an independent Texas state agency created by an amendment to the Texas Constitution in 1965, that is responsible for investigating allegations of judicial misconduct or judicial disability, and for disciplining judges.

---

*Subject to the Texas Sunset Act; will be reviewed in 2019.

JUDICIAL COUNCIL, TEXAS
205 West 14th Street, Suite 600, P.O. Box 12066, Austin 78711
512/463-1625 • *FAX: 512/463-1648*
www.txcourts.gov/tjc.aspx

OFFICERS:

The Honorable Nathan L. Hecht — Chair - Chief Justice, Supreme Court
The Honorable Sharon Keller — Vice Chair - Presiding Judge, Court of Criminal Appeals .

LEGISLATIVE MEMBERS:

Senator — The Honorable Judith Zaffirini
Senator — The Honorable Brandon Creighton
Representative — The Honorable Andrew Murr
Representative — The Honorable John T. Smithee

JUDICIAL MEMBERS:

The Honorable Gary Bellair — Presiding Judge, Ransom Canyon Municipal Court
The Honorable Bill J. Boyce — Justice, 14th Court of Appeals, Houston
The Honorable Bill Gravell, Jr. — Justice of the Peace, Pct. 3 Willliamson County
The Honorable Scott Jenkins — Judge, 53rd Judicial Civil District Court Travis County
The Honorable Kelly G. Moore — Judge 121st Judicial District, Terry & Yoakum
The Honorable Valencia Nash — Justice of the Peace, Pct. 1, Place 2, Dallas County
The Honorable Sherry Radack — Chief Justice, 1st Court of Appeals, Houston
The Honorable Polly Spencer — Judge (Ret.), Probate Court #1, Bexar County
The Honorable Edward J. Spillane III — Presiding Municipal Court Judge, College Station
The Honorable Vivian Torres — Judge, Medina County Court at Law

CITIZEN MEMBERS:

Information Services Group, Inc. — Carlos Amaral
Virtual Intelligence Providers LLC — Sonia Clayton
Lewis & Bockius LLP — Allyson Ho
Gibson, Dunn and Crutcher LLP — Ashley Johnson
Oliva, Saks, Garcia & Curiel LLP — Kenneth S. Saks
Baker Botts — Evan Young

STAFF:

Executive Director
 Office of Court Administration — David Slayton 512/463-1625

LAW EXAMINERS, BOARD OF*

205 W. 14th St., Suite 500, P.O. Box 13486, Austin 78711-3486
512/463-1621 • *FAX: 512/463-5300*
www.ble.texas.gov • Agency # 203

9 Members - 6 Years

Members are appointed by the Supreme Court

Harold "Al" Odom	Chair, Houston
Augustin Rivera, Jr.	Vice Chair, Corpus Christi
Barbara Ellis	Board Member, Austin
Teresa Ereon Giltner	Board Member, Dallas
C. Alfred Mackenzie	Board Member, Waco
Dwaine M. Massey	Board Member, Houston
Anna McKim	Board Member, Lubbock
Cynthia Orr	Board Member, San Antonio
Sandra Zamora	Board Member, Dallas

STAFF:

Executive Director	Susan Henricks	.512/463-8929
Executive Assistant	Kendelyn Schiller	.512/463-8926
Director, Character and Fitness	Lori S. Adelman	.512/463-9476
Director, Eligibility and Examination	Nahdiah Hoang	.512/463-6216

Subject to the Texas Sunset Act; will be reviewed in 2029.

LAW LIBRARY, TEXAS STATE

205 W. 14th St., Tom C. Clark Bldg., G01
P.O. Box 12367, Austin 78711-2367
512/463-1722 • *FAX: 512/463-1728*
www.sll.texas.gov • Agency # 243

3 Ex-Officio Members

The Honorable Nathan L. Hecht	Chief Justice of Supreme Court of Texas, 12-31-20
The Honorable Sharon Keller	Presiding Judge, Court of Criminal Appeals, 12-31-18
The Honorable Ken Paxton	Attorney General of Texas, 12-31-18

STAFF:

Director	Dale Propp
Assistant Director	Leslie Prather-Forbis
Chief Fiscal Officer	Amy Small
Network Administrator	Ruth Harrison

LICENSED COURT INTERPRETER
ADVISORY BOARD

205 W. 14th St., Ste. 600, P.O. Box 12066, Austin 78711-2066
512/475-4368 • *FAX: 512/463-1117*
www.txcourts.gov/jbcc/licensed-court-interpreters.aspx

5 Members - 6 Years

Members appointed by the Supreme Court

Melissa B. Fischer	Chair, San Antonio, 2-1-21
Robert Richter Jr.	Board Member, Houston, 2-1-19
Cynthia de Peña	Board Member, Mc Allen, 2-1-23
Luis Garcia	Board Member, Keller, 2-1-21
Melissa Wallace	Board Member, San Antonio, 2-1-19

OFFICE OF CAPITAL AND FORENSIC WRITS

1700 N. Congress Ave. Suite 460, Stephen F. Austin Building, Austin 78701
512/463-8600 • *FAX: 512/463-8590*
www.ocfw.texas.gov • Agency # 215

STAFF:

Director	Benjamin Wolff	.512/463-8502
Human Resources/ Senior Accountant	Sandra Justice	.512/463-8520

The Office of Capital and Forensic Writs is entrusted with advocating on behalf of indigent individuals sentenced to death in Texas. The Office works within the judicial system to safeguard the Constitutional rights of the individual through high quality legal representation, undertaken by a diverse staff.

PROCESS SERVER CERTIFICATION
ADVISORY BOARD

205 W. 14th St., Ste. 600, P.O. Box 12066, Austin 78711-2066
512/475-4368 • *FAX: 512/463-1117*
www.txcourts.gov/jbcc/process-server-certification.aspx

5 Members - 6 Years

Members appointed by the Supreme Court

Patrick Dyer	Chair, Missouri City, 2-1-21
Justiss Rasberry	Board Member, El Paso, 2-1-19
The Honorable Rhonda Hughey	Board Member, Kaufman, 2-1-19
Eric Johnson	Board Member, Rosharon, 2-1-21
Melissa K. Perez	Board Member, Waxahachie, 2-1-23

The Certification Division at the Office of Court Administration provides staff and support for the Advisory Board.

STATE PROSECUTING ATTORNEY
209 W. 14th Street, P.O. Box 13046, Austin 78711-3046
512/463-1660 • *FAX: 512/463-5724*
www.spa.texas.gov • Agency # 213

Stacey M. Soule	State Prosecuting Attorney
Emily Johnson-Liu	Assistant State Prosecuting Attorney
John R. Messinger	Assistant State Prosecuting Attorney
Sadie Jurney	Administrative Assistant

Prosecuting Attorney appointed by the Court of Criminal Appeals.

TEXAS INDIGENT DEFENSE COMMISSION
209 W. 14th St., Suite 202, Austin 78701
512/936-6994 • 866/499.0656 • *FAX: 512/463-5724*
www.tidc.texas.gov

13 Members

The Honorable Sharon Keller	Chair
The Honorable Nathan L. Hecht	Ex Officio Member
Sen. John Whitmire	Ex Officio Member, Houston
Sen. Brandon Creighton	Ex Officio Member, Conroe
Rep. Joseph "Joe" Moody	Ex Officio Member, El Paso
Rep. Andrew Murr	Ex Officio Member, Junction
The Honorable Sherry Radack	Ex Officio Member, Houston
The Honorable Vivian Torres	Ex Officio Member, Medina
Mr. Alex Bunin	Appointed Member, Houston, 2-1-19
The Honorable Jon H. Burrows	Appointed Member, Temple, 2-1-18
The Honorable Richard A. Evans	Appointed Member, 2-1-18
Mr. Don Hase	Appointed Member, Fort Worth, 2-1-19
The Honorable Missy Medary	Appointed Member, Corpus Christi, 2-1-18

STAFF:

Executive Director	Geoffrey Burkhart	512/936-6994
Deputy Director	Wesley Shackelford	512/936-6997
Grants Program Manager	Edwin Colfax	512/463-2508
Special Counsel	Scott Ehlers	512/936-7551
Grants Specialist	Doriana Torres	512/463/8015
Executive Assistant	Marissa Kubinski	512/936-6994
Budget & Accounting Analyst	Sharon Whitfield	512/936-6998
Senior Policy Monitor	Joel Lieurance	512/936-7560
Policy Monitor	Morgan Shell	512/463-2573
Fiscal Monitor	Debra Stewart	512/936-7561

AGENCIES, BOARDS & COMMISSIONS

A&M UNIVERSITY SYSTEM, THE TEXAS BOARD OF REGENTS

P.O. Box 15812, College Station 77841-5013
979/845-9600 • *FAX: 979/845-0835* • www.tamus.edu • Agency # 710

9 Members - 6 Year terms;

1 Student Regent - 1 Year term

Charles W. Schwartz	Chair, Houston, 2-1-19
Elaine Mendoza	Vice Chair, San Antonio, 2-1-23
Phil Adams	Board Member, Bryan/College Station, 2-1-21
Robert L. Albritton	Board Member, Fort Worth, 2-1-21
Anthony G. Buzbee	Board Member, Houston, 2-1-19
Morris E. Foster	Board Member, Austin, 2-1-19
Tim Leach	Board Member, Midland, 2-1-23
Bill Mahomes	Board Member, Dallas, 2-1-21
Cliff Thomas	Board Member, Victoria, 2-1-23
Stephen F. Shuchart	Student Regent, Houston, 5-31-18

Administration:
Executive Director,
Board of Regents   Vickie Spillers ....979/845-9600 / *Fax: 979/845-0835*

Office of the Chancellor:
Moore/Connally Building
301 Tarrow, 7th Floor
College Station, TX 77840
(979) 458-6000

Chancellor	John Sharp ....979/458-6000 / *Fax: 979/458-6044*
Executive Vice Chancellor & CFO	Billy Hamilton ....979/458-6000 / *Fax: 979/458-6044*
General Counsel	Ray Bonilla ....979/458-6120 / *Fax: 979/458-6150*
VC for Academic Affairs	James Hallmark ....979/458-6070 / *Fax: 979/458-6044*
VC for Business Affairs	Phillip Ray ....979/458-6000 / *Fax: 979/458-6044*
VC and Dean of Engineering	M. Katherine Banks ......979/845-1306 / *Fax: 979/845-4925*
VC and Dean of Agriculture and Life Sciences	Mark Hussey ....979/845-4747 / *Fax: 979/845-9938*
VC for Research	Jon Mogford ....979/458-6000 / *Fax: 979/458-6044*
VC for Marketing & Communications	Laylan Copelin ....979/458-6023 / *Fax: 979/458-6044*
Chief Auditor	Charlie Hrncir ....979/458-7100 / *Fax: 979/458-7111*
Chief Investment Officer and Treasurer	Maria Robinson 979/458-6221
Chief Information Officer	Mark Stone ....979/458-6450 / *Fax: 979/458-6044*
VC for Health Services & Dean of the College of Medicine	Carrie L. Byington, M.D. ...979/436-0202 / *Fax: 979/436-0092*

Texas A&M University Cont.

COMPONENT INSTITUTIONS:

Texas A&M University:
Michael Young, President
College Station, TX 77843-1246
979/845-2217 / *Fax: 979/845-5027*

Texas A&M University-Commerce:
Ray M. Keck III, President
P. O. Box 3011
Commerce, TX 75429-3011
903/ 886-5011

Texas A&M University-Corpus Christi:
Kelly Quintanilla, President
6300 Ocean Drive, Unit 5756
Corpus Christi, TX 78412-5756
361/825-2621 / *Fax: 361/825-5810*

Texas A&M University-Kingsville:
Steven H. Tallant, President
700 University Blvd., MSC 101
Kingsville, TX 78363-8202
361/593-3209 / *Fax: 361/593-3218*

Texas A&M University-Texarkana:
Emily F. Cutrer, President
7101 University Avenue
Texarkana, TX 75503
903/223-3001 / *Fax: 903/832-2032*

Prairie View A&M University:
Ruth Simmons, President
P. O. Box 519
Prairie View, TX 77446-0519
936/261-2111 / *Fax: 936/261-2115*

AGENCIES AND SERVICES:
College Station, TX 77843
Texas A&M AgriLife Research:
Craig Nessler, Director
979/845-8486 / *Fax: 979/458-4765*

Texas A&M AgriLife Extension Service:
Douglas Steele, Director
979/845-7967 / *Fax: 979/458-9542*

Texas A&M Engineering Experiment Station:
M. Katherine Banks, Director
979/458-2831 / *Fax: 979/845-4925*

Texas A&M Engineering Extension Service:
Gary Sera, Director
979/458-6800 / *Fax: 979/458-6829*

Texas A&M Forest Service:
Thomas G. Boggus, Director & State Forester .
979/458-6606 / *Fax: 979/458-6610*

Tarleton State University:
F. Dominic Dottavio, President
Tarleton Station
Stephenville, TX 76402
254/968-9100 / *Fax: 254/968-9920*

West Texas A&M University:
Walter V. Wendler, President
WT Box 60997
Canyon, TX 79016
806/651-2100 / *Fax: 806/651-2126*

Texas A&M International University:
Pablo Arenaz, President
5201 University Blvd.
Laredo, TX 78041-1900
956/326-2320 / *Fax: 956/326-2319*

Texas A&M University-Central Texas:
Marc A. Nigliazzo, President
1001 Leadership Place
Killeen, TX 76549
254/519-5720 / *Fax: 254/519-5450*

Texas A&M University-San Antonio:
Cynthia Teniente-Matson, President
One University Way, Suite 410
San Antonio, TX 78224
210/784-1602 / *Fax: 210/784-1619*

Texas A&M Transportation Institute:
Gregory D. Winfree, Director
979/845-1713 / *Fax: 979/845-9356*

Texas A&M Veterinary Medical Diagnostic Laboratory:
Bruce Akey, Director
979/845-2679 / *Fax: 979/845-1794*

Texas A&M Health Science Center:
Carrie L. Byington, M.D., Senior VP
8441 Riverside Parkway
Clinical Bldg. 1, Suite 3100
Bryan, TX 77807
979/436-0202 / *Fax: 979/436-0092*

ACCOUNTANCY, TX STATE BOARD OF PUBLIC*

333 Guadalupe, Tower 3, Suite 900, Austin 78701-3900
512/305-7800 • *FAX: 512/305-7875; 512/305-7854*
www.tsbpa.texas.gov • Agency # 457

15 Members - 6 Years

Manuel Cavazos IV, Esq., CPA	Presiding Officer, Austin, 1-31-23
Donna J. Hugly, CPA	Assistant Presiding Officer, Fredericksburg, 1-31-19
Steve D. Peña, CPA	Secretary, Georgetown, 1-31-19
Robert M. McAdams, CPA	Treasurer, San Antonio, 1-31-19
Susan Fletcher	Board Member, Frisco, 1-31-19
Lisa A. Friel, CPA	Board Member, San Antonio, 1-31-23
Jamie D. Grant	Board Member, Arlington, 1-31-23
James D, Ingram IV, CPA	Board Member, College Station, 1-31-23
Ross T. Johnson, CPA	Board Member, Houston, 1-31-21
Timothy L. LaFrey, Esq., CPA	Board Member, Austin, 1-31-21
Roselyn Morris, Ph.D., CPA	Board Member, San Marcos, 1-31-21
Benjamin Peña, CFE, CPA	Board Member, Brownsville, 1-31-21
Debra S. Sharp	Board Member, Houston, 1-31-23
Kimberly E. Wilkerson, Esq.	Board Member, Lubbock, 1-31-21
William Lawrence	Exec. Committee Member-at-Large, Highland Village, 1-31-19

STAFF:

Executive Director   William Treacy . . . . .512/305-7803 / *Fax: 512/305-7854*

DIVISIONS:

Administration, Information Resources and Accounting:
512/305-7800
accounting@tsbpa.texas.gov

General Automated Information Systems:
512/305-7870

Enforcement:
512/305-7866

Licensing:
512/305-7853

Continuing Professional Education:
512/305-7844

Qualifications:
512/305-7851

Peer Review:
512/305-7820

Information Resources:
512/305-7800

Public Information:
512/305-7804

The State Board of Public Accountancy regulates the practice of public accountants and administers the certified public accountant exam in Texas.

---

*Subject to the Texas Sunset Act; will be reviewed in 2019.

ACUPUNCTURE EXAMINERS,
TEXAS STATE BOARD OF*

333 Guadalupe, Tower 3, Suite 610, P.O. Box 2018, Austin 78768-2018
512/305-7010 • *FAX: 512/305-7051* • www.tmb.state.tx.us
Disciplinary Info Hotline: 800/248-4062
Consumer Complaints: 800/201-9353

9 Members - 6 Years

Allen Cline, L.Ac.	Presiding Officer, Austin, 1-31-19
Donna S. Guthery, L.Ac.	Board Member, Bellaire, 1-31-17
Claudia E. Harsh, M.D.	Board Member, Dallas, 1-31-19
Rachelle Webb, L.Ac.	Board Member, Austin, 1-31-19
Jeremy Wiseman M.D.	Board Member, Austin, 1-31-21
Raymond J. Graham	Public Member, El Paso, 1-31-17
Jingyu Gu, L.Ac.	Public Member, Austin, 1-31-17
Vacant	Board Member
Vacant	Public Member

STAFF:

Interim Executive Director	Scott Freshour, J.D. . . . . . . .512/305-7010 / *Fax: 512/305-7051*
Medical Director	Robert Bredt, M.D. . . . . .512/305-7019 / *Fax: 512/305-7051*
General Counsel	Scott Freshour, J.D. . . . . . . .512/305-7085 / *Fax: 512/305-7051*
Special Projects	Megan Goode . . . . .512/305-7044 / *Fax: 512/305-7051*
Board Coordinator/	
Executive Assistant	Laura Fleharty . . . . .512/305-7174 / *Fax: 512/305-7051*
Licensure Manager	Monique Johnston . . . . . . .512/305-7121 / *Fax: 512/305-7009*

The Texas State Board of Acupuncture Examiners is a division of The Texas Medical Board and regulates the practice of acupuncture in the state of Texas.

---

*Subject to the Texas Sunset Act; will be reviewed in 2029.

ADMINISTRATIVE HEARINGS, STATE OFFICE OF*

300 West 15th St., Suite 504, P.O. Box 13025, Austin 78711-3025
512/475-4993 • *FAX: 512/475-4994*
www.soah.texas.gov • Agency # 360

1 Member - 2 Years

Lesli G. Ginn   Chief Administrative Law Judge, Austin

Executive Offices:
Deputy Chief for Hearings   Gary W. Elkins 512/305-9384
General Counsel   Cynthia Villarreal-Reyna 512/936-6624
Executive Assistant   Norma Lopez .... 512/475-1276 / *Fax: 512/463-7791*
Program Specialist II   Angla Pardo .... 512/463-9726 / *Fax: 512/463-7791*

Human Resources:
Human Resources Director   Pamela Wood .... 512/305-9386 / *Fax: 512/936-0769*

Information Resources:
Information Resources Manager   Wendy Barron .... 512/463-1541 / *Fax: 512/463-4858*

Operations:
Chief Financial Officer   Kimberly Dudish .... 512/463-8575 / *Fax: 512/463-7527*

FIELD OFFICES:

Corpus Christi:
361/884-5023
Fax: 361/884-5427

Dallas:
214/962-3260
Fax: 214/962-3266

El Paso:
915/834-5650
Fax: 915/834-5657

Fort Worth:
817/731-1733
Fax: 817/377-3706

Houston:
713/957-0010
Fax: 713/812-1001

Lubbock:
806/792-0007
Fax: 806/792-0149

San Antonio:
210/308-6681
Fax: 210/308-6854

The judges hold contested case hearings and conduct mediations.

*Subject to the Texas Sunset Act; will be reviewed in 2027.

AFFORDABLE HOUSING CORPORATION, TEXAS STATE*

2200 East MLK Jr. Boulevard, P.O. Box 12637, Austin 78711-2637
512/477-3555 • 888/638-3555 • *FAX: 512/477-3557* • www.tsahc.org

5 Members - 6 Years

Robert "Bob" Jones	Chair, Corpus Christi, 2-1-15
William H. Dietz, Jr.	Vice Chair, Waco, 2-1-19
Gerry Evenwel	Board Member, Mt. Pleasant, 2-1-17
Alex Meade III	Board Member, Mission, 2-1-19
Jerry Romero	Board Member, El Paso, 2-1-15

STAFF:

President	David Long . . . . .512/477-3568 / *Fax: 512/477-3557*
Executive Vice President	Janie Taylor . . . . .512/477-3564 / *Fax: 512/477-3557*
Chief Financial Officer	Melinda Smith . . . . .512/904-1399 / *Fax: 512/477-3557*

The Legislature created the Texas State Affordable Housing Corporation in 1995 as a self-sustaining nonprofit corporation to help low-income Texans obtain affordable housing.

---

*Subject to the Texas Sunset Act; will be reviewed in 2023.

AGRICULTURE, TEXAS DEPARTMENT OF*

1700 N. Congress, 11th Floor, P.O. Box 12847, Austin 78711-2847
www.TexasAgriculture.gov • Agency # 551
Main Number: 512/463-7476
Customer Service: 800/835-5832
Relay Texas-Hearing Impaired: 800/735-2988
Agency Fax: 888/223-8861
TDA Fraud Hotline: 800/537-2834

1 Member - 4 Years

SID MILLER (R) Commissioner of Agriculture, 12-31-18

Spouse: Debra

Commissioner Miller was born in De Leon, Texas, and is an avid rodeo and horseshow participant who holds nine World Championships. He is a graduate of Tarleton State University in Stephenville, where he received a Bachelor of Science in Vocational Agriculture Education. He is a lifelong farmer, rancher and small business owner. Before being elected Commissioner of Agriculture, Commissioner Miller served 6 terms in the Texas House of Representatives.

Agriculture Commissioner	The Honorable Sid Miller	512/463-1408

COMMISSIONER'S STAFF:

Deputy Commissioner	Jason Fearneyhough	512/463-1408
Special Assistant to the Commissioner	Kevin Moomaw	512/475-1840
Executive Assistant/Scheduler	Rebecca Bustamante	512/463-1408

ADMINISTRATION:

Assistant Commissioner	Terry Keel	512/475-0133
Director for		
Licensing and Data Quality	Burney LaChance	512/463-7846
Agency Administration	Bertha Serna	512/475-0133
Chief of Operational Support	Michael Clark	512/463-7488
Administrator for		
Human Resources	Cynthia Mendoza	512/463-7423
Coordinator for Human Res.	Emilia Zarate	512/463-9305

AGRICULTURE & CONSUMER PROTECTION:

Administrator	Philip Wright	512/463-6514
Director for		
Consumer Service Protection	Leslie Smith	512/475-1620
Consumer Product Protection	Stuart Strnad	512/463-5706
Environmental and		
Biosecurity Programs	Dale Scott	512/936-2535
Ag. and Commodity Programs	Mike Mann	512/463-4753

EXTERNAL RELATIONS, COMMUNICATIONS AND LEGISLATIVE AFFAIRS:

Assistant Commissioner	Walt Roberts	512/936-9583
Director for Communications	Mark Loeffler	512/475-1669
Asst. Dir. for Communications	Jeremy Fuchs	512/463-9885
Director for Govt. Relations	Ilissa Nolan	512/463-7516

Agriculture, Dept. of Cont.

FINANCIAL SERVICES DIVISION:

Chief Financial Officer	Diana Warner	.512/463-9860
Administrator for		
Financial Compliance	April Bacon	.512/463-7493
Grants, Revenue & Cash Mgmt.	Marios Parpounas	.512/463-4793
Director for HUB/MWBE		
Programs CFO/ CIO	William "Butch" Grote	.512/475-0124

FOOD AND NUTRITION DIVISION:

Assistant Commissioner	Angela Olige	.512/463-8583
Administrator		
Food and Nutrition	Catherine Wright-Steele	.512/463-2164
Food and Nutrition	Tracy Mueck	.512/936-6723
Food and Nutrition	Robin Roark	.512/463-3910

OFFICE OF INTERNAL AUDIT:

Internal Auditor	Zoi Kondis	.512/463-8251

LEGAL DIVISION:

General Counsel	Tim Kleinschmidt	.512/463-6260
Lead Deputy General Counsel	Stephen Dillon	.512/463-0735
Deputy General Counsel/		
Ethics Officer	Susan Maldonado	.512/463-6591
Deputy General Counsel		
for Enforcement	AJ Salazar-Wilson	.512/463-2936

TRADE, BUSINESS DEVELOPMENT, WATER AND RURAL AFFAIRS:

Assistant Commissioner	Dan Hunter	.512/463-9132
Administrator for Office of		
Rural Affairs	Karen Reichek	.512/936-2450

FIELD OPERATIONS:

Liaison for Field Operations	Freddy Vest	.214/403-9563

REGIONAL AND SUB-OFFICES:

Region 1
West Texas Regional Office
Bob Tarrant, Regional Director
4502 Englewood Ave.
Lubbock, TX 79414
806/799-8555 / *Fax: 800/831-3746*

Region 2
North Texas Regional Office
Becky Dempsey, Regional Director
1720 Regal Row, Suite 118
Dallas, TX 75235
214/631-0265 / *Fax: 888/205-6335*

Region 3
Gulf Coast Regional Office
Jennifer Bailey, Regional Director
5425 Polk Street, G-20
Houston, TX 77023
713/921-8200 / *Fax: 888/223-5606*

Region 4
San Antonio Regional Office
Ken Weidenfeller, Regional Director
8918 Tesoro Dr., Suite 120
San Antonio, TX 78217
210/820-0288 / *Fax: 888/203-1235*

Region 5
Valley Regional Office
Jose Sanchez, Regional Director
900-B East Expressway 83
San Juan, TX 78589
956/787-8886 / *Fax: 800/909-8167*

*Subject to the Texas Sunset Act; will be reviewed in 2021.

ALCOHOLIC BEVERAGE COMMISSION, TEXAS (TABC)*

5806 Mesa Dr., P.O. Box 13127, Austin 78711-3127
512/206-3333 • *FAX: 512/206-3350* • www.tabc.texas.gov • Agency # 458

3 Members - 6 Years

Kevin J. Lilly	Chair, Houston, 11-15-21
Ida Louise "Weisie" Steen	Board Member, San Antonio, 11-15-19
Vacant	Board Member

Office of the Executive Director:

Executive Director	Bentley Nettles . . . . .512/206-3366 / *Fax: 512/206-3203*
Executive Assistant	Luann Dickerson . . . . .512/206-3217 / *Fax: 512/206-3203*

Deputy Executive Directors:

Chief of Staff	Matt Chaplin . . . . .512/206-3201 / *Fax: 512/206-3203*
Enforcement	Robert Saenz . . . . .512/206-3401 / *Fax: 512/206-3449*
Business & Revenue Operations	Dennis Beal . . . . .512/206-3373 / *Fax: 512/206-3399*

General Counsel/Legal Services:

General Counsel/Legal Services	Clark Smith . . . . .512/206-3230 / *Fax: 512/206-3226*

Chief Financial Officer:

CFO	Vanessa Mayo . . . . .512/206-3244 / *Fax: 512/206-3248*

Director:

Governmental Relations	Mariann H. Morelock . . . . .512/206-3347 / *Fax: 512/206-3203*
External Affairs	Jared Staples . . . . .512/206-3327 / *Fax: 512/206-3203*
Internal Affairs	Position Vacant . . . . .512/206-3426 / *Fax: 512/206-3207*

Division Directors:

Law Enforcement	Position Vacant . . . . .512/206-3271 / *Fax: 512/206-3449*
Investigations	Captain Ron Swenson . . . . .512/206-3301 / *Fax: 512/206-3449*
Audit	Dexter Jones . . . . .512/206-3302 / *Fax: 512/206-3449*
Ports of Entry	John Reney . . . . .512/206-3279 / *Fax: 512/206-3356*
Licensing	Jo Ann Joseph . . . . .512/206-3306 / *Fax: 512/206-3399*
Tax & Marketing Practices	Thomas Graham . . . . .512/206-3338 / *Fax: 512/206-3321*
Marketing Practices Supervisor	Andrea Maceyra . . . . .512/206-3411 / *Fax: 512/206-3321*
Human Resources	Donn Rupp . . . . .512/206-3215 / *Fax: 512/206-3350*
Innovation & Technology	Jay Webster . . . . .512/206-3452 / *Fax: 512/206-3281*
Education & Prevention	Mindy Carroll . . . . .512/206-3293 / *Fax: 512/206-3316*
Training	Albert Rodriguez . . . . .512/206-3238 / *Fax: 512/206-3269*

Public Information Officer:

Public Information Officer	Chris Porter . . . . .512/206-3462 / *Fax: 512/206-3203*

TABC REGIONAL/DISTRICT OFFICES:

Lubbock Regional Office (Region 1)
Major Mark Menn
Audit Regional Supervisor Tom Johnson
Licensing Regional Supervisor Kyle Russell
612 West Loop 289, Suite 100
Lubbock, TX 79416
806/793-3221 / *Fax: 806/793-3222*

Arlington Regional Office (Region 2)
Major Cathleen Cavazos
Audit Regional Supervisor Amanda Collins
Licensing Regional Supervisor Tana Travis
2225 East Randol Mill, Suite 200
Arlington, TX 76011
817/652-5912 / *Fax: 817/607-2492*

Alcoholic Beverage Comm. Cont.

Houston Regional Office (Region 3)
Major Marc Decatur
Regional Supervisor Nicole Phillips
Licensing Regional Supervisor Antoine Collins
427 West 20th St.
Suite 600
Houston, TX 77008-2497
713/426-7900 / *Fax: 713/426-7979*

Austin Regional Office (Region 4)
Major Victor Kuykendoll
Audit Regional Supervisor Josh Alexander
Licensing Patrick Connally
7700 Chevy Chase Dr., Suite 200
Austin, TX 78752
512/451-0231 / *Fax: 512/451-0240*

San Antonio Regional Office (Region 5)
Major Richard Jauregui
Audit Regional Supervisor Stacy Jackson
Licensing Regional Supervisor Yvette Price
Goliad Building, Suite 120
4203 Woodcock Drive
San Antonio, TX 78228
210/731-1720 / *Fax: 210/731-1759*

---

*Subject to the Texas Sunset Act; will be reviewed in 2019.

ALZHEIMER'S DISEASE & RELATED DISORDERS, TEXAS COUNCIL ON
512/776-6618 • 800/242-3399 • *FAX: 512/776-7254*

Agency Contact   Lynda Taylor, M.S.W. 512/776-6618

Advises and recommends needed actions for the benefit of persons with Alzheimer's disease and related disorders and their caregivers; disseminates information on services and related activities; coordinates services and activities of state agencies, associations and other service providers; and encourages statewide coordinated research.

ANGELINA AND NECHES RIVER AUTHORITY, BOARD OF DIRECTORS

210 E. Lufkin Avenue, P.O. Box 387, Lufkin 75902-0387
936/632-7795 • *FAX: 936/632-2564* • www.anra.org

9 Members - 6 Years

Jody Anderson	President, Lufkin, 9-5-19
Thomas R. "Tom" Murphy	Vice President, Crockett, 9-5-19
Patricia E. Dickey	Secretary/Treasurer, Crockett, 9-5-17
Skip Ogle	Secretary Pro-Tem, Tyler, 9-5-21
Louis A. Bronaugh	Director, Lufkin, 9-5-17
Julie Dowell	Director, Bullard, 9-5-17
David M. King	Director, Nacogdoches, 9-5-19
Dale Morton	Director, Nacogdoches, 9-5-21
Francis Spruiell	Director, Center, 9-5-21

STAFF:
General Manager   Kelley Holcomb . . . . .936/633-7543 / *Fax: 936/632-2564*

The board sets policy, provides oversight and employs a general manager for the Angelina and Neches River Authority. The Authority's jurisdiction covers all or part of 17 counties within the Neches River Basin which include Angelina, Anderson, Cherokee, Henderson, Houston, Jasper, Nacogdoches, Newton, Orange, Polk, Rusk, Sabine, San Augustine, Shelby, Smith, Trinity, and Van Zandt. ANRA's Service area is the equivalent of approximately 8,500 square miles of watershed. Recent population projections estimate the total population served at 600,000.

ANIMAL HEALTH COMMISSION, TEXAS*

2105 Kramer Lane, P.O. Box 12966, Austin 78711-2966
512/719-0700 • Toll Free: 800/550-8242 • *FAX: 512/719-0719*
www.tahc.texas.gov • Agency # 554

13 Members - 6 Years

Coleman Hudgins Locke	Chair, Hungerford, 9-6-21
Brandon Bouma	Commissioner, Plainview, 9-6-17
William F. Edmiston, Jr., D.V.M.	Commissioner, Eldorado, 9-9-19
Jim Eggleston	Commissioner, Weatherford, 9-6-21
Ken Jordan	Commissioner, San Saba, 9-9-19
Thomas "Tommy" Kezar	Commissioner, Dripping Springs, 9-6-17
Joe L. Leathers	Commissioner, Guthrie, 9-9-19
Thomas Eugene Oates	Commissioner, Huntsville, 9-9-19
Leo Vermedahl	Commissioner, Dalhart, 9-6-17
Mike Vickers, D.V.M.	Commissioner, Falfurrias, 9-6-17
Eric Dean White	Commissioner, Mason, 9-9-19
Vacant	Commissioner
Vacant	Commissioner

STAFF:

Executive Director	Andy Schwartz, D.V.M.	512/719-0704
Asst. Exec. Director Animal Health Programs	T. R. Lansford, D.V.M.	512/719-0712
Chief of Staff	Larissa Schmidt	512/719-0701
State Epidemiologist	Susan Rollo, D.V.M.	512/719-0713
Director of Financial and Procurement Services	Steven Luna	512/719-0755
Executive Assistant	Amanda Bernhard	512/719-0704
Dir. of Emergency Management	Jeff Turner	512/719-0786
General Counsel	Gene Snelson	512/719-0722
Governmental Industry Relations and Asst. General Counsel	Mary Thiel Luedeker	512/719-0760

FIELD OFFICES AND STAFF:

Region 1-Amarillo:
David Finch, D.V.M., Director
3822 Business Park Drive
Amarillo, TX 79110
806/354-9335 / *Fax: 806/354-2809*

Region 2-Hempstead:
Mark Michalke, D.V.M., Director
1739 13th Street, Suite 28
Hempstead, TX 77445
979/921-9481 / *Fax: 979/921-9992*

Region 3-Fort Worth:
Max Dow, D.V.M., Director
8751 Camp Bowie West, Suite 104
Fort Worth, TX 76116
817/244-2597
Fax: 817/560-1721

Region 4-Mt. Pleasant:
Hank Hayes, D.V.M., Director
313 W. Alabama, Suite 1
Mt. Pleasant, TX 75455
903/572-1966
Fax: 903/572-1114

Region 5-Beeville:
Brodie Miller, D.V.M., Director
1824 S. Washington Street
Beeville, TX 78102
361/358-3234
Fax: 361/358-0101

Region 6-Lampasas:
Pete Fincher, D.V.M., Director
1305 South Key Ave., Ste. 204
Lampasas, TX 76550
512/556-6277
Fax: 512/556-6415

Region 7-Rockdale:
Tommy Barton, D.V.M., Director
130 East Bell St.
Rockdale, TX 76567
512/446-2507
Fax: 512/446-5373

Region 8-Laredo:
T. R. Lansford, D.V.M., Director
500 East Mann Road
Laredo, TX 78041
956/568-5741
Fax: 956/568-5237

State-Federal Laboratory:
Rey Molina, Laboratory Supervisor
8200 Cameron Road, Ste. A186
Austin, TX 78754
512/832-6580
Fax: 512/832-6803

---

*Subject to the Texas Sunset Act; will be reviewed in 2021.

APPRAISER LICENSING AND CERTIFICATION BOARD, TEXAS*

1700 North Congress Ave., Suite 400, P.O. Box 12188, Austin 78711-2188
512/936-3001 • www.talcb.texas.gov • Agency # 329

9 Members - 6 Years

Jamie Wickliffe	Chair, Midlothian, 1-31-19
Ray "Chance" Bolton	Board Member, Bee Cave, 1-31-21
James Jeffries	Board Member, Georgetown, 1-31-23
Martha Gayle Lynch	Board Member, El Paso, 1-31-21
Clayton Black	Public Member, Stanton, 1-31-23
Tony Peña	Public Member, Lubbock, 1-31-21
Alejandro Sostre-Odio	Public Member, San Antonio, 1-31-19
Joyce Yannuzzi	Public Member, New Braunfels, 1-31-19
Earl "Buster" Renfrow	VLB Designee, Texas General Land Office

Appraisal Management Company Advisory Committee:

Chair	James Jeffries
AMC Member	Sara Jones Oates
AMC Member	Position Vacant
Public Member	Position Vacant
Public Member	Angelica Guerra

STAFF:

Commissioner	Douglas E. Oldmixon . . . . . .512/936-3088 / *Fax: 512/936-3788*
Deputy Commissioner/ General Counsel	Kristen Worman . . . . .512/936-3093 / *Fax: 512/936-3788*
Staff & Support Services	Priscilla Pipho . . . . .512/936-3590 / *Fax: 512/936-3551*
Standards & Enforcement Services	Troy Beaulieu . . . . .512/936-3623 / *Fax: 512/936-3621*
Information & Technology Services	Steve Spyropoulos 512/936-3288
Education & Licensing Services	Gwen Jackson . . . . .512/936-3094 / *Fax: 512/936-3899*
Reception & Communication Services	Lorie DeAnda . . . . .512/936-3807 / *Fax: 512/936-3798*

The board performs duties relating to the education, ethics, and certifying or licensing of real estate appraisers or appraiser trainees.

---

*Subject to the Texas Sunset Act; will be reviewed in 2019.

ARCHITECTURAL EXAMINERS, TEXAS BOARD OF*

333 Guadalupe St., Suite 2-350, P.O. Box 12337, Austin 78711-2337
512/305-9000 • *FAX: 512/305-8900* • www.tbae.state.tx.us • Agency # 459

9 Members - 6 Years

Debra Dockery, AIA	Chair, San Antonio, 1-31-17
Chad Davis	Vice Chair, Lubbock, 1-31-19
Jennifer Walker, AIA	Secretary, Lampasas, 1-31-21
Charles H. Anastos, AIA	Board Member, Corpus Christi, 1-31-19
Sonya Odell	Board Member, Dallas, 1-31-17
Bob Wetmore, AIA	Board Member, Austin, 1-31-21
Chase Bearden	Public Member, Austin, 1-31-21
Paula A. Miller	Public Member, The Woodlands, 1-31-17
Vacant	Public Member

STAFF:
Executive Director   Julie Hildebrand 512/305-8535

*Subject to the Texas Sunset Act; will be reviewed in 2025.

ARTS, TEXAS COMMISSION ON THE*

920 Colorado St., P.O. Box 13406, Austin 78711-3406
512/463-5535 • 800/252-9415 • *FAX: 512/475-2699*
www.arts.texas.gov • Agency # 813

9 Members - 6 Years

Dale W. Brock	Chair, Fort Worth, 8-31-17
S. Shawn Stephens	Vice Chair, Houston, 8-15-19
Mila B. Gibson	Secretary, Sweetwater, 8-31-21
Felix Noel Padrón, Jr.	Treasurer, San Antonio, 8-31-21
Marci L. Roberts	Parliamentarian, Marathon, 8-31-21
Rita E. Baca	Commissioner, El Paso, 8-31-17
David C. Garza	Commissioner, Brownsville, 8-31-17
Ronald "Ronnie" Sanders	Commissioner, San Antonio, 8-31-17
Kevin Yu	Commissioner, Dallas, 8-31-19

STAFF:

Executive Director	Gary Gibbs, Ph.D. 512/936-6561	*Fax: 512/475-2699*
Deputy Director	Jim Bob McMillan 512/936-6572	*Fax: 512/475-2699*
Director of Finance	Grant Weaver 512/936-6567	*Fax: 512/475-2699*
Director for Programs & Technology	Laura Wiegand 512/936-6565	*Fax: 512/475-2699*
Director of Communications	Anina Moore 512/936-6573	*Fax: 512/475-2699*
Executive Assistant	Dana Douglass Swann 512/936-6570	*Fax: 512/475-2699*

The commission encourages appreciation for fine arts in Texas, and acts in an advisory capacity regarding the construction and remodeling of state buildings and works of art.

*Subject to the Texas Sunset Act; will be reviewed in 2025.

ATHLETIC TRAINERS, ADVISORY BOARD OF

c/o TDLR, P.O. Box 12057, Austin 78711-2057
512/463-6599 • *FAX: 512/463-9468*
www.tdlr.texas.gov/at/atcmte.htm

5 Members - 6 Years

David J. Weir	Presiding Officer, College Station, 1-31-19
Darrell Ganus	Board Member, Kilgore, 1-31-21
Britney Webb	Board Member, Martindale, 1-31-21
Michael Fitch	Public Member, Dallas, 1-31-23
David Schmidt, M.D.	Public Member, San Antonio, 1-31-17

The board's purpose is to protect public health, safety, and welfare by establishing and enforcing qualifications and standards of practice for licensed athletic trainers.

ATTORNEY GENERAL, OFFICE OF THE

209 West 14th St., P.O. Box 12548, Austin 78711-2548
512/463-2100 • 800/252-8011 • *FAX: 512/475-2994*
www.texasattorneygeneral.gov • Agency # 302
Crime Victims: 800/983-9933
Consumer Protection: 800/621-0508
Child Support Enforcement: 800/252-8014
Open Government Hotline: 877/673-6839
Press Office: 512/463-2050

1 Member - 4 Years

KEN PAXTON (R) 51st Attorney General, 12-31-18
Spouse: Angela

Undergraduate- BA Baylor University, 1985; MBA-Baylor University,
1986; JD- University of Virginia School of Law, 1991. Practiced law
with Strasburger & Price- 1991-1995, and later served as in-house
counsel for J.C. Penney Company. Served in the Texas House of
Representatives, 2003-2013 and Texas State Senate, 2013-2014.
Attorney General of Texas, January 2015- present.

Attorney General	The Honorable Ken Paxton	.512/463-2191

STAFF:

First Assistant Attorney General	Jeffrey C. Mateer	.512/463-2191
Deputy First Assistant AG	Brantley Starr	.512/463-2191
Chief of Staff	Katherine Cary	.512/463-2191
Senior Advisor to the AG	Ben Williams	.512/463-2191
Senior Counsel to the AG	Michael Toth	.512/463-2191
Deputy AG for Civil Litigation	Jim Davis	.512/463-2191
Associate Deputy AG for Civil Litigation	Amanda Cochran-McCall	.512/463-2191
Deputy AG for Admin. and General Counsel	Amanda Crawford	.512/463-2191
Deputy AG for Child Support	Mara Friesen	.512/463-2191
Deputy Director for Child Support	Steve Roddy	.512/463-2191
Director of Law Enforcement	David Maxwell	.512/463-2191
Deputy AG for Criminal Justice	Adrienne McFarland	.512/463-2191
Chief Information Officer/ Information Resources Manager	Rudy Montoya	.512/463-2191
Director of Communications and Senior Advisor	Marc Rylander	.512/463-2191
Solicitor General	Scott Keller	.512/936-1700
Deputy Solicitor General	Cam Barker	.512/936-1700
Deputy Solicitor General	Matt Frederick	.512/936-1700
Director of Intergovt. Relations and Strategic Initiatives	Steve Pier	.512/463-2057
Director of Scheduling	Sarah Burgess	.512/936-1874
Director of Outreach	Amanda Sanders	.512/463-2191
Accounting	Keith Hafer	.512/473-2008

Office of Attorney General Cont.

Antitrust	David Talbot	512/936-1105
Administrative Law	Nichole Bunker-Henderson	512/475-4300
Admin. and Law Info. Technology	Sean Peterson	512/475-4616
Bankruptcy and Collections	Ron Del Vento	512/463-2173
Budget	Misti Hancock	512/475-4911
Child Support and Public Official Inquiry	Kathy McMichael	512/460-6000
Child Support Admin. Operations	Hayley Hall	512/460-6000
Child Support Contract Operations	Michael Gray	512/460-6000
Child Support Information Tech.	Lisa Petoskey	512/460-6000
Child Support Family Initiatives	Noelita Lugo	512/460-6000
Child Support Field Operations	Myra Sines	512/460-6000
Child Support Policy, Legal and Program Ops.	Al Ochoa	512/463-6000
Civil Medicaid Fraud	Ray Winter	512/463-2185
Constituent Affairs	Cyritha Riley Reed	512/475-4413
Consumer Protection	Paul Singer	512/463-2185
Contract and Asset Management	Louis Sellers	512/475-3382
Controller	Michele Price	512/463-2191
Crime Victim Services	Gene McCleskey	512/936-1200
Criminal Appeals	Ed Marshall	512/936-1400
Criminal Investigations	Cody Smirl	512/936-1400
Criminal Prosecutions	Lisa Tanner	512/463-2170
Environmental Protection	Priscilla Hubenak	512/463-2012
Financial Litigation & Charitable Trusts	Joshua Godbey	512/463-2018
General Counsel	John Ellis	512/475-3210
General Litigation	Angela Colmenero	512/463-2120
HUB Coordinator	Shawn Constancio	512/475-4411
Human Resources	Greg Simpson	512/463-2009
Information Governance and Logistical Operations	Margaret Hermesmeyer	512/936-1756
Internal Audit	Angelia Harris	512/475-4923
Law Enforcement Defense	Lacey Mase	512/936-1282
Legal Technical Support	David Falk	512/475-4625
Medicaid Fraud Control Unit	Stormy Kelly	512/463-2011
Office of Special Litigation	Position Vacant	512/463-2191
Ombudsman	Grace Meyer	512/936-1208
Open Records	Justin Gordon	512/936-6736
Opinion Committee	Jennie Hoelscher	512/463-2110
Procurement	Lisa Massock	512/475-4509
Public Finance	Leslie Brock	512/475-2929
Public Information Coordinator	Lauren Downey	512/475-4213
Tax Division	Jack Hohengarten	512/463-2002
Tort Litigation	Kara Kennedy	512/463-2197
Transportation	Randy Hill	512/463-2004

The Attorney General is the lawyer for the people of Texas and is charged by the Texas Constitution to defend the laws and the Constitution of the State of Texas, represent the State in litigation and approve public bond issues.

AUSTIN STATE HOSPITAL

c/o TX Dept. of State Health Services, 4110 Guadalupe St., Austin 78751
512/452-0381 • *FAX: 512/419-2163* •
www.dshs.state.tx.us/mhhospitals/AustinSH/default.shtm

ADMINISTRATION:

Superintendent	Alan Isaacson	.512/419-2100

STAFF:

Assistant Superintendent	Duane Harris	.512/419-2102
Administrative Assistant IV	Kathy Litaker	.512/419-2102
Chief Nurse Executive	Michael Robinson, MSN, RN-BC	.512/419-2928
Financial Officer	Patrick Pence	.512/419-2061
Service Director		
Child/Adolescent Services	Stacey Thompson	.512/419-2532
Service Director		
Specialty Services	Amie Grady-Chopra	.512/419-2862
Director		
Education/Rehabilitation	Karen Sams	.512/419-2617
Client Advocacy	Pareatha Madison, MAHS, BS	.512/419-2179
Reimbursement	Susan Williams	.512/419-2636
Community Relations	Cindy Reed	.512/419-2333

BANKING DEPARTMENT OF TEXAS*

2601 North Lamar, Austin 78705-4294
512/475-1300 • 877/276-5554 • *FAX: 512/475-1313*
www.dob.texas.gov • Agency # 451

DEPARTMENT STAFF:

Banking Commissioner	Charles G. Cooper	.512/475-1325 / *Fax: 512/475-1313*
Exec. Asst. to the Comm.	Anne Benites	.512/475-1325 / *Fax: 512/475-1313*
Deputy Commissioner	Robert Bacon	.512/475-1302 / *Fax: 512/475-1313*
Deputy Commissioner	Stephanie Newberg	.512/475-1280 / *Fax: 512/475-1313*
Exec. Asst.to the Deputy Comm.	Brenda Medina	.512/475-1332 / *Fax: 512/475-1313*
Director of		
Bank & Trust Supervision	Kurt Purdom	.512/475-1333 / *Fax: 512/475-1313*
Examination Support Activites	Chris Robinson	.512/475-1329 / *Fax: 512/475-1313*
Strategic Support	Wendy Rodriguez	.512/475-1320 / *Fax: 512/475-1313*
Human Resources	Lori Wright	.512/475-1345 / *Fax: 512/475-1313*
Administrative Services	Sami Chadli	.512/475-1316 / *Fax: 512/475-1313*
Information Services	Joe Broz	.512/475-1304 / *Fax: 512/475-1313*
Special Audits	Russell Reese	.512/475-1324 / *Fax: 512/475-1313*
Corporate Activities	Dan Frasier	.512/475-1322 / *Fax: 512/475-1313*
Financial Analyst	Krissna Jones	.512/475-1326 / *Fax: 512/475-1313*
Review Examiner	Kevin Wu	.512/475-1368 / *Fax: 512/475-1313*
Review Examiner	Jared Whitson	.512/475-1354 / *Fax: 512/475-1313*
Corporate Analyst	Mark Largent	.512/475-1351 / *Fax: 512/473-1313*
Corporate Analyst	Xazel Garcia	.512/475-1310 / *Fax: 512/475-1313*
General Counsel	Catherine Reyer	.512/475-1327 / *Fax: 512/475-1313*
Deputy General Counsel	Debby Loomis	.512/475-1282 / *Fax: 512/475-1313*
Special Counsel	Everette D. Jobe	.512/475-1321 / *Fax: 512/475-1313*
Assistant General Counsel	Ryan McCarthy	.512/475-1236 / *Fax: 512/475-1313*

Banking Dept. Cont.

Assistant General Counsel	Marcus Adams	.........512/475-1236 / *Fax: 512/475-1313*
Assistant General Counsel	Chris Bell	.............512/475-0439 / *Fax: 512/475-1313*
Review Examiner-Special Audits	Jesse Saucillo	..........512/475-1311 / *Fax: 512/475-1313*

REGIONAL OFFICES:

San Antonio:
2700 NE Loop 410, Suite 616
San Antonio, TX 78217

Regional Director	Kenneth Kuntschik	.......210/271-3923 / *Fax: 210/271-3948*
Regional Review Examiner	Allen Millsap	..........210/271-3923 / *Fax: 210/271-3948*

Dallas/Ft. Worth:
1201 N. Watson
Suite 210
Arlington, TX 76006-6120

Regional Director	Larry W. Walker	........972/241-1426 / *Fax: 972/241-1766*
Regional Review Examiner	Thomas Susany	.........972/241-1426 / *Fax: 972/241-1766*

Houston:
9610 Long Point Road
Suite 250
Houston, TX 77055-4259

Regional Director	Bobby Davenport	........713/932-6146 / Fax: 713/932-9405
Regional Review Examiner	Tony Adekoya	..........713/932-6146 / *Fax: 713/932-9405*

West Texas:
4413 82nd St., Suite 215
Lubbock, TX 79424-3366

Regional Director	Jeff Anderson	..........806/794-3763 / *Fax: 806/794-3764*
Regional Review Examiner	David Reed	............806/794-3763 / *Fax: 806/794-3764*

*Subject to the Texas Sunset Act; will be reviewed in 2019.

BLIND AND VISUALLY IMPAIRED, TEXAS SCHOOL FOR THE, GOVERNING BOARD

1100 West 45th St., Austin 78756-3494
512/454-8631; 800/872-5273 • *FAX: 512/206-9453*
www.tsbvi.edu • Agency # 771

9 Members - 6 Years

Mary K. Alexander	Board Member, Valley View, 1-31-21
Anne Corn, Ed.D.	Board Member, Austin, 1-31-17
Caroline K. Daley	Board Member, Kingwood, 1-31-17
Bobby Druesedow	Board Member, Glen Rose, 1-31-19
Michael E. Garrett	Board Member, Missouri City, 1-31-19
Michael P. Hanley	Board Member, Leander, 1-31-17
Joseph Muniz	Board Member, Harlingen, 1-31-21
B. Lee Sonnenberg	Board Member, Lubbock, 1-31-19
Tobie Wortham	Board Member, Royse City, 1-31-21

STAFF:

Superintendent	William Daugherty	512/206-9133
Chief Financial Officer	Pamela Darden, CPA	512/206-9422
Director of Center for School Resources	Susan Hauser	512/206-9273
Principal of Comprehensive Programs	Miles Fain	512/206-9251
Principal of Short Term Programs	Sara Merritt	512/206-9176
Director of Outreach Program	Cyral Miller	512/206-9242
Human Resources Director	Kate Oehlers SPHR	512/206-9132

BOND REVIEW BOARD, TEXAS

300 W. 15th St., Suite 409, P.O. Box 13292, Austin 78711-3292
512/463-1741 • *FAX: 512/475-4802* • www.brb.state.tx.us • Agency # 352

The Honorable Greg Abbott	Chair, Governor of Texas
The Honorable Dan Patrick	Vice Chair, Lt. Governor
The Honorable Glenn Hegar	Board Member, Comptroller of Public Accounts
The Honorable Joe Straus III	Board Member, Speaker of the House of Representatives

STAFF:

Interim Executive Director	Rob Latsha	512/463-1741
Chief Financial Officer	John Perryman	512/463-9890
Senior Financial Analyst	Justin Groll	512/475-4805
Accountant II	Doris Prescott	512/475-4801
Financial Analyst	Braxton Parsons	512/463-9891
Financial Analyst	Merit Dowling	512/475-0890
Accountant I	Denise James	512/463-1741
Accountant I	Hong Nguyen	512/463-4716

BRAZOS RIVER AUTHORITY

4600 Cobbs Drive, P.O. Box 7555, Waco 76714-7555
254/761-3100 • *FAX: 254/400-2194* • www.brazos.org • Agency # 30

21 Members - 6 Years

G. Dave Scott	Presiding Officer, Richmond, 2-1-19
F. LeRoy Bell	Assistant Presiding Officer, Tuscola, 2-1-19
Salvatore A. Zaccagnino	Secretary, Caldwell, 2-1-19
M.G. Christopher Steve Adams, Jr.	Board Member, Kyle, 2-1-17
Richard L. Ball	Board Member, Mineral Wells, 2-1-19
Peter G. Bennis	Board Member, Fort Worth, 2-1-19
Russel D. "Rusty" Boles	Board Member, Round Rock, 2-1-21
Paul J. Christensen	Board Member, Crawford, 2-1-17
Col. Robert M. Christian, (Ret.)	Board Member, Jewett, 2-1-17
Cynthia A. Flores	Board Member, Round Rock, 2-1-21
Roberta Jean "Jean" Grant	Board Member, Salado, 2-1-17
Charles R. "Rick" Huber III	Board Member, Granbury, 2-1-21
Carolyn H. Johnson	Board Member, Freeport, 2-1-17
Jim Lattimore	Board Member, Graford, 2-1-19
Wesley D. Lloyd	Board Member, Waco, 2-1-19
John Henry Luton	Board Member, Granbury, 2-1-21
Henry W. Munson	Board Member, Angleton, 2-1-17
William J. "Bill" Rankin	Board Member, Brenham, 2-1-21
Jarrod D. Smith	Board Member, Danbury, 2-1-17
Jeffery S. Tallas	Board Member, Sugar Land, 2-1-21
William W. "Ford" Taylor III	Board Member, Waco, 2-1-21

STAFF:
General Manager/CEO   Phillip J. Ford 254/761-3194

CANADIAN RIVER COMPACT COMMISSION

P.O. Box 1750, Amarillo 79105-1750 • 806/242-9651

1 Member - 6 Years

Roger S. Cox   Commissioner, Amarillo, 12-31-21

STAFF:
Interstate Compacts Coordinator   Suzy Valentine, P.E. . . . . . . .512/239-4730 / *Fax: 512/239-2214*

The Canadian River Compact Commission administers the Canadian River Compact to ensure that Texas receives its equitable share of quality water from the Canadian River and its tributaries as apportioned by the Compact. The Compact includes the states of New Mexico, Oklahoma, and Texas.

CANADIAN RIVER MUNICIPAL WATER AUTHORITY

P.O. Box 9, Sanford 79078-0009 • 806/865-3325 • *FAX: 806/865-3314*
www.crmwa.com/ • Agency # 598

17 Members - 2 Years

Steve Tucker	President, Slaton
Richard Ellis	Vice President, Levelland
Bill Carder	Board Member, Borger
Jerry Carlson	Board Member, Pampa
James O. Collins	Board Member, Lubbock
Tyke Dipprey	Board Member, Plainview
Rickey Dunn	Board Member, Brownfield
William Hallerberg	Board Member, Amarillo
Jay Dee House	Board Member, Tahoka
Jay House	Board Member, Lubbock
Glendon Jett	Board Member, Borger
Cris Norris	Board Member, Lamesa
Brian Pohlmeir	Board Member, Plainview
Lenny Sadler	Board Member, Amarillo
Mac Smith	Board Member, Pampa
Bruce Vaughn	Board Member, O'Donnell
Scott Wade	Board Member, Levelland

STAFF:

General Manager and Secy./Treas.	Kent Satterwhite . . . . .806/865-3325 / *Fax: 806/865-3314*
Deputy General Manager	Chad Pernell . . . . .806/865-3325 / *Fax: 806/865-3314*

CANCER PREVENTION AND RESEARCH INSTITUTE OF TEXAS*

1701 N. Congress Ave., P.O. Box 12097, Austin 78711-2097
512/463-3190 • *FAX: 512/475-2563* • www.cprit.texas.gov • Agency # 542

9 Members - 6 Years

Will Montgomery	Presiding Officer, Dallas, 2-1-23
Dee Margo	Assistant Presiding Officer, 1-31-21
Angelos Angelou	Board Member, Austin, 1-31-19
Pete Geren	Board Member, Ft. Worth, 1-31-19
Amy Mitchell	Board Member, Austin, 1-31-15
Mahendra C. Patel, M.D.	Board Member, San Antonio, 1-1-21
Craig Rosenfeld, M.D.	Board Member, Dallas, 1-31-17
Vacant	Board Member
Vacant	Board Member

STAFF:

Chief Executive Officer	Wayne Roberts	512/463-3190
Deputy Executive Officer and General Counsel	Kristen Doyle	512/463-3190
Chief Operating Officer	Heidi McConnell	512/463-3190
Chief Prevention and Communications Officer	Rebecca Garcia, Ph.D.	512/463-3190
Chief Scientific Officer	James Wilson, M.D.	512/463-3190
Chief Product Development Research Officer	Mike Lang	512/463-3190
Chief Compliance Officer	Vince Burgess	512/463-3190

The Oversight Committee serves as the governing body of CPRIT, which awards grants to expedite innovation in cancer research, to help bring lifesaving cancer products to Texans and to expand cancer prevention capabilities across the state.

---

*Subject to the Texas Sunset Act; will be reviewed in 2023.

CEMETERY COMMITTEE, TEXAS STATE

909 Navasota, Austin 78702 • 512/463-0605 • *FAX: 512/463-8811*
www.cemetery.texas.gov

3 Members - 6 Years

Benjamin M. Hanson	Chair, Austin, 2-1-21
Jim Bayless	Board Member, Austin, 2-1-23
Carolyn Hodges	Board Member, Houston, 2-1-19

STAFF:

Superintendent	Position Vacant	512/463-6023
Office Manager	Deborah Rothberger	512/463-6600
Director of Research	Position Vacant	512/463-0605
Senior Historian	Will Erwin	512/463-7875

CHIROPRACTIC EXAMINERS, TEXAS BOARD OF*

333 Guadalupe, Suite 3-825, Austin 78701
512/305-6700 • *FAX: 512/305-6705*
www.tbce.state.tx.us • Agency # 508

9 Members - 6 Years: 6 Licensed Chiropractors, 3 Public Members

Mark R. Bronson D.C.	Chair, Fort Worth, 2-1-21
Kenya S. Woodruff	Vice President, Dallas, 2-1-17
Karen Campion, D.C.	Secretary/Treasurer, College Station, 2-1-17
Nicholas Baucum, D.C.	Board Member, Corpus Christi, 2-1-21
Amy N. Gonzalez, D.C.	Board Member, Mansfield, 2-1-17
Michael P. Henry, D.C.	Board Member, Austin, 2-1-19
Gus Ramirez	Public Member, Tyler, 2-1-21
John Steinberg	Public Member, Marion, 2-1-19

STAFF:

Executive Director	Patricia Gilbert	512/305-6716
Executive Assistant	Lisa Agarwal	512/305-6906
Operations Manager	Jennifer Hertsenberg	512/305-6702
Chief Financial Officer	Arlethia R. Middleton	512/305-6703
General Counsel	Courtney Ebeier	512/305-6715
Programmer Analyst	Nikell Williams	512/305-7874

The mission of the Texas Board of Chiropractic Examiners is to execute the statutory authority of the Texas Chiropractic Act (Texas Occupations Code, Chapter 201) and to promote, preserve, and protect the health, safety, and welfare of the people of Texas by licensing skilled professionals and enforcing standards of practice.

*Subject to the Texas Sunset Act; will be reviewed in 2029.

COASTAL WATER AUTHORITY

1801 Main, Suite 800, Houston 77002 • 713/658-9020 • *FAX: 713/658-9429*

www.coastalwaterauthority.org

7 Members - 2 Years

4 Appointed by the Mayor of Houston; 3 Appointed by the governor

D. Wayne Klotz, P.E.	President, Harris County, 3-31-19
Tony L. Council, P.E.	First Vice President, Houston, 3-31-19
Douglas Walker	Second Vice President, Chambers County, 4-1-19
Alan D. Conner	Secretary/Treasurer, Liberty County, 4-1-18
Thomas Reiser	Director, Harris County, 4-1-19
Joseph J. Soliz	Director, Harris County, 3-31-18
Giti Zarinkelk, P.E.	Director, Harris County, 3-31-18

STAFF:

Executive Director	Donald R. Ripley, P.E.	713/658-9020
Chief Financial Officer	John J. Baldwin	713/658-9020
Chief Engineer	Greg Olinger, P.E.	713/658-9020

The board oversees the authority's provision of untreated surface water to the cities of Houston, Baytown and Deer Park.

COMPTROLLER OF PUBLIC ACCOUNTS

Lyndon B. Johnson Bldg., 111 E. 17th St., - P.O. Box 13528, Austin 78711-3528
512/463-4444 • 800/252-5555 • *FAX: 512/305-9711*
comptroller.texas.gov • Agency # 304

1 Member - 4 Years

GLENN HEGAR (R) Comptroller of Public Accounts, 12-31-18

BA-Texas A&M University; MA, JD-St. Mary's University; LLM-University of Arkansas

Elected in November 2014, Texas Comptroller Glenn Hegar is a vigilant steward of Texas tax dollars and a strong advocate for job growth in our economy. Hegar serves as Texas' treasurer, check writer, tax collector, procurement officer and revenue estimator. In the Texas Senate, Hegar oversaw all state and local revenue matters, during the 83rd legislative session, and he was instrumental in cutting $1 billion in taxes for Texas taxpayers and businesses. Hegar also served as chair of the Sunset Advisory Commission, working to eliminate inefficiency in government agencies.

Comptroller of Public Accounts	The Honorable Glenn Hegar	.512/463-0000

Executive Staff:

Deputy Comptroller and Chief Clerk	Mike Reissig	.512/463-4444
Chief of Staff	Lisa Craven	.512/463-4444
Scheduler/Executive Assistant to the Comptroller	Kim Buzard	.512/463-3991
Associate Deputy Comptroller for		
Fiscal	Phillip Ashley	.512/463-4444
Tax	Karey Barton	.512/463-4444
Operations & Support	Robert Wood	.512/463-4444
EA. to the DC/Associate for Tax	Cay Greene	.512/475-0255
EA to the Chief of Staff, Assoc. for Fiscal/Ops & Support	Bertha Valadez	.512/463-8943
General Counsel	Lita Gonzalez	.512/475-1125
Chief Revenue Estimator	Tom Currah	.512/936-2568

Division Directors:

Agency Administration	Robert Chapa	.512/463-4762
Audit	Denise Stewart	.512/463-4814
Assistant Director, Audit	Keith Womack	.512/463-7350
Assistant Director, Audit	Emma Fuentes	.512/305-9893
Communications and Info. Services	Lauren Willis	.512/936-2057
Agency Spokesperson	Chris Bryan	.512/936-5940
Criminal Investigations	Jim Harris	.512/936-2061
Data Analysis and Transparency	Will Counihan	.512/936-0758
Special Counsel to the Deputy Comptroller	Nancy Prosser	.512/463-3723
Economic Growth & Endangered Species Mgmt.	Robert Gulley	.512/463-4598
Educational Opportunities and Investments	Linda Fernandez	.512/463-4863
Enforcement	Dona Medlock	.512/463-4155
Fiscal Management	Rob Coleman	.512/463-7630
Assistant Director, Fiscal Mgmt.	Sandra Woodruff	.512/463-4947

Comptroller of Public Accounts Cont.

Chief Deputy General Counsel	Don Neal	512/463-6009
Information Security	Jesse Rivera	512/305-9883
Assistant Director, Info Security	Dave Boyd	512/936-6768
Information Technology	Jay Waldo	512/475-3469
Internal Audit	Cheryl Scott	512/463-4894
Legislative Affairs	Brooke Paup	512/463-7252
Property Tax Assistance	Mike Esparza	512/475-0288
Revenue Administration	Dovie Jackson	512/463-4041
Assistant Director, Rev. Admin.	Wayne Akridge	512/463-4100
State Energy Conservation Office (SECO)	Dub Taylor	512/463-8352
Special Counsel for Tax	William Hamner	512/475-0545
Tax Dispute Office	Tracy Hargrove	817/377-8855
Special Counsel for Tax Hearings	Kari Honea	512/463-8261
Tax Policy	Teresa Bostick	512/305-9952
Assistant Director, Tax Policy	Korry Castillo	512/463-3806
Statewide Procurement	Jette Withers	512/463-3938
Assistant Director, Statewide Procurement	Bobby Pounds	512/463-4941
CEO, TX Treasury Safekeeping Trust Company (TTSTC)	Paul Ballard	512/463-1870
Deputy Director & Deputy CIO, TTSTC, Investments	Danny Sachnowitz	512/475-3681
Chief Financial Officer, TTSTC, Finance	Frank Zahn	512/463-3129
Treasury Operations	Tom Smelker	512/463-1698
Unclaimed Property	Joani Bishop	512/463-4557

Division Managers:

Account Maintenance	Michael Elwell	512/475-1506
Application Services	Anh Selissen	512/463-9248
Banking & Electronic Processing	Rick Ochoa	512/463-6385
Budget & Internal Accounting	Shari Curtis	512/463-4771
Cash & Securities Management	Lynda Cantu	512/463-1306
Document Management	Juanita Robinson	512/305-9777
Educational Opportunities and Investment	Benito Navarro	512/463-2072
Fiscal Integrity	Mike Apperley	512/475-0724
Senior Advisor for Fiscal Research	John Heleman	512/475-0042
Deputy General Counsel		
Administrative Hearings	Jim Arbogast	512/463-8473
Agency Affairs	Victoria North	512/463-6243
Contracts	Jason Frizzell	512/936-6210
Litigation & Taxation	Murl Miller	512/936-8588
Open Records	Ruth Soucy	512/475-0411
Statewide Contracts	Position Vacant	
Special Counsel, Human Resources & Ethics	Shannon Gosewehr	512/463-2102
Human Resources	Diana Herring	512/463-3977
IT Fiscal Analysis and Support	Leslie Mitchell	512/463-8711

Media Relations	General Number	.512/463-4070
Organizational Development and Training	Susan Johnson	.512/463-3942
Planning and Architecture	Michael Telfeyan	.512/463-6133
Public Finance	Piper Montemayor	.512/463-6369
Records Management Officer	Stephen Quick	.512/463-7629
Revenue Accounting	Morris Bennett	.512/463-4152
Revenue Estimating	Dean Ferguson	.512/463-3990
Revenue Processing	Irma Martinez	.512/475-1075
Statewide Mail	Chris Christine	.512/463-9520
Contract Development & Data Mgmt.	Gerard MacCrossan	.512/463-4468
Statewide Fiscal Services	Lisa Nance	.512/475-0481
Statewide Fiscal Systems	Alice Alvarado	.512/475-0619
Statewide HUB Program	Laura Cagle-Hinojosa	.512/463-4583
Support Services	Stephen McDonald	.512/475-5654
Treasury Accounting	Macy Douglas	.512/463-8828

ENFORCEMENT OFFICES AND MANAGERS

2H06 Abilene Enforcement
Vanessa Zientek
1 Village Drive, Ste. 250
Abilene 79606-8248
325/695-4323

2II04 Amarillo Enforcement
Shell Collins
Park West Office Centre
7120 I-40 W., Bldg. A, Ste. 220
Amarillo 79106-2519
806/358-0148

2H40 Arlington Enforcement
Elmer Rogers
2108 E. Randol Mill Rd.
Ste. 100
Arlington 76011-8228
817/459-1155

Austin Enforcement
Call Center Hdq
Southcliff Bldg.
2015 S. IH 35, Ste. 300
Austin 78741-3809
512/475-0199

2H17 Austin Enforcement
Tricia Hampton
1711 San Jacinto Blvd.
Central Services Bldg.
Ste. 180
Austin 78701-1416
512/463-4865

2H25 Brownsville Enforcement
Natalia De La Garza
1655 Ruben Torres Sr. Blvd.
Ste. 104
Brownsville 78521-1597
956/542-8426

2H10 Corpus Christi
Enforcement
Diana Garcia
500 North Shoreline Blvd.
Ste. 1000
Corpus Christi 78401-0346
361/882-1234

2H51 Dallas NE Enforcement
Randy Brestrup
9221 LBJ Freeway, Ste. 100
Dallas 75243-3429
972/792-5800

2H53 Dallas SW Enforcement
Susan Ralstin
400 South Zang Blvd., Ste. 900
Dallas 75208-6644
214/944-2200

2H90 El Paso Enforcement
Fernando Alvarado
401 E. Franklin Ave., Ste. 160
El Paso 79901-1209
915/533-0506

2H31 Houston NW
Enforcement
Jesse Vela
1919 N. Loop West, Ste. 510
Houston 77008-1354
713/426-8200

2H76 Laredo Enforcement
Olga Espinoza
1202 East Del Mar Blvd.
Ste. 1
Laredo 78041-2400
956/722-2859

2II03 Lubbock Enforcement
Mary Mitchell
5012 50th St., Ste. 202
Lubbock 79414-3434
806/796-7772

2H18 Lufkin Enforcement
Tony Perez
306 Harmony Hill Dr., Ste. A
Lufkin 75901-5759
936/634-2621

2H33 Houston SE
Kimberly Henderson
2222 Bay Area Blvd., Ste. 108
Houston 77058
281/226-8010

2H11 McAllen Enforcement
Ninfa Garcia-Moreno
200 S.10th St., Ste. 301
McAllen 78501-4800
956/687-9227

2H02 Odessa Enforcement
Jessica Ford
4682 E. University, Ste. 200
Odessa 79762-8179
432/550-3027

2H07 San Angelo Enforcement
Vanessa Zientek
3127 Executive Drive
San Angelo 76904-6801
325/942-8364

2H60 San Antonio NW
Enforcement
Patricia Garza
10010 San Pedro Ave.,
Ste. 410
San Antonio 78216-3862
210/342-2300

2H19 Tyler Enforcement
Johnny Huff
3800 Paluxy Drive, Ste. 300
Tyler 75703-1661
903/534-0333

2H15 Waco Enforcement
Matthew Flaherty
801 Austin Ave., Ste. 810
Waco 76701-1937
254/752-3147

2H05 Wichita Falls
Jeff Surber
925 Lamar, Ste. 1900
Wichita Falls 76301-3414
940/761-4141

2H30 Houston SW
Enforcement
Rosa Dillon
Briar Hills One Bldg.
1011 Hwy. 6 South, Ste. 120
Houston 77077-1036
281/497-8442

AUDIT OFFICES AND MANAGERS

2I21 Abilene Audit
Sandra Obiedo
1 Village Dr., Ste. 250
Abilene 79606-8248
325/695-4323

2I04 Amarillo Audit
Sam Cross
Park West Office Centre
7120 I-40 West, Bldg. A
Ste. 240
Amarillo 79106-2500
806/358-0148

2I80 Austin Audit
Jeff McCulloch
2015 S. I-35
SouthCliff Bldg., Ste. 202
Austin 78741-3811
512/305-9800

2I31 Beaumont Audit
Belinda Renfrow
350 Pine St., Ste. 1435
Beaumont 77701-2437
409/832-0061

2I05 Business Activity
Research Team
Rusty Johnson
1700 N. Congress Ave.
SFA Bldg., Ste. 300
Austin 78701-1436
512/305-9899

2I71 Chicago Audit
Colleen Duczynski
1411 Opus Place
Executive Towers II, Ste. 125
Downer Grove, IL 60515
630/963-0761

2I10 Corpus Christi Audit
Ruben Barrera
500 North Shoreline Blvd.
Ste. 1015
Corpus Christi 78401-0399
361/882-1234

2I55 Dallas E Audit
Torii Wilde
9221 LBJ Freeway, Ste. 200
Dallas 75243-3455
972/792-5800

2I50 Dallas W Audit
Sandra Obiedo
2655 Villa Creek Dr., Ste. 270
Dallas 75234-7316
972/888-5300

2I90 El Paso Audit
Cassandra Blanco
401 E. Franklin Ave., Ste. 170
El Paso 79901-1206
915/533-0506

2I45 Euless Processing Center
Annette Drinkwater
831 W. Euless Blvd., Ste. 7
Euless 76040-4437
817/571-7707

2I40 Fort Worth Audit
Alex Gonzalez
Crosslands Plaza
6320 Southwest Blvd.
Ste. 201
Fort Worth 76109-6169
817/377-8855

2I30 Houston Central Audit
Sharon Barnes
1919 North Loop W., Ste. 311
Houston 77008-1394
713/426-8200

2I32 Houston S Audit
Brian King
2656 South Loop W., Ste. 400
Houston 77054-2600
713/314-5700

2I33 Houston W Audit
Maria Garcia
1260 Pin Oak Road, Ste. 210
Katy 77494-5600
281/371-5500

2I36 Houston North
Belinda Renfrow
One Northchase Park Bldg.
4201 FM 1960 West
Houston 77068

2I72 Los Angeles Audit
Joe Aghahowa
17777 Center Court Dr. N.
Ste. 700
Cerritos, CA 90703-8567
562/402-2000

2I03 Lubbock Audit
Sam Cross
6104 66th St., Ste. 300
Lubbock 79424-5935
806/794-4012

2I11 McAllen Audit
Laura Biemer
200 S. 10th St., Ste. 801
McAllen 78501-5538
956/687-9227

2I70 New York Audit
Adriana Alamilla
215 Lexington Ave., 19th Fl.
New York, N.Y. 10016-6023
646/742-1155

2I20 Odessa Audit
Rhonda Chambers
4682 E. University Blvd.,
Ste. 200
Odessa 79762-8104
432/550-3027

2I60 San Antonio Audit
Laura Biemer
5710 W. Hausman Rd.
Ste. 105
San Antonio 78249-1646
210/257-4600

2I74 Tulsa Audit
Hoyt Sizemore
7050 S. Yale Ave., Ste. 101
Tulsa, OK 74136-5707
918/622-4311

2I51 Tyler Audit
Vicki Taylor
3800 Paluxy Drive, Ste. 300
Tyler 75703-1663
903/534-0333

2I82 Waco Audit
Rusty Johnson
801 Austin Ave., Ste. 940
Waco 76701-1941
254/752-3147

CONSUMER CREDIT COMMISSIONER*

2601 N. Lamar Blvd., Austin 78705-4207
512/936-7600 • FAX: 512/936-7610 • www.occc.texas.gov • Agency # 466
Consumer Help Line: 800/538-1579

STAFF:

Commissioner	Leslie L. Pettijohn	512/936-7640
General Counsel	Michael Rigby	512/936-7623
Director of Consumer Protection	Rudy Aguilar	512/936-7627
Director of Strategic Comm., Administration & Planning	Juan V. Garcia	512/936-7620

*Subject to the Texas Sunset Act; will be reviewed in 2019.

COSMETOLOGY, ADVISORY BOARD ON

c/o TDLR, 920 Colorado St., P.O. Box 12157, Austin 78711-2157
512/463-6599 • FAX: 512/475-2871 • www.license.state.tx.us/cosmet/cosmet.htm

9 Members - 6 Years; 1 Ex Officio Member

Ron Robinson	Presiding Officer, Waco, 9-29-19
Anthony Anderson	Board Member, Spring Branch, 9-29-19
Natalie Caballero	Board Member, Lubbock, 9-29-19
Betty Neff	Board Member, Austin, 9-29-23
Aleshia Rivera	Board Member, Mount Pleasant, 9-29-19
Vanessa Robbins	Board Member, Houston, 9-29-21
Vacant	Board Member, Lubbock, 9-29-21
Claudia Avalos	Public Member, Richmond, 9-29-19
Mary Paschal-Lindsay	Public Member, Pearland, 9-29-23
Diane Salazar	Ex Officio Member, Austin

COUNCILS OF GOVERNMENTS

www.txregionalcouncil.org

Alamo Area Council Of Governments (AACOG):
Executive Director   Diane Rath
8700 Tesoro Drive, Suite 160
San Antonio 78217
210/362-5200 / *Fax: 210/824-4576*

Atascosa, Bandera, Bexar, Comal, Frio, Gillespie, Guadalupe, Karnes, Kendall, Kerr, McMullen, Medina, Wilson

Ark-Tex Council Of Governments (ARK-TEX COG):
Executive Director   Chris Brown
4808 Elizabeth St.
Texarkana 75503
903/832-8636 / *Fax: 903/832-3441*

Bowie, Cass, Delta, Franklin, Hopkins, Lamar, Morris, Red River, Titus, Miller County-Arkansas

Brazos Valley Council Of Governments (BVCOG):
Executive Director   Tom Wilkinson, Jr.
3991 E. 29th Street
P.O. Drawer 4128
Bryan 77805-4128
979/595-2800 / *Fax: 979/595-2810*

Brazos, Burleson, Grimes, Leon, Madison, Robertson, Washington

Capital Area Council Of Governments (CAPCOG):
Executive Director   Betty Voights
6800 Burleson Road
Bldg. 310, Suite 165
Austin 78744
512/916-6000 / *Fax: 512/916-6001*

Bastrop, Blanco, Burnet, Caldwell, Fayette, Hays, Lee, Llano, Travis, Williamson

Central Texas Council Of Governments (CTCOG):
Executive Director   Jim Reed
P.O. Box 729
Belton 76513-0729
254/770-2200 / *Fax: 254/770-2260*

Bell, Coryell, Hamilton, Lampasas, Milam, Mills, San Saba

Coastal Bend Council Of Governments (CBCOG):
Executive Director   John P. Buckner
2910 Leopard Street
Corpus Christi 78408
361/883-5743 / *Fax: 361/883-5749*

Aransas, Bee, Brooks, Duval, Jim Wells, Kenedy, Kleberg, Live Oak, Nueces, Refugio, San Patricio

Concho Valley Council Of Governments (CVCOG):
Executive Director   John Austin Stokes
2801 W. Loop 306, Suite A
San Angelo 76904
325/944-9666 / *Fax: 325/944-9925*

Coke, Concho, Crockett, Irion, Kimble, Mason, McCulloch, Menard, Reagan, Schleicher, Sterling, Sutton, Tom Green

Deep East Texas Council Of Governments (DETCOG):
Executive Director   Lonnie Hunt
210 Premier Drive
Jasper 75951
409/384-5704 / *Fax: 409/384-5390*

Angelina, Houston, Jasper, Nacogdoches, Newton, Polk, Sabine, San Augustine, San Jacinto, Shelby, Trinity, Tyler

East Texas Council Of Governments (ETCOG):
Executive Director   David Cleveland
3800 Stone Road
Kilgore 75662-6297
903/984-8641 / *Fax: 903/983-1440*

Anderson, Camp, Cherokee, Gregg, Harrison, Henderson, Marion, Panola, Rains, Rusk, Smith, Upshur, Van Zandt, Wood

Golden Crescent Regional Planning Commission (GCRPC):
Executive Director   Joe Brannan
1908 N. Laurent St., Ste. 600
Victoria 77901
361/578-1587 / *Fax: 361/578-8865*

Calhoun, DeWitt, Goliad, Gonzales, Jackson, Lavaca, Victoria

Heart Of Texas Council Of Governments (HOTCOG):
Executive Director   Russell Devorsky
1514 S. New Road
Waco 76711
254/292-1800 / *Fax: 254/756-0102*

Bosque, Falls, Freestone, Hill, Limestone, McLennan

Houston-Galveston Area Council:
Executive Director   Jack Steele
3555 Timmons Lane, #120
P.O. Box 22777
Houston 77227-2777
713/627-3200 / *Fax: 713/993-2414*

Austin, Brazoria, Chambers, Colorado, Fort Bend, Galveston, Harris, Liberty, Matagorda, Montgomery, Walker, Waller, Wharton

Lower Rio Grande Valley Development Council (LRGVDC):
Executive Director   Ron Garza
301 W. Railroad
Weslaco 78596
956/682-3481 / *Fax: 956/631-4670*

Cameron, Hidalgo, Willacy

Council of Governments Cont.

Middle Rio Grande Development Council (MRGDC):
Executive Director   Nick Gallegos
307 W. Nopal
Carrizo Springs 78834
830/876-3533 / *Fax: 830/876-9415*

Dimmit, Edwards, Kinney, LaSalle, Maverick, Real, Uvalde, Val Verde, Zavala

Nortex Regional Planning Commission (Nortex):
Executive Director   Dennis Wilde
P.O. Box 5144
Wichita Falls 76307-5144
940/322-5281 / *Fax: 940/322-6743*

Archer, Baylor, Clay, Cottle, Foard, Hardeman, Jack, Montague, Wichita, Wilbarger, Young

North Central Texas Council Of Governments (NCTCOG):
Executive Director   Mike Eastland
P.O. Box 5888
Arlington 76005-5888
817/640-3300 / *Fax: 817/640-7806*

Collin, Dallas, Denton, Ellis, Erath, Hood, Hunt, Johnson, Kaufman, Navarro, Palo Pinto, Parker, Rockwall, Somervell, Tarrant, Wise

Panhandle Regional Planning Commission (PRPC):
Executive Director   Kyle Ingham
P.O. Box 9257
Amarillo 79105-9257
806/372-3381 / *Fax: 806/373-3268*

Armstrong, Briscoe, Carson, Castro, Childress, Collingsworth, Dallam, Deaf Smith, Donley, Gray, Hall, Hansford, Hartley, Hemphill, Hutchinson, Lipscomb, Moore, Ochiltree, Oldham, Parmer, Potter, Randall, Roberts, Sherman, Swisher, Wheeler

Permian Basin Regional Planning Commission (PBRPC):
Executive Director   Terri Moore
P.O. Box 60660
Midland 79711-0660
432/563-1061 / *Fax: 432/563-1728*

Andrews, Borden, Crane, Dawson, Ector, Gaines, Glasscock, Howard, Loving, Martin, Midland, Pecos, Reeves, Terrell, Upton, Ward, Winkler

Rio Grande Council Of Governments (RGCOG):
Executive Director   Annette Gutierrez
8037 Lockheed, Ste. 100
El Paso 79925
915/533-0998 / *Fax: 915/532-9385*

Brewster, Culberson, El Paso, Hudspeth, Jeff Davis, Presidio, Doña Ana Co.-New Mexico

South East Texas Regional Planning Commission (SETRPC):
Executive Director   Shaun P. Davis
2210 Eastex Freeway
Beaumont 77703
409/899-8444 / *Fax: 409/347-0138*

Hardin, Jefferson, Orange

South Plains Association Of Governments (SPAG):
Executive Director   Tim Pierce
P.O. Box 3730, Freedom Station
Lubbock 79452-3730
806/762-8721 / *Fax: 806/765-9544*

Bailey, Cochran, Crosby, Dickens, Floyd, Garza, Hale, Hockley, King, Lamb, Lubbock, Lynn, Motley, Terry, Yoakum

South Texas Development Council (STDC):
Executive Director   Robert Mendiola
1002 Dicky Lane
P. O. Box 2187
Laredo 78044-2187
956/722-3995 / *Fax: 956/722-2670*

Jim Hogg, Starr, Webb, Zapata

Texoma Council Of Governments (TEXOMA):
Executive Director   Susan Thomas, Ph.D.
1117 Gallagher Dr., Suite 100
Sherman 75090
903/813-3512 / *Fax: 903/813-3511*

Cooke, Fannin, Grayson

West Central Texas Council Of Governments (WCTCOG):
Executive Director   Tom Smith
3702 Loop 322
Abilene 79602-7300
325/672-8544 / *Fax: 325/675-5214*

Brown, Callahan, Coleman, Comanche, Eastland, Fisher, Haskell, Jones, Kent, Knox, Mitchell, Nolan, Runnels, Scurry, Shackelford, Stephens, Stonewall, Taylor, Throckmorton

COUNSELORS, TEXAS STATE BOARD OF EXAMINERS OF PROFESSIONAL*

c/o HHSC, 1100 West 49th, P.O. Box 149347, MC 1982, Austin 78714-9347
512/834-6658 • *FAX: 512/834-6677* • www.dshs.state.tx.us/counselor

9 Members - 6 YearsP

Glenda Corley	Chair, Round Rock, 2-1-17
Loretta Bradley Ph.D.	Board Member, Lubbock, 2-1-21
Steven D. Christopherson	Board Member, Pasadena, 2-1-19
Brenda Compagnone	Board Member, San Antonio, 2-1-21
Christopher Taylor	Board Member, Dallas, 2-1-21
Sarah Abraham	Public Member, Sugar Land, 2-1-19
Lauren Polunsky Dreszer	Public Member, San Antonio, 2-1-17
Etienne Nguyen	Public Member, Houston, 2-1-17
Leslie F. Pohl	Public Member, Austin, 2-1-19

*Subject to the Texas Sunset Act; will be reviewed in 2019.

COUNTY AND DISTRICT RETIREMENT SYSTEM, TX

901 MoPac Expwy. So., Bldg. IV, Suite 500, P.O. Box 2034, Austin 78768-2034
512/328-8889 • 800/823-7782 • *FAX: 512/328-8887* • www.tcdrs.org

9 Members - 6 Years

Robert Eckels	Chair, Spring, 12-31-19
Bob Willis	Vice Chair, Livingston, 12-31-19
H.C. "Chuck" Cazalas	Board Member, , Corpus Christi, 12-31-17
Chris Davis	Board Member, Alto, 12-31-21
Mary Louise Garcia	Board Member, Fort Worth, 12-31-17
Deborah M. Hunt, CTA	Board Member, Georgetown, 12-31-21
Bridget McDowell	Board Member, Baird, 12-31-19
William "Bill" Metzger	Board Member, Dallas, 12-31-21
Kristeen Roe	Board Member, Bryan, 12-31-17

STAFF:
Executive Director   Amy Bishop . . . . .512/328-8889 / *Fax: 512/328-8887*

CREDIT UNION COMMISSION*

914 East Anderson Lane, Austin 78752-1699 • 512/837-9236 • *FAX: 512/832-0278*
www.cud.texas.gov • Agency # 469

9 Members - 6 Years

Allyson "Missy" Morrow	Chair, San Benito, 2-15-19
Beckie S. Cobb	Board Member, Deer Park, 2-15-21
Steve Gilman	Board Member, Houston, 2-15-21
James L "Jim" Minge	Board Member, Arlington, 2-15-23
Barbara Stewart	Board Member, Lone Star, 2-15-19
Ricky Ybarra	Board Member, Austin, 2-15-23
Yusuf Farran	Public Member, El Paso, 2-15-21
Sherrie Merket	Public Member, Midland, 2-15-23
Vik Vad	Public Member, Austin, 2-15-19

STAFF:

Commissioner	Harold E. Feeney	.512/837-9236
Deputy Commissioner	Robert W. Etheridge	.512/837-9236
Assistant Commissioner and		
General Counsel	Shari O. Shivers	.512/837-9236
Staff Services Officer	Michelle Archie	.512/837-9236

*Subject to the Texas Sunset Act; will be reviewed in 2021.

CRIMINAL JUSTICE, TEXAS BOARD OF*

209 West 14th Street, Suite 500, Price Daniel Bldg., P.O. Box 13084, Austin 78711-3084
512/475-3250 • *FAX: 512/305-9398* • www.tdcj.texas.gov • Agency # 696

9 Members - 6 Years

Dale Wainwright	Chair, Austin, 2-1-21
R. Terrell McCombs	Vice Chair, San Antonio, 2-1-19
E. F. "Mano" DeAyala	Board Member, Houston, 2-1-23
Tom Fordyce	Board Member, Huntsville, 2-1-21
Eric Gambrell	Board Member, Dallas, 2-1-19
Larry Miles	Board Member, Amarillo, 2-1-23
Patrick O'Daniel	Board Member, Austin, 2-1-23
Derrelynn Perryman	Board Member, Arlington, 2-1-21
Thomas Wingate	Board Member, Mission, 2-1-19

The Texas Board of Criminal Justice provides confinement, supervision, rehabilitation, and reintegration of the state's convicted felons.

*Subject to the Texas Sunset Act; will be reviewed in 2021.

CRIMINAL JUSTICE, TEXAS DEPARTMENT OF*

P.O. Box 99, Huntsville 77342-0099 - 209 W. 14th St., Suite 500,
P.O. Box 13084, Austin 78711-3084 • www.tdcj.texas.gov • Agency # 696

STAFF:

Executive Director	Bryan Collier	936/437-2101 / *Fax: 936/437-2123*
Deputy Executive Director	Oscar Mendoza	936/437-6251 / *Fax: 936/437-8925*
Chief of Staff	Jeff Baldwin	512/463-9776 / *Fax: 512/936-2169*
Director, Public Information	Position Vacant	936/437-6052 / *Fax: 936/437-6055*

ADMINISTRATIVE REVIEW AND RISK MANAGEMENT:
Division Director — Kelvin Scott — 936/437-4839 / *Fax: 936/437-4843*
P.O. Box 99
Huntsville, TX 77342-0099

BUSINESS AND FINANCE:
Chief Financial Officer — Jerry McGinty — 936/437-2107 / *Fax: 936/437-6381*
P.O. Box 4015
Huntsville, TX 77342-4015

COMMUNITY JUSTICE ASSISTANCE DIVISION:
Division Director — Carey Green — 512/305-9350 / *Fax: 512/305-9368*
209 W. 14th St., Ste. 400
Austin, TX 78701

CORRECTIONAL INSTITUTIONS DIVISION:
Division Director — Lorie Davis — 936/437-2170 / *Fax: 936/437-6325*
P.O. Box 99
Huntsville, TX 77342-0099

FACILITIES DIVISION:
Division Director — Frank Inmon — 936/437-7201 / *Fax: 936/437-7205*
2 Financial Plaza, Ste. 400
Huntsville, TX 77340

Criminal Justice, TX Dept. of (Cont.)

HEALTH SERVICES DIVISION:
Division Director   Dr. Lanette Linthicum, ...936/437-3542 / *Fax: 936/437-3541*
2 Financial Plaza, Suite 625
Huntsville, TX 77340

HUMAN RESOURCES DIVISION:
Division Director   Patty Garcia ....936/437-4088 / *Fax: 936/437-4068*
Two Financial Plaza, Suite 600
Huntsville, TX 77340

INFORMATION TECHNOLOGY DIVISION:
Chief Information Officer   Melvin Neely ....936/437-1270 / *Fax: 936/437-1011*
P.O. Box 4016
Huntsville, TX 77342-4016

INTERNAL AUDIT DIVISION:
Division Director   Chris Cirrito ....936/437-7100 / *Fax: 936/437-2821*
2 Financial Plaza, Ste. 130
Huntsville, TX 77340

MANUFACTURING AGRIBUSINESS & LOGISTICS:
Division Director   Bobby Lumpkin ....936/437-2189 / *Fax: 936/437-6096*
P.O. Box 4013
Huntsville, TX 77342-4013

OFFICE OF THE GENERAL COUNSEL:
General Counsel   Sharon Felfe Howell .....936/437-2141 / *Fax: 936/437-6994*
P.O. Box 13084
Austin, TX 78711-3084

OFFICE OF THE INSPECTOR GENERAL:
Inspector General   Bruce Toney ....512/671-2480 / *Fax: 512/671-2129*
P.O. Box 13084
Austin, TX 78711-3084

PAROLE DIVISION:
Division Director   Pamela Thielke ....512/406-5401 / *Fax: 512/406-5858*
8610 Shoal Creek
Austin, TX 78757

PRISON RAPE ELIMINATION ACT (PREA) OMBUDSMAN:
Ombudsman   Lynne Sharp ....936/437-2133 / *Fax: 936/437-6981*
P.O. Box 99
Huntsville, TX 77342-0099

PRIVATE FACILITY CONTRACT MONITORING/OVERSIGHT DIVISION:
Division Director   Cody Ginsel ....936/437-2810 / *Fax: 936/437-2873*
2 Financial Plaza, Ste. 300
Huntsville, TX 77340

REENTRY AND INTEGRATION DIVISION (RID):
Division Director   April Zamora ....512/671-2134 / *Fax: 512/671-2571*
4616 W. Howard Lane
Suite 200
Austin, TX 78728

REHABILITATION PROGRAMS DIVISION:
Division Director   Rene Hinojosa   . . . . .936/437-2180 / *Fax: 936/437-6299*
P.O. Box 99
Huntsville, TX 77342-0099

STATE COUNSEL FOR OFFENDERS:
Division Director   Rudolph Brothers . . . . .936/437-5203 / *Fax: 936/437-5293*
P.O. Box 4005
Huntsville, TX 77342-4005

VICTIM SERVICES DIVISION:
Division Director   Angela McCown   . . . . .512/406-5917 / *Fax: 512/452-1025*
8712 Shoal Creek Blvd., Suite 265
Austin, TX 78757

_____

*Subject to the Texas Sunset Act; will be reviewed in 2021.

DEAF, TEXAS SCHOOL FOR THE
1102 South Congress, Austin 78704
512/462-5353 • 800/332-3873 • *FAX: 512/462-5313*
www.tsd.state.tx.us • Agency # 772

9 Members - 6 Years

Eric Hogue	President, Wylie, 1-31-15
Shawn Saladin, Ph.D.	Vice President, Edinburg, 1-31-17
Angie O. Wolf	Secretary, Austin, 1-31-15
Shalia Cowan, Ed.D.	Board Member, Dripping Springs, 1-31-17
Ryan D. Hutchison	Board Member, Austin, 1-31-21
Tyran Lee	Board Member, Humble, 1-31-13
Susan K. Ridley	Board Member, Sugar Land, 1-31-13
David A. Saunders	Board Member, Waxahachie, 1-31-19
Vacant	Board Member

STAFF:
Superintendent   Claire Bugen . . . . .512/462-5300 / *Fax: 512/462-5313*
Chief Financial Officer   Justin Wedel . . . . .512/462-5351 / *Fax: 512/462-5359*
Director
     Support Operations   Russell O. West   . . . . .512/462-5603 / *Fax: 512/462-5723*
     Information Technology   Mari Liles . . . . .512/462-5407 / *Fax: 512/462-5313*
     Human Resources   Julie Dodd   . . . . .512/462-5321 / *Fax: 512/462-5643*
General Counsel   Leonard J. Schwartz . . . . . .512/462-5309 / *Fax: 512/462-5308*
Director of Outreach   Bobbie Beth Scoggins   . . . .512/462-5329 / *Fax: 512/462-5661*

The board functions like a local school district, and in addition to overseeing the provision of all TSD services, has specific responsibilities related to budget preparation, policy adoption and appointment of the superintendent.

DEMOGRAPHIC CENTER, TEXAS

1700 N. Congress Ave., Suite 220W, P.O. Box 13455, Austin 78711
512/463-8390 • *FAX: 512/463-7632* • demographics.texas.gov • Agency # 743

STAFF:

State Demographer	Lloyd Potter	.512/463-7659
Legislative and State Agency Liaison	Lila Valencia	.512/936-3542
Programmer Analyst	Saloni Rajput	.512/463-8423

DENTAL EXAMINERS, TEXAS STATE BOARD OF*

333 Guadalupe Street, Tower 3, Suite 800, Austin 78701-3942
512/463-6400 • *FAX: 512/463-7452* • www.tsbde.texas.gov • Agency # 504

11 Board Members - 6 Years:

6 Dentists, 3 Dental Hygienists and 2 Public Members

M. David Tillman, D.D.S.	Presiding Officer, Aledo, 2-1-21
Kimberly N. Haynes, D.M.D.	Dentist Member, College Station, 2-1-19
Bryan N. Henderson II, D.D.S.	Dentist Member, Dallas, 2-1-23
Robert G. McNeill, D.D.S., M.D.	Dentist Member, Dallas, 2-1-21
Jorge E. Quirch, D.D.S.	Dentist Member, Missouri City, 2-1-23
David H. Yu, D.D.S.	Dentist Member, Austin, 2-1-19
Lorie L. Jones, R.D.H.	Hygienist Member, Magnolia, 2-1-23
Margo Y. Melchor, R.D.H., Ed.D.	Hygienist Member, Houston, 2-1-21
Lois M. Palermo, R.D.H.	Hygienist Member, League City, 2-1-19
Vacant	Public Member
Vacant	Public Member

STAFF:

Executive Director	Kelly Parker	.512/475-0987 / *Fax: 512/463-7452*
Director of Dental Practice	Brooke Bell, D.D.S.	.512/463-6400 / *Fax: 512/463-7452*
Director of Finance and Admin.	Leticia Kappel	.512/305-7378 / *Fax: 512/463-7452*
General Counsel	Tyler Vance	.512/475-0977 / *Fax: 512/532-0637*
Director of Licensing	Christine Mendez	.512/475-0972 / *Fax: 512/463-7452*

The board oversees licensing and regulation of dental care providers in Texas, and enforces Texas laws regulating the practice of dentistry to protect the public health and safety and promote high quality and safe dental care.

*Subject to the Texas Sunset Act; will be reviewed in 2029.

DIABETES COUNCIL, TEXAS

c/o DSHS, P.O. Box 149347, Austin 78714-9347
512/776-7490 • *FAX: 512/776-7408* • /www.dshs.texas.gov/diabetes/default.shtm

11 Members - 6 Years; 3 Ex Officio Members

Kathy Ann LaCivita, MD	Chair, San Antonio, 2-1-21
Curtis Triplitt, PharmD	Vice Chair, San Antonio, 2-1-19
Jason M. Ryan, JD	Board Member, Houston, 21-19
Joan Colgin, RN, BSN, CDE	Board Member, Dallas, 2-1-21
Maria Duarte-Gardea, PhD, RD, LD	Board Member, El Paso, 2-1-17
Carley Gomez-Meade, DO	Board Member, Austin, 2-1-19
John Griffin, Jr., JD	Board Member, Victoria, 2-1-17
Aida Moreno-Brown, RD, LD	Board Member, El Paso, 2-21-21
William "David" Sanders	Board Member, Dallas, 2-1-21
Don Yarborough	Board Member, Garland, 2-1-17
Vacant	Board Member
Lisa Golden	Texas Workforce Commission
Rajendra Parikh, MD, MBA, CPE	Health and Human Services Commission
Vacant	Texas Department of State Health Services

STAFF:
Director   Melissa Cammack . . . . . .512/776-7490 / *Fax: 512/776-7408*

The council addresses issues affecting people with diabetes. Advises the Legislature on legislation that is needed to develop and maintain a statewide system of quality education services for all people with diabetes and health care professionals who offer diabetes treatment and education.

DIETITIANS ADVISORY BOARD

c/o TDLR, 920 Colorado St., P.O. Box 12157, Austin 78711-2157
512/463-6599 • *FAX: 512/463-9468* • www.tdlr.texas.gov

9 Members - 6 Years

Janet S. Hall, R.D., L.D.	Presiding Officer, Georgetown, 9-1-21
Irma Gutierrez	Board Member, Georgetown, 9-1-23
Matilde Ladnier	Board Member, Houston, 9-1-23
Aida Moreno-Brown, R.D., L.D.	Board Member, El Paso, 9-1-19
LeAnne C. Skinner	Board Member, Austin, 9-1-19
Mary Kate Weems, R.D. L.D.	Board Member, Waco, 9-1-21
Cynthia J. Comparin	Public Member, Dallas, 9-1-21
Grace White	Public Member, Watauga, 9-1-19
Vacant	Public Member

The board regulates the licensing and education of dietitians in Texas.

DISABILITIES, TX COUNCIL FOR DEVELOPMENTAL*

6201 E. Oltorf, Suite 600, Austin 78741
512/437-5432 • 800/262-0334 • *FAX: 512/437-5434* • tcdd.texas.gov

27 Members-6 Years and at the pleasure of the governor.

Mary M. Durheim	Chair, Spring, 2-1-11
John Thomas	Vice Chair, Weatherford, 2-1-17
Rebecca Hunter Adkins	Board Member, Lakeway, 2-1-15
Kimberly A. Blackmon	Board Member, Fort Worth, 2-1-15
Kristine Clark	Board Member, San Antonio, 2-1-17
Gladys Cortez	Board Member, McAllen, 2-1-17
Kristen L. Cox	Board Member, El Paso, 2-1-15
Mateo Delgado	Board Member, El Paso, 2-1-19
Stephen Gersuk	Board Member, Plano, 2-1-19
Ruth Mason	Board Member, Houston, 2-1-19
Scott McAvoy	Board Member, Cedar Park, 2-1-15
Michael Peace	Board Member, Poteet, 2-1-19
Dana S. Perry	Board Member, Brownwood, 2-1-15
Brandon Pharris	Board Member, Beaumont, 2-1-19
Vacant Position	Board Member, 2-1-19
Vacant Position	Board Member, 2-1-21
Lora Taylor	Board Member, Houston, 2-1-19
David Taylor	Board Member, El Paso, 2-1-17
Richard A. Tisch	Board Member, Spring, 2-1-15
Lisa Akers-Owen	Texas Health and Human Services Commission
Mary Faithfull	Disability Rights Texas
Rachel Jew	Texas Department of State Health Services
Jennifer Kaut	Texas Workforce Commission
Ron Roberts	Texas Education Agency
Amy Sharp	Texas Center for Disability Studies, UT Austin
Dan Zhang	Center on Disability and Development, Texas A&M
Vacant	Texas Health and Human Services Commission

STAFF:

Executive Director	Beth Stalvey	.512/437-5440 / *Fax: 512/437-5434*
Grants Management Director	Cynthia Ellison	.512/437-5436 / *Fax: 512/437-5434*
Communications Director	Joshua Ryf	.512/437-5441 / *Fax: 512/437-5434*
Operations Director	Martha Cantu	.512/437-5439 / *Fax: 512/437-5434*

*Subject to the Texas Sunset Act; will be reviewed in 2027.

EDUCATION AGENCY, TEXAS*

1701 N. Congress Ave., Austin 78701-1494
512/463-9734 • *FAX: 512/463-9838*
www.tea.texas.gov • Agency # 701

Commissioner of Education	Mike Morath	.512/463-8985
General Counsel	Von Byer	.512/463-9720

STAFF:

Deputy Commissioner of		
Operations	Megan Aghazadian	.512/463-8880
Educator Support	Martin Winchester	.512/463-8972
Finance	Kara Belew	.512/463-8880
Governance	A.J. Crabill	.512/936-1533
Technology	Melody Parrish	.512/463-2321
Chief Deputy of Academics	Penny Schwinn	.512/463-8934
Chief Investment Officer	Holland Timmins	.512/463-9169
Governmental Relations Director	Hunter Thompson, (Interim)	.512/463-9682
Director, Communications	Gene Acuna	.512/463-9000
Associate Commissioner		
Standards & Programs	Monica Martinez	.512/463-9087
Edu. Leadership & Quality	Ryan Franklin	.512/936-9831
Chief Financial Officer	Mary Ann Uranga Gill	.512/463-9189
Chief School Finance Officer	Leo Lopez	.512/463-9238

*Subject to the Texas Sunset Act; will be reviewed in 2025.

EDUCATION BOARD, SOUTHERN REGIONAL

592 Tenth St., N.W., Atlanta, GA 30318-5776
404/875-9211 • *FAX: 404/872-1477* • www.sreb.org

The Honorable Jimmie Don Aycock	Board Member, Killeen, 6-30-17
The Honorable Dan Branch	Board Member, Dallas, 6-30-15
The Honorable Rob Eissler	Board Member, The Woodlands, 6-30-16
The Honorable Michael L. Williams	Board Member, Austin, 6-30-14
The Honorable Greg Abbott	Ex Officio Member, Governor of Texas

STAFF:

President	David Spence .... .404/875-9211 / *Fax: 404/872-1477*
VP State Services	Gale F. Gaines	.404/879-5582

**Members - Governor of each of the 16 participating states and four citizens of each state (one of whom must be a legislator and one an educator) who are appointed by the governor for four-year staggered terms.

EDUCATION, STATE BOARD OF

c/o Texas Education Agency, 1701 N. Congress Ave., Austin 78701-1494
512/463-9007 • *FAX: 512/936-4319* • tea.texas.gov/sboe

15 Elected Members - 4 Years

Donna Bahorich	Chair, Houston, 1-1-21
Ruben Cortez, Jr.	Secretary, Brownsville, 1-1-19
Lawrence Allen, Jr.	Board Member, Houston, 1-1-19
Erika Beltran	Board Member, Fort Worth, 1-1-19
David Bradley	Board Member, Beaumont, 1-1-19
Barbara Cargill	Board Member, Conroe, 1-1-21
Keven M. Ellis	Board Member, Lufkin, 1-1-21
Patricia "Pat" Hardy	Board Member, Fort Worth, 1-1-19
Tom Maynard	Board Member, Florence, 1-1-21
Sue Melton-Malone	Board Member, Robinson, 1-1-21
Ken Mercer	Board Member, San Antonio, 1-1-21
Geraldine "Tincy" Miller	Board Member, Dallas, 1-1-19
Georgina C. Perez	Board Member, El Paso, 1-1-21
Marisa B. Perez	Board Member, Converse, 1-1-19
Marty Rowley	Board Member, Amarillo, 1-1-21

STAFF:

Director	Debbie Ratcliffe . . . . .512/463-9007 / *Fax: 512/936-4319*
Program Specialist	Lenny Sanchez . . . . .512/463-9007 / *Fax: 512/936-4319*
Program Specialist	Colleen Meuth . . . . .512/463-9007 / *Fax: 512/936-4319*

The board and education commissioner oversee the state's public school system.

EDUCATOR CERTIFICATION, STATE BOARD FOR

1701 N. Congress Ave., 5th Floor, Austin 78701-1494
512/936-9831 • *FAX: 512/936-8277*
www.tea.texas.gov • Agency # 701

15 Members - 6 Years

Jill Druesedow	Chair, Haskell, 2-1-19
Suzanne McCall	Vice Chair, Lubbock, 2-1-17
Laurie Bricker	Secretary, Houston, 2-1-19
Sandra D. Bridges	Board Member, Rockwall, 2-1-19
Rohanna Brooks-Sykes	Board Member, Spring, 2-1-21
Arturo J. "Art" Cavazos, Ed.D.	Board Member, Harlingen, 2-1-21
Susan Simpson Hull, Ph.D.	Board Member, Grand Prairie, 2-1-17
Scott Ridley, Ph.D.	Board Member, Lubbock, 2-1-17
Laurie J. Turner, Ed.D.	Board Member, Corpus Christi, 2-1-21
Carlos O. Villagrana	Board Member, Houston, 2-1-21
Tommy L. Coleman, J.D.	Public Member, Livingston, 2-1-19
Leon Leal	Public Member, Grapevine, 2-1-17
Sandie Mullins Moger	Public Member, Houston, 2-1-21
Rex Peebles, Ph.D.	Ex Officio Member
Martin Winchester	Ex Officio Member

STAFF:

Associate Comm. for Educator Leadership and Quality	Ryan Franklin . . . . .512/936-9831 / *Fax: 512/463-7795*
Director of	
Educator Preparation Programs	Tim Miller . . . . .512/475-1476 / *Fax: 512/936-8402*
Certification and Testing	Marilyn Cook . . . . .512/936-8400 / *Fax: 512/936-8402*
Educator Investigations	Doug Phillips . . . . .512/936-8400 / *Fax: 512/936-8404*

The board develops certification and continuing education requirements and standards of conduct for public school educators.

EDWARDS AQUIFER AUTHORITY
900 E. Quincy, San Antonio 78215
210/222-2204 • *FAX: 210/222-9869*
www.edwardsaquifer.org

15 Elected Directors - 4 Years; 2 Appointed Directors - 4 Years

Luana Buckner	Chair, Medina & Atascosa Counties, 12-1-18
Benjamin F. Youngblood	Vice Chair, Bexar County, 12-1-20
Enrique Valdivia	Secretary, Bexar County, 12-1-18
Ron Ellis	Treasurer, Bexar County, 12-1-18
Amy Lea Akers	Board Member, Hays & Caldwell Counties, 12-1-18
Rebekah Bustamante	Board Member, Bexar County, 12-1-18
Deborah Carington	Board Member, Bexar County, 12-1-20
Rader Gilleland	Board Member, Uvalde County, 12-1-18
Kathleen Krueger	Board Member, Comal County, 12-1-20
Don Laffere	Board Member, Uvalde County, 12-1-20
Byron Miller	Board Member, Bexar County, 12-1-20
Carol Patterson	Board Member, Bexar County, 12-1-18
Patrick Stroka	Board Member, Hays County, 12-1-20
Ronald J. Walton, Sr.	Board Member, Comal & Guadalupe Counties, 12-1-18
Scott Yanta	Board Member, Medina County, 12-1-20
Gary Middleton	SCTWAC Appointed Director, 12-1-20
J. Clark Ward	Appointed Director, Medina/Uvalde Counties, 12-1-20

STAFF:

General Manager	Roland Ruiz . . . . .210/222-2204 / *Fax: 210/222-9869*

EMERGENCY COMMUNICATIONS, COMMISSION ON STATE*

333 Guadalupe St., Suite 2-212, Austin 78701-3942
512/305-6911 • *FAX: 512/305-6937*
www.csec.texas.gov • Agency # 477
Poison Center: 800/222-1222

12 Members: 9 Appointed Commissioners - 6 Years;

3 Ex Officio Commissioners

William "Bill" Buchholtz	Presiding Officer, San Antonio, 9-1-21
Kay Alexander	Commissioner, Abilene, 9-1-19
James Beauchamp	Commissioner, Midland, 9-1-19
Sue Brannon	Commissioner, Midland, 9-1-17
Terry Henley	Commissioner, Meadows Place, 9-1-19
Rudy Madrid	Commissioner, 9-1-17
Jack D. Miller	Commissioner, Denton, 9-1-15
Ernestine Robles	Commissioner, Garden Ridge, 9-1-21
Vacant	Commissioner
Wayne Egeler	Ex Officio Member, Department of Information Resources
Brian H. Lloyd	Ex Officio Member, Public Utility Commission
Charles Smith	Ex Officio Member, Health and Human Services Comm.

STAFF:

Executive Director	Kelli Merriweather	512/305-6938
General Counsel	Patrick Tyler	512/305-6915
Chief Financial Officer	Kenneth Biddle	512/305-6914
Director of Programs	Susan Seet	512/305-6917
Assistant Director of Programs	Robert Gonzalez	512/305-6918
Poison Control Program Mgr.	Mia Villarreal	512/305-6916
Chief Program Tech. Officer	Kevin Rohrer	512/305-6780

The commission helps cities, counties, regional planning commissions and emergency communication districts implement and maintain enhanced 9-1-1 emergency communications; and administers the statewide poison control and prevention program through six regional poison control centers.

*Subject to the Texas Sunset Act; will be reviewed in 2023.

EMERGENCY MANAGEMENT COUNCIL, STATE

5805 N. Lamar Blvd., P.O. Box 4087, Austin 78773-0001
512/424-2208 • *FAX: 512/424-2444*
www.dps.texas.gov

31 Members - 29 state agencies; 2 volunteer organizations

American Red Cross (ARC)*
Department of Information Resources (DIR)
General Land Office (GLO)
State Auditor's Office (SAO)
State Comptroller of Public Accounts (CPA)
Texas AgriLife Extension Service
Texas Animal Health Commission (TAHC)
Texas Attorney General's Office (OAG)
Texas Commission on Environmental Quality (TCEQ)
Texas Commission on Fire Protection (TCFP)
Texas Department of Agriculture (TDA)
Texas Department of Criminal Justice (TDCJ)
Texas Department of Family Protective Services (DFPS)
Texas Department of Housing and Community Affairs (TDHCA)
Texas Department of Insurance (TDI)
Texas Department of Public Safety (TXDPS)
Texas Department of State Health Services (DSHS)
Texas Department of Transportation (TXDOT)
Texas Division of Emergency Management (TDEM)
Texas Education Agency (TEA)
Texas Engineering Extension Service (TEEX)
Texas Forest Service (TFS)
Texas Health & Human Services Commission (HHSC)
Texas Military Department
Texas Office of Court Administration
Texas Parks and Wildlife Department (TPWD)
Texas Procurement and Support Services (TPASS)
Texas Public Utility Commission (PUC)
Texas Railroad Commission (RRC)
Texas Workforce Commission (TWC)
The Salvation Army (TSA)*

STAFF:

Chief, Texas Division of
    Emergency Management   Chief W. Nim Kidd 512/424-2436

* The American Red Cross and Salvation Army are not state agencies

EMPLOYEES RETIREMENT SYSTEM OF TEXAS
200 East 18th St., P.O. Box 13207, Austin 78711-3207
512/867-7711 • 877/275-4377 • *FAX: 512/867-7334*
www.ers.texas.gov • Agency # 327

6 Members - 6 Years

Doug Danzeiser   Chair, Austin, 8-31-19
Cydney Donnell   Vice Chair, College Station, 8-31-18
J. Craig Hester   Appointed Member, Austin, 8-31-22
Ilesa Daniels   Elected Member, Houston, 8-31-21
Catherine Melvin   Elected Member, Austin, 8-31-23
Jeanie Wyatt   Appointed Member, San Antonio, 8-31-20

STAFF:

Executive Director   Porter Wilson 512/867-7176
Deputy Executive Director   Catherine Terrell 512/867-7238
Director of Governmental Relations Jennifer Chambers 512/867-7178
Chief Investments Officer   Tom Tull 512/867-7540
Deputy Executive Director &
  General Counsel   Paula A. Jones 512/867-7213
Internal Auditor   Tony Chavez 512/867-7443
Director of Benefit Contracts   Diana Kongevick 512/867-7151
Chief Information Officer   Chuck Turner 512/867-7412
Chief Financial Officer   Machelle Pharr 512/867-7667
Director of Customer Benefits   Robin Hardaway 512/867-7141
Director of Benefits
  Communications   Kathryn Tesar 512/867-7396

The board oversees a $28 billion retirement fund and program, and the administration of state employee and retiree health insurance benefits, a deferred compensation plan and a flexible benefits program.

ENGINEERS, TEXAS BOARD OF PROFESSIONAL*
1917 South IH 35, Austin 78741 • 512/440-7723 • *FAX: 512/440-0417*
www.engineers.texas.gov • Agency # 460

6 Professional Engineer Members - 6 Years; 3 Public Members - 6 Years

Daniel Wong, Ph.D., P.E.	Chair, Houston, 9-26-19
Edward L. Summers, Ph.D.	Treasurer, Austin, 9-26-17
Lamberto "Bobby" Balli, P.E.	Board Member, San Antonio, 9-26-21
Sam Kannappan, P.E.	Board Member, Baytown, 9-26-17
Sina K. Nejad, P.E., P.Eng	Board Member, Beaumont, 9-26-19
Cathy Norwood, P.E.	Board Member, Midland, 8-26-21
Kyle Womack, P.E.	Board Member, Horseshoe Bay, 9-26-17
Albert Cheng	Public Member, Houston, 9-26-21
Elvira Reyna	Public Member, Little Elm, 9-26-19

STAFF:

Executive Director	Lance Kinney, P.E.	512/440-3080
Deputy Executive Director	David Howell, P.E.	512/440-3054
Executive Assistant	Cristabel Bodden	512/440-3051
Director of Licensing	Rick Strong, P.E.	512/440-3050
Director of Compliance and Enforcement	Position Vacant	512/440-3087
Director of Financial Services	Jeff Mutscher	512/440-3063
Director of Operations	Janet Sobieski	512/440-3070
Human Resources	Suzanne Retiz, PHR	512/440-3067
Legislative Liaison	David Howell, P.E.	512/440-3054

*Subject to the Texas Sunset Act; will be reviewed in 2025.

ENVIRONMENTAL QUALITY, TEXAS COMMISSION ON (TCEQ)*

12100 Park 35 Circle, P.O. Box 13087, Austin 78711-3087
512/239-1000 • *FAX: 512/239-5533*
www.tceq.texas.gov • Agency # 582

3 Members - 6 Years

Bryan W. Shaw, Ph.D., P.E.	Chair, Elgin, 8-31-19
Toby Baker	Commissioner, Austin, 8-31-17
Jon Niermann	Commissioner, Austin, 8-31-21

Commissioner's Office: . . . .*523/29-5500 / Fax: 512/239/5533*

General Counsel	Tucker Royall	.512/239-5525 / *Fax: 512/239-5533*
Chief Auditor	Carlos Contreras	.512/239-0780 / *Fax: 512/239-5533*
Chief Clerk	Bridget C. Bohac	.512/239-3300 / *Fax: 512/239-5533*
Public Interest Counsel	Vic McWherter	.512/239-6363 / *Fax: 512/239-5533*

Executive Director and Staff: . . . .*512/239-3900 / Fax: 512/239-3939*

Executive Director	Richard A. Hyde, P.E.	.512/239-3900
Special Assistant	Lori Wilson	.512/239-1635
Executive Assistant	Barbara Robinson . . . . ,	.512/239-1279
Receptionist	Margaret Wilson	.512/239-3900
Deputy Executive Director	Stephanie Bergeron Perdue	.512/239-3900
Special Assistant	Emily Lindley	.512/239-4086
Technical Advisor	Minor Hibbs, P.E.	.512/239-6590

Communications and Intergovenmental Relations Division: **512/239-3500**

Director	Ryan Vise	.512/239-5022

Take Care of Texas Program: **512/239-3929**

Director	John Bentley	.512/239-6786

Environmental Assistance Division: **512/239-3100**

Director	Brian Christian	.512/239-5007

Toxicology Division: **512/239-1795**

Director	Michael Honeycutt, Ph.D.	.512/239-1793

Deputy Director:

Office of Admin. Services	John Racanelli	.512/239-0590 / *Fax: 512/239-0596*
Office of Air	Steve Hagle	.512/239-2104 / *Fax: 512/239-3341*
Office of Compliance & Enforcement	Ramiro Garcia	.512/239-5100 / *Fax: 512/239-4390*
Legal Services	Margi Ligarde	.512/239-0600 / *Fax: 512/239-0330*
Office of Waste	Brent Wade	.512/239-2300 / *Fax: 512/239-0659*
Office of Water	L'Oreal Stepney	.512/239-6696 / *Fax: 512/239-5737*

AREA DIRECTORS:

Border & Permian Basin-Regions 6,7,15,16:
Area Director   David A. Ramirez . . . . .956/425-6010 / *Fax: 956/412-5059*

Central Texas-Regions 9,11,13:
Area Director   Susan Jablonski, P.E. . . . . . .512/239-6731 / *Fax: 512/239-4390*

Coastal & East Texas-Regions 5,10,12,14:
Area Director   Kelly Keel Linden . . . . . . .512/239-3607 / *Fax: 512/239-4390*

North Central & West Texas-Regions 1,2,3,4,8:
Area Director   Randy J. Ammons . . . . . . .806/796-7092 / *Fax: 806/796-7107*

REGIONAL OFFICES:

Region 1:
Amarillo:
Regional Director   Brad Jones . . . . .806/353-9251 / *Fax: 806/358-9545*

Region 2:
Lubbock:
Regional Director   Gary Shipp, P.G. . . . . .806/796-7092 / *Fax: 806/796-7107*

Region 3:
Abilene:
Regional Director   Winona Henry, P.E. . . . . . .325/698-9674 / *Fax: 325/692-5869*

Region 4:
DFW:
Regional Director   Tony Walker . . . . .817/588-5800 / *Fax: 817/588-5700*

Region 5:
Tyler:
Regional Director   Leroy Biggers . . . . .903/535-5100 / *Fax: 903/595-1562*

Region 6:
El Paso:
Regional Director   Lorinda Gardner . . . . .915/834-4949 / *Fax: 915/834-4951*

Region 7:
Midland:
Regional Director   Lorinda Gardner . . . . .432/570-1359 / *Fax: 432/561-5512*

Region 8:
San Angelo:
Regional Director   Winona Henry, P.E. . . . . . .325/655-9479 / *Fax: 325/658-5431*

Region 9:
Waco:
Regional Director   David Van Soest . . . . .254/751-0335 / *Fax: 254/772-9241*

Region 10:
Beaumont:
Regional Director   Kathryn Sauceda . . . . .409/898-3838 / *Fax: 409/892-2119*

Region 11:
Austin:
Regional Director   David Van Soest . . . . .512/339-2929 / *Fax: 512/339-3795*

Region 12:
Houston:
Regional Director   Ashley K. Wadick . . . . .713/767-3500 / *Fax: 713/767-3520*

Region 13:
San Antonio:
Regional Director   Joel Anderson . . . . .210/490-3096 / *Fax: 210/545-4329*

Region 14:
Corpus Christi:
Regional Director   Susan Clewis . . . . .361/825-3100 / *Fax: 361/825-3101*

Region 15:
Harlingen:
Regional Director   Jamie A. Garza . . . . .956/425-6010 / *Fax: 956/412-5059*

Region 16:
Laredo:
Regional Director   Jamie A. Garza . . . . .956/791-6611 / *Fax: 956/791-6716*

Spill Reporting (24 Hours):
800/832-8224

Environmental Complaints and Non-Spill Emergencies:
888/777-3186

Toxicology Division:
877/992-8370

The commission oversees and establishes policy for the state's lead environmental permitting and enforcement agency.

---
*Subject to the Texas Sunset Act; will be reviewed in 2023.

ETHICS COMMISSION, TEXAS*

201 East 14th St., 10th Floor, P.O. Box 12070, Austin 78711-2070
512/463-5800 • *FAX: 512/463-5777*
www.ethics.state.tx.us • Agency # 356
Disclosure Filing Fax: 512/463-8808

8 Members - 4 Years

Steven D. Wolens	Chair, Dallas, 11-11-19
James Clancy	Commissioner, Portland, 11-19-17
Chad M. Craycraft	Commissioner, Dallas, 11-19-19
Randy Erben	Commissioner, Austin, 11-19-21
Chris Flood	Commissioner, Houston, 11-19-19
Mary K. Kennedy	Commissioner, Houston, 11-19-19
Thomas Ramsay	Commissioner, Mt. Vernon, 11-19-17
Joseph O. Slovacek	Commissioner, Houston, 11-19-21

STAFF:

Interim Executive Director	Seana Willing . . . . .512/463-5800 / *Fax: 512/463-5777*
General Counsel	Ian Steusloff . . . . .512/463-5800 / *Fax: 512/463-5777*
Director:	
Enforcement	Angela Goodwin . . . . .512/463-5800 / *Fax: 512/463-5777*
Disclosure Filing and	
Computer Services	Jessie Haug . . . . .512/463-5800 / *Fax: 512/463-5777*
Finance and Administration	Cristina Hernandez . . . . . . .512/463-5784 / *Fax: 512/463-5777*

The Texas Ethics Commission has eight commissioners. Four of the commissioners are appointed by the Governor, two are appointed by the Lieutenant Governor, and two are appointed by the Speaker of the Texas House of Representatives. Members of the Texas Senate and the Texas House of Representatives who represent each political party submit lists of nominees to the appropriate state official for appointment. The commissioners serve for four-year terms.

The commission is responsible for administering and enforcing laws concerning political contributions and expenditures, political advertising, lobbyist activities and the conduct of state officers and employees.

---

*Subject to the Texas Sunset Act; will be reviewed in 2025.

FACILITIES COMMISSION, TEXAS*

Central Services Bldg., 1711 San Jacinto, P.O. Box 13047, Austin 78711-3047
512/463-3446 • www.tfc.texas.gov • Agency # 303

7 Members - 6 Years

Robert D. Thomas	Chair, Austin, 1-31-21
Michael J. Novak	Vice Chair, San Antonio, 1-31-19
Steven Alvis	Commissioner, Houston, 1-31-23
William D. Darby	Commissioner, San Angelo, 1-31-15
Patti C. Jones	Commissioner, Lubbock, 1-31-21
Jack W. Perry	Commissioner, Houston, 1-31-19
Rigo Villarreal	Commissioner, Mission, 1-31-23

Office of the Executive Director:

Executive Director	Harvey Hilderbran	512/463-7598
Executive Assistant	Debbie Van Bibber	512/463-7598
Director		
Strategic Planning and Policy	Shyra Darr	512/936-4288
External Affairs & Comm.	Position Vacant	
Operations	Gerard Edimo	512/463-1767
Security and Safety Programs	Tommy Oates	512/463-3057

Office of General Counsel:

General Counsel	Kay Molina	512/475-2400
Assistant General Counsel	Naomi Gonzalez	512/463-3960

Chief Financial Office:

Chief Financial Officer	Position Vacant	
Director, Budget	Rob Reis	512/463-3540
Director, Accounting	Daniel Benjamin	512/463-3591
Director, Procurement	Richard Ehlert	512/463-0209
HUB Coordinator	Yolanda Strey	512/475-0453

Planning and Real Estate Management:

Deputy Executive Director	Peter Maass	512/463-9454
Director of Property Mgmt. Services	Kevin Myers	512/463-2360
Manager, State Leasing	Gayla Davis	512/475-2438

Facilities Design and Construction:

Deputy Executive Director	John Raff	512/463-3567
Director, Project Management	Marti Walsh	512/463-8247
Director, Human Resources	Catherine Camp	512/463-9996
Chief Technology Officer	Glenn Garvey	512/475-2488
Director, State/Federal Surplus	Kristy Fierro	512/463-3458
Director of Internal Audit	Amanda Jenami	512/463-1438

The Texas Facilities Commission (TFC) supports state government through strategic planning, asset management, design, construction, operation, maintenance, and leasing of state facilities and the reallocation and/or disposal of state and federal surplus property. TFC serves state agencies, legislative members/staff, and members of the general public that utilize the state facilities owned and managed or leased by TFC as well as the state agencies and their employees for whom construction and renovation projects are managed. TFC provides property management, repair, renovation, maintenance services, custodial, grounds, and utility services for its building inventory. The agency maintains a 24 hour, 7 day a week operation to ensure continuity of operations of vital building systems.

*Subject to the Texas Sunset Act; will be reviewed in 2021.

FAMILY AND PROTECTIVE SERVICES, TEXAS DEPARTMENT OF

701 W. 51st St., P.O. Box 149030, Austin 78714-9030
512/438-4800 • TxAbuseHotline.org
Abuse Hotline: 800/252-5400

The Texas Department of Family and Protective Services (DFPS) works with communities to protect children, the elderly, and people with disabilities from abuse, neglect, and exploitation. It also works to protect the health and safety of children in daycare, as well as foster care and other types of 24-hour care. We do this through investigations, services and referrals, regulation, and prevention programs.

DFPS has five major programs that do this important work:

Adult Protective Services
Protects the elderly and people with disabilities from abuse, neglect, and exploitation through investigations and services.

Child Protective Services
Protects children from abuse and neglect through investigations, services, foster care, and adoption.

Child Care Licensing
Regulates daycare, foster care, adoption agencies, residential treatment centers, before- and after-school programs, and maternity homes.

Statewide Intake
Takes reports of abuse, neglect, and exploitation from across the state through its Texas Abuse Hotline (1-800-252-5400) and through the website TxAbuseHotline.org

Prevention and Early Intervention
Manages community-based programs that prevent juvenile delinquency and child abuse and neglect.

FEED AND FERTILIZER CONTROL SERVICE, TEXAS/OFFICE OF THE TEXAS STATE CHEMIST

Texas A&M University System, P.O. Box 3160, College Station 77841-3160
979/845-1121 • *FAX: 979/845-1389* • otscweb.tamu.edu

STAFF:

State Chemist and Director, OTSC	Dr. Timothy Herrman	.979/845-1121 / *Fax: 979/845-1389*
Associate Director, OTSC	Ben Jones	.979/845-1121 / *Fax: 979/845-1389*
Associate Director	Sara Williams	.979/845-1121 / *Fax: 979/845-1389*
Associate Director	Mary Sasser	.979/845-1121 / *Fax: 979/845-1389*
Manager,		
Feed and Fertilizer Registration	Julie Mitchell	.979/845-1121 / *Fax: 979/845-1389*
Labeling	James Embry	.979/845-1121 / *Fax: 979/845-1389*
Quality Assurance	Megan Rooney	.979/845-1121 / *Fax: 979/845-1389*
Supervisory Staff Accountant	John W. See	.979/845-1121 / *Fax: 979/845-1389*
Sr. Administrative Coordinator	Lori J. Mendoza	.979/845-1121 / *Fax: 979/845-1389*
Outreach Coordinator	Prabha Vasudevan	.979/845-1121 / *Fax: 979/845-1389*

FINANCE COMMISSION OF TEXAS*

2601 North Lamar Blvd., Austin 78705
512/936-6222 • *FAX: 512/475-1505* • www.fc.texas.gov

11 Members - 6 Years

Stacy G. London, CMC	Chair, Houston, 2-1-20
H.J. "Jay" Shands III	Vice Chair, Lufkin, 2-1-18
Bob Borochoff	Public Member, Houston, 2-1-22
Molly Curl	Public Member, Richardson, 2-1-22
Phillip Holt	Consumer Credit Member, Bonham, 2-1-22
Lori B. McCool	Public Member, Boerne, 2-1-20
Matt Moore	Public Member, Amarillo, 2-1-22
Paul Plunket	Public Member, Dallas, 2-1-20
Vince E. Puente, Sr.	Public Member, Fort Worth, 2-1-18
Hector J. Cerna	Industry Banking Executive, Eagle Pass, 2-1-20
William Lucas	Industry Savings Executive, Center, 2-1-18

STAFF:

Banking Commissioner	Charles G. Cooper	.512/475-1300
Consumer Credit Commissioner	Leslie L. Pettijohn	.512/936-7640
Executive Director, Savings &		
Mortgage Lending Comm.	Caroline C. Jones	.512/475-1352
Executive Assistant	Anne Benites	.512/936-6222

The commission ensures banks, savings institutions, consumer credit grantors and other state-regulated financial entities under its purview operate responsibly to enhance the financial well-being of Texans.

*Subject to the Texas Sunset Act; will be reviewed in 2019.

FIRE PROTECTION, TEXAS COMMISSION ON*

1701 N. Congress, Suite 1-105, P.O. Box 2286, Austin 78768-2286
512/936-3838 • *FAX: 512/936-3808* • www.tcfp.texas.gov • Agency # 411

13 Members - 6 Years

Robert Moore	Presiding Officer, Bryan, 2-1-21
Tommy Anderson	Commissioner, Santa Fe, 2-1-21
Carlos Cortez, Jr.	Commissioner, Harlingen, 2-1-21
Kelly E. Doster	Commissioner, Frisco, 2-1-21
Joseph "Jody" Gonzalez	Commissioner, Krugerville, 2-1-19
Mike Jones	Commissioner, Burleson, 2-1-23
John T. McMakin	Commissioner, LaRue, 2-1-19
Bob Morgan	Commissioner, Fort Worth, 2-1-23
Lenny Perez	Commissioner, Brownsville, 2-1-19
Mala Sharma	Commissioner, Houston, 2-1-23
J.P. Steelman	Commissioner, Longview, 2-1-23
Steven C. Tull	Commissioner, Valley Mills, 2-1-21
Tivy Whitlock	Commissioner, San Antonio, 2-1-19

STAFF:

Executive Director	Tim Rutland	512/936-3812
Executive Assistant	Deborah Cowan	512/936-3812
Public Information Officer	Mark Roughton	512/936-3850

Created by the Legislature in 1969, the Texas Commission on Fire Protection's mission is to aid in the protection of lives and property of Texas citizens, through the development and enforcement of recognized professional standards for individuals and the fire service.

*Subject to the Texas Sunset Act; will be reviewed in 2021.

FORENSIC SCIENCE COMMISSION

1700 North Congress Avenue, Suite 445, Austin 78701
888/296-4232 • *FAX: 888/305-2432* • www.fsc.texas.gov

9 Members - 2 Years

Jeffrey J. Barnard, M.D.	Chair, Dallas, 9-1-17
Bruce Budowle Ph.D.	Board Member, North Richland Hills, 9-1-18
Mark Daniel	Board Member, Fort Worth, 9-1-17
Nancy Downing, Ph.D.	Board Member, Bryan, 9-1-18
Jasmine Drake, Ph.D.	Board Member, Conroe, 9-1-18
S. Robyn Hughes-Stamm, Ph.D.	Board Member, Spring, 9-1-18
Dennis "Pat" Johnson	Board Member, Austin, 9-1-17
Sarah Kerrigan, Ph.D.	Board Member, The Woodlands, 9-1-17
The Honorable Jarvis Parsons	Board Member, 9-1-17

STAFF:

General Counsel	Lynn M. Robitaille Garcia	512/936-0661
Associate General Counsel	Leigh M. Savage	512/936-0661
Commission Coordinator	Kathryn Adams	512/936-0770
Senior Scientific Advisor	D. Jody Koehler	512/936-0729

FOREST SERVICE, TEXAS A&M*
200 Technology Way, Suite 1281, College Station 77845
979/458-6600 • *FAX: 979/458-6610*
texasforestservice.tamu.edu • Agency # 576

Forest Resource Development & Sustainable Forestry Division:
200 Technology Way, Suite 1281
College Station 77845
979/458-6650 / *Fax: 979/458-6655*

Forest Resource Protection Division:
200 Technology Way, Suite 1162
College Station 77845
979/458-6507 / *Fax: 979/458-7347*

Forest Pest Management:
2127 S. First Street
Lufkin 75902-0310
936/639-8170 / *Fax: 936/639-8175*

STAFF:
Director & State Forester   Thomas G. Boggus 979/458-6600
Assoc. Director:
Forest Resource Dev. &
    Sustainable Forestry   Bill Oates 979/458-6650
    Forest Resource Protection   Mark Stanford 979/458-6507
Finance and Administration   Robby S. DeWitt 979/458-7301

*Subject to the Texas Sunset Act; will be reviewed in 2023.

FUNERAL SERVICE COMMISSION, TEXAS*
333 Guadalupe St., Suite 2-110, Austin 78701
512/936-2474 • *FAX: 512/479-5064* • www.tfsc.texas.gov • Agency # 513

7 Members - 6 Years

Jean "Jeanne" Olinger   Presiding Officer, Wichita Falls, 2-1-19
Larry Allen   Assistant Presiding Officer, Mesquite, 2-1-21
Greg Compean   Board Member, Richmond, 2-1-21
Dianne Hefley   Board Member, Amarillo, 2-1-23
Gary Shaffer   Board Member, San Angelo, 2-1-19
Kristin Tips   Board Member, San Antonio, 2-1-23
Jonathan Scepanski   Board Member, McAllen, 2-1-19

STAFF:
Executive Director   Janice McCoy ....512/936-2474 / *Fax: 512/479-5064*

*Subject to the Texas Sunset Act; will be reviewed in 2019.

GEOSCIENTISTS, TX BOARD OF PROFESSIONAL*

333 Guadalupe St., Tower 1, Suite 530, P.O. Box 13225, Austin 78711-3225
512/936-4400 • FAX: 512/936-4409 • www.tbpg.state.tx.us • Agency # 481

3 Public Members, 6 Professional Members -Term 3 Years

Charles T. Hallmark	Chair, Hearne, 2-1-19
W. David Prescott II	Vice Chair, Amarillo, 2-1-19
Becky L. Johnson	Secretary/Treasurer, Fort Worth, 2-1-17
Lindsey Bradford	Public Member, Edna, 2-1-21
Gregory C. Ulmer	Public Member, Houston, 2-1-17
Bereket Derie	Professional Member, Round Rock, 2-1-21
Steven Fleming	Professional Member, Midland, 2-1-21
Christopher C. Mathewson	Professional Member, College Station, 2-1-17
Vacant	Public Member

STAFF:

Executive Director	Charles Horton . . . . .512/936-4401 / Fax: 512/936-4409
Chief Financial Officer	Lisa Stockton . . . . .512/936-4404 / Fax: 512/936-4409
Operations Manager	Molly Roman . . . . .512/936-4405 / Fax: 512/936-4409
Enforcement Coordinator	T. Wesley McCoy . . . . .512/936-4410 / Fax: 512/936-4409
Licensing Coordinator	Elsa Paynes . . . . .512/936-4403 / Fax: 512/936-4409
Enforcement Specialist	Valerie Arnold . . . . .512/936-4402 / Fax: 512/936-4409

The board may set reasonable and necessary fees to be charged applicants and license holders, including fees for application, examination, licensure, and renewal of a license. In addition, the board shall base a fee for examination in a discipline of geoscience on the costs associated with preparing, administering, and grading that examination.

*Subject to the Texas Sunset Act; will be reviewed in 2019.

GUADALUPE-BLANCO RIVER AUTHORITY*

933 East Court Street, Seguin 78155 • 830/379-5822 • FAX: 830/379-9718
www.gbra.org

9 Members - 6 Years

Rusty Brockman	Chair, New Braunfels, 2-1-17
Dennis L. Patillo	Vice Chair, Victoria, 2-1-21
Don B. Meador	Secretary/Treasurer, San Marcos, 2-1-19
William R. Carbonara	Director, Cuero, 2-1-19
Oscar H. Fogle	Director, Lockhart, 2-1-17
Ronald J. Hermes	Director, Seguin, 2-1-21
Thomas O. "Tommy" Mathews	Director, Boerne, 2-1-21
Kenneth Motl	Director, Port Lavaca, 2-1-17
Vacant	Director

STAFF:

General Manager	Kevin Patteson . . . . .830/379-5822 / Fax: 830/379-1766

The board oversees water resources for communities in its 10-county district.

*Subject to the Texas Sunset Act; will be reviewed in 2019.

GULF COAST AUTHORITY
910 Bay Area Blvd., Houston 77058
281/488-4115 • *FAX: 281/488-3331*
www.gcatx.org

9 Members - 2 Years

Franklin Jones, Jr.	Chair, Harris County, 8-31-15
Rita Standridge	Vice Chair, Chambers County, 8-31-18
Stan Cromartie	Secretary, Galveston County, 8-31-16
Irvin Osborne-Lee	Treasurer, Harris County, 8-31-01
Nancy C. Blackwell	Board Member, Harris County, 8-31-17
Ron Crowder	Board Member, Galveston County, 8-31-15
Lamont Meaux	Board Member, Chambers County, 8-31-16
Chris Peden	Board Member, Galveston County, 8-31-15
Mark Schultz	Board Member, Chambers County, 8-31-16

STAFF:
General Manager   Lori Traweek ....281/488-4115 / *Fax: 281/488-3331*

The Board consists of nine directors from each county within the district, the governor of the State of Texas shall appoint one director from each county within the district, the county commissioners court of that county shall appoint one director and from each county within the district, the municipalities waste disposal council of that county, hereinafter created, shall appoint one director each. The Counties in the district are Harris County, Galveston County and Chambers County.

HEALTH AND HUMAN SERVICES COMMISSION, TX*

4900 North Lamar, P.O. Box 13247, Austin 78711-3247
512/424-6500 • www.hhs.texas.gov • Agency # 529

COMMISSIONER'S OFFICE:

Executive Commissioner	Charles Smith	512/424-6603
Chief Deputy Commissioner	Cecile Young	512/424-6502
Chief of Staff	Kara Crawford	512/424-6603
Deputy Chief of Staff	Hailey Kemp	512/487-3387
Chief Operating Officer	Heather Griffith Peterson	512/424-6603
Executive Clerk	Pam Wells	512/424-6554
Scheduler	Marissa Prifogle	512/424-6535

STAFF:

Chief Policy Officer	Victoria Ford	512/424-6932
Facilities Division	Mike Maples	512/438-2165
Information Technology Svcs.	Position Vacant	512/424-6990
Medical and Social Services Div.	Enrique Marquez	512/462-6573
State Medicaid Director	Stephanie Muth	512/707-6096
Policy and Rules	Constance Allison	737/867-8643
Financial Services	Greta Rymal	512/424-6993
Procurement and Contracting	Ron Pigott	512/424-4909
Regulatory Services	David Kostroun	512/424-6644
Social Services	Wayne Salter	512/424-4683
System Support Services	Chris Adams	512/424-6660
Chief Financial Officer	Trey Wood	512/707-6080
Director of Healthcare Quality Analytics, Research and Coordination Support	Matt Ferrara	512/380-4371
Business and Regional Services	Harriett Stephens	512/420-2887
Civil Rights	Jenny Hall	512/424-6615
Human Resources	Raette Hearne	512/487-3311
Ombudsman	Joel Schwartz	512/706-7281
Chief Legal Counsel	Karen Ray	512/424-6614
Govt. and Stakcholder Relations	Amanda Martin	512/487-3300
Communications	Bryan Black	512/424-6951
General Counsel	Carey Smith	512/424 6894
Internal Audit	Karin Hill	512/487-3450
Inspector General	Sylvia H. Kauffman	512/491-2000

STATE HOSPITAL SECTION:

Director	Tim Bray	512/206-5336 / *Fax: 512/206-5297*
Hospital Services Section	Peggy Perry	512/206-5184 / *Fax: 512/206-5297*
Austin State Hospital	Alan Isaacson	512/452-0381 / *Fax: 512/419-2163*
Big Spring State Hospital	Lorie Dunnam	432/267-8216 / *Fax: 432/268-7263*
Kerrville State Hospital	Leigh Ann Fitzpatrick	830/896-2211 / *Fax: 830/792-4926*
El Paso Psychiatric Center	Zulema Carrillo	915/534-5412 / *Fax: 915/534-5587*
North Texas State Hospital	James E. Smith	940/552-4000 / *Fax: 940/553-2500*
Rio Grande State Ctr. S. TX HCS	Sonia Hernandez-Keeble	956/364-8000 / *Fax: 956/364-8497*
Rusk State Hospital	Brenda Slaton	903/683-3421 / *Fax: 903/683-7101*
San Antonio State Hospital	Bob Arizpe	210/532-8811 / *Fax: 210/531-7876*
Terrell State Hospital	Dorothy Floyd	972/524-6452 / *Fax: 972/551-8053*
Waco Center for Youth	Chuck Russell	254/756-2171 / *Fax: 254/745-5398*

*Subject to the Texas Sunset Act; will be reviewed in 2023.

HEALTH PROFESSIONS COUNCIL
333 Guadalupe St., Suite 2-220, Austin 78701 • 512/305-8550
www.hpc.state.tx.us • Agency # 364

14 Members

Chris Kloeris, J.D.	Chair, Texas Optometry Board
Kelly Parker	Vice Chair, TX State Board of Dental Examiners
Allison Vordenbaumen Benz, R.Ph., M.S.	Board Member, Texas State Board of Pharmacy
Scott Freshour, J.D.	Board Member, Texas Medical Board
Patricia Gilbert	Board Member, Board of Chiropractic Examiners
John Helenberg	Board Member, Board of Veterinary Medical Exam.
Kara Holsinger, J.D.	Board Member, Office of the Attorney General
John Maline	Board Member, Board of Physical Therapy Exam.
Janice McCoy	Board Member, Funeral Service Commission
Tim Speer	Board Member, Dept. of State Health Services
Darrel Spinks, J.D.	Board Member, Board of Exam. of Psychologists
Katherine Thomas, M.N., R.N.	Board Member, Board of Nursing
Vacant	Board Member, Podiatric Medical Examiners
Vacant	Board Member, Texas Funeral Service Comm.

STAFF:

Administrative Officer	John Monk	.512/305-8551
Administrative Assistant	Rita Ybarra	.512/305-8550

HEALTH SERVICES, TX DEPARTMENT OF STATE

1100 West 49th Street, P.O. Box 149347, Austin 78714-9347
512/776-7111 • 888/963-7111 • www.dshs.texas.gov • Agency # 537

Commissioner's Office:

Commissioner	John Hellerstedt, M.D.512/776-7376 / *Fax: 512/776-7477*
Deputy Commissioner	Jennifer Sims . . . . . .512/776-7376 / *Fax: 512/776-7477*
Senior Advisor	Kirk Cole . . . . .512/776-7376 / *Fax: 512/776-7477*
Assistant Deputy Commissioner	Kirk Cole, (Interim) .512/776-7792 / *Fax: 512/776-7477*
Chief Financial Officer	Donna Sheppard . . . .512/776-7640 / *Fax: 512/776-7477*
Program Operations	Wanda Thompson . . .512/776-7789 / *Fax: 512/776-7177*
State Epidemiologist	Linda Gaul . . . . .512/776-7198 / *Fax: 512/776-7477*
Center for External Relations, Director	Ricky Garcia . . . . . .512/776-7404 / *Fax: 512/776-7624*
Communications Unit	Position Vacant . . . .512/776-6085 / *Fax: 512/776-7624*
Governmental Affairs Unit	Rachael Hendrickson .512/776-3765 / *Fax: 512/776-7624*
Media Relations/Press Office	Chris Van Deusen . . .512/776-7119 / *Fax: 512/776-7624*
Process Improvement	Mercy Bryant . . . . . .512/776-3482 / *Fax: 512/776-7624*
System Coordination Unit	Carolyn Bivens . . . .512/776-2370 / *Fax: 512/776-7624*
Health Policy and Performance	Peter Hajmasy . . . . .512/776-6537 / *Fax: 512/776-7624*
Office of Academic Affairs	Courtney Dezendorf .512/776-3685 / *Fax: 512/776-2822*

Division for Community Health Improvement:

Associate Commissioner	Manda Hall, M.D. . . .512/776-7321 / *Fax: 512/776-7358*

Division for Consumer Protection:

Associate Commissioner	Jon Huss . . . . .512/834-6660 / *Fax: 512/834-6635*

Division for Laboratory and Infectious Disease:

Associate Commissioner	Janna Zumbrun . . . .512/776-7729 / *Fax: 512/776-7229*

Division for Regional and Local Health Ops.:

Associate Commissioner	David Gruber . . . . . .512/776-7770 / *Fax: 512/776-7590*

Texas Center for Infectious Disease:

Hospital Administrator	Jessica Gutierrez-Rodriguez 210/534-8857
	. . . .*Fax: 210/531-4502*

Office of Border Public Health:

Administrator	Ronald J. Dutton . . . .512/776-7675 / *Fax: 512/776-7262*

DIVISION FOR REGIONAL AND LOCAL HEALTH REGIONS:

Public Health Region 1
Lubbock
Regional Medical Director
Kimberly Wolboldt, M.D.,
M.P.H.
806/744-3577 / *Fax: 783-6435*

Public Health Region 2/3
Arlington
Regional Medical Director
James A. Zoretic, M.D., M.P.H.
817/264-4500 / *Fax: 264-4506*

Public Health Region 4/5
Tyler
Regional Medical Director
Sharon Huff, M.D., M.S.
903/595-3585 / *Fax: 593-4187*

Public Health Region 6/5
S. Houston
Regional Medical Director,
Carlos Plasencia, M.D., MSPH
713/767-3000 / *Fax: 767-3049*

Public Health Region 7
Temple
Regional Medical Director,
Sharon Melville, M.D., M.P.H,
254/778-6744 / *Fax: 778-4066*

Public Health Region 8
San Antonio
Regional Medical Director,
Lillian Ringsdorf, M.D.,
M.P.H.
210/949-2000 / *Fax: 949-2015*

Public Health Region 9/10
El Paso
Regional Medical Director,
Mary Anderson, M.D., M.P.H.
915/834-7675 / *Fax: 834-7799*

Public Health Region 11
Harlingen
Regional Medical Director,
Emilie Prot, D.O., M.P.H.
956/423-0130 / *Fax: 444-3298*

Health Emergency
Preparedness and
Response Section
Director, Jeff Hoogheem
512/776-7219 / *Fax: 776-7472*

PROFESSIONAL LICENSING AND CERT. UNIT

c/o DSHS, P.O. Box 149347, MC 1982, Austin 78714-9347 • http://www.dshs.texas.gov

Chemical Dependency Counselor Licensing Program 512/834-6605
Code Enforcement Officer Registration Program 512/834-4512
Offender Education Programs 800/832-9623
Marriage and Family Therapists, State Board of Examiners of 512/834-6657
Massage Therapy Licensing Program 512/834-6657
Professional Counselors, Texas State Board of Examiners of 512/834-6658
Sex Offender Treatment, Council on 512/834-6628 x2929
Sanitarian Registration Program 512/834-4517
Social Worker Examiners, Board of 800/232-3162

HEARING INSTRUMENT FITTERS AND DISPENSERS ADVISORY BOARD

c/o TDLR, P.O. Box 12057, Austin 787111-2057
512/463-6599 • *FAX: 512/475-2874*
www.tdlr.texas.gov/hearing/hearing.htm

9 Members - 6 Years

Benjamin Norris	Presiding Officer, Elm Mott, 2-1-21
Jackie Cooper	Board Member, Spring, 2-1-23
Richard Davila II	Board Member, Lubbock, 2-1-19
James Fowler, M.D.	Board Member, Brownwood, 2-1-21
Gary A. Haun	Board Member, San Angelo, 2-1-23
Jesus Rangel	Board Member, Longview, 2-1-21
Amy Trost	Board Member, Seguin, 2-1-19
Vacant	Board Member
Vacant	Board Member

STAFF:
Executive Director   Brian Francis . . . . .512/463-3171 / *Fax: 512/475-2874*

HIGHER EDUCATION COORDINATING BOARD, TX*

1200 E. Anderson Lane, P.O. Box 12788, Austin 78711-2788
512/427-6101 • *FAX: 512/427-6127*
www.thecb.state.tx.us • Agency # 781

9 Members - 6 Years; 1 Student Representative serves 1 Year

Robert "Bobby" Jenkins, Jr.	Chair, Austin, 8-31-17
Stuart W. Stedman	Vice Chair, Houston, 8-31-21
John Steen	Secretary, San Antonio, 8-31-19
Arcilia Acosta	Board Member, Dallas, 8-31-19
S. Javaid Anwar	Board Member, Midland, 8-31-21
Fred Farias III, O.D.	Board Member, McAllen, 8-31-19
Rickey Raven	Board Member, Sugar Land, 8-31-21
Janelle Shepard	Board Member, Weatherford, 8-31-17
Andrias R. "Annie" Jones	Student Representative, McAllen, 5-31-18
Vacant	Board Member

STAFF:
Commissioner of Higher Education

Dr. Raymund Paredes . . .512/427-6101 / *Fax: 512/427-6127*

General Counsel William Franz . . . . .512/427-6143 / *Fax: 512/427-6127*

Internal Audit and
   Compliance, Director Mark Poehl . . . . .512/427-6161 / *Fax: 512/427-6127*

Academic Planning and Policy:
Deputy Commissioner & CAO David Gardner . . . . .512/427-6155 / *Fax: 512/427-6127*

Academic Quality and Workforce:
Assistant Commissioner Rex Peebles . . . . .512/427-6520 / *Fax: 512/427-6128*

Strategic Planning and Funding:
Assistant Commissioner Julie Eklund . . . . .512/427-6533 / *Fax: 512/427-6127*

College Readiness and Success:
Assistant Commissioner Jerel Booker . . . . .512/427-6247 / *Fax: 512/427-6444*

Agency Operations and Communications:
Deputy Commissioner/COO Linda Battles . . . . .512/427-6205 / *Fax: 512/427-6127*

Financial Services/CFO:
Assistant Commissioner Ken Martin . . . . .512/427-6173 / *Fax: 512/427-6169*

Information Solutions and Services:
Assistant Commissioner Zhenzhen Sun . . . . .512/427-6259 / *Fax: 512/427-6446*

Human Resources:
Director Tonia Scaperlanda . . . . . .512/427-6193 / *Fax: 512/427-6510*

External Relations:
Director John Wyatt . . . . .512/427-6586 / *Fax: 512/427-6127*

*Subject to the Texas Sunset Act; will be reviewed in 2025.

HISTORICAL COMMISSION, TEXAS*

1511 Colorado St., P.O. Box 12276, Austin 78711-2276
512/463-6100 • *FAX: 512/463-8222* • www.thc.texas.gov • Agency # 808

9 Members - 6 Years

John L. Nau III	Chair, Houston, 2-1-21
John Crain	Vice Chair, Dallas, 2-1-19
Earl P. Broussard	Board Member, Austin, 2-1-23
Monica Burdette	Board Member, Rockport, 2-1-21
Wallace B. Jefferson	Board Member, Austin, 2-1-19
Catherine McKnight	Board Member, Dallas, 2-1-23
Tom Perini	Board Member, Buffalo Gap, 2-1-23
Gilbert E. Peterson III	Board Member, Alpine, 2-1-19
Daisy Sloan White	Board Member, College Station, 2-1-23

STAFF:

Executive Director	Mark Wolfe	512/463-6383
Deputy Executive Director	Alvin Miller	512/463-5767
Government Relations	Vaughn Aldredge	512/463-5754
Director of Historic Sites	Joseph Bell	512/463-8801
Archeology Division Director	Pat Mercado-Allinger	512/463-8882
Architecture Division Director	Sharon Fleming	512/463-6268
Community Heritage Div. Director	Brad Patterson	512/936-2315
History Programs Division Director	Charles Sadnick	512/463-5854
Human Resources Director	Jada Louhela	512/936-2048
Public Information and Education	Chris Florance	512/463-4565
Chief Financial Officer	Corey Crawford	512/475-0774

The commission provides leadership and coordinates services to support projects commissioned by county historical commissions, historical societies, agencies and institutions interested in the preservation of archeological and historical heritage. The commission also acts as a clearinghouse and historical information center.

*Subject to the Texas Sunset Act; will be reviewed in 2019.

HOLOCAUST AND GENOCIDE COMMISSION, TEXAS*

1511 Colorado Street, P.O. Box 12276, Austin 78711-2276
512/463-5108 • *FAX: 512/463-6084* • thgc.texas.gov • Agency # 808

18 Members - 4 Years

Peter Tarlow Ph.D.	Chair, College Station, 2-1-19
Lynne Aronoff	Commissioner, Houston, 2-1-19
Fran Berg	Commissioner, Dallas, 2-1-17
Peter N. Berkowitz	Commissioner, Houston, 2-1-17
Anne Clutterbuck	Commissioner, Houston, 2-1-19
Laura Ehrenberg-Chesler	Commissioner, San Antonio, 4-13-17
Martin Fein	Commissioner, Houston, 2-1-17
Becky Keenan	Commissioner, Pearland, 2-1-19
Matthew A. Kornhauser	Commissioner, Houston, 2-1-19
The Honorable Elliott Naishtat	Commissioner, Austin, 5-10-17
Suzanne Ransleben	Commissioner, Rockport, 2-1-15
Ambassador Sichan Siv	Commissioner, San Antonio, 2-1-17
Rabbi Brian Strauss	Commissioner, Houston, 2-1-17
Gilbert Tuhabonye	Commissioner, Austin, 2-1-19
Alia Ureste	Commissioner, El Paso, 2-1-17
Mike Morath	Ex Officio Member, Commissioner of Education
Thomas P. Palladino	Ex Officio Member, Texas Veterans Commission
Dr. Raymund Paredes	Ex Officio Member, Commissioner of Higher Education

STAFF:

Executive Director	William McWhorter	.512/463-8815
Program Specialist	Lynn Santos	.512/463-2733
Program Specialist	Cheyanne Perkins	.512/463-5674
Education Coordinator	J.E. Wolfson	.512/936-8547
Education Specialist	Position Vacant	.512/463-0783

The commission was established to ensure that resources are available to students, educators and the general public regarding the Holocaust and other genocides. Created by Senate Bill (SB) 482, 81st Texas Legislature.

*Subject to the Texas Sunset Act; will be reviewed in 2021.

HOUSING AND COMMUNITY AFFAIRS, TEXAS DEPARTMENT OF*

221 East 11th Street, P.O. Box 13941, Austin 78711-3941
512/475-3800 • 800/525-0657 • *FAX: 800/733-5120*
www.tdhca.state.tx.us • Agency # 332

7 Members - 6 Years

J.B. Goodwin	Chair, Austin, 1-31-21
Paul Braden	Board Member, Dallas, 1-31-23
Leslie Bingham Escareño	Board Member, Brownsville, 1-31-19
Asusena Reséndiz	Board Member, San Antonio, 1-31-19
Sharon Thomason	Board Member, Wolfforth, 1-31-21
Leo Vasquez	Board Member, Houston, 1-31-23
Vacant	Board Member

DEPARTMENT SENIOR STAFF:

Executive Director	Tim Irvine	. . . . .512/475-3296 / *Fax: 512/469-9606*
Executive Admin. Coordinator	Terri Roeber	. . . . .512/475-3959 / *Fax: 512/469-9606*
Director of Internal Audit	Mark Scott	. . . . .512/475-3813 / *Fax: 512/475-3935*
Chief of External Affairs	Michael Lyttle	. . . . .512/475-4542 / *Fax: 512/469-9606*
General Counsel	Beau Eccles	. . . . .512/475-3932 / *Fax: 512/469-9606*
Executive Director of Manufactured Housing	Joe Garcia	. . . . .512/475-4999 / *Fax: 512/936-9635*
Chief of Compliance	Patricia Murphy	. . . . . . .512/475-3140 / *Fax: 512/475-3359*
Deputy Executive Director	Brooke Boston	. . . . .512/475-1762 / *Fax: 512/469-9606*
Deputy Executive Director	Tom Gouris	. . . . .512/475-1470 / *Fax: 512/469-9606*
Director of Asset Management	Raquel Morales	. . . . . . .512/475-2109 / *Fax: 512/475-3359*
Chief Investment Officer	Monica Galuski	. . . . . . .512/936-9268 / *Fax: 512/475-4798*
Director of Single Family Operations	Homero Cabello	. . . . . . .512/475-2118 / *Fax: 512/475-2365*
Director of Community Affairs	Michael DeYoung	. . . . . .512/475-2125 / *Fax: 512/475-3935*
Chief Financial Officer	David Cervantes	. . . . . . .512/475-3875 / *Fax: 512/472-7500*
Director of HOME and Homelessness Programs	Abigail Versyp	. . . . .512/475-2224 / *Fax: 512/475-1671*
Director of Multifamily Finance	Marni Holloway	. . . . . . .512/475-1676 / *Fax: 512/469-9606*
Director of Housing Resource Center	Elizabeth Yevich	. . . . . .512/463-7961 / *Fax: 512/475-0070*
Manager of Human Resources	Nicole Krueger	. . . . .512/475-3943 / *Fax: 512/475-3992*
Director of Information Systems	Curtis Howe	. . . . .512/475-1740 / *Fax: 512/475-2672*
Director of Real Estate Analysis	Brent Stewart	. . . . .512/475-2973 / *Fax: 512/475-4420*
Director of Texas Homeownership Program	Cathy Gutierrez	. . . . . . .512/475-0277 / *Fax: 512/475-4798*

The Texas Department of Housing and Community Affairs is committed to expanding fair housing choice and opportunities for Texans through affordable housing and homeownership, weatherization, and community-based services with the help of for-profits, nonprofits, and local governments.

*Subject to the Texas Sunset Act; will be reviewed in 2025.

INFORMATION RESOURCES, TEXAS DEPARTMENT OF (DIR)*

300 W.15th St., #1300, W.P. Clements Bldg, P.O. Box 13564, Austin 78711-3564
512/475-4700 • *FAX: 512/475-4759*
www.dir.texas.gov • Agency # 313

7 Voting Members - 6 Years; 3 Ex Officio Members

Ben Gatzke	Chair, Fort Worth, 2-1-23
Christian Alvarado	Board Member, Austin, 2-1-21
Charles Bacarisse	Board Member, Houston, 2-1-19
Mike Bell	Board Member, Spring, 2-1-23
Stuart Bernstein	Board Member, Austin, 2-1-21
Jay Dyer	Board Member, Austin, 2-1-19
Jeffrey Tayon	Board Member, Houston, 2-1-21
Bryan Collier	Ex Officio Member, Texas Dept. of Criminal Justice
Melody Parrish	Ex Officio Member, Texas Education Agency
George Rios	Ex Officio Member, Texas Parks and Wildlife Commission

STAFF:

Executive Director	Stacey Napier	512/475-4775
Executive Assistant	Chandra Thompson	512/936-7577
Public Affairs	Robert Armstrong	512/936-9851
CIO and Deputy Exec. Director	Todd Kimbriel	512/475-0579
General Counsel	Martin Zelinsky J.D.	512/463-9884
Chief Financial Officer	Nick Villalpando	512/936-2167
Chief Info.n Security Officer	Nancy Rainosek	512/463-1966
Chief Operations Officer	Dale Richardson	512/463-7370
Data Center Services Director	Sally Ward	512/463-9003

State agency whose goal is to promote the efficient use and management of information resources and assist the state leadership in achieving its goals through advice and recommendation on information resources issues.

---

*Subject to the Texas Sunset Act; will be reviewed in 2021.

INSURANCE, TEXAS DEPARTMENT OF*

333 Guadalupe, P.O. Box 149104, Austin 78714-9104
512/676-6000 • *FAX: 512/475-2005* • www.tdi.texas.gov • Agency # 454
Consumer Publications: 800/599-7467
Consumer Services: 800/252-3439
General Information: 800/578-4677

STAFF:

Commissioner of Insurance	Kent Sullivan	512/676-6020 / *Fax: 512/490-1045*
Internal Audit	Greg Royal	512/676-6200 / *Fax: 512/490-1024*
General Counsel and Chief Clerk	Norma Garcia	512/676-6586 / *Fax: 512/490-1064*
Legal Counsel	Michael Nored	512/676-6556 / *Fax: 512/490-1021*
Public Affairs	Stephanie Goodman	512/676-6935 / *Fax: 512/490-1025*
Government Relations	Melissa Hamilton	512/676-6602 / *Fax: 512/495-1025*
Public Information Office	Ben Gonzalez	512/676-6593 / *Fax: 512/490-1026*
Administrative Operations	Patricia David	512/676-6026 / *Fax: 512/490-1045*
Agency Affairs	Luke Bellsnyder	512/676-6028 / *Fax: 512/490-1025*
Information Technology Svcs.	Amy Lugo	512/676-6031 / *Fax: 512/490-1000*
Chief Financial Officer	Nancy Clark	512/676-6166 / *Fax: 512/490-1071*
Human Resources	Cynthia Olivier	512/676-6101 / *Fax: 512/490-1027*
Regulatory Policy	Cassie Brown	512/676-6610 / *Fax: 512/490-1045*
Financial Regulation	Doug Slape	512/676-6416 / *Fax: 512/490-1038*
Licensing Services	Mike Carnley	512/676-6476 / *Fax: 512/490-1038*
Compliance	Mark Einfalt	512/676-6210 / *Fax: 512/490-1045*
Consumer Protection	Melissa Hield	512/676-6213 / *Fax: 512/490-1003*
Enforcement	Leah Gillum	512/676-6357 / *Fax: 512/490-1020*
Fraud	Christopher Davis	512/676-6295 / *Fax: 512/490-1001*

Workers' Compensation:

Commissioner	Ryan Brannan	512/804-4400 / *Fax: 512/804-4401*

State Fire Marshal:

State Fire Marshal	Chris Connealy	512/676-6780 / *Fax: 512/490-1063*

The Texas Department of Insurance (TDI) regulates the business of insurance in Texas to ensure that Texas consumers have access to competitive and fair insurance products.

*Subject to the Texas Sunset Act; will be reviewed in 2023.

INTERSTATE MINING COMPACT COMMISSION (IMCC)

445-A Carlisle Drive, Herndon, VA 20170-4802
703/709-8654 • *FAX: 703/709-8655* • www.imcc.isa.us

Members appointed by the governor

J. Denny Kingsley   Director Surface Mining, TRC, Austin

............................512/463-8831 / *512/463-6709*

The Honorable Ryan Sitton   Commissioner, TRC, 12-31-20

....512/463-7144

STAFF:

Executive Director, IMCC	Gregory E. Conrad 703/709-8654
Deputy Executive Director	Beth A. Botsis 703/709-8654

INTERSTATE OIL AND GAS COMPACT COMMISSION

P.O. Box 53127, Oklahoma City, OK 73152-3127
405/525-3556 • *FAX: 405/525-3592* • www.iogcc.state.ok.us

Official Representative:

The Honorable Wayne Christian   Commissioner, Texas Railroad Commission

STAFF:

Executive Director   Mike Smith ....405/525-3556 / *Fax: 405/525-3592*

JAIL STANDARDS, TEXAS COMMISSION ON*

300 W. 15th St., Suite 503, P.O. Box 12985, Austin 78711-2985
512/463-5505 • *FAX: 512/463-3185*
www.tcjs.state.tx.us • Agency # 409

9 Members - 6 Years

Bill Stoudt	Chair, Longview, 1-31-19
Irene Armendariz	Board Member, Austin, 1-31-15
Allan Cain	Board Member, Carthage, 1-31-17
Jerry Lowry	Board Member, New Caney, 1-31-19
Larry May	Board Member, Sweetwater, 1-31-19
Esmaeil Porsa, M.D., MPH	Board Member, Parker, 1-31-17
Kelly Rowe	Board Member, Lubbock, 1-31-21
Dennis Wilson	Board Member, Groesbeck, 1-31-21
Vacant	Board Member

STAFF:
Executive Director   Brandon Wood . . . . .512/463-8236 / *Fax: 512/463-3185*

*Subject to the Texas Sunset Act; will be reviewed in 2021.

JUVENILE JUSTICE, TEXAS DEPARTMENT OF*
11209 Metric Boulevard, P.O. Box 12757, Austin 78711-2757
512/490-7130 • *FAX: 512/490-7717* • www.tjjd.texas.gov

13 Members - 6 Years

Scott W. Fisher	Chair, Bedford, 2-1-19
Edeska Barnes, Jr.	Board Member, Jasper, 2-1-21
The Honorable Carol Bush	Board Member, Waxahachie, 2-1-19
James Castro	Board Member, Bergheim, 2-1-23
Pama Hencerling	Board Member, Victoria, 2-1-23
The Honorable Lisa K. Jarrett	Board Member, San Antonio, 2-1-21
David "Scott" Matthew	Board Member, Georgetown, 2-1-19
MaryLou Mendoza	Board Member, San Antonio, 2-1-19
The Honorable Stephanie Moreno	Board Member, Beeville, 2-1-23
Candace T. "Candy" Noble	Board Member, Lucas, 2-1-21
The Honorable Allison Palmer	Board Member, San Angelo, 2-1-23
The Honorable Wesley C. Ritchey	Board Member, Dalhart, 2-1-21
James Smith	Board Member, Midland, 2-1-23

STAFF:

Executive Director	David Reilly . . . . .512/490-7004 / *Fax: 512/424-6099*
Chief of Staff	Chelsea Buchholtz 512/490-7779

*Subject to the Texas Sunset Act; will be reviewed in 2021.

LAND OFFICE, GENERAL

1700 N. Congress Ave., P.O. Box 12873, Austin 78711-2873
512/463-5001 • 800/998-4456 • www.glo.texas.gov • Agency # 305
Veterans Land Program: 800/252-8387

1 Member - 4 years

GEORGE P. BUSH (R) 28th Land Commissioner, 12-31-18

Spouse: Amanda

Born in Houston, Texas, April 24, 1976. Commissioner Bush has dedi-
cated his life to public service, working as a public school teacher
after graduating from Rice University and serving in Operation
Enduring Freedom in Afghanistan as an officer in the U.S. Naval
Reserve. Prior to serving as Texas Land Commissioner, Bush was a
successful businessman. He joined Akin Gump Strauss Hauer & Feld
LLP after earning his Juris Doctorate at the University of Texas
School of Law. He subsequently co-founded Pennybacker Capital
LLC, a real estate private equity firm, in 2007, and St. Augustine
Partners LLC, a Fort Worth-based investment firm focused on oil and
gas transactions and consulting for private businesses. Commissioner
Bush is the grandson of President George H.W. Bush, the son of former Florida Governor Jeb Bush
and the nephew of President George W. Bush. He lives in Austin with his wife, Amanda, who is an
attorney and partner at Jackson Walker, LLC, and their two sons, Prescott and Jack. Texas Land
Commissioner, January 2, 2015 to present.

Texas Land Commissioner	The Honorable George P. Bush	512/463-5001

STAFF:

Chief Clerk/ Deputy Land Commissioner	Mark Havens	512/936-4441
General Counsel	Jeff Gordon	512/463-7205
Chief Investment Officer	Rusty Martin	512/463-5120
Chief Information Officer	Cory Wilburn	512/463-5084
Chief Financial Officer	David Repp	512/475-0686
Chief Auditor	Tracey Hall	512/463-6078
Sr. Deputy Director of Asset Enhancement	Brian Carter	512/936-0902
Coastal Protection	Greg Pollock	512/463-5329
Community Development & Revitalization	Pete Phillips	512/475-5015
Veterans Programs	Matthew Elledge	512/463-2317
Director of Executive Admin.	Sandra Ortiz	512/936-1912
Director of Communications	Bryan Preston	512/936-0719
Deputy Director of Special Operations	Hector Valle	512/463-5331
Deputy Director Governmental Relations	Don Forse	512/936-3572
Veterans Land & Housing	Bill McLemore	512/463-5401
Veterans Homes	John Berkely	512/463-8764
Veterans Cemeteries	Eric Brown	512/463-5977
Oil Spill Prevention & Response	Jimmy A. Martinez	361/825-3001
Energy Resources	Robert Hatter	512/475-1542

Land Commission (Cont.)

Deputy Director
　Archives & Records　　　　Mark Lambert 512/463-5260
Deputy Director
　Coastal Resources　　　　David Green 512/463-9971
Deputy Director
　Construction Services　　　Jeff Kauffmann 512/936-3512
　Human Resources　　　　Stacey McClure 512/463-5128

LAND SURVEYING, TX BOARD OF PROFESSIONAL*

12100 Park 35 Circle, Building A, Suite 156, MC 230, Austin 78753
512/239-5263 • *FAX: 512/239-5253*
www.txls.texas.gov • Agency # 464

8 Appointed Members - 6 Years; 1 Ex Officio Member

Jon Hodde	Chair, Brenham, 1-31-19
James H. Cheatham	Board Member, Aledo, 1-31-21
Mary Chruszczak	Board Member, The Woodlands, 1-31-17
William D. Edwards	Board Member, Alvord, 1-31-21
Gerardo M. Garcia	Board Member, Laredo, 1-31-17
Paul P. Kwan	Board Member, Houston, 1-31-17
William "Bill" Merten	Board Member, Houston, 1-31-19
Andrew W. Paxton	Board Member, Lubbock, 1-31-21
The Honorable George P. Bush	Ex Officio Member

STAFF:
Executive Director　　　　　Marcelino A. Estrada . . . . . .512/239-5263 / *Fax: 512/239-5253*

The board protects Texas residents by regulating and licensing land surveyors.

---

*Subject to the Texas Sunset Act; will be reviewed in 2019.

LAVACA-NAVIDAD RIVER AUTHORITY

4631 FM 3131, P.O. Box 429, Edna 77957-0429
361/782-5229 • *FAX: 361/782-5310* • www.lnra.org

9 Members - 6 Years

Ronald Edwin Kubecka	President, Palacios, 5-1-21
Jerry Adelman	Vice President, Palacios, 5-1-17
Terri Parker	Secretary/Treasurer, Ganado, 5-1-17
Sandy Johs	Director, La Ward, 5-1-21
Glenn T. Martin	Director, Edna, 5-1-19
David Martin Muegge	Director, Edna, 5-1-17
Scott Sachtleben	Director, Ganado, 5-1-21
Leonard Steffek	Director, Edna, 5-1-19
Charlie Taylor	Director, Palacios, 5-1-19

STAFF:

General Manager	Patrick Brzozowski, P.E.	.361/782-5229
Deputy General Manager	Karen Gregory	.361/782-5229
Deputy General Manager	Doug Anders	.361/782-5229
Human Resource Manager	Jennifer Martin	.361/782-5229
Recreation Manager	Cammie Pearson	.361/782-5229
Land Management Manager	Chris Janak	.361/782-5229

The board oversees the storing, preservation and distribution of stream and river water in Jackson County.

LAW ENFORCEMENT, TEXAS COMMISSION ON*

6330 E. Highway 290, Suite 200, Austin 78723-1035
512/936-7700 • *FAX: 512/936-7714* • www.tcole.texas.gov • Agency # 407

9 Members - 6 Years

Joel W. Richardson	Presiding Officer, Canyon, 8-30-19
Patt Scheckel-Hollingsworth	Assistant Presiding Officer, Arlington, 8-30-17
Jason Hester	Secretary, Lago Vista, 8-30-19
Patricia Burruss	Board Member, Olmito, 8-30-19
Ron Hood	Board Member, Dripping Springs, 8-30-17
Kim Lemaux	Board Member, Arlington, 8-30-21
James Oakley	Board Member, Spicewood, 8-30-17
Sharon Breckenridge Thomas	Board Member, San Antonio, 8-30-21
Tim Whitaker	Board Member, Richmond, 8-30-21

STAFF:

Executive Director	Kim Vickers	.512/936-7712 / *Fax: 512/936-7714*
Legal	John Beauchamp	.512/936-7746
Director of		
Credentialing and Field Svcs.	Kenny Merchant	.512/936-7735
Enforcement and Special Svcs.	Michael Antu	.512/936-7750
Government Relations	Gretchen Grigsby	.512/936-7715
Fiscal and Staff Services	Brian Roth	.512/936-7725

*Subject to the Texas Sunset Act; will be reviewed in 2021.

LIBRARY AND ARCHIVES COMMISSION, TX STATE*
P.O. Box 12927, Austin 78711-2927
Lorenzo de Zavala State Archives, and Library Bldg., 1201 Brazos, Austin 78701
512/463-5455 • *FAX: 512/463-5436*
www.tsl.texas.gov • Agency # 306

7 Members - 6 Years

Michael C. Waters	Chair, Dallas, 9-28-19
Sharon T. Carr	Board Member, Katy, 9-28-17
Lynwood Givens	Board Member, Plano, 9-28-17
Larry G. Holt	Board Member, College Station, 9-28-21
Martha Wong	Board Member, Houston, 9-28-21
Vacant	Board Member
Vacant	Board Member

STAFF:

Director and Librarian	Mark Smith	512/463-6856 / *Fax: 512/463-5436*
Assistant State Librarian	Gloria Meraz	512/463-5459
Chief Operations and Fiscal Officer	Donna Osborne	512/463-5440
Director		
Information Technology Services	Steve Rapp	512/463-5481
Archives and Information Services	Jelain Chubb	512/463-5467
Talking Book Program	Ava Smith	512/463-5428
Library Dev. and Networking	Jennifer Peters	512/463-5456
State & Local Records Mgmt.	Craig Kelso	512/463-5534
Executive Assistant	Tracy Kuhn Lash	512/463-5460
Communications Officer	Stephen Siwinski	512/463-5514

*Subject to the Texas Sunset Act; will be reviewed in 2019.

LICENSING AND REGULATION, TEXAS DEPARTMENT OF*

E.O. Thompson SOB, 920 Colorado St., P.O. Box 12157, Austin 78711-2157
512/463-6599 • 800/803-9202 • *FAX: 512/463-9468*
www.tdlr.texas.gov • Agency # 452

7 Members - 6 Years

Mike Arismendez, Jr.	Chair, Shallowater, 2-1-21
Thomas F. Butler	Vice Chair, Deer Park, 2-1-19
Helen Callier	Board Member, Kingwood, 2-1-21
Rick Figueroa	Board Member, Brenham, 2-1-21
Catherine Rodewald	Board Member, Frisco, 2-1-17
Ravi Shah	Board Member, Carrollton, 2-1-17
Deborah A. Yurco	Board Member, Austin, 2-1-19

STAFF:

Executive Director	Brian E. Francis	512/463-3171
Deputy Executive Director	Carla James	512/463-3170
Chief of Staff	Nick Voinis	512/475-0362
Government Relations Officer	Steve Bruno	512/475-0351
Government Relations Officer	Eric Beverly	512/463-7574
Public Information Officer	Susan Stanford	512/463-3208
Budget Analyst	Tony Couvillon	512/463-7182

Division Directors:

Compliance	Position Vacant	512/463-2907
Customer Service	Trey Seals	512/936-8459
Education and Examination	Ray Pizarro	512/767-6810
Enforcement	Christina Kaiser	512/539-5611
Field Operations	Tanya Gauthreaux	512/583-7154
Human Resources	Sharon Homoya	512/463-3131
Financial Services	Jerry Daniels	512/463-3100
General Counsel	Brad Bowman	512/463-0859
Information Services	Jodi Ashlock	512/463-3572
Innovation	Randy Nesbitt	512/463-7135
Licensing	Dede McEachern	512/475-2896

FIELD OFFICES:

Fort Worth:
1501 Circle Drive,
Suite 215
Fort Worth, TX 76119
817/321-8350

Houston:
5425 Polk Ave.,
Suite G-80
Houston, TX 77023
713/924-6300

*Subject to the Texas Sunset Act; will be reviewed in 2019.

LOTTERY COMMISSION, TEXAS*

611 East 6th St., P.O. Box 16630, Austin 78761-6630
512/344-5000 • www.txbingo.org • Agency # 362
Lottery Customer Service: 800/375-6886
Texas Lottery Fax: 512/344-5080
Charitable Bingo Customer Service: 800/246-4677
Charitable Bingo Fax: 512/344-5142

5 Members - 6 Years

J. Winston Krause	Chair, Austin, 2-1-19
Carmen Arrieta-Candelaria	Commissioner, El Paso, 2-1-17
Doug Lowe	Commissioner, Houston, 2-1-17
Robert Rivera	Commissioner, Arlington, 2-1-21
Vacant	Commissioner

STAFF:

Executive Director	Gary Grief	512/344-5160 / *Fax: 512/478-3682*
Governmental Affairs Director	Nelda Treviño	512/344-5190 / *Fax: 512/344-5107*
Media Relations Director	Kelly Cripe	512/344-5131 / *Fax: 512/344-5490*
Charitable Bingo Ops. Director	Alfonso Royal	512/344-5155 / *Fax: 512/344-5142*
General Counsel	Bob Biard	512/344-5127 / *Fax: 512/344-5189*
Enforcement Director	Mario Valdez	512/344-5250 / *Fax: 512/344-5152*
Lottery Operations Director	Michael Anger	512/344-5181 / *Fax: 512/344-5253*
Retailer Services Manager	Ed Rogers	512/344-5389 / *Fax: 512/344-5448*
Products & Drawings Manager	Robert Tirloni	512/344-5406 / *Fax: 512/344-5242*
Security Manager	Jim Carney	512/344-5452 / *Fax: 512/344-5501*
Controller	Kathy Pyka	512/344-5410 / *Fax: 512/344-5066*
Administration Director	Mike Fernandez	512/344-5310 / *Fax: 512/344-5254*
Information Technology Manager	Joan Kotal	512/344-5315 / *Fax: 512/344-5101*
Human Resources Director	Jan Thomas	512/344-5243 / *Fax: 512/344-5240*

*Subject to the Texas Sunset Act; will be reviewed in 2025.

LOW-LEVEL RADIOACTIVE WASTE DISPOSAL COMPACT COMMISSION, TEXAS

505 W. 15th Street, Austin 78701 • 512/217-8045 • www.tllrwdcc.org/

6 Texas Members - 6 Years

Brandon T. Hurley	Chair, Grapevine, 9-1-19
John Matthew Salsman	Vice Chair, Driftwood, 9-1-17
Peter Bradford	Commissioner
The Hon. Richard H. Dolgener	Commissioner, Andrews, 9-1-21
Linda K. Morris	Commissioner, Waco, 9-1-21
Jane O'Meara Sanders, Ph.D.	Commissioner
Richard Saudek	Commissioner
Clint Weber	Commissioner, Fort Worth, 9-1-19
Robert Wilson	Commissioner, Lockhart, 9-1-17

STAFF:

Executive Director	Leigh Ing	512/217-8045
Deputy Executive Director	Andrew Tachovsky	512/291-7576

LOWER COLORADO RIVER AUTHORITY

P.O. Box 220, Austin 78767-0220 - 3700 Lake Austin Blvd., Austin 78703
512/473-3200 • 800/776-5272
www.lcra.org

15 members - 6 year terms

Timothy Timmerman	Chair, Travis County, 2-1-19
Thomas Michael Martine	Vice Chair, Blanco County, 2-1-19
Steve K. Balas	Secretary, Colorado County, 2-1-17
Lori A. Berger	Board Member, Fayette County, 2-1-21
Stephen F. "Steve" Cooper	Board Member, Wharton County, 2-1-17
Joseph M. "Joe" Crane	Board Member, Matagorda County, 2-1-21
Pamela Jo "PJ" Ellison	Board Member, Washingon County, 2-1-19
John M. Franklin	Board Member, Burnet County, 2-1-17
Raymond A. "Ray" Gill, Jr.	Board Member, Llano County, 2-1-17
Charles B. "Bart" Johnson	Board Member, Brown County, 2-1-21
Sandra Wright "Sandy" Kibby	Board Member, Comal County, 2-1-17
Robert "Bobby" Lewis	Board Member, Bastrop County, 2-1-19
George W. Russell	Board Member, Burnet County, 2-1-21
Franklin "Scott" Spears, Jr.	Board Member, Travis County, 2-1-19
Martha Leigh M. Whitten	Board Member, San Saba County, 2-1-21

Executive Office:
General Manager   Phil Wilson . . . . .512/578-3562 / *Fax: 512/578-3520*

The Lower Colorado River Authority is a conservation and reclamation district created by the Texas Legislature in 1934. It operates solely on the rates and fees it charges for services and has no taxing authority. LCRA serves customers and communities throughout Texas by managing the lower Colorado River; generating and transmitting electric power; providing a clean, reliable water supply; and offering access to nature at more than 40 parks, recreation areas and river access sites along the Texas Colorado River, from the Hill Country to the Gulf Coast. LCRA and its employees are committed to enhancing the lives of Texans through water stewardship, energy and community services.

LOWER NECHES VALLEY AUTHORITY

7850 Eastex Freeway, P.O. Box 5117, Beaumont 77726-5117
409/892-4011 • *FAX: 409/898-2468* • www.lnva.dst.tx.us/

9 Members - 6 Years

Caleb Spurlock	President, Woodville, 7-28-19
Ivy Pate	Vice President, Beaumont, 7-28-21
Olan Webb	Vice President, Silsbee, 7-28-17
Jeanie Turk	Secretary, Sour Lake, 7-28-21
Steve Lucas	Treasurer, Beaumont, 7-28-19
Lonnie Grissom	Board Member, Woodville, 7-28-21
Kal Kincaid	Board Member, Beaumont, 7-28-17
Steven M. McReynolds	Board Member, Groves, 7-28-19
Jordan Reese IV	Board Member, Beaumont, 7-28-17

STAFF:
General Manager   Scott Hall, P.E. . . . . .409/892-4011 / *Fax: 409/898-2468*

MANUFACTURED HOUSING, GOVERNING BOARD

1106 Clayton Lane, Ste. 270W, P.O. Box 12489, Austin 78711-2489
512/475-2200 • 800/500-7074 • *FAX: 512/475-1109*
www.tdhca.state.tx.us/mh/contacts.htm

5 Members - 6 Years

Michael H. Bray	Chair, El Paso, 1-31-17
Ronnie Richards	Board Member, Clear Lake Shores, 1-31-17
Kiran Shah	Board Member, Richmond, 1-31-19
Sheila Valles-Pankratz	Board Member, Mission, 1-31-21
Donnie W. Wisenbaker	Board Member, Sulphur Springs, 1-31-19

STAFF:
Executive Director   Joe Garcia . . . . .512/475-4999 / *Fax: 512/475-0495*

MARRIAGE AND FAMILY THERAPISTS, TEXAS STATE BOARD OF EXAMINERS OF*

c/o HHSC, P.O. Box 149347, MC 1982, Austin 78714-9347
512/834-6657 • *FAX: 512/834-6677* • www.dshs.texas.gov/mft

9 Members - 6 Years

Jennifer Smothermon, MA, LPC, LMFT	Chair, Abilene, 2-1-19
Sean Stokes, Ph.D, LPC, LMFT	Vice Chair, Denton, 2-1-17
Kenneth Bateman, Ed.D.	Board Member, Richardson, 2-1-21
Rick Bruhn, Ed.D., LPC, LMFT	Board Member, Huntsville, 2-1-17
Keith Rosenbaum, Ph.D, LPC, LMFT	Board Member, Joshua, 2-1-19
George Francis, IV, MBA	Public Member, Georgetown, 2-1-17
Rachel Logue	Public Member, The Hills, 2-1-21
Michael Miller, JD	Public Member, Belton, 2-1-19
Evelyn Husband Thompson	Public Member, Houston, 2-1-21

STAFF:
Executive Director   Cheryl Gomez 512/834-6628

The board adopts rules and regulations to license and regulate the qualifications and performance of marriage and family therapists in Texas.

---

*Subject to the Texas Sunset Act; will be reviewed in 2019.

MEDICAL BOARD, TEXAS*

333 Guadalupe, Tower 3, Suite 610, P.O. Box 2018, Austin 78768-2018
512/305-7010 • *FAX: 512/305-7051*
www.tmb.state.tx.us • Agency # 503
Consumer Complaint Hotline: 800/201-9353

19 Members - 6 Years

Sherif Zaafran, M.D.	President, Houston, 4-13-21
Kandace Farmer, D.O.	Board Member, Highland Village, 4-13-21
John Guerra, D.O.	Board Member, Mission, 4-13-17
J. Scott Holliday, D.O.	Board Member, University Park, 4-13-19
Jeffrey Luna, M.D.	Board Member, Livingston, 4-13-21
Margaret Carter McNeese, M.D.	Board Member, Houston, 4-13-19
Jayaram Naidu, M.D.	Board Member, Odessa, 4-13-21
Karl W. Swann, M.D.	Board Member, San Antonio, 4-13-19
Surendra K. Varma, M.D.	Board Member, Lubbock, 4-13-19
Julie K. Attebury	Public Member, Amarillo, 4-13-17
Michael Cokinos	Public Member, Houston, 4-13-21
Frank S. Denton	Public Member, Conroe, 4-13-19
LuAnn Morgan	Public Member, Midland, 4-13-21
Paulette Southard	Public Member, Alice, 4-13-15
Timothy Webb, J.D.	Public Member, Houston, 4-13-19
Vacant	Board Member
Vacant	Board Member
Vacant	Board Member
Vacant	Public Member

STAFF:

Interim Executive Director	Scott Freshour, J.D. . . . . . . .512/305-7010 / *Fax: 512/305-7051*
Medical Director	Dr. Robert Bredt . . . . .512/305-7019 / *Fax: 512/305-7051*
Board Coordinator	Laura Fleharty . . . . .512/305-7174 / *Fax: 512/305-7051*
Special Projects Manager	Megan Goode . . . . .512/305-7044 / *Fax: 512/305-7051*
Licensure Manager	Monique Johnston . . . . .512/305-7121 / *Fax: 512/305-7009*
General Counsel	Scott Freshour, J.D. . . . . . . .512/305-7085 / *Fax: 512/305-7051*

District One:

Public Member	Sharon J. Barnes
Public Member	Larry V. Buehler
Physician Member	David D. Davila, D.O.
Public Member	Position Vacant
Physician Member	Kathy C. Flanagan, M.D.
Physician Member	Stanley M. Duchman, M.D.
Physician Member	Courtney Townsend, M.D.

District Two:

Public Member	Lewis J. Benavides
Physician Member	Hari Reddy, D.O.
Public Member	Randall B. Isenberg
Physician Member	Melissa Tonn, M.D.
Physician Member	Todd Pollock, M.D., FACS
Public Member	Catherine "Trinka" Taylor

Medical Board (Cont.)

District Three:

Public Member	Betty Lou "Penny" Angelo
Physician Member	John P. McKinley
Public Member	David W. Miller, Ph.D.
Physician Member	Position Vacant
Physician Member	John S. Scott, Jr., D.O.
Public Member	Nancy Seliger

District Four:

Public Member	James H. Dickerson, Jr.
Public Member	Annette P. Raggette
Physician Member	Robert Hootkins, M.D., Ph.D.
Physician Member	Leah Raye Mabry, M.D.
Physician Member	Richard Newman, M.D.
Public Member	Phillip W. Worley

The board protects and enhances the public's health, safety and welfare by establishing and maintaining standards of excellence used in regulating the practice of medicine and ensuring quality health care for the citizens of Texas.

*Subject to the Texas Sunset Act; will be reviewed in 2029.

MEDICAL PHYSICISTS LICENSURE ADVISORY COMMITTEE

c/o Texas Medical Board, P.O. Box 2018, Austin 78768-2018
512/248-4062 • *FAX: 512/834-6677*
www.tmb.state.tx.us/page/licensing-medical-physicist

7 Members - 6 Years

Charles W. Beasley, Ph.D.	Chair, Bellaire, 10-29-17
Dianna D. Cody Ph.D.	Board Member, Friendswood, 10-29-17
Douglas A. Johnson, M.S.	Board Member, College Station, 10-29-17
Nikolaos Papanikolaou Ph.D.	Board Member, Shavano Park, 10-29-17
Alvin "Lee" Schlichtemeier, M.D.	Board Member, Plano, 10-29-17
Gregory P. Swanson M.D.	Board Member, Austin, 10-29-17
Kiran Shah, M.B.A.	Public Member, Houston, 10-29-17

STAFF:

Interim Executive Director	Scott Freshour, J.D. . . . . . . .512/305-7010 / *Fax: 512/305-7051*
Medical Director	Dr. Robert Bredt . . . . .512/305-7019 / *Fax: 512/305-7051*
Board Coordinator	Laura Fleharty . . . . .512/305-7174 / *Fax: 512/305-7051*
Special Projects Manager	Megan Goode . . . . .512/305-7044 / *Fax: 512/305-7051*
Licensure Manager	Monique Johnston . . . . .512/305-7121 / *Fax: 512/305-7009*
General Counsel	Scott Freshour, J.D. . . . . . . .512/305-7085 / *Fax: 512/305-7051*

MIDWESTERN STATE UNIVERSITY, BOARD OF REGENTS

3410 Taft Blvd., Wichita Falls 76308
940/397-4211 • *FAX: 940/397-4010* • www.mwsu.edu

9 Members - 6 Years; 1 Student Member - 1 Year

Samuel M. Sanchez	Chairman, Fort Worth, 2-25-18
Warren T. Ayres	Board Member, Wichita Falls, 2-25-22
Tiffany D. Burks	Board Member, Grand Prairie, 2-25-22
R. Caven Crosnoe	Board Member, Wichita Falls, 2-25-20
Fenton Lynwood Givens, Ph.D.	Board Member, Plano, 2-25-18
Charles "Jeff" Greg	Board Member, Seymour, 2-25-18
Shawn G. Hessing	Board Member, Fort Worth, 2-25-20
Nancy Marks	Board Member, Wichita Falls, 2-25-20
Shelley Sweatt, Ed.D.	Board Member, Wichita Falls, 2-25-22
Shayla Owens	Student Regent, Sherman, 5-31-18

President's Office:
President   Dr. Suzanne Shipley . . . . . . .940/397-4211 / *Fax: 940/397-4010*

Administration:
Provost and VP for
    Academic Affairs   Dr. James Johnston . . . . . . .940/397-4226 / *Fax: 940/397-4042*
VP Administration & Finance   Dr. Marilyn Fowlé . . . . . . .940/397-4275 / *Fax: 940/397-4302*
VP Student Affairs &
    Enrollment Management   Dr. Keith Lamb . . . . .940/397-4291 / *Fax: 940/397-4938*
VP University Advancement &
    Public Affairs   Anthony Vidmar . . . . .940/397-4782 / *Fax: 940/397-4814*
Director of Athletics   Kyle Williams . . . . .940/397-4748 / *Fax: 940/397-4892*

MIDWIVES ADVISORY BOARD

c/o TDLR, P.O. Box 12057, Austin 78711-2057
512/463-6599 • *FAX: 512/463-9468*
www.tdlr.tcxas.gov/midwives/midwives.htm

9 Members - 6 Years

Meredith Rentz Cook	Presiding Officer, Keller, 1-31-21
Brenda Buffington	Board Member, Livingston, 1-31-23
Janet Dirmeyer	Board Member, Comfort, 1-31-19
Laurie Fremgen	Board Member, Austin, 1-31-19
Charleta Guillory, M.D.	Board Member, Houston, 1-31-23
Destiny Hooper	Board Member, Pearland, 1-31-23
Victoria Meinhardt	Board Member, Austin, 1-31-21
Helen J. Nelson	Board Member, Grand Prairie, 1-31-19
Michael Nix M.D.	Board Member, Austin, 1-31-21

MOTOR VEHICLES BOARD, TX DEPARTMENT OF (TXDMV)*

4000 Jackson Ave., Austin 78731 • 888/368-4689 • www.txdmv.gov • Agency # 608

9 Members - 6 Years

Raymond Palacios, Jr.	Chair, 2-1-19
Blake Ingram	Vice Chair, 2-1-17
Robert "Barney" Barnwell III	Board Member, 2-1-19
Luanne Caraway	Board Member, 2-1-19
Brett Graham	Board Member, 2-1-17
Kate Hardy	Board Member, 2-1-21
Gary Painter	Board Member, 2-1-21
Guillermo "Memo" Treviño	Board Member, 2-1-21
John H. "Johnny" Walker III	Board Member, 2-1-17

STAFF:

Executive Director	Whitney Brewster	512/465-3001
Deputy Executive Director	Shelly Mellott	512/465-3001
Chief Financial Officer	Linda Flores	512/465-4125
General Counsel	David Duncan	512/465-4160
Government & Strategic Communications Director	Caroline Love	512/465-4019
Internal Audit Director	Sandra Menjivar-Suddeath	512/465-4118

*Subject to the Texas Sunset Act; will be reviewed in 2019.

MUNICIPAL RETIREMENT SYSTEM, TEXAS

1200 Interstate 35 North, P.O. Box 149153, Austin 78714-9153 • 512/476-7577 • 800/924-8677 • FAX: 512/474-9180 • www.tmrs.com

6 Members - 6 Years

Jim Parrish	Chair, Plano, 2-1-17
Bill Philibert	Vice Chair, Deer Park, 2-1-19
James P. Jeffers	Board Member, Nacogdoches, 2-1-21
David Landis	Board Member, Perryton, 2-1-21
Julie Oakley	Board Member, Lakeway, 2-1-19
Roel "Roy" Rodriguez	Board Member, McAllen, 2-1-17

STAFF:

Executive Director	David R. Gavia	512/476-7577
Chief Investment Officer	T.J. Carlson	512/476-7577

The board oversees the Texas Municipal Retirement System, which is responsible for providing a secure retirement benefit plan for more than 872 cities.

NUECES RIVER AUTHORITY*

200 East Nopal, Suite 206, P.O. Box 349, Uvalde 78802-0349
830/278-6810 • *FAX: 830/278-2025* • www.nueces-ra.org

20 Members - 6 Years

Gary A. Jones	President, Beeville, 2-1-17
Tomas Ramirez, III	Secretary/Treasurer, Devine, 2-1-21
W. Alston Beinhorn	Board Member, Catarina, 2-1-17
Allan P. Bloxsom III	Board Member, Kendalia, 2-1-21
Dane Bruun	Board Member, Corpus Christi, 2-1-19
Eric L. Burnett	Board Member, Portland, 2-1-21
Jesse Byron "Trace" Burton III	Board Member, San Antonio, 2-1-19
Amy Clark	Board Member, Three Rivers, 2-1-21
Mary Beth Delano	Board Member, Corpus Christi, 2-1-17
John Galloway	Board Member, Beeville, 2-1-17
Lindsey A. Koenig	Board Member, Orange Grove, 2-1-15
Joe C. McMillian	Board Member, Dilley, 2-1-19
Gary Moore	Board Member, Portland, 2-1-21
Travis Pruski	Board Member, Floresville, 2-1-21
David E. Purser	Board Member, Karnes City, 2-1-19
Dina Ramirez	Board Member, Karnes City, 2-1-19
Fidel R. Rul, Jr.	Board Member, Alice, 2-1-17
Rebecca Bradford	Executive Committee, Corpus Christi, 2-1-19
Dan Leyendecker, P.E.	2nd Vice President, Corpus Christi, 2-1-19
Roxana Proctor Tom	1st Vice President, Campbellton, 2-1-17

STAFF:

Executive Director	Con Mims . . . . .830/278-6810 / *Fax: 830/278-2025*

Corpus Christi Office:
602 N. Staples St., Suite 280
Corpus Christi, TX 78401

Deputy Executive Director	Ms. Rocky Freund . . . . . . .361/653-2110 / *Fax: 361/653-2115*

The Nueces River Authority has broad authority to preserve, protect, and develop surface water resources including flood control, irrigation, navigation, water supply, wastewater treatment, and water quality control. NRA serves all or parts of 22 counties in South Texas.

*Subject to the Texas Sunset Act; will be reviewed in 2019.

NURSING, TEXAS BOARD OF*

333 Guadalupe, Suite 3-460, Austin 78701 • 512/305-6811 • *FAX: 512/305-8101*
www.bon.texas.gov • Agency # 507

13 Members - 6 Years

Kathy Shipp, MSN, RN, FNP	President, Lubbock, 1-31-17
Patricia Clapp, BA	Vice President, Dallas, 1-31-19
Nina Almasy, MSN, RN	Board Member, Austin, 1-31-19
Deborah Bell, CLU, ChFC	Board Member, Abilene, 1-31-17
Laura Disque, MN, RN	Board Member, Edinburg, 1-31-19
Allison Edwards, DrPH, MS, RM, CNE	Board Member, Bellaire, 1-31-21
Diana Flores, MN, RN	Board Member, Helotes, 1-31-21
Doris Jackson, DHA, MSN, RN	Board Member, Pearland, 1-31-17
Kathy Leader-Horn, LVN	Board Member, Granbury, 1-31-21
Beverly Jean Nutall, LVN	Board Member, Bryan, 1-31-17
David E. Saucedo II	Public Member, El Paso, 1-31-21
Francis Stokes, BA	Public Member, Port Aransas, 1-31-21
Vacant	Board Member

STAFF:

Executive Director	Katherine A. Thomas, MN, RN, FAAN . . . . .512/305-6811 / *Fax: 512/305-8101*
Executive Assistant	Patricia Vianes-Cabrera . . . .512/305-6811 / *Fax: 512/305-8101*
Director of Operations	Mark Majek . . . . .512/305-6801 / *Fax: 512/305-7401*
Director of Enforcement	Anthony Diggs . . . . .512/305-6825 / *Fax: 512/305-6870*
Director of Nursing	Kristin K. Benton, MSN, RN512/305-6839 / *Fax: 512/305-7401*
General Counsel	James "Dusty" Johnston . . . .512/305-6821 / *Fax: 512/305-8101*

*Subject to the Texas Sunset Act; will be reviewed in 2029.

OCCUPATIONAL THERAPY EXAMINERS, TEXAS BOARD OF*

333 Guadalupe, Suite 2-510, Austin 78701-3942 • 512/305-6900 • *FAX: 512/305-6951*
www.ptot.texas.gov/page/ot-board

9 Members - 6 Years

Stephanie Johnston, OTR	Chair, Magnolia, 2-1-17
Todd Novosad, OTR	Vice Chair, Bee Cave, 2-1-19
DeLana Honaker, OTR, Ph.D.	Secretary, Amarillo, 2-1-17
Jennifer Clark, COTA	Board Member, Iola, 2-1-19
Sally Harris COTA	Board Member, Houston, 2-1-21
Amanda Ellis	Public Member, Austin, 2-1-19
William "Will" Hale	Public Member, Austin, 2-1-15
Pamela D. Nelon	Public Member, Fort Worth, 2-1-17
Vacant	Board Member

STAFF:

Executive Director	John Maline . . . . .512/305-6900 / *Fax: 512/305-6951*

*Subject to the Texas Sunset Act; will be reviewed in 2029.

OFFICE OF INJURED EMPLOYEE COUNSEL (OIEC)*
7551 Metro Center Dr., Suite 100, MS-50, Austin 78744-1609
512/804-4170 • *FAX: 512/804-4181*
www.oiec.texas.gov • Agency # 448

1 Member - 3 Years

Jessica Barta · · · · · · · · · · · · · · · · Public Counsel, Austin, 2-1-19

STAFF:
Deputy Public Counsel	Andria Franco	512/804-4170
Executive Assistant	Alejandra Hernandez	512/804-4176
General Counsel	Gina McCauley	512/804-4185
Human Resources Liaison	Sheila Henry	512/804-4190

*Subject to the Texas Sunset Act; will be reviewed in 2021.

ONE CALL BOARD OF TEXAS
8500 Shoal Creek Blvd., Ste. 4-120, P.O. Box 9764, Austin 78766-9764
512/467-2850 • 800/545-6005 • *FAX: 512/467-6664*
www.onecalltexas.com

12 Members - 3 Years

James "Jim" Wynn	Chair, Midland, 8-31-17
Rodney J. Unruh	Secretary, San Antonio, 8-31-17
Jeff Carroll	Board Member, Austin, 8-31-19
Roberto De Leon	Board Member, Corpus Christi, 8-31-19
Jesus A. Garza	Board Member, Kingsville, 8-31-18
James Schneider	Board Member, Austin, 8-31-18
Barry Calhoun	Public Member, Richardson, 8-31-19
Joseph Costa	Public Member, Allen, 8-31-17
Senaida "Sandy" Galvan	Public Member, San Antonio, 8-31-19
William O. "Bill" Geise	Public Member, Austin, 8-31-17
Jason Hartgraves	Public Member, Frisco, 8-31-18
Janie Walenta	Public Member, Quitman, 8-31-18

STAFF:
Executive Director · · · · · · · Donald M. Ward · · · · · · · .512/467-2850 / *Fax: 512/467-6664*

The board has authority over "Call Before You Dig" systems that notify underground facility operators of excavation plans so pipelines and utility lines can be marked to prevent accidents.

OPTOMETRY BOARD, TEXAS*

333 Guadalupe St., Suite 2-420, Austin 78701
512/305-8500 • *FAX: 512/305-8501*
www.tob.state.tx.us • Agency # 514

9 Members - 6 Years

John Coble, O.D.	Chair, Greenville, 1-31-17
Melvin G. Cleveland, Jr., O.D.	Vice Chair, Arlington, 1-31-19
Larry W. Fields	Secretary/Treasurer, Carthage, 1-31-17
Mario Gutierrez, O.D.	Board Member, San Antonio, 1-31-17
Ronald L. Hopping, O.D., M.P.H.	Board Member, Houston, 1-31-21
Carey A. Patrick O.D.	Board Member, Allen, 1-31-21
Virginia Sosa, O.D.	Board Member, Uvalde, 1-31-19
Judy Chambers	Public Member, Austin, 1-31-19
Rene D. Pena	Public Member, El Paso, 1-31-21

STAFF:
Executive Director   Chris Kloeris, J.D. . . . . .512/305-8500 / *Fax: 512/305-8501*

*Subject to the Texas Sunset Act; will be reviewed in 2029.

ORTHOTISTS AND PROSTHETISTS ADVISORY BOARD

c/o TDLR, P.O. Box 12057, Austin 78711-2057
512/463-6599 • *FAX: 512/463-9468* • www.tdlr.texas.gov/op/op.htm

7 Members - 6 Years

Miguel Mojica	Presiding Officer, Coppell, 2-1-23
David Ahrens	Board Member, Denton, 2-1-19
Randall Duncan	Board Member, McKinney, 2-1-23
Kevin Matthews	Board Member, Converse, 2-1-19
Cathcrinc Mizc	Board Member, Double Oak, 2-1-21
Kathryn Paszkowski	Board Member, Houston, 2-1-19
Sterling Phillips	Board Member, Lubbock, 2-1-21

PARDONS AND PAROLES, TEXAS BOARD OF (BPP)*

Price Daniel Bldg., 209 West 14th St., Suite 500, Austin 78701
512/936-6351 • www.tdcj.state.tx.us/bpp/
Fax: BPP Austin Central Office: 512/406-5482

7 Members - 6 Years

David Gutierrez	Chair, Gatesville, 2-1-21
James LaFavers	Board Member, Amarillo, 2-1-23
Brian Long	Board Member, Palestine, 2-1-23
Frederico Rangel	Board Member, Huntsville, 2-1-19
Ed Robertson	Board Member, Austin, 2-1-21
Col. Lionel F. "Fred" Solis	Board Member, San Antonio, 2-1-21
Cynthia Tauss	Board Member, Angleton, 2-1-19
Lee Ann Eck-Massingill	Parole Commissioner, Gatesville
Ira Evans	Parole Commissioner, Angleton
Troy Fox	Parole Commissioner, Austin
Roy Garcia	Parole Commissioner, Huntsville
Raymond Gonzalez	Parole Commissioner, Amarillo
James Hensarling	Parole Commissioner, Palestine
Elvis Hightower	Parole Commissioner, Austin
Paul Kiel	Parole Commissioner, Palestine
Marsha Moberley	Parole Commissioner, Amarillo
Anthony Ramirez	Parole Commissioner, San Antonio
Lynn Ruzicka	Parole Commissioner, Angleton
Wanda Saliagas	Parole Commissioner, Huntsville
Charles Speier	Parole Commissioner, San Antonio
Roel Tejeda	Parole Commissioner, Gatesville

STAFF:

Chair	David Gutierrez	512/936-6351
Chief of Staff	Timothy S. McDonnell	512/406-5452
General Counsel	Bettie L. Wells	512/463-1702
Director of Institutional Parole Operations	Tracy Long	936/437-2273
Director of Hearing Operations	Rachel Alderete	512/406-5452
Director of Public Information	Raymond Estrada	512/406-5870
Budget Director	Kyle Britt	936/291-2161
Clemency Director	Joe Lange	512/406-5852

*Subject to the Texas Sunset Act; will be reviewed in 2021.

PARKS AND WILDLIFE DEPARTMENT, TEXAS*
4200 Smith School Road, Austin 78744 • 512/389-4800 • *FAX: 512/389-4814*
www.tpwf.org • Agency # 802
Operation Game Thief: 800/792-4263
Department Information: 800/792-1112

9 Members - 6 Years

T. Dan Friedkin	Chair, Houston, 2-1-17
Ralph H. Duggins	Vice Chair, Fort Worth, 2-1-19
Annabel Benavides Galo	Board Member, Laredo, 2-1-19
Bill Jones	Board Member, Austin, 2-1-17
Jeanne W. Latimer	Board Member, San Antonio, 2-1-21
James H. Lee	Board Member, Houston, 2-1-19
S. Reed Morian	Board Member, Houston, 2-1-21
Richard "Dick" Scott	Board Member, Wimberley, 2-1-17
Kelcy L. Warren	Board Member, Dallas, 2-1-21
Lee Marshall Bass	Chairman-Emeritus, Fort Worth

STAFF:

Executive Director	Carter Smith	512/389-4802
Executive Asst. to the Director	Dee Halliburton	512/389-4802
Chief Operating Officer	Ann Bright	512/389-8558
Director of Conservation Programs	Ross Melinchuk	512/389-4868
General Counsel	Robert Sweeney	512/389-4433
Dir. of Intergovernmental Affairs	Harold Stone	512/389-4530
Chief Financial Officer	Mike Jensen	512/389-4803
Director of Coastal Fisheries	Robin Riechers	512/389-4636
Director of Inland Fisheries	Craig Bonds	512/389-4643
Director of Communication	Josh Havens	512/389-4557
Director of Human Resources	Pamela Wheeler	512/389-4808
Director of Information Tech.	George Rios	512/389-8066
Acting Director of Infrastructure	Jessica Davisson	512/389-4741
Director of Law Enforcement	Grahame Jones	512/389-4845
Director of State Parks	Brent Leisure	512/389-4866
Director of Wildlife	Clayton Wolf	512/389-8092
Chief Diversity & Inclusion	David Buggs	512/389-8575

*Subject to the Texas Sunset Act; will be reviewed in 2021.

PECOS RIVER COMPACT COMMISSION
P.O. Box 969, Marfa 79843 • 432/729-3225 • *FAX: 432/729-3224*

1 Member - 6 Years

Frederic "Rick" Tate Commissioner, Marfa, 1-23-23

STAFF:
Interstate Compacts Coordinator Suzy Valentine, P.E. . . . .512/239-4730 / *Fax: 512/239-2214*

PENSION REVIEW BOARD, STATE*

P.O. Box 13498, Austin 78711-3498 - 300 W. 15th, Suite 406, Austin 78701
512/463-1736 • 800/213-9425 • *FAX: 512/463-1882*
www.prb.state.tx.us • Agency # 338

7 Members - 6 Years

Josh McGee	Chair, Houston, 1-31-21
Keith Brainard	Vice Chair, Georgetown, 1-31-19
Andrew Cable	Board Member, Wimberley, 1-31-19
Stephanie Leibe	Board Member, Austin, 1-31-21
Robert Massengale	Board Member, Lubbock, 1-31-17
Robert May	Board Member, Austin, 1-31-19
Ernest Richards	Board Member, Irving, 1-31-21

STAFF:

Executive Director	Anu Anumeha	512/463-1736
Deputy Director	Michelle D. Kranes	512/463-1736
Staff Actuary	Kenneth J. Herbold	512/463-1736
Accountant	Wes Allen	512/463-1739
Accounting Technician	Eusebio Arizpe	512/463-1736
Management Analyst	Ashley Rendon	512/463-1736
Program Specialist	Joey Evans	512/463-8814
Program Specialist	Christine Taylor	512/463-1736
Research Specialist	Eloisa Mata	512/463-1736
Investment Analyst	Marc Chytil	512/463-1736
Financial Analyst	Bryan Burnham	512/463-1736
Financial Analyst	Reece Freeman	512/463-1736

*Subject to the Texas Sunset Act; will be reviewed in 2025.

PHARMACY, TEXAS STATE BOARD OF*

333 Guadalupe, Suite 3-500, Austin 78701-3903
512/305-8000 • *FAX: 512/305-8082*
www.pharmacy.texas.gov • Agency # 515
Consumer Complaints: 800/821-3205

11 Members - 6 Years

Jeanne D. Waggener, R.Ph.	President, Waco, 8-31-17
Jenny D. Yoakum, R.Ph.	Vice President, Longview, 8-31-21
Bradley A. Miller, Ph.T.R.	Treasurer, Austin, 8-31-19
Buford T. Abeldt, Sr., R.Ph.	Board Member, Lufkin, 8-31-19
Christopher M. Dembny, R.Ph.	Board Member, Richardson, 8-31-17
Suzan Kedron	Board Member, Dallas, 8-31-19
Alice G. Mendoza, R.Ph.	Board Member, Kingsville, 8-31-17
Phyllis Stine	Board Member, Abilene, 8-31-17
Isaac "Chip" Thornsburg	Board Member, Helotes, 8-31-21
Rebecca "Suzette" Tijerina R.Ph.	Board Member, San Antonio, 8-31-21
Dennis Wiesner, R.Ph.	Board Member, Austin, 8-31-19

STAFF:

Executive Director/Secretary	Allison Vordenbaumen Benz, R.Ph., M.S.	.512/305-2026
Director of Enforcement	Carol E. Fisher, R.Ph., M.P.A.	.512/305-8036
Director of Admin. Services and Licensing	Cathy Stella, PHR	.512/305-8013
General Counsel	Kerstin Arnold, J.D.	.512/305-8035

*Subject to the Texas Sunset Act; will be reviewed in 2029.

PHYSICAL THERAPY AND OCCUPATIONAL THERAPY EXAMINERS, EXECUTIVE COUNCIL OF*

333 Guadalupe, Suite 2-510, Austin 78701-3942 • 512/305-6900 • *FAX: 512/305-6951*
www.ptot.texas.gov • Agency # 533
Consumer Complaints: 800/821-3205

5 Members - 2 Years

Arthur Roger Matson	Presiding Officer, Georgetown, 2-1-17
Stephanie Johnston, O.T.R.	Board Member, Magnolia, 2-1-17
Barbara Sanders, P.T., Ph.D.	Board Member, Austin, 1-31-17
William "Will" Hale	Public Member, Austin, 2-1-15
Philip Vickers	Public Member, Fort Worth, 1-31-19

STAFF:

Executive Director	John Maline	.512/305-6900 / *Fax: 512/305-6951*

The council administratively supports the physical therapy and occupational therapy boards.

*Subject to the Texas Sunset Act; will be reviewed in 2029.

PHYSICAL THERAPY EXAMINERS, TEXAS BOARD OF*

333 Guadalupe, Suite 2-510, Austin 78701-3942
512/305-6900 • *FAX: 512/305-6951* • www.ptot.texas.gov/physical-therapy

9 Members - 6 Years

Harvey Aikman, P.T.	Chair, Mission, 1-1-21
Barbara Sanders, P.T., Ph.D.	Vice Chair, Austin, 1-31-17
Gary Gray, P.T.	Board Member, Midland, 1-31-17
Liesl Olson, P.T.	Board Member, Lubbock, 1-31-21
Jeffrey Tout, P.T.	Board Member, Granbury, 1-31-19
Glenda Clausell	Public Member, Houston, 1-31-21
Daniel Reyna, CPA	Public Member, Waco, 1-31-17
Philip Vickers	Public Member, Fort Worth, 1-31-19
Vacant	Board Member

STAFF:
Executive Director   John Maline . . . . .512/305-6900 / *Fax: 512/305-6951*

The board licenses and regulates physical therapy services in the state of Texas.

*Subject to the Texas Sunset Act; will be reviewed in 2029.

PHYSICIAN ASSISTANT BOARD, TEXAS*

333 Guadalupe, Tower 3, Suite 610, P.O. Box 2018, Austin 78768-2018
512/305-7010 • *FAX: 512/305-7051* • www.tmb.state.tx.us • Agency # 503
Consumer Complaint Hotline: 800/201-9353

13 Members - 6 Years

Jason Cooper, P.A.	Chair, Midland, 2-1-17
Clay Bulls, P.A.	Board Member, Abilene, 2-1-21
Jennifer Clarner, P.A.	Board Member, Austin, 2-1-17
Karrie Lynn Crosby, P.A.	Board Member, Waco, 2-1-21
Maribel "Monica" De Ponce	Board Member, McAllen, 2-1-21
Melinda A. Gottschalk, P.A.	Board Member, Round Rock, 2-1-19
Victor Ho, M.D.	Board Member, Houston, 2-1-21
Teralea Davis Jones, P.A.	Board Member, Beeville, 2-1-19
Felix Koo, M.D.	Board Member, San Antonio, 2-1-17
Michael Reis, M.D.	Board Member, Woodway, 2-1-19
Anna Arredondo Chapman	Public Member, Del Rio, 2-1-17
Jorge Martinez	Public Member, McAllen, 2-1-21
R. Blayne Rush	Public Member, Frisco, 2-1-19

STAFF:
Interim Executive Director	Scott Freshour, J.D. . . . . . . .512/305-7010 / *Fax: 512/305-7051*
Medical Director	Robert Bredt, M.D.. . . . . . . .512/305-7019 / *Fax: 512/305-7051*
Board Coordinator	Laura Fleharty . . . . .512/305-7174 / *Fax: 512/305-7051*
Licensure Manager	Monique Johnston . . . . . . .512/305-7121 / *Fax: 512/305-7009*
General Counsel	Scott Freshour, J.D. . . . . . . .512/305-7085 / *Fax: 512/305-7051*
Special Projects Manager	Megan Goode . . . . .512/305-7044 / *Fax: 512/305-7051*

*Subject to the Texas Sunset Act; will be reviewed in 2029.

PLUMBING EXAMINERS, TEXAS STATE BOARD OF*

929 East 41st Street, P.O. Box 4200, Austin 78765-4200
512/936-5200 • 800/845-6584 • *FAX: 512/450-0637*
www.tsbpe.texas.gov • Agency # 456

9 Members - 6 Years

Julio Cerda	Chair, Mission, 9-5-19
Ricardo Jose Guerra, P.E.	Secretary, Austin, 9-5-17
Enrique Castro	Board Member, El Paso, 9-5-17
Ben Friedman	Board Member, Dallas, 9-5-21
Janet Gallagher	Board Member, Pflugerville, 9-5-17
David A. Garza	Board Member, San Benito, 9-5-19
Milton Gutierrez	Board Member, Fort Worth, 9-5-21
Robi Jalnos, P.E.	Board Member, San Antonio, 9-5-21
Ed Thompson	Board Member, Tyler, 9-5-19

STAFF:

Executive Director	Lisa G. Hill	512/936-5233
Executive Assistant	Dawn Saravia	512/936-5226
Director of Financial Operations	Cori Briscoe	512/936-5225
Director of Enforcement	Steve Davis	512/936-5221
Staff Attorney	Lain Berry	512/936-5202

The board enforces plumbing regulations and oversees examinations and licensing of plumbers and plumbing inspectors in the state. The Board also investigates consumer complaints.

*Subject to the Texas Sunset Act; will be reviewed in 2019.

PODIATRIC MEDICAL EXAMINERS ADVISORY BOARD

E.O. Thompson SOB, 920 Colorado St., P.O. Box 12157, Austin 78711-2157
512/463-6599 • 800/803-9202 • *FAX: 512/463-9468*
www.tdlr.texas.gov • Agency # 512

9 Members - 6 Years

Travis A. Motley, D.P.M.	Presiding Officer, Colleyville, 2-1-23
Leslie Campbell, D.P.M.	Board Member, Plano, 2-1-21
Brian B. Carpenter, D.P.M.	Board Member, Paradise, 2-1-23
James Michael Lunsford, D.P.M.	Board Member, Spring Branch, 2-1-19
Joe E. Martin, Jr., D.P.M.	Board Member, College Station, 2-1-19
Renee Pietzsch, D.P.M.	Board Member, Georgetown, 2-1-21
Vacant	Public Member
Vacant	Public Member
Vacant	Public Member

The advisory board provides advice and recommendations to the Texas Department of Licensing and Regulation on technical matters relevant to the regulation of the practice of podiatry.

PORT FREEPORT
1100 Cherry Street, Freeport 77541
979/233-2667 • 800/362-5743 • *FAX: 979/373-0023*

6 Members - 6 Years

Paul Kresta	Chair, West Columbia/Damon, 5-31-21
John Hoss	Vice Chair, Freeport, 5-31-23
Shane Pirtle, P.E.	Secretary, Lake Jackson, 5-31-23
Bill Terry	Assistant Secretary, Brazoria/Sweeny, 5-31-19
Jason Cordoba	General Counsel
Rudy Santos	Commissioner, Angleton, 5-31-21
Ravi K. Singhania	Commissioner, Brazosport, 5-31-19

STAFF:

Executive Director/CEO	Phyllis Saathoff	.979/233-2667 x4304
Chief Financial Officer	John Mannion	.979/233-2667 x4366
Director of Business & Economic Development	Jason Miura	.979/233-2667 x4332
Director of Economic Development	Michael E. Wilson	.979/233-2667 x4325
Director of External Affairs	Position Vacant	.979/233-2667 x4341
Director of Engineering	Jason Hull	.979/233-2667 x4322
Director of Operations	Al Durel	.979/233-2667 x5340
Director of Protective Services	Chris Hogan	.979/233-2667 x5911
Controller	Mary Campus	.979/233-2667 x4320

PRESERVATION BOARD, STATE*
201 East 14th Street, Suite 950, P.O. Box 13286, Austin 78711-3286
512/463-5495 • *FAX: 512/475-3372* • www.tspb.texas.gov • Agency # 809

6 Members - 0 Year

The Honorable Greg Abbott	Chair, Austin
The Honorable Dan Patrick	Co-Vice Chair, Houston
The Honorable Joe Straus III	Co-Vice Chair, San Antonio
Rep. Charlie L. Geren	Board Member, Fort Worth
Sen. Lois W. Kolkhorst	Board Member, Brenham
Iris Moore	Public Member, Fort Worth, 2-1-19

STAFF:

Executive Director	Rod Welsh	.512/463-5495 / *Fax: 512/475-3372*

The board oversees preservation and maintenance of the Texas State Capitol, Capitol Visitors Center, Texas State Cemetery and the Texas Governor's Mansion, and operates the Bullock Texas State History Museum.

*Subject to the Texas Sunset Act; will be reviewed in 2025.

PRODUCE RECOVERY FUND BOARD

c/o Texas Dept. of Agriculture, SFA Bldg., P.O. Box 12847, Austin 78711-2847
512/936-2430 • *FAX: 512/463-8225*

5 Members - 6 Years

Becky Bonham	Board Member, 1-31-19
Ly H. Nguyen	Board Member, Houston, 1-31-15
Vacant	Board Member
Vacant	Board Member
Vacant	Board Member

STAFF:
Director   Mike Mann . . . . .512/463-4753/ *Fax: 888/215-4883*

PSYCHOLOGISTS, TEXAS STATE BOARD OF EXAMINERS OF*

333 Guadalupe, Suite 2-450, Austin 78701
512/305-7700 • *FAX: 512/305-7701*
www.tsbep.texas.gov/ • Agency # 520

9 Members - 6 Years

Tim F. Branaman, Ph.D.	Chair, Dallas, 10-31-19
Lou Ann Todd Mock, Ph.D.	Vice Chair, Bellaire, 10-31-19
Donna Lord Black, M.A.	Board Member, Frisco, 10-31-17
Jo Ann Campbell, M.S.	Board Member, Abilene, 10-31-17
Susan Fletcher, Ph.D.	Board Member, Plano, 10-31-21
Ronald Palomares, Ph.D.	Board Member, Dallas, 10-31-21
John Bielamowicz	Public Member, Waxahachie, 10-31-21
Angela A. Downes, J.D.	Public Member, Dallas, 10-31-19
John R. Huffman, J.D.	Public Member, Southlake, 10-31-17

STAFF:
Executive Director   Darrel Spinks, J.D. . . . . .512/305-7700 / *Fax: 512/305-7701*

*Subject to the Texas Sunset Act; will be reviewed in 2019.

PUBLIC FINANCE AUTHORITY, TEXAS*

300 West 15th St., Suite 411, P.O. Box 12906, Austin 78711-2906
512/463-5544 • *FAX: 512/463-5501*
www.tpfa.texas.gov • Agency # 347

7 Members - 6 Years

Billy M. Atkinson, Jr.	Chair, Sugar Land, 2-1-17
Ruth C. Schiermeyer	Vice Chair, Lubbock, 2-1-19
Gerald B. Alley	Secretary, Arlington, 2-1-19
Ramon Manning	Board Member, Houston, 2-1-21
Walker N. Moody	Board Member, Houston, 2-1-19
Rodney K. Moore	Board Member, Lufkin, 2-1-21
Robert T. Roddy, Jr.	Board Member, San Antonio, 2-1-17

STAFF:

Executive Director	Lee Deviney	512/463-9433
General Counsel	Kevin Van Oort	512/463-5681
Deputy Director	John Hernandez	512/463-3101
Director, Business Administration	Pamela Scivicque	512/463-3141

The Texas Public Finance Authority issues bonds and commercial paper to fund capital projects, equipment acquisitions and other programs as authorized by the Texas Legislature

*Subject to the Texas Sunset Act; will be reviewed in 2023.

PUBLIC INSURANCE COUNSEL, OFFICE OF*

333 Guadalupe, Suite 3-120, Austin 78701 • 512/322-4143 • *FAX: 512/322-4148*
www.opic.texas.gov • Agency # 359

1 Member - 2 Years

Melissa Hamilton   Public Counsel/Executive Director, Austin, 2-1-19

*Subject to the Texas Sunset Act; will be reviewed in 2023.

PUBLIC SAFETY, TEXAS DEPARTMENT OF*

5805 N. Lamar Blvd., P.O. Box 4087, Austin 78773-0001
512/424-2000 • *FAX: 512/424-5708* • www.dps.texas.gov • Agency # 405
Motorist Assistance: 800/525-5555
Motorcycle Safety: 800/292-5787
Missing Persons Hotline: 800/346-3243

5 Members - 6 Years

Steven P. Mach	Chair, Houston, 12-31-22
Manny Flores, Jr.	Board Member, Austin, 12-31-17
A. Cynthia "Cindy" Leon	Board Member, Mission, 1-1-20
Jason Pulliam	Board Member, San Antonio, 2-1-22
Randy Watson	Board Member, Burleson, 1-1-18

STAFF:

Director	Steven McCraw	512/424-7771
Deputy Director		
Law Enforcement	David Baker	512/424-7774
Homeland Security and Services	Robert Bodisch	512/424-2368
General Counsel	Phillip Adkins	512/424-2890
Inspector General	Rhonda Fleming	512/424-2054
Chief Auditor	Catherine Melvin	512/424-7573
Division Director		
Highway Patrol	Ron Joy	512/424-2113
Texas Rangers	Randall Prince	512/424-7700
Criminal Investigations	Thomas G. Ruocco	512/424-2130
ICT	John Jones	512/424-5768
Aircraft Operations	Billy Nabors	512/936-9201
Driver License	Amanda Arriaga	512/424-5232
Div. of Emergency Mgmt.	Chief W. Nim Kidd	512/424-2443
Regulatory Licensing	RenEarl Bowie	512/424-7731
Law Enforcement Support	David G. Baker	512/424-7901
Administration	Jessica Ballew	512/424-7772
Finance	Suzy Whittenton	512/424-2075
Information Technology Div.	Bryan Lane	512/424-2280
Assistant Division Director		
Chief Government Relations	Amy Clay	512/486-6450
Media/Communications	Katherine Cesinger	512/424-2011
Equal Employment Opportunity	Nathanael Haddox	512/424-5213
Government Relations	Kevin Meade	512/424-5076

Regional Commanders:

Garland	Commander Jack Webster	214/861-2460
Houston	Commander Duane Steen	281/517-1210
Weslaco	Commander Joe Rodriguez	956/565-7100
El Paso	Commander Orlando Alanis	915/849-4051
Lubbock	Commander Gary Albus	806/740-8711
San Antonio	Commander Freeman Martin	210/531-4325
Capitol District	Commander Joe Ortiz	512/463-3472

*Subject to the Texas Sunset Act; will be reviewed in 2019.

PRIVATE SECURITY BOARD-DPS

5806 Guadalupe, Bldg. I, P.O. Box 4087, Austin 78773-0001
512/424-7293 • *FAX: 512/424-7726* • www.txdps.state.tx.us/rsd/psb • Agency # 405

7 Members - 6 Years

Patricia "Patti" James	Chair, Houston, 1-21-21
Mark Smith	Secretary, Dallas, 1-31-17
Albert L. Black	Board Member, Austin, 1-31-17
Wade Hayden	Board Member, San Antonio, 1-31-19
Claude "C.D." Siems	Board Member, Houston, 1-31-21
Debbra Ulmer	Board Member, Houston, 1-31-19
Vacant	Board Member

STAFF:

Senior Manager	Chris Sims . . . . .512/424-7157 / *Fax: 512/424-5562*
Manager, Licensing & Registration	Huel Haynes . . . . .512/424-2697 / *Fax: 512/424-7284*

PUBLIC UTILITY COMMISSION OF TEXAS*

Wm. B. Travis Bldg., 1701 N. Congress, P.O. Box 13326, Austin 78711-3326
512/936-7120; 512/936-7000 • 888/782-8477 • *FAX: 512/936-7003*
www.puc.texas.gov • Agency # 473

3 Members - 6 Years

DeAnn Walker	Chair, Austin, 9-1-21
Arthur C. D'Andrea	Commissioner, Austin, 9-1-23
Brandy Marty Marquez	Commissioner, Austin, 9-1-19

STAFF:

Executive Director	Brian H. Lloyd 512/936-7040
Deputy Executive Director	Pamela Whittington 512/936-7245
Agency Counsel	Kasey Feldman-Thomason 512/936-7144
Director		
Finance & Administration	Thomas Gleeson 512/936-7095
External Affairs	Mike Hoke 512/936-7048
Communication	Position Vacant 512/936-7135
Commission Advising & Docket Mgmt.	Stephen Journeay 512/936-7215
Customer Protection	Chris Burch 512/936-7145
Oversight & Enforcement	Mick Long 512/936-7294
Infrastructure & Reliability	Keith Rogas 512/936-7325
Competitive Markets	Connie Corona 512/936-7232
Legal	Margaret Pemberton 512/936-7292
Rate Regulation	Darryl Tietjen 512/936-7436
Water Utility Regulation	Tammy Benter 512/936-7165

*Subject to the Texas Sunset Act; will be reviewed in 2023.

PUBLIC UTILITY COUNSEL, OFFICE OF*

1701 N. Congress Ave., Suite 9-180, P.O. Box 12397, Austin 78711-2397
512/936-7500 • *FAX: 512/936-7525* • www.opuc.texas.gov • Agency # 475

1 Appointed Member

Tonya Baer   Public Counsel, Austin, 2-1-19

STAFF:
Director, Administration   Brenda Sevier
Director, External Relations   Michele Gregg

The office represents Texas residential and small business consumers in utility proceedings that come before state and federal regulatory agencies and courts.

---

*Subject to the Texas Sunset Act; will be reviewed in 2023.

RACING COMMISSION, TEXAS*

8505 Cross Park Dr., Suite 110, P.O. Box 12080, Austin 78711-2080
512/833-6699 • *FAX: 512/833-6907* • www.txrc.texas.gov • Agency # 476

7 Members - 6 Years; 2 Ex-Officio Members

John T. Steen III	Chair, Houston, 2-1-19
Ronald F. Ederer	Vice Chair, Corpus Christi, 2-1-19
Gloria Hicks	Board Member, Corpus Christi, 2-1-17
Margaret L. Martin	Board Member, Boerne, 2-1-21
Robert Schmidt, M.D.	Board Member, Fort Worth, 2-1-17
Steven P. Mach	Ex Officio Member, Houston
The Honorable Sid Miller	Ex Officio Member, Stephenville
Vacant	Board Member
Vacant	Board Member

STAFF:

Executive Director	Chuck Trout	.512/833-6699 / *Fax: 512/833-6907*
Deputy Executive Director	Joel Speight	.512/490-4005 / *Fax: 512/833-6907*
Public Information Officer	Robert Elrod	.512/490-4032 / *Fax: 512/833-6907*
General Counsel	Devon Bijansky	.512/490-4003 / *Fax: 512/833-6907*
COS/Policy Dev. Officer	Jean Cook	.512/490-4011 / *Fax: 512/833-6907*
Chief Financial Officer	Adrianne Courtney	.512/490-4026 / *Fax: 512/833-6907*
Chief Steward/Judge	Ricky Walker	.512/490-4024 / *Fax: 512/833-6907*
Director of		
Administration	Gerry Dube	.512/490-4025 / *Fax: 512/833-6907*
Information Technology	Patricia Nalle	.512/490-4022 / *Fax: 512/833-6907*
Investigations	Jim Blodgett	.512/490-4002 / *Fax: 512/833-6907*
Licensing	Connie Estes	.512/490-4012 / *Fax: 512/833-6907*
Pari-Mutuels	Curley Trahan	.512/490-4027 / *Fax: 512/833-6907*
Veterinary Medical Director	Robert "Trey" James, DVM	.512/490-4033 / *Fax: 512/833-6907*

---

*Subject to the Texas Sunset Act; will be reviewed in 2023.

RAILROAD COMMISSION OF TEXAS*

Wm. B. Travis Bldg., 1701 N. Congress, P.O. Box 12967, Austin 78711-2967
512/463-7158 • *FAX: 512/463-7161* • www.rrc.texas.gov • Agency # 455
Toll Free outside Austin: 877/228-5740

3 Members - 6 Years

THE HONORABLE CHRISTI CRADDICK (R), Chair, 12-31-18
A native of Midland, Christi Craddick earned both her Bachelor's
Degree as a Plan II graduate and her Doctorate of Jurisprudence from
The University of Texas at Austin. During her career as an attorney,
she specialized in oil and gas, water, tax issues, electric deregulation
and environmental policy. As president of a grassroots advocacy firm,
she took the lead on work in coalition building in the public policy
arena and development and implementation of issue strategies.
In 2015, she was appointed to serve as the Governor's Designee on
Southern States Energy Board. .512/463-7140

THE HONORABLE RYAN SITTON (R), Commissioner, 12-31-20
Ryan Sitton is the 49th Commissioner of the Railroad Commission of
Texas. A native Texan, Sitton is a graduate of Texas A&M University
where he earned a degree in Mechanical Engineering before entering
the energy industry as an engineer. In 2006, Sitton and his wife
Jennifer founded PinnacleART, an engineering and technology company focused on reliability and integrity programs for the oil, gas and
petrochemical industries. In 2012 and 2013, Inc. Magazine recognized
PinnacleART as one of the top 1,500 fastest growing, privately held
companies in the world. For seven consecutive years, PinnacleART
has also been honored as an Aggie 100 recipient, an award celebrating
and recognizing the fastest growing Aggie-owned businesses in the
world 512/463-7144

THE HONORABLE WAYNE CHRISTIAN (R), Commissioner
12-31-22
Christian graduated from high school as valedictorian, and went on to
graduate from Stephen F. Austin State University with a B.B.A. in
General Business in 1973. After college, Christian found success in
the music industry with his country/gospel band, the Mercy River
Boys and went on to be finalist for a Grammy Award in 1979. In 1987,
Wayne Christian opened A financial services business and in 1996,
was elected to the House of Representatives as the first Republican
elected from Deep East Texas since Reconstruction after the Civil War.
During his time in the House, Christian was a leader for the conserva-
tive renaissance in the State of Texas and successfully assisted in the
fight to elect a Rep. majority in the Texas Legislature .512/463-7131

STAFF:

Interim Executive Director	Wei Wang . . . . .512/463-7068 / *Fax: 512/463-7000*
Chief Financial Officer	Wei Wang . . . . .512/463-5011 / *Fax: 512/463-7000*
General Counsel	Alexander Schoch . . . . .512/463-6715 / *Fax: 512/463-6989*
Director, Communications	Rich Parsons . . . . .512/936-3520 / *Fax: 512/463-7000*
Director, Enforcement	Megan Neal . . . . .512/463-6770 / *Fax: 512/463-6684*
Director, Oversight and Safety	Kari French . . . . .512/463-8559 / *Fax: 512/463-7962*

Director, Human Resources	Robbi Craig . . . . .512/463-6986 / *Fax: 512-463-0351*
Director, Administration .	Bill Dodson . . . . .512/463-5881 / *Fax: 512-463-5548*
Director, Hearings	Randall Collins . . . . .512/463-5928 / *Fax: 512/463-6989*
Director, Oil and Gas	Lori Wrotenbery . . . . .512/463-6810 / *Fax: 512/463-6780*
Director, Surface Mining	J. Denny Kingsley . . . . . . .512/305-8831 / *Fax: 512/463-6709*
Director, Government Affairs	Stacie Fowler . . . . .512/463-7086 / *Fax: 512/463-7000*
Chief Information Officer	Brandon Harris . . . . .512/463-7251 / *Fax: 512/463-8488*
Internal Auditor	Paul Delaney . . . . .512/463-6502 / *Fax: 512/463-7000*
Commission Secretary	Kathy Way . . . . .512/463-7865 / *Fax: 512/463-7161*

OIL AND GAS DIVISION OFFICES:

Santos Gonzales, Jr. Assistant Director
Austin Field Operations
512/463-6827 / *Fax: 512-463-7328*

Districts 1 and 2
Travis Baer, Director
115 E. Travis St., Suite 1610
San Antonio, TX 78205-1689
210/227-1313 / *Fax: 210-227-4822*

District 3
Peter Fisher, Director
1706 Seamist Dr., Suite 501
Houston, TX 77008-3135
713/869-5001 / *Fax: 713-869-9621*

District 4
William Thompson, District Director
10320 IH 37
Corpus Christi, TX 78410
361/242-3113 / *Fax: 361-242-9613*

Districts 5 and 6
Danny Sorrels, Director
2005 N. State Hwy. 42
Kilgore, TX 75662-5998
903/984-3026 / *Fax: 903-983-3413*

District 7B and 8A
Position Vacant, Director
3444 N. 1st, Suite 600
Abilene, TX 79603
325/677-3545 / *Fax: 325-677-7122*

District 7C
Bill Spaggins, Director
622 S. Oakes St., Suite J
San Angelo, TX 76903
325/657-7450 / *Fax: 325-657-7455*

Districts 8
Craig Pearson, Director
Conoco Towers
10 Desta Dr., Ste. 500 E
Midland, TX 79705
432/684-5581 / *Fax: 432-684-6005*

District 9
Kim Peterson, Director
First Texas Bldg.
5800 Kell Blvd.
Wichita Falls, TX 76301-6798
940/723-2153 / *Fax: 940-723-5088*

District 10
Cole Fraley, District Director
200 W. Foster
Pampa, TX 79065
806/665-1653 / *Fax: 806-665-4217*

---

*Subject to the Texas Sunset Act; will be reviewed in 2029.

REAL ESTATE COMMISSION, TEXAS*

1700 North Congress Ave., Suite 400, P.O. Box 12188, Austin 78711-2188
512/936-3000 • www.trec.texas.gov • Agency # 329

9 Members - 6 Years

Avis Wukasch	Chair, Georgetown, 1-31-19
Adrian A. Arriaga	Board Member, McAllen, 1-31-19
Bob Leonard	Board Member, San Antonio, 1-31-21
Jan Fite Miller	Board Member, Kemp, 1-31-23
Rayito Stephens	Board Member, Pearland, 1-31-21
DeLora Wilkinson	Board Member, Cypress, 1-31-23
T.J. Turner	Public Member, Austin, 1-31-21
Chart H. Westcott	Public Member, Dallas, 1-31-19
Micheal Williams	Public Member, Colleyville, 1-31-23

STAFF:

Executive Director	Douglas E. Oldmixon . . . . . .512/936-3088 / *Fax: 512/936-3788*
Deputy Executive Director/ General Counsel	Kerri Lewis . . . . .512/936-3284 / *Fax: 512/936-3788*
Staff & Support Services	Priscilla Pipho . . . . .512/936-3590 / *Fax: 512/936-3551*
Standards & Enforcement Services	Mark Moore . . . . .512/936-3057 / *Fax: 512/936-3809*
Information & Technology Services	Steve Spyropoulos 512/936-3242
Education & Licensing Services	Gwen Jackson . . . . .512/936-3094 / *Fax: 512/936-3864*
Reception & Communication Services	Lorie DeAnda . . . . .512/936-3000 / *Fax: 512/936-3798*

*Subject to the Texas Sunset Act; will be reviewed in 2019.

REAL ESTATE RESEARCH CENTER

Texas A&M University Real Estate Center, 2115 TAMU, College Station 77843-2115
979/845-2031 • *FAX: 979/845-5220* • www.recenter.tamu.edu

9 Members - 6 Years; 1 Ex Officio Member

Stephen D. "Doug" Roberts	Chair, Austin, 1-31-19
Mario A. Arriaga	Board Member, Conroe, 1-31-17
Russell Cain	Board Member, Port Lavaca, 1-31-17
Alvin Collins	Board Member, Andrews, 1-31-21
Jacquelyn K. Hawkins	Board Member, Austin, 1-31-17
W. Douglas Jennings	Board Member Fort Worth, 1-31-19
Elizabeth "Besa" Martin	Board Member, Boerne, 1-31-21
Walter F. "Ted" Nelson	Board Member, Houston, 1-31-19
Christopher Clark Welder	Board Member, San Antonio, 1-31-19
Bill Jones	Ex Officio Member, Temple, 1-31-17

STAFF:

Director	Gary Maler . . . . .979/845-9691 / *Fax: 979/845-5220*

RED RIVER AUTHORITY OF TEXAS*

3000 Hammon Road, P.O. Box 240, Wichita Falls 76307-0240
940/723-8697 • *FAX: 940/723-8531* • www.rra.texas.gov • Agency # 595

9 Members - 6 Years

Nathan J. "Jim" Bell IV	Board Member, Paris, 8-11-17
Todd Boykin	Board Member, Amarillo, 8-11-21
Cole Camp	Board Member, Amarillo, 8-11-19
Penny C. Carpenter	Board Member, Silverton, 8-11-19
Jerry B. Daniel	Board Member, Truscott, 8-11-21
Monty Johnson III	Board Member, Amarillo, 8-11-17
Mayfield McGraw	Board Member, Telephone, 8-11-17
G. Wilson Scaling II	Board Member, Henrietta, 8-11-21
Stephen A. Thornhill	Board Member, Denison, 8-11-19

STAFF:
General Manager   Curtis W. Campbell 940/723-8697

*Subject to the Texas Sunset Act; will be reviewed in 2019.

RED RIVER COMPACT COMMISSION

300 North Travis Street, Sherman 75090 • 903/870-0070 • *FAX: 903/870-0066*

1 Member - 6 Years

1 Ex Officio Member

Clyde Siebman	Commissioner, Sherman, 2-1-23
Richard A. Hyde, P.E.	Ex Officio Member, Austin

STAFF:
Interstate Compacts Coordinator   Suzy Valentine, P.E. . . . . . . .512/239-4730 / *Fax: 512/239-2214*

RIO GRANDE COMPACT COMMISSION

401 E. Franklin Avenue, Suite 560, El Paso 79901-1212
915/545-1133 • *FAX: 915/545-4433*

1 Member - 6 Years

Patrick R. Gordon   Commissioner, El Paso, 6-9-19

STAFF:
Technical Advisor   Curtis Seaton . . . . .512/239-0434 / *Fax: 512/239-2214*

The Rio Grande Compact Commission administers the Rio Grande Compact to ensure that Texas receives its equitable share of quality water from the Rio Grande and its tributaries as apportioned by the Rio Grande Compact. The Compact includes the states of Colorado, New Mexico, and Texas.

RISK MANAGEMENT, STATE OFFICE OF*

300 West 15th St., 6th Floor, P.O. Box 13777, Austin 78711-3777
512/475-1440 • *FAX: 512/370-9025* • www.sorm.state.tx.us • Agency # 479

5 Members - 2 Years and at the pleasure of the governor

Lloyd Garland, M.D.	Chair, Lubbock, 2-1-19
Rosemary A. Gammon, PAHM	Board Member, Plano, 2-1-21
Tomas Gonzalez	Board Member, El Paso, 2-1-17
Gerald Ladner, Sr.	Board Member, Austin, 2-1-21
John W. Youngblood	Board Member, Cameron, 2-1-19

STAFF:

Executive Director and State Risk Manager	Stephen S. Vollbrecht, J.D. 512/936-1508 / *Fax: 512/370-9025*
Deputy Executive Director	L. Todd Holt, M.Ed. . . . . .512/936-1502 / *Fax: 512/370-9025*
Division Chief of Internal Ops. and Chief Financial Officer	Stuart "Brad" Cargile . . . .512/936-1523 / *Fax: 512/370-9025*
Division Chief of Strategic Programs and Sr. Adv.	James Cox, MBA . . . . . . .512/936-1527 / *Fax: 512/370-9025*
Division Chief of Legal Svcs. & General Counsel	Deea Western, J.D. . . . . . .512/936-1465 / *Fax: 512/370-9025*
Governmental Relations Liaison	Paul S. Harris . . . . .512/936-1452 / *Fax: 512/370-9025*

*Subject to the Texas Sunset Act; will be reviewed in 2019.

SABINE RIVER AUTHORITY OF TEXAS

P.O. Box 579, Orange 77630 • 409/746-2192 • *FAX: 409/746-3780* • www.sratx.org

9 Members - 6 Years

Cary M. "Mac" Abney	Board Member, Marshall, 7-6-21
J. D. Jacobs, Jr.	Board Member, Rockwall, 7-6-19
David W. Koonce	Board Member, Center, 7-6-19
Stanley N. Mathews	Board Member, Pinehurst, 7-6-17
M. Sharon Newcomer	Board Member, Mauriceville, 7-6-17
Col. Jeanette Sterner (Ret.)	Board Member, Holly Lake Ranch, 7-6-21
Cliff R. Todd	Board Member, Long Branch, 7-16-17
Earl Williams	Board Member, Orange, 7-6-19
Laurie Woloszyn	Board Member, Longview, 7-6-21

STAFF:

Executive VP and General Manager	J. David Montagne
Assistant General Manager	
Operations	Clayton Henderson
Administration	E. Ann Galassi
Treasurer & Chief Administrative Officer	Debra L. Stagner
Chief Financial Officer	Holly Smith
Reg. Manager-Lower Basin	William R. "Bill" Hughes, Jr.
Reg. Manager - Upper Basin	Troy D. Henry
Water Resources Manager	Travis Williams

SABINE RIVER COMPACT COMMISSION
c/o TCEQ, P.O. Box 13087, MC-160, Austin 78711-3087
512/239-4730 • *FAX: 512/239-2214*

2 Members - 6 Years

Jerry F. Gipson   Commissioner, Longview, 7-12-22
Michael H. "Mike" Lewis   Commissioner, Newton, 7-12-19

STAFF:
Interstate Compacts Coordinator   Suzy Valentine, P.E. . . . . . . .512/239-4730 / *Fax: 512/239-2214*

SAN ANTONIO RIVER AUTHORITY
100 East Guenther Street, P.O. Box 839980, San Antonio 78283-9980
210/227-1373 • 866/345-7272 • *FAX: 210/227-4323* • www.sara-tx.org

12 Members - 6 Years

Michael W. Lackey, P.E.   Chairman, Bexar County District 3, 11-3-21
Darrell T. Brownlow, Ph.D.   Vice Chair, Wilson County, 11-3-19
Lourdes Galvan   Secretary, Bexar County District 2, 11-5-19
Jim Campbell   Treasurer, Bexar County District 4, 11-7-21
Alicia Lott Cowley   Board Member, Goliad County, 11-7-21
John Flieller   Board Member, Wilson County, 11-3-21
James Fuller, M.D.   Board Member, Goliad County, 11-13-19
Jerry G. Gonzales   Board Member, Bexar County District 1, 11-13-19
Hector R. Morales   Board Member, Bexar County At-Large, 11-7-21
Gaylon J. Oehlke   Board Member, Karnes County, 11-5-19
Deb Bolner Prost   Board Member, Bexar County At-Large, 11-13-22
H. B. "Trip" Ruckman, III   Board Member, Karnes County, 11-3-21

STAFF:
General Manager   Suzanne B. Scott . . . . .210/302-3613 / *Fax: 210/227-4323*

SAN JACINTO RIVER AUTHORITY

1577 Dam Site Road, P.O. Box 329, Conroe 77304
936/588-3111 • *FAX: 936/588-3043* • www.sjra.net

7 Members - 6 Years

Lloyd B. Tisdale	President, Conroe, 10-16-19
Fred Koetting	Vice President, The Woodlands, 10-30-21
Ronald Anderson	Treasurer, Mont Belvieu, 11-16-21
Jim Alexander, P.E.	Board Member, Magnolia, 10-16-19
Gary Renola	Board Member, Seabrook, 10-16-17
Vacant	Board Member
Vacant	Board Member

STAFF:

General Manager	Jace Houston	936/588-3111
Deputy General Manager	Ron Kelling, P.E.	936/588-3111
Director of Financial and Administrative Services	Tom Michel	936/588-3111
Director of Raw Water Enterprise	David Parkhill	936/588-3111

BRANCH OFFICES:

General Office:
Jace Houston, General Manager
1577 Dam Site Road
Conroe, TX 77304
936/588-3111 / *Fax: 936/588-3043*

Highlands Division:
Kim Wright, Division Manager
1108 East Canal Street
Highlands, TX 77562
281/843-3300

Woodlands Division:
Chris Meeks, Division Manager
2436 Sawdust Road
The Woodlands, TX 77380
281/367-9511 / *Fax: 281/362-4385*

Lake Conroe Division:
Bret Raley, Division Manager
Lake Conroe Dam
1561 Dam Site Road
Conroe, TX 77304
936/588-1111 / *Fax: 936/588-1114*

GRP Division:
Mark Smith, Division Manager
6627 Longmire Road
Conroe, TX 77304
936/588-1662 / *Fax: 936/588-7182*

SAVINGS AND MORTGAGE LENDING DEPARTMENT OF TEXAS*

2601 North Lamar, Suite 201, Austin 78705
512/475-1350 • *FAX: 512/475-1505*
www.sml.texas.gov • Agency # 450

Staff:

Commissioner	Caroline C. Jones	512/475-1038
General Counsel	Ernest Garcia	512/475-0787
Director of Licensing	Steven O'Shields	512/475-3679
EA to the Commissioner	Ruth Wright	512/475-1352
Director of Admin. and Finance	Antonia P. Antov	512/475-1296

*Subject to the Texas Sunset Act; will be reviewed in 2019.

SCHOOL LAND BOARD*

c/o GLO, SFA Office Bldg., 1700 N. Congress Ave., Austin 78701-1495
512/463-5001 • *FAX: 512/463-5248*

2 Members - 2 Years; 1 Ex Officio Member

Gilbert "Gil" Burciaga	Board Member, Austin, 8-29-19
Scott Rohrman	Board Member, Dallas, 8-31-19
The Honorable George P. Bush	Ex Officio Member, Texas Land Commissioner

*Subject to the Texas Sunset Act; will be reviewed in 2019.

SECURITIES BOARD, STATE*

208 E. 10th St., 5th Floor, P.O. Box 13167, Austin 78711-3167
512/305-8300 • *FAX: 512/305-8310* • www.ssb.texas.gov • Agency # 312

5 Members - 6 Years

Beth Ann Blackwood	Chair, Dallas, 1-20-19
David Appleby	Board Member, El Paso, 1-20-17
E. Wally Kinney	Board Member, Dripping Springs, 1-20-19
Miguel Romano, Jr.	Board Member, Austin, 1-20-21
Alan Waldrop	Board Member, Austin, 1-20-17

STAFF:

Securities Commissioner	Travis Iles	.512/305-8300
Deputy Commissioner	Clinton Edgar	.512/305-8300
Director		
Enforcement Division	Joe Rotunda	.512/305-8392
Inspections and Compliance Div.	Tommy Green	.512/305-8377
Registration Division	Clint Edgar	.512/305-8362
Services Division	Derek Lauterjung	.512/305-8321
General Counsel	Marlene Sparkman	.512/305-8300

BRANCH OFFICES:

Corpus Christi:
Angela Cole, Assistant Director
606 N. Carancahua, Suite 803
Corpus Christi, TX 78401-0659
361/887-1085 / *Fax: 361/884-7820*

Lubbock:
Sara Scribne, Assistant Director
4630 50th Street, Suite 614
Lubbock, TX 79414
806/762-8010 / *Fax: 806/762-6648*

Dallas:
Linda Bailey, AD-Inspections and Compliance
Jay Oman, AD Enforcement Division
8700 N Stemmons Freeway, Suite 144
Dallas, TX 75247-3714
214/630-8681 / *Fax: 214/630-8699*

San Antonio:
Judy Saenz, Assistant Director
115 E. Travis St., Suite 1105
San Antonio, TX 78205-1605
210/886-0073 / *Fax: 210/886-0153*

Houston:
Robert Abreo, AD-Inspections and Compliance Div.
Mogey Lovelle, AC-Enforcement Division
1919 N. Loop West, Suite 300
Houston, TX 77008-1366
713/426-0336 / *Fax: 713/426-6965*

*Subject to the Texas Sunset Act; will be reviewed in 2019.

SEED AND PLANT BOARD, STATE

c/o Texas Dept. of Agriculture, P.O. Box 629, Giddings 78942
512/463-4753 • *FAX: 888/205-7567* • www.texasagriculture.gov

6 Members - 2 Years

David Baltensperger	Chair, College Station, 3-14-18
Dr. Eric Hequet	Board Member, Lubbock, 9-1-18
Mike Mann	Board Member, Austin, 11-1-17
Dr. Roy Martens	Board Member, Alvin, 6-1-18
Jim Massey IV	Board Member, Robstown, 8-5-18
Larry McDowell	Board Member, Crosbyton, 6-1-18

SEX OFFENDER TREATMENT, COUNCIL ON

c/o HHSC, P.O. Box 149347, Mail Code 1982, Austin 78714-9347
512/834-4530 • *FAX: 512/834-6677* • www.dshs.texas.gov/csot

7 Members - 6 Years

Aaron Paul Pierce, LSOTP	Chair, Temple, 2-1-21
Terri L. Bauer, LCSW, LSOTP	Board Member, McKinney, 2-1-19
Ezio Leite, LSOTP	Board Member, North Richland Hills, 2-1-21
Emily Orozco-Crousen, LSOTP	Board Member, Abilene, 2-1-21
Charissa Dvorak	Public Member, Heath, 2-1-23
L ouis Gonzales III	Public Member, Round Rock, 2-1-19
James Taylor	Public Member, San Antonio, 2-1-21

STAFF:

Executive Director	Celeste Lunceford, MS, LPC-S, LSOTP . . . . . .512/834-4530 / *Fax: 512/834-6677*

SOCIAL WORKER EXAMINERS,
TEXAS STATE BOARD OF*

c/o HHSC, P.O. Box 149347, MC 1982, Austin 78714-9347
512/719-3521 • 800/232-3162 • *FAX: 512/834-6677*
www.dshs.texas.gov/socialwork

9 Members - 6 Years

Timothy Martel Brown, LCSW	Chair, Dallas, 2-1-19
Brian Brumley, LMSW	Board Member, Sumner, 2-1-21
Maria Castro, LBSW	Board Member, Weslaco, 2-1-19
Beverly Loss, LMSW	Board Member, Wolfe City, 2-1-21
Martha Mosier LCSW	Board Member, College Station, 2-1-17
Carol Rainey-Nivens, LBSW	Board Member, Denton, 2-1-17
Benny Morris	Public Member, Cleburne, 2-1-21
Denise V. Pratt	Public Member, Baytown, 2-1-17
Mark Talbot	Public Member, McAllen, 2-1-19

STAFF:

Executive Director	Alice Bradford 512/719-3521

*Subject to the Texas Sunset Act; will be reviewed in 2019.

SOIL AND WATER CONSERVATION BOARD, TEXAS STATE*

1497 Country View Lane, Temple 76504-8806
254/773-2250 • 800/792-3485 • *FAX: 254/773-3311* • www.tsswcb.texas.gov

7 Members - 2 Years

Jose Dodier	Chair, Zapata, 5-7-19
Barry Mahler	Vice Chair, Iowa Park, 5-7-19
Scott Buckles	Board Member, Stratford, 5-7-19
Marty H. Graham	Board Member, Rocksprings, 5-1-18
Jerry Nichols	Board Member, Nacogdoches, 5-1-18
Christine Y. "Tina" Buford	Governor Appointee, Harlingen, 2-1-18
Carl Ray Polk, Jr.	Governor Appointee, Lufkin, 2-1-19

STAFF:
Executive Director   Rex Isom 254/773-2250

*Subject to the Texas Sunset Act; will be reviewed in 2019.

SPEECH-LANGUAGE PATHOLOGISTS AND AUDIOLOGISTS ADVISORY BOARD

c/o TDLR, P.O. Box 12057, Austin 78711-2057
512/463-6599 • *FAX: 512/463-9468* • www.tdlr.texas.gov/slpa/slpa.htm

9 Members - 6 Years

Sherry Sancibrian	Presiding Officer, Lubbock, 9-1-21
Patricia Elaine Brannon, M.A., CCC-SLP	Board Member, San Antonio, 9-1-17
Cheval Bryant	Board Member, Sugar Land, 9-1-19
Cristen Plummer-Culp	Board Member, Round Rock, 9-1-19
Kimberly Ringer	Board Member, Pflugerville, 9-1-23
Michelle Tejada	Board Member, San Antonio, 9-1-21
Emanuel Bodner	Public Member, Houston, 9-1-21
Tammy Camp, M.D.	Public Member, Shallowater, 9-1-23
Elizabeth Sterling	Public Member, Austin, 9-1-19

STATE-FEDERAL RELATIONS, OFFICE OF*

660 Pennsylvania Ave SE, Suite 203, Washington, DC 20003
gov.texas.gov/osfr • 202/638-3927 • Agency # 300
Texas Office: 512/463-4375

Executive Director	Jerry Strickland	.512/463-4375
Washington Office	Wes Hambrick	.202/434-0218

*Subject to the Texas Sunset Act; will be reviewed in 2021.

STATEWIDE HEALTH COORDINATING COUNCIL, TX

c/o DSHS, P.O. Box 149347, Austin 78714-9347
512/776-7261 • *FAX: 512/776-7344* • www.dshs.state.tx.us/chs/shcc/

17 Members - 6 Years

Ayeez A. Lalji, D.D.S.	Chair, Sugar Land, 8-1-19
Carol Boswell, Ed.D.	Board Member, Andrews, 8-1-21
Andrew Crim	Board Member, Fort Worth, 8-1-19
Lourdes M. Cuellar, R.Ph.	Board Member, Houston, 8-1-17
Salil Deshpande, M.D.	Board Member, Houston, 8-1-19
Elva C. LeBlanc, Ph.D.	Board Member, Fort Worth, 8-1-19
Elizabeth Protas, Ph.D.	Board Member, League City, 8-1-17
Melinda Rodriguez, P.T., D.P.T.	Board Member, San Antonio, 8-1-21
Larry Safir	Board Member, McAllen, 8-1-17
Courtney Sherman, D.N.P.	Board Member, Fort Worth, 8-1-21
D. Bailey Wynne, R.Ph., M.H.A.	Board Member, Dallas, 8-1-17
Shaukat Zakaria	Board Member, Houston, 8-1-21
Yasser Zeid, M.D.	Board Member, Longview, 8-1-21
Jimmy Blanton, M.P.Aff	Texas Health and Human Services Commission
Kirk Cole	Texas Department of State Health Services
Trina Ita	Texas Health and Human Services Commssion
Stacey Silverman, Ph.D.	Texas Higher Education Coordinating Board

STAFF:
Coordinator   Matt Turner . . . . .512/776-7261 / *Fax: 512/776-7344*

STEPHEN F. AUSTIN STATE UNIVERSITY
BOARD OF REGENTS

Box 13026, SFA Station, Nacogdoches 75962
936/468-4048 • *FAX: 936/468-7048*
www.sfasu.edu/regents

9 Members - 6 Years

1 Student Regent

David Alders	Chair, Nacogdoches, 1-31-19
Brigettee Carnes Henderson	Vice Chair, Lufkin, 1-31-23
Alton Frailey	Secretary, Katy, 1-31-21
Nelda Luce Blair	Board Member, The Woodlands, 1-31-21
Scott Coleman, D.D.S.	Board Member, Houston, 1-31-21
Karen Gantt	Board Member, McKinney, 1-31-23
John R. "Bob" Garrett	Board Member, Tyler, 1-31-19
Tom Mason	Board Member, Dallas, 1-31-23
Ken E. Schaefer	Board Member, Brownsville, 1-31-19
Maggie Wright	Student Regent

OFFICE OF THE PRESIDENT:
President   Dr. Baker Pattillo
P.O. Box 6078 - SFA Station
Nacogdoches, TX 75962
936/468-2201 / *Fax: 936/468-2202*

SULPHUR RIVER BASIN AUTHORITY*

911 N. Bishop St., Suite C-104, Wake Village 75501
903/223-7887 • *FAX: 903/223-7988* • www.srbatx.org

7 Members - 6 Years

Michael Sandefur	President, Texarkana, 9-1-17
Brad Drake	Board Member, Paris, 9-1-17
Wally Kraft	Board Member, Paris, 2-1-17
Bret McCoy	Board Member, Omaha, 2-1-17
Michael Russell	Board Member, Clarksville, 2-1-17
Katie Stedman	Board Member, Mt. Pleasant, 2-1-17
Patricia Wommack	Board Member, Lone Star, 2-1-17

STAFF:
Office Administrator   Nancy Rose 903/223-7887

*Subject to the Texas Sunset Act; will be reviewed in 2029.

TEACHER RETIREMENT SYSTEM OF TEXAS

1000 Red River, Austin 78701 • 800/223-8778 • *FAX: 512/542-6585*
www.trs.texas.gov • Agency # 323
TDD: 512/542-6444

9 Members - 6 Years

Jarvis V. Hollingsworth	Chair, Missouri City, 8-31-23
Joe Colonnetta	Board Member, Dallas, 8-31-19
David Corpus	Board Member, Humble, 8-31-19
John Elliott	Board Member, Austin, 8-31-21
Greg Gibson, Ed.D.	Board Member, Schertz, 8-31-21
Christopher Moss	Board Member, Lufkin, 8-31-21
James "Dick" Nance	Board Member, Hallettsville, 8-31-23
Dolores Ramirez	Board Member, San Benito, 8-31-19
Nanette Sissney	Board Member, Whitesboro, 8-31-23

STAFF:

Executive Director	Brian Guthrie . . . . .512/542-6411 / *Fax: 512/542-6585*
Special Advisor to Exec. Dir.	Ray Spivey . . . . .512/542-6470 / *Fax: 512/542-6474*
Deputy Director	Ken Welch . . . . .512/542-6405 / *Fax: 512/542-6585*
Chief Investment Officer	Jerry Albright . . . . .512/542-6155 / *Fax: 512/542-5102*
Chief Audit Executive	Amy Barrett . . . . .512/542-6559 / *Fax: 512/542-6431*
General Counsel	Carolina de Onis . . . . .512/542-6457 / *Fax: 512/542-6529*
Chief Benefit Officer	Barbie Pearson . . . . .512/542-6731 / *Fax: 512/542-6585*
Chief Financial Officer	Don Green . . . . .512/542-6201 / *Fax: 512/542-6585*
Chief Health Care Officer	Katrina Daniel . . . . .512/542-6521 / *Fax: 512/542-6585*
Chief Information Officer	Chris Cutler . . . . .512/542-6234 / *Fax: 512/542-6528*
Director of Communications	Position Vacant . . . . .512/542-6508 / *Fax: 512/542-6426*
Director of Governmental Rel.	Merita Zoga . . . . .512/542-6857 / *Fax: 512/542-6474*
Director of Human Resources	Janet Bray . . . . .512/542-6511 / *Fax: 512/542-6571*
Director of Strategic Initiatives	Rebecca Merrill . . . . .512/542-6840 / *Fax: 512/542-6585*

TEXAS CIVIL COMMITMENT OFFICE (TCCO)
4614 West Howard Lane, Bldg. 2, Suite 350, Austin 78728
512/341-4421 • *FAX: 512/341-4645* • www.tcco.texas.gov

5 Members - 6 Years

Christy Jack	Chair, Fort Worth, 2-1-23
The Honorable Jose Aliseda	Board Member, Beeville, 2-1-19
Roberto Dominguez	Board Member, Mission, 2-1-23
Rona Stratton Gouyton	Board Member, Fort Worth, 2-1-21
Katie McClure	Board Member, Kingwood, 2-1-21

STAFF:
Executive Director   Marsha McLane ....512/341-4637 / *Fax: 512/341-4645*

TEXAS CORRECTIONAL OFFICE ON OFFENDERS WITH MEDICAL OR MENTAL IMPAIRMENTS ADVISORY COMMITTEE
c/o TDCJ, 4616 W. Howard Lane, Ste. 200, Austin 78728
512/671-2134 • *FAX: 512/671-2409* • www.tdcj.texas.gov

10 Members - 6 Years

The Honorable Robb Catalano	Chair, Fort Worth, 2-1-19
Martin Deleon	Board Member, Corpus Christi, 2-1-19
Kathy C. Flanagan, M.D.	Board Member, Houston, 2-1-19
Christopher C. Kirk	Board Member, Bryan, 2-1-17
Kathryn Kotrla	Board Member, Round Rock, 2-1-15
Trent Marshall	Board Member, Burleson, 2-1-19
Robert Morgan	Board Member, Lubbock, 2-1-17
Denise Oncken	Board Member, Houston, 2-1-15
Ross Taylor, M.D.	Board Member, Austin, 2-1-15
Vacant	Board Member

STAFF:
Director   April Zamora ....512/671-2134 / *Fax: 512/671-2409*

TEXAS EMERGENCY SERVICES RETIREMENT SYSTEM (TESRS)
208 E. 10th Street, 3rd Floor, Suite 309, Austin 78701
512/936-3372 • 800/919-3372 • *FAX: 512/936-3480*
www.tesrs.texas.gov • Agency # 326

9 Members - 6 Years

Frank R. Torres	Chair, Raymondville, 9-1-17
Ronald V. Larson	Secretary, Horizon City, 9-1-19
Andrew "Taylor" Allen	Board Member, Dallas, 9-1-19
Courtney Gibson Bechtol	Board Member, Rockport, 9-1-21
Dan Key	Board Member, Friendswood, 9-1-19
Jenny Moore	Board Member, Lake Jackson, 9-1-21
Pilar Rodriguez	Board Member, Edinburg, 9-1-21
Don R. Shipman	Board Member, Colleyville, 9-1-17
Stephen Williams	Board Member, Carthage, 9-1-17

STAFF:

Executive Director	Kevin Deiters	.512/936-3474 / *Fax: 512/936-3480*
Chief Financial Officer	Judy Johnson	.512/936-3422 / *Fax: 512/936-3480*
Staff Services Officer	Susannah Jones	.512/936-3473 / *Fax: 512/936-3480*
Accountant	Eliana Martinez	.512/936-3470 / *Fax: 512/936-3480*
Contract Manager	Shirley Hays	.512/936-9934 / *Fax: 512/936-3480*
Benefits Specialist	Cassandra Davis	.512/936-3478 / *Fax: 512/936-3480*
Benefits Specialist	Chana Kramer	.512/936-3424 / *Fax: 512/936-3480*
Data & Technology Officer	Jessica O'Brien	.512/936-3410 / *Fax: 512/936-3480*
Marketing Specialist	William Langford	.512/936-3423 / *Fax: 512/936-3480*

TEXAS SOUTHERN UNIVERSITY BOARD OF REGENTS
3100 Cleburne Street, Houston 77004
713/313-7992 • *FAX: 713/313-7901* • www.tsu.edu

9 Members - 6 Years

1 Student Regent

Glenn O. Lewis	Chair, Fort Worth, 2-1-19
Wesley G. Terrell	Vice Chair, Dallas, 2-1-21
Marilyn A. Rose	Second Vice Chair, Houston, 2-1-21
Erik D. Salwen	Secretary, Houston, 2-1-19
Sarah D. Monty-Arnoni	Board Member, Houston, 2-1-19
Oliver J. Bell	Board Member, Houston, 2-1-17
Gary L. Bledsoe	Board Member, Austin, 2-1-17
Samuel L. Bryant	Board Member, Austin, 2-1-17
Derrick M. Mitchell	Board Member, Houston, 2-1-21
Justin J. Lee	Student Regent, Beaumont, 5-31-18

STAFF:

Executive Administrator for Board Relations	Faith Ruiz . . . . .713/313-7900 / *Fax: 713/313-7901*

TEXAS STATE TECHNICAL COLLEGE
BOARD OF REGENTS

3801 Campus Dr., Waco 76705 • 254/867-4891 • *FAX: 254/867-3979* • www.tstc.edu/bor

9 Members - 6 Years

John Hatchel	Chair, Woodway, 8-31-17
Ivan Andarza	Vice Chair, Austin, 8-31-19
Tony Abad	Board Member, Waco, 8-31-21
Curtis Cleveland	Board Member, Waco, 8-31-21
Joe M. Gurecky	Board Member, Rosenberg, 8-31-17
Joe K. Hearne	Board Member, Dallas, 8-31-17
Keith Honey P.E.	Board Member, Longview, 8-31-19
Alejandro G. Meade III	Board Member, Mission, 8-31-21
Ellis M. Skinner II	Board Member, Dallas, 8-31-19

ADMINISTRATION:

Chancellor & CEO   Michael L. Reeser . . . . .254/867-4891 / *Fax: 254/867-3960*

TEXAS STATE UNIVERSITY SYSTEM
BOARD OF REGENTS
Thomas J. Rusk Bldg., 200 E. 10th Street, Suite 600, Austin 78701
512/463-1808 • *FAX: 512/463-1816*
www.tsus.edu • Agency # 758

9 Members - 6 Years; 1 Student Regent 1 Year

Rossanna Salazar	Chair, Austin, 2-1-17
Charlie Amato	Board Member, San Antonio, 2-1-19
Veronica M. Edwards	Board Member, San Antonio, 2-1-21
Jaime Garza, M.D.	Board Member, San Antonio, 2-1-17
J. David Montagne	Board Member, Beaumont, 2-1-21
Vernon Reaser, III	Board Member, Bellaire, 2-1-19
William Scott	Board Member, Nederland, 2-1-19
Alan L. Tinsley	Board Member, Madisonville, 2-1-21
Donna Williams	Board Member, Arlington, 2-1-17
Kaitlyn Tyra	Student Regent, Spring, 5-31-18

ADMINISTRATION:
Chancellor   Brian McCall 512/463-3280

COMPONENT UNIVERSITIES:

Lamar University:
Kenneth Evans, President
P.O. Box 10001
Beaumont, TX 77710
409/880-8405

Texas State University-San Marcos:
Denise M. Trauth, President
601 University Dr., JCK 1020
San Marcos, TX 78666
512/245-2121

Sam Houston State University:
Dana Hoyt, President
P.O. Box 2026, SHSU
Huntsville, TX 77341
936/294-1012

Lamar Institute of Technology:
Lonnie Howard, President
P.O. Box 10043
Beaumont, TX 77710
409/880-8185

Sul Ross State University:
William Kibler, President
Box C-100
Alpine, TX 79832
432/837-8000

Lamar State College-Orange:
J. Michael Shahan, President
410 Front Street
Orange, TX 77630
409/882-3314

Sul Ross State University
   Rio Grande College:
William Kibler, President
Box C-100
Alpine, TX 79832
432/837-8000

Lamar State College-Port Arthur:
Betty Reynard, President
P.O. Box 310
Port Arthur, TX 77641
409/984-6101

TEXAS TECH UNIVERSITY SYSTEM
BOARD OF REGENTS

P.O. Box 42011, Lubbock 79409-2011 • 806/742-2161 • *FAX: 806/742-4345*
www.texastech.edu

9 Members - 6 Years

Mickey L. Long	Chair, Midland, 1-31-21
John D. Esparza	Board Member, Austin, 1-31-19
L. Frederick "Rick" Francis	Board Member, El Paso, 1-31-19
Ronnie "Ron" Hammonds	Board Member, Houston, 1-31-21
Christopher M. Huckabee	Board Member, Fort Worth, 1-31-21
Tim Lancaster	Board Member, Abilene, 1-31-19
John D. Steinmetz	Board Member, Dallas, 1-31-23
Jeremy Stewart	Student Regent, Arlington, 5-31-17

Executive Assistant to the Board Ben Lock . . . . .806/742-0012 / *Fax: 806/742-8050*

ADMINISTRATION:

Chancellor	Robert L. Duncan . . . . .806/742-0012 / *Fax: 806/742-8050*
VC and Chief Financial Officer	Gary Barnes . . . . .806/742-9000 / *Fax: 806/742-2195*
VC and General Counsel	John Huffaker . . . . .806/742-2115 / *Fax: 806/742-1224*
VC for Governmental Relations	Martha Brown . . . . .806/742-2120 / *Fax: 806/742-1120*
VC for Institutional Advancement	Patrick Kramer . . . . .806/742-1764 / *Fax: 806/742-9754*
VC for Facilities Planning and Construction	Michael Molina . . . . .806/742-2116 / *Fax: 806/742-2241*
VC for Academic Affairs	John Opperman . . . . .512/463-3860 / *Fax: 512/936-8144*
Associate VC for Information Technology	Kay Rhodes . . . . .806/742-5170 / *Fax: 806/742-5168*
Chief Audit Executive	Kim Turner 806/742-3220
Chief of Staff	Christina Butts . . . . .806/742-0012 / *Fax: 806/742-8050*
VC for Communications and Marketing	Brett Ashworth . . . . .806/742-0057 / *Fax: 806/742-8050*

COMPONENT INSTITUTIONS:

Angelo State University:
President   Brian J. May, Ph.D. 325/942-2073

Texas Tech University Health Sciences Center:
President   Tedd L. Mitchell, M.D. .806/743-2900

Texas Tech University:
President   Lawrence Schovanec 806/742-2121

Texas Tech University Health Science Center El Paso:
President   Richard Lange, M.D. 915/215-4300

TEXAS WING, CIVIL AIR PATROL, USAF AUXILIARY

553 Terry Crawford Dr., Nacogdoches 75964
936/205-9013 • *FAX: 866/867-6764* • www.txwgcap.org

STAFF:

Texas Wing Commander	Sean Crandall, Col	.956/456-3590
Government Relations Director	Brooks Cima, Col	.832/632-1996
Government Relations Director	Dennis Cima, Lt Col	.832/632-1996
Texas Wing Sr. Administrator	Karen Smith	.936/205-9013

TEXAS WOMAN'S UNIVERSITY BOARD OF REGENTS

P.O. Box 425587, TWU Station, Denton 76204-5587
940/898-3250 • *FAX: 940/898-3244*
www.twu.edu/regents

9 Members - 6 Years

Nolan E. Perez, M.D.	Chair, Harlingen, 2-1-21
Melissa D. Tonn, M.D.	Vice Chair, Dallas, 2-1-17
Nancy Painter Paup	Board Member, Fort Worth, 2-1-19
George R. Schrader	Board Member, Dallas, 2-1-19
Mary Pincoffs Wilson	Board Member, Austin, 2-1-17
Rachel Lacobucci	Student Regent, 5-31-18
Vacant	Board Member
Vacant	Board Member
Vacant	Board Member

ADMINISTRATION:

Chancellor and President	Carine M. Feyten, Ph.D.	.940/898-3201

THE UNIVERSITY OF TEXAS SYSTEM
BOARD OF REGENTS

210 West Seventh St., Austin 78701 • 512/499-4402 • *FAX: 512/499-442*
www.utsystem.edu/board-of-regents • Agency # 720

9 Members - 6 Years; 1 Student Regent

Sara Martinez Tucker	Chairman, Dallas, 2-1-21
Jeffery D. Hildebrand	Vice Chairman, Houston, 2-1-19
Paul L. Foster	Vice Chairman, El Paso, 2-1-19
Ernest Aliseda	Board Member, McAllen, 2-1-19
David J. Beck	Board Member, Houston, 2-1-21
Kevin P. Eltife	Board Member, Tyler, 2-1-23
R. Steven Hicks	Board Member, Austin, 2-1-21
Janiece Longoria	Board Member, Houston, 2-1-23
Rad Weaver	Board Member, San Antonio, 2-1-23
Jaciel Castro	Student Regent, San Antonio, 5-31-18

General Counsel:
General Counsel to the Board   Francie A. Frederick . . . . . . .512/499-4402 / *Fax: 512/499-4425*

U.T. System Administration:
Chancellor   William H. McRaven . . . . . .512/499-4201 / *Fax: 512/499-4215*
Deputy Chancellor   David E. Daniel, Ph.D. . . . . .512/499-4201 / *Fax: 512/499-4215*
Executive VC for
   Academic Affairs   Steven Leslie, Ph.D. . . . . . . .512/499-4237 / *Fax: 512/499-4240*
Exec. VC for Health Affairs   Raymond S. Greenberg, M.D., Ph.D.
   .512/499-4224 / *Fax: 512/499-4313*
Exec. VC for Business Affairs   Scott C. Kelley, Ed.D. . . . . .512/499-4560 / *Fax: 512/499-4289*

INSTITUTIONS:

The University of Texas at Arlington:
UTA Box 19125
Arlington, TX 76019

President   Vistasp M. Karbhari, Ph.D. . . . .817/272-2101 / *Fax: 817/272-5656*

The University of Texas at Austin:
110 Inner Campus Drive, Stop G3400
Austin, TX 78712-3400

President   Gregory L. Fenves, Ph.D. . . . . .512/471-1232 / *Fax: 512/471-8102*

The University of Texas at Dallas:
800 W. Campbell Road
Richardson, TX 75080-3021

President   Richard Benson, Ph.D. . . . . .972/883-2201 / *Fax: 972/883-2237*

The University of Texas at El Paso:
500 W. University Ave.
Administration Bldg., Fifth Flr.
El Paso, TX 79968-0500

President   Diana S. Natalicio, Ph.D. . . . . . .915/747-5555 / *Fax: 915/747-5069*

The University of Texas cont.

The University of Texas of the Permian Basin:
4901 East University Blvd.
Odessa, TX 79762

President   Sandra K. Woodley, Ph.D. . . .432/552-2100 / *Fax: 432/552-2109*

The University of Texas Rio Grande Valley:
1201 W. University Drive
Edinburg, TX 78539

President   Guy H. Bailey, Ph.D. . . . . . . .956/296-1415 / *Fax: 956/296-1320*

The University of Texas at San Antonio:
One UTSA Circle
San Antonio, TX 78249-0601

President   Taylor Eighmy, Ph.D. . . . . . . .210/458-5112 / *Fax: 210/458-4655*

The University of Texas at Tyler:
3900 University Blvd.
Tyler, TX 75799

President   Michael Tidwell, Ph.D. . . . . .903/566-7119 / *Fax: 903/566-8368*

The University of Texas Southwestern Medical Center:
5323 Harry Hines Blvd.
Dallas, TX 75390-9002

President   Daniel K. Podolsky, M.D. . . .214/648-2508 / *Fax: 214/648-8690*

The University of Texas Medical Branch at Galveston:
301 University Blvd., Suite 6.100
Galveston, TX 77555-0129

President   David L. Callender, M.D. . . . .409/772-1902 / *Fax: 409/772-5064*

The University of Texas Health Science Center at Houston:
7000 Fannin, UCT 1707
Houston, TX 77030

President   Giuseppe N. Colasurdo, M.D. 713/500-3010 / *Fax: 713/500-3059*

The University of Texas Health Science Center at San Antonio:
7703 Floyd Curl Dr., MSC 7834
San Antonio, TX 78229-3900

President   William L. Henrich, M.D. . . .210/567-2050 / *Fax: 210/567-2025*

The University of Texas M. D. Anderson Cancer Center:
1515 Holcombe Blvd., Unit 1491
Houston, TX 77030

President   Peter W. T. Pisters, M.D. . . . .713/792-6000 / *Fax: 713/563-4500*

The University of Texas Health Science Center at Tyler:
11937 U.S. Hwy. 271
Tyler, TX 75708-3154

President   Kirk A. Calhoun, M.D. . . . . . .903/877-7750 / *Fax: 903/877-7759*

TRANSPORTATION, TEXAS DEPARTMENT OF (TXDOT)*

Dewitt C. Greer State Highway Building, 125 East 11th Street, Austin 78701-2483
512/463-8585 • *FAX: 512/463-9896* • www.txdot.gov • Agency # 601
Enforcement: 800/687-7846
Tourist/Travel Information: 800/452-9292

5 Members - 6 Years

J. Bruce Bugg, Jr.	Chairman, San Antonio, 2-1-21
Jeff Austin III	Commissioner, Tyler, 2-1-19
Tryon D. Lewis	Commissioner, Odessa, 2-1-21
Laura Ryan	Commissioner, Cypress, 2-1-23
Victor Vandergriff	Commissioner, Fort Worth, 2-1-19

STAFF:

Executive Director	James M. Bass . . . . .512/305-9501 / *Fax: 512/305-9567*
Deputy Executive Director	Marc D. Williams, P.E. . . . .512/305-9504 / *Fax: 512/463-0283*
Chief Engineer	Bill Hale, P.E. . . . . .512/305-9505 / *Fax: 512/463-0283*
Chief of Staff	Jesus "Chuy" Gonzalez . . .512/305-9502 / *Fax: 512/463-0283*
Chief Administrative Officer	Rich McMonagle . . . . .512/305-9518 / *Fax: 512/463-0283*
Chief Financial Officer	Brian D. Ragland, CPA . . .512/305-9507 / *Fax: 512/463-0283*
Chief Audit & Compliance Officer	Benito Ybarra . . . . .512/463-8637 / *Fax: 512/463-8593*
Project Finance, Debt and	
Strategic Contracts	Ben Asher . . . . .512/463-8611 / *Fax: 512/463-0283*
Director	
Strategy and Innovation	Darran T. Anderson . . . . . .512/305-9508 / *Fax: 512/463-0283*
Government Affairs Division	Jerry Haddican . . . . .512/463-6086 / *Fax: 512/463-9389*
Communication &	
Customer Service	Bob Kaufman . . . . .512/305-9503 / *Fax: 512/463-0283*
Aviation Division	David S. Fulton . . . . .512/416-4502 / *Fax: 512/416-4510*
Bridge Division	Gregg Freeby, P.E. . . . . . .512/416-2183 / *Fax: 512/416-3144*
Construction Division	Gina Gallegos . . . . .512/416-2559 / *Fax: 512/416-2539*
Design Division	Camille Thomason, P.E. . . .512/416-2653 / *Fax: 512/416-2599*
Environmental Affairs Division	Carlos Swonke . . . . .512/416-3001 / *Fax: 512/416-2746*
Federal Affairs Section	Andrea Lofye . . . . .512/463-6086 / *Fax: 512/463-9389*
Financial Management	Stephen Stewart . . . . .512/486-5555 / *Fax: 512/416-2085*
Fleet Operations Division	Dalton Pratt 817/370-3681
Information Management	Dana Glover 512/465-3058
Maritime	Dan Harmon 713/802-5157
Human Resources Division	David McMillan . . . . .512/486-5304 / *Fax: 512/486-5321*
Contract Services	Kenneth Stewart 512/416-4620
Professional Engineering	
Procurement Services Div.	Martin Rodin 512/416-2037
Procurement Division	Ken Wood 512/416-2401
State Legislative Affairs	Trent Thomas . . . . .512/463-6086 / *Fax: 512/463-9389*
Civil Rights	Michael Bryant . . . . .512/416-4700 / *Fax: 512/416-4711*
General Counsel	Jeff Graham . . . . .512/463-8630 / *Fax: 512/475-3070*
Public Transportation Division	Eric Gleason . . . . .512/374-5233 / *Fax: 512/374-5244*
Rail Division	Peter Espy . . . . .512/486-5230 / *Fax: 512/374-5244*
Research and Technology	
Implementation Division	Rocio Perez . . . . .512/416-4730 / *Fax: 512/475-7486*
Right of Way Division	Gus Cannon . . . . .512/416-2918 / *Fax: 512/416-2904*
Strategic Planning	Kent Marquardt 512/305-9562

TX Dept. of Transportation cont.
Director

Support Services Division	Andrew Chavez	...........................806/748-4576
Toll Operations	Richard Nelson	..........512/936-0903 / *Fax: 512/936-0970*
Traffic Operations Division	Michael Chacon	.........512/416-3200 / *Fax: 512/416-3214*
Trans. Planning and		
Program Div.	Peter Smith	.............512/486-5003 / *Fax: 512/486-5007*
Travel Information Division	Joan Henderson	.........512/486-5900 / *Fax: 512/486-5909*
Maintenance Division	C. Michael Lee, Interim	...512/416-3034 / *Fax: 512/416-2914*
Compliance and Ethics	Kristin Alexander	...........................512/465-3602
Occupational Safety Division	Samuel Salazar	..........512/416-3385 / *Fax: 512/416-3420*

DISTRICT ENGINEERS:

Abilene District
Carl Johnson, P.E.
4250 N. Clack St.
Abilene, TX 79601-9241
325/676-6800

Amarillo District
Brian Crawford, P.E.
5715 Canyon Dr.
Amarillo, TX 79110
806/356-3200

Atlanta District
Glenn Green, P.E. (Interim)
701 E. Main St.
Atlanta, TX 75551-2418
903/796-2851

Austin District
Terry McCoy, P.E.
7901 N. I-35
Austin, TX 78753
512/832-7000

Beaumont District
Tucker Ferguson, P.E.
8350 Eastex Freeway
Beaumont, TX 77708-1701
409/892-7311

Brownwood District
Elias Rmeili, P.E.
2495 Hwy. 183 North
Brownwood, TX 76802
325/646-2591

Bryan District
Lance W. Simmons, P.E.
2591 North Earl Rudder Frwy.
Bryan, TX 77803-5190
979/778-2165

Childress District
Marty Smith, P.E.
7599 U.S. Hwy. 287
Childress, TX 79201-9705
940/937-2571

Corpus Christi District
Chris Caron, P.E.
1701 S. Padre Island Dr.
Corpus Christi, TX 78416
361/808-2300

Dallas District
Kelly Selman, P.E.
4777 E. Hwy. 80
Mesquite, TX 75150-6643
214/320-6100

El Paso District
Bob Bielek
13301 Gateway Blvd. W.
El Paso, TX 79928-5410
915/790-4200

Fort Worth District
Loyl Bussell, P.E., Interim
2501 Southwest Loop 820
Fort Worth, TX 76133-2300
817/370-6500

Houston District
Quincy Allen, P.E.
7600 Washington Ave.
Houston, TX 77007
713/802-5000

Laredo District
David Salazar, P.E.
1817 Bob Bullock Loop
Laredo, TX 78043
956/712-7400

Lubbock District
Steve Warren, P.E.
135 Slaton Road
Lubbock, TX 79404-5201
806/745-4411

Lufkin District
Cheryl Flood, P.E.
1805 N. Timberland Drive
Lufkin, TX 75901
936/634-4433

Odessa District
John R. Speed, P.E.
3901 E. Highway 80
Odessa, TX 79761
432/498-4711

Paris District
Noel Paramanantham, P.E.
1365 N. Main St.
Paris, TX 75460-2697
903/737-9300

Pharr District
Pedro Alvarez, P.E.
600 West U.S. 83 Exp.
Pharr, TX 78577
956/702-6100

San Angelo District
Mark Jones, P.E.
4502 Knickerbocker Rd.
San Angelo, TX 76904
325/944-1501

San Antonio District
Mario Jorge, P.E.
4615 North West Loop 410
San Antonio, TX 78229
210/615-5802

Tyler District
Glenn Green, P.E.
2709 West Front St.
Tyler, TX 75702
903/510-9100

Wichita Falls District
Larry Tegtmeyer, P.E.
1601 Southwest Parkway
Wichita Falls, TX 76302-4906
940/720-7700

Waco District
Stan Swiatek, P.E.
100 South Loop Drive
Waco, TX 76703
254/867-2700

Yoakum District
Paul Reitz, P.E.
403 Huck St.
Yoakum, TX 77995-2804
361/293-4300

*Subject to the Texas Sunset Act; will be reviewed in 2029.

TRINITY RIVER AUTHORITY OF TEXAS

5300 S. Collins, P.O. Box 60, Arlington 76004-0060
817/467-4343 • *FAX: 817/465-0970* • www.trinityra.org

25 Members - 6 Years

Christina Melton Crain	President, Dallas County, 3-15-17
Kevin Maxwell	Vice President, Houston County, 3-15-21
Harold L. Barnard	Director, Ellis County, 3-15-17
Whitney Beckworth	Director, At Large, 3-15-23
Henry Borbolla III	Director, Tarrant County, 3-15-19
Steve Cronin	Director, San Jacinto County, 3-15-17
Amanda B. Davis	Director, Leon County, 3-15-17
Tommy G. Fordyce	Director, Walker County, 3-15-19
Martha A. Hernandez	Director, Tarrant County, 3-15-17
John W. Jenkins	Director, Chambers County, 3-15-21
Jess A. Laird	Director, Henderson County, 3-15-19
David B. Leonard	Director, Liberty County, 3-15-19
Victoria Lucas	Director, Kaufman County, 3-15-23
Dennis "Joe" McCleskey	Director, Trinity County, 3-15-17
Robert McFarlane, M.D.	Director, At Large, 3-15-23
James W. "Jim" Neale	Director, Dallas County, 3-15-19
Manny Rachal	Director, Polk County, 3-15-21
William Rodgers	Director, Tarrant County, 3-15-23
Amir A. Rupani	Director, At Large, 3-15-19
Ana Laura Saucedo	Director, Dallas County, 3-15-19
Dudley Skyrme	Director, Anderson County, 3-15-19
C. Dwayne Somerville	Director, Freestone County, 3-15-19
J. Carol Spillars	Director, Madison County, 3-15-17
Frank Steed, Jr.	Director, Navarro County, 3-15-23
Edward Williams III	Director, Dallas County, 3-15-23

STAFF:
General Manager   J. Kevin Ward 817/467-4343

Regional Offices:
Regional Mgr., Northern Region Fiona M. Allen 817/467-4343
Regional Mgr., Southern Region Jimmie R. Sims 936/295-5485

UNIFORM STATE LAWS, COMMISSION ON
111 N. Wabash Ave., Suite 1010, Chicago, IL 60602
312/450-6600 • *FAX: 312/450-6601*

10 Members - 6 Years

The Honorable Levi J. Benton	Commissioner, Houston, 9-30-16
Eric Hougland	Commissioner, Austin, 5-19-10
The Honorable Debra H. Lehrmann	Commissioner, Colleyville, 9-30-22
Peter K. Munson	Commissioner, Pottsboro, 9-30-20
Frank E. Perez	Commissioner, Brownsville, 9-30-16
Marilyn E. Phelan	Commissioner, Lubbock, 9-30-18
Harry L. Tindall	Commissioner, Houston, 9-30-18
Karen Roberts Washington	Commissioner, Dallas, 9-30-16
The Honorable Earl L. Yeakel, III	Commissioner, Austin, 9-30-18
Leonard Reese	Life Member, Austin
Rodney W. Satterwhite	Life Member, Midland
Vacant	Commissioner

STAFF:
Executive Director   Liza Karsai 312/450-6600

UNIVERSITY OF HOUSTON SYSTEM
BOARD OF REGENTS
4302 University Dr., 128 Ezekiel Cullen Bldg., Houston 77204-6001
832/842-3444 • *FAX: 713/743-3495* • www.uhsa.uh.edu • Agency # 783

9 Members - 6 Years; 1 Student Regent - 1 Year

Tilman J. Fertitta	Chair, Houston, 8-31-21
Welcome W. Wilson, Jr.	Vice Chair, Houston, 8-31-17
Spencer D. Armour III	Secretary, Midland, 8-31-17
Durga D. Agrawal	Board Member, Houston, 8-31-19
Beth Madison	Board Member, Houston, 8-31-21
Gerald W. McElvy	Board Member, Southlake, 8-31-21
Paula M. Mendoza	Board Member, Houston, 8-31-19
Peter K. Taaffe	Board Member, Austin, 8-31-19
Roger F. Welder	Board Member, Victoria, 8-31-17
Neelesh C. Mutyala	Student Regent, Houston, 5-31-18

STAFF:

Executive Administrator	Gerry Mathisen . . . . .832/842-3446/ *Fax: 713/743-3495*
Board Coordinator	Marquette D. Hobbs . . . . .832/842-3439/ *Fax: 713/743-3495*
Administrative Assistant	Brenda L. Robles . . . . . . .832/842-3444/ *Fax: 713/743-3495*

SYSTEM ADMINISTRATION:
128 Ezekiel Cullen Bldg.
4800 Calhoun
Houston 77204-6001

Chancellor, UH System and President, UH	Dr. Renu Khator . . . . .832/842-8820/ *Fax: 713/743-8837*
SVC and SVP for Academic Affairs, UH Syst. & Provost, UH	Dr. Paula Myrick Short . .832/842-0555 / *Fax: 832/842-5142*

Senior VC and VP for Admin.
and Fin. UH System and UH   Jim McShan . . . . .832/842-5550/ *Fax: 713/743-5551*
VC and VP Legal Affairs UH Syst. &
Gen. Counsel UH System & UH   Dona H. Cornell . . . . . .832/842-0949/ *Fax: 713/743-0948*
VC for Student Affairs & Enrollment UH Syst.
& VP for Student Affairs, UH   Dr. Richard Walker . . .713/743-5390 / *Fax: 713/743-5394*
IVC and VP for Research and
Tech. Transfer, UH System & UH   Dr. Amr Elnashai . . . .713/743-5797 / *Fax: 713/743-9577*
VC and VP Univ. Advancement,
UH Syst. & UH   Eloise Dunn Brice . . . .713/743-8872 / *Fax: 713/743-0946*
VC and VP Governmental &
Community Relations   Jason Smith . . . . .713/743-7189 / *Fax: 713/743-0900*
Associate VP for Division of Univ.
Marketing, Communication
& Media   Lisa Holdeman . . . . . .713/743-0945 / *Fax: 713/743-8185*

COMPONENT INSTITUTIONS:

University of Houston:
President   Dr. Renu Khator . . . . .713/743-8820 / *Fax: 713/743-8837*
4302 University Dr.
Houston, TX 77204-2018

UH-Clear Lake:
President   Dr. Ira K. Blake . . . . .281/283-2004 / *Fax: 281/283-2010*
2700 Bay Area Blvd.
Houston, TX 77058-1098

UH-Downtown:
President   Dr. Juan Sanchez Munoz . . .713/221-8001 / *Fax: 713/221-8075*
One Main Street
Houston, TX 77002

UH-Victoria:
President   Dr. Raymond V. Morgan, Jr. . .361/570-4848/*Fax: 361/570-4334*
3007 N. Ben Wilson
Victoria, TX 77901-5731

UNIVERSITY OF NORTH TEXAS SYSTEM
BOARD OF REGENTS

1901 Main Street, Dallas 75201 • 214/752-5533 • *FAX: 214/752-8827*
untsystem.edu/leadership/board-regents/regent- profiles • Agency # 769

9 Members - 6 Years; 1 Student Regent - 1 Year

Brint Ryan	Chair, Dallas, 5-22-21
Laura Wright	Vice Chair, Dallas, 5-22-21
Milton B. Lee	Board Member, San Antonio, 5-22-17
A.K. Mago	Board Member, Dallas, 5-22-21
Donald Potts	Board Member, Dallas, 5-22-17
Rusty Reid	Board Member, Fort Worth, 5-22-19
Gwyn Shea	Board Member, Irving, 5-22-19
Al Silva	Board Member, San Antonio, 5-22-17
Glen Whitley	Board Member, Hurst, 5-22-19
Haley Leverett	Student Regent, Ft. Worth, 5-31-18

ADMINISTRATION:
Chancellor   Lesa B. Roe 214/752-8585
Secretary to the Board of Regents Dr. Rosemary Haggett 214/752-5545

UPPER COLORADO RIVER AUTHORITY*

512 Orient, San Angelo 76903 • 325/655-0565 • *FAX: 325/655-1371* • www.ucratx.org

9 Members - 6 Years

Jeffie Harmon Roberts	Chair, Robert Lee, 2-1-17
John Nikolauk	Vice Chair, Eldorado, 2-1-19
William R. Hood	Secretary, Robert Lee, 2-1-15
Hyman D. Sauer	Treasurer, Eldorado, 2-1-17
Ronny Alexander	Board Member, Paint Rock, 2-1-15
Bill Holland	Board Member, San Angelo, 2-1-19
Eva Horton	Board Member, San Angelo, 2-1-15
Martin Lee	Board Member, Bronte, 2-1-19
Hugh Stone	Board Member, San Angelo, 2-1-17

STAFF:
Director of Operations   Chuck Brown . . . . .325/655-0565 / *Fax: 325/655-1371*
Office Manager   Ellen Groth . . . . .325/655-0565 / *Fax: 325/655-1371*

*Subject to the Texas Sunset Act; will be reviewed in 2029.

UPPER GUADALUPE RIVER AUTHORITY

Guadalupe Basin Natural Resource Center
125 Lehmann Drive, Suite 100, Kerrville 78028-5908
830/896-5445 • *FAX: 830/257-2621* • www.ugra.org

9 Members - 6 Years

Bob Waller	President, Kerrville, 2-1-19
Blake W. Smith	Vice President, Hunt, 2-1-21
Diane L. McMahon	Secretary, Kerrville, 2-1-21
James "Wayne" Musgrove	Treasurer, Mountain Home, 2-1-21
Mike L. Allen	Board Member, Ingram, 2-1-19
Aaron C. Bulkley	Board Member, Hunt, 2-1-19
Harold Danford	Board Member, Kerrville, 2-1-17
D. Michael "Mike" Hughes	Board Member, Ingram, 2-1-17
William R. Rector	Board Member, Kerrville, 2-1-17

STAFF:

General Manager	Ray Buck, Jr. . . . . .830/896-5445 / *Fax: 830/792-6763*
Assistant General Manager	Tammy Thompson . . .830/896-5456 x221 / *Fax: 830/792-6763*

UPPER NECHES RIVER MUNICIPAL WATER AUTHORITY

P.O. Box 1965, Palestine 75802 • 903/876-2237 • *FAX: 903/876-5200*

3 Members - 6 Years

Jay Steven Herrington D.D.S.	Board Member, Palestine, 2-1-21
William Barry James	Board Member, Palestine, 2-1-19
Milton Phillip Jenkins	Board Member, Palestine, 2-1-23

STAFF:

General Manager	Monty D. Shank . . . . .903/876-2237 / *Fax: 903/876-5200*

VETERANS COMMISSION, TEXAS*

SFA Bldg., 8th Floor, Ste. 800, 1700 N. Congress Avenue (78701)
P.O. Box 12277, Austin 78711-2277 • 512/463-6564 • *FAX: 512/475-2395*
www.tvc.state.tx.us • Agency # 403

5 Members - 6 Years

Eliseo Cantu, Jr.	Chair, Corpus Christi, 12-31-19
The Rev. Richard A. McLeon IV	Vice Chair, Henderson, 12-31-17
Jake Ellzey	Secretary, Midlothian, 12-31-17
Kevin Barber	Board Member, Houston, 12-31-21
Daniel P. Moran	Board Member, Cypress, 12-31-19

STAFF:

Executive Director	Thomas P. Palladino	.512/463-6564
Deputy Executive Director	Cruz Montemayor	.512/463-6564
General Counsel	Madeleine Connor	.512/463-3605
Division Director		
Resource Management	Chip Osborne	.512/463-3151
Program Operations	Shawn Deabay	.512/463-1466
Director		
Claims Rep. & Counseling	Victor Polanco	.512/463-8730
Human Resources	Glenn Tramel	.512/463-1295
Fund for Veterans' Assistance	Charles Catoe	.512/463-6535
Veterans Employment Services	Tim Shatto	.512/463-2678
Veterans Education	Position Vacant	.512/463-6160
Veterans Mental Health Prog.	Tim Keesling	.512/463-6091
Veterans Employment Services		
Operations Manager	Yolanda Moten	.512/463-8016
Communications and		
Veteran Outreach Manager	Elaine Zavala	.512/463-0680
Veterans Education Manager	Tina Marberry	.512/463-6441
Chief Financial Officer	Michelle Nall	.512/463-1657
Government Relations		
Program Manager	Justin Coleman	.512/463-8914
Veteran Entrepreneur		
Program Manager	Robyn Provost	.512/463-5173
Women Veterans		
Program Manager	Anna Baker	.512/463-0519
Information Resource		
Management Manager	Peter Donton	.512/463-2791

Claims Branch Offices:

Claims Northwest District	Gary Ivy	.254/299-9950
Claims Northeast District	Paula Taylor	.254/299-9950
Claims Southwest District	Michael Jaeger	.210/699-5308
Claims Southeast District	Julio Harros	.713/383-2756

Regional Veterans Employment Representatives:

South Texas Regional Office	Adrian King	.830/629-2010 x2607
Central Texas Regional Office	Tony Ramirez	.254/200-2014
North Texas Regional Office	James Martin	.214/290-1009
West Texas Regional Office	Lawrence Denton	.325/795-4333
Gulf Coast Regional Office	Ray Wilburn	.713/993-2416

*Subject to the Texas Sunset Act; will be reviewed in 2019.

VETERANS LAND BOARD*

SFA Bldg., 1700 Congress, Rm. 810, P.O. Box 12873, Austin 78711-2873
512/463-5060 • 800/252-8387 • *FAX: 512/475-1425* • www.texasveterans.com

2 Members - 4 Years; 1 Ex Officio Member

Andrew Cobos	Board Member, Houston, 12-29-18
Grant Moody	Board Member, San Antonio, 12-29-20
The Honorable George P. Bush	Ex Officio Member

STAFF:

Executive Secretary	Matthew Elledge	.512/463-2317
Assistant Executive Secretary	Bill McLemore	.512/463-5401

*Subject to the Texas Sunset Act; will be reviewed in 2019.

VETERINARY MEDICAL EXAMINERS TEXAS BOARD OF*

333 Guadalupe, #3-810, Austin 78701-3942 • 512/305-7555 • *FAX: 512/305-7556*
www.veterinary.texas.gov/ • Agency # 578
Toll-Free: 800/821-3205 • Human Resources/Legal Fax: 512/305-7574

9 Members - 6 Years

5 Veterinary Members; 1 Veterinary Technician; 3 Public Members - 6 years

Jessica Quillivan, DVM	President, Magnolia, 8-26-21
Keith Pardue	Vice President, Austin, 8-26-21
Lynn Criner DVM	Secretary, Missouri City, 8-26-21
Samantha Mixon, DVM	Board Member, Boerne, 8-26-23
Randall Skaggs, DVM	Board Member, Perryton, 8-26-23
Michael White, DVM	Board Member, Conroe, 8-26-19
Carlos Chacon	Public Member, Houston, 8-26-23
Vacant	Board Member
Vacant	Public Member

STAFF:

Executive Director	John Helenberg	.512/305-7561 / *Fax: 512/305-7574*
Director of Enforcement	Matthew West	.512/305-7560 / *Fax: 512/936-0837*
Director of Licensing & Examinations		.512/305-7558 / *Fax: 512/305-7556*
General Counsel	Michelle Griffin	.512/305-7572 / *Fax: 512/305-7574*
Accountant	Teresa Long	.512/305-7553 / *Fax: 512/305-7556*

*Subject to the Texas Sunset Act; will be reviewed in 2021.

WATER DEVELOPMENT BOARD, TEXAS*

1700 N. Congress Ave., Ste. 690, P.O. Box 13231, Austin 78711-3231
512/463-7847 • *FAX: 512/475-2053* • www.twdb.texas.gov • Agency # 580

3 Members - 6 Years

Bech K. Bruun	Chair, Corpus Christi, 2-1-19
Kathleen Jackson	Board Member, Beaumont, 2-1-23
Peter M. Lake	Board Member, Tyler, 2-1-21

BOARD STAFF:
Chief of Staff
   Chairman Bruun   Lauren Graber 512/463-7329
   Board Member Jackson   Jennifer White 512/463-7334
   Board Member Lake   Tara Rejino.............................512/463-7322
Scheduler and Exec. Asst. to Board Laura Rodriguez 512/463-7814

Executive Administrator and Staff:
Executive Administrator   Jeff Walker 512/463-7848
Scheduler and Executive Assistant
   to the Exec. Admin.   Gabriela Garcia 512/463-7159
Assistant Exec.Administrator   Amanda Lavin 512/463-9873
Deputy Exec. Admin.,
   Operations and Admin.   Edna Jackson 512/463-8006
Director Governmental Relations Tulsi Oberbeck 512/463-4864
Director of Communications   Merry Klonower 512/463-8165
Deputy Exec. Admin.,
   Water Science & Conservation Position Vacant 512/936-0861
Deputy Exec. Admin.,
   Water Supply & Infrastructure Jessica Zuba 512/475-3734
General Counsel   Todd Chenoweth 512/463-9105
Internal Auditor   Nicole Campbell 512/463-7978
Chief Financial Officer   Rebecca Trevino 512/936-0809
Texas Natural Resources Info. Sys.
   (TNRIS)   Richard Wade 512/463-4010

FIELD OFFICES:

Mesquite Field Office:
Raphael Castro
1515 E. Kearney, Suite 401
Mesquite, TX 75149
972/289-9890

Harlingen Field Office:
Juan Santana
1828 W. Jefferson
Harlingen, TX 78550
956/421-3599

Houston Field Office:
Scott Galaway
3920 Cypress Creek Pkwy.
Suite 330
Houston, TX 77068-3547
281/895-0722

Lubbock Field Office:
Jerry Millsaps
5012 50th Street
Lubbock, TX 79414
806/799-3565

*Subject to the Texas Sunset Act; will be reviewed in 2023.

WATER DISTRICTS, TEXAS MUNICIPAL WATER DISTRICTS:

Colorado River Municipal Water District:
P.O. Box 869
Big Spring, TX 79721-0869
432/267-6341
Fax: 432/267-3121

Northeast Texas Municipal Water District:
P.O. Box 955
Hughes Springs, TX 75656
903/639-7538
Fax: 903/639-2208
netmwd@aol.com

North Texas Municipal Water District:
P.O. Box 2408
Wylie, TX 75098
972/442-5405
Fax: 972/295-6440

Red Bluff Water Power Control District:
111 West Second Street
Pecos, TX 79772
432/445-2037
Fax: 432/445-2740

Tarrant Regional Water District:
800 E. Northside
Fort Worth, TX 76102
817/335-2491
Fax: 817/877-5137

Titus County Fresh Water Supply District #1:
P.O. Box 650
Mt. Pleasant, TX 75456-0650
903/572-1844
Fax: 903/572-0164

West Central Texas Municipal Water District:
P.O. Box 2362
Abilene, TX 79604
325/673-8254
Fax: 325/673-8272

WORKFORCE COMMISSION, TEXAS*

101 East 15th St., Austin 78778 • 512/463-2222
www.twc.state.tx.us • Agency # 320

3 Members - 6 Years

Andres Alcantar	Chair, Leander, 2-1-19
Julian Alvarez III	Commissioner, 2-1-23
Ruth Ruggero Hughs	Commissioner, Austin, 2-1-21

STAFF:

Executive Director	Larry Temple . . . . .512/463-0735 / *Fax: 512/475-2321*
Deputy Executive Director	Edward Serna . . . . .512/305-9636 / *Fax: 512/463-4935*
General Counsel	Les Trobman . . . . .512/475-4221 / *Fax: 512/463-1426*
Chief Financial Officer	Randy Townsend . . . . .512/463-2698 / *Fax: 512/463-5483*
Deputy Director	
Workforce Solutions	Reagan Miller 512/936-3563
Director	
Business Transformation-RPI	Alfredo Mycue . . . . .512/463-8721 / *Fax: 512/475-2321*
External Relations Division	Tom McCarty 512/936-2346
Operational Insight	Adam Leonard . . . . .512/936-5866 / *Fax: 512/475-1275*
Unemployment Insurance	
and Regulation Division	LaSha Lenzy . . . . .512/463-7234 / *Fax: 512/475-1275*
Internal Audit	Ashley Sagebiel . . . . .512/463-8024 / *Fax: 512/463-3243*
Regulatory Integrity Division	Paul Carmona . . . . .512/463-3454 / *Fax: 512/463-7804*
Employer Initiatives	Aaron Demerson . . . . . . .512/463-1473 / *Fax: 512/463-5483*
Workforce Development Div.	Courtney Arbour 512/936-8326
Rehabilitation Services Div.	Cheryl Fuller 512/936-3701
Civil Rights Division	Lowell Keig . . . . .512/463-4432 / *Fax: 512/463-2643*
Information Technology Div.	Lisa Richardson . . . . .512/936-3191 / *Fax: 512/936-3562*
Business Operations Division	Glenn Neal 512/463-5690

*Subject to the Texas Sunset Act; will be reviewed in 2027.

Notes and Changes

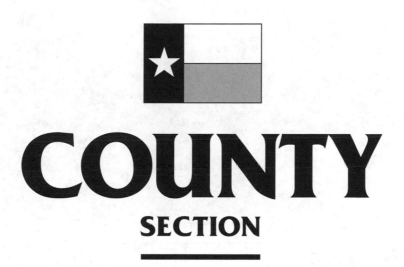

COUNTY

SECTION

COUNTY SECTION

The County Section of the TEXAS STATE DIRECTORY provides detailed information concerning the 254 counties of Texas and the public officials of each. The material is organized in the following fashion:

Name of county
Estimate of population   County Seat
Internet address
Mailing address of County Judge
Area Code and Telephone number of County Judge or Main County Number
Fax number for the county - this number is valid for each official unless
  a specific number is listed by his/her name

County Judge
District Attorney
County Attorney
District Clerk
County Clerk
County Treasurer
County Tax Assessor-Collector
Sheriff
County Auditor
Chief Appraiser
County Commissioners
Justices of the Peace
Constables

REFERENCE SECTION:
Texas Association of Counties
Top Fifteen Counties by Population
Top Ten Counties in Square Miles

ANDERSON COUNTY

Population: 58,458
County Seat:
  Palestine 75801

703 North Mallard, Suite 101
903 723-7406 / *Fax: 903 723-7494*
www.co.anderson.tx.us/

County Judge	Robert D. Johnston	723-7406 / *Fax: 723-7494*
Criminal District Attorney	Allyson Mitchell	723-7400 / *Fax: 723-7818*
District Clerk	Janice Staples	723-7412 / *Fax: 723-7491*
County Clerk	Mark Staples	723-7432 / *Fax: 723-4625*
County Treasurer	Tara Holliday	723-7408 / *Fax: 723-7804*
Tax Assessor-Collector	Teri Garvey	723-7423 / *Fax: 723-7801*
Sheriff	Greg Taylor	729-6068 / *Fax: 729-3022*
County Auditor	Karin Smith	723-7427 / *Fax: 723-7808*
Chief Appraiser	Carson Wages	723-2949 / *Fax: 723-5990*
Elections Official	Casey Brown	723-7438 / *Fax: 723-1223*
County Commissioner:		
Precinct 1	Greg Chapin	764-2646 / *Fax: 723-7821*
Precinct 2	Rashad Q. Mims	723-7480 / *Fax: 723-7821*
Precinct 3	Kenneth Dickson	876-2891 / *Fax: 723-7821*
Precinct 4	Joey Hill	549-2495 / *Fax: 723-7821*
Justice of the Peace:		
Precinct 1	Gary Thomas	764-5661 / *Fax: 764-0035*
Precinct 2	Carl Davis	723-7486 / *Fax: 723-7807*
Precinct 3	James Todd	723-7418 / *Fax: 723-7802*
Precinct 4	James Sharp	723-7419 / *Fax: 723-7834*
Constable:		
Precinct 1	Position Vacant	764-5874 / *Fax: 764-0035*
Precinct 2	Doug Lightfoot	723-7853 / *Fax: 723-7854*
Precinct 3	Kim Holliday	723-7869 / *Fax: 723-7802*
Precinct 4	James Muniz	723-7870 / *Fax: 723-7854*

ANDREWS COUNTY

Population: 18,202
County Seat:
  Andrews 79714

201 N. Main, Rm. 104
432 524 1401 / *Fax: 432 524-1470*
www.co.andrews.tx.us

County Judge	Richard H. Dolgener	524-1401 / *Fax: 524-1470*
District & County Attorney	Tim Mason	524-1405 / *Fax: 524-5839*
District Clerk	Sherry Dushane	524-1417
County Clerk	Position Vacant	524-1426 / *Fax: 524-1464*
Tax Assessor-Collector	Robin Harper	524-1409 / *Fax: 524-1450*
Sheriff	Rusty Stewart	523-5545 / *Fax: 523-5954*
County Auditor	Carol White	524-1410 / *Fax: 524-1440*
Chief Appraiser	Jackie Martin	523-9111 / *Fax: 523-3222*
Elections Official	Graciela Mendoza	524-1463 / *Fax: 524-1451*
County Commissioner:		
Precinct 1	Kerry Pack	524-1438 / *Fax: 524-1470*
Precinct 2	Brad Young	524-1439 / *Fax: 524-1470*
Precinct 3	Jeneane Anderegg	524-1460 / *Fax: 524-1470*
Precinct 4	Jim Waldrop	524-1466 / *Fax: 524-1470*

Justice of the Peace:
  Precinct 1   Mary Jane Baeza ....524-1412 / *Fax: 524-1475*
  Precinct 2   Neri Flores ....524-1413 / *Fax: 524-1475*
Constable:
  Precinct 1   Ronny Alaniz 523-5545
  Precinct 2   Dan Gomez 523-5545

ANGELINA COUNTY

Population: 90,667
County Seat:
  Lufkin 75902

P. O. Box 908
936 634-5413 / *Fax: 936 637-7452*
www.angelinacounty.net/

County Judge	Wes Suiter	.634-5413 / *Fax: 637-7452*
District Attorney, 159th Dist.	Joe Martin	.632-5090 / *Fax: 637-2818*
County Attorney	Cary D. Kirby	.639-3929 / *Fax: 639-3905*
District Clerk	Reba Squyres	.634-4312 / *Fax: 634-5915*
County Clerk	Amy Fincher	.634-8339 / *Fax: 634-8460*
County Treasurer	Deborah Huffman	.634-7312 / *Fax: 671-4892*
Tax Assessor-Collector	Billie Page	.634-8376 / *Fax: 634-2690*
Sheriff	Greg Sanches	.634-3331 / *Fax: 639-4510*
County Auditor	Janice Cordray	.634-8233 / *Fax: 634-4972*
Chief Appraiser	Tim Chambers	.634-8456 / *Fax: 634-8758*
Elections Official	Connie J. Brown	.671-5117 / *Fax: 634-2690*
County Commissioner:		
Precinct 1	Greg Harrison	.632-5531 / *Fax: 637-7452*
Precinct 2	Kenneth Timmons	.632-5531 / *Fax: 637-7452*
Precinct 3	Terry Pitts	.632-5531 / *Fax: 637-7452*
Precinct 4	Bobby Cheshire	.632-5531 / *Fax: 637-7452*
Justice of the Peace:		
Precinct 1	Billy Ball	.634-8334 / *Fax: 634-8336*
Precinct 2	Donnie Puckett	.637-3117 / *Fax: 637-3293*
Precinct 3	Pat Grubbs	.422-5533 / *Fax: 876-9912*
Precinct 4	Esther Barger	.829-3535 / *Fax: 829-3534*
Constable:		
Precinct 1	Tom Selman, Jr.	.465-0326 / *Fax: 634 8336*
Precinct 2	Trae Trevathan	.635-1435 / *Fax: 637-3293*
Precinct 3	Chad Wilson	.366-1060 / *Fax: 876-9912*
Precinct 4	Charles "Ray" Anthony	.829-2547 / *Fax: 829-3534*

ARANSAS COUNTY

Population: 25,176
County Seat:
  Rockport 78382

2840 Highway 35 N
361 790-0100 / *Fax: 361 727-2043*
www.aransascountytx.gov

County Judge	Burt Mills . . . . .790-0100 / *Fax: 727-2043*
District & County Attorney	Kristen Barnebey . . . . .790-0114 / *Fax: 790-0199*
District Clerk	Pam Heard . . . . .790-0128 / *Fax: 790-5211*
County Clerk	Valerie K. Amason . . . . .790-0122 / *Fax: 790-0119*
County Treasurer	Alma Cartwright . . . . .790-0132 / *Fax: 790-0165*
Tax Assessor-Collector	Jeri D. Cox . . . . .790-0160 / *Fax: 729-4373*
Sheriff	William "Bill" Mills . . . . .729-2222 / *Fax: 790-0164*
County Auditor	Suzy Wallace . . . . .790-0124 / *Fax: 790-0125*
Chief Appraiser	Mike Soto . . . . .729-9733 / *Fax: 729-9750*
Elections Official	Michele Bennett . . . . .729-7431 / *Fax: 790-0177*
County Commissioner:	
Precinct 1	Jack Chaney 463-6121
Precinct 2	Leslie "Bubba" Casterline . . . . .205-0993 / *Fax: 727-2043*
Precinct 3	Brian C. Olsen . . . . .386-0465 / *Fax: 727-2043*
Precinct 4	Betty Stiles . . . . .790-2955 / *Fax: 727-2043*
Justice of the Peace:	
Precinct 1	Diane Dupnik . . . . .790-0130 / *Fax: 790-5402*
Precinct 2	Diana McGinnis . . . . .790-0131 / *Fax: 790-5392*
Constable:	
Precinct 1	Harry "Doc" Thomas . . . . .790-0130 / *Fax: 790-5402*
Precinct 2	Charles Phillips . . . . .790-0131 / *Fax: 790-5392*

ARCHER COUNTY

Population: 9,067
County Seat:
  Archer City 76351

P.O. Box 458
940 574-4811 / *Fax: 940 574-2581*
www.co.archer.tx.us

County Judge	Randy Jackson . . . . .574-4811 / *Fax: 574-2581*
District Attorney, 97th Dist.	Casey Polhemus . . . . .894-6211 / *Fax: 894-6230*
County Attorney	David A. Levy . . . . .574-4724 / *Fax: 574-2230*
District Clerk	Lori Rutledge . . . . .574-4615 / *Fax: 574-2432*
County Clerk	Karren F. Winter . . . . .574-4302 / *Fax: 574-2876*
County Treasurer	Patricia A. Vieth . . . . .574-4822 / *Fax: 574-2432*
Tax Assessor-Collector	Dawn Vieth .574-4224 / *Fax: 574-4625*
Sheriff	Staci Williams Beesinger . . . . .574-2571 / *Fax: 574-2573*
County Auditor	Paul O. Wylie, Jr. . . . . .574-2303 / *Fax: 574-2581*
Chief Appraiser	Kimbra York . . . . .574-2172 / *Fax: 574-2509*
Elections Official	Vicki Wright . . . . .574-2645 / *Fax: 574-2655*
County Commissioner:	
Precinct 1	Richard Shelley . . . . .586-1315 / *Fax: 574-2581*
Precinct 2	Darin Wolf . . . . .423-6423 / *Fax: 574-2581*
Precinct 3	Pat Martin, III . . . . .563-3441 / *Fax: 574-2581*
Precinct 4	Darryl Lightfoot . . . . .583-5825 / *Fax: 574-2581*
Justice of the Peace:	
Precinct 1	C.T. McDaniel . . . . .574-4514 / *Fax: 574-2681*
Precinct 2	Corky Scarbrough 586-0237
Precinct 3	Lawrence J. Smith 563-2008
Precinct 4	Wayne L. Lindemann 541-2250

Constable:

Precinct 1	Doug Strange	.696-5727
Precinct 2	Jim Bob Wallace	.447-3770
Precinct 3	Position Vacant	
Precinct 4	Brett Hoff	.631-1387

ARMSTRONG COUNTY

Population: 1,933
County Seat:
  Claude 79019

P. O. Box 189
806 226-3221 / *Fax: 806 226-2030*
www.co.armstrong.tx.us

County Judge	Hugh Reed	.226-3221 / *Fax: 226-2030*
District Attorney, 47th Dist.	Randall C. Sims	.379-2325 / *Fax: 379-2823*
District & County Clerk	Tawnee Blodgett	.226-2081 / *Fax: 226-5301*
County Treasurer	Rachel Sanders	.226-3651 / *Fax: 226-4312*
Tax Assessor-Collector	Marissa Clement	.226-6021
Sheriff	Fleta Barnett	.226-3151 / *Fax: 226-3711*
Chief Appraiser	Debbie Stribling	.226-6021 / *Fax: 226-2654*
Elections Official	Jamie Craig	.226-4481 / *Fax: 226-2654*
County Commissioner:		
Precinct 1	Adam Ensey	.674-4602 / *Fax: 226-2030*
Precinct 2	Parker Stewart	.944-5247 / *Fax: 226-2030*
Precinct 3	Robert Harris	.226-3221 / *Fax: 226-2030*
Precinct 4	Philip Fletcher	.226-2078 / *Fax: 226-2030*
Justice of the Peace:	Dianne Samaniego	.226-2041 / *Fax: 226-4011*

ATASCOSA COUNTY

Population: 49,266
County Seat:
  Jourdanton 78026

1 Courthouse Circle Drive, Suite 101
830 769-3093 / *Fax: 830 769-2349*
www.atascosacountytexas.net

County Judge	Robert L. Hurley	.769-3093 / *Fax: 769-2349*
District Attorney, 81st Dist.	Audrey Gossett Louis	.393-2200 / *Fax: 393-2205*
County Attorney	Lucinda A. Vickers	.769-3573 / *Fax: 769-2757*
District Clerk	Margaret Littleton	.769-3011 / *Fax: 769-1332*
County Clerk	Diane Gonzales	.767-2511 / *Fax: 769-1021*
County Treasurer	Laura D. Pawelek	.769-3024 / *Fax: 767-2318*
Tax Assessor-Collector	Loretta Holley	.769-3842 / *Fax: 769-2115*
Sheriff	David Soward	.769-3434 / *Fax: 769-2721*
County Auditor	Ray Samson	.769-3620 / *Fax: 769-1183*
Chief Appraiser	Michelle L. Cardenas	.742-3591 / *Fax: 742-3044*
Elections Official	Janice Ruple	.769-1472 / *Fax: 769-1215*
County Commissioner:		
Precinct 1	Mark Gillespie	.769-2901 / *Fax: 769-2349*
Precinct 2	William "Bill" Torans	.742-3946 / *Fax: 769-2349*
Precinct 3	Eliseo Perez	.277-1213 / *Fax: 769-2349*
Precinct 4	Bill Carroll	.569-1147 / *Fax: 769-2349*
Justice of the Peace:		
Precinct 1	Michael Pascarella	.569-2801 / *Fax: 569-2829*
Precinct 2	Kyle Bradley	.772-3660 / *Fax: 772-5026*
Precinct 3	Orlando Carrasco	.769-2074 / *Fax: 769-2079*
Precinct 4	Jackie Bodden	.569-6614 / *Fax: 569-6664*

Atascosa County Cont.

Constable:

Precinct 1	Percy Medina	.569-2801 / *Fax: 569-2829*
Precinct 2	Edward Richter	.772-3660 / *Fax: 769-2349*
Precinct 3	Rick Luna	.277-1698 / *Fax: 277-1435*
Precinct 4	William Meadows	.569-6614 / *Fax: 569-6664*

AUSTIN COUNTY

Population: 30,609
County Seat:
  Bellville 77418

County Courthouse, One East Main
979 865-5911 / *Fax: 979 865-8786*
www.austincounty.com/

County Judge	Tim Lapham	.865-5911 / *Fax: 865-8786*
Criminal District Attorney	Travis Koehn	.865-5933 / *Fax: 865-5828*
District Clerk	Sue Murphy	.865-5911 / *Fax: 865-8350*
County Clerk	Carrie Gregor	.865-5911 / *Fax: 865-0336*
County Treasurer	Bryan Haevischer	.865-5911 / *Fax: 865-0982*
Tax Assessor-Collector	Kim Rinn	.865-8633 / *Fax: 865-0183*
Sheriff	Jack Brandes	.865-3112 / *Fax: 865-8271*
County Auditor	Billy Doherty	.865-5911 / *Fax: 865-5179*
Chief Appraiser	Carmen Ottmer	.865-9124 / *Fax: 865-3296*
Elections Official	Kim Rinn	.865-8633 / *Fax: 865-0183*
County Commissioner:		
Precinct 1	Mark Lamp	.865-2126 / *Fax: 865-2674*
Precinct 2	Robert "Bobby" Rinn	.357-4780 / *Fax: 357-4785*
Precinct 3	Randy R. Reichardt	.865-5441 / *Fax: 865-8786*
Precinct 4	Douglas W. King	.478-7121 / *Fax: 478-7453*
Justice of the Peace:		
Precinct 1	Richard Yancey	.865-9171 / *Fax: 865-8928*
Precinct 2	Wilfred W. Krause	.357-4477 / *Fax: 357-4470*
Precinct 3	Cheryl Kollatschny	.885-3195 / *Fax: 885-1156*
Precinct 4	Bernice Burger	.478-6723 / *Fax: 478-7453*
Constable:		
Precinct 1	Virgil Price	.865-3111 / *Fax: 865-8271*
Precinct 2	Dave Schulz	.865-3111 / *Fax: 865-8271*
Precinct 3	Ronnie Griffin	.885-3094 / *Fax: 885-6510*
Precinct 4	James Clark	.478-6723 / *Fax: 478-7453*

BAILEY COUNTY

Population: 7,150
County Seat:
  Muleshoe 79347

300 S. 1st Street, Ste. 100
806 272-3077 / *Fax: 806 272-4656*
www.co.bailey.tx.us

County Judge	Sherri Harrison	.272-3077 / *Fax: 272-4656*
District Attorney, 287th Dist.	Kathryn Gurley	.250-2050 / *Fax: 250-9053*
County Attorney	Jackie R. Claborn II	.272-4205 / *Fax: 272-3235*
District Clerk	Elaine Parker	.272-3165 / *Fax: 272-3124*
County Clerk	Robin Dickerson	.272-3044 / *Fax: 272-3538*
County Treasurer	Shonda Black	.272-3239 / *Fax: 272-4656*
Tax Assessor-Collector	Maria Gonzalez	.272-3022 / *Fax: 272-3124*
Sheriff	Richard Wills	.272-4268 / *Fax: 272-3879*
Chief Appraiser	Kaye Elliott	.272-5501 / *Fax: 272-3643*

County Commissioner:
Precinct 1	Gary Don Gartin	.570-8926 / *Fax: 272-4656*
Precinct 2	Mike Slayden	.946-7585 / *Fax: 272-4656*
Precinct 3	Cody Black	.543-0121 / *Fax: 272-4656*
Precinct 4	Juan Chavez	.946-8246 / *Fax: 272-4656*

Justice of the Peace:
Precinct 1	Daniel Guzman	.272-4300 / *Fax: 272-5375*
Constable:	Kent Wiley	.272-4245 / *Fax: 272-3235*

BANDERA COUNTY

Population: 21,374
County Seat:
Bandera 78003

500 Main St., P. O. Box 877
830 796-3781 / *Fax: 830 796-4210*
www.banderacounty.org/

County Judge	Richard A. Evans	.796-3781 / *Fax: 796-4210*
District Attorney, 198th Dist.	Scott Monroe	.315-2460 / *Fax: 315-2461*
County Attorney	Janna Lindig	.796-4075 / *Fax: 796-8218*
District Clerk	Tammy Kneuper	.796-4606 / *Fax: 796-8499*
County Clerk	Candy Wheeler	.796-3332 / *Fax: 796-8323*
County Treasurer	Terry Wheeler	.796-4197 / *Fax: 796-4538*
Tax Assessor-Collector	Gwenda L. Tschirhart, PCC, CTOP	.796-3731 / *Fax: 796-8140*
Sheriff	Daniel R. Butts	.796-4323 / *Fax: 796-3561*
County Auditor	Christina Moreno	.796-4573 / *Fax: 796-8139*
Chief Appraiser	Wendy M. Grams	.796-3039 / *Fax: 460-3672*
Elections Official	Gwenda L. Tschirhart, PCC, CTOP	.796-8146 / *Fax: 796-3321*

County Commissioner:
Precinct 1	Bruce Eliker	.210 722-1080 / *Fax: 796-4210*
Precinct 2	Robert "Bobby" Harris	.460-1654 / *Fax: 796-4210*
Precinct 3	Jack U. Moseley	.522-1500 / *Fax: 796-4210*
Precinct 4	Jordan "Jody" Rutherford	.796-5636 / *Fax: 796-4210*

Justice of the Peace:
Precinct 1	Michael P. Towers	.796-3593 / *Fax: 796-8169*
Precinct 2	Bobbie Jo Basinger	.751-3535 / *Fax: 751-2142*
Precinct 3	Eino Zapata	.589-7758 / *Fax: 589-2209*
Precinct 4	Lynn Holt	.796-3593 / *Fax: 796 8169*

Constable:
Precinct 1	Phillip Tobin	.460-8110
Precinct 2	Ernest Reich, III	.751-3575 / *Fax: 751-3054*
Precinct 3	Don Walters	.589-2473 / *Fax: 796-5899*
Precinct 4	Rod Chalmers	.460-1267 / *Fax: 796-8169*

BASTROP COUNTY

Population: 83,800
County Seat:
  Bastrop 78602

Co. Courthouse, 804 Pecan St.,
512 332-7201 / *Fax: 512 581-7103*
www.co.bastrop.tx.us/

County Judge	Paul Pape	.332-7201 / *Fax: 581-7103*
Criminal District Attorney	Bryan Goertz	.581-7125 / *Fax: 581-7133*
District Clerk	Sarah Loucks	.332-7244 / *Fax: 332-7249*
County Clerk	Rose Pietsch	.332-7234 / *Fax: 332-7241*
County Treasurer	Laurie Ingram	.581-7104 / *Fax: 581-7136*
Tax Assessor-Collector	Linda Harmon	.581-7161 / *Fax: 581-7167*
Sheriff	Maurice Cook	.549-5100 / *Fax: 549-5195*
County Auditor	Lisa Smith	.332-7222 / *Fax: 332-7272*
Chief Appraiser	Richard Petree, Interim	.303-1930 / *Fax: 303-4805*
Elections Official	Bridgette Escobedo	.581-7160 / *Fax: 581-4260*
County Commissioner:		
Precinct 1	Melvin Hamner	.581-4001
Precinct 2	Clara Beckett	.581-4002 / *Fax: 237-4986*
Precinct 3	Mark Meuth	.303-6800 / *Fax: 303-5795*
Precinct 4	Gary "Bubba" Snowden	.332-7267 / *Fax: 281-0351*
Justice of the Peace:		
Precinct 1	Donna Thomson	.581-4258 / *Fax: 581-4254*
Precinct 2	Raymah Davis	.581-7112 / *Fax: 332-7227*
Precinct 3	Katherine Hanna	.332-7288 / *Fax: 332-7250*
Precinct 4	Larry A. Dunne	.581-7162 / *Fax: 581-7163*
Constable:		
Precinct 1	Wayne Wood	.581-4010 / *Fax: 581-4025*
Precinct 2	August "Gus" Meduna, Jr.	.581-7113 / *Fax: 581-7155*
Precinct 3	Tim Sparkman	.332-7243 / *Fax: 581-4226*
Precinct 4	Salvador Abreo	.581-7166 / *Fax: 581-7168*

BAYLOR COUNTY

Population: 3,518
County Seat:
  Seymour 76380

109 N. Washington Street
940 889-3553 / *Fax: 940 889-8856*

County Judge	Rusty Stafford	.889-3553 / *Fax: 889-8856*
District Attorney, 50th Dist.	Jennifer A. Habert	.889-2852 / *Fax: 888-3036*
County Attorney	Cody Robinette	.889-5140 / *Fax: 889-3186*
District & County Clerk	Chris Jakubicek	.889-3322 / *Fax: 889-4300*
County Treasurer	Kevin Hostas	.889-1846 / *Fax: 889-3450*
Tax Assessor-Collector	Jeanette Holub	.889-3169 / *Fax: 889-6256*
Sheriff	Jason Zeissel	.889-3333 / *Fax: 889-3915*
Chief Appraiser	Beth Hrncirik	.888-5636 / *Fax: 888-5566*
Elections Official	Chris Jakubicek	.889-3169 / *Fax: 889-6256*
County Commissioner:		
Precinct 1	Rick Gillispie	.889-3553 / *Fax: 889-8856*
Precinct 2	John Edd Nelson	.889-3553 / *Fax: 889-8856*
Precinct 3	Don Emsoff	.889-3553 / *Fax: 889-8856*
Precinct 4	Larry Burnett	.889-3553 / *Fax: 889-8856*
Justice of the Peace:		
Precinct 1	Rick Jeter	.889-2662 / *Fax: 889-3915*
Precinct 2	Teresa Gray	.889-3300 / *Fax: 889-3915*

BEE COUNTY

Population: 32,688
County Seat:
  Beeville 78102

105 W. Corpus Christi St., Room 305
361 621-1556 / *Fax: 361 492-5980*
www.co.bee.tx.us

County Judge	Stephanie Moreno	.621-1556 / *Fax: 492-5980*
District Attorney, 156th Dist.	Jose Aliseda	.358-1007 / *Fax: 358-0505*
County Attorney	Michael Knight	.362-3237 / *Fax: 362-3208*
District Clerk	Zenaida Silva	.621-1562 / *Fax: 492-5984*
County Clerk	Mirella E. Davis	.621-1557 / *Fax: 492-5985*
Tax Assessor-Collector	Linda G. Bridge	.621-1554 / *Fax: 358-5417*
Sheriff	Alden E. Southmayd III	.362-3221 / *Fax: 362-3227*
County Auditor	April Cantu	.621-1551 / *Fax: 492-5989*
Chief Appraiser	Amanda Miller	.358-0193 / *Fax: 362-0140*
County Commissioner:		
Precinct 1	Carlos Salazar, Jr.	.621-1571 / *Fax: 492-5980*
Precinct 2	Dennis DeWitt	.621-1572 / *Fax: 492-5980*
Precinct 3	Sammy G. Farias	.621-1573 / *Fax: 492-5980*
Precinct 4	Kenneth Haggard	.621-1574 / *Fax: 492-5980*
Justice of the Peace:		
Precinct 1	Susana Salazar Contreras	.621-1558 / *Fax: 492-5982*
Precinct 2	Amy E. Shanklin	.621-1577 / *Fax: 492-5991*
Precinct 3	Abel Suniga	.621-1559 / *Fax: 492-5983*
Precinct 4	Esther Castro	.287-3436 / *Fax: 287-0578*
Constable:		
Precinct 1	Johnny "Dino" Sauceda	.362-5853 / *Fax: 492-5980*
Precinct 2	Mickie Ochoa	.362-5853 / *Fax: 492-5980*
Precinct 3	Kirk Delgado	.597-0646 / *Fax: 492-5980*
Precinct 4	Ronnie Olivares	.542-9139 / *Fax: 492-5980*

BELL COUNTY

Population: 336,383
County Seat:
  Belton 76513

P.O. Box 768 - County Courthouse
254 933-5105 / *Fax: 254 933-5179*
www.bellcountytx.com/

County Judge	Jon H. Burrows	.933-5105 / *Fax: 933-5179*
District Attorney, 27th Dist.	Henry L. Garza	.933-5215 / *Fax: 933-5238*
County Attorney	James E. Nichols	.933-5927 / *Fax: 933-5150*
District Clerk	Joanna Staton	.933-5197 / *Fax: 933-5199*
County Clerk	Shelley Coston	.933-5160 / *Fax: 933-5176*
County Treasurer	Charles E. Jones	.933-5250 / *Fax: 933-5303*
Tax Assessor-Collector	Shay Luedeke	.933-5320 / *Fax: 933-5325*
Sheriff	Eddy Lange	.933-5410 / *Fax: 933-5332*
County Auditor	Donna Eakin	.933-5115 / *Fax: 933-5918*
Chief Appraiser	Marvin Hahn	.939-5841 / *Fax: 939-3909*
Elections Official	Melinda Luedecke	.933-5774 / *Fax: 933-6754*
County Commissioner:		
Precinct 1	Russell T. Schneider	.933-5101 / *Fax: 933-5179*
Precinct 2	Tim Brown	.933-5102 / *Fax: 933-5179*
Precinct 3	Bill Schumann	.933-5103 / *Fax: 933-5179*
Precinct 4	John Fisher	.933-5104 / *Fax: 933-5179*

Bell County Cont.

Justice of the Peace:

Precinct 1	Theodore R. Duffield	.933-5183 / *Fax: 933-5768*
Precinct 2	Don Engleking	.933-5398 / *Fax: 933-5208*
Precinct 3, Pl. 1	David R. Barfield	.770-6822 / *Fax: 770-6820*
Precinct 3, Pl. 2	GW Ivey	.770-6831 / *Fax: 770-6833*
Precinct 4, Pl. 1	Claudia Brown	.634-5882 / *Fax: 634-3326*
Precinct 4, Pl. 2	Bill Cooke	.634-7612 / *Fax: 634-3875*

Constable:

Precinct 1	Linnie McCall	.933-5916 / *Fax: 933-5953*
Precinct 2	Rolly Correa	.933-5987 / *Fax: 933-5966*
Precinct 3	Thomas G. Prado	.770-6808 / *Fax: 770-6872*
Precinct 4	Edd Melton, III	.634-6263 / *Fax: 634-6740*

BEXAR COUNTY

Population: 1,913,559
County Seat:
  San Antonio 78205

101 W. Nueva St., 10th Floor, 100 Dolorosa
210 335-2011
www.bexar.org

County Judge	Nelson W. Wolff	.335-2626 / *Fax: 335-2926*
Criminal District Attorney	Nicholas LaHood	.335-2311 / *Fax: 335-2884*
District Clerk	Donna Kay McKinney	.335-2113 / *Fax: 335-3424*
County Clerk	Gerard C. Rickhoff	.335-2216 / *Fax: 335-2197*
Tax Assessor-Collector	Albert Uresti	.335-2251 / *Fax: 335-6573*
Sheriff	Javier Salazar	.335-6010 / *Fax: 335-6019*
County Auditor	Susan T. Yeatts CPA	.335-2301 / *Fax: 335-2996*
Chief Appraiser	Michael Amezquita	.224-8511 / *Fax: 242-2454*
Elections Official	Jacque Callanen	.335-8683 / *Fax: 335-0371*

County Commissioner:

Precinct 1	Sergio "Chico" Rodriguez	.335-2611 / *Fax: 335-2215*
Precinct 2	Paul Elizondo	.335-2612 / *Fax: 335-2264*
Precinct 3	Kevin Wolff	.335-2613 / *Fax: 335-3452*
Precinct 4	Tommy Calvert	.335-2614 / *Fax: 335-2926*

Justice of the Peace:

Precinct 1, Pl. 1	Robert Tejeda	.335-4500 / *Fax: 335-4501*
Precinct 1, Pl. 2	Ciro D. Rodriguez	.335-4500 / *Fax: 335-4501*
Precinct 2, Pl. 1	Roberto Vazquez	.335-4800 / *Fax: 684-4565*
Precinct 3, Pl. 1	William Donovan	.335-4700
Precinct 3, Pl. 2	Jeff Wentworth	.335-4708 / *Fax: 335-4705*
Precinct 4, Pl. 1	Rogelio Lopez, Jr.	.335-4920 / *Fax: 335-4920*
Precinct 4, Pl. 2	Yolanda Acuna-Uresti	.335-4925 / *Fax: 335-4920*

Constable:

Precinct 1	Ruben C. Tejeda	.335-2806 / *Fax: 335-2704*
Precinct 2	Michelle Barrientes Vela	.335-4850 / *Fax: 335-4865*
Precinct 3	Mark Vojvodich	.335-4750 / *Fax: 335-4789*
Precinct 4	Stan Ramos	.335-4950 / *Fax: 335-4971*

BLANCO COUNTY

Population: 11,305
County Seat:
 Johnson City 78636

P. O. Box 471
830 868-4266 / *Fax: 830 868-9112*
www.co.blanco.tx.us

County Judge	Brett Bray	.868-4266 / *Fax: 868-9112*
District Attorney, 33rd Dist.	Wiley B. "Sonny" McAfee	.512 756-5449 / *Fax: 512 756-8572*
County Attorney	Deborah Earley	.868-4447 / *Fax: 868-7788*
District Clerk	Debby Elsbury	.868-0973 / *Fax: 868-7788*
County Clerk	Laura Walla	.868-7357 / *Fax: 868-4158*
County Treasurer	Camille Swift	.868-4566 / *Fax: 868-7788*
Tax Assessor-Collector	Kristen Sultemeier Spies	.868-7178 / *Fax: 868-7788*
Sheriff	Don Jackson	.868-7104 / *Fax: 868-4577*
Chief Appraiser	Candice Fry	.868-4013 / *Fax: 868-7330*
Elections Official	Laura Walla	.868-7357 / *Fax: 868-4158*
County Commissioner:		
Precinct 1	Tommy Weir	.833-5331 / *Fax: 833-2667*
Precinct 2	James Sultemeier	.868-4471 / *Fax: 868-2585*
Precinct 3	Chris W. Liesmann	.825-3270 / *Fax: 825-3218*
Precinct 4	Paul Granberg	.833-1077 / *Fax: 833-2667*
Justice of the Peace:		
Precinct 1	Randy Brodbeck	.868-4888 / *Fax: 868-7788*
Precinct 4	H. R. "Bob" Riley, Jr.	.833-4212 / *Fax: 833-2667*
Constable:		
Precinct 1	Bobby Fenton	.868-4888 / *Fax: 868-4153*
Precinct 4	Ronnie Steubing	.833-4212 / *Fax: 833-2667*

BORDEN COUNTY

Population: 682
County Seat:
 Gail 79738

P. O. Box 156 - Courthouse, 101 Main
806 756-4391 / *Fax: 806 756-4405*
www.co.borden.tx.us/

County Judge	Ross D. Sharp	.756-4391 / *Fax: 756-4405*
District Attorney, 132nd Dist.	Ben R. Smith	.325 573-2462 / *Fax: 325 573-9339*
County Attorney	Marlo Holbrooks	.756-4351 / *Fax: 756-4405*
District & County Clerk	Jana Underwood	.756-4312 / *Fax: 756-4324*
County Treasurer	Shawna Gass	.756-4386 / *Fax: 756-4405*
Tax Assessor-Collector	Benny Allison	.756-4415 / *Fax: 756-4431*
Sheriff	Benny Allison	.756-4311 / *Fax: 756-4431*
Chief Appraiser	Tracy Cooley	.756-4484 / *Fax: 756-4419*
County Commissioner:		
Precinct 1	Monte Smith	.756-4391 / *Fax: 756-4405*
Precinct 2	Randy Adcock	.756-4391 / *Fax: 756-4405*
Precinct 3	Ernest Reyes	.756-4391 / *Fax: 756-4405*
Precinct 4	Joe Belew	.756-4391 / *Fax: 756-4405*
Justice of the Peace:	Jane Jones	.756-4380 / *Fax: 756-4405*

BOSQUE COUNTY

Population: 18,360
County Seat:
  Meridian 76665

P. O. Box 647
254 435-2382 / *Fax: 254 435-2152*
www.bosquecounty.us/

County Judge	Don Pool	.435-2382 / *Fax: 435-2152*
District Attorney, 220th Dist.	Adam Sibley	.435-2994 / *Fax: 435-2952*
County Attorney	Natalie Cobb Koehler	.435-2186 / *Fax: 435-2026*
District Clerk	Juanita Miller	.435-2334
County Clerk	Tab Ferguson	.435-2201 / *Fax: 435-2152*
County Treasurer	Carla Sigler	.435-6611
Tax Assessor-Collector	Arlene Swiney	.435-2301 / *Fax: 435-2822*
Sheriff	Anthony Malott	.435-2362 / *Fax: 435-2245*
County Auditor	Kent Reeves	.435-2611 / *Fax: 435-2558*
Chief Appraiser	Marilee Greenwood, RPA	.435-2304 / *Fax: 435-6139*
Elections Official	Crystal Denman	.435-6650 / *Fax: 435-9163*
County Commissioner:		
Precinct 1	Marvin "Wick" Wickman	.435-2285
Precinct 2	Durwood Koonsman	.797-4242
Precinct 3	Larry "Shotgun" Philipp	.675-8410
Precinct 4	Ronny Liardon	.675-8937
Justice of the Peace:		
Precinct 1	Jeff Hightower	.435-2921 / *Fax: 435-6906*
Precinct 2	Jamie W. Zander	.675-8939 / *Fax: 675-6747*
Constable:		
Precinct 1	Scott Ferguson	.435-2071 / *Fax: 435-2182*
Precinct 2	Bryan Prescher	.675-4461 / *Fax: 675-6747*

BOWIE COUNTY

Population: 97,549
County Seat:
  New Boston 75570

P. O. Box 248, 710 James Bowie Drive
903 628-6718 / *Fax: 903 628-6719*
www.co.bowie.tx.us/

County Judge	James Carlow	.628-6718 / *Fax: 628-6719*
Criminal District Attorney	Jerry Rochelle	.735-4800 / *Fax: 735-4819*
District Clerk	Jill Harrington	.628-6775 / *Fax: 628-6761*
County Clerk	Tina Petty	.628-6740 / *Fax: 628-6729*
County Treasurer	Donna Burns	.628-6721 / *Fax: 628-1071*
Tax Assessor-Collector	Treva Turner-Braley	.628-6730 / *Fax: 628-6780*
Sheriff	James Prince	.798-3149 / *Fax: 792-0959*
County Auditor	William Tye	.628-6710 / *Fax: 628-6836*
Chief Appraiser	Mike Brower	.793-8936 / *Fax: 792-8889*
Elections Official	George A. Stegall	.628-6810 / *Fax: 628-6811*
County Commissioner:		
Precinct 1	Sammy Stone	.838-8691 / *Fax: 838-0696*
Precinct 2	Tom Whitten	.838-6171 / *Fax: 831-5468*
Precinct 3	James Boyd Strain	.667-5116 / *Fax: 667-4164*
Precinct 4	Mike Carter	.628-2278 / *Fax: 628-4435*
Justice of the Peace:		

Precinct 1, Pl. 1 — Nancy Talley .... .798-3006 / *Fax: 798-3601*
Precinct 1, Pl. 2 — Gibson Hadaway .... .798-3038 / *Fax: 798-3601*
Precinct 2 — Stephen Young .... .628-6812 / *Fax: 628-6727*
Precinct 3, Pl. 1 — Gerrold Rankin .... .667-3891 / *Fax: 667-9931*
Precinct 4 — Mary Hankins .... .543-2279 / *Fax: 543-2279*
Precinct 5 — Susie Spelling .... .585-5428 / *Fax: 585-2111*
Constable:
Precinct 1 — Chris Lee .... .798-3038 / *Fax: 798-3958*
Precinct 2 — George Huggins, Jr. .... .628-6827 / *Fax: 628-6727*
Precinct 3 — Jeff Estes .... .667-3891 / *Fax: 667-9931*
Precinct 4 — Russell Crawford .... .543-2279 / *Fax: 543-2279*
Precinct 5 — Robbie Caudle .... .585-5428 / *Fax: 585-2111*

BRAZORIA COUNTY

Population: 349,500
County Seat:
  Angleton 77515

111 E. Locust, Suite 102-A
979 864-1200 / *Fax: 979 849-4655*
www.brazoria-county.com/

County Judge — Matt Sebesta .... .864-1200 / *Fax: 849-4655*
Criminal District Attorney — Jeri Yenne .... .864-1230 / *Fax: 864-1525*
District Clerk — Rhonda Barchak .... .864-1316 / *Fax: 864-1770*
County Clerk — Joyce Hudman .... .864-1362 / *Fax: 864-1358*
County Treasurer — Cathy Campbell CCT, CIO 864-1354
Tax Assessor-Collector — Ro'Vin Garrett, PCC .... .864-1320 / *Fax: 864-1346*
Sheriff — Charles Wagner .... .864-2392 / *Fax: 848-8003*
County Auditor — Connie Garner .... .864-1275 / *Fax: 864-1585*
Chief Appraiser — Cheryl Evans .... .849-7792 / *Fax: 849-7984*
County Commissioner:
Precinct 1 — Donald W. "Dude" Payne .... .265-3953 / *Fax: 265-5409*
Precinct 2 — Ryan Cade 864-1548
Precinct 3 — Stacy L. Adams .... .281 331-3197 / *Fax: 331-6586*
Precinct 4 — David Linder .... .345-1130 / *Fax: 345-2839*
Justice of the Peace:
Precinct 1, Pl. 1 — Jack Brown .... .297-4650 / *Fax: 297-4599*
Precinct 1, Pl. 2 — Milan Miller .... .233-4700 / *Fax: 233-8008*
Precinct 2, Pl. 1 — John Vasut .... .281 756-2410 / *Fax: 281 489-4435*
Precinct 2, Pl. 2 — Richard Davis .... .864-1402 / *Fax: 864-1637*
Precinct 3, Pl. 1 — Mike Merkel .... .281 331-3524 / *Fax: 281 756-0830*
Precinct 3, Pl. 2 — Gordon Starkenburg ...... .281 485-1528 / *Fax: 281 485-8720*
Precinct 4, Pl. 1 — Sharon Fox .... .713 844-1777 / *Fax: 281 489-5274*
Precinct 4, Pl. 2 — Sherry Kersh .... .345-2671 / *Fax: 345-3013*
Constable:
Precinct 1 — David Thacker .... .233-4188 / *Fax: 415-0610*
Precinct 2 — William Howell .... .281 756-2491 / *Fax: 281 756-2495*
Precinct 3 — Charles B. "Buck" Stevens . .281 997-9777 / *Fax: 281 412-7034*
Precinct 4 — James Brawner .... .345-2115 / *Fax: 345-6434*

COUNTY SECTION

BRAZOS COUNTY

Population: 220,371
County Seat:
  Bryan 77803

300 East 26th Street
979 775-7400 / *Fax: 979 361-4503*
www.co.brazos.tx.us/

County Judge	Duane Peters	.361-4102 / *Fax: 361-4503*
District Attorney, 85th Dist.	Jarvis Parsons	.361-4320 / *Fax: 361-4368*
County Attorney	Rod Anderson	.361-4300 / *Fax: 361-4357*
District Clerk	Marc Hamlin	.361-4230 / *Fax: 361-0197*
County Clerk	Karen McQueen	.361-4124 / *Fax: 361-4125*
County Treasurer	Laura Davis	.361-4345 / *Fax: 361-4347*
Tax Assessor-Collector	Kristeen Roe	.775-9930 / *Fax: 775-9938*
Sheriff	Christopher C. "Chris" Kirk	.361-4900 / *Fax: 361-4999*
County Auditor	Katie Conner	.361-4350 / *Fax: 361-4188*
Chief Appraiser	Mark Price	.774-4100 / *Fax: 774-4196*
Elections Official	Trudy Hancock	.361-5770 / *Fax: 361-5779*
County Commissioner:		
Precinct 1	Steve Aldrich	.361-4106 / *Fax: 361-4176*
Precinct 2	Sammy Catalena	.361-4115 / *Fax: 361-4176*
Precinct 3	Nancy Berry	.361-4105 / *Fax: 361-4176*
Precinct 4	Irma Cauley	.361-4111 / *Fax: 361-4176*
Justice of the Peace:		
Precinct 1	Mike McCleary	.695-0136 / *Fax: 695-0324*
Precinct 2	Tommy Munoz	.361-4190 / *Fax: 361-4373*
Precinct 3	Rick Hill	.693-2695 / *Fax: 764-1909*
Precinct 4	Louis Garcia, Jr.	.361-4402 / *Fax: 361-4502*
Constable:		
Precinct 1	Jeff W. Reeves	.695-0030 / *Fax: 695-0031*
Precinct 2	Donald Lampo	.361-4477 / *Fax: 361-4455*
Precinct 3	J.P. Ingram	.694-7901
Precinct 4	Isaac Butler, Jr.	.361-4266 / *Fax: 361-4564*

BREWSTER COUNTY

Population: 9,168
County Seat:
  Alpine 79831

P. O. Drawer 1630
432 837-2412 / *Fax: 432 837-1127*
www.brewstercountytx.com

County Judge	Eleazar Cano	.837-2412 / *Fax: 837-1127*
District Attorney, 83rd Dist.	Sandy Wilson	.336-3322 / *Fax: 336-8333*
County Attorney	Steve Houston	.837-6209 / *Fax: 837-7393*
District Clerk	JoAnn Salgado	.837-6216 / *Fax: 837-6217*
County Clerk	Berta Rios Martinez	.837-3366 / *Fax: 837-6217*
County Treasurer	Babett Mann	.837-6200 / *Fax: 837-9249*
Tax Assessor-Collector	Betty Jo Rooney	.837-2214 / *Fax: 837-3871*
Sheriff	Ronny Dodson	.837-3488 / *Fax: 837-5960*
Chief Appraiser	Denise Flores	.837-2558 / *Fax: 837-3871*
Elections Official	Berta Rios Martinez	.837-3366 / *Fax: 837-6217*
County Commissioner:		
Precinct 1	Betse Esparza	.837-7370 / *Fax: 837-1127*
Precinct 2	Hugh Garrett	.837-0187 / *Fax: 837-1127*
Precinct 3	Ruben Ortega	.294-1096 / *Fax: 837-1127*
Precinct 4	Mike Pallanez	.364-2468 / *Fax: 837-1127*

Justice of the Peace:
Precinct 1 Gilbert Valenzuela ....837-6214 / *Fax: 837-6217*
Precinct 2 Jim Burr 371-2127
Precinct 3 Susana Gonzales 386-4530
Constable:
Precinct 1 Henry Ogletree ....836-6317 / *Fax: 837-5960*
Precinct 2 Vacant
Precinct 3 Vacant

BRISCOE COUNTY

Population: 1,441
County Seat:
Silverton 79257

P. O. Box 153
806 823-2131 / *Fax: 806 823-2359*
www.co.briscoe.tx.us/

County Judge	Wayne Nance ....823-2131 / *Fax: 823-2359*
District Attorney, 110th Dist.	Wade Jackson ....983-2197 / *Fax: 823-2076*
County Attorney	Emily Teegardin ....823-2132 / *Fax: 823-2076*
District & County Clerk	Bena Hester ....823-2134 / *Fax: 823-2076*
County Treasurer	Mary Jo Brannon ....823-2133 / *Fax: 823-2076*
Tax Assessor-Collector	Jon Etta Ziegler ....823-2136 / *Fax: 823-2076*
Sheriff	Garrett Davis ....823-2135 / *Fax: 823-2141*
Chief Appraiser	Pat McWaters ....823-2161 / *Fax: 823-2359*
Elections Official	Bena Hester ....823-2134 / *Fax: 823-2076*
County Commissioner	
Precinct 1	Ken Wood ....847-2293 / *Fax: 823-2359*
Precinct 2	Wade Proctor 422-1177
Precinct 3	Danny Mac Francis 847-7139
Precinct 4	John Burson ....823-2020 / *Fax: 823-2359*
Justice of the Peace:	
Precinct 1	H.B. "Doc" Simpson ....823-2253 / *Fax: 823-2076*
Precinct 2	Dale Ramsey ....455-1278 / *Fax: 823-2359*

BROOKS COUNTY

Population: 7,200
County Seat:
  Falfurrias 78355

P. O. Box 515
361 325-5604 / *Fax: 361 895-9680*
www.co.brooks.tx.us/

County Judge	Judge Imelda Barrera . . . . .325-5604 / *Fax: 512 895-9680*
District Attorney, 79th Dist.	Carlos O. Garcia . . . . .325-5604 / *Fax: 895-9685*
County Attorney	David T. Garcia . . . . .325-5604 / *Fax: 512 895-9680*
District Clerk	Noe Guerra 325-5604
County Clerk	Elvaray B. Silvas . . . . .325-5604 / *Fax: 895-9680*
County Treasurer	Horacio Villarreal, III . . . . .325-5670 / *Fax: 325-4019*
Tax Assessor-Collector	Benny Martinez . . . . .325-5670 / *Fax: 895-9707*
Sheriff	Benny Martinez . . . . .325-3696 / *Fax: 325-1743*
County Auditor	August Patroelj . . . . .325-5670 / *Fax: 512 895-9707*
Chief Appraiser	Mary Lou Cantu, RPA 325-8122
Elections Official	Anna M. Garcia . . . . .325-5670 / *Fax: 512 895-9733*
County Commissioner:	
Precinct 1	Gloria Garza 325-3904
Precinct 2	Vicente Vargas 361-9002
Precinct 3	Armando Olivarez 522-8125
Precinct 4	Jose A. "Tony" Martinez 325-4195
Justice of the Peace:	
Precinct 1	Adela Quintanilla . . . . .667-3301 / *Fax: 895-9683*
Precinct 2	Oralia Lali Morales . . . . .667-3302 / *Fax: 895-9683*
Precinct 3	Sylvia Donnelly . . . . .667-3303 / *Fax: 895-9683*
Precinct 4	Rolando Garza . . . . .667-3304 / *Fax: 895-9683*
Constable:	
Precinct 1	Arturo Garcia . . . . .325-5670 / *Fax: 325-9571*
Precinct 2	Ramiro Gonzalez . . . . .325-5670 / *Fax: 325-9571*
Precinct 3	Frank Huerta . . . . .325-5670 / *Fax: 325-9571*
Precinct 4	Ruben M. Longoria . . . . .325-5670 / *Fax: 325-9571*

BROWN COUNTY

Population: 39,103
County Seat:
  Brownwood 76801

200 South Broadway
325 643-2828 / *Fax: 325 646-7013*
www.browncountytx.org

County Judge	E. Ray West, III . . . . .643-2828 / *Fax: 646-7013*
District Attorney, 35th Dist.	Micheal B. Murray . . . . .646-0444 / *Fax: 643-4053*
County Attorney	Shane Britton . . . . .646-7431 / *Fax: 643-4053*
District Clerk	Cheryl Jones . . . . .646-5514 / *Fax: 646-0878*
County Clerk	Sharon Ferguson . . . . .643-2594 / *Fax: 643-1685*
County Treasurer	Ann Krpoun . . . . .646-6033 / *Fax: 646-6033*
Tax Assessor-Collector	Christine Pentecost . . . . .643-1646 / *Fax: 643-1647*
Sheriff	Vance Hill . . . . .646-5510 / *Fax: 643-3238*
County Auditor	Jennifer Robison, CPA . . . . .646-0328 / *Fax: 646-0328*
Chief Appraiser	Brett McKibbon . . . . .643-5676 / *Fax: 646-8918*
Elections Official	Karen Opiela . . . . .646-4333 / *Fax: 646-6317*
County Commissioner:	
Precinct 1	Gary Worley . . . . .643-1985 / *Fax: 643-1356*
Precinct 2	Joel Kelton .643-1985 / *Fax: 643-1356*
Precinct 3	Wayne Shaw . . . . .643-1985 / *Fax: 643-1356*
Precinct 4	Larry Traweek . . . . .643-1985 / *Fax: 643-1356*

Justice of the Peace:

Precinct 1	Doug Hurt	.643-2688 / *Fax: 646-6437*
Precinct 2	Mike Holder	.643-5962 / *Fax: 641-2382*
Precinct 3	Bryan Thompson	.643-5962 / *Fax: 641-2382*
Precinct 4	Jim Cavanuagh	.646-6437 / *Fax: 646-6437*

Constable:

Precinct 1	Robert Mullins	.267-1750 / *Fax: 646-6437*
Precinct 2	David Hefner	.642-6744 / *Fax: 641-2382*
Precinct 3	Roy Parrack	.642-3260 / *Fax: 641-2382*
Precinct 4	Jim Byars	.642-7234 / *Fax: 646-6437*

BURLESON COUNTY

Population: 18,415
County Seat:
  Caldwell 77836

100 W. Buck
979 567-2333 / *Fax: 979 567-2372*
www.co.burleson.tx.us

County Judge	Mike Sutherland	.567-2333 / *Fax: 567-2372*
District Attorney, 21st Dist.	Julie Renken	.567-2350 / *Fax: 567-2375*
County Attorney	Susan R. Deski	.567-2340 / *Fax: 567-2373*
District Clerk	Dana Fritsche	.567-2336
County Clerk	Anna Schielack	.567-2329 / *Fax: 567-2376*
County Treasurer	Ken Prestenbach	.567-2307 / *Fax: 567-2366*
Tax Assessor-Collector	Curtis Doss	.567-2326 / *Fax: 567-2369*
Sheriff	Thomas Norsworthy	.567-4343 / *Fax: 567-0615*
County Auditor	Jimmy L. Mynar	.567-2331 / *Fax: 567-2390*
Chief Appraiser	Kim Orr	.567-2318 / *Fax: 567-2368*
Elections Official	Paula Bartnesky	.567-2000 / *Fax: 567-0789*

County Commissioner:

Precinct 1	Joe F. Baldwin, Jr.	.567-4996 / *Fax: 567-4996*
Precinct 2	Keith Schroeder	.272-8838 / *Fax: 272-5069*
Precinct 3	David Hildebrand	.567-3768 / *Fax: 567-6848*
Precinct 4	Carol Hill	.596-1022 / *Fax: 596-3612*

Justice of the Peace:

Precinct 1	James Baldwin	.535-4761 / *Fax: 535-7344*
Precinct 2	William J. "Bill" Orsak	.272-3656 / *Fax: 272-4501*
Precinct 3	Johnny Towslee	.567-2302 / *Fax: 567-0587*
Precinct 4	Robert Urbanosky	.596-1022 / *Fax: 596-3612*

Constable:

Precinct 1	Jason Muzny	.567-3993 / *Fax: 567-3993*
Precinct 2	Dennis J. Gaas	.272-3656 / *Fax: 272-4501*
Precinct 3	W. W. Warren	.567-2303 / *Fax: 567-0587*
Precinct 4	Wayne Wilhelm	.596-1412 / *Fax: 596-3795*

BURNET COUNTY

Population: 45,955
County Seat:
  Burnet 78611

220 South Pierce
512 756-5420 / *Fax: 512 715-5291*
www.burnetcountytexas.org/

County Judge ..... James Oakley ..... 756-5400 / *Fax: 715-5217*
District Attorney, 33rd Dist. ..... Wiley B. "Sonny" McAfee ..... 756-5449 / *Fax: 756-8572*
County Attorney ..... Eduardo "Eddie" Arredondo ..... 756-5476 / *Fax: 756-9290*
District Clerk ..... Casie Walker ..... 756-5450 / *Fax: 756-5023*
County Clerk ..... Janet Parker ..... 756-5406 / *Fax: 756-5410*
County Treasurer ..... Karrie Crownover ..... 756-5497 / *Fax: 715-5259*
Tax Assessor-Collector ..... Sheri Frazier ..... 756-5491 / *Fax: 756-1129*
Sheriff ..... Calvin Boyd ..... 756-8080 / *Fax: 756-4064*
County Auditor ..... Karen Hardin ..... 756-5466 / *Fax: 715-5264*
Chief Appraiser ..... Stan Hemphill ..... 756-8291 / *Fax: 756-7873*
Elections Official ..... Doug Ferguson ..... 715-5288 / *Fax: 715-5287*
County Commissioner:
  Precinct 1 ..... Jim Luther, Jr. ..... 715-5233 / *Fax: 715-5291*
  Precinct 2 ..... Russell Graeter ..... 715-5232 / *Fax: 715-5291*
  Precinct 3 ..... Billy Wall ..... 715-5236 / *Fax: 715-5291*
  Precinct 4 ..... Joe Don Dockery ..... 715-5235 / *Fax: 715-5291*
Justice of the Peace:
  Precinct 1 ..... Roxanne Nelson ..... 756-5421 / *Fax: 756-5402*
  Precinct 2 ..... Lisa Whitehead ..... 756-5453 / *Fax: 756-5402*
  Precinct 3 ..... Peggy L. Simon ..... 830 798-3212 / *Fax: 830 798-3214*
  Precinct 4 ..... Debbie Bindseil ..... 830 798-3205 / *Fax: 830 798-3216*
Constable:
  Precinct 1 ..... Leslie Ray 756-5456
  Precinct 2 ..... Garry Adams ..... 715-5237 / *Fax: 756-5402*
  Precinct 3 ..... Jimmy Ballard 830 798-3024
  Precinct 4 ..... Millicent "Missy" Bindseil ..... 830 798-3020 / *Fax: 830 798-3216*

CALDWELL COUNTY

Population: 40,336
County Seat:
  Lockhart 78644

110 South Main St.
512 398-1808 / *Fax: 512 398-1828*
www.co.caldwell.tx.us

County Judge ..... Ken Schawe ..... 398-1808 / *Fax: 398-1828*
Criminal District Attorney ..... Fred H. Weber ..... 398-1811 / *Fax: 398-1814*
District Clerk ..... Tina Morgan Freeman ..... 398-1806 / *Fax: 398-1805*
County Clerk ..... Carol Holcomb ..... 398-1804 / *Fax: 398-9925*
County Treasurer ..... Lori Rangel, CIO ..... 398-1800 / *Fax: 668-4947*
Tax Assessor-Collector ..... Darla Law ..... 398-1830 / *Fax: 398-1834*
Sheriff ..... Daniel C. Law ..... 398-6777 / *Fax: 376-4376*
County Auditor ..... Barbara Gonzales ..... 398-1801 / *Fax: 398-1829*
Chief Appraiser ..... Mary LaPoint ..... 398-5550 / *Fax: 398-5551*
Elections Official ..... Pam Ohlendorf ..... 668-4347 / *Fax: 398-1821*
County Commissioner:
  Precinct 1 ..... Hoppy Haden ..... 461-1108 / *Fax: 398-1828*
  Precinct 2 ..... Edward Moses ..... 830 832-7093 / *Fax: 398-1828*
  Precinct 3 ..... Edward Theriot ..... 618-2865 / *Fax: 398-1828*
  Precinct 4 ..... Joe Ivan Roland ..... 738-2172 / *Fax: 398-1828*

Justice of the Peace:
  Precinct 1   Matt Kiely . . . . .398-1810 / *Fax: 398-2785*
  Precinct 2   Homer Horne . . . . .830 875-5260 / *Fax: 830 875-6449*
  Precinct 3   Ben E. Brady . . . . .357-6729 / *Fax: 357-6833*
  Precinct 4   Raymond D. DeLeon . . . . .398-1841 / *Fax: 398-1837*
Constable:
  Precinct 1   Victor S. "Smitty" Terrell 376-8369
  Precinct 2   Tom Will 995-0272
  Precinct 3   Michael Jay Bell 743-5828
  Precinct 4   Arthur Villarreal 227-5900

CALHOUN COUNTY

Population: 21,397
County Seat:
  Port Lavaca 77979

211 S. Ann St., Suite 301
361 553-4600 / *Fax: 361 553-4444*
www.calhouncotx.org

County Judge	Michael "Mike" Pfeifer . . . . .553-4600 / *Fax: 553-4444*
Criminal District Attorney	Dan Heard .553-4422 / *Fax: 553-4421*
District Clerk	Anna Kabela . . . . .553-4630 / *Fax: 553-4637*
County Clerk	Anna Goodman . . . . .553-4411 / *Fax: 553-4420*
County Treasurer	Rhonda S. Kokena . . . . .553-4619 / *Fax: 553-4614*
Tax Assessor-Collector	Gloria Ann Ochoa . . . . .553-4433 / *Fax: 553-4442*
Sheriff	Bobbie John Vickery . . . . .553-4646 / *Fax: 553-4668*
County Auditor	Cynthia Mueller . . . . .553-4611 / *Fax: 553-4614*
Chief Appraiser	Jesse Hubbell . . . . .552-4560 / *Fax: 552-4787*
Elections Official	Dora Garcia . . . . .553-4440 / *Fax: 553-4442*

County Commissioner:
  Precinct 1   David Hall .552-9242 / *Fax: 553-8734*
  Precinct 2   Vern Lyssy . . . . .552-9656 / *Fax: 553-6664*
  Precinct 3   Clyde Syma . . . . .893-5346 / *Fax: 893-5309*
  Precinct 4   Kenneth W. Finster . . . . .785-3141 / *Fax: 785-5602*
Justice of the Peace:
  Precinct 1   Hope Kurtz . . . . .553-4621 / *Fax: 553-4626*
  Precinct 2   Calvin Anderle . . . . .553-4622 / *Fax: 553-4625*
  Precinct 3   Tanya Dimak . . . . .987-2930 / *Fax: 987-2940*
  Precinct 4   Wesley J. Hunt . . . . .983-2351 / *Fax: 983-4493*
  Precinct 5   Nancy T. Pomykal . . . . .983-2351 / *Fax: 983-4493*
Constable:
  Precinct 1   Eugene Menchaca 552-7917
  Precinct 2   William "Billy" Billings . . . . .553-4600 / *Fax: 553-4625*
  Precinct 3   Bruce Blevins . . . . .553-4607 / *Fax: 553-4444*
  Precinct 4   Kevin Koliba 550-8520

CALLAHAN COUNTY

Population: 14,167
County Seat:
  Baird 79504

100 W. 4th St., Suite 200
325 854-5805 / *Fax: 325 854-5806*
www.callahancounty.org

County Judge	Roger Corn	854-5805 / *Fax: 854-5806*
District & County Attorney	Shane Deel	854-5810 / *Fax: 854-5811*
District Clerk	Amber Tinsley	854-5825 / *Fax: 854-5826*
County Clerk	Nicole Crocker	854-5815 / *Fax: 854-5816*
County Treasurer	Jan Windham	854-5840 / *Fax: 854-5841*
Tax Assessor-Collector	Tammy T. Walker	854-5820 / *Fax: 854-5821*
Sheriff	Terry Joy	854-1444 / *Fax: 854-5998*
County Auditor	Sandra Rose	
Chief Appraiser	Brad Beam	854-5865 / *Fax: 854-5866*
Elections Official	Tammy T. Walker	854-5820 / *Fax: 854-5821*
County Commissioner:		
Precinct 1	Harold Hicks	854-5805 / *Fax: 854-5806*
Precinct 2	Bryan Farmer	854-5805 / *Fax: 854-5806*
Precinct 3	Tom F. Windham	854-5805 / *Fax: 854-5806*
Precinct 4	Erwin Clark	854-5805 / *Fax: 854-5806*
Justice of the Peace:		
Precinct 1	Tom Rumfield	893-4900 / *Fax: 893-4470*
Precinct 3	Steve Odom	854-5830 / *Fax: 854-5831*
Precinct 4	Burlie Taylor	254 725-7456 / *Fax: 254 725-6606*
Constable:		
Precinct 1	Ed C. Duncan	254 725-7456 / *Fax: 254 725-6606*

CAMERON COUNTY

Population: 425,194
County Seat:
  Brownsville 78520

1100 E. Monroe St
956 544-0830 / *Fax: 956 544-0801*
www.co.cameron.tx.us/

County Judge	Eddie Trevino, Jr.	544-0830 / *Fax: 544-0801*
District Attorney	Luis V. Saenz	544-0849 / *Fax: 550-1348*
District Clerk	Eric Garza	544-0838 / *Fax: 544-0841*
County Clerk	Sylvia Garza-Perez	544-0815 / *Fax: 544-0813*
County Treasurer	David A. Betancourt	544-0819 / *Fax: 550-1323*
Tax Assessor-Collector	Tony Yzaguirre, Jr.	544-0800 / *Fax: 544-0808*
Sheriff	Omar Lucio	554-6700 / *Fax: 554-6780*
County Auditor	Martha Galarza	544-0822 / *Fax: 544-0876*
Chief Appraiser	Richard Molina	399-9322 / *Fax: 361-6097*
Elections Official	Remi Garza	544-0809 / *Fax: 550-7298*
County Commissioner:		
Precinct 1	Sofia C. Benavides	574-8167 / *Fax: 544-0820*
Precinct 2	Alex Dominguez	983-5091 / *Fax: 983-5090*
Precinct 3	David A. Garza	361-8257 / *Fax: 361-8242*
Precinct 4	Gus Ruiz	427-8069 / *Fax: 427-8071*

Justice of the Peace:
Precinct 1 — Bennie Ochoa, III .... .943-2520 / *Fax: 943-0191*
Precinct 2, Pl. 1 — Linda Salazar .... .544-0857 / *Fax: 548-9573*
Precinct 2, Pl. 2 — Jonathan D. Gracia .... .544-0858 / *Fax: 550-1467*
Precinct 2, Pl. 3 — Mary Ester Sorola .... .547-7068 / *Fax: 547-7067*
Precinct 3, Pl. 1 — Chuy Garcia .... .361-4618 / *Fax: 361-4620*
Precinct 3, Pl. 2 — David Garza .... .361-8257 / *Fax: 361-8242*
Precinct 4 — Juan Mendoza .... .233-6105 / *Fax: 233-6151*
Precinct 5, Pl. 1 — Sallie Gonzalez .... .427-8057 / *Fax: 412-2457*
Precinct 5, Pl. 2 — Eloy Cano, Jr. .... .427-8058 / *Fax: 427-8034*
Precinct 5, Pl. 3 — Mike Trejo .... .797-1887 / *Fax: 797-9359*
Constable:
Precinct 1 — Pete Delgadillo .... .943-6757 / *Fax: 943-0199*
Precinct 2 — Abel Gomez, Jr. .... .544-0859 / *Fax: 550-1350*
Precinct 3 — Adrian Gonzalez .... .361-8228 / *Fax: 361-8274*
Precinct 4 — Merced Burnias .... .233-6156 / *Fax: 233-6162*
Precinct 5 — Eddie Solis .... .427-8052 / *Fax: 427-8051*

CAMP COUNTY

Population: 12,692
County Seat:
  Pittsburg 75686

126 Church St.
903 856-3845 / *Fax: 903 856-2309*
www.co.camp.tx.us/

County Judge — James "A.J." Mason .... .856-3845 / *Fax: 856-2309*
District Attorney, 76th Dist. — Charles C. Bailey .... .577-6726 / *Fax: 577 6729*
County Attorney — Angela Hammonds-Saucier .... .856-2409 / *Fax: 856-5278*
District Clerk — Teresa Bockmon .... .856-3221 / *Fax: 856-0560*
County Clerk — Elaine Young .... .856-2731 / *Fax: 856-6112*
County Treasurer — Kim Pittman .... .855-1756 / *Fax: 856-3078*
Tax Assessor-Collector — Gale Burns .... .856-3391 / *Fax: 856-0811*
Sheriff — Alan D. McCandless .... .856-6651 / *Fax: 856-6359*
County Auditor — Nanette Wilabay .... .856-3772 / *Fax: 856-3078*
Chief Appraiser — Jan Tinsley .... .856-6538 / *Fax: 856-6544*
County Commissioner:
  Precinct 1 — George French .... .856-3845 / *Fax: 856-2309*
  Precinct 2 — Steve Hudnall .... .856-3845 / *Fax: 856-2309*
  Precinct 3 — L. H. Calhoun Henderson .... .856-3845 / *Fax: 856-2309*
  Precinct 4 — Steve Lindley .... .856-3845 / *Fax: 856-2309*
Justice of the Peace: — Harold Kennington .... .856-3961 / *Fax: 855-0305*
Constable: — John Cortelyou .... .856-7853 / *Fax: 856-5278*

CARSON COUNTY

Population: 5,930
County Seat:
 Panhandle 79068

P. O. Box 369
806 537-3622 / *Fax: 806 537-2244*
www.co.carson.tx.us

County Judge	Daniel Looten	537-3622 / *Fax: 537-2244*
District Attorney, 100th Dist.	Luke Inman	447-0055 / *Fax: 866 233-2738*
County Attorney	Scott Sherwood	537-3591 / *Fax: 537-3592*
District & County Clerk	Celeste Bichsel	537-3873 / *Fax: 537-3623*
County Treasurer	Denise Salzbrenner	537-3753 / *Fax: 537-3724*
Tax Assessor-Collector	Jackie Moore	537-3412 / *Fax: 537-3795*
Sheriff	Loren Brand	537-3511 / *Fax: 537-2120*
County Auditor	Jackie West	537-3488 / *Fax: 537-3969*
Chief Appraiser	Donita Davis	537-3569 / *Fax: 537-5343*
County Commissioner:		
Precinct 1	Mike Britten	248-7277 / *Fax: 537-2244*
Precinct 2	James Martin	537-3954 / *Fax: 537-2244*
Precinct 3	Mike Jennings	537-5491 / *Fax: 537-2244*
Precinct 4	Kevin Howell	880-0294 / *Fax: 537-2244*
Justice of the Peace:		
Precinct 1	Kathleen Barkley	248-7444 / *Fax: 248-7444*
Precinct 2	Jean Hardman	537-3722 / *Fax: 537-2248*

CASS COUNTY

Population: 31,030
County Seat:
 Linden 75563

P. O. Box 825 (County Judge)
903 756-5181 / *Fax: 903 756-5732*
www.co.cass.tx.us

County Judge	Becky Wilbanks	756-5181 / *Fax: 756-5732*
Criminal District Attorney	Randal Lee	756-7541 / *Fax: 756-3210*
District Clerk	Jamie Albertson	756-7514 / *Fax: 756-5253*
County Clerk	Amy Varnell	756-5071 / *Fax: 756-8057*
County Treasurer	Donna Early	756-7626 / *Fax: 756-3018*
Tax Assessor-Collector	Angie Young	756-5513 / *Fax: 756-7431*
Sheriff	Larry Rowe	756-7511 / *Fax: 756-5434*
County Auditor	Tammy Wells	756-5067 / *Fax: 756-3018*
Chief Appraiser	Jordan Klein	756-7545 / *Fax: 756-3270*
County Commissioner:		
Precinct 1	Brett Fitts	756-5701 / *Fax: 756-5732*
Precinct 2	Jon Borseth	835-5761
Precinct 3	Paul Cothren	796-4502 / *Fax: 866 309-5411*
Precinct 4	Darrell Godwin	796-2766 / *Fax: 756-5732*
Justice of the Peace:		
Precinct 1	Barbara McMillon	756-5341 / *Fax: 756-3514*
Precinct 2	Gina Bassham	639-7268 / *Fax: 639-3769*
Precinct 3	Micki Henderson	796-3891 / *Fax: 796-9449*
Precinct 4	Bridget Smith	796-8493 / *Fax: 796-4690*
Constable:		
Precinct 1	Alton McWaters	756-5341 / *Fax: 756-3514*
Precinct 2	Anthony "Tony" Harrison	824-6947 / *Fax: 639-3789*
Precinct 3	John Smith	824-8545 / *Fax: 796-9449*
Precinct 4	Don Rich	824-1331 / *Fax: 796-4690*

CASTRO COUNTY

Population: 7,697
County Seat:
  Dimmitt 79027

100 E. Bedford, Room 111
806 647-4451 / *Fax: 806 647-4403*
www.co.castro.tx.us

County Judge	Carroll Gerber	.647-4451 / *Fax: 647-4403*
District & County Attorney	Shalyn Hamlin	.647-4445 / *Fax: 647-2089*
District & County Clerk	Joanna Blanco	.647-3338 / *Fax: 647-5438*
County Treasurer	Elaine Davis Flynt	.647-5534 / *Fax: 647-3052*
Tax Assessor-Collector	Pam Rickert	.647-5336 / *Fax: 647-5654*
Sheriff	Sal Rivera, Jr.	.647-3311 / *Fax: 647-2189*
Chief Appraiser	Jerry Heller	.647-5131 / *Fax: 647-5132*
County Commissioner:		
Precinct 1	Paul Ramirez	.647-6552 / *Fax: 647-4403*
Precinct 2	Tim Elliott	.647-5512 / *Fax: 647-4403*
Precinct 3	Michael Goolsby	.647-7107 / *Fax: 647-4403*
Precinct 4	Ralph Brookman	.240-1344 / *Fax: 647-4403*
Justice of the Peace:	Jo Campbell	.647-2328 / *Fax: 647-0508*
Constable:	John W. Kropp	.647-0515 / *Fax: 647-0508*

CHAMBERS COUNTY

Population: 39,676
County Seat:
  Anahuac 77514

P. O. Box 939 - 404 Washington Avenue
409 267-2440 / *Fax: 409 267-4453*
www.co.chambers.tx.us

County Judge	Jimmy Sylvia	.267-2440 / *Fax: 267-4453*
District Attorney, 344th Dist.	Cheryl Lieck	.267-2682 / *Fax: 267-3105*
County Attorney	Scott Peal	.267-2411 / *Fax: 267-8296*
District Clerk	Patti Henry	.267-2432 / *Fax: 267-8209*
County Clerk	Heather H. Hawthorne	.267-2418 / *Fax: 267-8405*
County Treasurer	Nicole "Nikki" Whittington	.267-2455 / *Fax: 267-3790*
Tax Assessor-Collector	Denise Hutter, PCC, CTOP	.267-2742 / *Fax: 267-8398*
Sheriff	Brian C. Hawthorne	.267-2500 / *Fax: 267-6858*
County Auditor	Tony Sims	.267-2405 / *Fax: 267-4434*
Chief Appraiser	Mitch McCullough	.267-3795 / *Fax: 267-6192*
County Commissioner:		
Precinct 1	Jimmy E. Gore	.926-8250 / *Fax: 296-3228*
Precinct 2	Larry G. George	.267-2409 / *Fax: 267-6685*
Precinct 3	Gary R. Nelson	.281 576-2243 / *Fax: 281 385-6392*
Precinct 4	A.R. "Rusty" Senac	.281 383-2011 / *Fax: 281 573-1823*
Justice of the Peace:		
Precinct 1	Yale Devillier	.296-8247 / *Fax: 296-8651*
Precinct 2	Randy Van Deventer	.267-2519 / *Fax: 267-3120*
Precinct 3	Tracy Woody	.252-4212 / *Fax: 252-4479*
Precinct 4	Blake Sylvia	.281 383-3197 / *Fax: 281 385-2158*
Precinct 5	R. M. "Bob" Wallace, Sr.	.267-2561 / *Fax: 389-2411*
Precinct 6	Larry Cryer	.267-2570 / *Fax: 281 573-1823*

COUNTY SECTION

Chambers County Cont.

Constable:

Precinct 1	Dennis Dugat	.267-2657
Precinct 2	Don R. Langford	.267-2516 / *Fax: 267-8342*
Precinct 3	Donnie Standley	.252-4345 / *Fax: 252-4479*
Precinct 4	Ben L. "Butch" Bean	.267-2609 / *Fax: 281 385-2158*
Precinct 5	C.R. Oldham	.267-2563 / *Fax: 389-2411*
Precinct 6	Robert Barrow	.267-2576 / *Fax: 281 573-1948*

CHEROKEE COUNTY

Population: 52,189
County Seat:
  Rusk 75785

Courthouse, 135 South Main St.
903 683-2324 / *Fax: 903 683-2393*
www.co.cherokee.tx.us

County Judge	Chris Davis	.683-2324 / *Fax: 683-2393*
District Attorney, 2nd Dist.	Elmer Beckworth	.683-2573 / *Fax: 683-2309*
County Attorney	Dana Young	.683-2423 / *Fax: 683-5931*
District Clerk	Janet Gates	.683-4533 / *Fax: 683-2971*
County Clerk	Laverne Lusk	.683-2350 / *Fax: 683-2457*
County Treasurer	Patsy J. Lassiter	.683-4935 / *Fax: 683-2393*
Tax Assessor-Collector	Linda Little	.683-5478 / *Fax: 683-2362*
Sheriff	James E. Campbell	.683-2271 / *Fax: 683-2813*
County Auditor	Amanda Dover	.683-2717 / *Fax: 683-2393*
Chief Appraiser	Lee Flowers	.683-2296 / *Fax: 683-6271*
Elections Official	Shannon Cornelius	.683-8409 / *Fax: 683-8419*
County Commissioner:		
Precinct 1	Kelly Traylor	.683-5060 / *Fax: 683-5891*
Precinct 2	Steven Norton	.936 858-4785 / *Fax: 936 858-4786*
Precinct 3	Patrick Reagan	.586-5811 / *Fax: 586-6521*
Precinct 4	Byron Underwood	.842-3535 / *Fax: 842-3541*
Justice of the Peace:		
Precinct 1	Brenda Dominy	.683-4663 / *Fax: 683-3476*
Precinct 2	Tony Johnson	.936 858-4732 / *Fax: 936 858-2271*
Precinct 3	Phillip Grimes	.586-9161 / *Fax: 586-0344*
Precinct 4	Rodney Wallace	.586-1065 / *Fax: 586-2524*
Constable:		
Precinct 1	Lynn Kelley	.571-9294
Precinct 2	Jack White	.721-3152
Precinct 3	Eddie Lee	.586-6211 / *Fax: 586-0344*
Precinct 4	Jamie Beene	.570-8054

CHILDRESS COUNTY

Population: 6,881
County Seat:
  Childress 79201

100 Avenue East NW, Box 1
940 937-2221 / *Fax: 940 937-0166*

County Judge	Jay Mayden	937-2221 / *Fax: 937-0166*
District Attorney, 100th Dist.	Luke Inman	806 447-0055 / *Fax: 866 233-2738*
County Attorney	Greg Buckley	937-6158 / *Fax: 937-3226*
District & County Clerk	Barbara Spitzer	937-6143 / *Fax: 937-3708*
County Treasurer	Brenda Overstreet	937-6271 / *Fax: 937-3479*
Tax Assessor-Collector	Kathy Dobbs	937-2232 / *Fax: 937-2250*
Sheriff	Mike Pigg	937-2535 / *Fax: 937-2395*
Chief Appraiser	Twila Butler	937-6062 / *Fax: 937-3368*
County Commissioner:		
Precinct 1	Jeremy Hill	937-2221
Precinct 2	Mark Ross	937-2221
Precinct 3	Lyall Foster	937-2221
Precinct 4	Rick Elliott	937-2221
Justice of the Peace:		
Precinct 1	Randall D. Rister	937-6145 / *Fax: 937-8086*
Constable:		
Precinct 1	Daniel Hernandez	937-2714

CLAY COUNTY

Population: 10,568
County Seat:
  Henrietta 76365

214 N. Main St.
940 538-4651 / *Fax: 940 538-5597*
www.co.clay.tx.us/

County Judge	Kenneth Liggett	538-4651 / *Fax: 538-5597*
District Attorney, 97th Dist.	Casey Polhemus	894-6211 / *Fax: 894-6203*
County Attorney	Seth Slagle	538-0533 / *Fax: 538-5567*
District Clerk	Marianne Bowles	538-4561 / *Fax: 538-0147*
County Clerk	Sasha Kelton	538-4631 / *Fax: 264-4160*
County Treasurer	Danja Bloodworth	538-5911 / *Fax: 538-5991*
Tax Assessor-Collector	Maribel Longoria	538-4356 / *Fax: 538-4624*
Sheriff	K.R. "Kenny" Lemons, Jr.	538-5611 / *Fax: 538-5800*
County Auditor	Ramona Seward	538-5560 / *Fax: 538-4008*
Chief Appraiser	Gerald Holland	538-4311 / *Fax: 538-4725*
County Commissioner:		
Precinct 1	Richard Lowery	636-4071 / *Fax: 538-4008*
Precinct 2	Johnny Gee	636-0140 / *Fax: 538-4008*
Precinct 3	John McGregor	781-4779 / *Fax: 538-4008*
Precinct 4	Richard Keen	704-2288 / *Fax: 538-4008*
Justice of the Peace:	John Swenson	538-6531 / *Fax: 264-4161*
Constable:	Sidney Kirk Horton	264-1314

COCHRAN COUNTY

Population: 3,012
County Seat:
  Morton 79346

100 North Main, Room 105
806 266-5508 / *Fax: 806 266-9027*
www.co.cochran.tx.us

County Judge	Pat Sabala Henry	.266-5508 / *Fax: 266-9027*
District Attorney, 286th Dist.	Christopher Dennis	.894-3130 / *Fax: 266-3543*
County Attorney	J. Collier Adams, Jr.	.266-5582 / *Fax: 266-5583*
District & County Clerk	Shanna Dewbre	.266-5450 / *Fax: 266-9027*
County Treasurer	Doris Sealy	.266-5161 / *Fax: 266-5629*
Tax Assessor-Collector	Treva Jackson	.266-5171 / *Fax: 266-5629*
Sheriff	Jorge De La Cruz	.266-5700 / *Fax: 266-8888*
County Auditor	Beverly McClellan	.266-5822 / *Fax: 266-5629*
Chief Appraiser	David Greener	.266-5584 / *Fax: 266-5737*
Elections Official	Cheryl Butler	.266-5181 / *Fax: 266-9027*
County Commissioner:		
Precinct 1	Timothy Roberts	.523-9223 / *Fax: 266-9027*
Precinct 2	Bruce Heflin	.891-4572 / *Fax: 266-9027*
Precinct 3	Eric Silhan	.525-2200 / *Fax: 266-9027*
Precinct 4	Reynaldo Morin	.893-5890 / *Fax: 266-9027*
Justice of the Peace:	Donna Schmidt	.266-5302 / *Fax: 266-8888*
Constable:	Ben Bristow	.266-0907

COKE COUNTY

Population: 3,195
County Seat:
  Robert Lee 76945

County Courthouse, 13 East 7th Street
325 453-2641 / *Fax: 325 453-2157*
www.co.coke.tx.us

County Judge	Roy Blair	.453-2641 / *Fax: 453-2157*
District Attorney, 51st Dist.	Allison Palmer	.659-6583 / *Fax: 658-6831*
County Attorney	Nicholas E. Arrott II	.453-2712 / *Fax: 453-2576*
District & County Clerk	Mary Grim	.453-2631 / *Fax: 453-2650*
County Treasurer	Hal Spain	.453-2713 / *Fax: 453-2328*
Tax Assessor-Collector	Josie Dean	.453-2614 / *Fax: 453-2328*
Sheriff	Wayne McCutchen	.453-2717 / *Fax: 453-2597*
County Auditor	Vallery Johnson	.453-2922 / *Fax: 453-2157*
Chief Appraiser	Gayle Sisemore	.453-4528 / *Fax: 453-4529*
County Commissioner:		
Precinct 1	Donald S. Robertson	.763-8946 / *Fax: 453-2157*
Precinct 2	Paul Williams	.660-6488 / *Fax: 453-2157*
Precinct 3	Marshall Millican	.473-0437 / *Fax: 453-2157*
Precinct 4	Joe Sefcik	.473-8503 / *Fax: 453-2157*
Justice of the Peace:		
Precinct 1	Jackie Walker	.453-4777 / *Fax: 453-2157*
Constable:		
Precinct 2	Marty Boyd	.453-2717 / *Fax: 453-2157*

COLEMAN COUNTY

Population: 8,541
County Seat:
  Coleman 76834

Courthouse, 100 West Live Oak St., Suite 203
325 625-4221 / *Fax: 325 625-4218*
www.co.coleman.tx.us

County Judge	Billy D. Bledsoe	.625-4218 / *Fax: 625-4218*
District Attorney, 42nd Dist.	Heath Hemphill	.625-1316 / *Fax: 625-1325*
County Attorney	Joe Lee Rose	.625-3731 / *Fax: 625-1724*
District Clerk	Margie Mayo	.625-2568 / *Fax: 625-3858*
County Clerk	Stacey Mendoza	.625-2889 / *Fax: 625-2889*
County Treasurer	Jerri Ann Chambers	.625-4221 / *Fax: 625-4221*
Tax Assessor-Collector	Jamie Trammell	.625-2153 / *Fax: 625-2154*
Sheriff	Les Cogdill	.625-3506 / *Fax: 625-3509*
Chief Appraiser	Bill Jones	.625-4155 / *Fax: 625-5134*
County Commissioner:		
Precinct 1	Mark Williams	.625-3211 / *Fax: 625-4221*
Precinct 2	Rick Beal	.348-9103 / *Fax: 625-4221*
Precinct 3	Scotty Lawrence	.357-4468 / *Fax: 625-4221*
Precinct 4	Alan Davis	.625-5807 / *Fax: 625-4221*
Justice of the Peace:	Nance Campbell	.625-4223 / *Fax: 625-4154*
Constable:	Joe D. Watson	.625-4218 / *Fax: 625-3509*

COLLIN COUNTY

Population: 944,366
County Seat:
  McKinney 75071

2300 Bloomdale Road, Suite 4192
972 424-1460
www.collincountytexas.gov

County Judge	Keith Self	.424-1460 / *Fax: 548-4699*
Criminal District Attorney	Greg Willis	.548-4323 / *Fax: 214 491-4860*
District Clerk	Lynn Finley	.548-4320
County Clerk	Stacey Kemp	.548-4185 / *Fax: 547-5731*
Tax Assessor-Collector	Kenneth L. Maun	.547 5020 / *Fax: 547-5040*
Sheriff	Jim Skinner	.547-5100 / *Fax: 547-5191*
County Auditor	Jeff May	.548-4641 / *Fax: 548-4696*
Chief Appraiser	Bo Daffin	.469 742-9200 / *Fax: 469 742-9209*
Elections Official	Bruce Sherbet	.547-1910 / *Fax: 547-1914*
County Commissioner:		
Precinct 1	Susan Fletcher	.548-4676 / *Fax: 548-4699*
Precinct 2	Cheryl Williams	.424-1460 / *Fax: 548-4699*
Precinct 3	John D. Thomas	.424-1460 / *Fax: 548-4699*
Precinct 4	Duncan Webb	.424-1460 / *Fax: 548-4699*
Justice of the Peace:		
Precinct 1	Paul Raleeh	.424-1460 / *Fax: 548-4188*
Precinct 2	Jerry Shaffer	.782-8671 / *Fax: 782-8559*
Precinct 3, Pl. 1	Chuck Ruckel	.881-3001 / *Fax: 881-3157*
Precinct 3, Pl. 2	John E. Payton	.881-3011 / *Fax: 881-3098*
Precinct 4	Mike Yarbrough	.731-7300 / *Fax: 731-7311*
Constable:		
Precinct 1	Shane Williams	.548-4419 / *Fax: 548-4785*
Precinct 2	Gary Edwards	.782-7211 / *Fax: 782-8559*
Precinct 3	Sammy Knapp	.881-3070 / *Fax: 881-4143*
Precinct 4	Joe Wright	.731-7320 / *Fax: 731-7330*

COUNTY SECTION

COLLINGSWORTH COUNTY

Population: 3,013
County Seat:
  Wellington 79095

Courthouse, 800 W. Avenue, Box 13
806 447-5408 / Fax: 806 447-5418
www.co.collingsworth.tx.us

County Judge	John A. James	.447-5408 / Fax: 447-5418
District Attorney, 100th Dist.	Luke Inman	.447-0055 / Fax: 866 233-2738
County Attorney	Keith Davis	.447-2518 / Fax: 447-2519
District & County Clerk	Jackie Johnson	.447-2408 / Fax: 447-2409
County Treasurer	Gina Harris	.447-2616 / Fax: 447-2251
Tax Assessor-Collector	Generah Manuel	.447-5606 / Fax: 447-2251
Sheriff	Kent Riley	.447-2588 / Fax: 447-5037
Chief Appraiser	Dwight Bowen	.447-5172 / Fax: 447-2198
County Commissioner:		
Precinct 1	Elmer Keller	.447-5408 / Fax: 447-5418
Precinct 2	Mike Hughs	.447-5408 / Fax: 447-5418
Precinct 3	Eddie Orr	.447-5408 / Fax: 447-5418
Precinct 4	Kirby Campbell	.447-5408 / Fax: 447-5418
Justice of the Peace:	Jo Rita Henard	.447-5555 / Fax: 447-5418
Constable:	Ronnie Ward	.447-2588 / Fax: 447-5418

COLORADO COUNTY

Population: 21,866
County Seat:
  Columbus 78934

P. O. Box 236 - 400 Spring Street, Room 113 (delivery)
979 732-2604 / Fax: 979 732-9389
www.co.colorado.tx.us/

County Judge	Ty Prause	.732-2604 / Fax: 732-9389
County Attorney	Jay Johannes	.732-8203 / Fax: 732-9115
District Clerk	Linda Holman	.732-2536 / Fax: 732-2916
County Clerk	Kimberly Menke	.732-6860 / Fax: 732-8852
County Treasurer	Joyce Stancik	.732-2865 / Fax: 732-2924
Tax Assessor-Collector	Mary Jane Poenitzsch, PCC	.732-2710 / Fax: 732-9622
Sheriff	R.H. "Curly" Wied	.732-2388 / Fax: 732-6431
County Auditor	Raymie Kana	.732-2791 / Fax: 732-2924
Chief Appraiser	Bill Mitchell	.732-8222 / Fax: 732-6485
County Commissioner:		
Precinct 1	Doug Wessels	.234-2071 / Fax: 234-2071
Precinct 2	Darrell Kubesch	.725-8416 / Fax: 725-8416
Precinct 3	Tommy Hahn	.732-3270 / Fax: 732-9922
Precinct 4	Darrell Gertson	.234-2633 / Fax: 234-3832
Justice of the Peace:		
Precinct 1	Billy Hefner	.732-2734 / Fax: 732-3022
Precinct 2	Chris Maddux	.725-8833 / Fax: 725-8671
Precinct 3	Francis Truchard	.732-6607 / Fax: 732-4729
Precinct 4	Stan Warfield	.234-2042 / Fax: 234-2851
Constable:		
Precinct 1	Richard LaCourse	.733-6720
Precinct 2	Lonnie Hinze	.725-8833
Precinct 3	Ivan V. Menke	.732-5352
Precinct 4	Darrell Stancik	.234-2534

COMAL COUNTY

Population: 130,021
County Seat:
  New Braunfels 78130

150 N. Seguin Avenue
830 221-1100 / *Fax: 830 608-2026*
www.co.comal.tx.us/

County Judge	Sherman Krause	.221-1105 / *Fax: 608-2026*
Criminal District Attorney		
District 22	Jennifer Anne Tharp	.221-1301 / *Fax: 608-2008*
District Clerk	Heather Kellar	.221-1251 / *Fax: 608-2006*
County Clerk	Bobbie Koepp	.221-1234 / *Fax: 620-3410*
County Treasurer	Renee Couch	.221-1220 / *Fax: 620-3482*
Tax Assessor-Collector	Cathy Talcott, PCC	.221-1353 / *Fax: 626-6871*
Sheriff	Mark W. Reynolds	.620-3400 / *Fax: 608-2082*
County Auditor	Jessie Rahe, Interim	.221-1201 / *Fax: 620-5592*
Chief Appraiser	Rufino "Hector" Lozano	.625-8597 / *Fax: 625-8598*
Elections Official	Bobbie Koepp	.221-1352 / *Fax: 608-2013*
County Commissioner:		
Precinct 1	Donna Eccleston	.221-1101 / *Fax: 608-2026*
Precinct 2	Scott Haag	.221-1102 / *Fax: 608-2026*
Precinct 3	Kevin Webb	.221-1103 / *Fax: 608-2026*
Precinct 4	Jen Crownover	.221-1104 / *Fax: 206-2026*
Justice of the Peace:		
Precinct 1	Tom Clark	.608-2025 / *Fax: 608-2085*
Precinct 2	Larry Shallcross	.387-7600 / *Fax: 438-3127*
Precinct 3	Mike Rust	.626-4888 / *Fax: 620-3465*
Precinct 4	Jennifer Saunders	.387-7700 / *Fax: 964-4798*
Constable:		
Precinct 1	Ben Scroggin	.643-3725 / *Fax: 608-2085*
Precinct 2	Mark Cheatum	.387-7602 / *Fax: 438-3127*
Precinct 3	Craig Ackerman	.626-4880 / *Fax: 620-3465*
Precinct 4	Shane Rapp	.387-7702 / *Fax: 964-4798*

COUNTY SECTION

COMANCHE COUNTY

Population: 13,906
County Seat:
  Comanche 76442

Courthouse, 101 W. Central
325 356-2466 / *Fax: 325 356-3710*

County Judge	James R. "Bob" Arthur	.356-2466 / *Fax: 356-3710*
District Attorney, 220th Dist.	Adam Sibley	.254 435-2994 / *Fax: 254 435-2952*
County Attorney	Craig Willingham	.356-2313 / *Fax: 356-3070*
District Clerk	Brenda Dickey	.356-2342 / *Fax: 356-2150*
County Clerk	Ruby Lesley	.356-2655 / *Fax: 356-5764*
County Treasurer	Patsy Phifer	.356-2838 / *Fax: 356-2838*
Tax Assessor-Collector	Grace Everhart	.356-3101 / *Fax: 356-5790*
Sheriff	Jeff Lambert	.356-7533 / *Fax: 356-3783*
County Auditor	Joey Boswell	.356-3834 / *Fax: 356-3710*
Chief Appraiser	JoAnn Hohertz	.356-5253 / *Fax: 356-1363*
County Commissioner:		
Precinct 1	Gary D. "Corky" Underwood	.356-3895 / *Fax: 356-3097*
Precinct 2	Russell Gillette	.356-5426 / *Fax: 356-5426*
Precinct 3	Sherman L. Sides	.254 879-2537 / *Fax: 254 879-2537*
Precinct 4	Jimmy Dale Johnson	.254 893-2184 / *Fax: 254 893-7284*
Justice of the Peace:	Johnny Conine	.356-3543 / *Fax: 356-5514*
Constable:	Mark McDonald	.356-5922 / *Fax: 356-3710*

CONCHO COUNTY

Population: 4,183
County Seat:
  Paint Rock 76866

P. O. Box 158 - 152 N. Roberts Ave.
325 732-4321 / *Fax: 325 732-4307*
www.co.concho.tx.us

County Judge	David Dillard	.732-4321 / *Fax: 732-4307*
District Attorney, 119th Dist.	John Best	.653-1912 / *Fax: 658-6813*
County Attorney	Bryan Clayton	.732-4315
District & County Clerk	Phyllis Lovell	.732-4322 / *Fax: 732-2040*
County Treasurer	Shawn L. Walston	.732-4279 / *Fax: 732-4279*
Tax Assessor-Collector	Chad Miller	.732-4460 / *Fax: 732-4761*
Sheriff	Chad Miller	.732-4312 / *Fax: 732-4761*
Chief Appraiser	Richard Petree, Interim	.732-4389 / *Fax: 732-4234*
County Commissioner:		
Precinct 1	Trey Bradshaw	.234-0206 / *Fax: 732-4307*
Precinct 2	Ralph Willberg	.456-1156 / *Fax: 732-4307*
Precinct 3	Gary Gierisch	.456-0683 / *Fax: 732-4307*
Precinct 4	Aaron B. "Sonny" Browning, Jr.	.456-0673 / *Fax: 732-4307*
Justice of the Peace:	Scott A. Spoonts	.732-4706 / *Fax: 732-4267*
Constable:	Vacant	.869-8921 / *Fax: 732-4307*

COOKE COUNTY

Population: 39,460
County Seat:
  Gainesville 76240

101 South Dixon
940 668-5435 / *Fax: 940 668-5440*
www.co.cooke.tx.us

County Judge	Jason Brinkley	.668-5435 / *Fax: 665-5440*
District Attorney, 235th Dist.	John Warren	.668-5466 / *Fax: 668-5499*
County Attorney	Edmund Zielinski	.668-5459 / *Fax: 668-5444*
District Clerk	Marci Gilbert	.668-5450 / *Fax: 668-5476*
County Clerk	Rebecca Lawson	.668-5521 / *Fax: 668-5486*
County Treasurer	Patricia Brennan	.668-5423 / *Fax: 668-5480*
Tax Assessor-Collector	Brandy Ann Carr	.668-5425 / *Fax: 668-5497*
Sheriff	Terry Gilbert	.665-3471 / *Fax: 665-3255*
County Auditor	Shelly Atteberry	.668-5493 / *Fax: 668-5442*
Chief Appraiser	Doug Smithson	.665-7651 / *Fax: 668-2587*
County Commissioner:		
Precinct 1	Gary Hollowell	.668-5481 / *Fax: 668-5527*
Precinct 2	B. C. Lemons	.668-5482 / *Fax: 668-5527*
Precinct 3	John Klement	.668-5483 / *Fax: 668-5527*
Precinct 4	Leon Klement	.668-5484 / *Fax: 668-5527*
Justice of the Peace:		
Precinct 1	Olivia Neu	.668-5463 / *Fax: 668-5411*
Precinct 4	Carroll Johnson	.726-3539 / *Fax: 726-5092*
Constable:		
Precinct 1	Chris Watson	.668-5463 / *Fax: 668-5411*
Precinct 4	Russell Harper	.726-3539 / *Fax: 726-5092*

CORYELL COUNTY

Population: 78,137
County Seat:
  Gatesville 76528

800 E. Main St., Ste. A
254 865-5911 / *Fax: 254 865-2040*
coryellcounty.org

County Judge	John E. Firth	.865-5911 / *Fax: 865-2040*
District Attorney, 52nd Dist.	Dustin Boyd	.865-5911 / *Fax: 865-5147*
County Attorney	Brandon Belt	.248-3180 / *Fax: 865-9080*
District Clerk	Janice M. Gray	.865-5911 / *Fax: 865-5064*
County Clerk	Barbara Simpson	.865-5911 / *Fax: 865-8631*
County Treasurer	Donna Medford	.865-5911 / *Fax: 865-2180*
Tax Assessor-Collector	Justin Carothers	.865-5911 / *Fax: 865-2519*
Sheriff	Scott A. Williams	.865-7201 / *Fax: 865-7774*
County Auditor	Ben Roberts	.865-5911 / *Fax: 865-1355*
Chief Appraiser	Mitch Fast	.865-6593 / *Fax: 865-1280*
Elections Official	Justin Carothers	.248-3142 / *Fax: 865-2519*
County Commissioner:		
Precinct 1	Kyle Matthews	.206-0663 / *Fax: 865-2040*
Precinct 2	Daren Moore	.223-1001 / *Fax: 865-2040*
Precinct 3	Don Jones	.223-1210 / *Fax: 865-2040*
Precinct 4	Ray Ashby	.679-9314 / *Fax: 865-2040*
Justice of the Peace:		
Precinct 1	John Guinn	.547-5993 / *Fax: 547-6007*
Precinct 2	F. W. "Bill" Price	.547-6517 / *Fax: 547-6007*
Precinct 3	Beverly Jones	.865-2912 / *Fax: 865-2978*
Precinct 4	Coy Latham	.865-5913 / *Fax: 865-2978*

COUNTY SECTION

Coryell County Cont.
Constable:

Precinct 1	Guy Beveridge	547-5993 / *Fax: 547-6007*
Precinct 2	Shawn Camp	547-6517 / *Fax: 547-6007*
Precinct 3	Dewey Jones	865-2912 / *Fax: 865-2978*
Precinct 4	Teddy Brock	865-5913 / *Fax: 865-2978*

COTTLE COUNTY

Population: 1,422
County Seat:
  Paducah 79248

Box 729, 9th & Richards St.
806 492-3613
www.co.cottle.tx.us

County Judge	Karl Holloway	492-3613
District Attorney, 50th Dist.	Jennifer A. Habert	940 889-2852 / *Fax: 940 888-3036*
County Attorney	John H. Richards	492-3340 / *Fax: 492-2032*
District & County Clerk	Vickey Wederski	492-3823 / *Fax: 492-2625*
County Treasurer	Crystal Tucker	492-3738 / *Fax: 492-2625*
Tax Assessor-Collector	Nakia Hargrave	492-3345 / *Fax: 492-3107*
Sheriff	Mark Box	492-2145 / *Fax: 492-2145*
Chief Appraiser	Nakia Hargrave	492-3345 / *Fax: 492-3107*
County Commissioner:		
Precinct 1	Jim Sweeney	492-3106 / *Fax: 492-3613*
Precinct 2	Vance D. Thompson	492-4343 / *Fax: 492-3613*
Precinct 3	Manuel Cruz, Jr.	492-3847 / *Fax: 492-3613*
Precinct 4	Marvin G. Powe	492-3613 / *Fax: 492-3613*
Justice of the Peace:		
Precinct 1	Hank White	492-3515 / *Fax: 492-2451*

CRANE COUNTY

Population: 5,063
County Seat:
  Crane 79731

201 W. 6th St.
432 558-1100 / *Fax: 432 558-1188*
www.co.crane.tx.us

County Judge	Vacant	558-1100 / *Fax: 558-1188*
District Attorney, 109th Dist.	Amanda Navarette	586-6608 / *Fax: 586-6036*
County Attorney	Carlos Rodriguez	558-1102 / *Fax: 558-1188*
District & County Clerk	Judy Crawford	558-3581 / *Fax: 558-1148*
County Treasurer	Cristy Tarin	558-3372 / *Fax: 558-1181*
Tax Assessor-Collector	Judy Crumrine	558-2622 / *Fax: 558-1198*
Sheriff	Andrew R. "Andy" Aguilar	558-3571 / *Fax: 558-3743*
County Auditor	Mendy Nichols	558-1121 / *Fax: 558-1185*
Chief Appraiser	Byron Bitner	558-1021 / *Fax: 558-1027*
County Commissioner:		
Precinct 1	Tom Brown	558-1101 / *Fax: 558-1188*
Precinct 2	Dennis Young	558-1101 / *Fax: 558-1188*
Precinct 3	Domingo Escobedo	558-1101 / *Fax: 558-1188*
Precinct 4	Ruby Martinez	558-1101 / *Fax: 558-1188*
Justice of the Peace:	Twilah Ward	558-1108 / *Fax: 558-1185*
Constable:	Rory Crumrine	558-1101 / *Fax: 558-1188*

CROCKETT COUNTY

Population: 3,772
County Seat:
  Ozona 76943

P. O. Drawer 1857
325 392-2965 / *Fax: 325 392-2391*
www.co.crockett.tx.us

County Judge	Fred Deaton	.392-2965 / *Fax: 392-2391*
District Attorney, 112nd Dist.	Laurie K. English	.392-2025 / *Fax: 392-8415*
County Attorney	Jody K. Upham	.392-3920 / *Fax: 392-2207*
District & County Clerk	Ninfa Preddy	.392-2022 / *Fax: 392-3742*
County Treasurer	Karen D. Webb	.392-3376 / *Fax: 392-9712*
Tax Assessor-Collector	Michelle Medley	.392-2674 / *Fax: 392-2906*
Sheriff	Robert F. "Bob" Rodriguez	.392-2661 / *Fax: 392-2045*
County Auditor	Janie Chandler	.392-3131 / *Fax: 392-5293*
Chief Appraiser	Janet Thompson	.392-8258 / *Fax: 392-2906*
County Commissioner:		
Precinct 1	Frank Tambunga	.392-2827 / *Fax: 392-1395*
Precinct 2	Pleas Childress, III	.392-3103 / *Fax: 392-2391*
Precinct 3	Wesley J. Bean	.392-2636 / *Fax: 392-2391*
Precinct 4	Eligio Martinez	.340-0937 / *Fax: 392-2391*
Justice of the Peace:		
Precinct 1	Evelyn C. Kerbow	.392-2253 / *Fax: 392-2365*
Constable:		
Precinct 1	Raymond Borrego	.392-2977 / *Fax: 392-2391*

CROSBY COUNTY

Population: 6,062
County Seat:
  Crosbyton 79322

201 West Aspen, Ste. 208
806 675-2011 / *Fax: 806 675-2403*
www.co.crosby.tx.us

County Judge	David Wigley	.675-2011 / *Fax: 675-2403*
District & County Attorney	Michael Sales	.675-2062 / *Fax: 675-2787*
District Clerk	Shari Smith	.675-2071 / *Fax: 675-2433*
County Clerk	Tammy Marshall	.675-2334 / *Fax: 675-2980*
County Treasurer	Debra Riley	.675-2241 / *Fax: 675-2403*
Tax Assessor-Collector	Anna R. Rodriquez	.675-2311 / *Fax: 675-2516*
Sheriff	Ethan Vallanueva	.675-7301 / *Fax: 675-2804*
County Auditor	Catie Wall	.675-2152 / *Fax: 675-2403*
Chief Appraiser	Kathy Lowrie Harris	.675-2356 / *Fax: 675-2838*
County Commissioner:		
Precinct 1	Larry McCauley	.675-2011 / *Fax: 675-2804*
Precinct 2	Frank Mullins	.675-2011 / *Fax: 675-2804*
Precinct 3	Donald Kirksey	.675-2011 / *Fax: 675-2804*
Precinct 4	James Caddell	.675-2011 / *Fax: 675-2804*
Justice of the Peace:	Irma Casias	.675-2523 / *Fax: 675-9105*
Constable:	Jimmy Isbell	.269-0169 / *Fax: 263-4474*

COUNTY SECTION

CULBERSON COUNTY

Population: 2,287
County Seat:
  Van Horn 79855

P. O. Box 927 - Courthouse, 300 LaCaverna
432 283-2059 / *Fax: 432 283-9234*
www.co.culberson.tx.us

County Judge	Carlos Urias	.283-2059 / *Fax: 283-9234*
District Attorney, 34th Dist.	Jaime Esparza	.915 546-2059 / *Fax: 915 533-5520*
County Attorney	Stephen L. Mitchell	.283-2391 / *Fax: 283-9234*
District & County Clerk	Linda McDonald	.283-2058 / *Fax: 283-2091*
County Treasurer	Susana R. Hinojos	.283-1419 / *Fax: 283-9234*
Tax Assessor-Collector	Amalia Hernandez	.283-2130 / *Fax: 283-1939*
Sheriff	Oscar Carrillo	.283-2060 / *Fax: 283-9002*
County Auditor	Mark A. Cabezuela	.283-1830 / *Fax: 283-7436*
Chief Appraiser	Maricel "Chello" Gonzalez	.283-2977 / *Fax: 283-0027*
County Commissioner:		
Precinct 1	Cornelio Garibay	.283-2877 / *Fax: 283-9234*
Precinct 2	Raul Rodriguez	.284-1959 / *Fax: 283-9234*
Precinct 3	Gilda Morales	.284-0156 / *Fax: 283-9234*
Precinct 4	Adrian Norman	.283-2738 / *Fax: 283-9234*
Justice of the Peace:		
Precinct 1	Rita Carrasco	.283-2609 / *Fax: 283-9272*
Precinct 2	AP Flores	.283-8439 / *Fax: 283-9234*
Precinct 3	Michael Davis	.283-1101 / *Fax: 283-7126*
Precinct 4	Betty Velez	.283-2999
Constable:		
Precinct 2	Thomas Burns	.283-1655
Precinct 4	Eric Ramirez	

DALLAM COUNTY

Population: 7,152
County Seat:
  Dalhart 79022

414 Denver Ave., Suite 301
806 244-2450 / *Fax: 806 244-2252*
www.dallam.org/county/

County Judge	Wesley C. "Wes" Ritchey	.244-2450 / *Fax: 244-2252*
District Attorney, 69th Dist.	David M. Green	.935-5654 / *Fax: 934-2155*
County Attorney	Jon King	.244-5711 / *Fax: 244-2252*
District & County Clerk	Terri Banks	.244-4751 / *Fax: 244-3751*
County Treasurer	Kenda McKay	.244-2530 / *Fax: 244-2252*
Tax Assessor-Collector	Jami Parr	.244-2801 / *Fax: 244-7801*
Sheriff	Shane Stevenson	.244-2313 / *Fax: 244-7513*
Chief Appraiser	Holly McCauley	.249-6767 / *Fax: 249-4124*
County Commissioner:		
Precinct 1	Carl McCarty	.244-2450 / *Fax: 244-2252*
Precinct 2	Corey Crabtree	.244-2450 / *Fax: 244-2252*
Precinct 3	Levi James	.244-2450 / *Fax: 244-2252*
Precinct 4	Floyd French	.244-2450 / *Fax: 244-2252*
Justice of the Peace:	Carol Smith	.244-4827 / *Fax: 244-1285*
Constable:	Bruce Scott	.244-2313 / *Fax: 244-7513*

DALLAS COUNTY

Population: 2,554,632
County Seat:
  Dallas 75202

411 Elm
214 653-7011 / *Fax: 214 653-7057*
www.dallascounty.org/

County Judge	Clay Jenkins	.653-7949 / *Fax: 653-6586*
Criminal District Attorney	The Honorable B Glasgow Glasgow	.653-3600 / *Fax: 653-5774*
District Clerk	Felicia Petri	.653-7301 / *Fax: 653-6634*
County Clerk	John Warren	.653-7099 / *Fax: 653-7176*
County Treasurer	Pauline Medrano	.653-7321 / *Fax: 653-7705*
Tax Assessor-Collector	John R. Ames, CTA	.653-7811 / *Fax: 653-7887*
Sheriff	Marian Brown	.653-3460 / *Fax: 653-3420*
County Auditor	Darryl D. Thomas	.653-6472 / *Fax: 653-6440*
Chief Appraiser	Ken Nolan	.631-0520 / *Fax: 653-7057*
Elections Official	Toni Pippins Poole	.819-6335 / *Fax: 819-6301*
County Commissioner:		
Precinct 1	Theresa Daniel	.653-6668 / *Fax: 653-7572*
Precinct 2	Mike Cantrell	.589-7090 / *Fax: 962-5799*
Precinct 3	John Wiley Price	.653-6671 / *Fax: 653-7057*
Precinct 4	Elba Garcia	.653-6670 / *Fax: 653-7994*
Justice of the Peace:		
Precinct 1, Pl. 1	Thomas G. Jones	.972 228-0280 / *Fax: 972 228-2737*
Precinct 1, Pl. 2	Valencia Nash	.972 228-2272 / *Fax: 972 228-2472*
Precinct 2, Pl. 1	Brian Hutcheson	.643-4773 / *Fax: 643-4772*
Precinct 2, Pl. 2	William "Bill" Metzger	.972 285-5429 / *Fax: 972 288-2461*
Precinct 3, Pl. 1	Albert B. Cercone	.321-4106 / *Fax: 321-4912*
Precinct 3, Pl. 2	Steven L. Seider	.904-3042 / *Fax: 904-3049*
Precinct 4, Pl. 1	Norris "Stretch" Rideaux	.751-4040 / *Fax: 751-4050*
Precinct 4, Pl. 2	Katy Hubener	.589-7000 / *Fax: 589-7048*
Precinct 5, Pl. 1	Sara Martinez	.943-6980 / *Fax: 943-2871*
Precinct 5, Pl. 2	Juan Jasso	.943-5981 / *Fax: 943-3695*
Constable:		
Precinct 1	Tracey Gulley	.972 228-0006 / *Fax: 972 228-2254*
Precinct 2	Ray Nichols	.643-4766 / *Fax: 643-4774*
Precinct 3	Ben Adamcik	.904-3160 / *Fax: 904-3170*
Precinct 4	Roy Williams, Jr.	.751-4065 / *Fax: 751-4080*
Precinct 5	Beth Villarreal	.943-1765 / *Fax: 943-3091*

COUNTY SECTION

DAWSON COUNTY

Population: 13,951
County Seat:
 Lamesa 79331

P. O. Drawer 1268
806 872-7544 / *Fax: 806 872-7496*
www.co.dawson.tx.us

County Judge	Foy O'Brien	.872-7544 / *Fax: 872-7496*
District Attorney, 106th Dist.	Philip Mack Furlow	.872-2259 / *Fax: 872-3174*
County Attorney	Steven Payson	.872-3310 / *Fax: 872-0494*
District Clerk	Pam Huse	.872-7373 / *Fax: 872-9513*
County Clerk	Gloria Vera	.872-3778 / *Fax: 872-2473*
County Treasurer	Julie Frizzell	.872-7474 / *Fax: 872-3395*
Tax Assessor-Collector	Sylvia Ortiz	.872-7181 / *Fax: 872-9643*
Sheriff	Matt Hogg	.872-7560 / *Fax: 872-9396*
County Auditor	Rick Dollahan	.872-5631 / *Fax: 872-3395*
Chief Appraiser	Norma Brock	.872-7060 / *Fax: 872-2364*
County Commissioner:		
Precinct 1	Ricky Minjarez	.201-3227 / *Fax: 872-7496*
Precinct 2	Joe Raines	.201-1496 / *Fax: 872-7496*
Precinct 3	Nicky Goode	.759-8659 / *Fax: 872-7496*
Precinct 4	Russell Cox	.759-4430 / *Fax: 872-7496*
Justice of the Peace:	Denise P. Dyess	.872-3744 / *Fax: 872-5915*
Constable:		
Precinct 1	Kent Parchman	.462-7766

DEAF SMITH COUNTY

Population: 19,737
County Seat:
 Hereford 79045

Courthouse, 235 E. 3rd Street
806 363-7000 / *Fax: 806 363-7022*
www.co.deaf-smith.tx.us

County Judge	D. J. Wagner	.363-7000 / *Fax: 363-7022*
District Attorney	Jim English	.364-3700 / *Fax: 363-7039*
District Clerk	Elaine Gerber	.364-3901 / *Fax: 363-7007*
County Clerk	Imelda DeLaCerda	.363-7077 / *Fax: 363-7023*
County Treasurer	Karen Smith	.363-7088 / *Fax: 363-7087*
Tax Assessor-Collector	Teresa Garth	.363-7044 / *Fax: 364-3787*
Sheriff	J. Dale Butler	.364-2311 / *Fax: 363-6656*
County Auditor	Trish Brown	.363-7066 / *Fax: 363-7087*
Chief Appraiser	Danny Jones	.364-0625 / *Fax: 364-6895*
County Commissioner:		
Precinct 1	Chris Kahlich	.363-7000 / *Fax: 363-7022*
Precinct 2	Jerry O'Connor	.363-7000 / *Fax: 363-7022*
Precinct 3	Mike Brumley	.363-7000 / *Fax: 363-7022*
Precinct 4	Dale Artho	.363-7000 / *Fax: 363-7022*
Justice of the Peace:	Karen Boren	.364-0999 / *Fax: 363-7037*
Constable:	Bryan Hedrick	.341-0999 / *Fax: 363-7022*

DELTA COUNTY

Population: 5,371
County Seat:
  Cooper 75432

903 395-4400 / *Fax: 903 395-2178*
www.deltacountytx.com

County Judge	Jason Murray	.395-4400 / *Fax: 395-2178*
District Attorney, 8th Dist.	Will Ramsay	.885-0641 / *Fax: 885-0640*
County Attorney	Jay Garrett	.395-4400 / *Fax: 395-2178*
District & County Clerk	Jane Jones	.395-4400 / *Fax: 395-4260*
County Treasurer	Bonnie Hobbs	.395-4400 / *Fax: 300-3573*
Tax Assessor-Collector	Dawn Maddox Stewart	.395-4400 / *Fax: 395-4638*
Sheriff	Ricky Smith	.395-2146 / *Fax: 395-2256*
Chief Appraiser	Kim Gregory RPA, CCA	.395-4118 / *Fax: 395-4455*
Elections Official	Jane Jones	.395-4400 / *Fax: 395-4260*
County Commissioner:		
Precinct 1	Eric Lair	.249-4556 / *Fax: 395-2178*
Precinct 2	Gary Anderson	.395-4924 / *Fax: 395-2178*
Precinct 3	Bobby Asbill	.243-2028 / *Fax: 395-2178*
Precinct 4	Mark Brantley	.458-1665 / *Fax: 395-2178*
Justice of the Peace:	Ginny G. Phifer	.395-4400 / *Fax: 395-4608*
Constable:	Marshall Lynch	.395-4400 / *Fax: 395-2178*

DENTON COUNTY

Population: 795,854
County Seat:
  Denton 76201

110 W. Hickory St., Courthouse-on-the-Square
940 349-2820 / *Fax: 940 349-2821*
www.dentoncounty.com

County Judge	Mary Horn	.349-2820 / *Fax: 349-2821*
Criminal District Attorney	Paul Johnson	.349-2600 / *Fax: 349-2601*
District Clerk	Sherri Adelstein	.349-2200 / *Fax: 349-2201*
County Clerk	Juli Luke	.349-2012 / *Fax: 349-5024*
County Treasurer	Cindy Yeatts Brown	.349-3150 / *Fax: 349-3151*
Tax Assessor-Collector	Michelle French	.349-3500 / *Fax: 349-3501*
Sheriff	Tracy Murphree	.349-1620 / *Fax: 349-1604*
County Auditor	James Wells	.349-3100 / *Fax: 349-3101*
Chief Appraiser	Rudy Durham	.349-3800 / *Fax: 349-3801*
Elections Official	Frank Phillips	.349-3200 / *Fax: 349-3201*
County Commissioner:		
Precinct 1	Hugh Coleman	.349-2810 / *Fax: 349-2811*
Precinct 2	Ron Marchant	.972 434-7140 / *Fax: 972 434-7141*
Precinct 3	Bobbie J. Mitchell	.972 434-4780 / *Fax: 972 434-4781*
Precinct 4	Andy Eads	.349-2801 / *Fax: 349-2803*
Justice of the Peace:		
Precinct 1	Joe Holland	.349-3170
Precinct 2	James DePiazza	.972 434-7200
Precinct 3	Becky Kerbow	.972 434-4750
Precinct 4	J.W. Hand	.972 434-3910
Precinct 5	Mike Oglesby	.349-3460
Precinct 6	Gary W. Blanscet	.972 434-7100
Constable:		
Precinct 1	Johnny Hammons	.349-3160
Precinct 2	Michael Truitt	.972 434-7220
Precinct 3	Jerry Raburn	.972 434-4770
Precinct 4	Tim Burch	.972 434-3980
Precinct 5	Doug Boydston	.349-3480
Precinct 6	Richard Bachus	.972 434-7120

COUNTY SECTION

DE WITT COUNTY

Population: 21,221
County Seat:
  Cuero 77954

307 N. Gonzales St.
361 275-0916 / *Fax: 361 275-0919*
www.co.dewitt.tx.us

County Judge	Daryl L. Fowler	.275-0916 / *Fax: 275-0919*
District Attorney, 24th Dist.	Rob Lassmann	.275-2612 / *Fax: 275-3282*
County Attorney	Raymond H. Reese	.275-0812 / *Fax: 275-0814*
District Clerk	Tabeth Gardner	.275-0931 / *Fax: 275-0934*
County Clerk	Natalie Carson	.275-0864 / *Fax: 275-0866*
County Treasurer	Carol Ann Martin	.275-0894 / *Fax: 275-0898*
Tax Assessor-Collector	Susie Dreyer	.275-0879 / *Fax: 275-5074*
Sheriff	Carl Bowen	.275-5734 / *Fax: 275-0936*
County Auditor	Carrie Rea	.275-0926 / *Fax: 275-0930*
Chief Appraiser	Beverly Malone	.275-5753 / *Fax: 275-9227*
Elections Official	Blanca McBride	.275-0859 / *Fax: 275-0860*
County Commissioner:		
Precinct 1	Curtis G. Afflerbach	.275-6441 / *Fax: 275-0919*
Precinct 2	James B. Pilchiek, Sr.	.293-2772 / *Fax: 275-0919*
Precinct 3	James Kaiser	.564-2321 / *Fax: 275-0919*
Precinct 4	Richard Randle	.275-3211 / *Fax: 275-0919*
Justice of the Peace:		
Precinct 1	Peggy J. Mayer	.275-3443 / *Fax: 275-9220*
Precinct 2	George W. Robinson	.564-9410 / *Fax: 564-9476*
Constable:		
Precinct 1	Kelly Phelps	.275-0916 / *Fax: 275-0919*
Precinct 2	Steven A. Wehlmann, Sr.	.275-4132

DICKENS COUNTY

Population: 2,226
County Seat:
  Dickens 79229

508 Crow St., P. O. Box 179
806 623-5532 / *Fax: 806 623-5319*
www.co.dickens.tx.us

County Judge	Kevin Brendle	.623-5532 / *Fax: 623-5319*
District Attorney, 110th Dist.	Wade Jackson	.983-2197 / *Fax: 983-2400*
County Attorney	Trey Poage, ProTem	.623-5288 / *Fax: 623-5319*
District & County Clerk	Becky Hill	.623-5531 / *Fax: 623-5240*
County Treasurer	Darla Thomason	.623-5542 / *Fax: 623-5319*
Tax Assessor-Collector	Rebecca Haney	.623-5216 / *Fax: 623-5319*
Sheriff	Terry Braly	.623-5533 / *Fax: 623-5369*
Chief Appraiser	Patti Abbott	.623-5258 / *Fax: 623-5259*
County Commissioner:		
Precinct 1	Dennis Wyatt	.623-5532 / *Fax: 623-5319*
Precinct 2	Mike Smith	.623-5532 / *Fax: 623-5319*
Precinct 3	Charlie Morris	.623-5532 / *Fax: 623-5319*
Precinct 4	Sheldon Parsons	.623-5532 / *Fax: 623-5319*
Justice of the Peace:	Nancy Stone	.623-5233 / *Fax: 623-5319*

DIMMIT COUNTY

Population: 11,012
County Seat:
  Carrizo Springs 78834

Courthouse Square, 103 N. 5th St.
830 876-2323 / *Fax: 830 876-4202*
www.dimmitcounty.org

County Judge	Francisco G. Ponce	.876-2323 / *Fax: 876-4202*
District Attorney, 293rd Dist.	Roberto Serna	.773-9268 / *Fax: 773-9371*
County Attorney	Daniel M. Gonzalez	.876-4236 / *Fax: 876-4219*
District Clerk	Maricela G. Gonzalez	.876-4243 / *Fax: 876-4244*
County Clerk	Mario Z. García	.876-4239 / *Fax: 876-4205*
County Treasurer	Estanislado Martinez	.876-4246 / *Fax: 876-4203*
Tax Assessor-Collector	Mary E. Sandoval	.876-4246 / *Fax: 876-4211*
Sheriff	Marion Boyd	.876-3508 / *Fax: 876-9263*
County Auditor	Carlos A. Pereda, Jr.	.876-4246 / *Fax: 876-4203*
Chief Appraiser	Norma Carrillo	.876-3420 / *Fax: 876-5137*
County Commissioner:		
Precinct 1	Mike Uriegas	.876-6543 / *Fax: 876-4202*
Precinct 2	Alonzo Carmona	.876-4234 / *Fax: 876-4235*
Precinct 3	Juan R. Carmona	.876-6215 / *Fax: 876-4202*
Precinct 4	Valerie Rubalcaba	.468-3849
Justice of the Peace:		
Precinct 1	Sonia G. Guerrero	.876-5486 / *Fax: 876-2778*
Precinct 2	Alberto Esquivel	.876-4210 / *Fax: 876-4202*
Precinct 3	Leticia Hernandez	.457-2643 / *Fax: 457-0065*
Precinct 4	Alfredo Martinez	.468-3530 / *Fax: 468-9111*
Constable:		
Precinct 1	Rudy Lopez	.876-2323
Precinct 2	Andres Arambula	.876-0041
Precinct 3	Ruth Ceniseros	.876-3500
Precinct 4	José Galván	.468-9252

DONLEY COUNTY

Population: 3,538
County Seat:
  Clarendon 79226

P. O. Box 909 - 300 A. Sully
806 874-3625 / *Fax: 806 874-1181*
www.co.donley.tx.us/

County Judge	John C. Howard, M.D.	.874-3625 / *Fax: 874-1181*
District Attorney, 100th Dist.	Luke Inman	.447-0055 / *Fax: 866 233-2738*
County Attorney	Landon Lambert	.874-0216 / *Fax: 874-1847*
District & County Clerk	Fay Vargas	.874-3436 / *Fax: 874-3351*
County Treasurer	Wanda Smith	.874-2328 / *Fax: 874-1181*
Tax Assessor-Collector	Linda Crump	.874-2193 / *Fax: 874-3165*
Sheriff	Charles "Butch" Blackburn, Jr.	.874-3533 / *Fax: 874-3458*
Chief Appraiser	Paula Lowrie	.874-2744 / *Fax: 874-5048*
County Commissioner:		
Precinct 1	Mark White	.874-0255 / *Fax: 874-1181*
Precinct 2	Daniel Ford	.662-5437 / *Fax: 874-1181*
Precinct 3	Andy Wheatly	.856-5930 / *Fax: 874-1181*
Precinct 4	Dan Sawyer	.874-2768 / *Fax: 874-1181*
Justice of the Peace:		
Precinct 1 $ 2	Pamela Mason	.874-2016 / *Fax: 874-9057*
Precinct 3 & 4	Denise Bertrand	.856-5914 / *Fax: 856-0017*
Constable:	Doug Wright	.856-5917 / *Fax: 874-1181*

DUVAL COUNTY

Population: 11,328
County Seat:
  San Diego 78384

400 E. Gravis St., P. O. Box 189
361 279-3322 / *Fax: 361 279-3310*
courthouse.duval-county.net

County Judge	Ricardo O. Carrillo	279-6208 / *Fax: 279-3310*
District Attorney, 229th Dist.	Omar Escobar	279-6220 / *Fax: 279-2646*
County Attorney	Baldemar Gutierrez	279-6223 / *Fax: 279-7365*
District Clerk	Richard Barton	279-6284 / *Fax: 279-8152*
County Clerk	Elodia M. Garza	279-6272 / *Fax: 279-3159*
County Treasurer	Sylvia Lazo	279-6330 / *Fax: 279-7440*
Tax Assessor-Collector	Roberto Elizondo	279-6332 / *Fax: 279-2193*
Sheriff	Romeo R. Ramirez	279-6209 / *Fax: 279-2670*
County Auditor	Matt Garza	279-6321 / *Fax: 279-7177*
Chief Appraiser	Brian Fields	279-3305 / *Fax: 279-2622*
Elections Official	Ana Martinez	279-6278 / *Fax: 279-8842*
County Commissioner:		
Precinct 1	Alejo Garcia	279-6215 / *Fax: 279-7038*
Precinct 2	Rene M. Perez	279-7456 / *Fax: 279-7547*
Precinct 3	David O. Garza	256-3911 / *Fax: 256-3549*
Precinct 4	Gilberto Uribe, Jr.	394-7487 / *Fax: 394-7487*
Justice of the Peace:		
Precinct 1	Geraldita "Tita" Martinez	279-6218
Precinct 2	Anabel Chapa-Canales	279-6245 / *Fax: 756-0008*
Precinct 3	Aida Estraca	256-3982 / *Fax: 256-3129*
Constable:		
Precinct 1	Bruno Valdez	279-6252 / *Fax: 279-3426*
Precinct 2	Ramiro G. Perez	539-4222 / *Fax: 539-4252*
Precinct 3	Raul Oliveira, III	227-0519 / *Fax: 256-3447*
Precinct 4	Arturo Martinez	460-0882

EASTLAND COUNTY

Population: 18,282
County Seat:
  Eastland 76448

100 W. Main, Suite 203
254 629-1263 / *Fax: 254 629-6090*
county.eastlandcountytexas.com/

County Judge	Rex Fields	629-1263 / *Fax: 629-6090*
Criminal District Attorney	Russell D. Thomason	629-2659 / *Fax: 629-3361*
District Clerk	Tessa K. Culverhouse	629-2664 / *Fax: 629-6070*
County Clerk	Cathy Jentho	629-1583 / *Fax: 629-8125*
County Treasurer	Christina Dodrill	629-2672 / *Fax: 629-6068*
Tax Assessor-Collector	Sandra "Sandy" Cagle	629-1564 / *Fax: 629-8252*
Sheriff	Wayne Bradford	629-1774 / *Fax: 629-2500*
County Auditor	Loretta Key	629-1082 / *Fax: 629-2080*
Chief Appraiser	Randy Clark	629-8597 / *Fax: 631-0628*
Elections Official	Laurie Mangum	629-6051 / *Fax: 631-0067*
County Commissioner:		
Precinct 1	Andy Maxwell	629-1303 / *Fax: 629-6090*
Precinct 2	John "Buzzy" Rutledge	647-1463 / *Fax: 629-6090*
Precinct 3	Ronnie Wilson	643-2532 / *Fax: 629-6090*
Precinct 4	Robert Rains	442-2160 / *Fax: 629-6090*

Justice of the Peace:
Precinct 1 — Ronnie White . . . . .629-1088 / *Fax: 629-6084*
Precinct 2 — D.J. Walker . . . . .629-1088 / *Fax: 629-6084*
Constable:
Precinct 1 — Larry Luther Jernigan, Sr. . . . . .631-8791 / *Fax: 629-6090*
Precinct 2 — Kenneth Payne . . . . .631-7371 / *Fax: 629-6090*

ECTOR COUNTY

Population: 161,393
County Seat:
Odessa 79761

300 N. Grant
432 498-4100 / *Fax: 432 498-4101*
www.co.ector.tx.us

County Judge	Ron Eckert	.498-4100 / *Fax: 498-4101*
District Attorney, 70th Dist.	Robert N. Bland, IV	.498-4230 / *Fax: 498-4293*
County Attorney	Dusty Gallivan	.498-4150 / *Fax: 498-4154*
District Clerk	Clarissa Webster	.498-4290 / *Fax: 498-4292*
County Clerk	Linda Haney	.498-4130 / *Fax: 498-4177*
County Treasurer	Cleopatra Anderson	.498-4061 / *Fax: 498-4038*
Tax Assessor-Collector	Barbara J. Horn	.498-4055 / *Fax: 498-4057*
Sheriff	Michael "Mike" Griffis	.335-3050 / *Fax: 335-3586*
County Auditor	David Austin	.498-4099 / *Fax: 498-4096*
Chief Appraiser	Anita Campbell	.332-6834 / *Fax: 332-1726*
Elections Official	Mitzi K. Scheible, CERA	.498-4030 / *Fax: 498-4009*
County Commissioner.		
Precinct 1	Eddy Shelton	.498-4001 / *Fax: 498-4005*
Precinct 2	Greg Simmons	.498-4002 / *Fax: 498-4005*
Precinct 3	Dale Childers	.498-4003 / *Fax: 498-4005*
Precinct 4	Armando S. Rodriguez	.498-4004 / *Fax: 498-4005*
Justice of the Peace:		
Precinct 1	Terry Lange	.498-4201 / *Fax: 498-4178*
Precinct 2	Position Vacant	.498-4202 / *Fax: 498-4178*
Precinct 3	Sherwood "Woody" Kupper	.498-4203 / *Fax: 498-4178*
Precinct 4	Eddy Spivey	.498-4204 / *Fax: 498-4178*
Constable:		
Precinct 1	Carl Watters	.498-2101 / *Fax: 335-3586*
Precinct 2	David Lewellen	.498-4202 / *Fax: 335-3586*
Precinct 3	Carl Rogers	.498-4203 / *Fax: 335-3586*
Precinct 4	Pete Anchondo	.498-4204 / *Fax: 335-3586*

COUNTY SECTION

EDWARDS COUNTY

Population: 1,896
County Seat:
  Rocksprings 78880

P. O. Box 348 - 400 Main
830 683-6122 / *Fax: 830 683-6385*
www.co.edwards.tx.us

County Judge	Souli A. Shanklin .... .683-6122 / *Fax: 683-6116*
District Attorney, 452nd Dist.	Tonya S. Ahlschwede ...... .325 347-8400 / *Fax: 325 347-8404*
County Attorney	Allen Ray Moody .... .683-6128 / *Fax: 683-6129*
District & County Clerk	Olga Lydia Reyes .... .683-2235 / *Fax: 683-5376*
County Treasurer	Lupe Sifuentes-Enriquez .... .683-5116 / *Fax: 683-6116*
Tax Assessor-Collector	Mark Bean .... .683-2337 / *Fax: 683-4195*
Sheriff	Pamela Elliott .... .683-4104 / *Fax: 683-4102*
County Commissioner:	
Precinct 1	Willliam Epperson 683-7066
Precinct 2	Lee Sweeten .... .210 912-8481
Precinct 3	Matt Fry 683-2266
Precinct 4	Andrew Barnebey 683-7645
Justice of the Peace:	Tommy M. Walker .... .683-5187 / *Fax: 683-2371*
Constable:	John Maxwell .... .683-7222 / *Fax: 597-6104*
Interim Chief Appraiser	Judy Harris .... .683-4189 / *Fax: 683-4193*

EL PASO COUNTY

Population: 840,597
County Seat:
  El Paso 79901

500 E. San Antonio Ave., Ste. 301
915 546-2000 / *Fax: 915 546-2217*
www.epcounty.com

County Judge	Ruben John Vogt .... .546-2098 / *Fax: 543-3888*
District Attorney, 34th Dist.	Jaime Esparza .... .546-2059 / *Fax: 533-5520*
County Attorney	Jo Anne Bernal .... .546-2050 / *Fax: 546-2133*
District Clerk	Norma Favela Barceleau .... .546-2029 / *Fax: 546-8139*
County Clerk	Delia Briones .... .546-2071 / *Fax: 546-2012*
Tax Assessor-Collector	Ruben P. Gonzalez .... .771-2300 / *Fax: 771-2360*
Sheriff	Richard Wiles .... .538-2006 / *Fax: 538-2028*
County Auditor	Edward A. Dion, C.P.A. .... .546-2040 / *Fax: 546-8172*
Chief Appraiser	Dinah L. Kilgore .... .780-2003 / *Fax: 780-2130*
Elections Official	Lisa Wise .... .546-2154 / *Fax: 546-2220*
County Commissioner:	
Precinct 1	Carlos Leon 546-2014
Precinct 2	David Stout .... .546-2111 / *Fax: 543-3817*
Precinct 3	Vincent Perez .... .546-2144 / *Fax: 543-3809*
Precinct 4	Andrew R. Haggerty .... .546-2044 / *Fax: 543-3854*
Justice of the Peace:	
Precinct 1	Robert Pearson .... .534-3917 / *Fax: 351-1731*
Precinct 2	Brian Haggerty .... .751-7575 / *Fax: 751-7623*
Precinct 3	Guadalupe Aponte .... .546-2170 / *Fax: 546-8188*
Precinct 4	Jesus Urenda .... .594-1143 / *Fax: 595-2647*
Precinct 5	John Chatman .... .859-3744 / *Fax: 859-9681*
Precinct 6, Pl. 1	Ruben Lujan .... .851-2019 / *Fax: 851-3694*
Precinct 6, Pl. 2	Enedina "Nina" Serna .... .855-3062 / *Fax: 855-3098*
Precinct 7	Kelly Dickson 886-2598

Constable:
Precinct 1   Oscar Ugarte .534-3917 / *Fax: 351-1731*
Precinct 2   Jeremiah Haggerty . . . . .757-9488 / *Fax: 751-7623*
Precinct 3   Hector Bernal . . . . .546-8137 / *Fax: 543-3898*
Precinct 4   Luis Aguilar . . . . .594-1143 / *Fax: 595-2647*
Precinct 5   Manny Lopez . . . . .859-3744 / *Fax: 859-8681*
Precinct 6   Javier Garcia . . . . .851-2019 / *Fax: 851-3694*
Precinct 7   Angie Sommers . . . . .886-2598 / *Fax: 886-2599*

ELLIS COUNTY

Population: 164,386
County Seat:
  Waxahachie 75165

101 W. Main St.
972 825-5000 / *Fax: 972 825-5010*
www.co.ellis.tx.us/

County Judge   Carol Bush . . . . .825-5011 / *Fax: 825-5012*
District & County Attorney   Patrick Wilson . . . . .825-5035 / *Fax: 825-5047*
District Clerk   Melanie P. Reed . . . . .825-5091 / *Fax: 825-5093*
County Clerk   Cindy Polley . . . . .825-5070 / *Fax: 825-5075*
County Treasurer   Cheryl Chambers . . . . .825-5127 / *Fax: 825-5129*
Tax Assessor-Collector   John Bridges . . . . .825-5150 / *Fax: 825-5151*
Sheriff   Charles Edge . . . . .825-4901 / *Fax: 825-4941*
County Auditor   Miykael Reeve . . . . .825-5120 / *Fax: 825-5124*
Chief Appraiser   Kathy Rodrigue . . . . .937-3552 / *Fax: 937-1618*
Elections Official   Jana Onyon, CERA . . . . .825-5195 / *Fax: 923-5194*
County Commissioner:
  Precinct 1   Randy Stinson 825-5330
  Precinct 2   Lane Grayson . . . . .825-5333 / *Fax: 875-9594*
  Precinct 3   Paul Perry . . . . .825-5340 / *Fax: 483-7478*
  Precinct 4   Kyle Butler 825-5305
Justice of the Peace:
  Precinct 1   Joyce Lindauer . . . . .825-5319 / *Fax: 875-6819*
  Precinct 2   Jackie Miller, Jr. . . . . .825-5022 / *Fax: 825-5025*
  Precinct 3   Curtis Polk .825-5030 / *Fax: 825-5033*
  Precinct 4   Steve Egan .825-5310 / *Fax: 723-8629*
Constable:
  Precinct 1   Roy Callender . . . . .825-5325 / *Fax: 875-6819*
  Precinct 2   Terry Nay . . . . .825-5027 / *Fax: 825-5029*
  Precinct 3   Mike McCorkle . . . . .825-5006 / *Fax: 825-5009*
  Precinct 4   Mike Jones .825-5316 / *Fax: 723-8629*

COUNTY SECTION

ERATH COUNTY

Population: 41,031
County Seat:
  Stephenville 76401

100 West Washington
254 965-1452 / *Fax: 254 965-1466*
www.co.erath.tx.us

County Judge	Tab Thompson .... 965-1452 / *Fax: 965-1466*
District Attorney, 266th Dist.	Alan Nash .... 965-1462 / *Fax: 965-5543*
County Attorney	Lisa Pence .... 965-1453 / *Fax: 965-1421*
District Clerk	Wanda Pringle .... 965-1486 / *Fax: 965-7516*
County Clerk	Gwinda Jones .... 965-1482 / *Fax: 965-5732*
County Treasurer	Donna Kelly .... 965-1483 / *Fax: 965-1447*
Tax Assessor-Collector	Jennifer Schlicke Carey .... 965-8630 / *Fax: 965-4025*
Sheriff	Matt Coates .... 965-3338 / *Fax: 965-3598*
County Auditor	Janet Martin .... 965-1484 / *Fax: 965-1401*
Chief Appraiser	Jerry Lee .... 965-5434 / *Fax: 965-5633*
County Commissioner:	
Precinct 1	Dee Stephens .... 965-7178 / *Fax: 965-1466*
Precinct 2	Herbert Brown .... 445-3122 / *Fax: 965-1466*
Precinct 3	Joe Brown .... 918-2113 / *Fax: 965-1466*
Precinct 4	Scot Jackson .... 965-3561 / *Fax: 965-1466*
Justice of the Peace:	
Precinct 1, 3 & $	Shawnee Bass .... 965-1489 / *Fax: 965-1400*
Precinct 2	Bart Greenway .... 445-2766 / *Fax: 445-4155*
Constable:	
Precinct 1, 3 & 4	Jason Schipper .... 965-1445 / *Fax: 965-1400*
Precinct 2	Lee Roy Gaitan .... 445-8114 / *Fax: 445-4155*

FALLS COUNTY

Population: 17,220
County Seat:
  Marlin 76661

125 Bridge Street, P.O. Box 458
254 883-1426 / *Fax: 254 883-3802*
www.co.falls.tx.us

County Judge	Jay T. Elliott .... 883-1426 / *Fax: 883-3802*
District & County Attorney	Kathryn J. "Jodi" Gilliam .... 883 1416 / *Fax: 883-1418*
District Clerk	Christy Wideman 883-1419
County Clerk	Linda Watkins .... 883-1408 / *Fax: 883-2260*
County Treasurer	Ernestine "Molly" Downes .... 883-1433 / *Fax: 883-1406*
Tax Assessor-Collector	Kayci Nehring .... 883-1436 / *Fax: 883-1438*
Sheriff	Ricky Scaman .... 883-1431 / *Fax: 803-3719*
County Auditor	Joan M. Kostiha .... 883-1404 / *Fax: 883-1406*
Chief Appraiser	Allen McKinley .... 883-2543 / *Fax: 883-6500*
Elections Official	Nicket Peoples-Taylor .... 883-1521 / *Fax: 804-0044*
County Commissioner:	
Precinct 1	Milton Albright 749-6076
Precinct 2	F.A. Green .... 644-0256 / *Fax: 883-3802*
Precinct 3	Jason Willberg 760-7585
Precinct 4	Nita Wuebker 709-7921
Justice of the Peace:	
Precinct 1	Jack Smith .... 883-1427 / *Fax: 883-1406*
Precinct 2	Debra Trotter .... 883-1428 / *Fax: 883-3640*
Precinct 3	Preble Polk .... 583-7506 / *Fax: 583-0356*
Precinct 4	Sharon Maxey .... 546-3700 / *Fax: 546-2016*

Constable:
  Precinct 1   Jonathan Shoemaker .... .230-2551 / *Fax: 883-1408*
  Precinct 2   Marion Humphrey 883-7117
  Precinct 3   Jerry Loren .... .733-4226 / *Fax: 583-0356*
  Precinct 4   James Maxey .... .546-3700 / *Fax: 546-2016*

FANNIN COUNTY

Population: 34,168   101 E. Sam Rayburn Dr., Suite 101
County Seat: 903 583-7455 / *Fax: 903 583-7811*
  Bonham 75418   www.co.fannin.tx.us

County Judge   Creta L. Carter II .... .583-7455 / *Fax: 583-7811*
Criminal District Attorney   Richard Glaser .... .583-7448 / *Fax: 583-7682*
District Clerk   Nancy Young 583-7459
County Clerk   Tammy Biggar .... .583-7486 / *Fax: 640-4241*
County Treasurer   David E. Woodson .... .583-7457 / *Fax: 640-5806*
Tax Assessor-Collector   Gail Young .... .583-7493 / *Fax: 583-1244*
Sheriff   Mark Johnson .... .583-2143 / *Fax: 583-4392*
County Auditor   Don Grammar .... .583-7451 / *Fax: 640-5806*
Chief Appraiser   Mike Jones .... .583-8701 / *Fax: 583-8015*
County Commissioner:
  Precinct 1   Gary Whitlock .... .965-7020 / *Fax: 583-7811*
  Precinct 2   Stan Barker .... .587-3455 / *Fax: 587-2025*
  Precinct 3   Jerry Magness .... .378-2941 / *Fax: 378-3941*
  Precinct 4   Dean Lackey .... .583-2039 / *Fax: 640-0748*
Justice of the Peace:
  Precinct 1   Royce W. Smithey .... .583-7489 / *Fax: 640-1826*
  Precinct 2   Position Vacant .... .587-2846 / *Fax: 587-2018*
  Precinct 3   Kenney Karl 378-0015
Constable:
  Precinct 1   Paul Holt .... .583-7489 / *Fax: 583-2803*
  Precinct 2   Jimmy Helms .... .587-2846 / *Fax: 587-2018*
  Precinct 3   Kevin Mayberry 227-8840

FAYETTE COUNTY

Population: 25,802
County Seat:
　La Grange 78945

County Courthouse, 151 N. Washington
979 968-6469 / *Fax: 979 968-8621*
www.co.fayette.tx.us/

County Judge	Edward F. Janecka ....968-6469 / *Fax: 968-8621*
District & County Attorney	Peggy S. Supak ....968-8402 / *Fax: 968-8404*
District Clerk	Linda Svrcek ....968-3548 / *Fax: 968-2618*
County Clerk	Julie Karstedt ....968-3251 / *Fax: 968-8531*
Tax Assessor-Collector	Rosalinda Adamcik ....968-3164 / *Fax: 968-5840*
Sheriff	Keith Korenek ....968-5856 / *Fax: 968-5080*
County Auditor	Kathy Kleiber ....968-3055 / *Fax: 968-8501*
Chief Appraiser	Richard Moring ....968-8383 / *Fax: 968-8385*
Elections Official	Terri B. Hefner ....968-6563 / *Fax: 968-6426*
County Commissioner:	
Precinct 1	Jason McBroom ....968-3358 / *Fax: 968-8478*
Precinct 2	Gary Weishuhn ....249-3166 / *Fax: 249-3906*
Precinct 3	Harvey Berckenhoff ......361 865-3524 / *Fax: 361 865-2975*
Precinct 4	Tom Muras ....743-3250 / *Fax: 743-5010*
Justice of the Peace:	
Precinct 1	Randy Albers ....968-3648 / *Fax: 968-9258*
Precinct 2	Sheila Coufal ....378-2573 / *Fax: 378-2824*
Precinct 3	Charles Zapalac ....361 865-3500 / *Fax: 361 865-2975*
Precinct 4	Dan Mueller ....743-4041 / *Fax: 743-3014*
Constable:	
Precinct 1	William "Billy" Roensch ....968-3648 / *Fax: 968-9258*
Precinct 2	Roger Wunderlich ....378-2573 / *Fax: 378-2824*
Precinct 3	Robert H. Chambers ......361 865-3500 / *Fax: 361 865-2975*
Precinct 4	Jason Strickland ....743-4041 / *Fax: 743-3014*

FISHER COUNTY

Population: 3,842
County Seat:
　Roby 79543

Courthouse, P. O. Box 306
325 776-2151 / *Fax: 325 776-2815*
www.co.fisher.tx.us

County Judge	Ken Holt ....776-2151 / *Fax: 776-2815*
District Attorney, 32nd Dist.	Ricky Thompson ....235-8639 / *Fax: 235-5886*
County Attorney	Michael Hall ....776-3251 / *Fax: 776-2815*
District Clerk	Gina Pasley ....776-2279 / *Fax: 776-3253*
County Clerk	Pat Thomson ....776-2401 / *Fax: 776-3274*
County Treasurer	Shana Haas ....776-3257 / *Fax: 776-2698*
Tax Assessor-Collector	Jonnye Lu Gibson ....776-2181 / *Fax: 776-2104*
Sheriff	H.T. Fillingim ....776-2273 / *Fax: 776-3269*
County Auditor	Becky Mauldin ....776-3255 / *Fax: 776-3258*
Chief Appraiser	Twyla Butler ....776-2733 / *Fax: 776-2636*
County Commissioner:	
Precinct 1	Gordon Pippin ....993-4561 / *Fax: 776-2815*
Precinct 2	Billy Henderson ....338-8917 / *Fax: 776-2815*
Precinct 3	Preston Martin ....575-9913 / *Fax: 776-2815*
Precinct 4	Scott Feagan ....235-7003 / *Fax: 776-2815*
Justice of the Peace:	
Precinct 1	Angie Pippin ....776-2482 / *Fax: 776-3264*

FLOYD COUNTY

Population: 5,869
County Seat:
  Floydada 79235

105 S. Main St.
806 983-4905 / *Fax: 806 983-4939*
www.co.floyd.tx.us

County Judge	Marty Lucke	.983-4905 / *Fax: 983-4939*
District Attorney, 110th Dist.	Wade Jackson	.983-2197 / *Fax: 983-2400*
County Attorney	Lex Herrington	.983-4924 / *Fax: 983-4933*
District Clerk	Patty Davenport	.983-4923 / *Fax: 983-4938*
County Clerk	Ginger Morgan	.983-4900 / *Fax: 983-4921*
County Treasurer	Lori Morales	.983-4910 / *Fax: 983-4926*
Tax Assessor-Collector	Delia G. Suarez	.983-4908 / *Fax: 983-4909*
Sheriff	Paul Raissez	.983-4901 / *Fax: 983-4904*
Chief Appraiser	Jim Finley	.983-5256 / *Fax: 983-6230*
County Commissioner:		
Precinct 1	Tanner Ray Smith	.777-1078 / *Fax: 983-4939*
Precinct 2	Lindan Morris	.983-7879 / *Fax: 983-4939*
Precinct 3	Nathan Johnson	.292-8823 / *Fax: 983-4939*
Precinct 4	Amado Morales	.983-7486 / *Fax: 983-4939*
Justice of the Peace:		
Precinct 1	Tali Jackson	.983-4911 / *Fax: 983-5542*
Precinct 2	Edward Marks	.652-3622 / *Fax: 652-3622*
Precinct 3	Edward Marks	.652-3622 / *Fax: 652-3622*
Precinct 4	Tali Jackson	.983-4911 / *Fax: 983-5542*

FOARD COUNTY

Population: 1,195
County Seat:
  Crowell 79227

P. O. Box 660
940 684-1424 / *Fax: 940 684-1918*

County Judge	Mark Christopher	.684-1424 / *Fax: 684-1426*
District Attorney, 46th Dist.	Staley Heatly	.553-3346 / *Fax: 552-9630*
County Attorney	Marshall Capps	.684-1443 / *Fax: 684-1426*
District & County Clerk	Debra Hopkins	.684-1365 / *Fax: 684-1918*
County Treasurer	Darcy Moore	.684-1818 / *Fax: 684-1918*
Tax Assessor-Collector	Mike Brown	.684-1501 / *Fax: 684-1947*
Sheriff	Mike Brown	.684-1501 / *Fax: 684-1947*
Chief Appraiser	Jo Ann Vecera	.684-1225 / *Fax: 684-1676*
County Commissioner:		
Precinct 1	Ricky Hammonds	.684-1424 / *Fax: 684-1426*
Precinct 2	Rockne Wisdom	.684-1424 / *Fax: 684-1426*
Precinct 3	Larry Wright	.684-1424 / *Fax: 684-1426*
Precinct 4	Anthony Hinsley	.684-1424 / *Fax: 684-1426*
Justice of the Peace:	Katy Marlow	.684-1917 / *Fax: 684-1317*
Constable:	Lee Hammonds	.655-3417 / *Fax: 684-1426*

FORT BEND COUNTY

Population: 732,167
County Seat:
  Richmond 77469

301 Jackson St.
281 342-3411 / *Fax: 281 341-8609*
www.fortbendcountytx.gov

County Judge	Robert E. "Bob" Hebert	.341-8608 / *Fax: 341-8609*
District Attorney	John Healey, Jr.	.341-4460 / *Fax: 341-4440*
County Attorney	Roy L. Cordes, Jr.	.341-4555 / *Fax: 341-4557*
District Clerk	Annie Rebecca Elliott	.341-4515 / *Fax: 341-4519*
County Clerk	Laura Richard	.341-8685 / *Fax: 341-8697*
County Treasurer	Jeff Council	.341-3750 / *Fax: 341-3757*
Tax Assessor-Collector	Patsy Schultz	.341-3710 / *Fax: 341-9267*
Sheriff	Troy Nehls	.341-4704 / *Fax: 341-4701*
County Auditor	Ed Sturdivant	.341-3760 / *Fax: 341-3774*
Chief Appraiser	Glen Whitehead	.344-8623 / *Fax: 344-8632*
Elections Official	John W. Oldham	.341-8670 / *Fax: 341-4418*
County Commissioner:		
Precinct 1	Vincent Morales	.344-9400 / *Fax: 342-0587*
Precinct 2	Grady Prestage	.403-8000 / *Fax: 403-8009*
Precinct 3	W.A. "Andy" Meyers	.238-1400 / *Fax: 238-1401*
Precinct 4	James Patterson	.980-2235 / *Fax: 980-9077*
Justice of the Peace:		
Precinct 1, Pl. 1	Gary Janssen	.832 471-2550 / *Fax: 832 471-2563*
Precinct 1, Pl. 2	Mary S. Ward	.341-3742 / *Fax: 341-3746*
Precinct 2	Joel C. Clouser, Sr.	.403-8080 / *Fax: 403-8089*
Precinct 3	George N. Lawrence	.238-1460 / *Fax: 238-1461*
Precinct 4	Justin M. Joyce	.491-6016 / *Fax: 242-2706*
Constable:		
Precinct 1	Mike Beard	.341-4536 / *Fax: 341-4545*
Precinct 2	Gary Majors	.403-8010 / *Fax: 403-8027*
Precinct 3	Wayne Thompson	.238-1430 / *Fax: 238-1431*
Precinct 4	Trever J. Nehls	.242-4014 / *Fax: 242-9030*

FRANKLIN COUNTY

Population: 10,832
County Seat:
  Mount Vernon 75457

200 N. Kaufman
903 537-2342 / *Fax: 903 537-2418*
co.franklin.tx.us

County Judge	Scott Lee	.537-2342 / *Fax: 537-2418*
District Attorney, 8th Dist.	Will Ramsay	.885-0641 / *Fax: 885-0640*
County Attorney	Gene Stump	.537-2342 / *Fax: 537-2418*
District Clerk	Ellen Jaggers	.537-8337 / *Fax: 537-8338*
County Clerk	Betty Crane	.537-2342 / *Fax: 537-2962*
County Treasurer	Betty Sue Allen	.537-8334 / *Fax: 537-8335*
Tax Assessor-Collector	Sue Ann Harper	.537-2358 / *Fax: 537-3483*
Sheriff	Ricky Jones	.537-4539 / *Fax: 537-2632*
County Auditor	Tina R. Phillips	.537-8333 / *Fax: 537-8335*
Chief Appraiser	Genea Burnaman	.537-2286 / *Fax: 537-2812*
County Commissioner:		
Precinct 1	Jerry Cooper	.632-4566 / *Fax: 537-8335*
Precinct 2	Larkin Jumper	.537-4263 / *Fax: 537-8335*
Precinct 3	Charlie Emerson	.588-2763 / *Fax: 537-8335*
Precinct 4	Sam Young	.860-3502 / *Fax: 860-3702*
Justice of the Peace:	Jim Alford	.537-2342 / *Fax: 537-2982*
Constable:	Randy Green	.537-4539 / *Fax: 537-2632*

FREESTONE COUNTY

Population: 20,172
County Seat:
  Fairfield 75840

Courthouse, 118 E. Commerce
903 389-3335 / *Fax: 903 389-3839*
www.co.freestone.tx.us

County Judge	Linda K. Grant	.389-3335 / *Fax: 389-3839*
District Attorney	Chris Martin	.389-3977 / *Fax: 389-5289*
District & County Attorney	Brian Evans	.389-3977 / *Fax: 389-5289*
District Clerk	Teresa F. Black	.389-2534 / *Fax: 389-8421*
County Clerk	Linda Jarvis	.389-2635 / *Fax: 389-6956*
County Treasurer	Kay Taylor	.389-2180 / *Fax: 389-5894*
Tax Assessor-Collector	Lisa Foree	.389-2336 / *Fax: 389-6533*
Sheriff	Jeremy Shipley	.389-3236 / *Fax: 389-5730*
County Auditor	Donna Lynn Williams	.389-3535 / *Fax: 389-0440*
Chief Appraiser	Bud Black	.389-5510 / *Fax: 389-5955*
County Commissioner:		
Precinct 1	Andy Bonner	.389-3709 / *Fax: 389-3839*
Precinct 2	Craig Oakes	.254 739-3444 / *Fax: 389-3839*
Precinct 3	Michael Daniels	.389-5305 / *Fax: 389-3839*
Precinct 4	Clyde Ridge, Jr.	.254 765-3888 / *Fax: 389-3839*
Justice of the Peace:		
Precinct 1	Theresa Farris	.389-8783 / *Fax: 389-2465*
Precinct 2	Debra Hamilton	.254 739-2518 / *Fax: 254 739-0939*
Precinct 3	Cinnamon Archibald	.389-3137 / *Fax: 389-9409*
Precinct 4	Shirley Mays	.389-0420 / *Fax: 389-0429*
Constable:		
Precinct 1	Buck Bonner	.389-4274 / *Fax: 389-2465*
Precinct 2	Lynn Clary	.254 739-2518 / *Fax: 254 739-0939*
Precinct 3	Pamela Lorraine Brackens	.390-0018
Precinct 4	Wade Harrison	.254 747-2372

COUNTY SECTION

FRIO COUNTY

Population: 19,041
County Seat:
  Pearsall 78061

Courthouse, 500 East San Antonio
830 334-2154 / *Fax: 830 334-0010*
www.co.frio.tx.us

County Judge	Arnulfo C. Luna	.334-2154 / *Fax: 334-0010*
District Attorney, 81st Dist.	Audrey Gossett Louis	.393-2200 / *Fax: 393-2205*
County Attorney	Joseph Sindon	.334-2162 / *Fax: 334-0015*
District Clerk	Ofelia Trevino	.334-8073 / *Fax: 334-0047*
County Clerk	Angie Tullis	.334-2214 / *Fax: 334-0021*
County Treasurer	Anna Luna Hernandez	.334-0040 / *Fax: 334-0033*
Tax Assessor-Collector	Anna Alaniz	.334-2152 / *Fax: 334-0006*
Sheriff	Albert De Leon	.334-3311 / *Fax: 334-0053*
County Auditor	Tracy Barrera	.334-0000 / *Fax: 334-0001*
Chief Appraiser	Luciano R. Gonzales, Jr.	.334-4163 / *Fax: 334-5568*
Elections Official	Carlos E. Segura	.334-3975 / *Fax: 334-3984*
County Commissioner:		
Precinct 1	Vickie "Coach" Camacho	.210 413-2670
Precinct 2	Richard Graf	.719-2715 / *Fax: 334-4510*
Precinct 3	Ruben Maldonado Sr.	.317-0114
Precinct 4	Jose "Pepe" Flores	.210 461-0563 / *Fax: 965-1170*
Justice of the Peace:		
Precinct 1	Shanna Jo Gates	.334-3668 / *Fax: 334-0034*
Precinct 2	James Sindon	.334-8292 / *Fax: 334-0080*
Precinct 3	Susana Ruiz-Belding	.334-2911 / *Fax: 334-2648*
Precinct 4	Larry Flores	.965-2009 / *Fax: 965-4148*
Constable:		
Precinct 1	Ricardo R. Ramirez	.334-3311 / *Fax: 334-0053*
Precinct 2	Rodolfo "Rudy" Ortegon, Jr.	.334-3311 / *Fax: 334-0053*
Precinct 3	Ted Nieto	.334-3311 / *Fax: 334-0053*
Precinct 4	Rene Lozano	.334-3311 / *Fax: 334-0053*

GAINES COUNTY

Population: 20,112
County Seat:
  Seminole 79360

P. O. Box 847
432 758-5411 / *Fax: 432 758-4031*
www.co.gaines.tx.us

County Judge	Tom Keyes	.758-5411 x4622 / *Fax: 758-4031*
District Attorney, 106th Dist.	Philip Mack Furlow	.806 872-2259 / *Fax: 806 872-3174*
County Attorney	Joe H. Nagy, Jr.	.758-4001 / *Fax: 758-4031*
District Clerk	Sharon Taylor	.758-4013 / *Fax: 758-4036*
County Clerk	Vicki Phillips	.758-4003 / *Fax: 758-1442*
County Treasurer	Michael Lord, Jr.	.758-4009 / *Fax: 758-4054*
Tax Assessor-Collector	Susan Shaw	.758-4008 / *Fax: 758-4035*
Sheriff	Ronny Pipkin	.758-9871 / *Fax: 758-4051*
County Auditor	Rick Dollahan	.758-4002 / *Fax: 758-4012*
Chief Appraiser	Gayla Harridge	.758-3263 / *Fax: 758-3674*
Elections Official	Patricia Roberson	.758-4041 / *Fax: 955-0150*

County Commissioner:
  Precinct 1 Brian Rosson .... .806 546-2423 / *Fax: 758-4031*
  Precinct 2 Craig Belt .... .758-4004 / *Fax: 758-4031*
  Precinct 3 David Murphree .... .758-4017 / *Fax: 758-4031*
  Precinct 4 Biz Houston .... .758-4018 / *Fax: 758-4031*
Justice of the Peace:
  Precinct 1 Tammy Clark .... .758-4015 / *Fax: 758-4037*
  Precinct 2 Calvin Sellers .... .806 546-2666
Constable:
  Precinct 1 Vacant .... .758-4056 / *Fax: 758-4031*

GALVESTON COUNTY

Population: 324,474
County Seat:
  Galveston 77550

722 Moody
409 766-2244 / *Fax: 409 766-4591*
www.co.galveston.tx.us/

County Judge Mark Henry .... .766-2244 / *Fax: 766-4591*
Criminal District Attorney Jack Roady .... .766-2355 / *Fax: 766-2290*
District Clerk John Kinard .... .766-2424 / *Fax: 766-2292*
County Clerk Dwight D. Sullivan, MBA .... .766-2200 / *Fax: 765-3160*
County Treasurer Kevin C. Walsh, C.P.A. .... .770-5395 / *Fax: 770-5386*
Tax Assessor-Collector Cheryl E. Johnson .... .766-2260 / *Fax: 766-2479*
Sheriff Henry Trochesset .... .766-2322 / *Fax: 766-6219*
County Auditor Randall Rice, CPA .... .770-5301 / *Fax: 765-3252*
Chief Appraiser Tommy Watson .... .935-1980 / *Fax: 935-4319*
County Commissioner:
  Precinct 1 Darrell A. Apffel 770-5474
  Precinct 2 Joseph Giusti .... .770-5475 / *Fax: 770-5998*
  Precinct 3 Stephen Holmes .... .770-5806 / *Fax: 770-5844*
  Precinct 4 Ken Clark .... .281 316-8744 / *Fax: 281 361-2000*
Justice of the Peace:
  Precinct 1 Alison Cox 770-5820
  Precinct 2 Jim Schweitzer 766-2250
  Precinct 3 Penny L. Pope 770-5455
  Precinct 4 Kathleen McCumber .... .281 316-8716
Constable:
  Precinct 1 Rick Sharp .... .281 316-8806 / *Fax: 765-3225*
  Precinct 2 Jimmy Fullen .... .770-5177 / *Fax: 770-6260*
  Precinct 3 Derreck Rose .... .765-2926 / *Fax: 770-6096*
  Precinct 4 Jerry Fisher .... .281 316-8711 / *Fax: 281 316-8737*

GARZA COUNTY

Population: 6,536
County Seat:
  Post 79356

300 West Main St.
806 495-4405 / *Fax: 806 495-4482*
www.garzacounty.net

County Judge	John Lee Norman	495-4405 / *Fax: 495-4482*
District Attorney, 106th Dist.	Philip Mack Furlow	872-2259 / *Fax: 872-3174*
County Attorney	Ted Weems	495-4440 / *Fax: 495-4496*
District & County Clerk	Jim Plummer	495-4430 / *Fax: 495-4431*
County Treasurer	LuAnne Terry	495-4422 / *Fax: 495-4424*
Tax Assessor-Collector	Nancy Wallace	495-4448 / *Fax: 495-4483*
Sheriff	Terry L. Morgan	990-4446 / *Fax: 495-4446*
Chief Appraiser	Irene Fry	495-3518 / *Fax: 495-2055*
County Commissioner:		
Precinct 1	Jeff Williams	495-4405 / *Fax: 495-4482*
Precinct 2	Charles Morris	495-4405 / *Fax: 495-4482*
Precinct 3	Ted Brannon	495-4405 / *Fax: 495-4482*
Precinct 4	Jerry Benham	495-4405 / *Fax: 495-4482*
Justice of the Peace:		
Precinct 1	Gordon Terry	495-4410 / *Fax: 495-4481*
Precinct 2	Angela Massey	495-4420 / *Fax: 495-4484*
Constable:		
Precinct 1	Daniel Yarbro	990-4810 / *Fax: 990-4750*
Precinct 2	Ronnie Gilbert	990-4810 / *Fax: 990-4750*

GILLESPIE COUNTY

Population: 26,303
County Seat:
  Fredericksburg 78624

101 West Main St.
830 997-7502 / *Fax: 830 992-2608*
www.gillespiecounty.org

County Judge	Mark Stroeher	997-7502 / *Fax: 992-2608*
District Attorney, 216th Dist.	Lucy Wilke	896-4744 / *Fax: 896-2620*
County Attorney	Chris Nevins	990-0675 / *Fax: 992-2615*
District Clerk	Jan Davis	997-6517 / *Fax: 992-2613*
County Clerk	Mary Lynn Rusche	997-6515 / *Fax: 997-9958*
County Treasurer	Laura Lundquist	997-6521 / *Fax: 990-2307*
Tax Assessor-Collector	Vicki J. Schmidt	997-6519 / *Fax: 990-2756*
Sheriff	Buddy Mills	997-7585 / *Fax: 997-9541*
County Auditor	Larry Crump	997-6777 / *Fax: 992-2654*
Chief Appraiser	Scott Fair	997-9807 / *Fax: 990-0860*
County Commissioner:		
Precinct 1	Charles Olfers	997-7503 / *Fax: 992-2608*
Precinct 2	William A. "Billy" Roeder	997-7503 / *Fax: 992-2608*
Precinct 3	Dennis W. Neffendorf	997-7503 / *Fax: 992-2608*
Precinct 4	Donnie Schuch	997-7503 / *Fax: 992-2608*
Justice of the Peace:		
Precinct 1	J.D. Hickman	997-6912 / *Fax: 997-1540*
Precinct 2	Carl E. Schoessow	997-9776 / *Fax: 997-1540*
Constable:		
Precinct 1	Hilario Villa Sr.	997-7585 / *Fax: 307-3448*
Precinct 2	Marshall Akin	997-7585 / *Fax: 997-9541*

GLASSCOCK COUNTY

Population: 1,362
County Seat:
  Garden City 79739

P. O. Box 67
432 354-2382 / *Fax: 432 354-2348*
www.co.glasscock.tx.us

County Judge	Kim Halfmann	.354-2639 / *Fax: 354-2348*
District & County Attorney	Hardy L. Wilkerson	.264-2220 / *Fax: 264-2222*
District & County Clerk	Rebecca Batla	.354-2371
County Treasurer	Alan Dierschke	.354-2415 / *Fax: 354-2348*
Tax Assessor-Collector	Tina Flores	.354-2489 / *Fax: 354-2661*
Sheriff	Keith Burnett	.354-2361 / *Fax: 354-2325*
Chief Appraiser	Priscilla A. Ginnetti	.354-2580 / *Fax: 354-2354*
County Commissioner:		
Precinct 1	Charles Gully	.413-8442
Precinct 2	Mark Halfmann	.354-2498
Precinct 3	Gary Jones	.270-8318
Precinct 4	Michael Hoch	.354-2360
Justice of the Peace:		
Precinct 1	Kay Donna Machicek	.354-2382 / *Fax: 354-2348*
Constable:		
Precinct 1	Mark Frysak	.354-2334 / *Fax: 354-2348*

GOLIAD COUNTY

Population: 7,741
County Seat:
  Goliad 77963

P. O. Box 677
361 645-3337 / *Fax: 361 645-3474*
www.co.goliad.tx.us

County Judge	Pat Calhoun	.645-3337 / *Fax: 645-3474*
District Attorney, 24th Dist.	Rob Lassmann	.275-2612 / *Fax: 275-3282*
County Attorney	Rob Baiamonte	.645-2184 / *Fax: 645-1711*
District & County Clerk	Mary Ellen Flores	.645-3294 / *Fax: 645-3858*
County Treasurer	Daphne Buelter	.645-3551 / *Fax: 645-4128*
Tax Assessor-Collector	Michelle Garcia	.645-3354 / *Fax: 645-8544*
Sheriff	Kirby Brumby	.645-3451 / *Fax: 645-2230*
County Auditor	William Larry Zermeno	.645-3345 / *Fax: 645-8518*
Chief Appraiser	Richard Miller	.645-2492 / *Fax: 645-3200*
County Commissioner:		
Precinct 1	Kenneth Edwards	.645-3174 / *Fax: 645-3174*
Precinct 2	Alonzo Morales	.645-1394 / *Fax: 645-1250*
Precinct 3	Mickey White	.564-4034 / *Fax: 564-4034*
Precinct 4	David Bruns	.645-8576 / *Fax: 645-8576*
Justice of the Peace:		
Precinct 1	Susan Moore	.645-3663 / *Fax: 645-8067*
Precinct 2	Steve Kennedy	.645-3320 / *Fax: 645-4127*
Constable:		
Precinct 1	Michael De La Garza	.645-4907 / *Fax: 645-8067*
Precinct 2	Mike Thompson	.935-8359 / *Fax: 645-4127*

GONZALES COUNTY

Population: 20,275
County Seat:
  Gonzales 78629

414 St. Joseph St., Suite 200
830 672-2327 / *Fax: 830 672-5477*
www.co.gonzales.tx.us/

County Judge	David Bird	.672-2327 / *Fax: 672-5477*
County Attorney	Paul Watkins	.672-6527 / *Fax: 672-5868*
District Clerk	Janice Sutton	.672-2326 / *Fax: 672-9313*
County Clerk	Sylvia Sheffield	.672-2801 / *Fax: 672-2636*
County Treasurer	Jo Ann Mercer	.672-2621 / *Fax: 672-2083*
Tax Assessor-Collector	Crystal Cedillo	.672-2841 / *Fax: 519-4256*
Sheriff	Matthew Atkinson	.672-6524 / *Fax: 672-2517*
County Auditor	Becky Weston	.672-6397 / *Fax: 672-6591*
Chief Appraiser	John Liford	.672-2879 / *Fax: 672-8345*
County Commissioner:		
Precinct 1	Kenneth O. "Dell" Whiddon	.672-3700 / *Fax: 672-5477*
Precinct 2	Donnie R. Brzozowski	.788-7351 / *Fax: 672-5477*
Precinct 3	Kevin T. LaFleur	.672-2265 / *Fax: 672-5477*
Precinct 4	Collie Boatright, Jr.	.582-1615 / *Fax: 582-1142*
Justice of the Peace:		
Precinct 1	Deidra D. Voigt	.672-3734 / *Fax: 672-5296*
Precinct 3	Jesse Almaraz	.788-7762 / *Fax: 788-7650*
Precinct 4	Darryl Becker	.582-1292 / *Fax: 582-1142*
Constable:		
Precinct 1	Leslie R. Pirkle	.672-4440 / *Fax: 672-5296*
Precinct 3	Derek Johnson	.788-7176 / *Fax: 788-7116*
Precinct 4	John J. Moreno	.582-1418 / *Fax: 582-1142*

GRAY COUNTY

Population: 23,316
County Seat:
  Pampa 79065

205 N. Russell
806 669-8007 / *Fax: 806 669-3048*
www.co.gray.tx.us

County Judge	Richard Peet	.669-8007 / *Fax: 669-3048*
District Attorney, 31st Dist.	Franklin McDonough	.669-8035 / *Fax: 669-8050*
County Attorney	Joshua M. Seabourn	.669-8003 / *Fax: 669-3048*
District Clerk	Jo Mays	.669-8010 / *Fax: 669-8053*
County Clerk	Susan Winborne	.669-8004 / *Fax: 669-8054*
County Treasurer	Scott Hahn	.669-8009 / *Fax: 669-8025*
Tax Assessor-Collector	Gaye Whitehead	.669-8018 / *Fax: 669-8051*
Sheriff	Michael Ryan	.669-8022 / *Fax: 669-8026*
County Auditor	Elaine Morris	.669-8001 / *Fax: 669-8021*
Chief Appraiser	Tyson Pronto	.665-0791 / *Fax: 665-1213*
Elections Official	Becky Sotelo	.669-8068 / *Fax: 669-4004*
County Commissioner:		
Precinct 1	Joe Wheeley	.669-8007 / *Fax: 669-3048*
Precinct 2	Gary Willoughby	.669-8007 / *Fax: 669-3048*
Precinct 3	John Mark Baggerman	.669-8007 / *Fax: 669-3048*
Precinct 4	Jeff Haley	.669-8007 / *Fax: 669-3048*

Justice of the Peace:
  Precinct 1 & 3 Joe Martinez .... .669-8032 / *Fax: 665-0481*
  Precinct 2   Connie Ogle .... .669-8015 / *Fax: 669-8066*
  Precinct 4   Mary Ann Carpenter .... .779-2721 / *Fax: 779-2721*
Constable:
  Precinct 1   Jason Rushing .... .669-8032 / *Fax: 669-8026*
  Precinct 2   Joe Montgomery .... .669-8002 / *Fax: 669-8066*

GRAYSON COUNTY

Population: 125,601
County Seat:
  Sherman 75090

100 West Houston
903 813-4200 / *Fax: 903 892-4085*
www.co.grayson.tx.us/

County Judge   Bill Magers .... .813-4228 / *Fax: 892-4085*
Criminal District Attorney   Joseph Brown .... .813-4361 / *Fax: 892-9933*
District Clerk   Kelly Ashmore .... .813-4352 / *Fax: 870-0609*
County Clerk   Wilma Blackshear Bush .... .813-4243 / *Fax: 870-0829*
County Treasurer   Gayla Hawkins .... .813-4251 / *Fax: 813-4263*
Tax Assessor-Collector   Bruce Stidham .... .892-8297 / *Fax: 893-4973*
Sheriff   Tom Watt .... .813-4408 / *Fax: 868-2977*
County Auditor   J. Richey Rivers .... .813-4245 / *Fax: 893-2707*
Chief Appraiser   Shawn Coker .... .870-1993 / *Fax: 892-3835*
Elections Official   Deana Patterson .... .893-8683 / *Fax: 891-4370*
County Commissioner:
  Precinct 1   Jeff Whitmire .... .813-4327 / *Fax: 868-8613*
  Precinct 2   David Whitlock .... .813-4325 / *Fax: 868-8613*
  Precinct 3   Phyllis James .... .813-4317 / *Fax: 868-8613*
  Precinct 4   Bart Lawrence .... .813-4318 / *Fax: 893-5207*
Justice of the Peace:
  Precinct 1   Larry Atherton .... .813-4346 / *Fax: 893-9264*
  Precinct 2   David Hawley .... .465-0984 / *Fax: 465-8521*
  Precinct 3   Mike Reeves .... .564-3550 / *Fax: 564-9127*
  Precinct 4   Rita Noel .... .482-6543 / *Fax: 482-6573*
Constable:
  Precinct 1   Thomas W. Carter .... .813-4342 / *Fax: 893-9264*
  Precinct 2   Mike Putman .... .465-0984 / *Fax: 463-2360*
  Precinct 3   Todd Booher .... .564-3550 / *Fax: 564-9127*
  Precinct 4   William R. Douglas .... .482-6543 / *Fax: 482-6573*

GREGG COUNTY

Population: 126,709
County Seat:
  Longview 75601

101 East Methvin
903 758-6181 / *Fax: 903 236-8456*
www.co.gregg.tx.us

County Judge	Bill Stoudt	236-8420 / *Fax: 237-2699*
Criminal District Attorney	Carl Dorrough	236-8440 / *Fax: 236-8490*
District Clerk	Barbara Duncan	237-2663 / *Fax: 236-8474*
County Clerk	Connie L. Wade	236-8430 / *Fax: 237-2574*
Tax Assessor-Collector	William Kirk Shields	237-2650 / *Fax: 237-2607*
Sheriff	Maxey Cerliano	236-8400 / *Fax: 753-3560*
County Auditor	Laurie Woloszyn	237-2680 / *Fax: 237-2695*
Chief Appraiser	Libby Neely	238-8823 / *Fax: 238-8830*
Elections Official	Kathryn Nealy	236-8458 / *Fax: 234-3126*
County Commissioner:		
Precinct 1	Ronnie McKinney	663-0400 / *Fax: 663-2475*
Precinct 2	R. Darryl Primo	759-3611 / *Fax: 759-6707*
Precinct 3	Gary W. Boyd	759-8962 / *Fax: 297-9140*
Precinct 4	John Mathis	981-1117 / *Fax: 981-1119*
Justice of the Peace:		
Precinct 1	B. H. Jameson	236-8470 / *Fax: 237-2598*
Precinct 2	Tim Bryan	237-2636 / *Fax: 297-3412*
Precinct 3	Talyna Carlson	845-2672 / *Fax: 845-6467*
Precinct 4	James Mathis	758-6342 / *Fax: 758-2684*
Constable:		
Precinct 1	James Plumlec	236-8427 / *Fax: 236-8424*
Precinct 2	Billy Fort	237-2600 / *Fax: 297-3412*
Precinct 3	Daniel Morgan	845-4896 / *Fax: 844-1722*
Precinct 4	Danny Craig II	236-4058 / *Fax: 758-2684*

GRIMES COUNTY

Population: 27,645
County Seat:
  Anderson 77830

P. O. Box 160
936 873-4400 / *Fax: 936 873-5065*
www.co.grimes.tx.us

County Judge	Joe Fauth III	873-4476 / *Fax: 873-5065*
District Attorney, 278th Dist.	Andria Bender	873-2137 / *Fax: 873-2688*
County Attorney	Jon C. Fultz	873-6455 / *Fax: 873-6457*
District Clerk	Diane LeFlore	873-4430 / *Fax: 873-2514*
County Clerk	David Pasket	873-4410 / *Fax: 873-3308*
County Treasurer	Janice A. Trant	873-4402 / *Fax: 873-4416*
Tax Assessor-Collector	Mary Ann Waters	873-4465 / *Fax: 873-4458*
Sheriff	Donald G. Sowell	873-6401 / *Fax: 873-2010*
County Auditor	Mary Nichols	873-4415 / *Fax: 873-2059*
Chief Appraiser	Mark Boehnke	873-2163 / *Fax: 873-2154*
Elections Official	Rebecca Duff	873-4424 / *Fax: 873-2083*

County Commissioner:
Precinct 1 — Chad Mallett 870-5179
Precinct 2 — David E. Dobyanski .... .571-5129 / *Fax: 894-3233*
Precinct 3 — Barbara Walker .... .873-3916 / *Fax: 873-3922*
Precinct 4 — Gary Husfeld .... .979 820-2926
Justice of the Peace:
Precinct 1 — Chris Acord .... .394-2060 / *Fax: 394-4110*
Precinct 2 — Lester Underwood .... .873-6452 / *Fax: 873-6410*
Precinct 3 — John Leflore .... .873-3900 / *Fax: 873-3923*
Constable:
Precinct 1 — Dale Schaper .... .394-6100 / *Fax: 394-4110*
Precinct 2 — Blake Jarvis .... .873-6409 / *Fax: 873-2010*
Precinct 3 — Wes Male 870-6286

GUADALUPE COUNTY

Population: 154,995
County Seat:
  Seguin 78155

101 E. Court Street
830 303-8867 / *Fax: 830 303-4064*
www.co.guadalupe.tx.us/

County Judge — Kyle Kutscher .... .303-8867 / *Fax: 303-4064*
County Attorney — David Willborn .... .303-6130 / *Fax: 379-9491*
District Clerk — Debi Crow .... .303-8873 / *Fax: 379-1943*
County Clerk — Teresa Kiel .... .303-8859 / *Fax: 401-0300*
County Treasurer — Linda Douglass .... .303-8868 / *Fax: 303-5757*
Tax Assessor-Collector — Daryl W. John .... .303-3421 / *Fax: 372-9940*
Sheriff — Arnold Zwicke .... .379-1224 / *Fax: 372-5408*
County Auditor — Kristen L. Klein .... .303-8855 / *Fax: 303-1541*
Chief Appraiser — Jamie Osborne .... .303-3313 / *Fax: 372-2874*
Elections Official — Lisa Adam .... .303-6363 / *Fax: 303-6373*
County Commissioner:
Precinct 1 — Greg Seidenberger .... .303-8857 x1314 / *Fax: 303-4064*
Precinct 2 — Jack Shanafelt .... .303-8857 x1362 / *Fax: 303-4064*
Precinct 3 — Jim Wolverton .... .303-8857 x1313 / *Fax: 303-4064*
Precinct 4 — Judy Cope .... .303-8857 x1329 / *Fax: 303-4064*
Justice of the Peace:
Precinct 1 — Darrell Hunter .... .372-4223 / *Fax: 372-3830*
Precinct 2 — Sheryl Sachtleben .... .379-2214 / *Fax: 379-3657*
Precinct 3 — Roy Richard, Jr. .... .210 945-6685 / *Fax: 210 945-8544*
Precinct 4 — Todd Friesenhahn .... .372-8916 / *Fax: 372-8924*
Constable:
Precinct 1 — Bobby Jahns .... .305-1673 / *Fax: 372-3830*
Precinct 2 — Jimmy Harless .... .379-2214 / *Fax: 379-3657*
Precinct 3 — Michael Skrobarcek .... .210 945-6685
Precinct 4 — Harvey Faulkner .... .372-8918 / *Fax: 372-8924*

HALE COUNTY

Population: 35,620
County Seat:
  Plainview 79072

Courthouse, 500 Broadway, Room 240
806 291-5214 / *Fax: 806 296-7786*
www.halecounty.org

County Judge	Bill A. Coleman	.291-5215 / *Fax: 296-7786*
District Attorney, 64th Dist.	Wally Hatch	.291-5241 / *Fax: 293-9618*
County Attorney	James M. Tirey	.291-5306 / *Fax: 291-5308*
District Clerk	Carla Cannon	.291-5226 / *Fax: 291-5206*
County Clerk	Latrice Kemp	.291-5261 / *Fax: 291-9810*
County Treasurer	Ida A. Tyler	.291-5209 / *Fax: 291-5313*
Tax Assessor-Collector	Roland Nash	.291-5276 / *Fax: 296-0876*
Sheriff	David Cochran	.296-2724 / *Fax: 296-5725*
County Auditor	Maretta Smithson	.291-5294 / *Fax: 291-5303*
Chief Appraiser	Nikki Branscum	.293-4226 / *Fax: 293-1834*
County Commissioner:		
Precinct 1	Harold King	.296-5863
Precinct 2	Mario Martinez	.667-2261
Precinct 3	Kenny Kernell	.239-2142 / *Fax: 288-5371*
Precinct 4	Benny Cantwell	.889-3381 / *Fax: 296-7786*
Justice of the Peace:		
Precinct 1	Sheron Collins	.291-5201 / *Fax: 291-5310*
Precinct 3	Karen Davis	.757-2476 / *Fax: 757-2481*
Constable:		
Precinct 1	Brent Hackett	.291-5208 / *Fax: 291-5310*
Precinct 3	Terry Timms	.292-9709 / *Fax: 757-2481*

HALL COUNTY

Population: 3,124
County Seat:
  Memphis 79245

512 W. Main, Suite 4
806 259-2511 / *Fax: 806 259-3083*
www.hallcountytexas.us

County Judge	Ray Powell	.259-2511 / *Fax: 259-3083*
District Attorney, 100th Dist.	Luke Inman	.447-0055 / *Fax: 866 233-2738*
County Attorney	John M. Deaver, II	.259-2651 / *Fax: 259-3317*
District & County Clerk	Raye Bailey	.259-2627 / *Fax: 259-5078*
County Treasurer	Janet Bridges	.259-2421 / *Fax: 259-2863*
Tax Assessor-Collector	Teresa Altman	.259-2125 / *Fax: 259-3322*
Sheriff	Tom Heck	.259-2151 / *Fax: 259-2137*
Chief Appraiser	Gina Chavira	.259-2393 / *Fax: 259-2384*
County Commissioner:		
Precinct 1	Winfred McQueen	.259-2963 / *Fax: 259-3083*
Precinct 2	Terry Lindsey	.867-2031 / *Fax: 259-5078*
Precinct 3	Gary Proffitt	.584-7545 / *Fax: 259-3083*
Precinct 4	James Fuston	.423-1120
Justice of the Peace:		
Precinct 1	Sherrie Stone	.259-3116 / *Fax: 259-5078*
Precinct 4	Cody Bell	.423-1498

HAMILTON COUNTY

Population: 8,449
County Seat:
  Hamilton 76531

102 North Rice
254 386-1200 / *Fax: 254 386-8727*
www.hamiltoncountytx.org

County Judge	W. Mark Tynes	.386-1200 x19 / *Fax: 386-1291*
District Attorney, 220th Dist.	Adam Sibley	.435-2994 / *Fax: 435-2952*
County Attorney	Mark Henkes	.386-3217 / *Fax: 386-8511*
District Clerk	Sandy Layhew	.386-1241 / *Fax: 386-1242*
County Clerk	Kiesha Bagwell	.386-1202 / *Fax: 386-8727*
County Treasurer	Shawna Dyer	.386-1260 / *Fax: 386-1262*
Tax Assessor-Collector	Terry Payne Short	.386-1200 x12 / *Fax: 386-1233*
Sheriff	Justin Caraway	.386-8128 / *Fax: 386-8762*
County Auditor	Kent Reeves	.386-1200 x17 / *Fax: 386-1271*
Chief Appraiser	Doyle Roberts	.386-8945 / *Fax: 386-8947*
County Commissioner:		
Precinct 1	Johnny Wagner	.386-8542 / *Fax: 386-8727*
Precinct 2	Keith Curry	.386-4942 / *Fax: 386-8727*
Precinct 3	Lloyd Huggins	.796-4133 / *Fax: 386-8727*
Precinct 4	Dickie Clary	.372-3339 / *Fax: 386-8727*
Justice of the Peace:		
Precinct 1	James Lively	.386-1200 x11 / *Fax: 386-1223*

HANSFORD COUNTY

Population: 5,599
County Seat:
  Spearman 79081

16 N.W. Court St.
806 659-4100 / *Fax: 806 659-4168*
www.co.hansford.tx.us

County Judge	Benny D. Wilson	.659-4100 / *Fax: 659-4168*
District Attorney, 84th Dist.	Mark Snider	.878-4036 / *Fax: 659-4168*
County Attorney	Cheryl Nelson	.659-4156 / *Fax: 844 272-7100*
District & County Clerk	Janet Torres	.659-4110 / *Fax: 659-4168*
County Treasurer	Wanda Wagner	.659-4125 / *Fax: 659-4168*
Tax Assessor-Collector	Linda Cummings	.659-4120 / *Fax: 659-4124*
Sheriff	Tim Glass	.659-4140 / *Fax: 659-2025*
County Auditor	Cindy Scribner	.659-4105 / *Fax: 659-4168*
Chief Appraiser	Brandi Thompson	.659-5575 / *Fax: 659-5109*
County Commissioner:		
Precinct 1	Ira G. "Butch" Reed	.659-4100 / *Fax: 659-4168*
Precinct 2	David Thomas	.659-4100 / *Fax: 659-4168*
Precinct 3	Tim Stedje	.659-4100 / *Fax: 659-4168*
Precinct 4	Danny Henson	.659-4100 / *Fax: 659-4168*
Justice of the Peace:	Bob Davis	.659-4165 / *Fax: 659-3715*

COUNTY SECTION

HARDEMAN COUNTY

Population: 3,764
County Seat:
 Quanah 79252

P. O. Box 30
940 663-2911 / *Fax: 940 663-2565*

County Judge	Ronald Ingram . . . . .663-2911 / *Fax: 663-2565*
District Attorney, 46th Dist.	Staley Heatly . . . . .553-3346 / *Fax: 552-9630*
County Attorney	Stanley Watson . . . . .663-5222 / *Fax: 663-6103*
District & County Clerk	Ellen London . . . . .663-2901 / *Fax: 663-5161*
County Treasurer	Mary Ann Naylor . . . . .663-5401 / *Fax: 663-2565*
Tax Assessor-Collector	Jan Evans . . . . .663-5221 / *Fax: 663-2770*
Sheriff	Pat Laughery . . . . .663-5374 / *Fax: 663-2597*
Chief Appraiser	Jan Evans . . . . .663-2532 / *Fax: 663-6490*
County Commissioner:	
Precinct 1	Chris Call . . . . .839-7187 / *Fax: 663-2565*
Precinct 2	Rodger Tabor . . . . .674-5155 / *Fax: 663-2565*
Precinct 3	Barry Haynes . . . . .839-6611 / *Fax: 663-2565*
Precinct 4	Rodney Foster . . . . .674-5030 / *Fax: 663-2565*
Justice of the Peace:	Linda Hollenbaugh . . . . .663-5932 / *Fax: 663-5947*
Constable:	Billy Walkup . . . . .663-2901 / *Fax: 663-5161*

HARDIN COUNTY

Population: 57,963
County Seat:
 Kountze 77625

300 Monroe Street
409 246-5120 / *Fax: 409 246-5195*
www.co.hardin.tx.us

County Judge	Wayne McDaniel . . . . .246-5120 / *Fax: 246-5195*
District Attorney, 88th Dist.	David Sheffield . . . . .246-5160 / *Fax: 246-5142*
County Attorney	Rebecca R. Walton . . . . .246-5165 / *Fax: 246-4389*
District Clerk	Dana Hogg . . . . .246-5150 / *Fax: 246-5288*
County Clerk	Glenda Alston . . . . .246-5185 / *Fax: 246-3208*
County Treasurer	Deborah McWilliams . . . . .246-5121 / *Fax: 246-5107*
Tax Assessor-Collector	Shirley M. Cook . . . . .246-5180 / *Fax: 246-4718*
Sheriff	Mark L. Davis . . . . .246 3441 / *Fax: 246-3277*
County Auditor	Angela Gore .246-5130 / *Fax: 246-5134*
Chief Appraiser	Crystal Smith . . . . .246-2507 / *Fax: 246-4714*
County Commissioner:	
Precinct 1	L. W. Cooper, Jr. . . . . .385-5501 / *Fax: 386-0752*
Precinct 2	Chris Kirkendall . . . . .246-3972 / *Fax: 246-3972*
Precinct 3	Ken Pelt . . . . .287-3300 / *Fax: 287-4775*
Precinct 4	Alvin Roberts . . . . .755-4584 / *Fax: 755-4902*
Justice of the Peace:	
Precinct 1	Chris Ingram . . . . .385-3740 / *Fax: 386-0276*
Precinct 2	Charles Brewer . . . . .385-7195 / *Fax: 385-7194*
Precinct 3	T.J. Hall . . . . .246-5115 / *Fax: 246-5191*
Precinct 4	Kent Walker .287-3211 / *Fax: 287-4000*
Precinct 5	Melissa Minton . . . . .755-2862 / *Fax: 755-7603*
Precinct 6	Jacqueline Werner . . . . .936 262-8271 / *Fax: 936 262-7311*

Constable:
Precinct 1	Carlos Montalvo ....234-9025 / *Fax: 386-0276*
Precinct 2	Ben Hawthorne ....385-7195 / *Fax: 385-7194*
Precinct 3	Bill Overstreet ....246-5115 / *Fax: 246-5191*
Precinct 4	Mark Ames 287-3211
Precinct 5	Danny Sullins 755-2962
Precinct 6	Ross Jordan 209-5336

HARRIS COUNTY

Population: 4,573,568
County Seat:
  Houston 77002

1001 Preston, Suite 911
713 755-4000 / *Fax: 713 755-8379*
www.co.harris.tx.us/

County Judge	Ed Emmett ....755-4000 / *Fax: 755-8379*
District Attorney	Kim Ogg ....755-5800 / *Fax: 755-6865*
County Attorney	Vince Ryan ....755-5101 / *Fax: 755-8924*
District Clerk	Chris Daniel ....832 927-5846 / *Fax: 832 927-0148*
County Clerk	Stan Stanart ....755-6411 / *Fax: 755-4638*
County Treasurer	Orlando Sanchez ....755-5120 / *Fax: 755-8842*
Tax Assessor-Collector	Ann H. Bennett ....274-8002 / *Fax: 274-2509*
Sheriff	Edward Gonzalez ....755-6044 / *Fax: 755-6228*
County Auditor	Mike Post 832 927-4560
Chief Appraiser	Roland Altinger ....812-5800 / *Fax: 957-5210*
County Commissioner:	
Precinct 1	Rodney Ellis ....755-6111 / *Fax: 755-6114*
Precinct 2	Jack Morman ....755-6220 / *Fax: 755-8810*
Precinct 3	Steve Radack ....755-6306 / *Fax: 755-8928*
Precinct 4	R. Jack Cagle ....755-6444 / *Fax: 755-8801*
Justice of the Peace:	
Precinct 1, Pl. 1	Eric William Carter ....274-0695 / *Fax: 437-4998*
Precinct 1, Pl. 2	David Patronella ....274-0600 / *Fax: 755-8805*
Precinct 2, Pl. 1	JoAnn Delgado ....281 481-9630 / *Fax: 281 484-2869*
Precinct 2, Pl. 2	George Risner ....274-6100 / *Fax: 437-4346*
Precinct 3, Pl. 1	Joe Stephens ....274-0760 / *Fax: 451-8074*
Precinct 3, Pl. 2	Don Coffey ....281 427-7449 / *Fax: 281 428-7485*
Precinct 4, Pl. 1	Lincoln Goodwin ....274-6556 / *Fax: 437-4608*
Precinct 4, Pl. 2	Laryssa Korduba ....274-2451 / *Fax: 281 274-2451*
Precinct 5, Pl. 1	Russ Ridgway 661-2276
Precinct 5, Pl. 2	Jeff Williams ....274-0800 / *Fax: 281 463-1059*
Precinct 6, Pl. 1	Richard Vara ....274-3985 / *Fax: 832 927-0007*
Precinct 6, Pl. 2	Armando Rodriguez ....921-6141 / *Fax: 921-1408*
Precinct 7, Pl. 1	Hilary H. Green 747-3553
Precinct 7, Pl. 2	Zinetta Burney ....274-0700 / *Fax: 437-4282*
Precinct 8, Pl. 1	Holly Williamson ....281 479-6900 / *Fax: 281 479-1407*
Precinct 8, Pl. 2	Louie Ditta ....281 488-8780 / *Fax: 713 437-4586*
Constable:	
Precinct 1	Alan Rosen ....755-5200 / *Fax: 755-3484*
Precinct 2	Chris Diaz ....477-2766 / *Fax: 477-5348*
Precinct 3	Sherman Eagleton ....281 427-4792 / *Fax: 281 457-1153*
Precinct 4	Mark Herman ....281 401-6205 / *Fax: 281 401-6287*
Precinct 5	Ted Heap ....281 492-3500 / *Fax: 281 398-5237*
Precinct 6	Silvia Trevino ....274-3400 / *Fax: 921-2334*
Precinct 7	May Walker ....643-6118 / *Fax: 643-3428*
Precinct 8	Phil Sandlin ....281 479-2525 / *Fax: 281 930-0494*

HARRISON COUNTY

Population: 68,636
County Seat:
  Marshall 75670

#1 Peter Whetstone Square, Room 214
903 935-8401 / *Fax: 903 935-4853*
www.harrisoncountytexas.org

County Judge	Hugh P. Taylor	935-8401 / *Fax: 935-4853*
Criminal District Attorney	Coke Solomon	935-8408 / *Fax: 938-9312*
District Clerk	Sherri Griffis	935-8409 / *Fax: 927-1918*
County Clerk	Patsy Cox	935-8403 / *Fax: 935-4877*
County Treasurer	Jamie Marie Noland	935-8404 / *Fax: 938-2693*
Tax Assessor-Collector	Veronica King	935-8411 / *Fax: 935-5564*
Sheriff	Tom McCool	923-4000 / *Fax: 935-4884*
County Auditor	Becky Haynes	935-8405 / *Fax: 923-8372*
Chief Appraiser	Robert Lisman	935-1991 / *Fax: 935-5648*
Elections Official	Mike McMurry	935-4822 / *Fax: 938-1509*
County Commissioner:		
Precinct 1	William Hatfield	935-8402 / *Fax: 935-4813*
Precinct 2	Zephaniah Timmins	935-8402 / *Fax: 935-4813*
Precinct 3	Phillip G. Mauldin	935-8402 / *Fax: 935-4813*
Precinct 4	Jay Ebarb	935-8402 / *Fax: 935-4813*
Justice of the Peace:		
Precinct 1	Megan Pinson	687-2370 / *Fax: 687-4374*
Precinct 2	Clarice "Brenda" Watkins	923-4009 / *Fax: 935-4866*
Precinct 3	Mike Smith	668-2050 / *Fax: 668-2979*
Precinct 4	Nancy George	923-4011 / *Fax: 927-1826*
Constable:		
Precinct 1	John C. Hickey, Jr.	687-2830 / *Fax: 687-4374*
Precinct 2	Brant Moore	923-4015
Precinct 3	Jim Weatherall	668-3611 / *Fax: 668-2979*
Precinct 4	Darryl Griffin	923-4013 / *Fax: 935-4813*

HARTLEY COUNTY

Population: 6,162
County Seat:
  Channing 79018

P. O. Box G - County Courthouse, 900 Main
806 235-3442 / *Fax: 806 635-5133*
www.co.hartley.tx.us

County Judge	Ronnie Gordon	235-3442 / *Fax: 635-5133*
District Attorney, 69th Dist.	David M. Green	935-5654 / *Fax: 934-2155*
County Attorney	Robert Elliott	235-2316 / *Fax: 635-5133*
District & County Clerk	Melissa Mead	235-3582 / *Fax: 235-2316*
County Treasurer	Dinkie Parman	235-3572 / *Fax: 635-5133*
Tax Assessor-Collector	Franky Scott	235-3142 / *Fax: 235-2003*
Sheriff	Franky Scott	235-3142 / *Fax: 235-2003*
Chief Appraiser	P. Jan Lowry	365-4515 / *Fax: 365-4582*
County Commissioner:		
Precinct 1	David Vincent	365-4466 / *Fax: 635-5133*
Precinct 2	David Ford	935-3259
Precinct 3	Chad Hicks	244-0820 / *Fax: 635-5133*
Precinct 4	Robert "Butch" Owens	244-3490 / *Fax: 635-5133*
Justice of the Peace:	Beth Moore	244-2939 / *Fax: 244-2299*

HASKELL COUNTY

Population: 5,678
County Seat:
  Haskell 79521

County Courthouse, 1 Avenue D
940 864-2851 / *Fax: 940 864-5722*
www.co.haskell.tx.us

County Judge	David C. Davis	.864-2851 / *Fax: 864-5722*
District Attorney, 39th Dist.	Mike Fouts	.864-2072 / *Fax: 864-3364*
County Attorney	Kristen L. Fouts	.864-2066 / *Fax: 864-5616*
District Clerk	Debbie Gressett	.864-2030 / *Fax: 864-5616*
County Clerk	Belia Abilia	.864-2451 / *Fax: 864-6164*
County Treasurer	Janis McDaniel	.864-3448 / *Fax: 864-6164*
Tax Assessor-Collector	Connie Benton	.864-2181 / *Fax: 864-6164*
Sheriff	Winston Stephens	.864-2345 / *Fax: 864-3370*
Chief Appraiser	Leah Robertson	.864-3805 / *Fax: 864-3075*
County Commissioner:		
Precinct 1	Bill Hester	.207-1336 / *Fax: 864-5722*
Precinct 2	Elmer Adams	.256-1566 / *Fax: 864-5722*
Precinct 3	Kenny Thompson	.325 370-4046 / *Fax: 864-5722*
Precinct 4	Neal Kreger	.256-3144 / *Fax: 864-5722*
Justice of the Peace:	Lynn Dodson	.864-2903 / *Fax: 864-6164*
Constable:		
Precinct 1	Kim Bassett	.864-2851 / *Fax: 864-6164*

HAYS COUNTY

Population: 199,344
County Seat:
  San Marcos 78666

712 South Stagecoach Trail
512 393-7779
www.co.hays.tx.us/

County Judge	Bert Cobb, M.D.	393-2205 / *Fax: 392-6500*
Criminal District Attorney	Wes Mau	393-7600 / *Fax: 393-7619*
District Clerk	Beverly Crumley	393-7660 / *Fax: 393-7674*
County Clerk	Liz Q. Gonzalez	393-7738 / *Fax: 393-7735*
County Treasurer	Michele Tuttle	393-2236 / *Fax: 393-2248*
Tax Assessor-Collector	Luanne Caraway	393-5545 / *Fax: 393-5547*
Sheriff	Gary Cutler	393-7808 / *Fax: 393-7879*
County Auditor	Marisol Villarreal-Alonzo, CPA	393-2283 / *Fax: 393-2248*
Chief Appraiser	David Valle	268-2522
Elections Official	Jennifer Anderson	393-7309 / *Fax: 393-2248*
County Commissioner:		
Precinct 1	Debbie Gonzales Ingalsbe	393-2243
Precinct 2	Mark Jones	262-2091 / *Fax: 268-1250*
Precinct 3	Lon Shell	847-3159 / *Fax: 847-7352*
Precinct 4	Ray Whisenant	858-7268 / *Fax: 858-2655*
Justice of the Peace:		
Precinct 1, Pl. 1	Jo Anne Prado	393-7871 / *Fax: 393-7641*
Precinct 1, Pl. 2	Maggie Hernandez Moreno	393-7871 / *Fax: 393-7641*
Precinct 2	Beth Smith	268-3151 / *Fax: 268-4901*
Precinct 3	Andrew Cable	847-2000
Precinct 4	Terry Kyle	858-7446 / *Fax: 858-4799*
Precinct 5	Scott J. Cary	295-2700 / *Fax: 312-9384*
Constable:		
Precinct 1	David L. Peterson	393-7730 / *Fax: 393-7720*
Precinct 2	Michael Torres	268-0785 / *Fax: 268-4901*
Precinct 3	Ray Helm	847-5532 / *Fax: 847-7352*
Precinct 4	Ron E. Hood	858-7605 / *Fax: 858-4799*
Precinct 5	John Ellen	295-3030 / *Fax: 295-4213*

HEMPHILL COUNTY

Population: 4,208
County Seat:
  Canadian 79014

400 Main Street, Suite 200
806 323-6521
www.co.hemphill.tx.us

County Judge	George Briant	323-6521 / *Fax: 323-5271*
District Attorney, 31st Dist.	Franklin McDonough	669-8035 / *Fax: 669-8050*
County Attorney	Kyle Miller	323-5521 / *Fax: 323-8602*
District & County Clerk	Lisa Johnson	323-6212 / *Fax: 323-8125*
County Treasurer	Kay Smallwood	323-6671 / *Fax: 323-8491*
Tax Assessor-Collector	Debbie Ford	323-6661 / *Fax: 323-9745*
Sheriff	Nathan Lewis	323-5324 / *Fax: 323-5260*
Chief Appraiser	Pam Scates	323-8022 / *Fax: 323-8430*
County Commissioner:		
Precinct 1	Dawn E. Webb	217-1638
Precinct 2	Tim Alexander	323-8853
Precinct 3	Curt McPherson	670-0382 / *Fax: 375-2369*
Precinct 4	Nicholas Thomas	323-2601 / *Fax: 323-9113*
Justice of the Peace:	Larry Dunnam	323-5123 / *Fax: 323-8517*

HENDERSON COUNTY

Population: 81,179
County Seat:
  Athens 75751

125 N. Prairieville St., Room 100
903 675-6120 / *Fax: 903 675-6190*
www.henderson-county.com

County Judge	Richard Sanders	675-6120 / *Fax: 675-6190*
District Attorney, 173rd Dist.	Mark W. Hall	675-6100 / *Fax: 675-6196*
County Attorney	Clint Davis	675-6112 / *Fax: 675-6192*
District Clerk	Betty Herriage	675-6115 / *Fax: 677-7274*
County Clerk	Mary Margaret Wright	675-6140 / *Fax: 675-6105*
County Treasurer	Michael Bynum	675-6119 / *Fax: 677-7297*
Tax Assessor-Collector	Peggy Goodall	675-6134 / *Fax: 670-7230*
Sheriff	Botie Hillhouse	675-9275 / *Fax: 677-6344*
County Auditor	Ann Marie Lee	675-6145 / *Fax: 675-7298*
Chief Appraiser	Bill Jackson	675-9296 / *Fax: 675-4223*
Elections Official	Denise Hernandez	675-6149 / *Fax: 670-1061*

County Commissioner:
Precinct 1	Ken Hayes	489-1665 / *Fax: 489-1447*
Precinct 2	Wade McKinney	425-2611 / *Fax: 425-0121*
Precinct 3	Charles "Chuck" McHam	469-3430 / *Fax: 469-3096*
Precinct 4	Ken Geeslin	676-4054 / *Fax: 676-4064*

Justice of the Peace:
Precinct 1	Randy Daniel	677-6373 / *Fax: 677-6376*
Precinct 2	Kevin Pollock	432-4334 / *Fax: 432-2517*
Precinct 3	James A. "Tony" Duncan	849-2222 / *Fax: 849-6111*
Precinct 4	Milton Adams	876-2711 / *Fax: 876-2867*
Precinct 5	Belinda Brownlow	489-0474 / *Fax: 489-1454*

Constable:
Precinct 1	Kay Langford	677-6373 / *Fax: 677-6376*
Precinct 2	Mitch Baker	432-4237 / *Fax: 432-2517*
Precinct 3	David Grubbs	849-6699 / *Fax: 849-6111*
Precinct 4	John Floyd	876-3635 / *Fax: 876-2867*
Precinct 5	Brad Miers	489-2740 / *Fax: 489-2743*

COUNTY SECTION

HIDALGO COUNTY

Population: 848,037
County Seat:
  Edinburg 78539

P.O. Box 1356
956 318-2600 / *Fax: 956 318-2699*
www.hidalgocounty.us

County Judge	Ramon Garcia	318-2600 / *Fax: 318-2699*
Criminal District Attorney	Ricardo Rodriguez	318-2300 / *Fax: 381-5127*
District Clerk	Laura Hinojosa	318-2200 / *Fax: 318-2251*
County Clerk	Arturo Guajardo, Jr.	318-2100 / *Fax: 318-2105*
County Treasurer	Norma G. Garcia	318-2506 / *Fax: 318-2507*
Tax Assessor-Collector	Pablo "Paul" Villarreal, Jr.	318-2157 / *Fax: 318-2733*
Sheriff	J.E. "Eddie" Guerra	383-8114 / *Fax: 383-6179*
County Auditor	Maria Arcilla "Arcy" Duran	318-2511 / *Fax: 318-2577*
Chief Appraiser	Rolando Garza	381-8466 / *Fax: 289-2120*
Elections Official	Yvonne Ramon	318-2570 / *Fax: 393-2039*
County Commissioner:		
Precinct 1	David Fuentes	968-8733 / *Fax: 969-1417*
Precinct 2	Eduardo "Eddie" Cantu	787-1891 / *Fax: 787-4683*
Precinct 3	Joe Flores	585-4509 / *Fax: 205-7009*
Precinct 4	Joseph Palacios	383-3112 / *Fax: 381-5905*
Justice of the Peace:		
Precinct 1, Pl. 1	Gilbert Saenz	447-3995 / *Fax: 447-9522*
Precinct 1, Pl. 2	Jesus Morales	968-0707 / *Fax: 968-8827*
Precinct 2, Pl. 1	Robert "Bobby" Contreras	784-3540 / *Fax: 784-3541*
Precinct 2, Pl. 2	Jaime Munoz	787-1986 / *Fax: 292-7052*
Precinct 3, Pl. 1	Luis J. Garza	519-8422 / *Fax: 519-1796*
Precinct 3, Pl. 2	Marcos Ochoa	581-2124 / *Fax: 581-2134*
Precinct 4, Pl. 1	Charlie Espinoza	380-4473 / *Fax: 380-4029*
Precinct 4, Pl. 2	Homero A. Jasso	292-7015 / *Fax: 383-7430*
Precinct 5, Pl. 5	Position Vacant	
Constable:		
Precinct 1	Celestino Avila	447-3775 / *Fax: 447-8614*
Precinct 2	Martin Cantu	784-3510 / *Fax: 784-8687*
Precinct 3	Lazaro "Larry" Gallardo, Jr.	581-6800 / *Fax: 519-4245*
Precinct 4	Atanacio "JR" Gaitan	383-8560 / *Fax: 383-8565*
Precinct 5	Danny Marichalar	

HILL COUNTY

Population: 35,621
County Seat:
  Hillsboro 76645

P. O. Box 457
254 582-4020 / *Fax: 254 582-4028*
www.co.hill.tx.us

County Judge	Justin Lewis ....582-4020 / *Fax: 582-4028*
District Attorney, 66th Dist.	Mark Pratt ....582-4070 / *Fax: 582-4036*
County Attorney	David Holmes ....582-4047 / *Fax: 582-4013*
District Clerk	Angelia Orr ....582-4042 / *Fax: 582-4035*
County Clerk	Nicole Tanner ....582-4030 / *Fax: 582-4003*
County Treasurer	Rhonda Burkhart ....582-4050 / *Fax: 582-4019*
Tax Assessor-Collector	Krystal "Krissi" Hightower ....582-4000 / *Fax: 582-4001*
Sheriff	Rodney Watson ....582-5313 / *Fax: 582-3848*
County Auditor	Susan Swilling ....582-4060 / *Fax: 582-4033*
Chief Appraiser	Mike McKibben 582-2508
Elections Official	Aaron Torres ....582-4072 / *Fax: 582-4073*
County Commissioner:	
Precinct 1	Andrew Montgomery ....874-5435 / *Fax: 582-4028*
Precinct 2	Larry Crumpton ....694-3787 / *Fax: 582-4028*
Precinct 3	Scotty Hawkins ....623-4236 / *Fax: 582-4028*
Precinct 4	Martin Lake ....687-2711 / *Fax: 582-4028*
Justice of the Peace:	
Precinct 1	Martis Ward ....694-3140 / *Fax: 694-5503*
Precinct 2	Shane Brassell ....582-4025 / *Fax: 582-4005*
Precinct 3	Brad Henley 530-1034
Precinct 4	Charles Jones 687-2424
Constable:	
Precinct 1	Bill Wilkins 337-0245
Precinct 2	Justin Girsh 582-4040
Precinct 3	Larry Armstrong 582-4040
Precinct 4	Collin Yeaman 337-0245

HOCKLEY COUNTY

Population: 23,612
County Seat:
  Levelland 79336

802 Houston St., Suite 101
806 894-6856 / *Fax: 806 894-6820*
www.co.hockley.tx.us

County Judge	Sharla Baldridge	.894-6856 / *Fax: 894-6820*
District Attorney, 286th Dist.	Christopher Dennis	.894-3130 / *Fax: 894-3543*
County Attorney	Anna Hord	.894-5455 / *Fax: 894-3543*
District Clerk	Dennis Price	.894-8527 / *Fax: 894-3891*
County Clerk	Irene Gonzalez Gumula	.894-3185 / *Fax: 894-6917*
County Treasurer	Denise Bohannon	.894-3718 / *Fax: 894-6917*
Tax Assessor-Collector	Debra Bramlett	.894-4938 / *Fax: 894-6917*
Sheriff	Ray Scifres	.894-3126 / *Fax: 894-3161*
County Auditor	Linda Barnette	.894-6070 / *Fax: 894-6917*
Chief Appraiser	Gregg Kelly	.894-9654 / *Fax: 894-9671*
Elections Official	Cheryl Smart	.894-4938 / *Fax: 894-1102*
County Commissioner:		
Precinct 1	Curtis Thrash	.894-4092 / *Fax: 894-6820*
Precinct 2	Larry R. Carter	.894-4092 / *Fax: 894-6820*
Precinct 3	J. L. "Whitey" Barnett	.894-4092 / *Fax: 894-6820*
Precinct 4	Tommy Clevenger	.894-4092 / *Fax: 894-6820*
Justice of the Peace:		
Precinct 1	Sue Coker	.559-7732
Precinct 2	Linda Canon	.229-2022
Precinct 4	Larry Wood	.470-1833
Precinct 5	Brenda Nock	.894-4104 / *Fax: 894-1101*
Constable:		
Precinct 1	Kenny Greenlee	.562-3551
Precinct 2	Robert L. Dalton	.229-6236 / *Fax: 229-6236*
Precinct 4	Jennifer Kinney	.299-1106
Precinct 5	Lance Scott	.441-0497 / *Fax: 894-6917*

HOOD COUNTY

Population: 56,799
County Seat:
  Granbury 76048

1200 W. Pearl Street
817 579-3200 / *Fax: 817 579-3213*
www.co.hood.tx.us

County Judge	Darrell Cockerham	.579-3200 / *Fax: 579-3213*
District Attorney, 355th Dist.	Rob Christian	.579-3245 / *Fax: 579-3247*
County Attorney	Matt Mills	.579-3216 / *Fax: 579-3218*
District Clerk	Tonna T. Hitt	.579-3236 / *Fax: 579-3239*
County Clerk	Katie Lang	.579-3222 / *Fax: 408-3459*
County Treasurer	Kathy Davis	.579-3208 / *Fax: 579-3254*
Tax Assessor-Collector	Teresa McCoy	.579-3295 / *Fax: 579-9303*
Sheriff	Roger Deeds	.579-3316 / *Fax: 408-2794*
County Auditor	Becky Kidd	.579-3210 / *Fax: 326-5520*
Chief Appraiser	Greg Stewart	.573-2471 / *Fax: 573-6451*
Elections Official	Jenise "Crickett" Miller	.408-2525 / *Fax: 408-2592*
County Commissioner:		
Precinct 1	James Deaver	.579-3300 / *Fax: 579-0396*
Precinct 2	Lloyd "Butch" Barton	.579-3300 / *Fax: 579-0396*
Precinct 3	Bruce White	.579-3300 / *Fax: 579-0396*
Precinct 4	Steve Berry	.579-3300 / *Fax: 579-0396*

Justice of the Peace:
  Precinct 1   Roger Howell . . . . .408-2660 / *Fax: 408-2661*
  Precinct 2   Martin Castillo . . . . .579-3290 / *Fax: 579-3345*
  Precinct 3   Kathryn Gwinn . . . . .579-3202 / *Fax: 326-6071*
  Precinct 4   Danny Tuggle . . . . .408-2530 / *Fax: 573-3836*
Constable:
  Precinct 1   Delton Thrasher . . . . .408-2602 / *Fax: 408-2603*
  Precinct 2   DeWayne Hart . . . . .579-3291 / *Fax: 408-3466*
  Precinct 3   Kathy Jividen . . . . .408-2560 / *Fax: 326-8263*
  Precinct 4   Chad Jordan . . . . .579-3204 / *Fax: 573-3426*

HOPKINS COUNTY

Population: 36,595
County Seat:
  Sulphur Springs 75482

118 Church Street
903 438-4081 / *Fax: 903 438-4007*
www.hopkinscountytx.org

County Judge   Robert Newsom . . . . .438-4006 / *Fax: 438-4007*
District Attorney, 8th Dist.   Will Ramsay 885-0641
County Attorney   Dusty Hyde Rabe 438-4017
District Clerk   Cheryl Fulcher 438-4081
County Clerk   Debbie Shirley . . . . .438-4074 / *Fax: 438-4110*
County Treasurer   Jim Thompson 438-4003
Tax Assessor-Collector   Debbie Jenkins 438-4063
Sheriff   Lewis Tatum . . . . .438-4040 / *Fax: 438-4062*
County Auditor   Shannah Walker 438-4011
Chief Appraiser   Cathy Singleton . . . . .885-2173 / *Fax: 885-2175*
County Commissioner:
  Precinct 1   Mickey Earl Barker 438-4031
  Precinct 2   Mike Odell 438-4032
  Precinct 3   Wade Bartley 438-4033
  Precinct 4   Danny Evans 438-4034
Justice of the Peace:
  Precinct 1   B.J. Teer 438-4026
  Precinct 2   Brad Cummings 438-4036
Constable:
  Precinct 1   Norman Colyer 438-4001
  Precinct 2   Bill Allan 438-4002

HOUSTON COUNTY

Population: 23,131
County Seat:
  Crockett 75835

P.O. Box 370 - 401 E. Goliad
936 544-3255 / *Fax: 936 544-8053*
www.co.houston.tx.us

County Judge	Jim Lovell	.544-3255 / *Fax: 544-8053*
District Attorney, 349th Dist.	Donna Gordon Kaspar	.544-3255 / *Fax: 544-2790*
County Attorney	Daphne Session	.544-3255 / *Fax: 544-9811*
District Clerk	Carolyn Rains	.544-3255 / *Fax: 544-9523*
County Clerk	Bridget Lamb	.544-3255 / *Fax: 544-1954*
County Treasurer	Dina Herrera	.544-3255 / *Fax: 546-5519*
Tax Assessor-Collector	Danette Millican	.544-3255 / *Fax: 544-2711*
Sheriff	Darrel Bobbitt	.544-2862 / *Fax: 544-8061*
County Auditor	Melissa Mosley, CPM	.544-3255 / *Fax: 544-3260*
Chief Appraiser	Carey Minter	.544-9655 / *Fax: 544-8213*
County Commissioner:		
Precinct 1	Gary Lovell	.687-2381 / *Fax: 544-8053*
Precinct 2	Willie E. Kitchen	.544-3255 / *Fax: 544-8053*
Precinct 3	Pat Perry	.636-7439 / *Fax: 544-8053*
Precinct 4	Kennon Kellum	.655-3255 / *Fax: 544-8053*
Justice of the Peace:		
Precinct 1	Clyde Black	.544-2564 / *Fax: 544-1460*
Precinct 2	Ronnie Jordan	.544-9561 / *Fax: 544-1460*
Constable:		
Precinct 1	Morris Luker	.544-2481 / *Fax: 544-1460*
Precinct 2	Kenneth "Red" Smith	.545-0445 / *Fax: 544-1460*

HOWARD COUNTY

Population: 37,157
County Seat:
  Big Spring 79720

300 Main, Room 207
432 264-2202 / *Fax: 432 264-2206*
www.co.howard.tx.us

County Judge	Kathryn Wiseman	.264-2202 / *Fax: 264-2206*
District Attorney, 118th Dist.	Hardy L. Wilkerson	.264-2220 / *Fax: 264-2222*
County Attorney	Josh Hamby	.264-2205 / *Fax: 264-2206*
District Clerk	Colleen Barton	.264-2223 / *Fax: 264-2256*
County Clerk	Brent Zitterkopf	.264-2213 / *Fax: 264-2215*
County Treasurer	Sharon Adams	.264-2218 / *Fax: 264-0675*
Tax Assessor-Collector	Tiffany Sayles	.264-2232 / *Fax: 264-2282*
Sheriff	Stan Parker	.264-2231 / *Fax: 264-9117*
County Auditor	Jackie Olson	.264-2210 / *Fax: 264-2201*
Chief Appraiser	Lisa Reyes	.263-8301 / *Fax: 263-8303*
Elections Official	Jodi Duck	.264-2273 / *Fax: 264-2275*
County Commissioner:		
Precinct 1	Oscar Garcia	.213-2040 / *Fax: 264-2206*
Precinct 2	Craig Bailey	.816-5270 / *Fax: 264-2206*
Precinct 3	Jimmie Long	.264-2202 / *Fax: 264-2201*
Precinct 4	John Cline	.263-7158 / *Fax: 264-2206*

Justice of the Peace:
Precinct 1, Pl. 1   Bennie Green . . . . .264-2226 / *Fax: 264-2227*
Precinct 1, Pl. 2   Robert Fitzgibbons . . . . .264-2228 / *Fax: 264-2268*
Precinct 2   Connie Shaw . . . . .394-4000 / *Fax: 394-4005*
Constable:
Precinct 1   Kneel Stallings . . . . .264-2244 / *Fax: 264-5355*

HUDSPETH COUNTY

Population: 3,404   P. O. Box 68
County Seat: 915 369-2321 / *Fax: 915 369-2361*
Sierra Blanca 79851

COUNTY SECTION

County Judge   Mike Doyal .369-2321 / *Fax: 369-2361*
District Attorney, 34th Dist.   Jaime Esparza . . . . .546-2059 / *Fax: 533-5520*
County Attorney   C. R. "Kit" Bramblett . . . . .877-4173 / *Fax: 877-7146*
District & County Clerk   Virginia Doyal . . . . .369-2301 / *Fax: 369-0055*
County Treasurer   Gwen Wilbanks . . . . .369-3511 / *Fax: 369-0055*
Tax Assessor-Collector   Patricia Rose . . . . .369-2331 / *Fax: 369-3005*
Sheriff   Arvin West . . . . .369-2161 / *Fax: 369-2126*
County Auditor   Yolanda Esparza . . . . .369-4147 / *Fax: 369-2407*
Chief Appraiser   Adolfo M. Ramirez . . . . .369-4118 / *Fax: 369-3621*
County Commissioner:
Precinct 1   Wayne West . . . . .432 940-6593 / *Fax: 369-3039*
Precinct 2   Manuel Galindo, Jr. . . . . .769-3852 / *Fax: 769-9331*
Precinct 3   Jim Ed Miller . . . . .769-3840 / *Fax: 769-3490*
Precinct 4   Larry Brewton . . . . .964-2666 / *Fax: 964-2275*
Justice of the Peace:
Precinct 1   Julie Sanchez . . . . .369-4141 / *Fax: 369-2721*
Precinct 2   Margie Aquilar . . . . .769-3887 / *Fax: 769-3450*
Precinct 3   Nikol Endres . . . . .988-2457 / *Fax: 988-2457*
Precinct 4   Davi Gardner . . . . .964-2678 / *Fax: 964-2394*
Constable:
Precinct 1   John Schuller . . . . .986-2558 / *Fax: 369-3005*
Precinct 2   Johnny Schuller 543-0206
Precinct 3   Tony Endres . . . . .857-6467 / *Fax: 592-1043*
Precinct 4   George Dean . . . . .227-1038 / *Fax: 369-2361*

HUNT COUNTY

Population: 90,231
County Seat:
  Greenville 75403

2507 Lee Street, P. O. Box 1097
903 408-4100 / *Fax: 903 453-6935*
www.huntcounty.net

County Judge	John Horn	.408-4146 / *Fax: 408-4299*
District Attorney, 196th Dist.	Noble D. Walker, Jr.	.408-4180 / *Fax: 408-4296*
County Attorney	Joel Littlefield	.408-4112 / *Fax: 408-4297*
District Clerk	Stacey Landrum	.408-4172 / *Fax: 408-4289*
County Clerk	Jennifer Lindenzweig	.408-4130 / *Fax: 408-4287*
County Treasurer	Delores Shelton	.408-4171 / *Fax: 408-4285*
Tax Assessor-Collector	Randy Wineinger	.408-4000 / *Fax: 455-3202*
Sheriff	Randy Meeks	.453-6800 / *Fax: 453-6822*
County Auditor	Tammi Byrd	.408-4120 / *Fax: 408-4280*
Chief Appraiser	Brent South	.454-3510
Elections Official	Almina D. Cook	.454-5467 / *Fax: 454-7905*
County Commissioner:		
Precinct 1	Eric Evans	.408-4195 / *Fax: 408-4298*
Precinct 2	Tod McMahan	.408-4195 / *Fax: 408-4298*
Precinct 3	Phillip Martin	.408-4195 / *Fax: 408-4298*
Precinct 4	Jim Latham	.408-4195 / *Fax: 408-4298*
Justice of the Peace:		
Precinct 1, Pl. 1	Wayne Money	.453-6922
Precinct 1, Pl. 2	Sheila Linden	.453-6930
Precinct 2	Jennifer Reeves	.886-6726
Precinct 3	Aaron Williams	.496-7974
Precinct 4	David McNabb	.356-2904 / *Fax: 356-4737*
Constable:		
Precinct 1	Terry Jones	.453-6891 / *Fax: 453-6965*
Precinct 2	Wayne "Doc" Pierce	.886-7937 / *Fax: 886-8387*
Precinct 3	Don Morrison	.450-6261
Precinct 4	Kent Layton	.356-4543

HUTCHINSON COUNTY

Population: 21,382
County Seat:
  Stinnett 79083

P. O. Box 790
806 878-4000 / *Fax: 806 878-4048*
www.co.hutchinson.tx.us/

County Judge	Cindy Irwin	.878-4000 / *Fax: 878-4048*
District Attorney, 84th Dist.	Mark Snider	.878-4036 / *Fax: 878-4038*
County Attorney	Michael D. Milner	.273-0134 / *Fax: 273-0123*
District Clerk	Robin Stroud	.878-4017 / *Fax: 878-4042*
County Clerk	Jan Barnes	.878-4002 / *Fax: 878-3497*
County Treasurer	Kathy Sargent	.878-4010 / *Fax: 878-4029*
Tax Assessor-Collector	Carrie D. Kimmell	.878-4005 / *Fax: 878-4008*
Sheriff	Kirk A. Coker	.274-6343 / *Fax: 273-0117*
County Auditor	Mark Dill	.878-4015 / *Fax: 878-4040*
Chief Appraiser	Joe Raper	.274-2294 / *Fax: 273-3400*
County Commissioner:		
Precinct 1	Larry Coffman	.273-0135
Precinct 2	Jerry D. Hefner	.681-1559 / *Fax: 878-4048*
Precinct 3	S. T. "Red" Isbell, Jr.	.878-3902
Precinct 4	Eddie Whittington	.672-3690
Justice of the Peace:		
Precinct 1	Shila Hart	.878-4024 / *Fax: 878-3036*
Precinct 2	Yadi Rodriguez	.273-0103 / *Fax: 273-0112*
Constable:		
Precinct 1	Kendell McWilliams	.878-4030 / *Fax: 878-3036*
Precinct 2	Ron Cromer	.273-0113 / *Fax: 273-0112*

IRION COUNTY

Population: 1,636
County Seat:
  Mertzon 76941

P. O. Box 770 - 209 North Park View
325 835-4361 / *Fax: 325 835-2008*
www.co.irion.tx.us

County Judge	Tom Aiken	.835-4361 / *Fax: 835-2008*
District Attorney, 51st Dist.	Allison Palmer	.659-6583 / *Fax: 947-3562*
County Attorney	James F. Ridge, Jr.	.835-7101 / *Fax: 835-2276*
District & County Clerk	Molly Criner	.835-2421 / *Fax: 835-7941*
County Treasurer	Carolyn Huelster	.835-4111 / *Fax: 835-7047*
Tax Assessor-Collector	Joyce Gray	.835-7771 / *Fax: 835-2195*
Sheriff	W. A. Estes	.835-2551 / *Fax: 835-7024*
Chief Appraiser	Byron Bitner	.835-3551 / *Fax: 835-2018*
County Commissioner:		
Precinct 1	Tia Paxton	.650-3509 / *Fax: 835-2008*
Precinct 2	Jeff Davidson	.835-7690 / *Fax: 835-2008*
Precinct 3	John Nanny	.876-5108 / *Fax: 835-2008*
Precinct 4	Beaver McManus	.949-6998 / *Fax: 835-2008*
Justice of the Peace:		
Precinct 1	Donna Smith	.835-4141 / *Fax: 632-2940*

COUNTY SECTION

JACK COUNTY

Population: 9,291
County Seat:
 Jacksboro 76458

100 N. Main Street, Suite 206
940 567-2241 / *Fax: 940 567-5502*
www.jackcounty.org

County Judge	Mitchell G. Davenport	.567-2241 / *Fax: 567-5502*
District Attorney, 271st Dist.	Greg Lowery	.567-6261 / *Fax: 567-2696*
County Attorney	Brad Dixon	.567-3321 / *Fax: 567-6306*
District Clerk	Tracie Pippin	.567-2141 / *Fax: 567-2696*
County Clerk	Vanessa James	.567-2111 / *Fax: 567-6441*
County Treasurer	Kim Gibby	.567-2251 / *Fax: 567-5029*
Tax Assessor-Collector	Sharon Robinson	.567-2352 / *Fax: 567-5322*
Sheriff	Tom Spurlock	.567-2161 / *Fax: 567-2144*
County Auditor	Lisa Perry	.567-2663 / *Fax: 567-5978*
Chief Appraiser	Kathy Conner	.567-6301 / *Fax: 567-3640*
County Commissioner:		
Precinct 1	John R. Berry	.567-5318
Precinct 2	James L. Brock	.798-2781
Precinct 3	Henry D. Birdwell, Jr.	.567-3981
Precinct 4	Terry Ward	.567-2971
Justice of the Peace:		
Precinct 1	Stacy Spurlock	.567-2001 / *Fax: 567-5029*
Constable:		
Precinct 1	Clyde E. Watson, Sr.	.567-3194

JACKSON COUNTY

Population: 14,674
County Seat:
 Edna 77957

115 W. Main, Room 207
361 782-2352 / *Fax: 361 782-5253*
www.co.jackson.tx.us

County Judge	Dennis Simons	.782-2352 / *Fax: 782-5253*
Criminal District Attorney	Pam Guenther	.782-7170 / *Fax: 782-3730*
District Clerk	Sharon Mathis	.782-3812 / *Fax: 782-3056*
County Clerk	Barbara Earl	.782-3563 / *Fax: 782-3132*
County Treasurer	Mary Horton	.782-3402 / *Fax: 782-0856*
Tax Assessor-Collector	Monica Hyek Foster	.782-3473 / *Fax: 782-3645*
Sheriff	A.J. "Andy" Louderback	.782-3371 / *Fax: 782-7574*
County Auditor	Michelle Darilek	.782-2072 / *Fax: 782-0856*
Chief Appraiser	Damon Moore	.782-7115 / *Fax: 782-0369*
County Commissioner:		
Precinct 1	Wayne Hunt	.782-2804 / *Fax: 782-5253*
Precinct 2	Wayne Bubela	.771-2475 / *Fax: 771-2467*
Precinct 3	Johnny E. Belicek	.782-2033 / *Fax: 782-3707*
Precinct 4	Dennis Karl	.872-2345 / *Fax: 872-2345*
Justice of the Peace:		
Precinct 1	Darren Stancik	.782-5259 / *Fax: 782-7039*
Precinct 2	Cynthia Poulton	.771-2249 / *Fax: 771-2278*
Constable:		
Precinct 1	J.W. "Cisco" Marek	.781-2441 / *Fax: 782-7574*
Precinct 2	Curt Gabrysch	.771-2248 / *Fax: 771-2778*

JASPER COUNTY

Population: 34,339
County Seat:
Jasper 75951

121 North Austin St., Room 106
409 384-2612 / *Fax: 409 384-9745*
www.co.jasper.tx.us

County Judge	Mark Allen	384-2612 / *Fax: 384-9745*
Criminal District Attorney	Steve Hollis	384-4362 / *Fax: 384-1309*
District Clerk	Kathy Kent	384-2721 / *Fax: 383-7501*
County Clerk	Debbie Newman	384-2632 / *Fax: 384-7198*
County Treasurer	Rene Kelley	384-2461 / *Fax: 489-1013*
Tax Assessor-Collector	Bobby Biscamp	384-4685 / *Fax: 384-8226*
Sheriff	Mitchel Newman	384-5417 / *Fax: 384-7016*
County Auditor	Renee Weaver	384-5212 / *Fax: 384-7346*
Chief Appraiser	Lori Barnett	384-2544 / *Fax: 384-7416*
County Commissioner:		
Precinct 1	Charles Shofner, Jr.	384-8112 / *Fax: 384-4744*
Precinct 2	Roy Parker	384-5343 / *Fax: 489-1215*
Precinct 3	Willie Stark	423-4791 / *Fax: 423-7467*
Precinct 4	Vance Moss	994-3711 / *Fax: 994-4205*
Justice of the Peace:		
Precinct 1	Ronald Billingsley	384-2958 / *Fax: 383-0184*
Precinct 2	Freddie Miller	384-4534 / *Fax: 383-1965*
Precinct 3	Mike Smith	423-2281 / *Fax: 423-4235*
Precinct 4	Daniel Whitten	994-2595 / *Fax: 994-2250*
Precinct 5	Brett Holloway	698-9335 / *Fax: 698-9314*
Precinct 6	Steve Conner	276-1440
Constable:		
Precinct 1	Jimmy W. Hensarling	224-1264
Precinct 2	Niles Nichols	382-2167
Precinct 3	Ronnie C. Hutchinson	423-2281
Precinct 4	Gene Hawthorne	994-2430
Precinct 5	Mike Poindexter	382-7866
Precinct 6	Joe Sterling	276-1440

JEFF DAVIS COUNTY

Population: 2,244
County Seat:
Fort Davis 79734

P. O. Box 836
432 426-3968 / *Fax: 432 426-2292*
www.co.jeff-davis.tx.us

County Judge	Jeannette M. Duer	426-3968 / *Fax: 426-2292*
District Attorney, 83rd Dist.	Sandy Wilson	837-0990 / *Fax: 837-0995*
County Attorney	Teresa Todd	426-4434 / *Fax: 426-4431*
District & County Clerk	Jennifer Wright	462-3251 / *Fax: 426-3760*
County Treasurer	Cecilia G. Davis	426-3242 / *Fax: 426-2940*
Tax Assessor-Collector	Bill Kitts	426-3213 / *Fax: 426-3937*
Sheriff	Bill Kitts	426-3213 / *Fax: 426-3937*
Chief Appraiser	Gary Zeitler	426-3210 / *Fax: 426-3437*
County Commissioner:		
Precinct 1	Jody Adams	
Precinct 2	Kerith Sproul	206 434-3018
Precinct 3	Curtis Evans	
Precinct 4	Albert Miller	467-2971 / *Fax: 426-2095*
Justice of the Peace:	Mary Ann Luedecke	426-3045 / *Fax: 426-2677*
Constable:	Clay Woods	426-4430 / *Fax: 426-2292*

JEFFERSON COUNTY

Population: 250,798
County Seat:
  Beaumont 77701

1149 Pearl St.
409 835-8400 / *Fax: 409 839-2311*
www.co.jefferson.tx.us/

County Judge	Jeff Branick	.835-8466 / *Fax: 839-2311*
Criminal District Attorney	Bob Wortham	.835-8550 / *Fax: 835-8573*
District Clerk	Jamie Smith	.835-8580 / *Fax: 835-8527*
County Clerk	Carolyn L. Guidry	.835-8475 / *Fax: 839-2394*
County Treasurer	Tim Funchess	.835-8509 / *Fax: 839-2347*
Tax Assessor-Collector	Allison N. Getz	.835-8516 / *Fax: 835-8589*
Sheriff	Zena Stephens	.835-8411 / *Fax: 784-5817*
County Auditor	Patrick Swain	.835-8500 / *Fax: 839-2369*
Chief Appraiser	Angela Bellard	.727-4611 / *Fax: 727-5621*
County Commissioner:		
Precinct 1	Eddie Arnold	.835-8442 / *Fax: 835-8628*
Precinct 2	Brent Weaver	.719-5950 / *Fax: 722-1916*
Precinct 3	Michael Sinegal	.983-8300 / *Fax: 983-8303*
Precinct 4	Everette Alfred	.835-8443 / *Fax: 784-5803*
Justice of the Peace:		
Precinct 1, Pl. 1	Kenneth W. Dollinger	.835-8522 / *Fax: 835-8523*
Precinct 1, Pl. 2	Nancy Beaulieu	.835-8457 / *Fax: 839-2393*
Precinct 2	Marc DeRouen	.983-8325 / *Fax: 989-3680*
Precinct 4	Ray S. Chesson	.434-5460 / *Fax: 794-1637*
Precinct 6	Ransom "Duce" Jones	.839-2333 / *Fax: 726-2504*
Precinct 7	Brad Burnett	.719-5900 / *Fax: 724-2148*
Precinct 8	Tom Gillam, III	.983-8330 / *Fax: 983-8320*
Constable:		
Precinct 1	Earl White	.835-8450 / *Fax: 839-2350*
Precinct 2	Christopher Bates	.983-8335 / *Fax: 983-8320*
Precinct 4	Bryan Werner	.434-5450 / *Fax: 794-3156*
Precinct 6	Dana A. Baker, Sr.	.839-2339 / *Fax: 726-2589*
Precinct 7	Robert "Bobby" Adams	.719-5990 / *Fax: 721-6017*
Precinct 8	Eddie J. Collins	.983-8311 / *Fax: 983-8303*

JIM HOGG COUNTY

Population: 5,177
County Seat:
  Hebbronville 78361

P. O. Box 729
361 527-3015 / *Fax: 361 527-5843*
co.jim-hogg.tx.us/

County Judge	Humberto Gonzalez	.527-3015
District Attorney, 229th Dist.	Omar Escobar	.527-4056 / *Fax: 527-4032*
County Attorney	Rodolfo Gutierrez	.527-3015 / *Fax: 527-3483*
District & County Clerk	Zonia G. Morales	.527-4031 / *Fax: 232-5875*
County Treasurer	Gloria "Gigi" Benavides	.527-3015 / *Fax: 288-8576*
Tax Assessor-Collector	Norma Liza Hinojosa	.527-3015 / *Fax: 288-1640*
Sheriff	Erasmo "Kiko" Alarcon, Jr.	.527-3015 / *Fax: 527-4310*
County Auditor	Marissa Garcia	.527-3015 / *Fax: 527-5436*
Chief Appraiser	Jorge Arellano, CPA	.527-4033 / *Fax: 527-4034*

County Commissioner:

Precinct 1	H.D. "Beto" Martinez	527-3015 / *Fax: 527-4393*
Precinct 2	Abelardo Alaniz	527-3015 / *Fax: 527-4393*
Precinct 3	Sandalio Ruiz	527-3015 / *Fax: 527-4393*
Precinct 4	Cynthia G. Betancourt	527-3015 / *Fax: 527-4393*

Justice of the Peace:

Precinct 1	Alma Rios Silguero	527-3015 / *Fax: 288-7031*
Precinct 2	Julia Huff	527-5830 / *Fax: 288-7031*
Precinct 3	Marissa M. Garza	527-5830 / *Fax: 288-7031*
Precinct 4	Lucia C. Dominguez	288-7031

Constable:

Precinct 1	Basilio Galvan	527-3015 / *Fax: 527-4310*
Precinct 2	Carlos Guerra	527-3015 / *Fax: 527-4310*
Precinct 3	Rene Molina	527-3015 / *Fax: 527-4310*
Precinct 4	Amando Garza	527-3015 / *Fax: 527-4310*

JIM WELLS COUNTY

Population: 40,004
County Seat:
 Alice 78332

200 N. Almond
361 668-5706 / *Fax: 361 668-8671*
www.co.jim-wells.tx.us

County Judge	Pedro "Pete" Trevino, Jr.	668-5706 / *Fax: 668-8671*
District Attorney, 79th Dist.	Carlos O. Garcia	668-5716 / *Fax: 668-9974*
County Attorney	Michael Guerra	668-5700 / *Fax: 668-5768*
District Clerk	David Guerrero	668-5732 / *Fax: 668-5717*
County Clerk	J.C. Perez, III	668-5702 / *Fax: 661-1372*
County Treasurer	Becky Dominguez	668-5713 / *Fax: 668-8671*
Tax Assessor-Collector	Mary C. Lozano	668-5720 / *Fax: 668-5754*
Sheriff	Danny J. Bueno	668-0341 / *Fax: 668-0569*
County Auditor	Noe Gamez	668-5701 / *Fax: 664-6366*
Chief Appraiser	J. Sidney Vela	668-9656 / *Fax: 668-6423*
Elections Official	Maria Antonia "Tonie" Kuhlman	668-5711 / *Fax: 664-4276*

County Commissioner:

Precinct 1	Margie H. Gonzalez	668-5763 / *Fax: 668-2899*
Precinct 2	Ventura Garcia, Jr.	668-5704 / *Fax: 668-5704*
Precinct 3	Carlos Gonzalez	384-2747 / *Fax: 384-0417*
Precinct 4	Emede Garcia	348-3213 / *Fax: 348-2951*

Justice of the Peace:

Precinct 1	Juan Rodriguez, Jr.	668-5719 / *Fax: 661-0697*
Precinct 3	Karin Knolle	547-9796 / *Fax: 547-0990*
Precinct 4	Sylvia I. Johnson	348-2773 / *Fax: 348-3821*
Precinct 5	Luz Paiz	384-2486 / *Fax: 384-0417*
Precinct 6	Jose L. Rodriguez	664-9987 / *Fax: 668-6384*

Constable:

Precinct 1	Jesus "Chuy" Salinas	668-5859 / *Fax: 668-8671*
Precinct 3	Jim Long	460-1008 / *Fax: 547-1009*
Precinct 4	Frank Davila, Jr.	660-4518 / *Fax: 346-2218*
Precinct 5	Robert Vasquez, Sr.	384-2486 / *Fax: 384-0417*
Precinct 6	Bartolo Guajardo, Jr.	668-4065 / *Fax: 460-0787*

JOHNSON COUNTY

Population: 163,213
County Seat:
  Cleburne 76033

Johnson County Courthouse, 2 Main Street
817 556-6300 / *Fax: 817 556-6359*
www.johnsoncountytx.org/

County Judge	Roger Harmon	556-6360 / *Fax: 556-6359*
District Attorney, 18th Dist.	Dale Hanna	556-6802 / *Fax: 556-6816*
County Attorney	Bill Moore	556-6330 / *Fax: 556-6331*
District Clerk	David Lloyd	556-6839 / *Fax: 556-6120*
County Clerk	Becky Ivey	556-6323 / *Fax: 556-6170*
County Treasurer	Kathy Blackwell	556-6341 / *Fax: 556-6342*
Tax Assessor-Collector	Scott Porter	558-0122 / *Fax: 556-0826*
Sheriff	Adam King	556-6058 / *Fax: 556-6051*
County Auditor	J. R. "Kirk" Kirkpatrick	556-6305 / *Fax: 556-6075*
Chief Appraiser	Jim Hudspeth	558-8100 / *Fax: 645-3105*
Elections Official	Patty Bourgeois	556-6197 / *Fax: 556-6048*
County Commissioner:		
Precinct 1	Rick Bailey	645-0441 / *Fax: 202-9203*
Precinct 2	Kenny Howell	297-1926 / *Fax: 447-0500*
Precinct 3	Jerry Stringer	790-5333 / *Fax: 790-3393*
Precinct 4	Larry Woolley	558-9400 / *Fax: 202-8952*
Justice of the Peace:		
Precinct 1	Ronny McBroom	556-6032 / *Fax: 556-6198*
Precinct 2	Jeff Monk	558-0111 / *Fax: 447-5911*
Precinct 3	Pat Jacobs	558-0111 / *Fax: 790-2592*
Precinct 4	Johnny Bekkelund	556-6388 / *Fax: 556-6036*
Constable:		
Precinct 1	Matt Wylie	556-6163 / *Fax: 556-6868*
Precinct 2	Adam Crawford	202-2967 / *Fax: 295-6887*
Precinct 3	Mike White	558-0111 / *Fax: 790-2592*
Precinct 4	Tim Kinman	556-6363 / *Fax: 556-6083*

JONES COUNTY

Population: 19,871
County Seat:
  Anson 79501

P. O. Box 148
325 823-3741 / *Fax: 325 823-4223*
www.co.jones.tx.us

County Judge	Dale Spurgin	823-3741 / *Fax: 823-4223*
District Attorney, 259th Dist.	Joe Edd Boaz	823-2742 / *Fax: 823-2322*
County Attorney	Chad Cowan	823-3771 / *Fax: 823-4223*
District Clerk	Lacey Hansen	823-3731 / *Fax: 823-3289*
County Clerk	LeeAnn Jennings	823-3762 / *Fax: 823-3979*
County Treasurer	Amber Thompson	823-3742 / *Fax: 823-2065*
Tax Assessor-Collector	Mary Ann Lovelady	823-2437 / *Fax: 823-4246*
Sheriff	Greg Arnwine	823-3201 / *Fax: 823-2099*
County Auditor	Gwen Bailey	823-3919 / *Fax: 823-4592*
Chief Appraiser	Kim McLemore	823-2422 / *Fax: 823-2424*

County Commissioner:
- Precinct 1 — James Clawson ....576-3081 / *Fax: 823-4223*
- Precinct 2 — Steve Lefevre ....773-3331 / *Fax: 823-4223*
- Precinct 3 — Ross Davis ....537-2674 / *Fax: 823-4223*
- Precinct 4 — Joe Whitehorn ....280-8870 / *Fax: 823-4223*
- Justice of the Peace: — Cheryl Guernsey ....823-3761 / *Fax: 823-4205*
- Constable: — Danny Jimenez ....823-3201 / *Fax: 823-4223*

KARNES COUNTY

Population: 15,577
County Seat:
 Karnes City 78118

210 W. Calvert Ave. Ste. 160
830 780-3732 / *Fax: 830 780-4538*
www.co.karnes.tx.us

County Judge	Walter R. Long, Jr.	780-3732 / *Fax: 780-4538*
District Attorney, 81st Dist.	Audrey Gossett Louis	393-2200 / *Fax: 393-2205*
County Attorney	Jennifer Dillingham	780-3736 / *Fax: 780-4790*
District Clerk	Denise Rodriguez	780-2562 / *Fax: 780-3227*
County Clerk	Carol Swize	780-3938 / *Fax: 780-4576*
County Treasurer	Vi Malone	780-2312 / *Fax: 780-4530*
Tax Assessor-Collector	Brenda Janysek	780-2431 / *Fax: 780-4530*
Sheriff	Dwayne Villanueva	780-3931 / *Fax: 780-3273*
County Auditor	Lajuana Kasprzyk	780-2721 / *Fax: 780-4530*
Chief Appraiser	Brian Stahl	780-2433 / *Fax: 780-4436*
Elections Official	Stacy Mika	780 2246 / *Fax: 780-4576*

County Commissioner:
- Precinct 1 — Shelby Dupnik 299-1524
- Precinct 2 — Pete Jauer 623-6610
- Precinct 3 — Mary Lozano 623-1344
- Precinct 4 — David Reynolds 583-6389

Justice of the Peace:
- Precinct 1 — Rachel Vasquez Garcia ....583-2102 / *Fax: 583-9229*
- Precinct 2 — Caroline Korzekwa ....254-3226 / *Fax: 254-3226*
- Precinct 3 — Delia Villanueva ....780-4373 / *Fax: 780-2262*
- Precinct 4 — David Sotello ....239-4459 / *Fax: 239-7449*

Constable:
- Precinct 1 — Dennis Fenner 534-8246
- Precinct 2 — Donald Hons 210 334-1012
- Precinct 3 — Fernando Martinez 534-5968
- Precinct 4 — Fernando Rios III 299-2699

KAUFMAN COUNTY

Population: 115,487
County Seat:
  Kaufman 75142

100 W. Mulberry
972 932-4331 / *Fax: 972 932-1368*
www.kaufmancounty.org

County Judge	Bruce Wood .... .932-0218 / *Fax: 932-1368*
Criminal District Attorney	Erleigh Norville Wiley 932-4331 x1260
District Clerk	Rhonda Hughey .... .932-0228 / *Fax: 932-1337*
County Clerk	Laura Hughes .... .932-0200 / *Fax: 962-8018*
County Treasurer	Ronnie Oldfield .... .932-0280 / *Fax: 932-1415*
Tax Assessor-Collector	Brenda Samples .... .932-0288 / *Fax: 932-1413*
Sheriff	Bryan Beavers .... .932-4337 / *Fax: 932-9752*
County Auditor	Karen Cooper .... .932-0240 / *Fax: 932-7628*
Chief Appraiser	Chris Peace .... .932-6081 / *Fax: 932-4749*
County Commissioner:	
Precinct 1	Michael D. Hunt .... .932-0284 / *Fax: 469 376-4062*
Precinct 2	Skeet Phillips .... .564-4054 / *Fax: 564-0113*
Precinct 3	Terry Barber .... .563-5362 / *Fax: 551-1832*
Precinct 4	Jakie Allen .... .469 376-4620 / *Fax: 903 498-4033*
Justice of the Peace:	
Precinct 1	Mary Bardin .... .932-9747 / *Fax: 962-2653*
Precinct 2	Patricia B. Ashcroft 564-3786
Precinct 3	Mike Smith .... .563-9723 / *Fax: 932-1368*
Precinct 4	Johnny Adams .... .469 376-4620 / *Fax: 903 498-2012*
Constable:	
Precinct 1	Shawn Mayfield 932-9798
Precinct 2	Jason Johnson .... .564-4054 / *Fax: 552-2727*
Precinct 3	Keith Stephens .... .563-3121 / *Fax: 563-2960*
Precinct 4	Chad Jones .... .469 376-4620 / *Fax: 903 498-4033*

KENDALL COUNTY

Population: 41,161
County Seat:
  Boerne 78006

201 E. San Antonio Ave.
830 249-9343 / *Fax: 830 249-9478*
www.co.kendall.tx.us/

County Judge	Darrel L. Lux .... .249-9343 / *Fax: 249-9478*
Criminal District Attorney	
District 451	Nicole Bishop .... .249-9343 / *Fax: 249-4176*
District Clerk	Susan Jackson .... .249-9343 / *Fax: 249-1763*
County Clerk	Darlene Herrin .... .249-9343 / *Fax: 249-3472*
County Treasurer	Sheryl D'Spain .... .249-9343 / *Fax: 249-9340*
Tax Assessor-Collector	James A. Hudson .... .249-9343 / *Fax: 249-4701*
Sheriff	Al Auxier .... .249-9721 / *Fax: 249-8027*
County Auditor	Corinna Speer .... .249-9343 / *Fax: 249-2813*
Chief Appraiser	Shelby Presley .... .249-8012 / *Fax: 249-3975*
Elections Official	Staci Decker .... .331-8701 / *Fax: 331-8295*

County Commissioner:
  Precinct 1   Christina Bergmann . . . . .249-9343 / *Fax: 249-9478*
  Precinct 2   Richard W. Elkins . . . . .249-9343 / *Fax: 249-9340*
  Precinct 3   Tommy Pfeiffer 249-9343 x339
  Precinct 4   Don Durden 210 414-9099
Justice of the Peace:
  Precinct 1   Lawrence James . . . . .249-9343 / *Fax: 249-7046*
  Precinct 2   Leon Brimhall . . . . .249-8404 / *Fax: 249-8408*
  Precinct 3   Debby S. Hudson . . . . .249-2820 / *Fax: 249-1544*
  Precinct 4   Frieda Pressler . . . . .995-2031 / *Fax: 995-5181*
Constable:
  Precinct 1   Donald White 210 383-1353 x339
  Precinct 2   James R. Schmidt 210 367-9479
  Precinct 3   Gene Serene . . . . .249-2820 / *Fax: 249-1544*
  Precinct 4   Brian Vaughan . . . . .995-3386 / *Fax: 995-3386*

KENEDY COUNTY

Population: 410   151 N. Mallory Street, P.O. Box 37
County Seat: 361 294-5224 / *Fax: 361 294-5244*
  Sarita 78385   www.co.kenedy.tx.us/

County Judge   Louis E. Turcotte, III . . . . .294-5224 / *Fax: 294-5244*
District Attorney, 105th Dist.   John T. Hubert . . . . .595-8544 / *Fax: 595-8522*
County Attorney   Allison Strauss . . . . .294-5292 / *Fax: 294-5303*
District & County Clerk   Veronica Vela . . . . .294-5220 / *Fax: 294-5218*
County Treasurer   Cynthia Salinas . . . . .294-5304 / *Fax: 294-5218*
Tax Assessor-Collector   Sandra Garcia-Burns . . . . .294-5202 / *Fax: 294-5710*
Sheriff   Ramon Salinas III . . . . .294-5205 / *Fax: 294-5260*
Chief Appraiser   Thomas Denney . . . . .294-5333 / *Fax: 866 303-6553*
Elections Official   Diego L. Villarreal Interim . . . . .294-5255 / *Fax: 294-5218*
County Commissioner:
  Precinct 1   Joe Recio . . . . .294-5224 / *Fax: 294-5244*
  Precinct 2   Israel Vela, Jr. . . . . .294-5224 / *Fax: 294-5244*
  Precinct 3   Sarita Hixon . . . . .595-5551 / *Fax: 595-7050*
  Precinct 4   Gumecinda "Cindy" Gonzalez . . . . .216-5298 / *Fax: 294-5294*
Justice of the Peace:
  Precinct 1   Andrew Turcotte . . . . .294-5785 / *Fax: 294-5788*
  Precinct 2   Jerry Miller . . . . .294-5298 / *Fax: 294-5788*
  Precinct 3   Cecilia Schulz . . . . .294-5786 / *Fax: 294-5788*
  Precinct 4   Patricia Fain . . . . .294-5787 / *Fax: 294-5788*

KENT COUNTY

Population: 804
County Seat:
 Jayton 79528

P.O. Box 6 - 101 Main Street
806 237-3373 / *Fax: 806 237-2632*
www.kentcountytexas.us

County Judge	Jim White	.237-3373 / *Fax: 237-2632*
District Attorney, 39th Dist.	Mike Fouts	.940 864-2072 / *Fax: 940 864-3364*
County Attorney	Bill Ballard	.237-3975 / *Fax: 237-2632*
District & County Clerk	Craig Harrison	.237-3881 / *Fax: 237-2300*
County Treasurer	Shawna Doss	.237-3075 / *Fax: 237-2632*
Tax Assessor-Collector	William Scogin	.237-3746 / *Fax: 237-3306*
Sheriff	William Scogin	.237-3801 / *Fax: 237-3306*
County Auditor	Position Vacant	.237-2002 / *Fax: 237-2295*
Chief Appraiser	Cindy Watson	.237-3066 / *Fax: 237-3067*
County Commissioner:		
Precinct 1	Roy W. Chisum	.237-6413 / *Fax: 237-2632*
Precinct 2	Don Long	.284-5432 / *Fax: 237-2632*
Precinct 3	Daryl Ham	.237-9832 / *Fax: 237-2632*
Precinct 4	Robert Graham	.237-2938 / *Fax: 237-2632*
Justice of the Peace:		
Precinct 4	David Parker	.237-3646 / *Fax: 237-2632*

KERR COUNTY

Population: 51,589
County Seat:
 Kerrville 78028

Courthouse, 700 Main St.
830 792-2200 / *Fax: 830 792-2218*
www.co.kerr.tx.us

County Judge	Tom Pollard	.792-2211 / *Fax: 792-2218*
District Attorney, 198th Dist.	Scott Monroe	.315-2460 / *Fax: 315-2461*
District Attorney, 216th Dist.	Lucy Wilke	.896-4744 / *Fax: 896-2620*
County Attorney	Heather Stebbins	.792-2220 / *Fax: 792-2228*
District Clerk	Robbin Burlew	.792-2287 / *Fax: 257-8262*
County Clerk	Rebecca Bolin	.792-2255 / *Fax: 792-2274*
County Treasurer	Tracy Soldan	.792-2275 / *Fax: 257-9228*
Tax Assessor-Collector	Diane Bolin	.792-2243 / *Fax: 792-2253*
Sheriff	W. R. "Rusty" Hierholzer	.896-1216 / *Fax: 896-7380*
County Auditor	Brenda Doss	.792-2235 / *Fax: 792-2238*
Chief Appraiser	Sharon Constantinides	.895-5223 / *Fax: 895-5227*
County Commissioner:		
Precinct 1	Harley David Belew	.792-2213 / *Fax: 792-2218*
Precinct 2	Tom Moser	.792-2214 / *Fax: 792-2218*
Precinct 3	Jonathan Letz	.792-2216 / *Fax: 792-2218*
Precinct 4	Bob Reeves	.792-2217 / *Fax: 792-2218*
Justice of the Peace:		
Precinct 1	Mitzi French	.792-2230 / *Fax: 792-2278*
Precinct 2	J.R. Hoyne	.792-6444 / *Fax: 792-6414*
Precinct 3	Kathy Mitchell	.792-2233 / *Fax: 792-2279*
Precinct 4	Bill Ragsdale	.896-9031 / *Fax: 792-3005*

Constable:
  Precinct 1   Tommy Rodriguez .... .792-2223 / *Fax: 792-2278*
  Precinct 2   Charlie Hicks .... .315-2475 / *Fax: 792-6414*
  Precinct 3   Kenneth Wilke .... .792-2240 / *Fax: 792-2279*
  Precinct 4   Gene Huffaker .... .896-9035 / *Fax: 896-9034*

KIMBLE COUNTY

Population: 4,641
County Seat:
  Junction 76849

Courthouse, 501 Main
325 446-3353 / *Fax: 325 446-2986*
www.co.kimble.tx.us

County Judge   Delbert R. Roberts .... .446-2724 / *Fax: 446-2986*
District Attorney, 452nd Dist.   Tonya S. Ahlschwede .... .347-8400 / *Fax: 347-8404*
County Attorney   Donnie J. Coleman .... .446-2378 / *Fax: 446-9427*
District & County Clerk   Haydee Torres .... .446-3353 / *Fax: 446-2986*
County Treasurer   Jolene Williams .... .446-2847 / *Fax: 446-4506*
Tax Assessor-Collector   Hilario Cantu .... .446-2357 / *Fax: 446-2986*
Sheriff   Hilario Cantu .... .446-2766 / *Fax: 446-4341*
Chief Appraiser   Kandy Dick .... .446-2357 / *Fax: 446-4361*
County Commissioner:
  Precinct 1   Billy Braswell 446-3066
  Precinct 2   Charles McGuire 446-2277
  Precinct 3   Dennis Dunagan .... .446-2524 / *Fax: 446-2986*
  Precinct 4   Chad Gipson 446-3375
Justice of the Peace:
  Precinct 1   Josh Cantrell .... .446-2281 / *Fax: 446-3691*
Constable: Bryan Payne .... .446-4565 / *Fax: 446-4341*

KING COUNTY

Population: 286
County Seat:
  Guthrie 79236

P.O. Box 127
806 596-4411 / *Fax: 806 596-4030*

County Judge   Duane Daniel .... .596-4411 / *Fax: 596-4030*
District Attorney, 50th Dist.   Jennifer A. Habert .... .940 889-2852 / *Fax: 940 888-3036*
County Attorney   David Hajek .... .940 256-3271 / *Fax: 596-4664*
District & County Clerk   Jammye D. Timmons .... .596-4412 / *Fax: 596-4664*
County Treasurer   Denise Beck .... .596-4319 / *Fax: 596-4010*
Tax Assessor-Collector   Sadie Spitzer .... .596-4318 / *Fax: 596-4030*
Sheriff   Mike McWhirter .... .596-4413 / *Fax: 596-4316*
Chief Appraiser   Kala Briggs .... .596-4588 / *Fax: 596-4041*
County Commissioner:
  Precinct 1   Reggie Hatfield .... .596-4341 / *Fax: 596-4664*
  Precinct 2   Larry Rush .... .596-4571 / *Fax: 596-4664*
  Precinct 3   Doris Tidmore .... .596-4520 / *Fax: 596-4664*
  Precinct 4   Jay Hurt .... .596-4389 / *Fax: 596-4664*
Justice of the Peace: Melody Pettiet .... .596-4481 / *Fax: 596-4664*

KINNEY COUNTY

Population: 3,742
County Seat:
  Brackettville 78832

P.O. Drawer 348
830 563-2401 / *Fax: 830 563-3104*
www.co.kinney.tx.us

County Judge	James T. "Tully" Shahan	.563-2401 / *Fax: 563-9163*
District Attorney	Mike Bagley	.775-0505 / *Fax: 775-0352*
County Attorney	Todd Durden	.563-2240 / *Fax: 563-2644*
District & County Clerk	Isela Ramon	.563-2521 / *Fax: 563-2644*
County Treasurer	Diana Gutierrez	.563-2777 / *Fax: 563-2644*
Tax Assessor-Collector	Martha Pena Padron	.563-2688 / *Fax: 563-9563*
Sheriff	Brad Coe	.563-2788 / *Fax: 563-9114*
County Auditor	Donieta O'Keeffe	.563-2384 / *Fax: 563-2644*
Chief Appraiser	Gene Slate	.563-2323 / *Fax: 563-9292*
County Commissioner:		
Precinct 1	Mark Frerich	.563-2401 / *Fax: 563-3104*
Precinct 2	Joe Montalvo	.563-2091
Precinct 3	Dennis Dodson	.563-2401 / *Fax: 563-3104*
Precinct 4	Pat Melancon	.563-9493
Justice of the Peace:	Narce Villarreal	.563-2881 / *Fax: 563-3077*
Constable:	Ben Vasquez	.563-2788 / *Fax: 563-9114*

KLEBERG COUNTY

Population: 30,607
County Seat:
  Kingsville 78363

P.O. Box 752, Kingsville, 78364
361 595-8585 / *Fax: 361 592-0838*
www.co.kleberg.tx.us

County Judge	Rudy Madrid	.595-8585 / *Fax: 592-0838*
District Attorney, 105th Dist.	John T. Hubert	.595-8545 / *Fax: 595-8522*
County Attorney	Kira Talip	.595-8583 / *Fax: 595-4726*
District Clerk	Jennifer Whittington	.595-8561 / *Fax: 595-8525*
County Clerk	Stephanie G. Garza	.595-8548 / *Fax: 593-1355*
County Treasurer	Priscilla Alaniz Cantu	.595-8535 / *Fax: 593-1367*
Tax Assessor-Collector	Melissa T. De La Garza	.595-8542 / *Fax: 595-8546*
Sheriff	Richard Kirkpatrick	.595-8500 / *Fax: 595-7870*
County Auditor	Melissa S. Green	.595-8526 / *Fax: 595-8536*
Chief Appraiser	Tina Flores	.595-5775 / *Fax: 595-7984*
County Commissioner:		
Precinct 1	David Rosse	.595-8529 / *Fax: 595-8530*
Precinct 2	Joe G. Hinojosa	.595-8532 / *Fax: 595-8537*
Precinct 3	Roy Cantu	.296-3623 / *Fax: 296-3796*
Precinct 4	Crystal L. Runyon	.595-8588 / *Fax: 595-8599*
Justice of the Peace:		
Precinct 1	Andy Gonzalez	.595-1387 / *Fax: 595-1308*
Precinct 2	Carmen Cortez	.595-8571 / *Fax: 595-8537*
Precinct 3	Chris Lee	.296-3214 / *Fax: 296-3613*
Precinct 4	Esequiel DeLaPaz	.595-8586 / *Fax: 595-8599*
Constable:		
Precinct 1	Position Vacant	.595-1379
Precinct 2	Omar Rosales	.595-8582 / *Fax: 595-8503*
Precinct 3	Del Moral	.296-3706 / *Fax: 296-3706*
Precinct 4	Amando Vidal	.595-8589 / *Fax: 595-8599*

KNOX COUNTY

Population: 3,731
County Seat:
  Benjamin 79505

P.O. Box 77
940 459-2191 / *Fax: 940 459-2022*
www.knoxcountytexas.org

County Judge	Stan Wojcik	.459-2191 / *Fax: 459-2022*
District Attorney, 50th Dist.	Jennifer A. Habert	.889-2852 / *Fax: 888-3036*
County Attorney	Lina L Reyes-Trevino	.459-2241 / *Fax: 459-2022*
District & County Clerk	Lisa Cypert	.459-2441 / *Fax: 459-2005*
County Treasurer	Rosie Ake	.459-2251 / *Fax: 459-2005*
Tax Assessor-Collector	Mitzi Welch	.459-2411 / *Fax: 459-2004*
Sheriff	Dean W. Homstad	.459-2211 / *Fax: 459-2016*
Chief Appraiser	Mitzi Welch	.459-3891 / *Fax: 459-2004*
Elections Official	Lisa Cypert	.459-2441 / *Fax: 459-2005*
County Commissioner:		
Precinct 1	Johnny McCown	.256-1341 / *Fax: 459-2022*
Precinct 2	Daniel Godsey	.657-5311 / *Fax: 459-2022*
Precinct 3	Jimmy Urbanczyk	.203-0377 / *Fax: 459-2022*
Precinct 4	Nathan Urbanczyk	.422-4076 / *Fax: 459-2022*
Justice of the Peace:	Pam Oliver	.459-3181 / *Fax: 459-4191*

LA SALLE COUNTY

Population: 7,640
County Seat:
  Cotulla 78014

101 Courthouse Square
830 879-4430 / *Fax: 830 879-4431*
www.co.la-salle.tx.us/

County Judge	Joel Rodriguez, Jr.	.483-5139 / *Fax: 483-5110*
District Attorney, 81st Dist.	Audrey Gossett Louis	.393-2200 / *Fax: 393-2205*
County Attorney	Elizabeth Martinez	.483-5127 / *Fax: 483-5105*
District & County Clerk	Margarita Esqueda	.483-5120 / *Fax: 483-5100*
County Treasurer	Thelma Treviño	.483-5143 / *Fax: 483-5109*
Tax Assessor-Collector	Dora A. Gonzales	.483-5134 / *Fax: 483-5102*
Sheriff	Miguel Rodriguez	.879-3044 / *Fax: 483-5105*
County Commissioner:		
Precinct 1	Nocl "Noni" Niavez	.202-0031 / *Fax: 483-5100*
Precinct 2	Joaquin Alba	.483-0163 / *Fax: 483-5100*
Precinct 3	Erasmo "Mito" Ramirez, Jr.	.202-0478 / *Fax: 483-5100*
Precinct 4	Raul Ayala	.202-1205 / *Fax: 483-5100*
Justice of the Peace:		
Precinct 1	Vicki Rodriguez	.483-5147 / *Fax: 483-5111*
Precinct 2	Frank Weikel	.956 948-0586 / *Fax: 956 948-5085*
Precinct 3	George Trigo	.879-4128 / *Fax: 879-4443*
Precinct 4	Janie Meglorino	.202-0096 / *Fax: 373-4581*
Constable:		
Precinct 1	Oscar Tellez	.879-3044 / *Fax: 483-5100*
Precinct 2	Rene Maldonado	.879-3044 / *Fax: 483-5100*
Precinct 3	Hector Ramirez	.202-7872 / *Fax: 483-5100*
Precinct 4	Guy Meglorino	.202-7971 / *Fax: 483-5100*
Chief Interim Appraiser	Gary Zeitler	.879-4756 / *Fax: 879-4067*

COUNTY SECTION

LAMAR COUNTY

Population: 51,102
County Seat:
  Paris 75460

County Courthouse, 119 N. Main St.
903 737-2410 / *Fax: 903 785-3858*
www.co.lamar.tx.us/

County Judge	M. C. "Chuck" Superville, Jr.	737-2410 / *Fax: 785-3858*
District & County Attorney	Gary Young	737-2470 / *Fax: 737-2455*
District Clerk	Shawntel Golden	737-2428 / *Fax: 785-4905*
County Clerk	Ruth Sisson	737-2420 / *Fax: 782-1100*
County Treasurer	Nicki Bridgers	737-2419 / *Fax: 734-4421*
Tax Assessor-Collector	Haskell Maroney	737-2423 / *Fax: 737-2425*
Sheriff	Scott Cass	737-2400 / *Fax: 737-2498*
County Auditor	Kayla Hall	737-2466 / *Fax: 737-2451*
Chief Appraiser	Jerry Patton	785-7822 / *Fax: 785-8322*
Elections Official	Tricia Johnson	782-1116 / *Fax: 782-1123*
County Commissioner:		
Precinct 1	Lawrence Malone	737-2467 / *Fax: 737-2469*
Precinct 2	Lonnie Layton	737-2467 / *Fax: 737-2469*
Precinct 3	Ronnie Bass	737-2467 / *Fax: 737-2469*
Precinct 4	Keith Mitchell	737-2467 / *Fax: 737-2469*
Justice of the Peace:		
Precinct 1	Don Denison	737-2400 / *Fax: 737-2490*
Precinct 2	Crystal Duke	346-3671 / *Fax: 782-1115*
Precinct 3	Tim Risinger	737-2439 / *Fax: 782-1115*
Precinct 4	Jimmy Steed	737-2441 / *Fax: 782-1115*
Precinct 5, Pl. 1	Cindy Cooper Ruthart	737-2439 / *Fax: 782-1115*
Precinct 5, Pl. 2	Gene Hobbs	737-2441 / *Fax: 737-2490*
Constable:		
Precinct 1	Travis Rhodes	737-8867 / *Fax: 737-2490*
Precinct 2	Mike Ford	737-2437 / *Fax: 737-2490*
Precinct 3	Steven Hill	785-5023
Precinct 4	Richard E. "Rick" Easterwood	737-2437
Precinct 5	Jimmy Hodges	737-2438 / *Fax: 737-2490*

LAMB COUNTY

Population: 13,100
County Seat:
  Littlefield 79339

100 6th Drive
806 385-4222 / *Fax: 806 385-6485*
www.co.lamb.tx.us

County Judge	James M. "Mike" DeLoach	385-4222 / *Fax: 385-6485*
District & County Attorney	Scott A. Say	385-4222 / *Fax: 358-6485*
District Clerk	Stephanie Chester	385-4222 / *Fax: 385-3554*
County Clerk	Tonya Ritchie	385-4222 / *Fax: 385-6485*
County Treasurer	Jerry Yarbrough	385-4222 / *Fax: 385-6485*
Tax Assessor-Collector	Brenda Goheen	385-4222 / *Fax: 385-6485*
Sheriff	Gary Maddox	385-7900 / *Fax: 385-9400*
County Auditor	Gina Jones	385-4222 / *Fax: 385-6485*
Chief Appraiser	Lesa Ann Kloiber	385-6474 / *Fax: 385-6944*
Elections Official	Tonya Ritchie	385-4222 / *Fax: 385-6485*

County Commissioner:

Precinct 1	Cory DeBerry	.385-4222 / *Fax: 385-6485*
Precinct 2	Kent Lewis	.385-4222 / *Fax: 385-6485*
Precinct 3	Danny Short	.385-4222 / *Fax: 385-6485*
Precinct 4	Jimmy Young	.385-4222 / *Fax: 385-6485*

Justice of the Peace:

Precinct 1	Becky DeBerry	.285-7771 / *Fax: 285-3024*
Precinct 2	Christi Clark	.257-2110 / *Fax: 257-2273*
Precinct 3	Al Mann	.385-4222 / *Fax: 385-6485*
Precinct 4	Matt Hanna	.227-2048 / *Fax: 227-2044*

LAMPASAS COUNTY

Population: 20,540
County Seat:
  Lampasas 76550

501 E. 4th St.
512 556-8271 / *Fax: 512 556-8270*
www.co.lampasas.tx.us/

County Judge	Wayne Boultinghouse	.556-8271 / *Fax: 556-8270*
District Attorney	John Greenwood	.556-8282 / *Fax: 556-4572*
District Clerk	Cody L. Reed	.556-8271 / *Fax: 556-9463*
County Clerk	Connie Hartmann	.556-8271 / *Fax: 556-8270*
County Treasurer	Nelda DeRiso	.556-8271 / *Fax: 556-8270*
Tax Assessor-Collector	Linda Crawford	.556-8271 / *Fax: 556-4825*
Sheriff	Jess Ramos	.556-8255 / *Fax: 556-5809*
Chief Appraiser	Melissa Gonzales	.556-8058 / *Fax: 556-4660*
Elections Official	Mark Bishop	.556-8271 / *Fax: 564-1424*

County Commissioner:

Precinct 1	Bobby Carroll	.556-8271 / *Fax: 556-8270*
Precinct 2	Jim Lindeman	.556-8271 / *Fax: 556-8270*
Precinct 3	Lewis Bridges	.556-8271 / *Fax: 556-8270*
Precinct 4	Mark Rainwater	.556-8271 / *Fax: 556-8270*

Justice of the Peace:

Precinct 1	Andrew Garcia, Jr.	.564-1845 / *Fax: 564-1696*
Precinct 2	Cameron Brister	.752-3497 / *Fax: 752-8397*
Precinct 3	Cameron Brister	.752-3497 / *Fax: 752-8397*
Precinct 4	Greg Chapman	.932-2182 / *Fax: 932-3884*

Constable:

Precinct 1	Bob Montgomery	.556-6488 / *Fax: 564-1696*
Precinct 2	John W. Harris	.734-9020 / *Fax: 752-8397*
Precinct 3	John W. Harris	.734-9020 / *Fax: 752-8397*
Precinct 4	Forest Spence	.932-2182 / *Fax: 932-3884*

COUNTY SECTION

LAVACA COUNTY

Population: 19,567
County Seat:
  Hallettsville 77964

P.O. Box 243
361 798-2301 / *Fax: 361 798-5490*
www.co.lavaca.tx.us

County Judge	Tramer J. Woytek	.798-2301 / *Fax: 798-5490*
County Attorney	John Stuart Fryer	.798-4757 / *Fax: 798-2816*
District Clerk	Sherry T. Henke	.798-2351 / *Fax: 798-5674*
County Clerk	Elizabeth A. Kouba	.798-3612 / *Fax: 798-1610*
County Treasurer	Karen Bludau	.798-2181 / *Fax: 798-4724*
Tax Assessor-Collector	Deborah A. Sevcik	.798-3601 / *Fax: 798-5229*
Sheriff	Micah Harmon	.798-2121 / *Fax: 798-1890*
County Auditor	Shana Opela	.798-2711 / *Fax: 798-5046*
Chief Appraiser	Gregory Cook	.798-4396 / *Fax: 798-2653*
Elections Official	Christine Brown	.798-3594 / *Fax: 798-4016*
County Commissioner:		
Precinct 1	Edward Pustka	.798-4822 / *Fax: 798-5490*
Precinct 2	Ronald Berckenhoff	.596-4541 / *Fax: 798-5490*
Precinct 3	R.W. Brown	.594-2000 / *Fax: 798-5490*
Precinct 4	Dennis W. Kocian	.798-3490 / *Fax: 798-5490*
Justice of the Peace:		
Precinct 1	Mark Ivey	.798-3945 / *Fax: 798-9541*
Precinct 2	Travis Hill	.596-8308 / *Fax: 596-8888*
Precinct 3	Wayne Denson	.594-8505
Precinct 4	Hallie Hall	.293-9146 / *Fax: 293-5818*
Constable:		
Precinct 1	Mike Buchanek	.798-3945
Precinct 2	Charles Greive	.772-1742 / *Fax: 979 743-2601*
Precinct 3	Larry W. Hlavac	.594-3709 / *Fax: 594-3709*
Precinct 4	Andy Anderson	.798-5553

LEE COUNTY

Population: 17,198
County Seat:
  Giddings 78942

200 South Main, Room 107
979 542-3178 / *Fax: 979 542-2988*
www.co.lee.tx.us

County Judge	Paul E. Fischer	.542-3178 / *Fax: 542-2988*
District & County Attorney	Martin Placke	.542-3233 / *Fax: 542-1226*
District Clerk	Lisa Teinert	.542-2947 / *Fax: 542-2444*
County Clerk	Sharon Blasig	.542-3684 / *Fax: 542-2623*
County Treasurer	Melinda "Lyndy" Krause	.542-2161 / *Fax: 540-2739*
Tax Assessor-Collector	David Matthijetz	.542-2640 / *Fax: 542-3787*
Sheriff	Rodney W. Meyer	.542-2800 / *Fax: 542-1446*
County Auditor	Maxine Siegmund	.542-3103 / *Fax: 540-2740*
Chief Appraiser	James Orr	.542-9618
Elections Official	Carla R. Arldt	.540-2731 / *Fax: 540-2732*
County Commissioner:		
Precinct 1	Maurice Pitts, Jr.	.542-6065 / *Fax: 542-6065*
Precinct 2	Charles Murray	.542-2522 / *Fax: 542-2522*
Precinct 3	Alan Turner	.512 542-6897
Precinct 4	Steve Knobloch	.542-1388 / *Fax: 542-2839*

Justice of the Peace:
Precinct 2 Michael York ....542-3030 / *Fax: 542-0234*
Precinct 3 Don M. Milburn ....773-2267 / *Fax: 773-4866*
Precinct 4 Danita W. Smith ....884-4001 / *Fax: 884-1501*
Constable:
Precinct 2 Vernon J. Surman ....540-2732 / *Fax: 903 540-3733*
Precinct 3 Farah Ramsey ....773-2268 / *Fax: 773-4866*
Precinct 4 Donald Whitsel ....884-6000 / *Fax: 884-1501*

LEON COUNTY

Population: 17,342
County Seat:
  Centerville 75833

P.O. Box 429
903 536-2331 / *Fax: 903 536-7044*
www.co.leon.tx.us

County Judge Byron Ryder ....536-2331 / *Fax: 536-7044*
District Attorney, 369th Dist. Hope Knight ....536-7161 / *Fax: 536-8000*
County Attorney James Caleb Henson ....536-2131 / *Fax: 536-7044*
District Clerk Beverly Wilson ....536-2227 / *Fax: 536-5058*
County Clerk Christie Wakefield ....536-2352 / *Fax: 536-7581*
County Treasurer Brandi S. Hill ....536-2915 / *Fax: 536-5135*
Tax Assessor-Collector Robin Shafer ....536-2543 / *Fax: 536-2431*
Sheriff Kevin Ellis ....536-2749 / *Fax: 536-4357*
County Auditor Melissa Abney ....536-2709 / *Fax: 536-5801*
Chief Appraiser Jeff Beshears ....536-2252 / *Fax: 536-2377*
Elections Official Donna Golden ....536-4469 / *Fax: 536-1773*
County Commissioner:
Precinct 1 Jocy Sullivan ....536-3299 / *Fax: 536-7044*
Precinct 2 David Ferguson ....545-2471 / *Fax: 545-2471*
Precinct 3 Dean Stanford ....626-4656 / *Fax: 626-4656*
Precinct 4 David Grimes ....936 396-3427 / *Fax: 936 396-1978*
Justice of the Peace:
Precinct 1 Lori Reid ....322-4795 / *Fax: 322-8205*
Precinct 2 Jack Keeling ....536-2523 / *Fax: 536-3625*
Precinct 4 Jerry Grimes ....529-1261 / *Fax: 529-1269*
Constable:
Precinct 1 Chris Johnson 626-5377
Precinct 2 George Holleman ....979 412-1715 / *Fax: 536-6402*
Precinct 4 Position Vacant

LIBERTY COUNTY

Population: 79,682
County Seat:
  Liberty 77575

1923 Sam Houston
936 336-4665 / *Fax: 936 336-4518*
www.co.liberty.tx.us/

County Judge	Jay Knight	.336-4665 / *Fax: 336-4518*
District Attorney, 253rd Dist.	Logan Pickett	.336-4610 / *Fax: 336-4644*
County Attorney	Matthew Poston	.336-4650 / *Fax: 336-4568*
District Clerk	Donna Brown	.336-4682 / *Fax: 336-1115*
County Clerk	Paulette Williams	.336-4670 / *Fax: 334-8174*
County Treasurer	Kim Harris	.336-4621 / *Fax: 336-4637*
Tax Assessor-Collector	Richard L. Brown	.336-4629 / *Fax: 336-2866*
Sheriff	Bobby Rader	.336-4500 / *Fax: 336-4545*
County Auditor	Dewayne Gott	.336-4605 / *Fax: 336-4638*
Chief Appraiser	Lana McCarty	.336-5722 / *Fax: 336-8390*
County Commissioner:		
Precinct 1	Bruce Karbowski	.587-4922
Precinct 2	Greg Arthur	.281 592-1172 / *Fax: 298-9737*
Precinct 3	James "Boo" Reaves	.281 592-1653 / *Fax: 281 593-0178*
Precinct 4	Leon Wilson	.258-5202 / *Fax: 258-9685*
Justice of the Peace:		
Precinct 1	Stephen Herbert	.336-4558 / *Fax: 334-3207*
Precinct 2	Ronnie Davis	.587-4010 / *Fax: 587-4951*
Precinct 3	Cody Parrish	.298-9407 / *Fax: 298-3827*
Precinct 4	Larry Wilburn	.258-2461 / *Fax: 258-2010*
Precinct 5	Wade Brown	.281 592-9229 / *Fax: 281 592-1404*
Precinct 6	Ralph Fuller	.281 593-8422 / *Fax: 281 593-8414*
Constable:		
Precinct 1	Justin Johnson	.336-4587 / *Fax: 334-3216*
Precinct 2	Les Hulsey	.587-4920 / *Fax: 587-4950*
Precinct 3	Mark "Mad Dog" Davison	.298-3687
Precinct 4	Robbie Thornton	.258-4711
Precinct 5	David Hunter	.281 593-3189 / *Fax: 281 592-1404*
Precinct 6	John Joslin	.281 593-8418 / *Fax: 281 593-8414*

LIMESTONE COUNTY

Population: 24,104
County Seat:
  Groesbeck 76642

200 W. State, Suite 101
254 729-3810 / *Fax: 254 729-2643*
www.co.limestone.tx.us

County Judge	Daniel Burkeen	.729-3810 / *Fax: 729-2643*
District & County Attorney	Roy DeFriend	.729-3814 / *Fax: 729-5699*
District Clerk	Carol Jenkins	.729-3206 / *Fax: 729-2960*
County Clerk	Peggy Beck	.729-5504 / *Fax: 729-2951*
County Treasurer	Carol Pickett	.729-3314 / *Fax: 729-2342*
Tax Assessor-Collector	Stacy Hall	.729-3405 / *Fax: 729-3533*
Sheriff	Dennis Wilson	.729-3278 / *Fax: 729-8342*
County Auditor	Debbie Watson	.729-3817 / *Fax: 729-5626*
Chief Appraiser	Karen Wietzikoski	.729-3009 / *Fax: 729-5534*
Elections Official	Jennifer Southard	.729-4997 / *Fax: 729-4993*

County Commissioner:
Precinct 1	John McCarver	.729-3810 / *Fax: 729-2643*
Precinct 2	Sonny Baker	.729-3810 / *Fax: 729-2643*
Precinct 3	Jerry Allen	.729-3810 / *Fax: 729-2643*
Precinct 4	Bobby Forrest	.729-3810 / *Fax: 729-2643*
Justice of the Peace:		
Precinct 1	Marcus Hanna	.729-2933 / *Fax: 729-3151*
Precinct 2	Mike Bell	.786-4938 / *Fax: 786-4916*
Precinct 3	Sherri LeNoir	.729-3630 / *Fax: 729-3060*
Precinct 4	Ray Jones	.562-7113 / *Fax: 562-9667*
Constable:		
Precinct 1	Scott Smith	.729-2933 / *Fax: 729-3151*
Precinct 2	Ray Forrester	.786-4938 / *Fax: 786-4916*
Precinct 3	Glenn Shoemaker	.729-5409 / *Fax: 729-2643*
Precinct 4	Kevin Nickels	.562-7379 / *Fax: 562-9667*

LIPSCOMB COUNTY

Population: 3,552
County Seat:
Lipscomb 79056

P.O. Box 69
806 862-4131 / *Fax: 806 862-2603*
www.co.lipscomb.tx.us

County Judge	Willis V. Smith	.862-4131 / *Fax: 862-2603*
District Attorney, 31st Dist.	Franklin McDonough	.669-8035 / *Fax: 669-8050*
County Attorney	Matthew D. Bartosicwicz	.658-4545 / *Fax: 658-4524*
District & County Clerk	Kim Blau	.862-3091 / *Fax: 862-3004*
County Treasurer	Kimberly Long	.862-3821 / *Fax: 862-3004*
Tax Assessor-Collector	Sharla Bradshaw	.862-2911 / *Fax: 862-3004*
Sheriff	Kenneth M. Eggleston	.862-2611 / *Fax: 862-2214*
Chief Appraiser	Angela Peil	.624-2881 / *Fax: 624-2003*
County Commissioner:		
Precinct 1	Juan Cantu	.658-4889 / *Fax: 862-2603*
Precinct 2	Merle Miller	.435-0684 / *Fax: 862-2603*
Precinct 3	Scotty Schilling	.653-5591 / *Fax: 862-2603*
Precinct 4	Randy Immel	.852-3131 / *Fax: 852-2801*
Justice of the Peace:		
Precinct 1	Nancy Shepherd	.862-3844 / *Fax: 862-2603*

COUNTY SECTION

LIVE OAK COUNTY

Population: 12,156
County Seat:
  George West 78022

P.O. Box 487
361 449-2733 / *Fax: 361 449-3155*
www.co.live-oak.tx.us/

County Judge	Jim Huff	.449-2733 / *Fax: 449-3155*
District Attorney, 156th Dist.	Jose Aliseda	.621-1550 / *Fax: 358-0505*
County Attorney	Dwayne McWilliams	.449-2733 / *Fax: 449-9488*
District Clerk	Melanie Matkin	.449-2733 / *Fax: 449-2992*
County Clerk	Ida Briseno Vasquez	.449-2733 / *Fax: 449-3155*
County Treasurer	Nancy Coquat	.449-8027 / *Fax: 449-3626*
Tax Assessor-Collector	Mari Gonzales	.449-2733 / *Fax: 449-3068*
Sheriff	Larry R. Busby	.449-2271 / *Fax: 449-3035*
County Auditor	Tragina Smith	.449-2733 / *Fax: 449-3626*
Chief Appraiser	Debra D. Morin, RPA, RTA, CCA	.449-2641 / *Fax: 449-2774*
County Commissioner:		
Precinct 1	Richard Lee	.449-7021 / *Fax: 449-3155*
Precinct 2	Donna Mills	.786-7432 / *Fax: 449-3155*
Precinct 3	Willie James	.449-7303 / *Fax: 449-3155*
Precinct 4	Emilio Garza	.449-2733 / *Fax: 449-3155*
Justice of the Peace:		
Precinct 1	Elizabeth Ellis	.449-8046/ *Fax: 449-1156*
Precinct 2	Virginia Tanguma	.786-3211 / *Fax: 449-8045*
Precinct 3	Jimmie E. Jones	.449-2733 / *Fax: 449-3064*
Precinct 4	Endercio Chapa, Jr.	.449-2733 / *Fax: 449-3258*
Constable:		
Precinct 1	Position Vacant	.449-2271 / *Fax: 449-3035*
Precinct 2	Vincent Roberts	.449-2271 / *Fax: 449-3035*
Precinct 3	James M. Baker	.449-2271 / *Fax: 449-3035*
Precinct 4	Robert Baker	.449-2271 / *Fax: 449-3035*

LLANO COUNTY

Population: 19,993
County Seat:
  Llano 78643

801 Ford Street, Room 101
325 247-7730 / Fax: 325 247-7732
www.co.llano.tx.us

County Judge	Mary Cunningham	.247-7730 / *Fax: 247-7732*
District Attorney, 33rd Dist.	Wiley B. "Sonny" McAfee	.247-5755 / *Fax: 247-5274*
County Attorney	Rebecca Lange	.247-7733 / *Fax: 247-7737*
District Clerk	Joyce Gillow	.247-5036 / *Fax: 248-0492*
County Clerk	Marci Hadeler	.247-4455 / *Fax: 247-2406*
County Treasurer	Teresa Kassell	.247-7743 / *Fax: 247-7745*
Tax Assessor-Collector	Kris Fogelberg	.247-4165 / *Fax: 247-5205*
Sheriff	Bill Blackburn	.247-5767 / *Fax: 247-3273*
County Auditor	Cindy Lent	.247-3783 / *Fax: 247-3162*
Chief Appraiser	Gary Eldridge	.247-3065 / *Fax: 247-4656*
Elections Official	Cindy Ware	.247-5425 / *Fax: 247-5624*
County Commissioner:		
Precinct 1	Peter Jones	.830 598-2296 / *Fax: 830 598-5231*
Precinct 2	Linda Raschke	.512 793-6181 / *Fax: 512 793-6215*
Precinct 3	Mike Sandoval	.512 793-2007 / *Fax: 512 793-2010*
Precinct 4	Jerry Don Moss	.247-2788 / *Fax: 247-3745*

Justice of the Peace:
  Precinct 1   Beatrice "Bebe" Piatt . . . . . .830 598-2296 / *Fax: 830 598-5231*
  Precinct 2   Linda Ballard . . . . .512 793-2332 / *Fax: 512 793-6215*
  Precinct 3   Era Marion . . . . .512 793-2016 / *Fax: 512 793-2017*
  Precinct 4   Brian Alexander . . . . .247-3178 / *Fax: 247-3745*
Constable:
  Precinct 1   Gary Olfers . . . . .830 598-2296 / *Fax: 830 598-5231*
  Precinct 2   Richard Harris . . . . .512 793-2332 / *Fax: 512 793-6215*
  Precinct 3   William "Bill" Edwards . . . .512 793-2012 / *Fax: 512 793-2013*
  Precinct 4   Joe Simpson, Jr. . . . . .247-2788 / *Fax: 247-3745*

LOVING COUNTY

Population: 81
County Seat:
  Mentone 79754

Courthouse, 100 Bell St.
432 377-2362 / *Fax: 432 377-2701*
www.lovingcountytexas.com/

County Judge	Skeet Lee Jones . . . . .377-2362 / *Fax: 377-2701*
District Attorney, 143rd Dist.	Randall W. "Randy" Reynolds . . . . .445-2010 / *Fax: 445-2015*
District & County Clerk	Mozelle Carr . . . . .377-2441 / *Fax: 377-2701*
County Treasurer	Regina Wilkinson . . . . .377-2311 / *Fax: 377-2701*
Tax Assessor-Collector	Chris H. Busse . . . . .377-2411 / *Fax: 377-2025*
Sheriff	Chris H. Busse . . . . .377-2411 / *Fax: 377-2025*
County Auditor	Linda Clark . . . . .377-2511 / *Fax: 469 646-4916*
Chief Appraiser	Sherlene Burrows, RPA, RTA ,CTA . .377-2201 / *Fax: 377-2011*
Elections Official	Mozelle Carr . . . . .377-2441 / *Fax: 469 646-4921*
County Commissioner:	
Precinct 1	Harlan Hopper . . . . .377-2261 / *Fax: 377-2701*
Precinct 2	Ysidro Renteria . . . . .448-5090 / *Fax: 377-2701*
Precinct 3	Tom E. Jones . . . . .448-0692 / *Fax: 377-2701*
Precinct 4	William "Bill" Wilkinson . . . . .661-4139 / *Fax: 377-2701*
Justice of the Peace:	Phyllis Young . . . . .377-2001 / *Fax: 377-2202*
Constable:	Brandon Wintana Jones . . . . .614-7559 / *Fax: 377-2701*

LUBBOCK COUNTY

Population: 300,961
County Seat:
  Lubbock 79408

P.O. Box 10536
806 775-1335 / *Fax: 806 775-7950*
www.co.lubbock.tx.us/

County Judge	Tom Head	.775-1679 / *Fax: 775-7950*
Criminal District Attorney	Matt D. Powell	.775-1100 / *Fax: 775-7930*
District Clerk	Barbara Sucsy	.775-1585 / *Fax: 775-7992*
County Clerk	Kelly J. Pinion	.775-1076 / *Fax: 775-1074*
County Treasurer	Chris Winn	.775-1616 / *Fax: 775-7988*
Tax Assessor-Collector	Ronnie Keister	.775-1344 / *Fax: 775-7951*
Sheriff	Kelly Rowe	.775-1469 / *Fax: 775-7991*
County Auditor	Jackie Latham, CPA	.775-1097 / *Fax: 775-7917*
Chief Appraiser	Tim Radloff	.762-5000 / *Fax: 762-2451*
Elections Official	Dorothy Kennedy	.775-1339 / *Fax: 775-7980*
County Commissioner:		
Precinct 1	Bill McCay	.775-1335 / *Fax: 775-7950*
Precinct 2	Mark E. Heinrich	.775-1335 / *Fax: 775-7950*
Precinct 3	Gilbert A. Flores	.775-1335 / *Fax: 775-7950*
Precinct 4	Patti C. Jones	.775-1335 / *Fax: 775-7950*
Justice of the Peace:		
Precinct 1	Jim Hansen	.775-1547 / *Fax: 775-7956*
Precinct 2	Jim Dulin	.775-1555 / *Fax: 775-7972*
Precinct 3	Aurora Chaides-Hernandez	.775-1328 / *Fax: 775-7937*
Constable:		
Precinct 1	Paul Hanna	.775-1538 / *Fax: 775-1678*
Precinct 2	Jody A. Barnes	.535-2601 / *Fax: 775-1678*
Precinct 3	Marina Garcia	.775-1535 / *Fax: 775-1678*
Precinct 4	C. J. Peterson	.775-1537 / *Fax: 775-1678*

LYNN COUNTY

Population: 5,951
County Seat:
 Tahoka 79373

P.O. Box 1167
806 561-4222 / *Fax: 806 561-4234*
www.co.lynn.tx.us/

County Judge — Mike Braddock .... .561-4222 / *Fax: 561-4234*
District Attorney, 106th Dist. — Philip Mack Furlow .... .872-2259 / *Fax: 872-3174*
County Attorney — Rebekah Filley .... .561-5286 / *Fax: 561-5287*
District Clerk — Sandra Laws .... .561-4274 / *Fax: 561-4151*
County Clerk — Susan Tipton .... .561-4750 / *Fax: 561-4988*
County Treasurer — Amy Schuknecht .... .561-4055 / *Fax: 561-6145*
Tax Assessor-Collector — Donna Willis .... .561-4112 / *Fax: 561-4277*
Sheriff — Abraham Vega .... .561-4505 / *Fax: 561-4658*
Chief Appraiser — Marquita Scott .... .561-5477 / *Fax: 561-4057*
County Commissioner:
 Precinct 1 — Matt Woodley .... .903 217-2120 / *Fax: 561-4234*
 Precinct 2 — John Hawthorne .... .831-5020 / *Fax: 561-4234*
 Precinct 3 — Don Blair .... .759-7215 / *Fax: 561-4234*
 Precinct 4 — Larry Durham .... .893-2338 / *Fax: 561-4234*
Justice of the Peace:
 Precinct 1 — Nancy Guilliams .... .561-4337 / *Fax: 561-6257*
 Precinct 4 — Ed L. Follis, Jr. .... .428-3711 / *Fax: 428-3711*

MADISON COUNTY

Population: 14,149
County Seat:
 Madisonville 77864

103 W. Trinity, Suite 113
936 241-6200 / *Fax: 936 241-6201*
www.co.madison.tx.us

County Judge — C.E. McDaniel, Jr. .... .241-6202 / *Fax: 241-6201*
Criminal District Attorney — Brian Risinger .... .348-7049 / *Fax: 348-7052*
District Clerk — Rhonda Savage 241-6212
County Clerk — Susanne Morris .... .241-6210 / *Fax: 241-6211*
County Treasurer — Judi Delesandri .... .348-5141 / *Fax: 241-6206*
Tax Assessor-Collector — Karen M. Lane .... .348-2654 / *Fax: 348-2655*
Sheriff — Travis Neelcy .... .348-2755 / *Fax: 348-3763*
County Auditor — Toni McBee-Joyner .... .241-6221 / *Fax: 241-6222*
Chief Appraiser — Matthew Newton .... .348-2783 / *Fax: 348-6188*
Elections Official — Earl C. Parker, Jr. 349-0132
County Commissioner:
 Precinct 1 — Ricky Driskell .... .241-6241 / *Fax: 241-6251*
 Precinct 2 — Thomas Collard .... .241-6242 / *Fax: 241-6252*
 Precinct 3 — Carl L. Cannon .... .348-1619 / *Fax: 241-6253*
 Precinct 4 — Sam Cole .... .348-4033 / *Fax: 241-6254*
Justice of the Peace:
 Precinct 1 — Jon Stevens .... .348-5151 / *Fax: 348-3989*
 Precinct 2 — Jon Stevens .... .348-5151 / *Fax: 348-3989*
 Precinct 3 — Lew Plotts, Jr. .... .348-5151 / *Fax: 348-3989*
 Precinct 4 — Lew Plotts, Jr. .... .348-5151 / *Fax: 348-3989*
Constable:
 Precinct 1 — James Weathers .... .348-6013 / *Fax: 241-6219*
 Precinct 2 — Charles D. Turner .... .348-6013 / *Fax: 241-6220*

MARION COUNTY

Population: 10,398
County Seat:
 Jefferson 75657

102 W. Austin, Rm. 205
903 665-3261 / *Fax: 903 665-8732*
www.co.marion.tx.us

County Judge	Lex A. Jones	665-3261 / *Fax: 665-8732*
District & County Attorney	Angela Smoak	665-2611 / *Fax: 665-3348*
District Clerk	Susan Anderson	665-2441 / *Fax: 665-2102*
County Clerk	Vickie Smith	665-3971 / *Fax: 665-7936*
County Treasurer	Terrie S. Neuville	665-2472 / *Fax: 665-8732*
Tax Assessor-Collector	Karen Jones	665-3281 / *Fax: 665-3132*
Sheriff	David McKnight	665-7201 / *Fax: 665-7590*
County Auditor	Shanna Solomon	665-7240 / *Fax: 665-8732*
Chief Appraiser	Ann Lummus	665-2519 / *Fax: 665-2576*
County Commissioner:		
Precinct 1	J.R. Ashley	665-8336 / *Fax: 665-8732*
Precinct 2	Joe McKnight	665-8336 / *Fax: 665-8732*
Precinct 3	Glenn Dorough	665-8336 / *Fax: 665-8732*
Precinct 4	C.W. Treadwell	665-8336 / *Fax: 665-8732*
Justice of the Peace:		
Precinct 1	Lena Pope	665-2392 / *Fax: 665-2392*
Precinct 2	JoAnn Nutt	665-3581
Constable:		
Precinct 1	David Capps	665-7892
Precinct 2	Natashia Wison	665-3581

MARTIN COUNTY

Population: 5,589
County Seat:
 Stanton 79782

P.O. Box 1330
432 607-3535 / *Fax: 432 756-2992*
co.martin.tx.us

County Judge	Bryan Cox	607-3535 / *Fax: 756-2992*
District Attorney, 118th Dist.	Hardy L. Wilkerson	264-2220 / *Fax: 264-2222*
County Attorney	James J. Napper	756-2838 / *Fax: 756-2992*
District & County Clerk	Linda Gonzales	756-3412 / *Fax: 607-2212*
County Treasurer	Cynthia O'Donnell	756-3631 / *Fax: 756-2992*
Tax Assessor-Collector	Kathy Hull	756-3997 / *Fax: 756-2992*
Sheriff	James B. Ingram Brad	756-3336 / *Fax: 607-2992*
Chief Appraiser	Marsha Graves	756-2823 / *Fax: 756-2825*
Elections Official	Helen Floyd	607-3580 / *Fax: 607-2542*
County Commissioner:		
Precinct 1	Kenny Stewart	661-5084 / *Fax: 756-2992*
Precinct 2	Robin Barnes	756-2231 / *Fax: 756-2992*
Precinct 3	Bobby Holland	756-3411 / *Fax: 756-2992*
Precinct 4	Koy Blocker	459-2231 / *Fax: 756-2992*
Justice of the Peace:		
Precinct 1	Jarrell W. Hedrick	756-3711 / *Fax: 756-2992*
Precinct 2	Pam McAnally	756-3445 / *Fax: 756-2992*

MASON COUNTY

Population: 4,080
County Seat:
 Mason 76856

P.O. Box 1726
325 347-5556 / *Fax: 325 347-6868*
www.co.mason.tx.us

County Judge	Jerry Bearden	.347-5556 / *Fax: 347-6868*
District Attorney, 452nd Dist.	Tonya S. Ahlschwede	.347-8400 / *Fax: 347-8404*
County Attorney	Rebekah Whitworth	.347-5614 / *Fax: 294-4074*
District & County Clerk	Pam Beam	.347-5253 / *Fax: 347-6868*
County Treasurer	Polly McMillan	.347-5251 / *Fax: 347-6868*
Tax Assessor-Collector	James "Buster" Nixon	.347-6937 / *Fax: 347-6194*
Sheriff	James "Buster" Nixon	.347-5252 / *Fax: 347-6194*
Chief Appraiser	Ted Smith	.347-5989 / *Fax: 347-5302*
County Commissioner:		
Precinct 1	Reggie Loeffler	.347-2734
Precinct 2	Wilburn Frey	.429-6329
Precinct 3	Buddy Schuessler	.347-2509
Precinct 4	Stephen Mutschink	.347-5638
Justice of the Peace:		
Precinct 1	James Treg Hudson	.347-5412 / *Fax: 326 347-6035*

MATAGORDA COUNTY

Population: 36,613
County Seat:
 Bay City 77414

1700 Seventh Street, Room 301
979 244-7605 / *Fax: 979 245-3697*
www.co.matagorda.tx.us

County Judge	Nate McDonald	.244-7605 / *Fax: 245-3697*
District Attorney, 23rd Dist.	Steven E. Reis	.244-7657 / *Fax: 245-9409*
County Attorney	Denise Fortenberry	.244-7645 / *Fax: 244-7647*
District Clerk	Jamie C. Bludau	.244-7621 / *Fax: 244-7624*
County Clerk	Janet Hickl	.244-7680 / *Fax: 244-7688*
County Treasurer	Carmen Andrews	.244-7606 / *Fax: 244-7694*
Tax Assessor-Collector	Cristyn Hallmark	.244-7670 / *Fax: 244-7678*
Sheriff	Frank D. "Skipper" Osborne	.241-3202 / *Fax: 244-3255*
County Auditor	Kristen Kubecka	.244-7611 / *Fax: 241 7628*
Chief Appraiser	Vince Maloney	.244-2031 / *Fax: 244-4254*
County Commissioner:		
Precinct 1	Gary Graham	.245-3914
Precinct 2	Kent Pollard	.863-7861
Precinct 3	James Gibson	.361 972-2719
Precinct 4	Charles Frick	.361 588-6866
Justice of the Peace:		
Precinct 1	Jason K. Sanders	.244-7666 / *Fax: 244-7696*
Precinct 2	Suzan Thompson	.863-2035
Precinct 3	Amy Tapia	.361 972-5313
Precinct 4	Mark Finlay	.843-5601
Precinct 6	Ray Taggart	.245-0358
Constable:		
Precinct 1	Precious K. Smith	.244-7605
Precinct 2	Frank Craft, Jr.	.245-9122
Precinct 3	Jesse Alvarez, Jr.	.244-7605
Precinct 4	Pedro Medina	.244-7605
Precinct 6	William "Bill" Orton, Jr.	.244-7612

COUNTY SECTION

MAVERICK COUNTY

Population: 57,666
County Seat:
  Eagle Pass 78852

500 Quarry Street, Suite 3
830 773-3824 / *Fax: 830 773-6450*
www.co.maverick.tx.us/

County Judge	David R. Saucedo	773-3824 / *Fax: 773-6450*
District Attorney, 293rd Dist.	Roberto Serna	773-9268 / *Fax: 773-9379*
County Attorney	Jaime "AJ" Iracheta	773-3520 / *Fax: 757-2863*
District Clerk	Leopoldo Vielma	773-2629 / *Fax: 773-4439*
County Clerk	Sara Montemayor	773-2829 / *Fax: 752-4479*
County Treasurer	Rito J. Valdez III	773-2413 / *Fax: 757-6957*
Tax Assessor-Collector	Isamari Sanchez-Villarreal	773-9273 / *Fax: 773-6378*
Sheriff	Tom Schmerber	773-2321 / *Fax: 752-1413*
County Auditor	Sandra Watkins	773-3708 / *Fax: 773-4749*
Chief Appraiser	Maggie Mata-Duran	773-0255 / *Fax: 773-8652*
Elections Official	Teodoro Roy Schmerber	757-4175 / *Fax: 757-4337*
County Commissioner:		
Precinct 1	Jerry Morales	773-7672 / *Fax: 773-6473*
Precinct 2	Rosy Cantu	752-4472 / *Fax: 773-6450*
Precinct 3	Pete Venegas	773-1716 / *Fax: 773-7730*
Precinct 4	Roberto Ruiz	773-1057 / *Fax: 752-1210*
Justice of the Peace:		
Precinct 1	Kina Mancha	757-9201 / *Fax: 752-1664*
Precinct 2	Dora Madera	752-1323 / *Fax: 757-4475*
Precinct 3, Pl. 1	David J. Castañeda	757-2710 / *Fax: 325-7050*
Precinct 3, Pl. 2	Jeannie Smith	758-5993/ *Fax: 758-5998*
Precinct 4	Teresa Melendrez	773-9616 / *Fax: 757-1105*
Constable:		
Precinct 1	Rudy Valdez	968-0735
Precinct 2	Jaime S. Rios	513-3539 / *Fax: 773-6450*
Precinct 3, Pl. 1	Mario A. Hernandez	325-0132 / *Fax: 773-1418*
Precinct 3, Pl. 2	Samuel "Sam" Chacon	335-9541 / *Fax: 757-5514*
Precinct 4	Jose Regalado	325-5135

MCCULLOCH COUNTY

Population: 8,352
County Seat:
  Brady 76825

199 Courthouse Square
325 597-0733 / *Fax: 325 597-2980*
www.co.mcculloch.tx.us

County Judge	Danny Neal	597-0733 / *Fax: 597-2980*
District Attorney, 452nd Dist.	Tonya S. Ahlschwede	347-8400 / *Fax: 347-8404*
County Attorney	Mark Marshall	597-9151 / *Fax: 597-9152*
District Clerk	Michelle Pitcox	597-0733 / *Fax: 597-0606*
County Clerk	Tina A. Smith	597-2400 / *Fax: 597-1731*
County Treasurer	Steven Estes	597-0733 / *Fax: 597-1814*
Tax Assessor-Collector	Silvia Campos	597-2400 / *Fax: 597-8306*
Sheriff	John Dagen	597-2290 / *Fax: 597-1662*
Chief Appraiser	Zane Brandenberger	597-1627 / *Fax: 597-2408*

County Commissioner:
  Precinct 1   Jim Quinn 456-7691
  Precinct 2   Gene Edminston 597-0733
  Precinct 3   Jason Ray Behrens 597-0733
  Precinct 4   Brent Deeds 597-0733
Justice of the Peace: Margaret Sawyer . . . . .597-8000 / *Fax: 792-8040*

MCLENNAN COUNTY

Population: 252,626   501 Washington Ave.
County Seat: 254 757-5000
  Waco 76701   www.co.mclennan.tx.us/

County Judge   Scott M. Felton . . . . .757-5049 / *Fax: 757-5196*
Criminal District Attorney Abel Reyna . . . . .757-5084 / *Fax: 757-5021*
District Clerk   Jon Gimble . . . . .757-5054 / *Fax: 757-5060*
County Clerk   J.A. "Andy" Harwell . . . . .757-5140 / *Fax: 757-5146*
County Treasurer   Bill Helton . . . . .757-5020 / *Fax: 759-2832*
Tax Assessor-Collector   Randy H. Riggs . . . . .757-5130 / *Fax: 757-2666*
Sheriff   Parnell McNamara . . . . .757-5095 / *Fax: 757-5091*
County Auditor   Stan Chambers . . . . .757-5156 / *Fax: 757-5157*
Chief Appraiser   Andrew J. Hahn, Jr. . . . . .752-9864 / *Fax: 752-8225*
Elections Official   Kathy E. Van Wolfe . . . . .757-5043 / *Fax: 757-5041*
County Commissioner:
  Precinct 1   Kelly Snell . . . . .757-5061 / *Fax: 757-5007*
  Precinct 2   Lester Gibson .757-5062 / *Fax: 757-5007*
  Precinct 3   Will Jones . . . . .757-5063 / *Fax: 757-5007*
  Precinct 4   Ben Perry . . . . .757-5064 / *Fax: 757-5007*
Justice of the Peace:
  Precinct 1, Pl. 1   Dianne Hensley . . . . .757-5040 / *Fax: 714-2899*
  Precinct 1, Pl. 2   W. H. "Pete" Peterson . . . . .757-5128 / *Fax: 757-5035*
  Precinct 2   James E. Lee, Jr. . . . . .752-9353 / *Fax: 752-9526*
  Precinct 3   David W. Pareya . . . . .826-3341 / *Fax: 826-3595*
  Precinct 4   Brian Richardson . . . . .840-4225 / *Fax: 840-9748*
  Precinct 5   Fernando Villarreal . . . . .752-4242 / *Fax: 752-0227*
Constable:
  Precinct 1   Walt Strickland . . . . .757-5026 / *Fax: 757-5056*
  Precinct 2   John Johnson .752-9196 / *Fax: 752-9526*
  Precinct 3   David A. Maler . . . . .826-5771 / *Fax: 826-3595*
  Precinct 4   Stan Hickey . . . . .840-3388 / *Fax: 840-9748*
  Precinct 5   Freddie Cantu . . . . .752-3199 / *Fax: 752-0227*

MCMULLEN COUNTY

Population: 884
County Seat:
  Tilden 78072

P.O. Box 237
361 274-3341 / *Fax: 361 274-3693*
www.co.mcmullen.tx.us

County Judge	James E. Teal ....274-3900 / *Fax: 274-3693*
District Attorney, 156th Dist.	Jose Aliseda ....358-1007 / *Fax: 358-0505*
County Attorney	Kimberly Dreider-Dusek ....274-3723 / *Fax: 566-2218*
District & County Clerk	Mattie Sadovsky ....274-3215 / *Fax: 274-3858*
County Treasurer	Judy Wyatt ....274-3685 / *Fax: 274-3693*
Tax Assessor-Collector	Bessilia Guerrero ....274-3233 / *Fax: 274-3618*
Sheriff	Emmett Shelton ....274-3311 / *Fax: 274-3736*
Chief Appraiser	Juan Saucedo ....274-3638 / *Fax: 261 274-3618*
County Commissioner:	
Precinct 1	Hilario "Larry" Garcia 274-3224
Precinct 2	Murray Swaim 274-3341
Precinct 3	Scotty McClaugherty
Precinct 4	Maximo G. Quintanilla 274-3263
Justice of the Peace:	Debora Garza ....274-3372 / *Fax: 274-3758*
Constable:	Craig Franklin ....274-3341 / *Fax: 274-3693*

MEDINA COUNTY

Population: 49,558
County Seat:
  Hondo 78861

1100 16th Street
830 741-6000 / *Fax: 830 741-6015*
www.medinacountytexas.org

County Judge	Chris Schuchart ....741-6020 / *Fax: 741-6025*
District Attorney, 38th Dist.	Daniel J. Kindred ....741-6187 / *Fax: 741-6033*
County Attorney	Kim Havel ....741-6080 / *Fax: 741-6015*
District Clerk	Cindy Fowler ....741-6070 / *Fax: 741-6015*
County Clerk	Gina Champion ....741-6040 / *Fax: 741-6015*
County Treasurer	Debbie Southwell ....741-6110 / *Fax: 741-6119*
Tax Assessor-Collector	Melissa Lutz ....741-6100 / *Fax: 741-6105*
Sheriff	Randy R. Brown ....741-6150 / *Fax: 741-6156*
County Auditor	Eduardo Lopez ....741-6091 / *Fax: 741-6094*
Chief Appraiser	Johnette Dixon ....741-3035 / *Fax: 276-2199*
Elections Official	Patricia Barton ....741-6009 / *Fax: 741-6007*
County Commissioner:	
Precinct 1	Timothy "Tim" Neuman ....741-6016 / *Fax: 741-6018*
Precinct 2	Larry Sittre ....931-4000 / *Fax: 741-6119*
Precinct 3	David Lynch ....741-8008 / *Fax: 741-6119*
Precinct 4	Jerry Beck ....665-8015 / *Fax: 665-8016*
Justice of the Peace:	
Precinct 1	Glenn Klaus ....741-6050 / *Fax: 741-6052*
Precinct 2	Mark P. Haby ....931-4010 / *Fax: 931-4015*
Precinct 3	Clyde "Bubba" Howse ....741-6031 / *Fax: 741-6015*
Precinct 4	Phil Montgomery ....665-8020 / *Fax: 665-8021*
Constable:	
Precinct 1	Don Berger ....741-6050 / *Fax: 741-6015*
Precinct 2	Jim Przybylski ....931-4010 / *Fax: 931-4015*
Precinct 3	Stephen Duffy ....363-7258 / *Fax: 741-6015*
Precinct 4	Malcolm Watson ....663-4005 / *Fax: 665-8021*

MENARD COUNTY

Population: 2,340
County Seat:
  Menard 76859

P.O. Box 1038, 206 E. San Saba Ave.
325 396-4682 / *Fax: 325 396-2047*
www.co.menard.tx.us

County Judge	Richard Cordes	.396-4789 / *Fax: 396-2047*
District Attorney, 452nd Dist.	Tonya S. Ahlschwede	.347-8400 / *Fax: 347-8404*
County Attorney	Tom Roberson	.396-4682 / *Fax: 396-2047*
District & County Clerk	Ann Kothmann	.396-4682 / *Fax: 396-2047*
County Treasurer	Robert Bean	.396-2748 / *Fax: 396-2047*
Tax Assessor-Collector	Tim Powell	.396-4523 / *Fax: 396-2047*
Sheriff	Buck Miller	.396-4705 / *Fax: 396-2458*
Chief Appraiser	Kayla Wagner	.396-4784 / *Fax: 396-2916*
County Commissioner:		
Precinct 1	Boyd Murchison	.396-4386 / *Fax: 396-2047*
Precinct 2	Jay Cunningham	.656-3978 / *Fax: 396-2047*
Precinct 3	Ed Keith	.396-2566
Precinct 4	Larry Burch	.396-4789
Justice of the Peace:	Robert Hernandez	.396-2239
Constable:	Lee Callan	.396-4705

COUNTY SECTION

MIDLAND COUNTY

Population: 163,783
County Seat.
  Midland 79701

500 N. Loraine St., Suite 1100
432 688-4310 / *Fax: 432 688-4931*
www.co.midland.tx.us

County Judge	Mike Bradford	.688-4310 / *Fax: 688-4988*
District Attorney, 142nd Dist.	Laura A. Nodolf	.688-4411 / *Fax: 688-4938*
County Attorney	Russell Malm	.688-4490 / *Fax: 688-4931*
District Clerk	Ross Bush	.688-4500 / *Fax: 688-4934*
County Clerk	Alison Haley	.688-4400 / *Fax: 688-4925*
County Treasurer	Mitzi Baker	.688-4880 / *Fax: 688-4917*
Tax Assessor-Collector	Karen Hood	.688-4810 / *Fax: 688-4916*
Sheriff	Gary Painter	.688-4600 / *Fax: 688-4970*
County Auditor	Veronica Morales	.688-4860 / *Fax: 688-4911*
Elections Official	Deborah Land	.688-4890 / *Fax: 688-4912*
County Commissioner:		
Precinct 1	Scott Ramsey	.684-8822 / *Fax: 688-0066*
Precinct 2	Robert "Robin" Donnelly	.688-4802
Precinct 3	Luis D. Sanchez	.688-4803 / *Fax: 688-4988*
Precinct 4	Randy Prude	.685-1980 / *Fax: 685-1242*
Justice of the Peace:		
Precinct 1	Terry M. Luck	.688-4741 / *Fax: 688-4960*
Precinct 2	David M. Cobos	.688-4722 / *Fax: 688-4949*
Precinct 3	Billy G. Johnson, Jr.	.688-4733 / *Fax: 688-4960*
Precinct 4	John Barton	.688-4734 / *Fax: 688-4949*
Constable:		
Precinct 1	David Criner	.688-4711 / *Fax: 688-4965*
Precinct 2	Mark Wohleking	.688-4700 / *Fax: 688-4949*
Precinct 3	Jeffrey N. Rowland	.688-4713 / *Fax: 688-4960*
Precinct 4	Charles Hall	.688-4701 / *Fax: 688-4950*

MILAM COUNTY

Population: 24,167
County Seat:
  Cameron 76520

102 South Fannin
254 697-7000 / *Fax: 254 697-7002*
www.milamcounty.net/

County Judge	Dave Barkemeyer .... 697-7000 / *Fax: 697-7002*
District & County Attorney	Bill Torrey .... 697-7013 / *Fax: 697-7016*
District Clerk	Karen Berry .... 697-7052 / *Fax: 697-7056*
County Clerk	Barbara Vansa .... 697-7049 / *Fax: 697-7055*
County Treasurer	Linda Acosta .... 697-7032 / *Fax: 697-7028*
Tax Assessor-Collector	Sherry Mueck .... 697-7017 / *Fax: 697-7020*
Sheriff	David Greene .... 697-7033 / *Fax: 697-7037*
County Auditor	Danica Lara .... 697-7026 / *Fax: 697-7028*
Chief Appraiser	Dyann White .... 697-6638 / *Fax: 697-8059*
County Commissioner:	
Precinct 1	Richard "Opey" Watkins .... 593-3171 / *Fax: 593-9265*
Precinct 2	Donald Shuffield .... 697-7054 / *Fax: 697-7061*
Precinct 3	John "Barney" Fisher ..... 512 446-2580 / *Fax: 512 446-6293*
Precinct 4	Jeff Muegge .... 512 898-2115 / *Fax: 512 898-2115*
Justice of the Peace:	
Precinct 1	Sam Berry .... 697-7004 / *Fax: 697-7005*
Precinct 2	Sam Berry .... 697-7008 / *Fax: 697-7009*
Precinct 3	Andy Isaacs .... 512 446-5214 / *Fax: 512 446-3098*
Precinct 4	Gary Northcott .... 512 898-5252 / *Fax: 512 898-5424*
Constable:	
Precinct 1	John Anderle 281 723-6192
Precinct 2	Charlie West 697-7000
Precinct 3	Jay Beathard 482-3015
Precinct 4	Michael M. Moehling, Jr. 512 862-3361

MILLS COUNTY

Population: 5,064
County Seat:
  Goldthwaite 76844

1011 4th Street, P.O. Box 483
325 648-2222 / *Fax: 325 648-2806*
www.co.mills.tx.us

County Judge	Kirkland A. Fulk .... 648-2222 / *Fax: 648-2806*
District Attorney, 35th Dist.	Micheal B. Murray .... 646-0444 / *Fax: 643-4053*
County Attorney	Gerald Hale .... 648-2233 / *Fax: 648-2353*
District & County Clerk	Carolyn Foster .... 648-2711 / *Fax: 648-3251*
County Treasurer	Terrena Busby .... 648-2636 / *Fax: 648-3546*
Tax Assessor-Collector	Lori Fariss .... 648-3879 / *Fax: 648-2324*
Sheriff	Clint Hammonds .... 648-2245 / *Fax: 648-3797*
Chief Appraiser	Codi A. McCarn RPA, CCA .... 648-2253 / *Fax: 648-3458*
County Commissioner:	
Precinct 1	Mike Wright .... 648-2222 / *Fax: 648-2806*
Precinct 2	Jed Garren .... 648-2222 / *Fax: 648-2806*
Precinct 3	Robert Hall .... 648-2222 / *Fax: 648-2806*
Precinct 4	Jason Williams .... 648-2222 / *Fax: 648-2806*
Justice of the Peace:	Kimberly Avants .... 648-2278 / *Fax: 648-3478*

MITCHELL COUNTY

Population: 9,013
County Seat:
  Colorado City 79512

349 Oak Street
325 728-3481 / *Fax: 325 728-5322*

County Judge	Ray Mayo	.728-8439 / *Fax: 728-8697*
District Attorney, 32nd Dist.	Ricky Thompson	.728-3457 / *Fax: 728-8697*
County Attorney	Sterling T. Burleson II	.728-3457 / *Fax: 728-3944*
District Clerk	Belinda Blassingame	.728-5918 / *Fax: 728-8697*
County Clerk	Debby Carlock	.728-3481 / *Fax: 728-5322*
County Treasurer	Jennifer Riveria	.728-8356 / *Fax: 728-8399*
Tax Assessor-Collector	Sylvia Clanton	.728-2606 / *Fax: 728-3963*
Sheriff	Patrick Toombs	.728-5261 / *Fax: 728-8319*
County Auditor	Heidi Harris	.728-2196 / *Fax: 728-2266*
Chief Appraiser	Linda McSpadden	.728-5028 / *Fax: 728-8024*
Elections Official	Debby Carlock	.728-3481 / *Fax: 728-5322*
County Commissioner:		
Precinct 1	Randy Anderson	.728-2735 / *Fax: 728-8697*
Precinct 2	Jeremy Strain	.728-2735 / *Fax: 728-8697*
Precinct 3	Jesse Munoz	.728-2735 / *Fax: 728-8697*
Precinct 4	Billy H. Preston	.728-2735 / *Fax: 728-2266*
Justice of the Peace:		
Precinct 1	Rick Grissam	.728-8906 / *Fax: 728-2002*
Precinct 2	James Williams	.728-5162 / *Fax: 728-8185*

MONTAGUE COUNTY

Population: 19,675
County Seat:
  Montague 76251

P.O. Box 564, Nocona, 76255
940 894-2401 / *Fax: 940 894-3999*
www.co.montague.tx.us

County Judge	Rick Lewis	.894-2401 / *Fax: 894-3999*
District Attorney, 97th Dist.	Casey Polhemus	.894-6211 / *Fax: 894-6203*
County Attorney	Clay Riddle	.894-2261 / *Fax: 894-2805*
District Clerk	Lesia Darden	.894-2571 / *Fax: 894-2077*
County Clerk	Glenda Henson	.894-2461 / *Fax: 894-6601*
County Treasurer	Linda McGaughey	.894-2161 / *Fax: 894-3110*
Tax Assessor-Collector	Sydney Nowell	.894-3881 / *Fax: 894-2012*
Sheriff	Marshall W. Thomas	.894-2871 / *Fax: 894-2114*
County Auditor	Jennifer Essary	.894-6090 / *Fax: 894-3110*
Chief Appraiser	Kim Haralson	.894-6011 / *Fax: 894-6599*
Elections Official	Ginger Wall	.894-2540 / *Fax: 894-2543*
County Commissioner:		
Precinct 1	Roy L. Darden	.964-2388 / *Fax: 894-3110*
Precinct 2	Mike Mayfield	.872-1741 / *Fax: 894-3110*
Precinct 3	Mark Murphey	.825-3742 / *Fax: 894-3110*
Precinct 4	Bob Langford	.995-2667 / *Fax: 894-3110*
Justice of the Peace:		
Precinct 1	David Allen	.894-2541 / *Fax: 894-2544*
Precinct 2	Karen Reynolds	.894-2542 / *Fax: 894-2545*
Constable:		
Precinct 1	Stefanie Horton	.841-1150 / *Fax: 894-2553*
Precinct 2	Ronnie Reynolds	.841-0919 / *Fax: 894-2553*

COUNTY SECTION

MONTGOMERY COUNTY

Population: 549,928
County Seat:
  Conroe 77301

501 N. Thompson, Suite 401
936 756-0571 / *Fax: 936 760-6919*
www.mctx.org

County Judge	Craig Doyal	539-7812 / *Fax: 760-6919*
District Attorney, 9th Dist.	Brett W. Ligon	539-7800 / *Fax: 760-6940*
County Attorney	J D Lambright	539-7828 / *Fax: 760-6920*
District Clerk	Barbara Adamick	539-7855 / *Fax: 538-8138*
County Clerk	Mark Turnbull	539-7885 / *Fax: 760-6927*
County Treasurer	Stephanne Davenport	539-7844 / *Fax: 760-6960*
Tax Assessor-Collector	Tammy McRae	539-7897 / *Fax: 760-6992*
Sheriff	Rand Henderson	760-5872 / *Fax: 538-7797*
County Auditor	Phyllis Martin	539-7820 / *Fax: 788-8390*
Chief Appraiser	Tony Bilinosky	756-3354 / *Fax: 539-8629*
Elections Official	Suzie Harvey	539-7843 / *Fax: 788-8340*
County Commissioner:		
Precinct 1	Mike Meador	539-7815 / *Fax: 539-7874*
Precinct 2	Charlie Riley	539-7816 / *Fax: 760-6954*
Precinct 3	James Noack	539-7817 / *Fax: 281 298-7321*
Precinct 4	Jim Clark	521-8919 / *Fax: 521-8918*
Justice of the Peace:		
Precinct 1	Wayne Mack	856-7949 / *Fax: 788-8399*
Precinct 2	Trey Spikes	538-3788 / *Fax: 538-7732*
Precinct 3	Edie Connelly	281 364-4284 / *Fax: 539-7959*
Precinct 4	James Metts	521-8970 / *Fax: 521-8947*
Precinct 5	Matt Masden	281 259-6494 / *Fax: 760-6989*
Constable:		
Precinct 1	Philip Cash	539-7821 / *Fax: 856-9408*
Precinct 2	Gene DeForest	539-7854 / *Fax: 539-7935*
Precinct 3	Ryan Gable	281 364-4211 / *Fax: 281 465-3504*
Precinct 4	Kenneth "Rowdy" Hayden	521-8985 / *Fax: 521-8985*
Precinct 5	David Hill	281 259-6493 / *Fax: 281 259-6462*

MOORE COUNTY

Population: 22,851
County Seat:
  Dumas 79029

715 Dumas Ave., Room 202
806 935-5588 / *Fax: 806 935-5697*
www.co.moore.tx.us

County Judge	J. D. "Rowdy" Rhoades	935-5588 / *Fax: 935-5697*
District Attorney, 69th Dist.	David M. Green	935-5654 / *Fax: 934-2155*
County Attorney	Scott Higginbotham	935-2407 / *Fax: 935-6690*
District Clerk	Diane Hoefling	935-4218 / *Fax: 935-6325*
County Clerk	Brenda McKanna	935-2009 / *Fax: 935-9004*
County Treasurer	Pam Cox	935-2019 / *Fax: 935-6847*
Tax Assessor-Collector	Nikki McDonald	935-2008 / *Fax: 935-2344*
Sheriff	J.E. "Bo" DeArmond	935-4145 / *Fax: 935-2699*
County Auditor	James Allen	935-7919 / *Fax: 935-3753*
Chief Appraiser	Alfonso Venegas, Interim	935-4193 / *Fax: 935-2792*

County Commissioner:
  Precinct 1   Daniel Garcia . . . . .934-3248 / *Fax: 935-5697*
  Precinct 2   Genevie Sheets . . . . .935-6761 / *Fax: 935-5697*
  Precinct 3   Dee Vaughan . . . . .935-6269 / *Fax: 935-5697*
  Precinct 4   Lynn Cartrite 930-5545
Justice of the Peace:
  Precinct 1   Barbara Mulanax . . . . .935-3920 / *Fax: 935-4614*
  Precinct 2   Sue Sims . . . . .948-5362 / *Fax: 948-0037*

MORRIS COUNTY

Population: 12,988   500 Broadnax
County Seat: 903 645-3691 / *Fax: 903 645-5729*
  Daingerfield 75638   www.co.morris.tx.us

COUNTY SECTION

County Judge   Lynda Munkres . . . . .645-3691 / *Fax: 645-5729*
District & County Attorney   Steve Cowan . . . . .645-2021 / *Fax: 645-7666*
District Clerk   Gwen Ashworth . . . . .645-2321 / *Fax: 645-3433*
County Clerk   Scott Sartain . . . . .645-3911 / *Fax: 645-4026*
County Treasurer   Nita Beth Traylor . . . . .645-2916 / *Fax: 645-5729*
Tax Assessor-Collector   Kim Thomasson . . . . .645-2446 / *Fax: 645-5351*
Sheriff   Jack Martin . . . . .645-2232 / *Fax: 645-7228*
County Auditor   Shanna Solomon . . . . .645-2717 / *Fax: 645-5729*
Chief Appraiser   Summer Golden . . . . .645-5601 / *Fax: 645-2694*
County Commissioner:
  Precinct 1   Dennis Allen . . . . .645-3691 / *Fax: 645-5729*
  Precinct 2   Weldon Lilley . . . . .645-3691 / *Fax: 645-5729*
  Precinct 3   Michael Clair . . . . .645-3691 / *Fax: 645-5729*
  Precinct 4   Todd Freeman . . . . .645-3691 / *Fax: 645-5729*
Justice of the Peace:
  Precinct 1   Nikita Fridia . . . . .645-3691 / *Fax: 645-5729*
  Precinct 2   Jennifer Easley . . . . .645-3031 / *Fax: 645-7228*
Constable:
  Precinct 2   Kerry B. McCoy . . . . .645-7202 / *Fax: 645-7228*

MOTLEY COUNTY

Population: 1,100
County Seat:
  Matador 79244

701 Dundee, P.O. Box 719
806 347-2334 / *Fax: 806 347-2072*

County Judge	James B. "Jim" Meador	.347-2334 / *Fax: 347-2220*
District Attorney, 110th Dist.	Wade Jackson	.983-2197 / *Fax: 983-2400*
County Attorney	Tom Edwards	.347-2333 / *Fax: 347-2343*
District & County Clerk	Jamie Martin	.347-2621 / *Fax: 347-2220*
County Treasurer	Misty Jones	.347-2800 / *Fax: 347-2220*
Tax Assessor-Collector	Jana Marshall	.347-2252 / *Fax: 347-2220*
Sheriff	Robert Fisk	.347-2234 / *Fax: 347-2692*
Chief Appraiser	Jim Finley	.983-5256 / *Fax: 983-6230*
County Commissioner:		
Precinct 1	Guy Campbell	.347-2334 / *Fax: 347-2072*
Precinct 2	Donnie L. Turner	.347-2334 / *Fax: 347-2072*
Precinct 3	Franklin Jameson	.347-2334 / *Fax: 347-2072*
Precinct 4	David Stafford	.347-2334 / *Fax: 347-2072*
Justice of the Peace:	Libby Cruse	.347-2204 / *Fax: 347-2161*

NACOGDOCHES COUNTY

Population: 65,747
County Seat:
  Nacogdoches 75961

101 W. Main Street, Suite 170
936 560-7755 / *Fax: 936 560-7841*
www.co.nacogdoches.tx.us/

County Judge	Mike Perry	.560-7755 / *Fax: 560-7841*
District Attorney, 145th Dist.	Nicole D. Lostracco	.560-7766 / *Fax: 560-6036*
County Attorney	John Fleming	.560-7789 / *Fax: 560-7809*
District Clerk	Loretta Cammack	.560-7741 / *Fax: 560-7839*
County Clerk	June Clifton	.560-7733 / *Fax: 559-5926*
County Treasurer	Denise Baublet	.560-7804 / *Fax: 560-7846*
Tax Assessor-Collector	Kim Morton	.560-7767 / *Fax: 564-2217*
Sheriff	Jason Bridges	.560-7794 / *Fax: 560-6446*
County Auditor	Jessica Corley	.560-7761 / *Fax: 560-7702*
Chief Appraiser	Gary Woods	.560-3447 / *Fax: 560-1894*
Elections Official	Todd Stallings	.560-7825 / *Fax: 560-7838*
County Commissioner:		
Precinct 1	Jerry Don Williamson	.560-7709 / *Fax: 560-7841*
Precinct 2	Jerry D. Stone	.560-7784 / *Fax: 560-7841*
Precinct 3	Robin Dawley	.560-7756 / *Fax: 560-7841*
Precinct 4	Elton Milstead	.560-7738 / *Fax: 560-7841*
Justice of the Peace:		
Precinct 1	Kerry Williamson	.560-4867 / *Fax: 560-6487*
Precinct 2	Dorothy Tigner-Thompson	.560-7726 / *Fax: 560-7892*
Precinct 3	LeAnn Goerner	.560-7889 / *Fax: 569-7009*
Precinct 4	David Perkins	.569-9365 / *Fax: 568-0131*
Constable:		
Precinct 1	William Sowell	.569-6727 / *Fax: 560-3259*
Precinct 2	Clarence Y. Yarbrough	.560-7779 / *Fax: 560-7892*
Precinct 3	Roger Dudley	.554-0449 / *Fax: 569-7009*
Precinct 4	David Stone	.715-0317 / *Fax: 568-0131*

NAVARRO COUNTY

Population: 49,647
County Seat:
  Corsicana 75110

300 W. 3rd Avenue, Suite 102, Corsicana, 75151
903 654-3035 / *Fax: 903 872-0778*
www.co.navarro.tx.us/

County Judge	H. M. Davenport, Jr.	654-3025 / *Fax: 872-0778*
Criminal District Attorney	R. Lowell Thompson	654-3045 / *Fax: 872-6858*
District Clerk	Joshua B. Tackett	654-3040 / *Fax: 654-3088*
County Clerk	Sherry Dowd	654-3035 / *Fax: 872-7329*
County Treasurer	Ryan Douglas	654-3090 / *Fax: 875-3391*
Tax Assessor-Collector	Mike Dowd	654-3080 / *Fax: 874-5675*
Sheriff	Elmer Tanner	654-3001 / *Fax: 654-3044*
County Auditor	Terri Gillen	654-3095 / *Fax: 654-3097*
Chief Appraiser	Karen Morris	872-6161 / *Fax: 874-0604*
Elections Official	Danda Parker	875-3330 / *Fax: 875-3331*
County Commissioner:		
Precinct 1	Jason Grant	654-3031 / *Fax: 874-6053*
Precinct 2	Richard "Dick" Martin	654-3032 / *Fax: 874-6053*
Precinct 3	Eddie Moore	654-3033 / *Fax: 874-6053*
Precinct 4	James Olsen	654-3034 / *Fax: 874-6053*
Justice of the Peace:		
Precinct 1	Vicki Gray	654-3055 / *Fax: 654-3092*
Precinct 2	Darrell Waller	654-3058 / *Fax: 654-3092*
Precinct 3	Jackie Freeland	875-3363 / *Fax: 654-3092*
Precinct 4	Connie Hickman	654-3060 / *Fax: 654-3092*
Constable:		
Precinct 1	Mike Davis	654-2580 / *Fax: 875-3980*
Precinct 2	David Foreman	654-3308 / *Fax: 396-2278*
Precinct 3	Bobby J. Rachel	956-4942
Precinct 4	Kipp Thomas	357-0158

NEWTON COUNTY

Population: 13,963
County Seat:
  Newton 75966

P.O. Drawer 1380
409 379-5691 / *Fax: 409 379-2107*
www.co.newton.tx.us

County Judge	Paul Price	379-5691 / *Fax: 379-2107*
Criminal District Attorney	Courtney Tracy Ponthier	379-8600 / *Fax: 379-8603*
District Clerk	Bree Allen	379-3951 / *Fax: 379-9087*
County Clerk	Sandra Duckworth	379-5341 / *Fax: 379-9049*
County Treasurer	Ginger Siau	379-8127 / *Fax: 379-5623*
Tax Assessor-Collector	Melissa J. Burks, PCC	379-4241 / *Fax: 379-5944*
Sheriff	Billy E. Rowles	379-3636 / *Fax: 379-3071*
County Auditor	Elizabeth A. Holloway	379-5755 / *Fax: 379-3359*
Chief Appraiser	Margie Herrin	379-3710 / *Fax: 379-4020*
Elections Official	Sandra Duckworth	379-5341 / *Fax: 379-9049*
County Commissioner:		
Precinct 1	William L. Fuller	423-5206 / *Fax: 379-2107*
Precinct 2	Thomas Gill	565-2028 / *Fax: 379-2107*
Precinct 3	Gary Fomby	565-4015 / *Fax: 565-4015*
Precinct 4	Gene Thompson	746-3935 / *Fax: 746-9799*

COUNTY SECTION

Newton County Cont.

Justice of the Peace:
Precinct 1   Connie Smith .... 397-4545 / *Fax: 397-4455*
Precinct 2   Brenda Smith .... 565-9944 / *Fax: 565-1017*
Precinct 3   Mike Greer .... 379-2169 / *Fax: 379-2058*
Precinct 4   Dana Ashmore .... 746-7190 / *Fax: 746-9843*
Constable:
Precinct 1   Odis Lane 423-3693
Precinct 2   Les Amburn 698-7487
Precinct 3   Holton C. "Bubba" Johnson 489-5032
Precinct 4   Jimmy Lavergne 920-3181

NOLAN COUNTY

Population: 14,673
County Seat:
  Sweetwater 79556

100 East Third Street
325 235-2263 / *Fax: 325 236-9416*
www.co.nolan.tx.us

County Judge   Whitley May .... .235-2263 / *Fax: 236-9416*
District Attorney, 32nd Dist.   Ricky Thompson .... .235-8639 / *Fax: 235-5886*
County Attorney   Lisa W. Peterson .... .235-5469 / *Fax: 236-9416*
District Clerk   Jamie Clem .... .235-2111 / *Fax: 430-6089*
County Clerk   Sharla Keith .... .235-2462 / *Fax: 235-4635*
County Treasurer   Jeanne P. Wells .... .236-6932 / *Fax: 235-1271*
Tax Assessor-Collector   Kathy Bowen .... .235-3271 / *Fax: 236-9506*
Sheriff   David Warren .... .235-5471 / *Fax: 235-5750*
County Auditor   Judy Kasper .... .235-5857 / *Fax: 235-1271*
Chief Appraiser   Brenda Klepper .... .235-8421 / *Fax: 235-8165*
County Commissioner:
Precinct 1   Terry Willman .... .235-3355 / *Fax: 236-9416*
Precinct 2   Doug Alexander .... .235-3355 / *Fax: 236-9416*
Precinct 3   Tommy White .... .235-3355 / *Fax: 236-9416*
Precinct 4   Tony Lara .... .235-3355 / *Fax: 236-9416*
Justice of the Peace: Sharon Gardner .... .235-5482 / *Fax: 235-5750*
Constable: Stephen F. Smith ll .... .829-2723 / *Fax: 235-5750*

NUECES COUNTY

Population: 361,320
County Seat:
  Corpus Christi 78401

901 Leopard, Room 303
361 888-0444 / *Fax: 361 888-0445*
www.nuecesco.com

County Judge   Loyd Neal .... .888-0444 / *Fax: 888-0445*
District Attorney, 105th Dist.   Mark A. Gonzalez .... .888-0410 / *Fax: 888-0700*
County Attorney   Laura Garza Jimenez .... .888-0391 / *Fax: 888-0577*
District Clerk   Anne Lorentzen .... .888-0450 / *Fax: 888-0571*
County Clerk   Kara Sands .... .888-0580 / *Fax: 888-0329*
Tax Assessor-Collector   Kevin Kieschnick .... .888-0230 / *Fax: 888-0236*
Sheriff   Jim Kaelin .... .887-2222 / *Fax: 887-2206*
County Auditor   Dale Atchley .... .888-0556 / *Fax: 888-0584*
Chief Appraiser   Ramiro "Ronnie" Canales .... .881-9978 / *Fax: 887-6138*

County Commissioner:
Precinct 1 — Mike Pusley .... 888-0245 / *Fax: 888-0284*
Precinct 2 — Joe A. Gonzalez .... 888-0296 / *Fax: 888-0239*
Precinct 3 — John Marez .... 387-1151 / *Fax: 387-9868*
Precinct 4 — Brent Chesney .... 888-0268 / *Fax: 888-0470*

Justice of the Peace:
Precinct 1, Pl. 1 — Joe Benavides .... 888-0201 / *Fax: 888-0279*
Precinct 1, Pl. 2 — Henry Santana .... 888-0210 / *Fax: 888-0321*
Precinct 1, Pl. 3 — Robert "Bobby" Balderas .... 241-1222 / *Fax: 242-2677*
Precinct 2, Pl. 1 — Jo Woolsey .... 853-4079 / *Fax: 853-4092*
Precinct 2, Pl. 2 — Thelma L. Rodriguez .... 937-2614 / *Fax: 937-1015*
Precinct 3 — Larry L. Lawrence .... 584-2420 / *Fax: 584-1521*
Precinct 4 — Duncan Neblett .... 749-5661 / *Fax: 749-0231*
Precinct 5, Pl. 1 — Robert "Bobby" Gonzalez .... 767-5205 / *Fax: 767-5206*
Precinct 5, Pl. 2 — Hermilo Pena, Jr. .... 998-2101 / *Fax: 998-2101*

Constable:
Precinct 1 — Robert Cisneros .... 888-0503 / *Fax: 888-0777*
Precinct 2 — Mitchell Clark .... 937-6306 / *Fax: 937-1121*
Precinct 3 — Jimmy Rivera .... 387-7211 / *Fax: 584-2177*
Precinct 4 — Robert "Bobby" Sherwood .... 749-5212 / *Fax: 749-4684*
Precinct 5 — Frank Flores, III .... 767-5204 / *Fax: 767-5249*

OCHILTREE COUNTY

Population: 10,936
County Seat:
Perryton 79070

511 S. Main
806 435-8031 / *Fax: 806 435-2081*
www.co.ochiltree.tx.us

County Judge — Earl McKinley .... 435-8031 / *Fax: 435-2081*
District & County Attorney — Jose N. Meraz .... 435-8035 / *Fax: 435-8069*
District Clerk — Shawn Bogard .... 435-8054 / *Fax: 435-8058*
County Clerk — Stacey Brown .... 435-8039 / *Fax: 435-2081*
County Treasurer — Janet Reynolds .... 435-8046 / *Fax: 648-1309*
Tax Assessor-Collector — Linda Womble .... 435-8060 / *Fax: 435-2899*
Sheriff — Terry L. Bouchard .... 435-8000 / *Fax: 435-8011*
County Auditor — Jim Dear .... 435-8044 / *Fax: 648-1309*
Chief Appraiser — Burton Jones .... 435-9623 / *Fax: 435-4198*

County Commissioner:
Precinct 1 — Duane Pshigoda .... 435-6169 / *Fax: 435-2081*
Precinct 2 — David Peckenpaugh .... 435-8031 / *Fax: 435-2081*
Precinct 3 — Richard Burger .... 435-8031 / *Fax: 435-2081*
Precinct 4 — Dempsey Malaney .... 435-8031 / *Fax: 435-2081*

Justice of the Peace:
Precinct 1 — Braden Karber .... 435-8020 / *Fax: 435-2081*

Constable: — Dwain Read .... 435-8000 / *Fax: 435-8011*

OLDHAM COUNTY

Population: 2,085
County Seat:
  Vega 79092

P.O. Box 571
806 267-2722 / *Fax: 806 267-2671*
www.co.oldham.tx.us

County Judge	Don R. Allred	.267-2607 / *Fax: 267-2671*
County Attorney	Kent Birdsong	.267-2233
District & County Clerk	Darla Lookingbill	.267-2667 / *Fax: 267-2671*
County Treasurer	Sherri Johnson	.267-2329 / *Fax: 267-2671*
Tax Assessor-Collector	Linda Brown	.267-2280 / *Fax: 267-0354*
Sheriff	Brent Warden	.267-2162 / *Fax: 267-2362*
County Auditor	Charlotte Cook	.267-2722 / *Fax: 267-2671*
Chief Appraiser	Leann Voyles	.267-2442 / *Fax: 267-2471*
County Commissioner:		
Precinct 1	Quincy Taylor	.267-2564
Precinct 2	Larry Groneman	.267-2607
Precinct 3	Roger Morris, III	.267-2883
Precinct 4	Billy Don Brown	.538-6350
Justice of the Peace:	Kristy Homfeld	.267-2619 / *Fax: 267-2838*

ORANGE COUNTY

Population: 83,278
County Seat:
  Orange 77630

123 South 6th Street
409 882-7740 / *Fax: 409 882-7079*
www.co.orange.tx.us/

County Judge	Stephen Brint Carlton	.882-7070 / *Fax: 882-7079*
District & County Attorney	John D. Kimbrough	.883-6764 / *Fax: 883-9322*
District Clerk	Vickie Edgerly	.882-7825 / *Fax: 882-7083*
County Clerk	Brandy Robertson	.882-7055 / *Fax: 882-7012*
County Treasurer	Christy Khoury	.882-7991 / *Fax: 882-7066*
Tax Assessor-Collector	Karen Fisher	.882-7971 / *Fax: 882-7912*
Sheriff	Keith Merritt	.882-7958 / *Fax: 670-4156*
County Auditor	Pennee Schmitt	.882-7020 / *Fax: 882-7029*
Chief Appraiser	Mike Cedars	.745-4777 / *Fax: 745-4112*
Elections Official	Tina Jo Barrow	.882-7973 / *Fax: 670-4176*
County Commissioner:		
Precinct 1	Johnny Trahan	.746-2593 / *Fax: 882-7079*
Precinct 2	Barry Burton	.745-2223 / *Fax: 745-9926*
Precinct 3	John Gothia	.882-5308 / *Fax: 882-7079*
Precinct 4	Jody Crump	.769-6724 / *Fax: 783-9830*
Justice of the Peace:		
Precinct 1	Hershel Stagner	.882-7800 / *Fax: 882-7001*
Precinct 2	Derry Dunn	.882-7805 / *Fax: 882-7808*
Precinct 3	Joy Dubose-Simonton	.882-5310 / *Fax: 882-5314*
Precinct 4	Rodney Price	.769-2284 / *Fax: 769-0918*
Constable:		
Precinct 1	Chris Humble	.882-7810
Precinct 2	David Cagle	.882-78115
Precinct 3	Mark Philpott	.882-7812
Precinct 4	Jimmy Lane Mooney	.769-0513

PALO PINTO COUNTY

Population: 28,382
County Seat:
  Palo Pinto 76484

P.O. Box 190
940 659-1253 / *Fax: 888 965-1552*
www.co.palo-pinto.tx.us/

County Judge	David Nicklas	659-1253 / *Fax: 888 965-1552*
District Attorney, 29th Dist.	Kriste Burnett	659-1251 / *Fax: 659-3885*
County Attorney	Jimmy A. Ashby	659-1278 / *Fax: 659-4210*
District Clerk	Janie Glover	659-1224 / *Fax: 659-2590*
County Clerk	Janette K. Green	659-1277 / *Fax: 844 769-4976*
County Treasurer	Tanya Fallin	659-1260 / *Fax: 659-3572*
Tax Assessor-Collector	Stacy Choate	659-1271 / *Fax: 659-3628*
Sheriff	Brett McGuire	659-2085 / *Fax: 659-3801*
County Auditor	Phyllis Banks	659-1276 / *Fax: 659-2590*
Chief Appraiser	Donna Rhoades	659-1281 / *Fax: 659-2618*
Elections Official	Judith S. Evans	659-1217 / *Fax: 659-2289*
County Commissioner:		
Precinct 1	Gary Glover	659-1210 / *Fax: 659-2590*
Precinct 2	Louis Ragle	659-1210 / *Fax: 659-2590*
Precinct 3	Michael Pierce	659-1210 / *Fax: 659-2590*
Precinct 4	Jeff Fryer	659-1210 / *Fax: 659-2590*
Justice of the Peace:		
Precinct 1	Todd Baker	659-1202 / *Fax: 659-2356*
Precinct 2	Shane Long	950 329-1539
Precinct 3	Shawn Humphries	779-3551 / *Fax: 779-2947*
Precinct 4	C. L. Hodgkins, Jr.	254 672-5381 / *Fax: 254 672-5990*
Precinct 5	Bobby Hart	325-3201 / *Fax: 325-4011*
Constable:		
Precinct 1	Rod Price	745-1207 / *Fax: 659-2590*
Precinct 2	Marc Moon	659-2085 / *Fax: 659-3801*
Precinct 3	Mike Santifer	659-2085
Precinct 4	Abel Saldana	254 210-2110
Precinct 5	Scott Mitcham	682-1853

PANOLA COUNTY

Population: 24,417
County Seat:
  Carthage 75633

110 S. Sycamore, Room 216-A
903 693-0391 / *Fax: 903 693-2726*
www.co.panola.tx.us

County Judge	Lee Ann Jones	.693-0391 / *Fax: 693-2726*
Criminal District Attorney	Danny Buck Davidson	.693-0310 / *Fax: 693-0368*
District Clerk	Debra Johnson	.693-0306 / *Fax: 693-6914*
County Clerk	Bobbie Davis	.693-0302 / *Fax: 693-0328*
County Treasurer	Joni W. Reed	.693-0325 / *Fax: 693-4125*
Tax Assessor-Collector	Debbie Crawford	.693-0340 / *Fax: 693-2726*
Sheriff	Kevin Lake	.693-0333 / *Fax: 693-9366*
County Auditor	Sidney Burns	.693-0320 / *Fax: 693-2726*
Chief Appraiser	Douglas McPhail	.693-2891 / *Fax: 693-8229*
Elections Official	Cheyenne Lampley	.693-0370 / *Fax: 693-7283*
County Commissioner:		
Precinct 1	Ronnie LaGrone	.693-0385 / *Fax: 693-2726*
Precinct 2	John Gradberg	.693-0385 / *Fax: 693-2726*
Precinct 3	Craig M. Lawless	.693-0385 / *Fax: 693-2726*
Precinct 4	Dale LaGrone	.693-0385 / *Fax: 693-2726*
Justice of the Peace:		
Precinct 1	David Gray	.693-0375 / *Fax: 694-2674*
Precinct 2	Toni Hughes	.693-0377 / *Fax: 693-4708*
Precinct 3	Toni Hughes	.693-0377 / *Fax: 693-4708*
Precinct 4	David Gray	.693-0375 / *Fax: 694-2674*
Constable:		
Precinct 1	Bryan Murff	.693-0333 / *Fax: 693-9366*
Precinct 2	Mitch Norton	.693-0385 / *Fax: 693-0342*
Precinct 3	Mitch Norton	.693-0385 / *Fax: 693-0342*
Precinct 4	Bryan Murff	.693-0333 / *Fax: 693-9366*

PARKER COUNTY

Population: 131,437
County Seat:
  Weatherford 76086

1 Courthouse Square
817 598-6148 / *Fax. 817 598-6199*
www.co.parker.tx.us

County Judge	Mark Riley	.598-6148 / *Fax: 598-6199*
District Attorney, 43rd Dist.	Donald Schnebly	.598-6124 / *Fax: 599-7628*
County Attorney	John Forrest	.594-8409 / *Fax: 594-8414*
District Clerk	Sharena Gilliland	.598-6114 / *Fax: 598-6131*
County Clerk	Jeane Brunson	.598-6163 / *Fax: 594-9540*
County Treasurer	Jenny Barnwell	.598-6150 / *Fax: 598-6180*
Tax Assessor-Collector	Jennifer "Jenny" Gentry	.598-6139 / *Fax: 598-6133*
Sheriff	Larry Fowler	.594-8845 / *Fax: 594-7809*
County Auditor	Mike Rhoten	.598-6104 / *Fax: 598-6181*
Chief Appraiser	Larry Hammonds	.596-0077 / *Fax: 613-8096*
Elections Official	Don Markum	.598-6185 / *Fax: 598-6183*
County Commissioner:		
Precinct 1	George Conley	.220-7218 / *Fax: 220-7220*
Precinct 2	Craig Peacock	.594-4022
Precinct 3	Larry D. Walden	.594-0371 / *Fax: 594-4496*
Precinct 4	Steve Dugan	.596-0004 / *Fax: 596-5016*

Justice of the Peace:
  Precinct 1   Wayne Hayes 682 229-2104
  Precinct 2   Kelly Green 682 229-2171
  Precinct 3   Dusty Vinson...............................598-6086
  Precinct 4   Kirk D. Martin 441-9396
Constable:
  Precinct 1   Charlie Hunt ....523-0027 / *Fax: 220-2000*
  Precinct 2   Joe Harris, Jr. 682 229-2167
  Precinct 3   Glen Praytor ....598-6193 / *Fax: 598-6171*
  Precinct 4   Scott Jones ....441-9396 / *Fax: 682 229-2227*

PARMER COUNTY

Population: 9,748
County Seat:
  Farwell 79325

P.O. Box 506
806 481-3383 / *Fax: 806 481-9548*
parmercounty.org

County Judge   Trey Ellis ....481-3383 / *Fax: 481-9548*
District Attorney, 287th Dist.   Kathryn Gurley ....250-2050 / *Fax: 250-9053*
County Attorney   Jeff W. Actkinson ....481-3361 / *Fax: 481-9060*
District Clerk   Sandra Warren ....481-3419 / *Fax: 481-9416*
County Clerk   Gerri Bowers ....481-3691 / *Fax: 481-9548*
County Treasurer   Altha Herington ....481-9152 / *Fax: 481-9154*
Tax Assessor-Collector   Awyna Sanchez ....481-3845 / *Fax: 481-9548*
Sheriff   Randy Geries ....481-3303 / *Fax: 481-3305*
County Auditor   Larry Johnston ....481-9151 / *Fax: 481-9154*
Chief Appraiser   Jill Timms ....251-1405 / *Fax: 251-1121*
County Commissioner:
  Precinct 1   Kirk Frye ....265-7514 / *Fax: 481-9548*
  Precinct 2   Steve Cockerham ....225-7295 / *Fax: 481-9548*
  Precinct 3   Kenny White ....225-7237 / *Fax: 481-9548*
  Precinct 4   Lloyd Bradshaw ....946-8255 / *Fax: 481-9548*
Justice of the Peace:
  Precinct 1   JoBeth Gipson ....250-2412 / *Fax: 250-2414*
  Precinct 2   Sandra Clayton 251-1356
  Precinct 3   Pamela Haseloff ....481-9964 / *Fax: 481-9965*

PECOS COUNTY

Population: 16,160
County Seat:
  Fort Stockton 79735

103 W. Callaghan
432 336-2792 / *Fax: 432 336-6640*
www.co.pecos.tx.us/

County Judge	Joe Shuster	336-2792 / *Fax: 336-6640*
District Attorney, 83rd Dist.	Sandy Wilson	336-3322 / *Fax: 336-8333*
District Attorney, 112nd Dist.	Laurie K. English	336-6294 / *Fax: 336-3839*
County Attorney	Frank Lacy	336-3742 / *Fax: 336-2299*
District Clerk	Gayle Henderson	336-3503 / *Fax: 336-6437*
County Clerk	Liz Chapman	336-7555 / *Fax: 336-7557*
County Treasurer	Barry McCallister	336-3461 / *Fax: 336-2638*
Tax Assessor-Collector	Santa Acosta	336-3386 / *Fax: 336-3382*
Sheriff	Cliff Harris	336-3521 / *Fax: 336-2519*
County Auditor	Kay Hardwick	336-2216 / *Fax: 336-5365*
Chief Appraiser	Sam Calderon III	336-7587 / *Fax: 336-2665*
County Commissioner:		
Precinct 1	Tom Chapman	336-6261 / *Fax: 336-6134*
Precinct 2	Lupe Dominguez	336-5085 / *Fax: 336-8098*
Precinct 3	Mickey Jack Perry	639-2841 / *Fax: 639-2510*
Precinct 4	Santiago Cantu, Jr.	336-6281 / *Fax: 336-9624*
Justice of the Peace:		
Precinct 1	Ruben Salinas	336-3281 / *Fax: 336-6829*
Precinct 3	Cathy Ervine	639-2350 / *Fax: 639-2158*
Precinct 4	Deborah S. Braden	536-2538 / *Fax: 536-0117*
Precinct 6	Donna Wooten	836-4449 / *Fax: 836-4390*
Constable:		
Precinct 1	Oscar Gallegos	290-7444
Precinct 3	Merejildo G. "Junior" Dominguez	290-5257 / *Fax: 639-2158*
Precinct 4	William King	536-2230
Precinct 6	Don Jackson	836-4349

POLK COUNTY

Population: 48,080
County Seat:
  Livingston 77351

101 West Church St.
936 327-6813 / *Fax: 936 327-6891*
www.co.polk.tx.us

County Judge	Sydney Murphy	327-6813 / *Fax: 327-6891*
Criminal District Attorney	Lee Hon	327-6868 / *Fax: 327-6875*
District Clerk	Bobbye Richards	327-6814 / *Fax: 327-6851*
County Clerk	Schelana Hock	327-6804 / *Fax: 327-6874*
County Treasurer	Terri Williams	327-6816 / *Fax: 327-6853*
Tax Assessor-Collector	Leslie Burks	327-6801 / *Fax: 327-6885*
Sheriff	Kenneth Hammack	327-6810 / *Fax: 327-5574*
County Auditor	Louis Ploth	327-6811 / *Fax: 327-6898*
Chief Appraiser	Chad Hill	327-2461 / *Fax: 327-2545*
County Commissioner:		
Precinct 1	Bob Willis	365-2222 / *Fax: 365-4237*
Precinct 2	Ronnie Vincent	646-5929 / *Fax: 646-5712*
Precinct 3	Milton Purvis	398-4171 / *Fax: 398-5950*
Precinct 4	Tommy Overstreet	327-6866 / *Fax: 327-6863*

Justice of the Peace:

Precinct 1	Darrell Longino	.327-6841 / *Fax: 327-6884*
Precinct 2	Sarah Arnett	.646-3674 / *Fax: 646-4197*
Precinct 3	Robert Johnson	.398-4114 / *Fax: 398-5574*
Precinct 4	Jamie Jones	.327-6865 / *Fax: 327-6861*

Constable:

Precinct 1	Scott Hughes	.327-2807 / *Fax: 327-7018*
Precinct 2	Bill Cunningham	.646-3691 / *Fax: 646-4197*
Precinct 3	Ray Myers	.398-2875
Precinct 4	Dana "Bubba" Piper	.327-5085

POTTER COUNTY

Population: 123,268
County Seat:
  Amarillo 79101

500 S. Fillmore, Ste. 103
806 379-2250 / *Fax: 806 379-2446*
www.co.potter.tx.us

County Judge	Nancy Tanner	.379-2250 / *Fax: 379-2446*
District Attorney, 47th Dist.	Randall C. Sims	.379-2325 / *Fax: 379-2823*
County Attorney	Scott Brumley	.379-2255
District Clerk	Caroline Woodburn	.379-2310 / *Fax: 372-5061*
County Clerk	Julie Smith	.379-2275 / *Fax: 379-2296*
County Treasurer	Leann R. Jennings	.349-4834 / *Fax: 349-4845*
Tax Assessor-Collector	Sherri Aylor	.342-2600 / *Fax: 342-2637*
Sheriff	Brian L. Thomas	.379-2903 / *Fax: 379-2919*
County Auditor	Kerry Hood	.349-4801 / *Fax: 349-4808*
Chief Appraiser	Jeffrey Dagley	.358-1601 / *Fax: 355-8426*
Elections Official	Melynn Huntley	.379-2299 / *Fax: 379-2249*

County Commissioner:

Precinct 1	H. R. Kelly	.379-2421
Precinct 2	Mercy Murguia	.379-2422
Precinct 3	Leon Church	.379-2423
Precinct 4	Alphonso Vaughn	.379-2424

Justice of the Peacc:

Precinct 1	Debbie Horn	.349-4880 / *Fax: 349-4887*
Precinct 2	Richard Herman	.379-2390 / *Fax: 379-2845*
Precinct 3	Gary Jackson	.355-3070 / *Fax: 352-0129*
Precinct 4	Thomas Jones	.379-2817 / *Fax: 379-2829*

Constable:

Precinct 1	Darryl Wertz	.349-4880 / *Fax: 349-4887*
Precinct 2	Georgia Estrada	.379-2436
Precinct 3	Mike Duval	.355-3070 / *Fax: 352-0129*
Precinct 4	Idella Jackson	.379-2817

PRESIDIO COUNTY

Population: 7,466
County Seat:
  Marfa 79843

P.O. Box 606
432 729-4452 / *Fax: 432 729-4453*
www.co.presidio.tx.us

County Judge	Cindy Rice Guevara	.729-4452 / *Fax: 729-4453*
District Attorney, 83rd Dist.	Sandy Wilson	.729-4452
County Attorney	Arvel "Rod" Ponton	.729-4054 / *Fax: 729-3743*
District & County Clerk	Virginia Pallarez	.729-4812 / *Fax: 729-4313*
County Treasurer	Frances Garcia	.729-4076 / *Fax: 729-4071*
Tax Assessor-Collector	Natalia Williams	.729-4081 / *Fax: 729-4920*
Sheriff	Danny Dominguez	.729-4308 / *Fax: 729-3171*
County Auditor	Patricia Roach	.423 729-1990 / *Fax: 729-1995*
Chief Appraiser	Cynthia Ramirez	.729-3431 / *Fax: 729-4722*
County Commissioner:		
Precinct 1	Brenda Silva-Bentley	.386-2328 / *Fax: 729-4453*
Precinct 2	Eloy Aranda	.229-4599 / *Fax: 729-4453*
Precinct 3	Position Vacant	.488-6409
Precinct 4	Loretto Vasquez	.729-3287 / *Fax: 729-4453*
Justice of the Peace:		
Precinct 1	David Beebe	.729-4831 / *Fax: 729-3368*
Precinct 2	Juanita Bishop	.229-3705 / *Fax: 229-4336*
Constable:		
Precinct 1	Esteban Marquez	.729-3488 / *Fax: 729-4453*
Precinct 2	Esteban Steve Coker	.229-3604 / *Fax: 229-4336*

RAINS COUNTY

Population: 11,290
County Seat:
  Emory 75440

167 E. Quitman St.
903 473-5019 / *Fax: 903 473-4298*
www.co.rains.tx.us

County Judge	Wayne Wolfe	.473-5000 / *Fax: 473-4298*
District & County Attorney	Robert Vititow	.473-5000 / *Fax: 474-1108*
District Clerk	Deborah Traylor	.473-5000 / *Fax: 473-5008*
County Clerk	Linda Wallace	.473-5000 / *Fax: 473-5086*
County Treasurer	Teresa Northcutt	.473-5000 / *Fax: 473-5065*
Tax Assessor-Collector	Shelia Floyd	.473-5018 / *Fax: 473-4583*
Sheriff	David Traylor	.473-5000 / *Fax: 473-3008*
County Auditor	Kristi Ratliff	.473-5000 / *Fax: 508-2859*
Chief Appraiser	Sherri McCall	.473-2391 / *Fax: 473-4040*
County Commissioner:		
Precinct 1	Patsy Marshall	.473-5021 / *Fax: 953-1008*
Precinct 2	Mike Willis	.473-5022 / *Fax: 473-5088*
Precinct 3	Mike Godwin	.473-5000 / *Fax: 473-4298*
Precinct 4	Joe Humphrey	.473-5024 / *Fax: 473-4298*
Justice of the Peace:	Don Smith	.473-5050 / *Fax: 473-5090*
Constable:	Steve Holman	.473-5061 / *Fax: 473-5090*

RANDALL COUNTY

Population: 131,527
County Seat:
  Canyon 79015

501 16th Street, Suite 303
806 468-5500 / *Fax: 806 468-5503*
www.randallcounty.com

County Judge	Ernie Houdashell	468-5500 / *Fax: 468-5503*
Criminal District Attorney	James A. Farren	468-5570 / *Fax: 468-5566*
District Clerk	Jo Carter	468-5600 / *Fax: 468-5604*
County Clerk	Renee Calhoun	468-5505 / *Fax: 468-5509*
County Treasurer	Glenna Canada	468-5536 / *Fax: 468-5502*
Tax Assessor-Collector	Christina McMurray	468-5540 / *Fax: 468-5541*
Sheriff	Joel W. Richardson	468-5800 / *Fax: 468-5768*
County Auditor	Karon Kantor	468-5533 / *Fax: 468-5529*
Chief Appraiser	Jim Childers	358-1601 / *Fax: 355-8426*
Elections Official	Shannon Lackey	468-5510 / *Fax: 468-5634*
County Commissioner:		
Precinct 1	Christy Dyer	468-5500 / *Fax: 468-5503*
Precinct 2	Mark Benton	468-5500 / *Fax: 468-5503*
Precinct 3	Bob Robinson	458-5500 / *Fax: 468-5503*
Precinct 4	Buddy DeFord	468-5500 / *Fax: 456-5503*
Justice of the Peace:		
Precinct 1	J. Tracy Byrd	468-5606 / *Fax: 468-5607*
Precinct 4	Clay Houdashell	468-5658 / *Fax: 468-5661*
Constable:		
Precinct 1	Chris Tinsley	468-5642 / *Fax: 468-5607*
Precinct 4	Chris Johnson	468-5683

REAGAN COUNTY

Population: 3,812
County Seat:
  Big Lake 76932

P.O. Box 100
325 884-2665 / *Fax: 325 884-1503*

County Judge	Larry Isom	884-2665 / *Fax: 884-1503*
District Attorney, 112nd Dist.	Laurie K. English	392-2025 / *Fax: 392-8415*
County Attorney	Chad Elkins	884-2247 / *Fax: 884-4164*
District & County Clerk	Terri Curry	884-2442 / *Fax: 884-1503*
County Treasurer	Ginna Hruska	884-2090 / *Fax: 884-4160*
Tax Assessor-Collector	Cynthia Aguilar	884-2131 / *Fax: 884-4104*
Sheriff	Jeff N. Garner	884-2424 / *Fax: 884-2252*
County Auditor	Terrie Schneemann	884-2233 / *Fax: 884-4138*
Chief Appraiser	Stephanie Wilson	884-3275 / *Fax: 884-2149*
County Commissioner:		
Precinct 1	Jim O'Bryan	277-1382 / *Fax: 884-1503*
Precinct 2	Tim Sellman	226-3238 / *Fax: 884-1503*
Precinct 3	Tommy Holt	650-5496 / *Fax: 884-1503*
Precinct 4	Thomas Strube	432 397-2340 / *Fax: 884-1503*
Justice of the Peace:	Patty Creech	884-3482 / *Fax: 884-4110*

COUNTY SECTION

REAL COUNTY

Population: 3,463
County Seat:
  Leakey 78873

P.O. Box 446
830 232-5304 / *Fax: 830 232-6040*
www.co.real.tx.us

County Judge	W.B. "Sonny" Sansom	.232-5304 / *Fax: 232-6040*
District Attorney, 38th Dist.	Daniel J. Kindred	.278-2916 / *Fax: 278-4731*
County Attorney	Bobby Jack Rushing	.232-6461 / *Fax: 232-5443*
District & County Clerk	D'Ann Green	.232-5202 / *Fax: 232-6888*
County Treasurer	Mairi E. Gray	.232-6627 / *Fax: 232-6681*
Tax Assessor-Collector	Donna Brice	.232-6210 / *Fax: 232-6701*
Sheriff	Nathan T. Johnson	.232-5201 / *Fax: 232-5102*
Chief Appraiser	Michael Mann	.232-6248 / *Fax: 232-4168*
County Commissioner:		
Precinct 1	Manuel Rubio	.232-6623 / *Fax: 232-6040*
Precinct 2	Bryan Shackelford	.232-5756 / *Fax: 232-6040*
Precinct 3	Ramon R. Ybarra, Jr.	.279-6787
Precinct 4	Joe B. Connell	.597-5159 / *Fax: 232-6040*
Justice of the Peace:		
Precinct 1	Dianne Rogers	.232-6630 / *Fax: 232-6040*
Precinct 2	Dianne Rogers	.232-6630 / *Fax: 232-6040*
Precinct 3	Dianne Rogers	.597-6149 / *Fax: 597-5365*
Precinct 4	Dianne Rogers	.597-6149 / *Fax: 597-5365*
Constable:		
Precinct 1	Kevin Chisum	.232-5599 / *Fax: 232-5102*

RED RIVER COUNTY

Population: 12,083
County Seat:
  Clarksville 75426

400 N. Walnut St.
903 427-2680 / *Fax: 903 427-5510*
www.co.red-river.tx.us/

County Judge	L. D. Williamson	.427-2680 / *Fax: 427-5510*
District & County Attorney	Val Varley	.427-2009 / *Fax: 427-5316*
District Clerk	Janice Gentry	.427-3761 / *Fax: 427-1201*
County Clerk	Shawn Weemes	.427-2401 / *Fax: 427-3589*
County Treasurer	Sandra Embrey	.427-3748 / *Fax: 427-3748*
Tax Assessor-Collector	Tonya R. Martin	.427-3009 / *Fax: 427-3009*
Sheriff	Jim Caldwell	.427-3838 / *Fax: 427-5913*
County Auditor	Camille Hines	.427-2131 / *Fax: 427-5216*
Chief Appraiser	Christie Ussery	.427-4181 / *Fax: 427-5434*
County Commissioner:		
Precinct 1	Donnie Gentry	.632-5963 / *Fax: 427-5510*
Precinct 2	David Hutson	.925-2753 / *Fax: 427-5510*
Precinct 3	Jeff Moore	.684-3548 / *Fax: 427-5510*
Precinct 4	Wayne Johnson	.697-3390 / *Fax: 427-5510*
Justice of the Peace:	Shelley Benton	.427-3322 / *Fax: 427-8011*
Constable:	Barnaby Resendiz	.427-3322 / *Fax: 427-8011*

REEVES COUNTY

Population: 14,841
County Seat:
  Pecos 79772

100 East 4th Street
432 445-5418 / *Fax: 432 445-5389*

County Judge	Won Joo Bang, M.D.	445-5418 / *Fax: 445-5389*
District Attorney, 143rd Dist.	Randall W. "Randy" Reynolds	445-2010 / *Fax: 445-2015*
County Attorney	Alva Alvarez	445-5480 / *Fax: 445-7044*
District Clerk	Pat Tarin	445-2714 / *Fax: 445-7455*
County Clerk	Dianne O. Florez	445-5467 / *Fax: 445-3997*
County Treasurer	Zulema Rodriguez	445-2631 / *Fax: 445-3147*
Tax Assessor-Collector	Rosemary Chabarria	445-5473 / *Fax: 445-5096*
Sheriff	Arturo "Art" Granado	445-4901 / *Fax: 445-9403*
County Auditor	Lynn Owens	445-2346 / *Fax: 445-3268*
Chief Appraiser	John Huddleston	445-5122 / *Fax: 271-4002*
County Commissioner:		
Precinct 1	Rojelio "Roy" Alvarado	445-5542
Precinct 2	Louise Moore	940-1965
Precinct 3	Paul Hinojos	923-1250
Precinct 4	Tony Trujillo	448-8061 / *Fax: 445-7245*
Justice of the Peace:		
Precinct 1	Roger Harrison	445-2619 / *Fax: 445-1492*
Precinct 2	Jim Riley	447-2569 / *Fax: 447-2572*
Precinct 3	Rosendo Carrasco	375-2663 / *Fax: 375-0175*
Precinct 4	Heriberto Rodriguez	445-2628 / *Fax: 445-8977*
Constable:		
Precinct 1	Position Vacant	
Precinct 2	Jerry Matta	
Precinct 3	Jose Alfredo Saldana	
Precinct 4	Jay Bob Haney	

COUNTY SECTION

REFUGIO COUNTY

Population: 7,400
County Seat:
 Refugio 78377

808 Commerce, Room 104
361 526-4434 / *Fax: 361 526-5100*
www.co.refugio.tx.us

County Judge	Robert E. Blaschke	.526-4434 / *Fax: 526-5100*
District Attorney, 24th Dist.	Rob Lassmann	.275-2612 / *Fax: 275-3282*
County Attorney	Deborah A. Bauer	.526-4123 / *Fax: 526-1763*
District Clerk	Ruby Garcia	.526-2721 / *Fax: 526-5942*
County Clerk	Ida M. Ramirez	.526-2233 / *Fax: 526-1325*
County Treasurer	Rita Trojcak	.526-4223 / *Fax: 526-1553*
Tax Assessor-Collector	Ida M. Turner	.526-2023 / *Fax: 526-2279*
Sheriff	Raul "Pinky" Gonzales	.526-2351 / *Fax: 526-1668*
County Auditor	Margie Moeller	.526-2245 / *Fax: 526-5389*
Chief Appraiser	Connie Raymond	.526-5994 / *Fax: 526-4144*
Elections Official	Rachael B. Garcia	.526-2151 / *Fax: 526-2102*
County Commissioner:		
Precinct 1	Ann Lopez	.526-2897 / *Fax: 526-5100*
Precinct 2	David Vega	.543-4378 / *Fax: 543-4451*
Precinct 3	Gary D. Bourland	.526-2017 / *Fax: 526-5100*
Precinct 4	Rod Bernal	.286-3214 / *Fax: 286-3014*
Justice of the Peace:		
Precinct 1	Lorraine M. Lopez	.526-4877 / *Fax: 526-1494*
Precinct 2	Emi Pullin Riemenschneider	.526-1635 / *Fax: 526-1758*
Constable:		
Precinct 1	Mark Moore	.526-4877 / *Fax: 526-4347*
Precinct 2	Johnnie J. Garza	.526-2351 / *Fax: 526-1668*

ROBERTS COUNTY

Population: 925
County Seat:
 Miami 79059

P.O. Box 478
806 868-3721 / *Fax: 806 868-3381*

County Judge	Rick L. Tennant	.868-3721 / *Fax: 868-3381*
District Attorney, 31st Dist.	Franklin McDonough	.669-8035 / *Fax: 669-8050*
County Attorney	William P. Weiman	.868-2019 / *Fax: 868-3381*
District & County Clerk	Toni Rankin	.868-2341 / *Fax: 868-3381*
County Treasurer	Amy Tennant	.868-2411 / *Fax: 868-3381*
Tax Assessor-Collector	Hether Williams	.868-3611 / *Fax: 868-4019*
Sheriff	Dana Miller	.868-3121 / *Fax: 868-6521*
County Commissioner:		
Precinct 1	Cleve Wheeler	.868-2100
Precinct 2	Ken Gill	.868-5201
Precinct 3	Kelly Flowers	.323-2180
Precinct 4	James F. Duvall	.669-9432
Justice of the Peace:		
Precinct 1	Tresa "Teda" Seuhs	.868-4111

ROBERTSON COUNTY

Population: 17,247
County Seat:
  Franklin 77856

P.O. Box 427
979 828-3542 / *Fax: 979 828-2944*
www.co.robertson.tx.us

County Judge	Charles Ellison	.828-3542 / *Fax: 828-2944*
District & County Attorney	W. Coty Siegert	.828-3205 / *Fax: 828-3300*
District Clerk	Barbara Axtell	.828-3636 / *Fax: 828-5523*
County Clerk	Stephanie Sanders	.828-4130 / *Fax: 828-1260*
County Treasurer	Mindy Turner	.828-3201 / *Fax: 828-2497*
Tax Assessor-Collector	Michael Brewer	.828-3337 / *Fax: 828-4011*
Sheriff	Gerald Yezak	.828-3299 / *Fax: 828-5845*
County Auditor	Candace Anderson	.828-3474 / *Fax: 828-1725*
Chief Appraiser	Nancy Commander	.828-5800 / *Fax: 828-5137*
Elections Official	Raymond Rodriguez	.828-5726 / *Fax: 828-4584*
County Commissioner:		
Precinct 1	Keith Petitt	.364-2832 / *Fax: 364-3913*
Precinct 2	Donald Threadgill	.279-3876 / *Fax: 279-3876*
Precinct 3	Keith Nickelson	.828-4413
Precinct 4	Robert Bielamowicz	.254 746-7850 / *Fax: 254 746-7222*
Justice of the Peace:		
Precinct 1	Keith Folterman	.364-2750 / *Fax: 364-2127*
Precinct 2	Ramona Aguirre	.279-2301 / *Fax: 279-6251*
Precinct 3	Melanie Green	.828-3929 / *Fax: 828-2109*
Precinct 4	Frederick Webber	.254 746-7836 / *Fax: 254 746-7773*
Constable:		
Precinct 1	Vince Angele	.828-2122 / *Fax: 828-1477*
Precinct 2	Craig Boyett	.828-2122 / *Fax: 828-1477*
Precinct 3	Chris Sanders	.828-2122 / *Fax: 828-1477*
Precinct 4	LeAnthony Dykes	.254 746-7836 / *Fax: 828-1477*

ROCKWALL COUNTY

Population: 93,032
County Seat:
 Rockwall 75087

101 East Rusk, Room 202
972 204-6200 / *Fax: 972 204-6009*
www.rockwallcountytexas.com

County Judge	David Sweet	.204-6000 / *Fax: 204-6009*
Criminal District Attorney	Kenda Culpepper	.204-6800 / *Fax: 204-6809*
District Clerk	Kay McDaniel	.204-6500 / *Fax: 204-6509*
County Clerk	Shelli Miller	.204-6300 / *Fax: 204-6309*
County Treasurer	David Peek	.204-6100 / *Fax: 204-6109*
Tax Assessor-Collector	Kim Sweet	.204-6130 / *Fax: 204-6139*
Sheriff	Harold Eavenson	.204-7001 / *Fax: 204-7029*
County Auditor	Lisa Constant Wylie	.204-6050 / *Fax: 204-6059*
Chief Appraiser	Patricia Davis	.771-2034 / *Fax: 771-6871*
Elections Official	Chris Lynch	.204-6201
County Commissioner:		
Precinct 1	Cliff Sevier	.204-6010 / *Fax: 204-6009*
Precinct 2	Lee Gilbert	.204-6020 / *Fax: 204-6009*
Precinct 3	Dennis Bailey	.204-6030 / *Fax: 204-6009*
Precinct 4	David Magness	.204-6040 / *Fax: 204-6009*
Justice of the Peace:		
Precinct 1	Jack James	.204-6740 / *Fax: 204-6749*
Precinct 2	Nancy Beaty	.204-6730 / *Fax: 204-6739*
Precinct 3	Mark Russo	.204-6720 / *Fax: 204-6729*
Precinct 4	Liana Bell Whitten	.204-6710 / *Fax: 294-6719*
Constable:		
Precinct 1	John Benedetto	.204-7210 / *Fax: 204-6749*
Precinct 2	Trey Chaney	.204-7220 / *Fax: 204-6739*
Precinct 3	Tom Egan	.204-7230 / *Fax: 204-6009*
Precinct 4	Randy Parks	.204-7240

RUNNELS COUNTY

Population: 10,477
County Seat:
 Ballinger 76821

613 Hutchings Avenue
325 365-2633 / *Fax; 325 365-3408*
www.co.runnels.tx.us

County Judge	Barry Hilliard	.365-2633 / *Fax: 365-3408*
District Attorney, 119th Dist.	John Best	.653-1912 / *Fax: 658-6831*
County Attorney	Kenneth Slimp	.365-2337 / *Fax: 365-3408*
District Clerk	Tammy Burleson	.365-2638 / *Fax: 365-9229*
County Clerk	Julia Miller	.365-2720 / *Fax: 365-3408*
County Treasurer	Ann Strube	.365-2428 / *Fax: 365-4823*
Tax Assessor-Collector	Robin M. Burgess	.365-2339 / *Fax: 365-5884*
Sheriff	Carl L. Squyres	.365-2121 / *Fax: 365-5807*
County Auditor	Cindy Winchester	.365-2221 / *Fax: 365-3607*
Chief Appraiser	Larry Reagan	.365-3583 / *Fax: 365-5563*
County Commissioner:		
Precinct 1	Robert Moore	.365-3615
Precinct 2	Ronald Presley	.754-4025 / *Fax: 754-4405*
Precinct 3	Roy Mints	.743-2566 / *Fax: 365-3408*
Precinct 4	Richard W. Strube	.468-2551

Justice of the Peace:
  Precinct 1
  Precinct 2
Constable:
  Precinct 1
  Precinct 2

Glenda Wood .... 365-2137 / *Fax: 365-4823*
Richard Hamilton .... 754-4270 / *Fax: 754-5734*

Wayne Poehls 365-9215
Archie Jobe 754-5743

RUSK COUNTY

Population: 54,084
County Seat:
  Henderson 75652

115 North Main St.
903 657-0302 / *Fax: 903 657-0300*
www.co.rusk.tx.us

County Judge   Joel Hale .... 657-0302 / *Fax: 657-0300*
District & County Attorney   Micheal Jimerson .... 657-2265 / *Fax: 657-0329*
District Clerk   Terri P. Willard .... 657-0353 / *Fax: 657-1914*
County Clerk   Trudy McGill .... 657-0330 / *Fax: 657-2387*
County Treasurer   Andy Vinson .... 657-0352 / *Fax: 657-0634*
Tax Assessor-Collector   Lanita Whitehead .... 657-0338 / *Fax: 657-0388*
Sheriff   Jeff Price .... 657-3581 / *Fax: 655-0934*
County Auditor   Ronald Moody .... 657-0304 / *Fax: 657-9132*
Chief Appraiser   Terry Decker .... 657-3578 / *Fax: 657-9073*
Elections Official   Kathie Wittner .... 657-0321 / *Fax: 657-0319*
County Commissioner:
  Precinct 1   W. D. "Bill" Hale .... 657-3030 / *Fax. 657-1927*
  Precinct 2   Tammy Pepper .... 836-4347 / *Fax: 657-0324*
  Precinct 3   Greg Gibson .... 822-3211 / *Fax: 657-0324*
  Precinct 4   Harold Howell .... 854-4627 / *Fax: 657-0324*
Justice of the Peace:
  Precinct 1   Jerdy Wolverton .... 834-3753 / *Fax: 834-3837*
  Precinct 2   Bonnie F. Miller .... 947-6440 / *Fax: 947-6292*
  Precinct 3   Jackie Risinger .... 822-3737 / *Fax: 822-3735*
  Precinct 4   Darlene Childress .... 854-4220 / *Fax: 854-4316*
  Precinct 5   Joe Sorrells .... 657-0308 / *Fax: 657-0310*
Constable:
  Precinct 1   Sammy Nichols .... 895-2491 / *Fax: 838-3738*
  Precinct 2   Chuck McDonald .... 947-6440 / *Fax: 947-6292*
  Precinct 3   Kenneth Miley .... 822-3737 / *Fax: 822-3735*
  Precinct 4   David Guy .... 863-2598 / *Fax: 854-4316*
  Precinct 5   Jimmy Skinner .... 657-0470 / *Fax: 657-0310*

SABINE COUNTY

Population: 11,414
County Seat:
 Hemphill 75948

P.O. Drawer 580 (County Clerk)
409 787-3543 / *Fax: 409 787-2044*
www.co.sabine.tx.us

County Judge	Daryl Melton	.787-3543 / *Fax: 787-2044*
District Attorney, 1st Dist.	J. Kevin Dutton	.787-2901 / *Fax: 787-3884*
County Attorney	Robert G. Neal	.787-2988 / *Fax: 787-3884*
District Clerk	Lisa Pitre	.787-2912 / *Fax: 787-2623*
County Clerk	Janice McDaniel	.787-3786 / *Fax: 787-3795*
County Treasurer	Tricia Woods Jacks	.787-2210 / *Fax: 787-4973*
Tax Assessor-Collector	Martha Stone	.787-2257 / *Fax: 787-4753*
Sheriff	Thomas N. Maddox	.787-2266 / *Fax: 787-2150*
County Auditor	Malinda Bryan	.787-5226 / *Fax: 787-1787*
Chief Appraiser	Sandra Helander	.787-2777 / *Fax: 787-4186*
County Commissioner:		
Precinct 1	Thomas Clark	.787-2501 / *Fax: 787-2044*
Precinct 2	Jimmy McDaniel	.579-4212 / *Fax: 787-2044*
Precinct 3	Charles Ellison	.586-9040 / *Fax: 787-2044*
Precinct 4	Fayne Warner	.625-3050 / *Fax: 787-2044*
Justice of the Peace:		
Precinct 1	Roger Gay	.787-3719 / *Fax: 787-3025*
Precinct 2	Jamie Brasher	.787-5248 / *Fax: 787-3466*
Constable:		
Precinct 1	Position Vacant	

SAN AUGUSTINE COUNTY

Population: 8,517
County Seat:
 San Augustine 75972

100 W. Columbia, Room 105
936 275-2762 / *Fax: 936 275-2538*
www.co.san-augustine.tx.us

County Judge	Samye Johnson	.275-2762 / *Fax: 275-2538*
District Attorney, 1st Dist.	J. Kevin Dutton	.275-9903 / *Fax: 275-9905*
County Attorney	Wesley Hoyt	.275-0971 / *Fax: 275-0055*
District Clerk	Carmen Brown	.275-2231 / *Fax: 275-2389*
County Clerk	Margo Noble	.275-2452 / *Fax: 275-2263*
County Treasurer	Pam Smith	.275-9472 / *Fax: 275-0441*
Tax Assessor-Collector	Regina A. Barthol	.275-2300 / *Fax: 275-9579*
Sheriff	Robert P. Cartwright	.275-2424 / *Fax: 275-5133*
County Auditor	Position Vacant	.288-0128 / *Fax: 275-0441*
Chief Appraiser	Evelyn Watts	.275-3496 / *Fax: 275-4120*
Elections Official	Deborah K. Woods	.275-0989 / *Fax: 275-0129*
County Commissioner:		
Precinct 1	Position Vacant	.275-2762 / *Fax: 275-2538*
Precinct 2	Edward Wilson	.275-2762 / *Fax: 275-2538*
Precinct 3	Joey Holloway	.275-2762 / *Fax: 275-2538*
Precinct 4	David McEachern	.275-2762 / *Fax: 275-2538*
Justice of the Peace:		
Precinct 1	Shelia Ponder	.275-3552 / *Fax: 275-4057*
Precinct 2	Ardis Mosby	.275-3552 / *Fax: 275-4057*
Precinct 3	Billy Williams	.275-3552 / *Fax: 275-4057*
Precinct 4	J. D. Miller	.275-3552 / *Fax: 275-4057*

Constable:
Precinct 1	Shannon Brazeal	.275-3552 / *Fax: 275-4057*
Precinct 2	Alex J. Garner	.275-3552 / *Fax: 275-4057*
Precinct 3	Joey Watson	.275-3552 / *Fax: 275-4057*
Precinct 4	Ben Miller	.275-3552 / *Fax: 275-4057*

SAN JACINTO COUNTY

Population: 27,397
County Seat:
  Coldspring 77331

1 State Highway 150, Room 5
936 653-4331 / *Fax: 936 653-3970*
www.co.san-jacinto.tx.us

County Judge	John Lovett	.653-2199 / *Fax: 653-3970*
Criminal District Attorney	Robert Trapp	.653-2601 / *Fax: 653-2143*
District Clerk	Rebecca "Becky" Capers	.653-2909 / *Fax: 653-4659*
County Clerk	Dawn Wright	.653-2324 / *Fax: 653-8312*
County Treasurer	Amanda Washburn	.653-2353 / *Fax: 653-2870*
Tax Assessor-Collector	Patricia Dianne Griffiths	.653-3292 / *Fax: 653-2533*
Sheriff	Greg Capers	.653-4367 / *Fax: 653-5058*
County Auditor	Kimberley Wooley	.653-4461
Chief Appraiser	Kelly Foxworth	.653-1450 / *Fax: 653-5271*
Elections Official	Vicki Shelly	.653-5804 / *Fax: 653-5808*
County Commissioner:		
Precinct 1	Laddie McAnally	.653-5045 / *Fax: 653-5747*
Precinct 2	Donny Marrs	.628-3267 / *Fax: 628-6716*
Precinct 3	Thomas Bonds	.281 592-1109 / *Fax: 281 592-1898*
Precinct 4	Mark Nettuno	.377-2481 / *Fax: 377-2273*
Justice of the Peace:		
Precinct 1	Beth Sewell	.653-4578 / *Fax: 653-5604*
Precinct 2	Harris Blanchette	.628-6477 / *Fax: 628-3953*
Precinct 3	Randy Ellisor	.281 592-4400 / *Fax: 281 592-4410*
Precinct 4	Greg Magee	.377-2131 / *Fax: 377-3453*
Constable:		
Precinct 1	Roy Rogers	.653-5614 / *Fax: 653-5614*
Precinct 2	Roy Pippin, Jr.	.628-1439 / *Fax: 628-1130*
Precinct 3	Sam Houston	.281 592-0919 / *Fax: 281 592-4410*
Precinct 4	Alvin Wyatt	.377-5412 / *Fax: 377-5412*

COUNTY SECTION

SAN PATRICIO COUNTY

Population: 66,479
County Seat:
  Sinton 78387

400 W. Sinton, Room 109
361 364-9300 / *Fax: 361 364-6118*
www.co.san-patricio.tx.us

County Judge	Terry Simpson	364-9301 / *Fax: 364-6118*
District Attorney, 36th Dist.	Sam Smith	364-9390 / *Fax: 364-9490*
County Attorney	Tamara Cochran-May	364-9338 / *Fax: 364-9440*
District Clerk	Laura Miller	364-9377 / *Fax: 364-9477*
County Clerk	Gracie Alaniz-Gonzales	364-9350 / *Fax: 364-9450*
County Treasurer	Denise Janak	364-9335 / *Fax: 364-9435*
Tax Assessor-Collector	Dalia Sanchez	364-9373 / *Fax: 364-9473*
Sheriff	Leroy Moody	364-9600 / *Fax: 364-6110*
County Auditor	David Wendel	364-9312 / *Fax: 364-9412*
Chief Appraiser	Robert Cencie	364-5402 / *Fax: 364-1198*
Elections Official	Pamela Ann Hill	364-6121 / *Fax: 364-6132*
County Commissioner:		
Precinct 1	Nina Trevino	364-6170 / *Fax: 364-6171*
Precinct 2	Richard Ott	643-1460 / *Fax: 643-2267*
Precinct 3	Alma V. Moreno	547-2132 / *Fax: 547-0639*
Precinct 4	Howard J. Gillespie	758-5276 / *Fax: 758-7657*
Justice of the Peace:		
Precinct 1	Yolanda Guerrero	364-9620 / *Fax: 364-6139*
Precinct 2	Daniel Garza	587-3600 / *Fax: 368-2548*
Precinct 4	Karen Diaz	587-3620 / *Fax: 643-6800*
Precinct 5	Nere Villarreal	587-3640 / *Fax: 547-2265*
Precinct 6	Susan Price	587-3660 / *Fax: 758-8567*
Precinct 8	Elvia L. Hernandez	587-3680 / *Fax: 528-3994*
Constable:		
Precinct 1	Joe Gaitan	364-9584 / *Fax: 364-6139*
Precinct 2	Steve Garcia	587-3603 / *Fax: 368-2548*
Precinct 4	Parnel Haynes	587-3620 / *Fax: 643-6800*
Precinct 5	Val Ramirez	547-2244 / *Fax: 547-0180*
Precinct 6	Ronald "Ron" Howe	587-3665 / *Fax: 758-5155*
Precinct 8	Terry Gonzales	528-2738 / *Fax: 528-3994*

SAN SABA COUNTY

Population: 6,334
County Seat:
 San Saba 76877

500 E. Wallace
325 372-3635 / *Fax: 325 372-6484*
www.co.san-saba.tx.us

County Judge	Byron Theodosis	372-3635 / *Fax: 372-6484*
District Attorney, 33rd Dist.	Wiley B. "Sonny" McAfee	247-5755 / *Fax: 247-5274*
County Attorney	Randy Robinson	372-3747 / *Fax: 372-5653*
District & County Clerk	Kim Wells	372-3614 / *Fax: 372-5425*
County Treasurer	Lois VanBeck	372-3337 / *Fax: 372-6484*
Tax Assessor-Collector	Matthew Boswell	372-5325 / *Fax: 372-5425*
Sheriff	Matthew Boswell	372-5551 / *Fax: 372-3277*
Chief Appraiser	Jan Vanderburg	372-5031 / *Fax: 372-3325*
County Commissioner:		
Precinct 1	Otis Judkins	372-7877 / *Fax: 372-6484*
Precinct 2	Rickey Lusty	372-8502 / *Fax: 372-6484*
Precinct 3	Kenley Kroll	372-8385 / *Fax: 372-6484*
Precinct 4	Pat Pool	372-1309 / *Fax: 372-6484*
Justice of the Peace:	Sharon Blossman	372-5746 / *Fax: 372-4574*

SCHLEICHER COUNTY

Population: 3,283
County Seat:
 Eldorado 76936

P.O. Box 536
325 853-2593 / *Fax: 325 853-2603*

County Judge	Charlie Bradley	853-2593
District Attorney, 51st Dist.	Allison Palmer	655-6116 / *Fax: 658-6831*
County Attorney	Clint T. Griffin	853-2594 / *Fax: 853-2594*
District & County Clerk	Mary Ann Gonzalez	853-2833 / *Fax: 853-2768*
County Treasurer	Jennifer L. Henderson	853-2596 / *Fax: 853-2596*
Tax Assessor-Collector	Vanessa Covarrubiaz	853-3066 / *Fax: 853-3066*
Sheriff	David R. Doran	853-2737 / *Fax: 853-2713*
Chief Appraiser	Liza Trevino	853-2737 / *Fax: 853-2713*
Elections Official	Rosemary Adame	853-2302
County Commissioner:		
Precinct 1	Johnny F. Mayo	853-2420
Precinct 2	Lynn Meador	853-2808
Precinct 3	Kirk Griffin	853-2305
Precinct 4	Matt Brown	853-2496
Justice of the Peace:	Phil Edmiston	853-2766 / *Fax: 853-2766*

COUNTY SECTION

SCURRY COUNTY

Population: 17,592
County Seat:
　Snyder 79549

1806 25th St., Suite 200
325 573-8576 / *Fax: 325 515-7575*
www.co.scurry.tx.us

County Judge	Ricky Fritz	573-8576 / *Fax: 515-7575*
District Attorney, 132nd Dist.	Ben R. Smith	573-2462 / *Fax: 573-9339*
County Attorney	Michael W. Hartman	573-7440 / *Fax: 573-1266*
District Clerk	Candace Jones	573-5641 / *Fax: 573-1081*
County Clerk	Melody Appleton	573-5332 / *Fax: 573-7396*
County Treasurer	Nelda Colvin	573-5382 / *Fax: 515-7575*
Tax Assessor-Collector	Jana Young	573-9316 / *Fax: 574-1687*
Sheriff	Trey Wilson	573-3551 / *Fax: 573-4456*
County Auditor	Angela Sanchez	573-7121 / *Fax: 515-7575*
Chief Appraiser	Larry Crooks	573-8549 / *Fax: 573-8458*
County Commissioner:		
Precinct 1	Terry D. Williams	573-1502 / *Fax: 515-7575*
Precinct 2	Marianne Randals	573-7197 / *Fax: 515-7575*
Precinct 3	Shawn McCowen	573-7165 / *Fax: 515-7575*
Precinct 4	Jim Robinson	573-7345 / *Fax: 515-7575*
Justice of the Peace:		
Precinct 1	Norma Martinez	573-5406 / *Fax: 574-1912*
Precinct 2	Ricki Webb	574-1352 / *Fax: 574-1381*

SHACKELFORD COUNTY

Population: 3,430
County Seat:
　Albany 76430

225 South Main St., P.O. Box 2797
325 762-2232 / *Fax: 325 762-3966*

County Judge	Ross Montgomery	762-2232 / *Fax: 762-3966*
District Attorney, 259th Dist.	Joe Edd Boaz	823-2742 / *Fax: 823-2322*
County Attorney	Colton Johnson	762-2232
District & County Clerk	Cheri Hawkins	762-2232 / *Fax: 762-3756*
County Treasurer	Tammy Brown	762-9440 / *Fax: 762-9441*
Tax Assessor-Collector	Edward "Ed" Miller	762-2232 / *Fax: 762-2830*
Sheriff	Edward "Ed" Miller	762-2000 / *Fax: 762-3432*
Chief Appraiser	Clayton Snyder	762-2207 / *Fax: 762-2205*
County Commissioner:		
Precinct 1	Steve Riley	762-2741 / *Fax: 762-3966*
Precinct 2	Larry Cauble	
Precinct 3	Lanham Martin	201-7420 / *Fax: 762-3966*
Precinct 4	Cody Jordan	228-4256 / *Fax: 762-3966*
Justice of the Peace:	James Breeden	762-2232 / *Fax: 762-3704*

SHELBY COUNTY

Population: 24,872
County Seat:
  Center 75935

200 San Augustine St., Box 6
936 598-3863 / *Fax: 936 598-3146*
www.co.shelby.tx.us

County Judge	Allison Harbison	598-3863 / *Fax: 598-3146*
District Attorney, 123rd Dist.	Stephen Shires	598-2489 / *Fax: 598-4106*
County Attorney	Gary Rholes	598-6100 / *Fax: 598-9184*
District Clerk	Lori Oliver	598-4164 / *Fax: 598-3323*
County Clerk	Jennifer Fountain	598-6361 / *Fax: 598-3701*
County Treasurer	Ann Blackwell	598-3581 / *Fax: 598-3952*
Tax Assessor-Collector	Debora Riley	598-4441 / *Fax: 598-8942*
Sheriff	Willis Blackwell	598-5601 / *Fax: 598-7893*
County Auditor	Clint Porterfield	598-3535 / *Fax: 598-3952*
Chief Appraiser	Robert N. Pigg	598-6171 / *Fax: 598-7096*
County Commissioner:		
Precinct 1	Roscoe McSwain	598-6136 / *Fax: 598-3818*
Precinct 2	Jimmy Lout	598-6136 / *Fax: 598-3818*
Precinct 3	Charles Barr	598-6136 / *Fax: 598-3818*
Precinct 4	Bradley Allen	598-6136 / *Fax: 598-3818*
Justice of the Peace:		
Precinct 1	Melissa Crouch	598-3735 / *Fax: 598-4161*
Precinct 2	Marla Denby	598-7797
Precinct 3	Margie Anderson	269-3527 / *Fax: 269-9695*
Precinct 4	Jenny Hicks	248-4510 / *Fax: 248-4510*
Precinct 5	Mike Crouch	254-3922 / *Fax: 254-3994*
Constable:		
Precinct 1	Zack Warr	591-4283
Precinct 2	Jamie Hagler	332-0993
Precinct 3	Roy Cheatwood	269-3839
Precinct 4	Jacob "Jake" Metcalf	903 472-8891
Precinct 5	Robert Hairgrove	254-3704

SHERMAN COUNTY

Population: 3,179
County Seat:
  Stratford 79084

701 N. 3rd St., P.O. Box 165
806 366-2021 / *Fax: 806 366-3011*
www.co.sherman.tx.us

County Judge	Terri Beth Carter	366-2021 / *Fax: 366-3011*
District Attorney, 69th Dist.	David M. Green	935-5654 / *Fax: 934-2155*
County Attorney	Kimberly Allen	366-2270 / *Fax: 366-3130*
District & County Clerk	Gina Gray	366-2371 / *Fax: 366-5670*
County Treasurer	Doris Parsons	366-5842 / *Fax: 366-2168*
Tax Assessor-Collector	Valerie McAlister	366-2150 / *Fax: 366-2854*
Sheriff	Ted Allen	366-5551 / *Fax: 366-3142*
Chief Appraiser	Teresa Edmond	366-5566 / *Fax: 366-2565*
County Commissioner:		
Precinct 1	Dana Buckles	366-2021 / *Fax: 366-3011*
Precinct 2	Randy Williams	396-2050 / *Fax: 366-3011*
Precinct 3	Jeff Crippen	827-7338 / *Fax: 366-3011*
Precinct 4	David Davis	753-6042 / *Fax: 366-3011*
Justice of the Peace:	Brenda Acker	366-5645 / *Fax: 366-7648*

SMITH COUNTY

Population: 222,702
County Seat:
 Tyler 75702

200 E. Ferguson, Suite 100
903 590-4600 / *Fax: 903 590-4615*
www.smith-county.com/

County Judge	Nathaniel Moran	590-4600 / *Fax: 590-4615*
Criminal District Attorney	Matt Bingham III	590-1721 / *Fax: 590-1719*
District Clerk	Lois Rogers	590-1660 / *Fax: 590-1661*
County Clerk	Karen Phillips	590-4670 / *Fax: 590-4689*
County Treasurer	Kelli White	590-4730 / *Fax: 590-4733*
Tax Assessor-Collector	Gary Barber	590-2920 / *Fax: 590-2939*
Sheriff	Larry Smith	590-2660 / *Fax: 590-2659*
County Auditor	Ann Wilson, CPA	590-4700 / *Fax: 590-4716*
Chief Appraiser	Michael D. Barnett	510-8600 / *Fax: 510-8621*
Elections Official	Karen Nelson	590-4777 / *Fax: 590-4778*
County Commissioner:		
Precinct 1	Jeff Warr	590-4601 / *Fax: 590-4615*
Precinct 2	Cary Nix	590-4602 / *Fax: 590-4615*
Precinct 3	Terry Phillips	590-4603 / *Fax: 590-4615*
Precinct 4	JoAnn Hampton	590-4604 / *Fax: 590-4615*
Justice of the Peace:		
Precinct 1	Quincy Beavers, Jr.	590-2601 / *Fax: 590-2607*
Precinct 2	Gary Alfred	590-4830 / *Fax: 561-3310*
Precinct 3	James Meredith	590-4729 / *Fax: 590-4739*
Precinct 4	Mitch Shamburger	590-4870 / *Fax: 877-4528*
Precinct 5	James R. Cowart	590-4890 / *Fax: 882-0354*
Constable:		
Precinct 1	Henry Jackson	590-2610 / *Fax: 590-2608*
Precinct 2	Andy Dunklin	590-4840 / *Fax: 561-6647*
Precinct 3	Jim Blackmon	590-4745 / *Fax: 842-2668*
Precinct 4	Josh Joplin	590-4871 / *Fax: 877-2201*
Precinct 5	Jeff McClenny	590-4901 / *Fax: 882-0354*

SOMERVELL COUNTY

Population: 8,945
County Seat:
 Glen Rose 76043

P.O. Box 851
254 897-2322 / *Fax: 254 897-7314*
www.co.somervell.tx.us/

County Judge	Danny Chambers	897-2322 / *Fax: 897-7314*
District Attorney	Dale Hanna	817 556-6800 / *Fax: 817 556-6816*
County Attorney	Andrew Lucas	897-2277 / *Fax: 897-2600*
District & County Clerk	Michelle Reynolds	897-4427 / *Fax: 897-3233*
County Treasurer	Susanne Graves	897-4814 / *Fax: 897-2931*
Tax Assessor-Collector	Darlene Chambers	897-2419 / *Fax: 897-3018*
Sheriff	Alan E. West	897-2242 / *Fax: 897-9414*
County Auditor	Brian Watts	897-2923 / *Fax: 897-2931*
Chief Appraiser	Wes Rollen	897-4094 / *Fax: 897-3258*
Elections Official	Christy Covey	897-9470 / *Fax: 897-7703*

County Commissioner:

Precinct 1	Larry Hulsey	.897-2206 / *Fax: 897-7703*
Precinct 2	John Curtis	.897-2206 / *Fax: 897-7703*
Precinct 3	Kenneth Wood	.897-2206 / *Fax: 897-7703*
Precinct 4	Don Kranz	.897-2206 / *Fax: 897-7703*

Justice of the Peace:

Precinct 1	Ronnie Webb	.897-2120 / *Fax: 897-7725*
Precinct 2	Scott May	.897-2120 / *Fax: 897-7725*

Constable:

Precinct 1	Mike Reynolds	.898-3926 / *Fax: 897-2195*
Precinct 2	Jeff Slaton	.898-3927 / *Fax: 897-2195*

STARR COUNTY

Population: 63,241
County Seat:
  Rio Grande City 78582

100 N. FM 3167, Suite 202
956 716-4800 / *Fax: 956 352-6573*
www.co.starr.tx.us/

County Judge	Eloy Vera	.716-4800 x8497 / *Fax: 352-6573*
District Attorney, 229th Dist.	Omar Escobar	.716-4800 x8553 / *Fax: 487-8697*
County Attorney	Victor Canales	.716-4800 x8629 / *Fax: 487-8692*
District Clerk	Eloy R. Garcia	.716-4800 x8482 / *Fax: 487-8493*
County Clerk	Dennis D. Gonzalez	.716-4800 x8047 / *Fax: 487-8674*
County Treasurer	Fernando Pena	.716-4800 x2013 / *Fax: 716-8223*
Tax Assessor-Collector	Maria Ameida Salinas	.716-4800 x4822 / *Fax: 716-8178*
Sheriff	Rene "Orta" Fuentes	.487-5571 / *Fax: 487-0021*
County Auditor	Boyd Carter	.716-4802 / *Fax: 487-8720*
Chief Appraiser	Rosalva Guerra	.487-5613 / *Fax: 487-8555*
Elections Official	Rafael Rodolfo Monatalvo	.716-4800 x8007 / *Fax: 716-8222*

County Commissioner:

Precinct 1	Jaime M. Alvarez	.849-2606 / *Fax: 849-4328*
Precinct 2	Raul Pena III	.849-7371 / *Fax: 849-3532*
Precinct 3	Eloy Zarate	.487-2120 / *Fax: 488-9242*
Precinct 4	Ruben D. Saenz	.487-2922 / *Fax: 487-3694*

Justice of the Peace:

Precinct 1	Jesse Barrera, Jr.	.317-1170 / *Fax: 317-1173*
Precinct 2	Ramiro Guillen	.849-1253 / *Fax: 849-9873*
Precinct 3	Salvador Zarate	.487-7049 / *Fax: 487-8522*
Precinct 4	Martin Martinez	.716-4800 x8244 / *Fax: 487-8582*
Precinct 5	Antonia S. Treviño	.481-3210 / *Fax: 481-3210*
Precinct 6	Ramon De La Cruz	.487-7180 / *Fax: 488-9242*
Precinct 7	Raul Vidal	.848-5717 / *Fax: 848-5713*
Precinct 8	Jose F Perez, Jr.	.849-7450 / *Fax: 847-1091*

Constable:

Precinct 1	Daniel "Danny" Muniz	.849-4558 / *Fax: 847-1103*
Precinct 2	Emilio Montalvo	.849-1253 / *Fax: 849-9873*
Precinct 3	Santiago Zarate	.487-7049 / *Fax: 487-8522*
Precinct 4	Haime Eli Martinez	.716-4800 / *Fax: 487-8582*
Precinct 6	Jose A. Garza	.487-7180 / *Fax: 488-8242*
Precinct 7	Sonny Gonzalez	.848-5717 / *Fax: 848-5713*
Precinct 8	Fermin Orta	.849-7450 / *Fax: 847-1091*

STEPHENS COUNTY

Population: 9,199
County Seat:
  Breckenridge 76424

200 West Walker
254 559-2190 / *Fax: 254 559-7296*
www.co.stephens.tx.us

County Judge	Gary L. Fuller	.559-2190 / *Fax: 559-7296*
District Attorney, 90th Dist.	Dee H. Peavy	.940 549-4132 / *Fax: 940 549-7151*
County Attorney	Gary D. Trammel	.559-9091 / *Fax: 559-5823*
District Clerk	Christie Coapland	.559-3151 / *Fax: 559-8127*
County Clerk	Jackie Ensey	.559-3700 / *Fax: 559-5892*
County Treasurer	Sharon Trigg	.559-3181 / *Fax: 559-9645*
Tax Assessor-Collector	Christie Latham	.559-2732 / *Fax: 559-2960*
Sheriff	Will Holt	.559-2481 / *Fax: 559-2882*
Chief Appraiser	Terry Sullivan	.559-8233 / *Fax: 559-2897*
County Commissioner:		
Precinct 1	Ed Russell	.559-2371 / *Fax: 559-7296*
Precinct 2	D. C. Sikes	.559-2371 / *Fax: 559-7296*
Precinct 3	Will H. Warren	.559-2371 / *Fax: 559-7296*
Precinct 4	Rickie R. Carr	.559-2371 / *Fax: 559-7296*
Justice of the Peace:		
Precinct 1	Michael Roach	.559-5322 / *Fax: 559-1127*
Constable:	Dan R. Young	.559-5322 / *Fax: 559-2882*

STERLING COUNTY

Population: 1,285
County Seat:
  Sterling City 76951

P.O. Box 819
325 378-3481 / *Fax: 325 378-3111*
www.co.sterling.tx.us

County Judge	Leslie Mackie	.378-3481 / *Fax: 378-3111*
District Attorney, 51st Dist.	Allison Palmer	.659-6583 / *Fax: 658-6831*
County Attorney	Lilli A. Hensley	.378-5621
District & County Clerk	Jerri McCutchen	.378-5191 / *Fax: 378-3111*
County Treasurer	Rhea McGinnis	.378-8511 / *Fax: 378-8481*
Tax Assessor-Collector	Julie Thomason	.378-3041 / *Fax: 378-2266*
Sheriff	Tim Sanders	.378-4771 / *Fax: 378-2071*
Chief Appraiser	Ronnie Krejci	.378-7711 / *Fax: 378-2266*
County Commissioner:		
Precinct 1	Ross Copeland	.378-3481 / *Fax: 378-3111*
Precinct 2	Edward Michulka, Jr.	.378-2303
Precinct 3	Tommy Wright, Jr.	.378-2311
Precinct 4	Reed Stewart	.378-2156
Justice of the Peace:	Stacy Dyer	.378-3761 / *Fax: 378-2011*

STONEWALL COUNTY

Population: 1,391
County Seat:
  Aspermont 79502

P.O. Drawer P (County Clerk)
940 989-2272 / *Fax: 940 989-3105*

County Judge	Ronnie Moorhead	.989-3393 / *Fax: 989-3105*
District Attorney, 39th Dist.	Mike Fouts	.864-2072 / *Fax: 864-3364*
County Attorney	Riley Branch	.989-2608 / *Fax: 989-3015*
District & County Clerk	Holly McLaury	.989-2272 / *Fax: 989-2032*
County Treasurer	Anya Mullen	.989-3520 / *Fax: 989-3566*
Tax Assessor-Collector	Jim B. Ward	.989-2633 / *Fax: 989-2715*
Sheriff	William M. "Bill" Mullen	.989-3333 / *Fax: 989-3334*
Chief Appraiser	Debra Smith	.989-3363 / *Fax: 989-3695*
County Commissioner:		
Precinct 1	David Hoy	.989-3572 / *Fax: 989-2715*
Precinct 2	Jan Hawkins	.989-2814 / *Fax: 989-2715*
Precinct 3	Kirk Meador	.806 254-6881 / *Fax: 989-2715*
Precinct 4	Gary Myers	.806 254-2253 / *Fax: 989-2715*
Justice of the Peace:	Mike English	.989-2213 / *Fax: 988-4418*

SUTTON COUNTY

Population: 4,000
County Seat:
  Sonora 76950

300 E. Oak St., Suite 4
325 387-2711
www.co.sutton.tx.us/

County Judge	Steve Smith	.387-2711
District Attorney, 112nd Dist.	Laurie K. English	.392-2025 / *Fax: 392-8415*
County Attorney	David W. Wallace	.387-6551 / *Fax: 387-6554*
District & County Clerk	Rachel Chavez Duran	.387-3815 / *Fax: 387-6028*
County Treasurer	Janalyn Jones	.387-2886 / *Fax: 387-2886*
Tax Assessor-Collector	Kathy S. Marshall	.387-2342 / *Fax: 387-2031*
Sheriff	Oscar G. Chavez, Sr.	.387-2288 / *Fax: 387-5245*
County Auditor	Maura Weingart	.387-5380 / *Fax: 387-2379*
Chief Appraiser	Mary Bustamante	.387-2809 / *Fax: 387-2265*
County Commissioner:		
Precinct 1	Miguel Villanueva	.387-5300
Precinct 2	Bob Brockman	.226-0255
Precinct 3	Carl Teaff	.226-3471
Precinct 4	Fred Perez	.387-5249
Justice of the Peace:		
Precinct 1	Joseph Harris	.387-3322 / *Fax: 387-6122*

COUNTY SECTION

SWISHER COUNTY

Population: 7,516
County Seat:
  Tulia 79088

County Courthouse, 119 S. Maxwell
806 995-3504 / *Fax: 806 995-2214*
www.co.swisher.tx.us

County Judge	Harold Keeter	.995-3504 / *Fax: 995-2214*
County Attorney	J. Michael Criswell	.995-3505 / *Fax: 995-1525*
District & County Clerk	C.J. Chasco	.995-3294 / *Fax: 995-4121*
County Treasurer	Tricia Speed	.995-2204 / *Fax: 995-1464*
Tax Assessor-Collector	Deborah Lemons	.995-3513 / *Fax: 995-4572*
Sheriff	Jimmy McCaslin	.995-3326 / *Fax: 995-3367*
Chief Appraiser	Frank Reeves	.995-4118 / *Fax: 995-4079*
Elections Official	Richelle Culifer	.995-2363 / *Fax: 995-4121*
County Commissioner:		
Precinct 1	Lloyd Rahlfs	.558-2158
Precinct 2	Joe Bob Thompson	.668-4766
Precinct 3	Joe Murrell	.995-2810
Precinct 4	Larry Buske	.684-2354
Justice of the Peace:		
Precinct 1	Sharla Miller	.995-4407 / *Fax: 995-3371*

TARRANT COUNTY

Population: 1,971,711
County Seat:
  Fort Worth 76196

100 E. Weatherford
817 884-1441 / *Fax: 817 884-2793*
www.tarrantcounty.com

County Judge	Glen Whitley	.884-1441 / *Fax: 884-2793*
Criminal District Attorney	Sharen Wilson	.884-1400 / *Fax: 884-1667*
District Clerk	Thomas A. Wilder	.884-1574 / *Fax: 884-1484*
County Clerk	Mary Louise Garcia	.884-1195 / *Fax: 884-3295*
Tax Assessor-Collector	Position Vacant	.884-1850 / *Fax: 884-1555*
Sheriff	Bill E. Waybourn	.884-3099 / *Fax: 212-6987*
County Auditor	S. Renee Tidwell	.884-1205 / *Fax: 884-1104*
Chief Appraiser	Jeffery D. Law	.284-0024 / *Fax: 595-6198*
Elections Official	Frank Phillips	.831-8683 / *Fax: 831-6475*
County Commissioner:		
Precinct 1	Roy Charles Brooks	.370-4500 / *Fax: 370-4503*
Precinct 2	Andy Nguyen	.548-3900 / *Fax: 548-3903*
Precinct 3	Gary Fickes	.581-3600 / *Fax: 581-3603*
Precinct 4	J. D. Johnson	.238-4400 / *Fax: 238-4403*
Justice of the Peace:		
Precinct 1	Ralph Swearingin, Jr.	.884-1395 / *Fax: 884-1912*
Precinct 2	Mary Tom Curnutt	.548-3925 / *Fax: 548-3923*
Precinct 3	Russ Casey	.481-8112 / *Fax: 581-3631*
Precinct 4	Jacquelyn Wright	.238-4425 / *Fax: 238-4430*
Precinct 5	Sergio L. DeLeon	.884-1438 / *Fax: 884-3323*
Precinct 6	Gary Ritchie	.370-4525 / *Fax: 850-2345*
Precinct 7	Matt Hayes	.473-5101 / *Fax: 850-2328*
Precinct 8	Lisa R. Woodard	.531-5625 / *Fax: 531-5666*

Constable:
  Precinct 1   Dale Clark .884-1385 / *Fax: 212-6846*
  Precinct 2   David Woodruff . . . . .548-3910 / *Fax: 548-3914*
  Precinct 3   Darrell Huffman . . . . .581-3610 / *Fax: 581-3622*
  Precinct 4   Joe D. Johnson . . . . .238-4410 / *Fax: 238-4413*
  Precinct 5   Ruben Garcia . . . . .884-1892 / *Fax: 884-3292*
  Precinct 6   Jon Siegel .370-4510 / *Fax: 370-4514*
  Precinct 7   Clint C. Burgess . . . . .473-5110 / *Fax: 473-5109*
  Precinct 8   Michael R. Campbell . . . . .531-5610 / *Fax: 531-5656*

TAYLOR COUNTY

Population: 137,438   300 Oak St., Suite 200
County Seat: 325 674-1235 / *Fax: 325 674-1365*
  Abilene 79602   www.taylorcountytexas.org

County Judge   Downing A. Bolls, Jr. . . . . .674-1235 / *Fax: 674-1365*
Criminal District Attorney James Hicks .674-1261 / *Fax: 674-1306*
District Clerk   Tammy Robinson . . . . .674-1316 / *Fax: 674-1307*
County Clerk   Larry G. Bevill . . . . .674-1202 / *Fax: 674-1279*
County Treasurer   Lesa Hart Crosswhite . . . . .674-1231 / *Fax: 738-8513*
Tax Assessor-Collector   Jan Dukes .674-1224 / *Fax: 674-1394*
Sheriff   Ricky Bishop . . . . .674-1300 / *Fax: 672-8066*
County Auditor   Elijah Anderson . . . . .674-1252 / *Fax: 674-1372*
Chief Appraiser   Gary Earnest . . . . .676-9381 / *Fax: 676-7877*
Elections Official   Freda Ragan . . . . .674-1216 / *Fax: 674-1340*
County Commissioner:
  Precinct 1   Randy Williams . . . . .674-1235 / *Fax: 674-1365*
  Precinct 2   Kyle Kendrick . . . . .674-1235 / *Fax: 674-1365*
  Precinct 3   Brad Birchum . . . . .674-1235 / *Fax: 674-1365*
  Precinct 4   Chuck Statler . . . . .674-1235 / *Fax: 674-1365*
Justice of the Peace:
  Precinct 1, Pl. 1   Mike McAuliffe . . . . .674-1338 / *Fax: 674-1250*
  Precinct 1, Pl. 2   Sparky Dean . . . . .674-1267 / *Fax: 738-8514*
  Precinct 2   Robert J. Jones . . . . .928-5114 / *Fax: 928-1119*
  Precinct 3   Bobby Shea . . . . .554-7893 / *Fax: 554-7384*
  Precinct 4   Frank Cleveland . . . . .583-2341 / *Fax: 583-7384*
Constable:
  Precinct 1   Dwight Kinney . . . . .674-1319 / *Fax: 738-8533*
  Precinct 2   James P. Tuck . . . . .271-8176 / *Fax: 928-1119*
  Precinct 3   DeWayne Bush . . . . .738-8540 / *Fax: 674-1398*

TERRELL COUNTY

Population: 864
County Seat:
  Sanderson 79848

P.O. Drawer 4810
432 345-2421 / *Fax: 432 345-2653*
www.co.terrell.tx.us

County Judge	Santiago Flores	.345-2421 / *Fax: 345-2653*
District Attorney, 63rd Dist.	Mike Bagley	.830 775-0505 / *Fax: 345-2740*
County Attorney	Kenneth Bellah	.345-2914 / *Fax: 345-2926*
District & County Clerk	Martha Allen	.345-2391 / *Fax: 345-2740*
County Treasurer	Ana Barron	.345-2992 / *Fax: 345-2992*
Tax Assessor-Collector	Keith Hughes	.345-2499 / *Fax: 345-2499*
Sheriff	Keith Hughes	.345-2525 / *Fax: 345-3056*
Chief Appraiser	Blain Chriesman	.345-2251 / *Fax: 345-2526*
County Commissioner:		
Precinct 1	Dale Carruthers	.312-8274
Precinct 2	Michelle Marquez	.345-2141
Precinct 3	Arnulfo "Arnie" Serna	.557-7179 / *Fax: 345-2653*
Precinct 4	Jon Tom Lowrance	.345-2507
Justice of the Peace:		
Precinct 1	Corina Arredondo	.345-2341
Precinct 2	Corina Arredondo	.345-2341
Precinct 3	Shelly Cleveland	.345-2660
Precinct 4	Shelly Cleveland	.345-2660

TERRY COUNTY

Population: 12,264
County Seat:
  Brownfield 79316

500 West Main, Room 102
806 637-6421 / *Fax: 806 637-9782*
www.co.terry.tx.us

County Judge	J.D. "Butch" Wagner	.637-6421 / *Fax: 637-9782*
District & County Attorney	Jo'Shae Ferguson-Worley	.637-4984 / *Fax: 637-4947*
District Clerk	Paige Lindsey	.637-4202 / *Fax: 637-1333*
County Clerk	Kim Carter	.637-8551 / *Fax: 637-4874*
County Treasurer	Karen Grigsby	.637-3616 / *Fax: 637-9782*
Tax Assessor-Collector	Rexann W. Furlow	.637-7534 / *Fax: 637 9215*
Sheriff	Larry Gilbreath	.637-2212 / *Fax: 637-9424*
County Auditor	Janice Hudson	.637-3797 / *Fax: 637-9782*
Chief Appraiser	Eddie Olivas	.637-6966 / *Fax: 637-4675*
Elections Official	Krystal Valetin	.637-3806 / *Fax: 637-3807*
County Commissioner:		
Precinct 1	Mike Swain	.637-6421 / *Fax: 637-9782*
Precinct 2	Kirby Keesee	.637-6421 / *Fax: 637-9782*
Precinct 3	Shorty Martinez	.637-6421 / *Fax: 637-9782*
Precinct 4	John Franks	.637-6421 / *Fax: 637-9782*
Justice of the Peace:		
Precinct 1	Angie Garza	.637-4757 / *Fax: 637-2758*

THROCKMORTON COUNTY

Population: 1,565
County Seat:
  Throckmorton 76483

P.O. Box 700
940 849-8805 / *Fax: 940 849-8841*

County Judge	Trey Carrington	.849-8805 / *Fax: 849-8841*
District Attorney, 39th Dist.	Mike Fouts	.864-2072 / *Fax: 864-3364*
County Attorney	Jeff Mathiews	.849-8810 / *Fax: 849-8811*
District & County Clerk	Dianna Moore	.849-8815 / *Fax: 849-8816*
County Treasurer	Brenda Rankin	.849-8840 / *Fax: 849-8841*
Tax Assessor-Collector	Doc Wigington	.849-8855 / *Fax: 849-8856*
Sheriff	Doc Wigington	.849-8855 / *Fax: 849-8856*
Chief Appraiser	Dede Smith	.849-5691 / *Fax: 849-5692*
County Commissioner:		
Precinct 1	Casey Wells	.849-8805 / *Fax: 849-8806*
Precinct 2	John Jones	.849-8805 / *Fax: 849-8806*
Precinct 3	Lance Sullivan	.849-8805 / *Fax: 849-8806*
Precinct 4	Joe Edd Chandler	.849-8805 / *Fax: 849-8806*
Justice of the Peace:	Bobby Thompson	.849-8830 / *Fax: 849-8831*

TITUS COUNTY

Population: 34,170
County Seat:
  Mount Pleasant 75455

100 West First St., Suite 200, Mt. Pleasant, 75455
903 577-6791 / *Fax: 903 577-6793*
www.co.titus.tx.us/

County Judge	Brian P. Lee	.577-6791 / *Fax: 577-6793*
District Attorney, 76th Dist.	Charles C. Bailey	.577-6726 / *Fax: 577-6729*
County Attorney	John M. Cobern	.572-0382 / *Fax: 577-7540*
District Clerk	Debra Abston	.577-6724 / *Fax: 577-6719*
County Clerk	Joan Newman	.577-6796 / *Fax: 572-5078*
County Treasurer	Sheryl Preddy	.572-8723 / *Fax: 577-6718*
Tax Assessor-Collector	Judy Cook	.577-6712 / *Fax: 577-6714*
Sheriff	Tim Ingram	.572-6641 / *Fax: 577-8038*
County Auditor	Carl Johnson, Jr.	.572-8101 / *Fax: 572-1467*
Chief Appraiser	Shirley Grant	.572-7939 / *Fax: 572-5147*
Elections Official	Krissy Lytle	.575-0902 / *Fax: 575-1117*
County Commissioner:		
Precinct 1	Albert T. Riddle	.430 222-2151
Precinct 2	Mike Fields	.572-7172 / *Fax: 577-6793*
Precinct 3	Dana Applewhite	.575-0478 / *Fax: 577-6793*
Precinct 4	Jimmy Parker	.572-0402 / *Fax: 577-6793*
Justice of the Peace:		
Precinct 1	Kay McNutt	.577-6760 / *Fax: 572-0971*
Precinct 2	Paula Dyke	.577-6756 / *Fax: 572-0921*
Constable:		
Precinct 1	Chris Durant	.577-6762 / *Fax: 572-0971*
Precinct 2	Ray Barrett	.577-6766 / *Fax: 572-0921*

COUNTY SECTION

TOM GREEN COUNTY

Population: 119,995
County Seat:
  San Angelo 76903

112 W. Beauregard
325 653-7329 / *Fax: 325 658-7871*
www.co.tom-green.tx.us/

County Judge	Steve Floyd	.653-3318 / *Fax: 659-3258*
District Attorney, 51st Dist.	Allison Palmer	.659-6583 / *Fax: 658-6831*
District Attorney, 119th Dist.	John Best	.659-6583 / *Fax: 658-6831*
County Attorney	Chris Taylor	.659-6562 / *Fax: 655-6430*
District Clerk	Sheri Woodfin	.659-6579 / *Fax: 659-3241*
County Clerk	Elizabeth "Liz" McGill	.659-6553 / *Fax: 659-3251*
County Treasurer	Dianna Spieker	.659-6520 / *Fax: 659-6440*
Tax Assessor-Collector	Becky Robles	.659-6539 / *Fax: 659-3450*
Sheriff	David Jones	.655-8111 / *Fax: 655-5393*
County Auditor	Nathan Cradduck	.659-6521 / *Fax: 658-6703*
Chief Appraiser	Bill Benson	.658-5575 / *Fax: 657-8197*
Elections Official	Vona Hudson	.659-6541 / *Fax: 657-9226*
County Commissioner:		
Precinct 1	Ralph Hoelscher	.659-6511 / *Fax: 659-5441*
Precinct 2	Aubrey DeCordova	.659-6512 / *Fax: 659-5441*
Precinct 3	Rick Bacon	.659-6513 / *Fax: 659-5441*
Precinct 4	Bill Ford	.659-6514 / *Fax: 659-5441*
Justice of the Peace:		
Precinct 1	Susan Werner	.659-6444 / *Fax: 659-6459*
Precinct 2	J.P. McGuire	.949-2415 / *Fax: 949-5706*
Precinct 3	Fred Buck	.657-9922 / *Fax: 657-0162*
Precinct 4	Eddie Howard	.659-6424 / *Fax: 659-6418*
Constable:		
Precinct 1	Mike McGee	.659-6442
Precinct 2	Deen Dickson	.949-2416
Precinct 3	James Smith	.653-5232 / *Fax: 657-0162*
Precinct 4	Randy Harris	.659-6408 / *Fax: 659-6418*

TRAVIS COUNTY

Population: 1,190,186
County Seat:
  Austin 78767

P.O. Box 1748
512 854-9020 / *Fax: 512 854-9535*
www.traviscountytx.gov

County Judge	Sarah Eckhardt	.854-9555 / *Fax: 854-9535*
District Attorney, 53rd Dist.	Margaret Moore	.854-9400 / *Fax: 854-4206*
County Attorney	David Escamilla	.854-9415 / *Fax: 854-9316*
District Clerk	Velva Price	.854-9457 / *Fax: 854-4744*
County Clerk	Dana DeBeauvoir	.854-9188 / *Fax: 854-4526*
County Treasurer	Dolores Ortega Carter	.854-9365 / *Fax: 854-9361*
Tax Assessor-Collector	Bruce Elfant	.854-9473 / *Fax: 854-9056*
Sheriff	Sally Hernandez	.854-9770 / *Fax: 854-3289*
County Auditor	Nicki Riley	.854-9125 / *Fax: 854-9164*
Chief Appraiser	Marya Crigler	.834-9317 / *Fax: 835-5371*

County Commissioner:
Precinct 1 — Jeff Travillion ....854-9111 / *Fax: 854-4897*
Precinct 2 — Brigid Shea ....854-9222 / *Fax: 854-6446*
Precinct 3 — Gerald Daugherty ....854-9333 / *Fax: 854-9376*
Precinct 4 — Margaret Gomez ....854-9444 / *Fax: 854-4886*
Justice of the Peace:
Precinct 1 — Yvonne M. Williams ....854-7700 / *Fax: 929-3047*
Precinct 2 — Randall Slagle ....854-4545 / *Fax: 854-4535*
Precinct 3 — Susan K. Steeg ....854-6763 / *Fax: 854-2197*
Precinct 4 — Raúl Arturo González ....854-9479 / *Fax: 854-9480*
Precinct 5 — Nicholas Chu ....854-9049 / *Fax: 854-9640*
Constable:
Precinct 1 — Danny Thomas ....854-7510 / *Fax: 929-0981*
Precinct 2 — Adan Ballesteros ....854-9697 / *Fax: 854-9196*
Precinct 3 — Stacy Suits ....854-2107 / *Fax: 854-2117*
Precinct 4 — George Morales III ....854-9488 / *Fax: 854-4452*
Precinct 5 — Carlos Lopez ....854-9100 / *Fax: 854-4228*

TRINITY COUNTY

Population: 14,434
County Seat:
Groveton 75845

P.O. Box 457
936 642-1746 / *Fax: 936 642-1046*
www.co.trinity.tx.us

County Judge — Doug Page ....642-1746 / *Fax: 642-1046*
District Attorney, 258th Dist. — Bennie Schiro ....642-2401 / *Fax: 642-2040*
County Attorney — Joe Warner Bell ....642-1725 / *Fax: 642-2362*
District Clerk — Kristen Raiford ....642-1118 / *Fax: 642-0002*
County Clerk — Shasta Bergman ....642-1208 / *Fax: 642-3004*
County Treasurer — Bob Dockens ....642-1443 / *Fax: 642-0578*
Tax Assessor-Collector — Mylinda Madden "Lindy" Warren ....642-1637 / *Fax: 642-2609*
Sheriff — Woody Wallace ....642-1424 / *Fax: 642-2869*
County Auditor — Bonnie Kennedy ....642-2233 / *Fax: 642-0432*
Chief Appraiser — Gary Gallant ....642-1502 / *Fax: 642-2336*
County Commissioner:
Precinct 1 — Grover Worsham ....642-1261 / *Fax: 642-1261*
Precinct 2 — Richard Chamberlin ....594-0645 / *Fax: 594-0664*
Precinct 3 — Neal Smith ....594-9354 / *Fax: 594-8364*
Precinct 4 — Jimmy Brown ....831-2562 / *Fax: 831-2562*
Justice of the Peace:
Precinct 1 — Danny Martin ....642-1224 / *Fax: 642-0327*
Precinct 2 — Lyle Stubbs ....594-2011 / *Fax: 594-5904*
Precinct 3 — Hayne Huffman ....594-3456 / *Fax: 594-9440*
Precinct 4 — Sam "Rod" Blair III ....831-3778 / *Fax: 831-3779*
Constable:
Precinct 1 — Tommy Park ....642-1224 / *Fax: 642-0327*
Precinct 2 — Mark Cole ....642-1424 / *Fax: 642-2869*
Precinct 3 — Carl Casey 594-2072
Precinct 4 — Reggie Olive ....831-3778 / *Fax: 831-3779*

TYLER COUNTY

Population: 22,171
County Seat:
  Woodville 75979

100 W. Bluff
409 283-2141 / *Fax: 409 331-0028*
www.co.tyler.tx.us

County Judge	Jacques L. Blanchette	.283-2141 / *Fax: 331-0028*
District Attorney	Lou Cloy	.283-8136 / *Fax: 283-6128*
District Clerk	Chyrl Pounds	.283-2162
County Clerk	Donece Gregory	.283-2281 / *Fax: 283-8049*
County Treasurer	Sue Saunders	.283-3054 / *Fax: 283-6305*
Tax Assessor-Collector	Lynette Cruse	.283-2734 / *Fax: 283-5967*
Sheriff	Bryan Weatherford	.283-2172 / *Fax: 283-8656*
County Auditor	Jackie Skinner	.283-3652 / *Fax: 283-6305*
Chief Appraiser	David Luther	.283-3736 / *Fax: 283-8439*
County Commissioner:		
Precinct 1	Martin Nash	.283-7013 / *Fax: 283-6307*
Precinct 2	James "Rusty" Hughes	.283-7013 / *Fax: 283-6307*
Precinct 3	Mike Marshall	.283-7623 / *Fax: 283-6307*
Precinct 4	Jack Walston	.283-7623 / *Fax: 283-6307*
Justice of the Peace:		
Precinct 1	Trisher Ford	.283-3631 / *Fax: 283-5043*
Precinct 2	Martha Dawson	.283-3631 / *Fax: 283-5043*
Precinct 3	Milton Powers	.837-8447 / *Fax: 283-5043*
Precinct 4	James D. Moore	.429-9500 / *Fax: 429-3488*
Constable:		
Precinct 1	Dale Freeman	.781-2731 / *Fax: 331-0015*
Precinct 2	John Fuller	.936 969-2300
Precinct 3	Tony Reynolds	.837-5204 / *Fax: 283-6305*
Precinct 4	Jim Zachary	.429-0509

UPSHUR COUNTY

Population: 39,985
County Seat:
  Gilmer 75644

P.O. Box 730
903 843-4001 / *Fax: 903 843-5492*
www.countyofupshur.com/

County Judge	Dean Fowler	.843-4003 / *Fax: 843-0827*
Criminal District Attorney	Billy Byrd	.843-5513 / *Fax: 843-3661*
District Clerk	Karen Bunn	.680-8288 / *Fax: 843-3540*
County Clerk	Terri Ross	.843-4015 / *Fax: 843-4504*
County Treasurer	Brandy Vick	.843-4027 / *Fax: 843-3478*
Tax Assessor-Collector	Luana Howell	.843-3085 / *Fax: 843-3083*
Sheriff	Larry Webb	.843-2541 / *Fax: 843-2368*
County Auditor	Brandy Lee	.843-4001 / *Fax: 843-4818*
Chief Appraiser	Sarah Curtis	.843-3041 / *Fax: 843-5764*
County Commissioner:		
Precinct 1	Paula Gentry	.680-8154 / *Fax: 843-4301*
Precinct 2	Don Gross	.680-8156 / *Fax: 843-4301*
Precinct 3	Frank Berka	.680-8333 / *Fax: 843-4301*
Precinct 4	Mike Spencer	.680-8334 / *Fax: 843-4301*

Justice of the Peace:
  Precinct 1   Wyone Manes .... .734-6269 / *Fax: 734-6769*
  Precinct 2   Lyle Potter .... .843-5023 / *Fax: 843-4772*
  Precinct 3   Rhonda Welch .... .680-8350 / *Fax: 844-0103*
  Precinct 4   Rebecca Skinner .... .843-4039 / *Fax: 843-5347*
Constable:
  Precinct 1   Gene Dolle 680-8399
  Precinct 2   Jason Weeks .... .968-4233 / *Fax: 843-4772*
  Precinct 3   Stanley Jenkins 734-4954
  Precinct 4   Larry Sewell .... .725-6813 / *Fax: 843-5347*

UPTON COUNTY

Population: 3,487
County Seat:
  Rankin 79778

205 East 10th Street, P.O. Box 482
432 693-2321 / *Fax: 432 693-2243*
www.co.upton.tx.us

County Judge   Bill Eyler .... .693-2321 / *Fax: 693-2243*
District Attorney, 112nd Dist. Laurie K. English .... .336-6294 / *Fax: 336-3839*
County Attorney   Paige Skehan .... .693-2222 / *Fax: 693-2243*
District & County Clerk   LaWanda McMurray .... .693-2861 / *Fax: 693-2129*
County Treasurer   Sharon Harper .... .693-2401 / *Fax: 693-2333*
Tax Assessor-Collector   Monica Zarate .... .693-2572 / *Fax: 693-2333*
Sheriff   Dan W. Brown .... .693-2422 / *Fax: 693-2303*
County Auditor   Christy Hodges .... .693-2312 / *Fax: 693-2333*
Chief Appraiser   Sheri Stephens .... .652-3221 / *Fax: 652-3372*
County Commissioner:
  Precinct 1   Pete Jackson .... .301-0015 / *Fax: 693-2243*
  Precinct 2   Tommy Owens .... .693-2591 / *Fax: 693-2243*
  Precinct 3   Mike Smart .... .208-1562 / *Fax: 693-2243*
  Precinct 4   Leon Patrick .... .652-3696 / *Fax: 693-2243*
Justice of the Peace:
  Precinct 1   Paige Lopez .... .693-2473 / *Fax: 693-2326*
  Precinct 2   Dorie Hord .... .693-2919 / *Fax: 693-2326*
  Precinct 3   Martha Silva .... .652-4320 / *Fax: 652-9702*
  Precinct 4   Corina Navarrete .... .652-8222 / *Fax: 652-9702*
Constable: Larry Hollingsworth 530-8247

COUNTY SECTION

UVALDE COUNTY

Population: 27,863
County Seat:
 Uvalde 78801

#3 Courthouse Square
830 278-3216 / *Fax: 830 278-8703*
www.uvaldecounty.com/

County Judge	William R. Mitchell	278-3216 / *Fax: 278-8703*
District Attorney, 38th Dist.	Daniel J. Kindred	278-2916 / *Fax: 278-4731*
County Attorney	John P. Dodson	278-6510 / *Fax: 278-6585*
District Clerk	Christina Ovalle	278-3918 / *Fax: 591-1344*
County Clerk	Donna M. Williams	278-6614 / *Fax: 278-8692*
County Treasurer	Joni Deorsam	278-5821 / *Fax: 278-8809*
Tax Assessor-Collector	Rita C. Verstuyft	278-3225 / *Fax: 486-0062*
Sheriff	Charles Mendeke	278-1321 / *Fax: 278-2986*
County Auditor	Alice Chapman	591-0181 / *Fax: 278-9506*
Chief Appraiser	Roberto Valdez	278-1106 / *Fax: 278-8150*
Elections Official	Melissa M. Jones	591-2724 / *Fax: 278-2541*
County Commissioner:		
Precinct 1	Randy Scheide	278-7017 / *Fax: 278-3355*
Precinct 2	Mariano Pargas, Jr.	261-9112
Precinct 3	Jerry W. Bates	232-6262 / *Fax: 232-5393*
Precinct 4	Raul T. Flores	278-3119
Justice of the Peace:		
Precinct 1	Steven T. Kennedy	278-3921 / *Fax: 278-6662*
Precinct 2	Bobby McIntosh	988-2462 / *Fax: 988-2137*
Precinct 3	Bill Schaeffer	966-3445
Precinct 4	Eulalio Diaz, Jr.	278-3904 / *Fax: 278-8750*
Precinct 6	Neto Luna	278-8123
Constable:		
Precinct 1	Johnny J. Field	275-4187 / *Fax: 278-6662*
Precinct 2	Weldon McCutchen	988-2462
Precinct 3	Jimmy D. Mangum	210 260-0612
Precinct 4	David Valdez	591-6534
Precinct 6	Robert A. Moss	317-3052

VAL VERDE COUNTY

Population: 48,230
County Seat:
 Del Rio 78841

400 Pecan, Del Rio, 78840
830 774-7501 / *Fax: 830 775-9406*
www.valverdecounty.org/

County Judge	Efrain V. Valdez	774-7501 / *Fax: 775-9406*
District Attorney, 63rd Dist.	Mike Bagley	774-7562 / *Fax: 775-0352*
County Attorney	Ana Markowski Smith	774-7571 / *Fax: 774-1235*
District Clerk	Jo Ann Cervantes	774-7538 / *Fax: 774-7643*
County Clerk	Generosa "Janie" Garcia-Ramon	774-7564 / *Fax: 774-7608*
County Treasurer	Aaron Rodriguez	774-7587 / *Fax: 775-4768*
Tax Assessor-Collector	Beatriz I. Munoz	774-7533 / *Fax: 775-7282*
Sheriff	Joe Frank Martinez	774-7513 / *Fax: 775-9678*
County Auditor	Matthew Weingardt	774-7585 / *Fax: 775-9198*
Chief Appraiser	Cherry T. Sheedy	774-4602 / *Fax: 775-2101*

County Commissioner:
Precinct 1   Martin Wardlaw . . . . .774-7656 / *Fax: 774-7661*
Precinct 2   Lewis Owens . . . . .774-7656 / *Fax: 774-7661*
Precinct 3   Robert Nettleton . . . . .774-7656 / *Fax: 774-7661*
Precinct 4   Gustavo Flores . . . . .774-7656 / *Fax: 774-7661*

Justice of the Peace:
Precinct 1   Jim Bob Barrera . . . . .774-7545 / *Fax: 774-7546*
Precinct 2   Antonio "Tony" Faz III . . . . .774-7579 / *Fax: 774-2514*
Precinct 3   Pat Cole . . . . .774-7511 / *Fax: 774-7512*
Precinct 4   Hilda C. Lopez . . . . .774-7581 / *Fax: 774-7278*

Constable:
Precinct 1   Jesse James Treviño . . . . .774-7545 / *Fax: 774-7546*
Precinct 2   Berry West . . . . .774-7579 / *Fax: 774-2514*
Precinct 3   Steve Berg . . . . .774-7511 / *Fax: 774-7512*
Precinct 4   Gerardo "Jerry" Hernandez . . . . .774-7699 / *Fax: 774-7278*

VAN ZANDT COUNTY

Population: 55,099
County Seat:
  Canton 75103

121 E. Dallas
903 567-7555 / *Fax: 903 567-7216*
www.vanzandtcounty.org/

County Judge   Don Kirkpatrick . . . . .567-4071 / *Fax: 567-7216*
Criminal District Attorney Chris Martin .567-4104 / *Fax: 567-6258*
District Clerk   Karen Wilson . . . . .567-6576 / *Fax: 567-1283*
County Clerk   Pamela Pearman . . . . .567-6503 / *Fax: 567-6722*
County Treasurer   Teri Pruitt . . . . .567-2551 / *Fax: 567-7351*
Tax Assessor-Collector   Shirley Chisham . . . . .567-6511 / *Fax: 567-2944*
Sheriff   Dale Corbett .567-4133 / *Fax: 567-5317*
County Auditor   Sandy Hill . . . . .567-2171 / *Fax: 567-4700*
Chief Appraiser   Scott Hyde . . . . .567-6171 / *Fax: 567-6600*

County Commissioner:
Precinct 1   Brandon Brown . . . . .567-2166 / *Fax: 567-5473*
Precinct 2   Virgil Melton, Jr. . . . . .567-2166 / *Fax: 567-5473*
Precinct 3   Keith Pearson . . . . .567-2166 / *Fax: 567-5473*
Precinct 4   Tim West . . . . .567-2166 / *Fax: 567-5473*

Justice of the Peace:
Precinct 1   Pam Harvath .962-3471 / *Fax: 962-4676*
Precinct 2   Sandra Plaster . . . . .567-6569 / *Fax: 567-4699*
Precinct 3   Herbert Dunn . . . . .873-3592 / *Fax: 873-3662*
Precinct 4   Scott Shinn . . . . .833-5705 / *Fax: 833-5829*

Constable:
Precinct 1   Mickey Henson . . . . .962-6032 / *Fax: 962-4676*
Precinct 2   Jesse Ison . . . . .848-7912 / *Fax: 567-4699*
Precinct 3   Robert Tisdale . . . . .873-2733 / *Fax: 873-3662*
Precinct 4   Pat Jordan . . . . .833-5705 / *Fax: 833-5829*

VICTORIA COUNTY

Population: 92,667
County Seat:
  Victoria 77901

101 N. Bridge, Room 102
361 575-4558 / *Fax: 361 573-7585*
www.vctx.org/

County Judge	Ben Zeller	575-4558 / *Fax: 573-7585*
District Attorney	Stephen B. Tyler	575-0468 / *Fax: 576-4139*
District Clerk	Cathy Stuart	575-0581 / *Fax: 572-5682*
County Clerk	Heidi Easley	575-1478 / *Fax: 575-6276*
County Treasurer	Sean K. Kennedy	575-8588 / *Fax: 576-4912*
Tax Assessor-Collector	Rena Scherer	576-3671 / *Fax: 576-0477*
Sheriff	T. Michael O'Connor	575-0651 / *Fax: 574-8019*
County Auditor	Judy McAdams	575-8451 / *Fax: 573-0636*
Chief Appraiser	John Haliburton	576-3621 / *Fax: 578-1662*
Elections Official	Vicki Vogel	576-0124 / *Fax: 582-5940*
County Commissioner:		
Precinct 1	Danny Garcia	575-8711 / *Fax: 573-7585*
Precinct 2	Kevin M. Janak	575-7932 / *Fax: 573-7585*
Precinct 3	Gary Burns	578-8212 / *Fax: 573-7585*
Precinct 4	Clint Ives	575-5221 / *Fax: 573-7585*
Justice of the Peace:		
Precinct 1	Mary Ann Rivera	573-0836 / *Fax: 573-1835*
Precinct 2	Stuart Posey	575-0012 / *Fax: 573-5515*
Precinct 3	Robert B. Whitaker	575-0246 / *Fax: 575-1202*
Precinct 4	John Miller	573-5073 / *Fax: 572-0441*
Constable:		
Precinct 1	Jesse Garza	580-5748
Precinct 2	James Calaway	580-5763
Precinct 3	Kenneth Easley, Jr.	580-5760
Precinct 4	Kyle R. Dalton	935-6774

WALKER COUNTY

Population: 71,986
County Seat:
  Huntsville 77340

1100 University Ave.
936 436-4910 / *Fax: 936 436-4914*
www.co.walker.tx.us

County Judge	Danny Pierce	436-4910 / *Fax: 436-4914*
Criminal District Attorney	David Weeks	435-2441 / *Fax: 435-2449*
District Clerk	Robyn Flowers	436-4972 / *Fax: 436-4973*
County Clerk	Kari French	436-4922 / *Fax: 436-4928*
County Treasurer	Amy Klawinsky	436-4927 / *Fax: 436-0888*
Tax Assessor-Collector	Diana McRae	436-4950 / *Fax: 436-4951*
Sheriff	Clint McRae	435-2400 / *Fax: 435-2440*
County Auditor	Patricia Allen	436-4940 / *Fax: 436-4949*
Chief Appraiser	Raymond Kiser	295-0402 / *Fax: 295-3061*
County Commissioner:		
Precinct 1	Danny Kuykendall	295-3641 / *Fax: 436-4914*
Precinct 2	Ronnie White	295-6963 / *Fax: 294-0761*
Precinct 3	Bill Daugette	295-7984 / *Fax: 730-1528*
Precinct 4	Jimmy D. Henry	344-6558 / *Fax: 344-0701*

Justice of the Peace:

Precinct 1	Janie Hartnett Farris	436-4966 / *Fax: 436-4965*
Precinct 2	Mike Countz	436-4977 / *Fax: 436-4980*
Precinct 3	Mark Holt	436-4988 / *Fax: 436-4987*
Precinct 4	Stephen Cole	435-8750 / *Fax: 435-8049*

Constable:

Precinct 1	John Hooks	436-4964 / *Fax: 436-4963*
Precinct 2	Shane Loosier	436-4979 / *Fax: 436-4980*
Precinct 3	Steve Hill	436-4990 / *Fax: 436-4987*
Precinct 4	Gene Bartee	435-8028 / *Fax: 435-8049*

WALLER COUNTY

Population: 49,060
County Seat:
  Hempstead 77445

836 Austin St.
979 826-3357 / *Fax: 979 826-2112*
www.co.waller.tx.us/

County Judge	Trey Duhon	826-7700 / *Fax: 826-2112*
Criminal District Attorney	Elton Mathis	826-7718 / *Fax: 826-7722*
District Clerk	Liz Pirkle	826-7735 / *Fax: 826-7738*
County Clerk	Debbie Hollan	826-7711 / *Fax: 826-7771*
County Treasurer	Joan Sargent	826-7707 / *Fax: 826-7709*
Tax Assessor-Collector	Ellen C. Shelburne	826-7620 / *Fax: 826-7619*
Sheriff	Glenn Smith	826-8282 / *Fax: 826-7667*
County Auditor	Alan R. Younts	826 7740 / *Fax: 826-8317*
Chief Appraiser	Chris Barzilla	921-0060 / *Fax: 921-0377*
Elections Official	Christy A. Eason	826-7643

County Commissioner:

Precinct 1	John A. Amsler	826-7700
Precinct 2	Russell Klecka	826-7700 / *Fax: 826-2112*
Precinct 3	Jeron Barnett	826-7700
Precinct 4	Justin Beckendorff	281 375-5231 / *Fax: 281 375-7751*

Justice of the Peace:

Precinct 1	Charles Karisch	826-7745 / *Fax: 826-7748*
Precinct 2	Delores Hargrave	936 372-2193 / *Fax: 936 931-5206*
Precinct 3	Marian Elaine Jackson	826-7637 / *Fax: 826-7639*
Precinct 4	Ted Krenek	281 375-5233 / *Fax: 281 375-7757*

Constable:

Precinct 1	Bo Hashaw	826-7745 / *Fax: 826-7748*
Precinct 2	Glenn White	936 931-1914 / *Fax: 936 372-9234*
Precinct 3	Herschel Smith	826-7635 / *Fax: 826-7639*
Precinct 4	Joe Trimm	281 375-5233 / *Fax: 281 375-7757*

WARD COUNTY

Population: 11,095
County Seat:
  Monahans 79756

400 South Allen
432 943-3200 / *Fax: 432 943-5010*
www.co.ward.tx.us

County Judge	Greg M. Holly . . . . .943-3209 / *Fax: 943-5010*
District Attorney, 143rd Dist.	Randall W. "Randy" Reynolds . . . . . .943-5038 / *Fax: 943-3626*
County Attorney	Hal Upchurch . . . . .943-4211 / *Fax: 943-7404*
District Clerk	Patricia Oyerbides . . . . .943-2751 / *Fax: 943-3810*
County Clerk	Denise Valles . . . . .943-3294 / *Fax: 943-6054*
County Treasurer	Teresa Perry-Stoner . . . . .943-2841 / *Fax: 943-8517*
Tax Assessor-Collector	Vicki Heflin . . . . .943-2546 / *Fax: 943-2745*
Sheriff	Mikel Strickland . . . . .943-6703 / *Fax: 943-6265*
County Auditor	Ellen Friar .943-2921 / *Fax: 943-8517*
Chief Appraiser	Norma Valdez . . . . .943-3224 / *Fax: 943-3226*
Elections Official	Denise Valles
County Commissioner:	
Precinct 1	Jubentino "Tino" Sanchez . . . . .445-6827 / *Fax: 943-8517*
Precinct 2	Larry Hanna . . . . .943-6343 / *Fax: 943-8517*
Precinct 3	Dexter Nichols . . . . .943-2921 / *Fax: 943-8517*
Precinct 4	Eddie Nelms . . . . .943-2921 / *Fax: 943-8517*
Justice of the Peace:	
Precinct 1	Pasqual Olibas . . . . .943-7227 / *Fax: 943-3138*
Precinct 2	Elizabeth Polanco . . . . .943-7237 / *Fax: 943-5250*
Constable:	
Precinct 1	Bill Clayton 943-3362
Precinct 2	James P. Hammond 943-3013

WASHINGTON COUNTY

Population: 35,131
County Seat:
  Brenham 77833

100 E. Main, Suite 104
979 277-6200 / *Fax: 979 277-6221*
www.co.washington.tx.us/

County Judge	John Brieden III . . . . .277-6200 / *Fax: 277-6221*
District Attorney, 21st Dist.	Julie Renken . . . . .277-6247 / *Fax: 277-6237*
County Attorney	Renee Ann Mueller . . . . .277-6200 / *Fax: 277-6215*
District Clerk	Tammy Brauner . . . . .277-6200 / *Fax: 277-6239*
County Clerk	Beth Rothermel . . . . .277-6200 / *Fax: 277-6278*
County Treasurer	Peggy Kramer . . . . .277-6224 / *Fax: 277-6286*
Tax Assessor-Collector	Dorothy "Dot" Borchgardt . . . . .277-6200 / *Fax: 277-6282*
Sheriff	Otto Hanak .277-6251 / *Fax: 277-6258*
County Auditor	Sharon Stolz .277-6229 / *Fax: 277-6238*
Chief Appraiser	Willy Dilworth . . . . .277-3740 / *Fax: 277-3741*
County Commissioner:	
Precinct 1	Don Koester .277-6200 / *Fax: 277-6221*
Precinct 2	Luther Hueske . . . . .277-6200 / *Fax: 277-6221*
Precinct 3	Kirk Hanath . . . . .277-6275 / *Fax: 277-6276*
Precinct 4	Joy Fuchs .277-6200 / *Fax: 277-6221*
Justice of the Peace:	
Precinct 1	Douglas Zwiener . . . . .277-6260 / *Fax: 277-6296*
Precinct 2	Douglas Cone . . . . .836-5008 / *Fax: 353-0041*
Precinct 3	Ken Tofel . . . . .277-6200 / *Fax: 277-6226*
Precinct 4	William Kendall . . . . .289-2921 / *Fax: 289-5001*

Constable:
  Precinct 1   Ken Holle . . . . .251-2577 / *Fax: 277-6296*
  Precinct 2   Carroll C. "Butch" Faske 836-0610
  Precinct 3   David Blakey, Jr. . . . . .289-3599 / *Fax: 277-6226*
  Precinct 4   Position Vacant . . . . .451-5771 / *Fax: 289-5001*

WEBB COUNTY

Population: 275,291   1000 Houston Street, Laredo, 78040
County Seat: 956 523-4600 / *Fax: 956 523-5065*
  Laredo 78042   www.webbcounty.com

County Judge   Tano E. Tijerina . . . . .523-4600 / *Fax: 523-5065*
District Attorney, 49th Dist.   Isidro R. Alaniz . . . . .523-4900 / *Fax: 523-5054*
County Attorney   Marco Montemayor . . . . .523-4044 / *Fax: 523-5005*
District Clerk   Esther Degollado . . . . .523-4268 / *Fax: 523-5063*
County Clerk   Margie R. Ibarra . . . . .523-4251 / *Fax: 523-5035*
County Treasurer   Delia Perales . . . . .523-4150 / *Fax: 523-5014*
Tax Assessor-Collector   Norma C. Farabough . . . . .523-4200 / *Fax: 523-5050*
Sheriff   Martin Cuellar . . . . .523-4500 / *Fax: 523-5059*
County Auditor   Conrado Hein . . . . .523-4016 / *Fax: 523-5001*
Chief Appraiser   Martin Villarreal . . . . .718-4091 / *Fax: 718-3041*
Elections Official   Oscar Villarreal, CERA . . . . .523-4050 / *Fax: 523-5006*
County Commissioner:
  Precinct 1   Jesse Gonzalez . . . . .523-4660 / *Fax: 523-5116*
  Precinct 2   Rosaura Tijerina . . . . .523-4624 / *Fax: 523-5080*
  Precinct 3   John C. Galo . . . . .523-4625 / *Fax: 523-4662*
  Precinct 4   Jaime Canales . . . . .523-4652 / *Fax: 523-5017*
Justice of the Peace:
  Precinct 1, Pl. 1   Hector Liendo . . . . .523-4295 / *Fax: 523-5056*
  Precinct 1, Pl. 2   Oscar Liendo . . . . .523-4303 / *Fax: 523-5057*
  Precinct 2, Pl. 1   Ramiro Veliz, Jr. . . . . .721-2502 / *Fax: 718-8567*
  Precinct 2, Pl. 2   Danny Dominguez . . . . .791-6263 / *Fax: 791-6462*
  Precinct 3   Alfredo Garcia . . . . .523-4850 / *Fax: 361 747-5486*
  Precinct 4   Jose "Pepe" Salinas . . . . .721-2510 / *Fax: 718-8561*
Constable:
  Precinct 1   Rudy Rodriguez, Jr. . . . . .523-4316 / *Fax: 523-5071*
  Precinct 2   Mike Villarreal . . . . .523-4780 / *Fax: 791-1147*
  Precinct 3   Adrian Cortez . . . . .523-4860 / *Fax: 361 747-5777*
  Precinct 4   Harold DeVally . . . . .523-5100 / *Fax: 718-8694*

COUNTY SECTION

WHARTON COUNTY

Population: 41,214
County Seat:
Wharton 77488

100 S. Fulton, Suite 100
979 532-4612 / *Fax: 979 532-1970*
www.co.wharton.tx.us

County Judge	Phillip S. Spenrath	.532-4612 / *Fax: 532-1970*
District Attorney, 329th Dist.	Dawn Allison	.532-8051 / *Fax: 532-8467*
County Attorney	G. A. "Trey" Maffett, III	.532-2591 / *Fax: 532-1251*
District Clerk	Kendra Charbula	.532-5542 / *Fax: 532-1299*
County Clerk	Sandra K. Sanders	.532-2381 / *Fax: 532-8426*
County Treasurer	Donna Thornton	.532-2971 / *Fax: 532-3786*
Tax Assessor-Collector	Patrick Kubala	.532-3312 / *Fax: 532-3897*
Sheriff	Shannon Srubar	.532-1550 / *Fax: 531-0473*
County Auditor	Barbara Starling	.532-2640 / *Fax: 532-8820*
Chief Appraiser	Tylene Gamble	.532-8931 / *Fax: 532-5691*
Elections Official	Cindy Richter	.532-0193 / *Fax: 282-2034*
County Commissioner:		
Precinct 1	Richard Zahn	.532-1991 / *Fax: 532-0838*
Precinct 2	D.C. "Chris" King	.335-7541 / *Fax: 335-6029*
Precinct 3	Steven Goetsch	.543-0091 / *Fax: 543-0092*
Precinct 4	Doug Mathews	.543-3561 / *Fax: 543-9062*
Justice of the Peace:		
Precinct 1	Jeanette Krenek	.532-3941 / *Fax: 531-0758*
Precinct 2	Cynthia L. Kubicek	.335-6210 / *Fax: 335-6312*
Precinct 3	Dennis Korenek	.648-2363
Precinct 4	Timmy Drapela	.543-4322 / *Fax: 543-1568*
Constable:		
Precinct 1	Michael L. Hubenak	.532-3941
Precinct 2	John A. Szymanski	.335-6210 / *Fax: 335-6312*
Precinct 3	Robert L. Holder	.648-2022 / *Fax: 648-2359*
Precinct 4	Shawn Ferguson	.543-1147 / *Fax: 543-1568*

WHEELER COUNTY

Population: 5,692
County Seat:
Wheeler 79096

401 Main St., P.O. Box 486
806 826-5961 / *Fax: 806 826-3282*
www.co.wheeler.tx.us

County Judge	Jerry Dan Hefley	.826-5961 / *Fax: 826-3282*
District Attorney, 31st Dist.	Franklin McDonough	.669-8035 / *Fax: 669-8050*
County Attorney	Leslie Standerfer	.826-2042 / *Fax: 826-0717*
District Clerk	Sherri Jones	.826-5931 / *Fax: 826-0346*
County Clerk	Margaret Dorman	.826-5544 / *Fax: 826-3282*
County Treasurer	Renee Warren	.826-3122 / *Fax: 826-0502*
Tax Assessor-Collector	Scott Porter	.826-3131 / *Fax: 826-3282*
Sheriff	Wes Crites	.826-5537 / *Fax: 826-3458*
Chief Appraiser	Kimberly Morgan	.826-5900 / *Fax: 826-5960*
County Commissioner:		
Precinct 1	Steve Walker	.826-3186 / *Fax: 826-3282*
Precinct 2	Bob Hink	.826-9010 / *Fax: 826-3282*
Precinct 3	David W. Simpson	.256-2852 / *Fax: 256-2813*
Precinct 4	John Walker	.256-3054 / *Fax: 256-5398*

Justice of the Peace:
  Precinct 1   Mark Brown .826-5768 / *Fax: 826-0610*
  Precinct 2   Rick Walden . . . . .256-2552 / *Fax: 256-2751*
Constable:
  Precinct 1   Mack Marshall . . . . .826-5537 / *Fax: 826-3458*
  Precinct 2   Kenneth Martindale . . . . .826-5537 / *Fax: 826-3458*

WICHITA COUNTY

Population: 132,080   900 7th Street, Suite 260
County Seat: 940 766-8101 / *Fax: 940 766-8289*
  Wichita Falls 76301   www.co.wichita.tx.us/

County Judge   Woodrow "Woody" Gossom, Jr. . . . . .766-8101 / *Fax: 766-8289*
Criminal District Attorney   Maureen Shelton . . . . .766-8113 / *Fax: 766-8177*
District Clerk   Patti Flores . . . . .766-8190 / *Fax: 766-8181*
County Clerk   Lori Bohannon . . . . .766-8195 / *Fax: 716-8554*
County Treasurer   R. J. Bob Hampton . . . . .766-8297 / *Fax: 766-8196*
Tax Assessor-Collector   Tommy Smyth . . . . .766-8298 / *Fax: 766-8176*
Sheriff   David Duke . . . . .766-8170 / *Fax: 766-8102*
County Auditor   Deborah A. Stevens . . . . .766-8138 / *Fax: 766-8152*
Chief Appraiser   Lisa Stephens-Musick . . . . .322-2435 / *Fax: 322-8190*
County Commissioner:
  Precinct 1   Mark A. Beauchamp . . . . .766-8106 / *Fax: 766-8251*
  Precinct 2   Lee Harvey . . . . , ...766-8106 / *Fax: 766-8251*
  Precinct 3   Barry Mahler .766-8106 / *Fax: 766-8251*
  Precinct 4   Jeff Watts . . . . .766-8106 / *Fax: 766-8251*
Justice of the Peace:
  Precinct 1, Pl. 1   Janice Sons .766-8141 / *Fax: 766-8282*
  Precinct 1, Pl. 2   Mike Little . . . . .766-8143 / *Fax: 766-8283*
  Precinct 2   Nancy Viavattene . . . . .569-1140 / *Fax: 569-3368*
  Precinct 3   Marc Newman . . . . .592-9388 / *Fax: 592-2638*
  Precinct 4   Judy Baker . . . . .766-8129 / *Fax: 495-4098*
Constable:
  Precinct 1   Mark Brewer . . . . .766-8150 / *Fax: 766-8251*
  Precinct 2   Thomas L. "Tom" Black . . . . .781-3947 / *Fax: 569-3445*
  Precinct 3   David W. Blackerby . . . . .781-4116 / *Fax: 592-4861*
  Precinct 4   James Gowen . . . . .761-8130 / *Fax: 495-4098*

COUNTY SECTION

WILBARGER COUNTY

Population: 12,527
County Seat:
  Vernon 76384

1700 Wilbarger St.
940 553-2300 / *Fax: 940 553-1766*
www.co.wilbarger.tx.us/

County Judge	Greg Tyra	553-2300 / *Fax: 553-1766*
District Attorney, 46th Dist.	Staley Heatly	553-3346 / *Fax: 552-9630*
County Attorney	Cornell "Cory" Curtis	553-3521 / *Fax: 553-2305*
District Clerk	Brenda Peterson	553-3411 / *Fax: 553-2316*
County Clerk	Jana Kennon	552-5486 / *Fax: 553-2320*
County Treasurer	Joann Carter	553-2302 / *Fax: 553-2348*
Tax Assessor-Collector	Chris Quisenberry	552-9341 / *Fax: 553-2324*
Sheriff	Bill Price	552-6205 / *Fax: 553-2318*
County Auditor	Sid Beebe	553-2308 / *Fax: 553-2320*
Chief Appraiser	Sandy Burkett	553-1857 / *Fax: 552-9541*
County Commissioner:		
Precinct 1	Richard Jacobs	552-5712
Precinct 2	Phillip Graf	552-7742
Precinct 3	Kelly Joe Neel	553-2300
Precinct 4	Joshua Patterson	839-5204
Justice of the Peace:		
Precinct 1, Pl. 1	Gene Morton	553-2306 / *Fax: 553-2328*
Precinct 2	Lewis Templeton	553-2307 / *Fax: 553-3321*
Constable:		
Precinct 1	Kenny Alexander	553-2304 / *Fax: 553-2328*
Precinct 2	Paul Miller	553-2305 / *Fax: 553-1766*

WILLACY COUNTY

Population: 21,661
County Seat:
  Raymondville 78580

576 W. Main St.
956 689-3393 / *Fax: 956 689-4817*
www.co.willacy.tx.us

County Judge	Aurelio "Keter" Guerra, Jr.	689-3393 / *Fax: 689-4817*
County Attorney	Annette C. Hinojosa	689-2164 / *Fax: 689-5280*
District Clerk	Isabel Adame	689-2532 / *Fax: 689-5713*
County Clerk	Terry Flores	689-2710 / *Fax: 689-9849*
County Treasurer	Ruben Cavazos	689-2772 / *Fax: 689-2735*
Tax Assessor-Collector	Elizabeth Barnhart	689-3621 / *Fax: 689-3910*
Sheriff	Larry G. Spence	689-5576 / *Fax: 689-3867*
County Auditor	Ida C. Martinez	689-3422 / *Fax: 689-6127*
Chief Appraiser	Agustin Lopez	689-5979 / *Fax: 689-0585*
Elections Official	Mary Hope Barrera	689-2387
County Commissioner:		
Precinct 1	Eliberto Guerra	689-4214 / *Fax: 689-2735*
Precinct 2	Oscar De Luna	689-4214 / *Fax: 689-2735*
Precinct 3	Henry De La Paz	689-4214 / *Fax: 689-2735*
Precinct 4	Eduardo "Eddy" Gonzales	689-4214 / *Fax: 689-2735*

Justice of the Peace:
Precinct 1   Yesenia Rosas 699-5018
Precinct 2   Juan Salinas, Jr. .... .689-6255 / *Fax: 689-5341*
Precinct 3   Juan Silva .... .699-2940 / *Fax: 689-5341*
Precinct 4   Juan Salinas, Jr. .... .689-3381 / *Fax: 689-5341*
Precinct 5   Rudy Cantu .... .642-3381 / *Fax: 689-5341*
Constable:
Precinct 1   Carlos Ybarra .... .689-3393 / *Fax: 689-4817*
Precinct 2   Jose Salazar .... .689-3393 / *Fax: 689-4817*
Precinct 3   Ben Vera .... .966-6955 / *Fax: 689-4817*
Precinct 4   Albert Garza .... .244-5512 / *Fax: 689-4817*
Precinct 5   Antonio Trevino .... .689-3393 / *Fax: 689-4817*

WILLIAMSON COUNTY

Population: 505,250
County Seat:
Georgetown 78626

405 Martin Luther King St.
512 943-1226 / *Fax: 512 943-1188*
www.wilco.org

County Judge   Dan A. Gattis .... .943-1550 / *Fax: 943-1662*
District Attorney, 26th Dist.   Shawn Dick .... .943-1234 / *Fax: 943-1255*
County Attorney   Dee Hobbs .... .943-1111 / *Fax: 943-1120*
District Clerk   Lisa David .... .943-1212 / *Fax: 943-1222*
County Clerk   Nancy E. Rister, C.I.O. .... .943-1515 / *Fax: 943-1616*
County Treasurer   Scott Heselmeyer . . .. .943-1540 / *Fax: 943-1590*
Tax Assessor-Collector   Larry Gaddes .... .943-1954 / *Fax: 943-3578*
Sheriff   Robert Chody .... .943-1300 / *Fax: 943-1393*
County Auditor   Jerri Jones 943-1500
Chief Appraiser   Alvin Lankford .... .930-3787 / *Fax: 930-0391*
Elections Official   Chris Davis .... .943-1630 / *Fax: 943-1634*
County Commissioner:
Precinct 1   Terry Cook .... .244-8610 / *Fax: 244-8616*
Precinct 2   Cynthia Long .... .260-4280 / *Fax: 260-4284*
Precinct 3   Valerie Covey .... .943-3370 / *Fax: 943-3376*
Precinct 4   Larry Madsen .... .943-3761 / *Fax: 943-3798*
Justice of the Peace:
Precinct 1   Dain Johnson .... .244-8618 / *Fax: 244-8603*
Precinct 2   Edna Staudt .... .260-4210 / *Fax: 260-4215*
Precinct 3   Bill Gravell, Jr. 943-1501
Precinct 4   Judy Schier Hobbs 352-4155
Constable:
Precinct 1   Vinnie Cherrone .... .244-8650 / *Fax: 244-8662*
Precinct 2   Rick Coffman .... .260-4270 / *Fax: 260-4275*
Precinct 3   Kevin Stofle .... .943-1434 / *Fax: 943-1440*
Precinct 4   Marty Ruble .... .238-2181 / *Fax: 352-4186*

WILSON COUNTY

Population: 49,106
County Seat:
  Floresville 78114

1420 3rd Street
830 393-7303 / *Fax: 830 393-7327*
www.co.wilson.tx.us

County Judge	Richard L. Jackson	.393-7303 / *Fax: 393-7327*
District Attorney, 81st Dist.	Audrey Gossett Louis	.393-2200 / *Fax: 393-2205*
County Attorney	Tom Caldwell	.393-7305 / *Fax: 393-7358*
District Clerk	Deborah Bryan	.393-7322 / *Fax: 393-7319*
County Clerk	Eva S. Martinez	.393-7308 / *Fax: 393-7334*
County Treasurer	Jan Hartl	.393-7310 / *Fax: 393-7393*
Tax Assessor-Collector	Dawn Polasek-Barnett	.393-7313 / *Fax: 393-7359*
Sheriff	Joe D. Tackitt, Jr.	.393-2535 / *Fax: 393-7402*
County Auditor	Tom Dupnick	.393-7304 / *Fax: 393-7384*
Chief Appraiser	Jennifer Coldeway	.393-3065 / *Fax: 393-7755*
County Commissioner:		
Precinct 1	Albert Gamez, Jr.	.391-0451 / *Fax: 393-7345*
Precinct 2	Paul W. Pfeil	.210 414-5971 / *Fax: 484-2519*
Precinct 3	Ernest "Skip" Hajek	.534-9859
Precinct 4	Larry A. Wiley	.391-0234
Justice of the Peace:		
Precinct 1	Johnny Tejada Villarreal	.393-5112 / *Fax: 393-5213*
Precinct 2	Sara Canady	.484-2356 / *Fax: 484-2890*
Precinct 3	Harold Schott	.779-2285 / *Fax: 779-4425*
Precinct 4	Clara J. Rutland	.393-4052 / *Fax: 393-5149*
Constable:		
Precinct 1	Thomas "Wedo" Silvas	.534-6321
Precinct 2	Devin Keen	.477-8744
Precinct 3	Curtis Fowler	.210 663-2288 / *Fax: 393-7327*
Precinct 4	Jerry "Jay" Talley Jr.	.321-1102 / *Fax: 393-7327*

WINKLER COUNTY

Population: 7,970
County Seat:
  Kermit 79745

P.O. Drawer Y - 100 E. Winkler
432 586-6658 / *Fax: 432 586-3223*
www.co.winkler.tx.us

County Judge	Charles M. Wolf	.586-6658 / *Fax: 586-3223*
District Attorney, 109th Dist.	Amanda Navarette	.586-3700 / *Fax: 586-3208*
County Attorney	Thomas D. Duckworth, Jr.	.586-2596 / *Fax: 586-3535*
District Clerk	Sherry Terry	.586-3359 / *Fax: 586-2998*
County Clerk	Shethelia Reed	.586-3401
County Treasurer	Shannon Nutt	.586-6604 / *Fax: 586-3223*
Tax Assessor-Collector	Minerva Soltero	.586-3465 / *Fax: 586-6925*
Sheriff	Darin Mitchell	.586-3461 / *Fax: 586-3902*
County Auditor	Jeanna Willhelm	.586-3161 / *Fax: 586-3223*
Chief Appraiser	Connie Carpenter	.586-2832 / *Fax: 586-3674*
Elections Official	Shethelia Reed	.586-3401
County Commissioner:		
Precinct 1	Billy Stevens	.586-2233 / *Fax: 586-3223*
Precinct 2	Robbie Wolf	.527-3537 / *Fax: 586-3223*
Precinct 3	Hope F. Williams	.586-2233 / *Fax: 586-3223*
Precinct 4	Billy Ray Thompson	.586-2233 / *Fax: 586-3223*

Justice of the Peace:
Precinct 1   Erma "Kaki" Coleman 586-2671
Precinct 2   Glenda Mixon 527-3450
Constable:
Precinct 1   Richard Leroy Crow 586-6658
Precinct 2   Carl Garrett .... .208-4583 / *Fax: 586-3223*

WISE COUNTY

Population: 63,207
County Seat:
  Decatur 76234

P.O. Box 393
940 627-5743 / *Fax: 940 627-6926*
www.co.wise.tx.us/

County Judge	J.D. Clark .... .627-5743 / *Fax: 627-6926*
District Attorney, 271st Dist.	Greg Lowery .... .627-5257 / *Fax: 627-6404*
County Attorney	James Stainton .... .627-3321 / *Fax: 627-7194*
District Clerk	Brenda Rowe .... .627-5535 / *Fax: 627-0705*
County Clerk	Sherry Lemon .... .627-3351 / *Fax: 627-2138*
County Treasurer	Katherine Canova Hudson .... .627-3540 / *Fax: 627-3573*
Tax Assessor-Collector	Monte S. Shaw, PCC .... .627-3523 / *Fax: 627-7237*
Sheriff	Lane Akin .... .627-5971 / *Fax: 627-3797*
County Auditor	Ann McCuiston .... .627-5744 / *Fax: 627-3388*
Chief Appraiser	Michael Hand .... .627-3081 / *Fax: 627-5187*
Elections Official	Sabra Srader .... .626-4453 / *Fax: 626-4283*
County Commissioner:	
Precinct 1	Danny White .... .627-5810 / *Fax: 627-0735*
Precinct 2	Kevin Burns .... .427-4881 / *Fax: 427-2210*
Precinct 3	Harry Lamance .... .433-5365 / *Fax: 433-5511*
Precinct 4	Gaylord Kennedy .... .683-4153 / *Fax: 683-3541*
Justice of the Peace:	
Precinct 1	Jan Morrow .... .627-2694 / *Fax: 627-5417*
Precinct 2	Callie Manning .... .626-4206 / *Fax: 626-4243*
Precinct 3	Mandy Hopkins Hays .... .433-2969 / *Fax: 433-3062*
Precinct 4	Clay Poynor .... .683-4244 / *Fax: 683-3747*
Constable:	
Precinct 1	Dennis Hudson 389-1870
Precinct 2	Larry Short 626-4206
Precinct 3	Position Vacant .... .433-2969 / *Fax: 433-3062*
Precinct 4	Kevin P. Huffman .... .683-3750 / *Fax: 683-3747*

COUNTY SECTION

WOOD COUNTY

Population: 43,865
County Seat:
  Quitman 75783

100 Main Street
903 763-2716 / *Fax: 903 763-2902*
www.mywoodcounty.com

County Judge	Bryan Jeanes	763-2716 / *Fax: 763-2902*
Criminal District Attorney	Jim Wheeler	763-4515 / *Fax: 763-5105*
District Clerk	Jenica Turner	763-2361 / *Fax: 763-1511*
County Clerk	Kelley Price	763-2711 / *Fax: 763-5641*
County Treasurer	Becky Burford	763-4186 / *Fax: 763-1316*
Tax Assessor-Collector	Carol Taylor	763-2261 / *Fax: 763-5753*
Sheriff	Tom Castloo	763-2201 / *Fax: 763-5464*
County Auditor	Terri Sellars	763-2921 / *Fax: 763-5039*
Chief Appraiser	Tracy Nichols	763-4946 / *Fax: 763-4183*
Elections Official	Laura Wise	763-2400 / *Fax: 763-2401*
County Commissioner:		
Precinct 1	Virgil J. Holland	763-2716 / *Fax: 763-2902*
Precinct 2	Jerry Gaskill	763-2716 / *Fax: 763-2902*
Precinct 3	Mike Simmons	763-2716 / *Fax: 763-2902*
Precinct 4	Russell Acker	763-2716 / *Fax: 763-2902*
Justice of the Peace:		
Precinct 1	Tony Gilbreath	763-2713 / *Fax: 763-4246*
Precinct 2	Wes Criddle	569-3802 / *Fax: 569-6270*
Precinct 3	Jerry Parker	769-3517 / *Fax: 769-9631*
Precinct 4	Cindy Weems	342-3079 / *Fax: 342-9903*
Constable:		
Precinct 1	Stephen Bowser	763-2713 / *Fax: 763-4246*
Precinct 2	Kelly Smith	569-5495 / *Fax: 569-6270*
Precinct 3	Gary Dixon	769-3517 / *Fax: 769-9631*
Precinct 4	Scott Price	342-5203 / *Fax: 342-9903*

YOAKUM COUNTY

Population: 8,788
County Seat:
  Plains 79355

P.O. Box 456
806 456-7491 / *Fax: 806 456-6175*
www.co.yoakum.tx.us

County Judge	Jim Barron	456-7491 / *Fax: 456-6175*
Criminal District Attorney	Bill Helwig	456-7491 / *Fax: 456-2441*
District Clerk	Sandra Roblez	456-7491 / *Fax: 456-8767*
County Clerk	Deborah L. Rushing	456-7491 / *Fax: 456-2258*
County Treasurer	Barbara Wright	456-7491 / *Fax: 456-6175*
Tax Assessor-Collector	Jan Parrish	456-7491 / *Fax: 456-7118*
Sheriff	David Bryant	456-2377 / *Fax: 456-5431*
County Auditor	Darinda McWhirter	456-7491 / *Fax: 456-6175*
Chief Appraiser	David Greener	456-7101 / *Fax: 456-7102*
County Commissioner:		
Precinct 1	Woodson "Woody" Lindsey	592-3601 / *Fax: 456-6175*
Precinct 2	Ray Marion	592-3287 / *Fax: 592-0063*
Precinct 3	Tommy Box	456-4371 / *Fax: 456-6175*
Precinct 4	Tim Addison	456-6525 / *Fax: 456-6175*
Justice of the Peace:		
Precinct 1	Marc Traweek	456-7491 / *Fax: 456-4263*
Precinct 2	Troy Scott	592-3963 / *Fax: 592-7563*

YOUNG COUNTY

Population: 18,834
County Seat:
  Graham 76450

316 4th St., Rm. 108
940 549-2030 / *Fax: 940 521-9482*
www.co.young.tx.us

County Judge	John Charles Bullock	.549-2030 / *Fax: 521-9482*
District Attorney, 90th Dist.	Dee H. Peavy	.549-4132 / *Fax: 549-7151*
County Attorney	Christopher D. Baran	.549-8486 / *Fax: 549-8675*
District Clerk	Jamie Freeze Land	.549-0029 / *Fax: 549-4874*
County Clerk	Kay J. Hardin	.549-8432 / *Fax: 521-0305*
County Treasurer	Ann Daily	.549-2633 / *Fax: 521-9486*
Tax Assessor-Collector	Nancy Thomas	.549-1393 / *Fax: 549-5160*
Sheriff	Travis Babcock	.549-1555 / *Fax: 549-0011*
County Auditor	Cheryl Roberts	.549-1786 / *Fax: 549-4266*
Chief Appraiser	Luke Robbins	.549-2392 / *Fax: 549-7271*
Elections Official	Lauren Sullivan	.521-9483 / *Fax: 221-2104*
County Commissioner:		
Precinct 1	Mike Sipes	.549-0337 / *Fax: 549-4266*
Precinct 2	Matt Pruitt	.362-4301 / *Fax: 549-4266*
Precinct 3	Stacey K. Rogers	.564-5070 / *Fax: 549-4266*
Precinct 4	Jimmy R. Wiley	.378-2414 / *Fax: 549-4266*
Justice of the Peace:		
Precinct 1	Robert D. Dial	.549-3636 / *Fax: 549-7426*
Precinct 3	Stan Mahler	.564-5001 / *Fax: 564-3536*
Constable:		
Precinct 1	Tommy Martin	.549-1555 / *Fax: 549-0011*
Precinct 3	Position Vacant	.564-5029 / *Fax: 564-3536*

ZAPATA COUNTY

Population: 14,272
County Seat:
  Zapata 78076

201 E. 7th Avenue, Suite 115
956 765-9920 / *Fax: 956 765-9926*
www.co.zapata.tx.us/

County Judge	Joseph Rathmell	.765-9920 / *Fax: 765-9926*
District Attorney, 49th Dist.	Isidro R. Alaniz	.523-4900 / *Fax: 721-2434*
County Attorney	Alfonso Figueroa	.765-9905 / *Fax: 765-9932*
District Clerk	Dora Martinez Castanon	.765-9930 / *Fax: 765-9931*
County Clerk	Mary Jayne Villarreal-Bonoan	.765-9915 / *Fax: 765-9933*
County Treasurer	Romeo Salinas, CIO	.765-9925 / *Fax: 765-9748*
Tax Assessor-Collector	Luis Lauro Gonzalez	.765-9971 / *Fax: 765-8638*
Sheriff	Alonso Lopez	.765-9960 / *Fax: 765-9941*
County Auditor	Triunfo Gonzalez	.765-9910 / *Fax: 765-8606*
Chief Appraiser	Amada Gonzalez	.765-9988 / *Fax: 765-9991*
County Commissioner:		
Precinct 1	Paco Mendoza	.285-9496 / *Fax: 765-9926*
Precinct 2	Olga M. Elizondo	.765-6804 / *Fax: 765-3526*
Precinct 3	Eddie Martinez	.765-8449 / *Fax: 765-9926*
Precinct 4	Norberto Garza	.334-4858 / *Fax: 765-9926*

Zapata County Cont.
Justice of the Peace:
Precinct 1	Ana Guerra .... 765-9165 / *Fax: 765-8978*
Precinct 2	Juana Maria B. Gutierrez .... 765-5333 / *Fax: 765-3526*
Precinct 3	Fernando Munoz, Jr. .... 765-9945 / *Fax: 765-8978*
Precinct 4	Ramon Benavides .... 765-6655 / *Fax: 765-6756*

Constable:
Precinct 1	Mario H. Garcia .... 765-9960 / *Fax: 765-9941*
Precinct 2	Daniel Arriaga .... 830 374-2116 / *Fax: 830 347-2895*
Precinct 3	Eloy "Jay" Martinez .... 765-9988 / *Fax: 765-9941*
Precinct 4	Baldemar Montes .... 765-9960 / *Fax: 765-9941*

ZAVALA COUNTY

Population: 12,307
County Seat:
  Crystal City 78839

200 E. Uvalde St., Suite 9
830 374-3810 / *Fax: 830 374-5634*
www.co.zavala.tx.us

County Judge	Joe Luna .... 374-3810 / *Fax: 374-5634*
District Attorney, 293rd Dist.	Roberto Serna .... 773-9268 / *Fax: 773-9379*
County Attorney	Eduardo Serna .... 374-3734 / *Fax: 374-3007*
District Clerk	Rachel Ramirez .... 374-3456 / *Fax: 374-2632*
County Clerk	Oralia G. Trevino .... 374-2331 / *Fax: 374-5955*
County Treasurer	Elizabeth Rodriguez .... 374-2442 / *Fax: 374-2634*
Tax Assessor-Collector	Cindy M. Rivera .... 374-2351 / *Fax: 374-2634*
Sheriff	Euscvio E. Salinas, Jr. .... 374-3615 / *Fax: 374-5933*
County Auditor	Carlos A. Pereda, Jr. .... 374-2214 / *Fax: 374-2634*
Chief Appraiser	John Tapia .... 374-3475 / *Fax: 374-3076*

County Commissioner:
Precinct 1	Isidro Cantu .... 374-3810 / *Fax: 376-9021*
Precinct 2	Miguel "Mike" Acosta .... 374-3810 / *Fax: 374-2895*
Precinct 3	Jesse Gonzales .... 486-7240 / *Fax: 374-5634*
Precinct 4	Fred E. Enriquez .... 374-3810 / *Fax: 365-4702*

Justice of the Peace:
Precinct 1	Paula Mae De Leon .... 376-4609 / *Fax: 376-9021*
Precinct 2	Xavier Espinosa .... 374-2116 / *Fax: 374-2895*
Precinct 3	Luis Hinojosa .... 374-5197 / *Fax: 374-2895*
Precinct 4	Lucy Leal .... 365-4276 / *Fax: 365-4702*

Constable:
Precinct 1	John A. Simpson .... 376-4216 / *Fax: 376-4344*
Precinct 2	Jose Angel Flores .... 374-3615 / *Fax: 374-2895*
Precinct 3	Jesse M. Lopez .... 374-3615 / *Fax: 374-5933*
Precinct 4	Alvin Lewis .... 365-2704 / *Fax: 365-4702*

TEXAS ASSOCIATION OF COUNTIES

1210 San Antonio St., P.O. Box 2131, Austin 78768
512/478-8753 • *FAX: 512/478-0519* • www.county.org

OFFICERS:

President	The Hon. Larry Gallardo	.956/581-6800
President-Elect	The Hon. Renee Couch	.830/221-1221
Vice President	The Hon. Kim Halfmann	.432/354-2639

MEMBERS:

Dallas Co. Tax Assessor Coll.	The Hon. John R. Ames, CTA	.214/653-7811
Denton County Treasurer	The Hon. Cindy Yeatts Brown	.940/349-3150
Tom Green County Auditor	The Hon. Nathan Cradduck	.325/659-6521
112th District Attorney	The Hon. Laurie K. English	.432/336-6294
Bandera County District Clerk	The Hon. Tammy Kneuper	.830/796-4606
Hunt County Clerk	The Hon. Jennifer Lindenzweig	.903/408-4130
Travis County Constable	The Hon. Carlos Lopez	.512/854-9100
Sheriff Lamb Couty	The Hon. Gary Maddox	.806/385-7900
Ellis County JP	The Hon. Jackie Miller, Jr.	.972/825-5022
Leon County Judge	The Hon. Byron Ryder	.903/536-2331
Victoria County Judge	The Hon. Ben Zeller	.361/757-4558

Ex Officio Members:

Chaplain	The Hon. Don R. Allred	.806/267-2607
NACO Representative	The Hon. Connie Hickman	.903/654-3060
NACO Representative	The Hon. Jon Burrows	.254/933-5105
Immediate Past President	The Hon. Joyce Hudman	.979/864-1970

STAFF:

Gene Terry	Executive Director	.512/478-8753 / *512/478-0519*

COUNTY SECTION

TOP TEN COUNTIES IN TEXAS IN SQUARE MILES

Brewster	6,193 sq.mi.	Val Verde	3,170 sq.mi.
Pecos	4,764 sq.mi.	Crockett	2,807 sq.mi.
Hudspeth	4,571 sq.mi.	Reeves	2,636 sq.mi.
Presidio	3,856 sq.mi.	Terrell	2,358 sq.mi.
Culberson	3,812 sq.mi.		
Webb	3,357 sq.mi.		

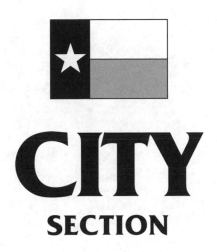

CITY

SECTION

CITY SECTION

The City Section of the TEXAS STATE DIRECTORY is designed to provide a listing of most elected officials of incorporated cities in the State. The material is organized in the following manner:

Name of city, General ZIP code
Population　　　　　(County ID)
Mailing address of city
General information telephone number of city (including area code)
FAX number
City URL
Mayor
Mayor Pro Tem (Mayor PT) Deputy Mayor Pro Tem (Deputy Mayor PT)
Commissioners (Comm.), Alderpersons (Ald.), Councilpersons (Coun.), or
　　Representative (Rep.)
Manager (Mgr.), Secretary (Secy.), Clerk (Clk.), or Administrator (Admin.)
Director of Finance (Dir. of Fin.)
Attorney (Atty.)
Chief of Police (C.P.) or Marshal (Mar.), Fire Chief/Marshal (F.C or FM.)
Director of Public Safety (Dir. P.S.), Volunteer Fire Dept. Fire Chief (V.F.D.F.C)

ABBOTT 76621
Pop: 376　　　　　(Hill)
P.O. Box 44
254 582-3911 - *Fax: 582-3911*
Mayor-Anthony R. Pustejovsky
Comm.-Ryan Kaska
Comm.-Kevin Scheler
Atty.-Stephanie W. Johnson
V.F.D.F.C.-Bradley Matthys

ABERNATHY 79311
Pop: 2748　　　　(Hale-Lubbock)
811 Ave. D
P.O. Box 310
806 298-2546 - *Fax: 298-2968*
www.cityofabernathy.org
Mayor-Sharon Kester-Fair
Mayor PT-Michael Macias
Ald.-William Atchley
Ald.-Victor Cavazos
Ald.-Ron Johnson
Ald.-Jay Stephen
City Mgr.-Mike Cypert
City Secy.-Krista Adames
Atty.-Todd Hurd
C.P.-Vacant
V.F.D.F.C.-Kelley Vandygriff

ABILENE 79604
Pop: 122315　　　(Jones-Taylor)
555 Walnut
P.O. Box 60
325 676-6202 - *Fax: 676-6229*
www.abilenetx.com
Mayor-Anthony Williams
Coun.-Donna Albus
Coun.-Weldon Hurt

Coun.-Bruce Kreitler
Coun.-Kyle McAlister
Coun.-Shane Price
Coun.-Steve Savage
City Mgr.-Robert Hanna
City Secy.-Rosa A. Rios
P.A.-Melissa Denson
Atty.-Stanley E. Smith
C.P.-Stan Standridge
F.C.-Larry Bell

ACKERLY 79713
Pop: 224　　　　(Dawson-Martin)
P.O. Box 37
432 353-4868 - *Fax: 353-4301*
Mayor-Scott Ragle
Mayor PT-Joe Dean Hall
Ald.-Kornelius Enns
Ald.-Ralph Gomez
Ald.-Jim Kays
Ald.-David Sanderson
Ald.-Chris Spivey
City Secy.-Judy Kays
F.C.-Scott Ragle

ADDISON, TOWN OF
Pop: 15075　　　　(Dallas)
5300 Belt Line Rd.
P.O. Box 9010
Addison, TX 75001-9010
972 450-7001 - *Fax: 450-7043*
www.addisontx.gov
Mayor-Joe Chow
Mayor PT-Ivan Hughes
Dep. Mayor PT-Jim Duffy
Coun.-Al Angell

Coun.-Tom Braun
Coun.-Paul Walden
Coun.-Lori Ward
City Mgr.-Wes Pierson
Deputy CM-Cheryl Delaney
Deputy CM-Ashley Mitchell
City Secy.-Laura M. Bell
C.P.-Paul Spencer
F.C.-David Jones

ADRIAN 79001
Pop: 164　　　　(Oldham)
P.O. Box 222
806 538-6223 - *Fax: 536-0046*
Mayor-Finis Brown
Ald.-Emily Acevedo
Ald.-Maggie Gruhlkey
Ald.-Juliet Harris
Ald.-Dale Rich
Ald.-Joshua Smith
City Secy.-Mildred Petty

AGUA DULCE 78330
Pop: 834　　　　(Nueces)
P.O. Box 297
361 998-2532 - *Fax: 998-2262*
Mayor-John Howard
Mayor PT-Kenny Riley
Ald.-Elaine Black
Ald.-Ramon Ovalle
Ald.-Freddy Perez
Ald.-Carl Vajdos
City Secy.-Ninfa Acuna
Atty.-Hal George
Dir. P.S.-David Pena

ALAMO 78516
Pop: 19246 (Hidalgo)
420 N. Tower Rd.
956 787-0006 - *Fax: 787-6807*
www.alamotexas.org
Mayor-Diana Martinez
Mayor PT-Maria Pilar Garza
Comm.-Robert De La Garza
Comm.-Molly Gallegos
Comm.-Pete Morales
City Mgr.-Luciano Ozuna, Jr.
Dir. Fin-Yvette Mendoza
City Secy.-Margot Saenz
Atty.-Damian Orozco
F.C.-Rolando Espinoza

ALAMO HEIGHTS
Pop: 7031 (Bexar)
6116 Broadway
San Antonio, TX 78209
210 822-3331 - *Fax: 822-8197*
www.alamoheightstx.gov
Mayor-Bobby Rosenthal
Coun.-Lynda Billa Burke
Coun.-Lawson Jessee
Coun.-Fred Prassel
Coun.-John Savage
Coun.-Wes Sharples
City Mgr.-Mark Browne
Dir. Fin-Robert Galindo
City Secy.-Jennifer Reyna
Atty.-Michael S. Brenan
C.P.-Rick Pruitt
F.C.-Buddy Kuhn
Dir. P.W.-Patrick Sullivan

ALBA 75410
Pop: 523 (Wood)
903 765-2396 - *Fax: 765-9043*
www.albatexas.org/
Mayor-Preston "Sonny" Hass
Mayor PT-Marja Heinert
Ald.-Larry Harris
Ald.-Larry Jones
Ald.-Tammy Kirkpatrick
Ald.-Jonathan Mize
City Secy.-Lindy McCarty
Atty.-Jim D. McLeroy
C.P.-Tim Koonce
F.C.-Shawn Newland

ALBANY 76430
Pop: 2034 (Shackelford)
425 South 2nd St.
P.O. Box 3248
325 762-3133 - *Fax: 762-3849*
www.albanytexas.org
Mayor-Rodney Alexander
Ald.-Lester Galbreath
Ald.-Susan Montgomery
Ald.-Joe Tidwell
Ald.-Carolyn Waller
Ald.-James Waters
City Mgr.-Billy Holson
City Secy.-Becky Wiloth

Atty.-William "Pat" Chesser
C.P.-Lynn Wilkins
F.C.-Kyle Tischler

ALEDO 76008
Pop: 3194 (Parker)
P.O. Box 1
817 441-7016 - *Fax: 441-7520*
www.aledo-texas.com
Mayor-Kit Marshall
Mayor PT-Kimberly Hiebert
Coun.-Jean E. Bailey
Coun.-Daniel Herbert
Coun.-Spencer Perry
Coun.-Robert Wood
City Secy.-Deana McMullen
City Admin.-Ken Pfeifer
Atty.-Betsy Elam
Dir. P.W.-David Fain

ALICE 78333
Pop: 18706 (Jim Wells)
P.O. Box 3229
361 668-7210 - *Fax: 668-4353*
www.ci.alice.tx.us
Mayor-Jolene B. Vanover
Coun.-Cynthia Carrasco
Coun.-Pete Crisp
Coun.-Vacant
Coun.-Vacant
Int. Mgr.-Diana L. Lopez
Clk.-Diana L. Lopez
C.P.-Rex Ramon
F.C.-Dean Van Nest
Interim City Attorne-John Lemon

ALLEN 75013
Pop: 100412 (Collin)
305 Century Parkway
214 509-4100 - *Fax: 509-4118*
www.cityofallen.org
Mayor-Stephen Terrell
Mayor PT-Gary L. Caplinger
Coun.-Baine Brooks
Coun.-Carl Clemlencich
Coun.-Kurt Kizer
Coun.-Robin L. Sedlacek
Coun.-Vacant
City Mgr.-Peter H. Vargas
City Secy.-Shelley B. George
P.A.-Debra Morris
Atty.-Peter G. Smith
C.P.-Brian Harvey
F.C.-Bill Hawley

ALMA 75119
Pop: 354 (Ellis)
972 825-7938 - *Cell: 834-6445*
www.cityofalmatx.com
Mayor-Bob Peters
Mayor PT-Kyle Wilson
Ald.-Alan Braswell
Ald.-Marvin Dorton
Ald.-Jason Griffin
Ald.-Dave Prachel

City Secy.-Linda Calvert
Atty.-Michael B. Halla
V.F.D.F.C.-Brian Mundie

ALPINE 79830
Pop: 5941 (Brewster)
100 North 13th St.
432 837-3301 - *Fax: 837-2044*
cityofalpine.com
Mayor-Andres "Andy" Ramos
Coun.-Maria Curry
Coun.-Lucy Escovedo
Coun.-Jim Fitzgerald
Coun.-Ramon Olivas
Coun.-Rick Stephens
Int. Mgr.-J. Horry
Dir. Fin-Megan Antrim
City Secy.-Cynthia Salas
Atty.-Mick McKamie
C.P.-Russell Scown
F.C.-Mark Scudder

ALTO 75925
Pop: 1227 (Cherokee)
936 858-4711 - *Fax: 858-4761*
www.altotexas.org
Mayor-Jimmy Allen
Mayor PT-El Thacker
Coun.-Steve Cox
Coun.-Jerry Flowers
Coun.-Carey Palmer
Coun.-Randy Selman
City Secy.-Vacant
Atty.-Jimmy Cassels
C.P.-Jeremy Jackson
F.C.-Terry Black

ALTON 78573
Pop: 15127 (Hidalgo)
956 432-0760 - *Fax: 432-0766*
www.alton-tx.gov/
Mayor-Salvador Vela
Mayor PT-Arturo R. Galvan, Jr.
Comm.-Richard Arevalo
Comm.-Emilio Cantu Jr.
Comm.-Ricardo Garza
City Mgr.-Jorge Arcaute
Dir. Fin-Rosie Tello
City Secy.-Baudelia Rojas
Atty.-Ricardo "Ric" Gonzalez
C.P.-Enrique Sotelo
F.C.-Javier Garcia
Dir. P.W.-Rudy Garza

ALVARADO 76009
Pop: 4095 (Johnson)
104 W. College
817 790-3351 - *Fax: 783-7925*
www.cityofalvarado.org
Mayor-Dewayne "Coach" Richters
Mayor PT-Shawn Goulding
Coun.-Michael Bennett
Coun.-Cherry Bryant
Coun.-Beverly Short
Coun.-Arrdeen Vaughan

Coun.-Jacob Wheat
City Mgr.-Clint Davis
Dir. Fin-Kelle Whitfill
City Secy.-Debbie Thomas
Atty.-Ashley Dierker
C.P.-Brad Anderson
F.C.-Richard VanWinkle
Dir. P.W.-Michael Dwiggins

ALVIN 77511
Pop: 26954   (Brazoria)
216 W. Sealy St.
281 388-4200 - *Fax: 388-4294*
www.alvin-tx.gov
Mayor-Paul Horn
Mayor PT-Brad Richards
Coun.-Gabe Adame
Coun.-Adam Arendell
Coun.-Scott Reed
Coun.-Chris Sanger
Coun.-Glenn Starkey
Coun.-Keith Thompson
City Mgr.-Sereniah Breland
City Secy.-Dixie Roberts
Atty.-Suzanne Hanneman
C.P.-Robert Lee
V.F.D.F.C.-Rex Klesel

ALVORD 76225
Pop: 1426   (Wise)
P.O. Box 63
940 427-5916 - *Fax: 427-2471*
Mayor-Roy King
Mayor PT-Kirk Gibson
Coun.-Jim Enochs
Coun.-Troy Gregg
Coun.-Debra McKelvain
Coun.-Michael Nivens
City Secy.-Patience Barnes
Atty.-James E. Shepherd
F.C.-Sam Hahn

AMARILLO
Pop: 201332   (Potter-Randall)
P.O. Box 1971
Amarillo, TX 79105-1971
806 378-3000 - *Fax: 378-9394*
www.amarillo.gov
Mayor-Ginger Nelson
Coun.-Elaine Hays
Coun.-Freda Powell
Coun.-Eddy Sauer
Coun.-Howard Smith
City Mgr.-Jared Miller
City Secy.-Frances Hibbs
P.A.-Trent Davis
Atty.-Mick McKamie
C.P.-Ed Drain
F.C.-Jeff Greenlee

AMES
Pop: 1075   (Liberty)
P.O. Box 8094
Liberty, TX 77575-2694
936 336-7278 - *Fax: 336-8856*
cityofamestexas.com
Mayor-John White
Mayor PT-David Papillion
Ald.-Janet Carrier
Ald.-Louise Donatto
Ald.-Robert Walters
Ald.-Dwight N. Webb
City Secy.-Lillie Bernard
Atty.-Brandon Davis

AMHERST 79312
Pop: 669   (Lamb)
P.O. Box 560
806 246-3421 - *Fax: 246-3575*
Mayor-Dwayne Montgomery
Comm.-Steve Campbell
Comm.-Clinton Sawyer
City Secy.-Rosa Angel
F.C.-Bob Mills

ANAHUAC 77514
Pop: 2289   (Chambers)
501 Miller St.
P.O. Box 578
409 267-6681 - *Fax: 267-6839*
www.anahuac.us
Mayor-Cheryl Sanders
Mayor PT-Charlie Henry
Coun.-Deidre Crews
Coun.-Janice Jircik
Coun.-Sean Perry
Coun.-Danny Thompson
City Secy.-Julie Harvill
City Admin.-Ken Bays
Atty.-Richard Ferguson and
   Richard Baker
V.F.D.F.C.-Vacant

ANDERSON 77830
Pop: 232   (Grimes)
P.O. Box 592
936 873-3102 - *Fax: 873-3102*
www.townofandersontexas.com
Mayor-Gail M. Sowell
Mayor PT-Erna M. Freeman
Ald.-Joe Boudreaux
Ald.-Carol DeBose
Ald.-Karen McDuffie
Ald.-Harold J. Minor
City Secy.-Cndy Olivieri
Atty.-Michael Casaretto

ANDREWS 79714
Pop: 13832   (Andrews)
111 Logsdon
432 523-4820 - *Fax: 523-6372*
www.cityofandrews.org
Mayor-Flora H. Braly

Mayor PT-Pam Brownlee
Coun.-Lynn Fisher
Coun.-Carolyn Jones
Coun.-John McLeod
Coun.-Bradley Sears
City Mgr.-Glen E. Hackler
Dir. Fin-Steve Eggleston
City Secy.-Sara Copeland
Atty.-John L. Pool
C.P.-Ronny McCarver
F.C.-Vernon Hobbs Jr.

ANGLETON 77515
Pop: 19964   (Brazoria)
121 S. Velasco
979 849-4364 - *Fax: 849-5561*
www.angleton.tx.us
Mayor-Jason A. Perez
Mayor PT-Hardwick Bieri
Coun.-Carl Herbst
Coun.-Bonnie McDaniel
Coun.-Williams M. Tigner
Coun.-Cody Vasut
City Mgr.-Scott L. Albert
City Secy.-Dana Alsobrook
Atty.-J. Grady Randle
C.P.-David Ashburn
F.C.-Chris Hogan

ANGUS
Pop: 438   (Navarro)
6008 S. I-45 West
Corsicana, TX 75109
903 874-3513 - *Fax: 874-3513*
Mayor-Julie Humphries
Mayor PT-Ken Cook
Ald.-Roy Lynn McCain
Ald.-Kathy McKissack
Ald.-Eben Stover
Ald.-Phillis Tidwell
City Secy.-Trina Jeffers
F.C.-Dale Farmer

ANNA 75409
Pop: 10950   (Collin)
P.O. Box 776
972 924-3325 - *Fax: 924-2620*
annatexas.gov
Mayor-Nate Pike
Mayor PT-Justin Burr
Coun.-John Beazley
Coun.-Nathan Bryan
Coun.-Rene Martinez
Coun.-Lee Miller
Coun.-Chris Reeves
City Mgr.-Vacant
City Secy.-Carrie L. Smith
Atty.-Clark H. McCoy, Jr.
C.P.-Vacant
Dir. P.W.-Joseph Johnson
Fire Chief/E.M.C.-Tim Gothard

ANNETTA
Pop: 2830 (Parker)
450 Thunder Head Lane
P.O. Box 1150
Aledo, TX 76008
817 441-5770 - *Fax: 441-5666*
www.annettatx.gov
Mayor-Bruce Pinckard
Mayor PT-Kent Stasey
Ald.-Danny Coffman
Ald.-Shane Mudge
Ald.-Rico Remigio
Ald.-Mark Wohl
City Secy.-Jamee Long
Clk.-Diana Kotlinski
City Admin.-Bruce Pinckard
Atty.-Drew Larkin

ANNETTA NORTH
Pop: 574 (Parker)
P.O. Box 1238
Aledo, TX 76008-1238
817 222-8405
www.annettanorth.com
Mayor-Robert Schmidt
Mayor PT-Robert Watson
Ald.-Morgan Bodie
Ald.-Lee Callaway
Ald.-Kenneth Hall
Ald.-Stonie Hamilton
Town Secy.-Sheila Elmore
Atty.-Taylor Olson Adkins etal

ANNETTA SOUTH
Pop: 577 (Parker)
P.O. Box 61
Aledo, TX 76008-0061
682 352-5442
annettasouth.org
Mayor-Charles Marsh
Mayor PT-William Gordon
Coun.-David Goolsby
Coun.-Scott Hayes
Coun.-Philip Kuntz
Coun.-Don Larson
City Secy.-Ellen Woodward
Atty.-George Staples

ANNONA 75550
Pop: 300 (Red River)
P.O. Box 107
903 697-3681 - *Fax: 697-2601*
Mayor-George English, Sr.
Mayor PT-Veronica Harris
Ald.-Greg Bogan
Ald.-Howard English, Jr.
Ald.-Kimberly Turner
City Secy.-Ellie Wolf
P.A.-George English Sr.
F.C.-Bobby Brem

ANSON 79501
Pop: 2391 (Jones)
1314 Commercial Ave.
325 823-2411 - *Fax: 823-2641*
https://anson-tx.us

Mayor-Sara Alfaro
Mayor PT-Keith Gilbert
Coun.-Evelyn Edwards
Coun.-Jeannie Free
Coun.-Robert Patterson
Coun.-Linda Powell
City Mgr.-Ervin Campbell
City Secy.-Juanita Burleson
Atty.-Chad Cowan
C.P.-Vacant
F.C.-Perry Thompson

ANTHONY, TOWN OF
Pop: 5518 (El Paso)
401 Wildcat Drive
P.O. Box 1269
Anthony, TX 79821-1269
915 886-3944 - *Fax: 886-3115*
townofanthony.org
Mayor-Martin Lerma
Mayor PT-Benjamin Romero
Ald.-Joanna Carrasco
Ald.-Eduardo "Eddie" Chavez
Ald.-Joe Garcia
Ald.-Shawn Weeks
Town Clk.-Mary Carter
Atty.-Enrique Palomares
C.P.-Carlos Enriquez

ANTON 79313
Pop: 1133 (Hockley)
P.O. Box 127
806 997-2801 - *Fax: 997-5026*
Mayor-Blake Cate
Ald.-Tommy Alvarado
Ald.-Garland Cooper
Ald.-Greg Hodges
Ald.-Clayton Hubble
Ald.-Nicky Jezisek
City Mgr.-Mike Sea
City Secy.-Lisa Richardson
Atty.-Rush Wells
C.P.-David Kinney
F.C.-Douglas Mitchell

APPLEBY 75965
Pop: 483 (Nacogdoches)
936 554-6716
Mayor-Gerald Hebert, Sr.
Comm.-Tom Bush
Comm.-Mike Center
Comm.-Tom Rosner
Comm.-Mike Worsham
Comm.-Vacant
City Secy.-Mike Center

AQUILLA 76622
Pop: 101 (Hill)
P.O. Box 190
254 694-6942 - *Fax: 694-7632*
Mayor-James Hamner, Sr.
Coun.-James Hamner Jr.
Coun.-Kyle McCurdy
Coun.-Scotty Myers
Coun.-Gerald Schrunk
F.C.-James Hamner, Sr.

ARANSAS PASS 78335
Pop: 8565 (Aransas-Nueces-
San Patricio)
P.O. Box 2000
361 758-5301 - *Fax: 758-4854*
www.aransaspasstx.gov
Mayor-Ramiro Gomez
Mayor PT-Carrie Scruggs
Coun.-Vickie Abrego
Coun.-William Ellis
Coun.-Janet Moore
City Mgr.-Gary Edwards
City Secy.-Mary Juarez
Atty.-Allen S. Lawrence, Jr.
C.P.-Eric Blanchard
F.C.-William Cox

ARCHER CITY 76351
Pop: 1813 (Archer)
P.O. Box 367
940 574-4570 - *Fax: 574-4995*
www.archercity.org
Mayor-Kelvin Green
Mayor PT-Paula Bradley
Ald.-Zachary Beck
Ald.-Debra Haehn
Ald.-Gregg Miller
Ald.-Ben Tucker
City Mgr.-George Huffman
City Secy.-Kim Whitsitt
Atty.-Jay A. Cantrell
C.P.-Justin Perron
F.C.-William Petit

ARCOLA 77583
Pop: 2006 (Fort Bend)
13222 Hwy. 6
281 431-0606 - *Fax: 431-1523*
www.arcolatexas.org
Mayor-Mary Etta Anderson
Mayor PT-Florence Jackson
Coun.-Greg Abarr
Coun.-Evelyn Jones
Coun.-Rosie Rojas
Coun.-Glenn Sanco
City Secy.-Sally Cantu
Atty.-James L. Dougherty, Jr.

ARGYLE, TOWN OF 76226
Pop: 4022 (Denton)
P.O. Box 609
940 464-7273 - *Fax: 464-7274*
www.argyletx.com
Mayor-Donald G. Moser
Mayor PT-Marla Hawkesworth
Coun.-Jon Donahue
Coun.-Joey Hasty
Coun.-Todd Mankin
Coun.-Ronald Schmidt
Town Mgr.-Vacant
Dir. Fin-Kim Collins
Town Secy.-Kristi Gilbert
Atty.-Matthew Boyle
C.P.-William T. "Tom" Tackett
Dir. P.W.-Troy Norton

ARLINGTON
Pop: 387148 (Tarrant)
101 W. Abram St.
P.O. Box 90231
Arlington, TX 76004
817 459-6122 - *Fax: 459-6120*
www.arlingtontx.gov
Mayor-Jeff Williams
Mayor PT-Sheri Capehart
Dep. Mayor PT-Michael Glaspie
Coun.-Victoria Farrar-Myers
Coun.-Charlie Parker
Coun.-Robert Shepard
Coun.-Roxanne Thalman
Coun.-Kathryn Wilemon
Coun.-Lana Wolff
City Mgr.-Trey Yelverton
City Secy.-Mary Supino
Atty.-Teris Solis
C.P.-Will Johnson
F.C.-Don Crowson

ARP 75750
Pop: 987 (Smith)
P.O. Drawer 68
903 859-6131 - *Fax: 859-3110*
Mayor-Terry Lowry
Coun.-Roger Frazier
Coun.-Vacant
City Secy.-Tracey Pritchett
Atty.-John Hardy
C.P.-Craig Robinson
F.C.-Mack Arnold

ASHERTON 78827
Pop: 1146 (Dimmit)
1001 Carter St.
P.O. Box 450
830 468-3314 - *Fax: 468-3671*
Mayor-Max Silva Jr.
Comm.-Alex Bustamante Jr.
Comm. Norma T. Garza
City Secy.-Odelia T. Gonzalez
Clk.-Elvira O. Ramirez
Atty.-Charles W. Downing
F.C.-Juan Rosas

ASPERMONT 79502
Pop: 857 (Stonewall)
P.O. Box 277
940 989-3585 - *Fax: 989-2692*
Mayor-Lane Smith
Coun.-Jackie Bingham
Coun.-Rusty Harris
Coun.-Chris Lipham
Coun.-Ralph R. Riddel III
Coun.-Vacant
City Secy.-Tammy Gibson
City Admin.-Lorenzo Calamaco
Atty.-Lois A. Rockefeller
F.C.-Jimmy Pittcock

ATHENS 75751
Pop: 13121 (Henderson)
508 E. Tyler St.
903 675-5131 - *Fax: 675-7562*
www.athenstexas.us
Mayor-Monte Montgomery
Mayor PT-Tres Winn
Coun.-Toni Clay
Coun.-Ed McCain
Coun.-Joe Whatley
City Mgr.-Elizabeth Borstad
City Secy.-Bonnie Hambrick
Atty.-Blake E. Armstrong
C.P.-Michael D. Hill, Jr.
F.C.-John McQueary

ATLANTA 75551
Pop: 5762 (Cass)
903 796-2192 - *Fax: 796-5833*
www.atlantatexas.org/
Mayor-Vacant
Mayor PT-Dean McDuff
Coun.-Chad Clements
Coun.-Chris E. Collins, Sr.
Coun.-Arlie Kyzer
Coun.-Randy Pennington
City Mgr.-David Cockrell
City Secy.-Danica Porter
Atty.-James Verschoyle
C.P.-Jay Womack
F.C.-Robin Betts

AUBREY 76227
Pop: 3593 (Denton)
107 S. Main St.
940 440-9343 - *Fax: 365-1215*
www.aubreytx.gov
Mayor-Janet Meyers
Mayor PT-Jeff Perry
Dep. Mayor PT-Oscar Pearson
Coun.-Deborah Goin
Coun.-Jeff M. Miller
Coun.-Christopher Rich
City Secy.-Jenny Huckabee
Atty.-David Berman
C.P.-Tommy Payne
F.C.-Mike Starr

AURORA 76078
Pop: 1331 (Wise)
817 636-2783 - *Fax: 887-3352*
www.auroratexas.gov
Mayor-Terry Solomon
Mayor PT-Jason Brummal
Ald.-Rick Boland
Ald.-William "Bill" McCurdy
Ald.-Rick Smith
Ald.-Joe Smith
Ald.-Jackie Stone
City Admin.-Toni Kelly Wheeler
Atty.-Betsy Elam

AUSTIN
Pop: 921781 (Travis-Williamson)
P.O. Box 1088
Austin, TX 78767-1088
512 974-2000
austintexas.gov
Mayor-Steve Adler
Mayor PT-Kathie Tovo
Coun.-Allison Alter
Coun.-Greg Casar
Coun.-James Flannigan
Coun.-Delia Garza
Coun.-Ora Houston
Coun.-Ann Kitchen
Coun.-Leslie Pool
Coun.-Sabino "Pio" Renteria
Coun.-Ellen Troxclair
City Mgr.-Spencer Cronk
Clk.-Jannette Goodall
Atty.-Anne Morgan
C.P.-Brian Manley
F.C.-Rhoda Mae Kerr

AUSTWELL 77950
Pop: 151 (Refugio)
P.O. Box 147
361 286-3523 - *Fax: 286-3902*
Mayor-Mary Canales
Comm.-Molly Grace Garcia
Comm.-Vacant
City Secy.-Sheila Sitka
Atty.-Hal George

AVERY 75554
Pop: 448 (Red River)
250 US BUS HWY 82
903 684-3825 - *Fax: 684-3168*
Mayor-Khristopher Posey
Mayor PT-Alex Ackley
Ald.-Terry Merritt
Ald.-George Merritt
Ald.-Wesley Roseberry
Ald.-Vickie Roseberry
City Secy.-Kathryne Porter
Atty.-Troy Hornsby
V.F.D.F.C.-Gary Tucek

AVINGER 75630
Pop: 449 (Cass)
P.O. Box 356
903 562-1000 - *Fax: 562-1002*
Mayor-Marvin Parvino
Mayor PT-Jeff Patterson
Ald.-Margaret Ford
Ald.-Earmon Montgomery
Ald.-Jacquelyn Salmon
Ald.-Harold Tress
Clk.-Pam Downs
Atty.-Rick Shelton
F.C.-Kyle Downs

AZLE 76020
Pop: 11962 (Parker-Tarrant)
613 SE Parkway
817 444-2541 - *Fax: 444-7149*
www.cityofazle.org
Mayor-Alan Brundrett
Mayor PT-Bill Jones
Coun.-Lee Barrett
Coun.-William Chambers
Coun.-David McClure
Coun.-Rouel Rothenberger, Jr.
Coun.-Christopher Simpson
City Mgr.-Tom Muir
Dir. Fin-Renita Bishop
City Secy.-Yael Forgey
C.P.-Rick Pippins
F.C.-Thomas "Will" Scott
Dir. P.S.-Rick White

BAILEY 75413
Pop: 291 (Fannin)
P.O. Box 159
903 583-6111 - *Fax: 583-6111*
Mayor-Kenneth Burks
Coun.-Robert Stephen
Coun.-Clifton Wright
City Secy.-Brittany Hibdon
Atty.-John H. Skotnik

BAILEY'S PRAIRIE, VILLAGE OF
Pop: 753 (Brazoria)
P.O. Box 71
Angleton, TX 77516-0071
979 849-0134
www.baileysprairie.org
Mayor-Jo Mapel
Mayor PT-Michelle Powless
Ald.-Oscar Greak
Ald.-Cheryl McBeth
Ald.-Judith McEyla
Ald.-John Ontiveros
City Secy.-Donna Dues

BAIRD 79504
Pop: 1762 (Callahan)
328 Market St.
325 854-1212 - *Fax: 854-5941*
Mayor-Donny Smith
Mayor PT-Brian Patterson
Coun.-Hector Aguirre
Coun.-Saundra Collins
Coun.-Jim Dobbs
City Secy.-Lori Higgins
Clk.-Dela Pickens
Atty.-Forrest McCray
Mar.-Eric Howard

BALCH SPRINGS
Pop: 25318 (Dallas)
13503 Alexander Rd.
Balch Springs, TX 75181
972 286-4477 - *Fax: 286-4279*
www.cityofbalchsprings.com
Mayor-Steven Gorwood
Mayor PT-Wanda Adams
Coun.-Tartisha Hill
Coun.-Sammy Moon
Coun.-Charlene Rushing
Coun.-Helen Shelby
City Mgr.-Susan Cluse
City Secy.-Cindy Gross
Atty.-Monte Akers
C.P.-Jon Haber
F.C.-Randy Smith
Dir. P.W.-William Freeman

BALCONES HEIGHTS 78201
Pop: 3271 (Bexar)
3300 Hillcrest Drive
210 735-9148 - *Fax: 735-4954*
www.balconesheights.org
Mayor-Suzanne de Leon
Mayor PT-Miguel C. Valverde
Coun.-Jack Burton
Coun.-Lamar Gillian
Coun.-Stephen Lara
Coun.-Charles White
Dir. Fin-Floyd Messick
City Secy.-Delia Sanchez
City Admin.-David Harris
Atty.-Frank J. Garza
C.P.-Darrell Volz
F.C.-Brock Ward

BALLINGER 76821
Pop: 3735 (Runnels)
P.O. Box 497
325 365-3511 - *Fax: 365-3445*
www.ballinger-tx.com
Mayor-Sam Mallory
Comm.-Phillip Arp
Comm.-Eloyed Fuentes
Comm.-Bob McDaniel
Coun.-Richard "Rick" Morrish
City Mgr.-Vacant
City Secy.-Bonita F. Shields
Atty.-E. J. "Ebb" Grindstaff
C.P.-Stanley Maresch
F.C.-Clyde Kresta

BALMORHEA 79718
Pop: 520 (Reeves)
P.O. Box 323
432 375-2307 - *Fax: 375-2200*
cityofbalmorhea.com/
Mayor-John L. Davis
Ald.-Trena Jurado
Ald.-Josue Mendoza
Ald.-Karen Smith
Ald.-Benito Vasquez
Ald.-Ike Ward

Clk.-Sandra Navarrete
Atty.-Trent Graham
F.C.-Richard Galindo

BANDERA 78003
Pop: 859 (Bandera)
P.O. Box 896
830 796-3765 - *Fax: 796-4247*
cityofbandera.org
Mayor-Suzanne Schauman
Mayor PT-Rebeca Gibson
Coun.-Glenn Clark
Coun.-Toni Kunz
Coun.-Christine Morse
Coun.-Lynn Palmer
City Secy.-Jill Shelton
City Admin.-Linda S. Coones
Atty.-Daniel Santee
Mar.-Will Dietrich
F.C.-Max Konz

BANGS 76823
Pop: 1603 (Brown)
P.O. Box 188
325 752-6223 - *Fax: 752-7500*
cityofbangs.org/
Mayor-Eric Bishop
Mayor PT-Marisa Craddock
Coun.-Toby Bowers
Coun.-Danny Marney
Coun.-Waymond Sheppard
Coun.-Carrol Wells
City Secy.-Nan Billings
City Admin.-Vacant
Atty.-Mark Bessent
C.P.-Jorge Camarillo
V.F.D.F.C.-Chief Larry Loman

BARDWELL 75101
Pop: 688 (Ellis)
P.O. Box 271
100 Planter's Gin Rd
972 646-5332 - *Fax: 646-5117*
Mayor-J.B. Lowry Jr.
Mayor PT-Dionne Sauers
Comm.-Tommy Lee Aguilar
Int. City Secy.-Christy Gatlin
Atty.-Donald Stout
C.P.-Michael Spurgeon
F.C.-Michael Anthony

BARRY 75102
Pop: 257 (Navarro)
P.O. Box 99
903 695-0948
Mayor-Charles Worsham
Mayor PT-Lori Armstrong
Ald.-Charlie Allen
Ald.-Ann Elmore
Ald.-Jack Herod
Ald.-Pamela Rose
City Secy.-Aaron Allen
F.C.-Mike Ball

BARSTOW 79719
Pop: 366 (Ward)
P.O. Box 98
432 445-6838
Mayor-Olga Abila
Ald.-Elia Florez
Ald.-Carole Guerrero
Ald.-Linda Martinez
Ald.-Armondo Ortiga
Ald.-Dora Villanueva
City Secy.-Delma Lerma

BARTLETT 76511
Pop: 2799 (Bell-Williamson)
140 W. Clark
P.O. Drawer H
254 527-3219 - *Fax: 527-4280*
Mayor-James Grant
Mayor PT-Ray Uson
Coun.-Mona Burnett
Coun.-Ramona Hall
Coun.-Monique Mathis
Coun.-Sharon Randig
City Admin/Secy-Sabra Davis
Atty.-Zach Evans
C.P.-Markus Holt
F.C.-Steve Wenetreck

BARTONVILLE,
TOWN OF
Pop: 1705 (Denton)
1941 E. Jeter Road
Bartonville, TX 76226
817 430-4052 - *Fax: 430-9433*
www.townofbartonville.com
Mayor-Bill Scherer
Mayor PT-Jeff Traylor
Ald.-Jaclyn Carrington
Ald.-Jim Murphy
Ald.-Josh Phillips
Ald.-Clay Sams
Town Secy.-Tammy Dixon
Town Adm..-Michael Montgomery
Atty.-Ed Voss
C.P.-Corry Blount
F.C.-Mac Hohenberger

BASTROP 78602
Pop: 8278 (Bastrop)
512 332-8800 - *Fax: 332-8819*
www.cityofbastrop.org
Mayor-Connie Schroeder
Mayor PT-Gary Schiff
Coun.-Bill Ennis
Coun.-Deborah Jones
Coun.-Lyle Nelson
Coun.-Willie Lewis Peterson
City Mgr.-Lynda Humble
City Secy.-Ann Franklin
Clk.-Phyllis Mathison
Atty.-Alan J. Bojorquez
C.P.-Steve Adcock
F.C.-Mark Wobus

BAY CITY 77414
Pop: 17604 (Matagorda)
1901 5th St.
979 245-2137 - *Fax: 323-1626*
www.cityofbaycity.org
Mayor-Mark Bricker
Mayor PT-Bill D. Cornman
Coun.-Jason Childers
Coun.-Julie Estlinbaum
Coun.-Chrystal Folse
Coun.-Becca Sitz
Dir. Fin-Scotty Jones
City Secy.-David Holubec
Atty.-George E. Hyde
C.P.-Robert Lister
F.C.-Randy Frontz

BAYOU VISTA 77563
Pop: 1503 (Galveston)
2929 Highway 6, #100
409 935-8348 - *Fax: 935-1205*
Mayor-Daniel S. Konya
Mayor PT-James L. Cook
Ald.-Robert Althaus
Ald.-Tami Inman
Ald.-Carlos Price
Ald.-Louis Wortham
City Secy.-Lisa Mitchell
Atty.-Gregg & Gregg, P.C.
C.P.-Jimmie Gillane
F.C.-John Venzke

BAYSIDE 78340
Pop: 332 (Refugio)
P.O. Box 194
361 529-6520 - *Fax: 529-6409*
Mayor-Sandra B. Spada
Mayor PT-Sharon Scott
Coun.-Evelyn Barnes
Coun.-Gloria Derrough
Coun.-Severa Flores
Coun.-Trey Fricks
City Secy.-Connie Cramer
Atty.-Hal George
F.C.-Bob Cramer

BAYTOWN
Pop: 78971 (Chambers-Harris)
P.O. Box 424
Baytown, TX 77522-0424
281 422-8281 - *Fax: 420-6586*
www.baytown.org
Mayor-Stephen H. DonCarlos
Coun.-Laura Alvarado
Coun.-Heather Betancourth
Coun.-David Himsel
Coun.-Robert C. Hoskins
Coun.-Charles Johnson
Coun.-Chris Presley
City Mgr.-Rick Davis
Clk.-Leticia Brysch
P.M.-Drew Potts, CPPO, C.P.M.
Atty.-Ignacio Ramirez, Sr.
C.P.-Keith Dougherty
F.C.-Shon Blake

BAYVIEW, TOWN OF 78566
Pop: 403 (Cameron)
104 S. San Ramon
956 233-6445 - *Fax: 233-4343*
Mayor-Gary Paris
Mayor PT-Mark Mullendor
Ald.-Ron Heinz
Ald.-Jeneria L. Lewis
Ald.-Gabriel Najera
Ald.-Robert Steenbock
Town Secy.-Carmen Amaya
Atty.-David Irwin

BEACH CITY 77523
Pop: 2561 (Chambers)
12723 FM 2354
281 383-3180
Fax: 855 743-0559
www.beachcitytx.us
Mayor-Billy Combs
Mayor PT-Jackey Lasater
Ald.-Dana Colquitt
Ald.-Paul Newman
Ald.-Ray Smith
Ald.-Douglas Walker
City Secy.-Evonne Donnelly
Atty.-Daniel Jackson

BEAR CREEK,
VILLAGE OF
Pop: 417 (Hays)
6705 W. Hwy 290, #502
P.M.B. 244
Austin, TX 78735-8400
www.vilbc.org
Mayor-Bruce Upham
Comm.-Allan Brushwood
Comm.-Douglas Burns
City Secy.-Kathryn Rosenbluth
Atty.-Barney Knight

BEASLEY 77417
Pop: 778 (Fort Bend)
319 South 3rd St.
P.O. Box 122
979 387-2775 - *Fax: 387-2423*
Mayor-Kenneth Reid
Mayor PT-Dale Lindemann
Coun.-Alfred Becan
Coun.-Teresa Cisneros
Coun.-Jenni Lindeman
Coun.-Yvonne Meyer
City Secy.-G. B. Michulka
Atty.-Scott Bounds
F.C.-Dale Lindemann

CITY SECTION

BEAUMONT 77701
Pop: 118083 (Jefferson)
409 880-3745 - *Fax: 880-3740*
beaumonttexas.gov
Mayor-Becky Ames
Coun.-Michael D. Getz
Coun.-Virginia H. Jordan
Coun.-Robin Mouton
Coun.-W.L. Pate, Jr.
Coun.-Audwin M. Samuel
Coun.-Gethrel Williams-Wright
City Mgr.-Kyle Hayes
Clk.-Tina Broussard
P.A.-Patrick Bardwell
Atty.-Tyrone E. Cooper
C.P.-James Singletary
F.C.-Anne Huff

BECKVILLE 75631
Pop: 858 (Panola)
P.O. Box 97
903 678-3661 - *Fax: 678-2318*
Mayor-Gene Mothershed
Ald.-James Broomly
Ald.-Christie Moon
Ald.-William Morrison
Ald.-Marlyn Rogers
Ald.-Larry Thompson
City Secy.-Peggy Harris
Atty.-Rick McPherson
F.C.-Robert Fite

BEDFORD 76021
Pop: 49160 (Tarrant)
2000 Forest Ridge, Bldg. A
817 952-2101 - *Fax: 952-2103*
www.bedfordtx.gov
Mayor-Jim Griffin
Mayor PT-Roger Fisher
Coun.-Michael Boyter
Coun.-Dave Gebhart
Coun.-Amy Sabol
Coun.-Rusty Sartor
Coun.-Roy Turner
City Mgr.-Brian Bosshardt
City Secy.-Michael Wells
Atty.-Stanton Lowry
C.P.-Jeff Gibson
F.C.-Sean Fay

BEDIAS 78731
Pop: 450 (Grimes)
936 395-1119
www.bedias.com/
Mayor-Mackie Bobo-White
Mayor PT-Robert Upchurch
Ald.-Shirley Ray Curtis
Ald.-James Garrett
Ald.-Randall Richards
Ald.-Walter Rogers
City Secy.-Sharon Allen
Atty.-Matthew Bobo

BEE CAVE 78738
Pop: 6117 (Travis)
4000 Galleria Parkway
512 767-6600 - *Fax: 767-6619*
www.beecavetexas.gov
Mayor-Caroline Murphy
Mayor PT-Bill Goodwin
Coun.-Kara King
Coun.-Marie Lowman
Coun.-Tom Matzen
Coun.-Monty Parker
City Mgr.-Travis Askey
City Secy.-Kaylynn Holloway
Atty.-Patty Akers
C.P.-Gary Miller

BEEVILLE 78102
Pop: 13250 (Bee)
400 N. Washington
361 358-4641 - *Fax: 358-7355*
www.beevilletx.org/
Mayor-David B. Carabajal
Mayor PT-John Fulghum
Coun.-Bebe Adamez
Coun.-Randy Forbes
Coun.-Benny Rey Puente
City Mgr.-William DiLibero
City Secy.-Gabriela Hernandez
Atty.-Frank W. Warner
C.P.-Robert Bridge
F.C.-Bill Burris

BELLAIRE 77401
Pop: 18584 (Harris)
7008 S. Rice Ave.
713 662-8222 - *Fax: 662-8212*
www.bellairetx.gov
Mayor-Andrew Friedberg
Mayor PT-Roman F. Reed
Coun.-Michael Fife
Coun.-Pat B. McLaughlan
Coun.-David R. Montague
Coun.-Gus E. Pappas
Coun.-Trisha S. Pollard
City Mgr.-Paul A. Hofmann
Clk.-Tracy L. Dutton
Atty.-Alan P. Petrov
C.P.-Byron Holloway
F.C.-Darryl Anderson

BELLEVUE 76228
Pop: 351 (Clay)
P.O. Box 261
940 928-2109 - *Cell: 928-2109*
Mayor-Robert Ratliff
Mayor PT-Kenneth Ford
Coun.-John Barnett
Coun.-Renee Ellis
Coun.-Marsha Hanson
Coun.-Herbert Mikeworth
City Secy.-James Allen
F.C.-Mark Hanson

BELLMEAD 76705
Pop: 10650 (McLennan)
3015 Bellmead Dr.
254 799-2436 - *Fax: 799-5969*
www.bellmead.com
Mayor-Doss Youngblood
Mayor PT-Mark Pace
Coun.-Travis Gibson
Coun.-Alfreda Love
Coun.-Gary Moore
Coun.-William B. Ridings
City Mgr.-Everett "Bo" Thomas
Int. City Secy.-Patricia Ervin
Atty.-Charles Buenger
C.P.-Lydia Alvarado
F.C.-William Hlavenka Jr.

BELLS 75414
Pop: 1441 (Grayson)
P.O. Box 95
903 965-7744 - *Fax: 965-0250*
www.cityofbells.org/
Mayor-Angela LeBlanc
Mayor PT-Roger Goodwin
Ald.-Tammy Hartline
Ald.-John Ramsey
Ald.-Diane Snavely
Ald.-Jennifer Washburn
City Secy.-Joanna Duevel
Atty.-Christina Tillett
C.P.-Lee Culley
F.C.-Jim Cockrill

BELLVILLE 77418
Pop: 4432 (Austin)
30 S. Holland
979 865-3136 - *Fax: 865-9485*
www.cityofbellville.com
Mayor-Joe Ed Lynn
Ald.-Wayne Browning
Ald.-James Harrison
Ald.-Clay Kistler
Ald.-Douglas D. Lottridge
Ald.-John Moore
City Secy.-Betty Hollon
City Admin.-Shawn Jackson
Atty.-Charley Smith
C.P.-Larry Matthews
F.C.-Mike Kasprowicz

BELTON 76513
Pop: 20186 (Bell)
P.O. Box 120
254 933-5800 - *Fax: 933-5822*
www.beltontexas.gov
Mayor-Marion Grayson
Mayor PT-Craig Pearson
Coun.-John R. Holmes, Sr.
Coun.-Dan Kirkley
Coun.-David K. Leigh
Coun.-Guy O'Banion
Coun.-Paul Sanderford
City Mgr.-Sam A. Listi
Clk.-Amy M. Casey
Atty.-John Messer
F.C.-Bruce Pritchard
CP-Gene Ellis

BENAVIDES 78341
Pop: 1319 (Duval)
P.O. Drawer R
361 256-3283 - *Fax: 256-3915*
Mayor-Sijfredo "Chacho" Flores
Ald.-Natividad "Tivita" Charo
Ald.-Juan H. Garcia
Ald.-Robert "Chachi" Garcia
Ald.-Estela G. Saenz
Ald.-Alonzo Saenz
City Secy.-Debbie Garcia
C.P.-Corando "Cory" Martinez
F.C.-Juan Garcia

BENBROOK 76126
Pop: 23480 (Tarrant)
817 249-3000 - *Fax: 249-0884*
www.benbrook-tx.gov
Mayor-Jerry B. Dittrich
Coun.-Rickie Allison
Coun.-Renee Franklin
Coun.-Larry Marshall, M.D.
Coun.-Ron Sauma
Coun.-Mark Washburn
Coun.-Jim Wilson
City Mgr.-Andy Wayman
City Secy.-Joanna King
Atty.-Betsy Elam
C.P.-James Mills
F.C.-Tommy Davis

BENJAMIN 79505
Pop: 258 (Knox)
P.O. Box 286
940 459-3131 - *Fax: 459-2017*
Mayor-Joy Lynn Pool
Mayor PT-Jenny Jones
Coun.-Dylan Benson
Coun.-Jim Cowen
Coun.-Shannon Ewing
Coun.-Charles Jones
City Secy.-Linda Griffith
F.C.-Mike Moorhouse

BERRYVILLE 75763
Pop: 1035 (Henderson)
903 876-3763 - *Fax: 876-5486*
www.cityofberryville.org
Mayor-Ron Hewlett
Coun.-Lee Danner
Coun.-Bobbie Evans
Coun.-Gayla Leary
Coun.-Susan Morgan
Coun.-Terry Stubbins
City Secy.-Brenda Lankford
Atty.-Gregg Porter
F.C.-Chris Moore

BERTRAM 78605
Pop: 1433 (Burnet)
P.O. Box 1604
512 355-2197 - *Fax: 355-3182*
http://www.cityofbertram.org
Mayor-Cynthia Anderson
Mayor PT-Kim Klose
Ald.-Mike Dickinson
Ald.-Pat Turner
Ald.-Adam Warden
Ald.-Jean Worrell
City Secy.-Georgina Hernandez
Atty.-Michael Guevara
C.P.-James Wilson
F.M.-Brian Klosterhoff

BEVERLY HILLS
Pop: 2053 (McLennan)
3418 Memorial Drive
Waco, TX 76711
254 752-2584 - *Fax: 752-0003*
www.beverlyhillstexas.net/
Mayor-David Gonzales
Mayor PT-Michael Thompson
Coun.-Tony Garcia
Coun.-Joe Frank Holder
Coun.-Lance Leuschner
Coun.-Kurt Vance
City Secy.-Angel Flores
Atty.-Dan Francis
F.C.-Debra Bruce
Dir. P.S.-Debra Bruce

BEVIL OAKS 77713
Pop: 1226 (Jefferson)
7525 Sweetgum Rd.
409 753-1475 - *Fax: 753-1404*
www.cityofbeviloaks.com/
Mayor-Rebecca M. Ford
Coun.-Jim Andrews
Coun.-Douglas Emmons
Coun.-Danny Fruge
Coun.-Michelle Nelson
Coun.-Mark Theobald
Coun.-Martha Vautrot
Atty.-Dru Montgomery
F.C.-Chris Gonzales

BIG LAKE 76932
Pop: 3667 (Reagan)
P.O. Box 310
325 884-2511 - *Fax: 884-3195*
www.biglaketx.com/
Mayor-Phil Pool
Ald.-Robin Collins
Ald.-Melvin Davis Jr.
Ald.-John Long
Ald.-David Melms
Ald.-Cliff Miller
City Secy.-Stacey Stroud
Atty.-Melanie Spratt-Anderson
F.C.-Alan Garner

BIG SANDY 75755
Pop: 1365 (Upshur)
P.O. Box 986
903 636-4343 - *Fax: 636-4413*
Mayor-Sonny Parsons
Mayor PT-Sue Jones
Ald.-Michael Baggett
Ald.-Cindy Bauter
Ald.-Don Cochran
Ald.-Ronnie Norman
City Secy.-Laura Rex
Atty.-Andy Tefteller
C.P.-Tim Scott
F.C.-Jeff Jones

BIG SPRING 79720
Pop: 29008 (Howard)
310 Nolan St.
432 264-2514 - *Fax: 263-8310*
www.mybigspring.com
Mayor-Larry McLellan
Coun.-Raul Benavides
Coun.-Jim DePauw
Coun.-Carmen Harbour
Coun.-Raul J. Marquez
Coun.-Terry McDaniel
Coun.-Howard Stewart
City Mgr.-Todd Darden
Dir. Fin-Donald Moore
City Secy.-Donald Moore
Atty.-Marianne Landers Banks
C.P.-Chad Williams
F.C.-Craig Ferguson

BIG WELLS 78830
Pop: 767 (Dimmit)
P.O. Box 68
1302 East Grand Avenue
830 457-2218 - *Fax: 457-2494*
Mayor-David Rosa
Comm.-Joseph P. Martinez
Comm.-Evett Talamentes
City Secy.-Barbara Cowell

BISHOP 78343
Pop: 3186 (Nueces)
P.O. Box 356
203 East Main St.
361 584-2567 - *Fax: 584-3253*
Mayor-Tem Miller
Mayor PT-Albert Guajardo
Coun.-Bill Boswell
Coun.-Janie Dominguez
Coun.-Robert Gaona
Coun.-Nathan Garza
City Secy.-Cynthia L. Contreras
Atty.-Gerald L. Benadum
C.P.-Billy Durbin
F.C.-Carl Hill

BISHOP HILLS
Pop: 182 (Potter)
#6 Manchester Road
Amarillo, TX 79124
806 352-6602 - *Fax: 463-7794*
Mayor-Betty Benham
Ald.-Veronica Akins
Ald.-J.D. Davis
Ald.-Ronald Gjerde
Ald.-Carolyn Hudnell
Ald.-Jon Moffett
Clk.-Wade Blake
Atty.-Angelique Weaver

BLACKWELL 79506
Pop: 304 (Coke-Nolan)
325 282-2082 - *Fax: 282-3073*
Mayor-Laura Rozzlle
Ald.-Lana Goodman
Ald.-Kay Kovach
Ald.-James Ottaberry
Ald.-Bryan Shipman
Ald.-Miller Walker
City Secy.-Shirley Duncan-Lemley
Atty.-Peter Sheridan
F.C.-Randy Pieper

BLANCO 78606
Pop: 1902 (Blanco)
P.O. Box 750
830 833-4525 - *Fax: 833-4121*
www.cityofblanco.com
Mayor-Martha Herden
Mayor PT-Martin Sauceda
Coun.-Martha Gosnell
Coun.-Matt Lewis
Coun.-Keith McClellan
Coun.-Tony Vela
City Secy.-Jessica Gardner
City Admin.-Vacant
Atty.-Alan Borjorquez
C.P.-Mike Ritchey
F.C.-Mark McMain

BLANKET 76432
Pop: 391 (Brown)
P.O. Box 38
325 748-3171 - *Fax: 748-3171*
Mayor-Judy Eoff
Mayor PT-Scotty Isham
Ald.-Mo Amos
Ald.-Arthur Larkin
City Secy.-Rose Wigham
Atty.-Mark Bessent

BLOOMBURG 75556
Pop: 412 (Cass)
P.O. Box 198
903 728-5323 - *Fax: 728-5398*
Mayor-Melvin Timmons
Mayor PT-Delores Simmons
Ald.-Candie Harris
Ald.-Shirley Hill
Ald.-Janice Hooker
Ald.-Jerrell Ritchie
City Secy.-Suzanne Bishop

Atty.-Brian Simmons
C.P.-Daniel Roberts
F.C.-Dakota Huddleston

BLOOMING GROVE 76626
Pop: 837 (Navarro)
P.O. Box 237
903 695-2711 - *Fax: 695-2482*
bloominggrovetx.com
Mayor-Gary S. Patterson
Mayor PT-James "Bubba" Jones
Ald.-Eva Marshall
Ald.-Susan McCall
Ald.-Phillip McCullouch
Ald.-Alva Smith
City Secy.-Beth Nemeth
Atty.-Kerri Donica
C.P.-Thomas "T.C." Lawhon
F.C.-Chad Marshall

BLOSSOM 75416
Pop: 1569 (Lamar)
P.O. Box 297
903 982-5900 - *Fax: 982-6599*
www.cityofblossom.tx.citygovt.org
Mayor-Charlotte Burge
Mayor PT-Bradley Sessums
Coun.-Carrie Couch
Coun.-Nick Holloway
Coun.-Jeff Stover
Coun.-Patti Wilson
City Secy.-Stacy Prestridge
Atty.-Michael Mosher
F.C.-Billy Forbis

BLUE MOUND
Pop: 2488 (Tarrant)
301 S. Blue Mound Rd.
Fort Worth, TX 76131-1026
817 232-0663 - *Fax: 232-4435*
www.bluemoundtexas.org
Mayor-Alan Hooks
Mayor PT-Mary Smith
Coun. Dean Batie
Coun.-Linda Copeland
Coun.-Thomas A. Crotzer
Coun.-Margie Hooks
City Secy.-Kathryn Sanchez
Atty.-Ashley D. Dierker
C.P.-Randy Baker
F.C.-Shawn Fannan

BLUE RIDGE 75424
Pop: 926 (Collin)
200 S. Main St.
972 752-5791 - *Fax: 752-9160*
www.blueridgecity.com/
Mayor-Rhonda Williams
Ald.-Kevin Bell
Ald.-Allen Cunnyngham
Ald.-Christina Porath
Ald.-Amber Wood
Ald.-Gerald Young
City Secy.-Edie Sims
Atty.-Andy Messer
F.C.-John Bowers

BLUM 76627
Pop: 442 (Hill)
P.O. Box 613
254 874-5772 - *Fax: 874-5702*
Mayor-Chryle Hackler
Ald.-Lisa Bandy
Ald.-Willie Mosely Jr.
Ald.-Tamra Nawara
Ald.-Jack Williams
City Secy.-Barbara Hamel
Atty.-Stephanie W. Johnson
F.C.-Brandon Munn

BOERNE 78006
Pop: 13515 (Kendall)
P.O. Box 1677
830 249-9511 - *Fax: 249-9264*
www.ci.boerne.tx.us/
Mayor-Mike Schultz
Mayor PT-Nina Woolard
Coun.-Joe Anzollitto
Coun.-Charlie E. Boyd IV
Coun.-Ron Cisneros
Coun.-Craig Colvin
City Mgr.-Ron Bowman
City Secy.-Lori Carroll
Atty.-Kirsten Cohoon
C.P.-Jim Kohler
F.C.-Doug Meckel
F.M.-Mark Mattick
Dir. P.W.-Michael Mann

BOGATA 75417
Pop: 1104 (Red River)
P.O. Box 400
903 632-5315 - *Fax: 632-4631*
www.cityofbogata.com
Mayor-Vincent Lum
Mayor PT-Danny Eudy
Coun.-Tonya Bush
Coun.-Alice Perry
Coun.-Don Roach
Coun.-Teresa White
City Secy.-Jennifer Duffer
Atty.-Jay Garrett
C.P.-David A. Short
F.C.-Jerry Hutson

BONHAM 75418
Pop: 10225 (Fannin)
514 Chestnut
903 583-7555 - *Fax: 583-5761*
www.cityofbonham.org
Mayor-Roy V. Floyd
Mayor PT-H. L. Compton
Coun.-Jerry Gay
Coun.-Kevin Hayes
Coun.-Tony Rodriguez
Coun.-Bob Thomas
Coun.-John Trubey
City Mgr.-Sean Pate
City Secy.-Heather Stockton
Atty.-Christina Tillett
C.P.-Mike Bankston
F.C.-Vacant

BONNEY 77583
Pop: 321   (Brazoria)
19025 F.M. 521
281 595-2269 - *Fax: 595-2269*
www.bonneytexas.gov
Mayor-Raymond Cantu
Ald.-Manuel Cantu
Ald.-Bevelria Doyle
Ald.-Tony Gonzalez
Ald.-Jennifer Winans
Ald.-Vacant
City Secy.-L. F. "Jae" Barkalow
Atty.-Stephen M. Coleman

BOOKER 79005
Pop: 1620   (Lipscomb-Ochiltree)
P.O. Box M
806 658-4579 - *Fax: 658-9627*
Mayor-C.J. Skipper
Ald.-Darren Chisum
Ald.-Robert Flores
Ald.-David Hearon
Ald.-Jeff Monk
Ald.-Vacant
City Secy.-Karen Haddon
Atty.-Matt Bartosiewicz
C.P.-Dwain Read
F.C.-Andrew Skipper

BORGER 79007
Pop: 12,755   (Hutchinson)
806 273-0900 - *Fax: 273-0974*
borgertx.gov/
Mayor-Marvin "Bubba" Dickson
Mayor PT-Karen Felker
Coun.-James Marrs II
Coun.-Odis McClellan
Coun.-Milton Ooley
City Mgr.-Eddie Edwards
City Secy.-Stella Sauls
Atty.-Angelique Weaver
C.P.-Bruce Roberts
F.C.-Bob Watson
Dir. P.W.-Ted B. Dodd

BOVINA 79009
Pop: 1748   (Parmer)
806 251-1116 - *Fax: 251-1805*
www.cityofbovina.net/
Mayor-Frank Gonzalez, Jr.
Ald.-Josue Gonzales
Ald.-Matt Hromas
Ald.-Daniel Mayberry
Ald.-Yolanda Robledo
Ald.-Jeff Steelman
City Mgr.-Cesar Marquez
City Secy.-Lesley Gama
Atty.-Slater Elza
C.P.-Eric Geske
F.C.-Cesar Marquez

BOWIE 76230
Pop: 5218   (Montague)
304 Lindsey St.
940 872-1114
www.cityofbowietx.com
Mayor-Gaylynn Burris
Coun.-Wayne Bell
Coun.-Doug Boyd
Coun.-Jim Graham
Coun.-Terry Gunter
Coun.-Chuck Malone
City Secy.-Sandy Page
Atty.-Tracey Jennings
C.P.-Guy Green
F.C.-Doug Page

BOYD 76023
Pop: 1349   (Wise)
P.O. Box 216
940 433-5166 - *Fax: 433-8241*
www.cityofboyd.com/
Mayor-Rodney E. Holmes
Mayor PT-Mark Culpepper
Ald.-Gary Brown
Ald.-Vince Estel
Ald.-Tim Hammonds
Ald.-Letty Thome
City Secy.-Alicia Smith
City Admin.-Greg Arrington
Atty.-Walter W. Leonard
C.P.-Dwayne Taylor

BRACKETTVILLE 78832
Pop: 1734   (Kinney)
119 W Springs Street
P.O. Box 526
830 563-2412 - *Fax: 563-2906*
cityofbrackettville.weebly.com
Mayor-Andres Rodriguez
Mayor PT-Rene A. Villarreal
Ald.-Charles W. Hall
Ald.-Francisca "Chica" Hernandez
Ald.-Zandra I. Negrette
Ald.-Isauro Rivas
City Admin.-Veronica Garcia
Atty.-Eddie Morales
C.P.-Javier Ibanez

BRADY 76825
Pop: 5577   (McCulloch)
P.O. Box 351
325 597-2152 - *Fax: 597-2068*
www.bradytx.us
Mayor-Anthony Groves
Mayor PT-Rey Garza
Coun.-James Griffin
Coun.-Jane Huffman
Coun.-Shelly Perkins
Coun.-Jeffrey Sutton
City Mgr.-Kim Lenoir
Dir. Fin-Lisa Remini
City Secy.-Tina Keys
Atty.-George E. Hyde
C.P.-Steve Thomas
F.C.-Brian Meroney

BRAZORIA 77422
Pop: 3104   (Brazoria)
201 S. Main
979 798-2489 - *Fax: 798-2018*
www.cityofbrazoria.org
Mayor-BobbyJo Newell
Mayor PT-Gary Kersh
Ald.-Stephanie M. Cribbs
Ald.-Gail Logsdon
Ald.-Susan S. Parker
Ald.-Roger Shugart
City Mgr.-Teresa Borders
City Secy.-Sheila Williams
Atty.-R.C. "Charlie" Stevenson
C.P.-Neal Longbotham
F.C.-Duane Stahl
Dir. P.S.-David Jordan

BRAZOS COUNTRY
Pop: 512   (Austin)
316 Pecan Grove
Sealy, TX 77474
979 885-7264 - *Fax: 877-0110*
Mayor-Charles A. Kalkomey
Mayor PT-Gary Craig
Ald.-Randal Beckley
Ald.-Robert Ray
Ald.-Sharon Smith
Ald.-Robert Wadsworth
City Secy. Linda Williams
Atty.-J. Grady Randle

BRECKENRIDGE 76424
Pop: 5446   (Stephens)
105 North Rose Ave.
254 559-8287 - *Fax: 559-7322*
www.breckenridgetx.gov
Mayor-Jimmy McKay
Mayor PT-Tom Cyprian
Comm.-Russell Blue
Comm.-Rob Durham
Comm.-David Wimberley
City Mgr. Andy McCuistion
City Secy.-Heather Robertson-
    Caraway
Atty.-Lois A. Rockefeller
C.P.-Larry Mahan
F.C.-Calvin Chaney

BREMOND 76629
Pop: 954   (Robertson)
201 S. Dallas
P.O. Box E
254 746-7730 - *Fax: 746-7140*
www.bremondtexas.org
Mayor-Ricky Swick
Mayor PT-Melissa Wilganowski
Coun.-Dorothy Boudreaux
Coun.-Andy Burnett
Coun.-Roger Kujawa
Coun.-Donnie Mikolajewski
City Secy.-Debbie Zan
Atty.-Molly Hedrick
C.P.-Roger Maddox
F.C.-Kevin Jefferson

CITY SECTION

BRENHAM 77834
Pop: 16752 (Washington)
P.O. Box 1059
979 337-7200 - *Fax: 337-7568*
www.cityofbrenham.org
Mayor-Milton Y. Tate, Jr.
Mayor PT-Andrew Ebel
Coun.-Susan Cantey
Coun.-Daniel "Danny" Goss
Coun.-W. "Keith" Herring
Coun.-Charlie Pyle
Coun.-Weldon C. Williams, Jr.
City Mgr.-James Fisher
City Secy.-Jeana Bellinger
P.A.-Sara Parker
Atty.-Cary Bovey
C.P.-Craig Goodman
F.C.-Ricky Boeker

BRIARCLIFF, VILLAGE OF
Pop: 1536 (Travis)
302 Sleat Dr.
Briarcliff, TX 78669
512 264-2274 - *Fax: 264-3514*
www.briarclifftx.com/board.php
Mayor-Al Hostetler
Mayor PT-Dave Hertel
Ald.-Bobbi Bowles
Ald.-Jeff Elliott
Ald.-James Johnston
Ald.-Jo Ann Richmond
Tres.-Jeff Elliott
Clk.-Tina Linder
City Admin.-Aaron Johnson
Atty.-Ken Campbell
C.P.-Lou DeLira

BRIAROAKS
Pop: 490 (Johnson)
P.O. Box 816
Burleson, TX 76097
817 295-4249
Mayor-James Dunn
Mayor PT-Andy Bode
Coun.-Richard Foster
Coun.-Bill W. Henshaw
Coun.-Carolyn Johnson
Coun.-Vacant
City Secy.-Mary Foster

BRIDGE CITY 77611
Pop: 7909 (Orange)
P.O. Box 846
409 735-6801 - *Fax: 735-3349*
www.bridgecitytex.com
Mayor-David Rutledge
Coun.-Eric Andrus
Coun.-Lucy Fields
Coun.-Tammi Fisette
Coun.-Terri Gauthier
Coun.-Carl Harbert
Coun.-Kirk Roccaforte
City Mgr.-Jerry D. Jones
Dir. Fin-Karen Morgan
City Secy.-Sherry Tisdale

P.A.-Jeanie McDowell
Atty.-Paul M. Fukuda
C.P.-Paul T. Davis

BRIDGEPORT 76426
Pop: 6479 (Wise)
900 Thompson St.
940 683-3415 - *Fax: 683-3401*
www.cityofbridgeport.net
Mayor-Randy Singleton
Mayor PT-David Correll
Coun.-Bobby Brazier
Coun.-Kevin Lopez
Coun.-Jimmy Meyers
Coun.-Billy Fred Walker
City Mgr.-Jesica McEachern
Dir. Fin-Blu Kostelich
City Secy.-Erika McComis
Atty.-Robert M. Allibon
C.P.-Steve Stanford
F.C.-Terry Long
Dir. P.W.-James Elliott

BROADDUS 75929
Pop: 194 (San Augustine)
P.O. Box 149
936 872-3303 - *Fax: 872-3303*
Mayor-Shirley Parker
Mayor PT-Laura Williams
Ald.-Wanda Dixon
Ald.-Linda Mutters
Ald.-Luanne Newborn
Ald.-Joe Osenbaugh
City Secy.-Kathleen Scherffius
F.C.-Gary Williams

BRONTE 76933
Pop: 951 (Coke)
P.O. Box 370
325 473-3501 - *Fax: 473-2048*
www.brontetexas.org
Mayor-Gerald Sandusky
Mayor PT-David Bedford
Coun.-Paul Gohman
Coun.-Jim Rodriguez
Coun.-Wade Stautzenberger
Coun.-Stormy Vaughn
City Secy.-Crystal L. Blevins
Atty.-Eileen M. Hayman
F.C.-Bill Torres

BROOKSHIRE 77423
Pop: 5260 (Waller)
P.O. Box 160
281 375-5050 - *Fax: 375-5045*
www.cityofbrookshire.org/
Mayor-Eric Scott
Mayor PT-Marilyn F. Vaughn
Ald.-Kim C. Branch
Ald.-Jason Campos
Ald.-Eric Green
Ald.-Vacant
City Secy.-Claudia J. Harrison
Atty.-Arthur Lee "Art" Pertile, III
C.P.-Brandal Jackson
F.C.-Lyndon Stamps
Dir. P.W.-Earnest Kelley

BROOKSIDE VILLAGE 77581
Pop: 1637 (Brazoria)
6243 Brookside Rd.
281 485-3048 - *Fax: 485-9551*
www.brooksidevillage-tx.org
Mayor-Craig Bailey
Mayor PT-Jana Largent
Coun.-Earnest Byrd
Coun.-Donald Flynn
Coun.-Glenda Hundl
Coun.-Greg Thomas
City Secy.-Rosie Fonseca
Atty.-Dick H. Gregg, III
C.P.-Sonny Atkins
F.C.-Craig Bailey

BROWNDELL
Pop: 194 (Jasper)
291 Circle Drive
P.O. Box 430
Brookeland, TX 75931
409 698-2044 - *Fax: 698-2044*
Mayor-Thyatria Young
Coun.-Tincy Brooks
Coun.-Donna Brooks
Coun.-Becky Hall
Coun.-Annatta Seastrunk
City Secy.-Rena Brooks
Atty.-Vacant

BROWNFIELD 79316
Pop: 9548 (Terry)
201 W. Broadway
806 637-4547 - *Fax: 637-9369*
ci.brownfield.tx.us/
Mayor-Tom Hesse
Mayor PT-Leon Pope
Coun.-Ray McFarland
Coun.-Chuck Nave
Coun.-Ricky Rocha
Coun. Teresa Sparks
Coun.-Mike Swaringen
Coun.-Mary Valdonado
City Mgr.-Eldon Jobe
City Secy.-Kelly Burris
P.A.-Eldon Jobe
Atty.-Lina L Reyes-Trevino
C.P.-Tony Serbantez
F.C.-Dennis Rowe

BROWNSBORO 75756
Pop: 1104 (Henderson)
P.O. Box 303
903 852-2401 - *Fax: 852-6762*
www.brownsboro.us
Mayor-Josh W. Fulgham
Mayor PT-Doug Schaffer
Coun.-Charles Cox
Coun.-Glen D. Vest
Coun.-M. Len Vest
Coun.-Dusty Wise
City Secy.-Sonyia Foster
Atty.-Jay Mills
C.P.-Thomas Robertson
F.C.-Robert Chambers

BROWNSVILLE
Pop: 184568 (Cameron)
P.O. Box 911
Brownsville, TX 78522-0911
956 546-4357 - *Fax: 546-2130*
www.cob.us
Mayor-Tony Martinez
Comm.-Cesar de Leon
Comm.-Rose M. Gowen
Comm.-Ricardo Longoria, Jr.
Comm.-Joel Munguia
Comm.-Ben Neece
Comm.-Jessica Tetreau
City Mgr.-Vacant
City Secy.-Griselda Rosa
P.A.-Roberto Luna
Atty.-Vacant
C.P.-Orlando Rodriguez
Int. F.C.-Jarrett V. Sheldon

BROWNWOOD
Pop: 19803 (Brown)
P.O. Box 1389
Brownwood, TX 76804-1389
325 646-5775 - *Fax: 646-0938*
brownwoodtexas.gov/1
Mayor-Stephen E. Haynes
Coun.-Jerry DeHay
Coun.-HD Jones
Coun.-Larry Mathis
Coun.-Ed McMillian
Coun.-Draco Miller
City Mgr.-Emily Crawford
City Secy.-Christi Wynn
P.A.-Mary Brown
Atty.-William "Pat" Chesser
C.P.-Terry Nichols
F.C.-Eddy Wood

BRUCEVILLE - EDDY
Pop: 1897 (McLennan-Falls)
143 Wilcox Dr. #A
Eddy, TX 76524
254 859-5964 - *Fax: 859-5700*
www.bruceville-eddy.org
Mayor-Connally Bass
Mayor PT-Gary L. Lucas
Coun.-Jason Dean
Coun.-Frank Holt
Coun.-Allen Trigg Sr.
Coun.-Halbert Wilcox
City Secy.-Esther Moreno
City Admin.-Koni Billings
Atty.-Alan J. Bojorquez
C.P.-W. "Bill" McLean
F.C.-Ron Engelke

BRYAN
Pop: 83301 (Brazos)
P.O. Box 1000
Bryan, TX 77805-1000
979 209-5000 - *Fax: 209-5003*
www.bryantx.gov
Mayor-Andrew Nelson
Coun.-Ben Hardeman
Coun.-Prentiss Madison
Coun.-Reuben Marin
Coun.-Greg Owens
Coun.-Buppy Simank
Coun.-Mike Southerland
City Mgr.-Kean Register
City Secy.-Mary Lynne Stratta
Atty.-Janis Hampton
C.P.-Eric Buske
F.C.-Randy McGregor

BRYSON 76427
Pop: 558 (Jack)
940 392-2241 - *Fax: 392-2251*
www.cityofbrysontexas.com/
Mayor-Sheila Birdwell
Mayor PT-Lutitia Ford
Coun.-Roger Foster
Coun.-Ray Jennings
Coun.-Joe Lake
Coun.-Vacant
City Secy.-Frank Hefner
Atty.-Tracey Jennings
F.C.-Charles Hauger
Dir. P.W.-Clifford Smith

BUCKHOLTS 76518
Pop: 514 (Milam)
254 593-3111 - *Fax: 593-0005*
www.buckholts.org
Mayor-Kathy Mayes
Coun.-Keith Janicek
Coun.-Antonio Villanueva
City Secy.-Vacant
Atty.-James Parker
C.P.-Shawn Newsom
F.C.-Robert Rodriguez

BUDA 78610
Pop: 14644 (Hays)
121 Main St.
P.O. Box 1380
512 312-0084 - *Fax: 312-1889*
www.ci.buda.tx.us
Mayor-George Haehn
Mayor PT-Wiley Hopkins
Coun.-Paul Daugereau
Coun.-Remy Fallon
Coun.-David Nuckles
Coun.-Evan Ture
Coun.-Lee Urbanovsky
City Mgr.-Kenneth Williams
Dir. Fin-June Ellis
City Secy.-Alicia Ramirez
Clk.-Alicia Ramirez
Atty.-Cathrine Gonzales
C.P.-Bo Kidd
F.C.-Clay Huckaby

BUFFALO 75831
Pop: 1907 (Leon)
P.O. Box 219
903 322-5909 - *Fax: 322-2142*
www.buffalotex.com/
Mayor-Royce Dawkins
Coun.-Dorothy Farmer
Coun.-Glenn Hightower
Coun.-Martin Housler
Coun.-Dianne Ryder
Coun.-Jerry Salazar
City Secy.-Debbie Waters
Atty.-Jerry Nowlin
C.P.-Lance Pavelka
F.C.-Shaine Reeder

BUFFALO GAP 79508
Pop: 472 (Taylor)
P.O. Box 506
325 572-3347 - *Fax: 572-5127*
Mayor-David L. Perry
Mayor PT-Howard Renick
Ald.-Doris Dillard
Ald.-Nancy Henderson
Ald.-James Mabes
Ald.-Mickey Stewart
City Secy.-Cindy Husbands
Atty.-Lois A. Rockefeller
F.C.-Dana Sowell

BUFFALO SPRINGS
Pop: 482 (Lubbock)
99-B Pony Express Trail
Lubbock, TX 79404-1907
806 790-4324
Mayor-Dennis Wardroup
Mayor PT-Meggan Wilkes
Ald.-Kim Archer
Ald.-Tommy Delavan
Ald.-Tammy Leer
Ald.-Roger Trammel
City Secy.-Donna Trammel
Atty. Lina L Reyes-Trevino
C.P.-Stewart Naron
F.C.-John Keys, Jr.

BULLARD 75757
Pop: 3043 (Cherokee-Smith)
P.O. Box 107
903 894-7223 - *Fax: 894-8163*
www.bullardtexas.net
Mayor-Pam Frederick
Mayor PT-Shirley Coe
Coun.-Mark Anderson
Coun.-Ralph Britt
Coun.-Shane Neally
Coun.-David Rhodes
City Mgr.-Jay Abercrombie
City Secy.-Doris Crockett
Atty.-Robert Davis
C.P.-Gary Lewis
F.C.-Justin Walker

BULVERDE 78163
Pop: 5303 (Comal)
30360 Cougar Bend
830 438-3612 - *Fax: 438-4339*
www.bulverdetx.gov
Mayor-Bill Krawietz
Mayor PT-Gene Hartman
Coun.-Yvonne L. Chapman
Coun.-Kirk Harrison
Coun.-Robert W. "Rob" Hurst
Coun.-Ray Jeffrey
Coun.-David Payne
City Mgr.-Danny Batts
Dir. Fin-Ginger Hofstetter
City Secy.-Jeannette Hugghins
C.P.-Gary Haecker

BUNKER HILL VILLAGE
Pop: 3952 (Harris)
11977 Memorial Dr.
Houston, TX 77024
713 467-9762 - *Fax: 827-8752*
www.bunkerhilltx.gov
Mayor-Jay Williams
Coun.-Jay Janecek
Coun.-Robert P. Lord
Coun.-Laurie Rosenbaum
Coun.-Susan B. Schwartz
Coun.-Jay Smyre
City Secy.-Britique L. Williams
City Admin.-Karen Glynn, P.E.
Atty.-Olson & Olson
C.P.-Ray Schultz
F.C.-David Foster

BURKBURNETT 76354
Pop: 11046 (Wichita)
501 Sheppard Rd.
940 569-2263 - *Fax: 569-4192*
www.burkburnett.org
Mayor-Mike Tugman
Mayor PT-Frank Ducos
Comm.-Randy Brewster
Comm.-Jeremy Duff
Comm.-Don Harly
Comm.-Bill Lindenborn
Comm.-Marguerite Love
City Mgr.-Mike Whaley
Clk.-Janelle Dolan
City Admin.-Trish Holley
Atty.-Michael Guevara
C.P.-Ed Stahr

BURKE 75941
Pop: 741 (Angelina)
936 829-5707
www.burketexas.com
Mayor-John Thomas Jones
Mayor PT-Glen Howard Maxwell
Ald.-Wayne Hodges
Ald.-Paul Mettlen
Ald.-Larry Gene Morris
Ald.-Charlotte Morris
City Mgr.-Clint Jones
City Secy.-Charlotte Morris

BURLESON 76028
Pop: 42328 (Johnson-Tarrant)
141 W. Renfro
817 426-9661 - *Fax: 426-9376*
www.burlesontx.com
Mayor-Ken Shetter
Mayor PT-Dan McClendon
Coun.-Stuart Gillaspie
Coun.-Rick Green
Coun.-Todd Hulsey
Coun.-Ronnie Johnson
Coun.-Dan Strong
City Mgr.-Dale Cheatham
City Secy.-Amanda McCrory
P.M.-Justin Scharnhorst
Atty.-Allen Taylor
C.P.-Billy Cordell
F.C.-Ken Freeman
Dir. P.W.-Aaron Russell, P.E.

BURNET 78611
Pop: 6380 (Burnet)
P.O. Box 1369
512 756-6093 - *Fax: 756-8560*
www.cityofburnet.com
Mayor-Crista Goble Bromley
Coun.-Tres Clinton
Coun.-Paul Farmer
Coun.-Joyce Laudenschlager
Coun.-Danny Lester
Coun.-Milton Phair
Coun.-Cindia Talamantez
City Mgr.-David Vaughn
Dir. Fin-Patricia Langford
City Secy.-Kelly Dix
Atty.-Charles E. "Charlie" Zech
C.P.-Paul Nelson
F.C.-Mark Ingram

BURTON 77835
Pop: 312 (Washington)
P.O. Box 255
979 289-3402 - *Fax: 289-3418*
cityofburton-tx.gov/
Mayor-David B. Zajicek
Mayor PT-Robert Brouillette
Ald.-Jeff Eckhardt
Ald.-Nathan D. Kalkhake
Ald.-Samuel Patterson
Ald.-Dale Schwartz
City Secy.-Angela Weyand
Atty.-Michael Casaretto
C.P.-Gregory Rolling
F.C.-Ronnie Stanley

BYERS 76357
Pop: 492 (Clay)
P.O. Box 265
940 529-6149 - *Fax: 529-6549*
Mayor-Carl Barnhill
Mayor PT-Shannon Nelms
Ald.-Virginia Clayton
Ald.-Norrieca Dalton
Ald.-Gary Jetton
City Secy.-Lorrie Yuknick
Atty.-James Rasmussen
F.C.-Will Harding

BYNUM 76631
Pop: 196 (Hill)
P.O. Box 8
254 623-4400 - *Fax: 623-4400*
Mayor-Vacant
Mayor PT-John Robertson
Coun.-George Lowery
Coun.-Diane Nowlin
Coun.-David Waller
Coun.-Vacant
City Secy.-Mada Lane Barron
Atty.-Stephanie W. Johnson

CACTUS 79013
Pop: 3179 (Moore)
P.O. Box 365
806 966-5458 - *Fax: 966-5771*
Mayor-Socorro Marquez
Ald.-Rene Aguilar
Ald.-Lorenzo Castaneda
Ald.-Raul Ceniceros
Ald.-Rene Davila
Ald.-Armando Vencor
City Mgr.-Aldo Gallego
City Secy.-Christina Hernandez
Clk.-Teresa Rodriguez
Atty.-Robert L. Elliott, III
C.P.-Maribel Tarzon
F.C.-Juan Gomez

CADDO MILLS 75135
Pop: 1338 (Hunt)
P.O. Box 490
903 527-3116 - *Fax: 527-4582*
www.cityofcaddomills.com
Mayor-Dwayne Pattison
Mayor PT-Ben Bentley
Ald.-Paul Baker
Ald.-Chris Dumire
Ald.-Ron Olson
Ald.-Cade Richardson
City Mgr.-Matt McMahan
City Secy.-Pam Miller
Atty.-Andy Messer
C.P.-Bryan Barrett
F.C.-Chris Taylor

CALDWELL 77836
Pop: 4104 (Burleson)
107 S. Hill
979 567-3901 - *Fax: 567-9233*
www.caldwelltx.gov
Mayor-Norris L. McManus
Mayor PT-Adrian B. Carlson
Ald.-Jonnie Vic Barnett
Ald.-Kavon Novak
Ald.-James C. Wilde
Ald.-Allan G. Willis
City Secy.-Melissa G. Gonzalez
City Admin.-Johnny Price
P.A.-William L. Broaddus
Atty.-Barney Knight
C.P.-Charles Barnes
F.C.-David Pevehouse

CALLISBURG 76240
Pop: 353   (Cooke)
59 Campbell St.
940 665-9809
Fax: 866 384-1785
www.callisburgtx.com/
Mayor-Nathan Caldwell
Mayor PT-Mike Medford
Ald.-Carla Neilson
Ald.-Danny Powell
Ald.-Vacant
Ald.-Vacant
City Secy.-Marlye Howe
Atty.-James Tidwell
F.C.-Sam Stanford

CALVERT 77837
Pop: 1192   (Robertson)
P.O. Box 505
979 364-2881 - *Fax: 364-2028*
Mayor-Marcus D. Greaves
Ald.-Bobbie J. Alford
Ald.-Kervin Babers
Ald.-J. Matthew Evans
Ald.-Barry Satterwhite
Ald.-Gilsie Wiese
Atty.-Bryan F. "Rusty" Russ, Jr.
C.P.-Mike Holt
F.C.-Joe Jackson

CAMERON 76520
Pop: 5552   (Milam)
P.O. Box 833
254 697-6646 - *Fax: 697-3040*
www.camerontexas.net
Mayor-Connie Anderle
Coun.-Robert Davis Jr.
Coun.-Virgie Hardeman
Coun.-Roselee Mondrik
Coun.-Robert "Bobby" Schiller
Coun.-Melissa Williams
Coun.-Daniel Willie
City Mgr.-J. Rhett Parker
City Secy.-Amy Harris
Atty.-Art Rodriguez
C.P.-Lonnie Goschas
F.C.-Henry Horelica

CAMP WOOD 78833
Pop: 706   (Real)
P.O. Box 130
830 597-2265 - *Fax: 597-5365*
http://cityofcampwood.com
Mayor-Jesse Chevez
Coun.-Josh Cox
Coun.-Juan Gomez
Coun.-Brianna Taylor
Coun.-Domingo Tobar
Coun.-Johnie Wooldridge
City Secy.-Jamie Hidalgo
Clk.-Patsy Ruiz
Atty.-E. Dwain Psencik
F.C.-Josh Cox

CAMPBELL 75422
Pop: 638   (Hunt)
P.O. Box 27
903 862-3191 - *Fax: 862-2149*
Mayor-Ken Padilla
Mayor PT-Charles Herring
Ald.-Kim Coffman
Ald.-Bonnie Massey
Ald.-Fay Morgan
Ald.-James Zimmer
City Secy.-Kay Lowery
Atty.-Jim D. McLeroy

CANADIAN 79014
Pop: 2649   (Hemphill)
6 Main St.
806 323-6473 - *Fax: 323-5398*
cityofcanadiantexas.com
Mayor-Rob Talley
Mayor PT-Jonathan Frederick
Coun.-Blake Beedy
Coun.-Bob Gober
Coun.-Gary Prater
Coun.-Joe Schaef
City Mgr.-Joe Jarosek
City Secy.-Kimberly Sloat
Atty.-Angelique Weaver
F.C.-Scott Brewster
Dir. P.W.-Tommy Wyatt

CANEY CITY 75148
Pop: 217   (Henderson)
15241 Barron Rd.
903 489-1844 - *Fax: 489-2576*
Mayor-Ronald Welch
Mayor PT-Sandra Youngblood
Ald.-Diane Borden
Ald.-Lamar Mathews
Ald.-Gwen O'Dell
Ald.-Lance Peck
City Secy.-Cynthia Dosier
Atty.-Blake E. Armstrong
C.P.-John Chism
V.F.D.F.C.-Russell Hutchinson

CANTON 75103
Pop: 3581   (Van Zandt)
201 N. Buffalo St.
903 567-1841 - *Fax: 567-1793*
cantontx.gov/index.php
Mayor-Lou Ann Everett
Mayor PT-Shawn Stewart
Coun.-Cindy Malouf
Coun.-Nathan Moore
Coun.-Connie Odic
Coun.-Scott Perkins
City Mgr.-Lonny Cluck
City Secy.-Debra Johnson
Atty.-Jeff Moore
C.P.-Brad Allison
F.C.-Bud Sanford

CANYON 79015
Pop: 13303   (Randall)
301 16th St.
806 655-5000 - *Fax: 655-5025*
www.canyontx.com
Mayor-Gary Hinders
Mayor PT-Justin Richarson
Comm.-Cody Jones
Comm.-Paul R. Lyons
Comm.-Roger Remlinger
City Mgr.-Randy Criswell
Clk.-Gretchen Mercer
P.A.-Chris Sharp
Atty.-Chuck Hester
C.P.-Dale Davis
F.C.-Mike Webb

CARBON 76435
Pop: 272   (Eastland)
P.O. Box 414
254 639-2002 - *Fax: 639-2002*
Mayor-Corey Hull
Mayor PT-Leo Gillentine
Ald.-Dale Griffin
Ald.-Lindsey McGaha
Ald.-Tena Walker
Ald.-Michael Williams
City Secy.-Sylvia Gosnell

CARL'S CORNER 76645
Pop: 173   (Hill)
Box 500
972 333-9937 - *Fax: 254 582-9047*
Mayor-Carl Cornelius
Ald.-Pedro Benetez
Ald.-Allen Cartwright
Ald.-Joe Condo
Ald.-Linda Cornelius
Ald.-Susan Ezell
Ald.-Mike Shaw
City Secy.-Linda Cornelius
Atty.-Dave Wagner
F.C.-Lew Crow

CARMINE 78932
Pop: 250   (Fayette)
P.O. Box 76
979 278-3273 - *Fax: 278-3310*
www.carminetx.com
Mayor-Jerry Knox
Mayor PT-Wade Eilers
Coun.-Susan Bathe
Coun.-Madonna Morris
Coun.-Virginia Psencik
Coun.-Brion Williams
City Secy.-Jacklyn Robbins
Atty.-Angela Flores Beck

CARRIZO SPRINGS 78834
Pop: 5368 (Dimmit)
P.O. Box 329
830 876-2476 - *Fax: 876-3127*
www.cityofcarrizo.org/
Mayor-Dina Balderas
Mayor PT-Sofia Morones
Coun.-Jesse Johnson
Coun.-Sandra Little
Coun.-Oscar Puente
City Mgr.-Lamar Schulz
City Secy.-Melissa M. Guerra
Atty.-Robert "Bobby" Maldonado
F.C.-Mario Garcia

CARROLLTON 75011
Pop: 119097(Collin-Dallas-
   Denton)
P.O. Box 110535
972 466-3001 - *Fax: 466-3252*
www.cityofcarrollton.com
Mayor-Kevin Falconer
Mayor PT-Doug Hrbacek
Coun.-Glen Blanscet
Coun.-Frances Cruz
Coun.-Mike Hennefer
Coun.-James Lawrence
Coun.-Young Sung
Coun.-John Sutter
City Mgr.-Erin Rinehart
Dir. Fin-Bob Scott
City Secy.-Laurie Garber
P.M.-Vince Priolo
Atty.-Meredith A. Ladd
C.P.-Derick Miller
F.C.-Greg Salmi

CARTHAGE 75633
Pop: 6883 (Panola)
P.O. Box 400
903 693-3868 - *Fax: 693-3882*
www.carthagetexas.com
Mayor-Lynn C. Vincent
Comm.-Ida M. Beck
Comm.-John W. Cooke
Comm.-Jerry T. Hanszen
Comm.-Olin Joffrion
City Mgr.-Steve Williams
City Secy.-Dana Clark
Atty.-Robert Underwood
C.P.-Jim Vanover
F.C.-Brodie Akins

CASHION
Pop: 348 (Wichita)
354 Baker Road
Wichita Falls, TX 76305
940 855-8511
Mayor-Debra Carr
Mayor PT-Edwin Smith
Comm.-Steve Carr
City Secy.-Vacant
Atty.-Jay Cantrell

CASTLE HILLS
Pop: 4237 (Bexar)
209 Lemonwood Dr.
San Antonio, TX 78213
210 342-2341 - *Fax: 342-4525*
www.cityofcastlehills.com/
Mayor-Tim Howell
Mayor PT-JR Trevino
Ald.-Douglas Gregory
Ald.-Amy McLin
Ald.-Frank Paul
Ald.-Maretta Scott
City Mgr.-Curt Van De Walle
City Secy.-Minerva Gonzales
Atty.-Michael S. Brenan
C.P.-Wayne Davis
F.C.-Darrell Dover

CASTROVILLE 78009
Pop: 2909 (Medina)
1209 Fiorella St.
830 931-4070 - *Fax: 931-6373*
www.castrovilletx.gov
Mayor-Timothy J. Kelley
Mayor PT-Eric Cherry
Coun.-Paul Carey
Coun.-Phil King
Coun.-Victor M. Ortiz, Jr.
Coun.-Phyllis Santleben
City Secy.-Debra Howe
City Admin.-Marie Gelles
Atty.-Habib H. Erkan, Jr.
C.P.-Chris Filline
V.F.D.F.C.-Rick Lair

CEDAR HILL 75104
Pop: 48084 (Dallas-Ellis)
285 Uptown Blvd., Bldg. #100
972 291-5100 - *Fax: 291-5199*
www.cedarhilltx.com
Mayor-Rob Franke
Mayor PT-Stephen Mason
Coun.-Daniel C. Haydin, Jr.
Coun.-Jami McCain
Coun.-Chris Parvin
Coun.-Clifford Shaw
Coun.-Wallace Swayze
City Mgr.-Greg Porter
City Secy.-Belinda Berg
Atty.-Ron G. MacFarlane Jr.
C.P.-Steve Rhodes
F.C.-John Ballard

CEDAR PARK 78613
Pop: 57957 (Travis-Williamson)
450 Cypress Creek Road
Building One
512 401-5000 - *Fax: 250-8602*
www.cedarparktexas.gov
Mayor-Matt Powell
Coun.-Kristyne Bollier
Coun.-Cobby Caputo
Coun.-Anne Duffy
Coun.-Heather R. Jefts
Coun.-Stephen Thomas

Coun.-Corbin Van Arsadale
City Mgr.-Brenda Eivens
City Secy.-LeAnn M. Quinn
Atty.-J.P. LeCompte
C.P.-Sean Mannix
F.C.-James Mallinger

CELESTE 75423
Pop: 814 (Hunt)
P.O. Box 399
903 568-4512 - *Fax: 568-4448*
www.cityofceleste.org
Mayor-Larry Godwin
Ald.-Doug Milton
Ald.-Jason Minter
Ald.-Fred Reynolds
Ald.-Felicia White
Ald.-Josh Zachary
City Secy.-Jenoa Lipsey
Atty.-Ronnie Lyon
C.P.-Dan Turrentine

CELINA 75009
Pop: 7320 (Collin)
142 N. Ohio St.
972 382-2682 - *Fax: 382-3736*
www.celina-tx.gov
Mayor-Sean Terry
Mayor PT-Chad Anderson
Ald.-Andy Hopkins
Ald.-Mindy Koehne
Ald.-Wayne Nabors
Ald.-Carmen Roberts
Ald.-Bill Webber
City Mgr.-Jason W. Laumer
City Secy.-Vicki Faulkner
Atty.-Lance Vanzant
C.P.-Tony Griggs
F.C.-Mark Metdker

CENTER 75935
Pop: 5193 (Shelby)
P.O. Box 1744
936 598-2941 - *Fax: 598-2615*
www.centertexas.org
Mayor-David Chadwick
Mayor PT-Leigh Porterfield
Coun.-Randy Collard
Coun.-Howell Howard
Coun.-Joyce Johnson
Coun.-Jerry Lathan
Coun.-Terry Scull
City Mgr.-Chad D. Nehring
City Secy.-Barbara Boyd
Atty.-Jim Payne
C.P.-Jim Albers
F.C.-Keith Byndom

CENTERVILLE 75833
Pop: 892 (Leon)
P.O. Box 279
903 536-2515 - *Fax: 536-6402*
www.centervilletx.gov
Mayor-Noal Ray Goolsby
Mayor PT-Bobby Walters
Coun.-Jim Carrigan
Coun.-Tammy Chafins

Coun.-Carole Dickey
Coun.-John Lee Walters
City Secy.-Teresa Bates
Atty.-Charles Olson
F.C.-Johnny Franks
Dir. P.W.-George Holleman

CHANDLER 75758
Pop: 2734 (Henderson)
P.O. Box 425
903 849-6853 - *Fax: 849-4663*
www.chandlertx.com
Mayor-Libby Fulgham
Mayor PT-Janeice Lunsford
Ald.-Kari Bersano
Ald.-Conley Cade
Ald.-Marshall Crawford, Jr.
Ald.-Brandon Delaney
City Secy.-Ronda Cockerham
City Admin.-John Taylor
Atty.-Blake E. Armstrong
F.C.-Robert York

CHANNING 79018
Pop: 363 (Hartley)
P.O. Box 34
806 235-3106 - *Fax: 235-0811*
Mayor-Brent Loudder
Comm.-Johnathan Hall
Comm.-Nedra Hunnicut
City Secy.-Kelly Garrison
Atty.-Robert L. Elliott, III
F.C.-Larry L. Miller

CHARLOTTE 78011
Pop: 1637 (Atascosa)
P.O. Box 216
830 277-1414 - *Fax: 277-1632*
Mayor-Buddy Lee Daughtry
Mayor PT-Mark T. Wilson
Ald.-Zoraida Casares
Ald.-Patty Garza
Ald.-Matthew E. Mayberry
Ald.-Christie Rankin
City Secy.-Gracie S. Garcia
Atty.-Charles E. "Charlie" Zech

CHESTER 75936
Pop: 312 (Tyler)
P.O. Box 87
936 969-2360 - *Fax: 969-2087*
Mayor-Floyd Petri
Mayor PT-Gale Williams
Ald.-Charlotte Barnes
Ald.-John Wayne Davis
Ald.-Hoke Hart
Ald.-Jimmy Herrington
City Secy.-Annette Hickman

CHICO 76431
Pop: 1002 (Wise)
P.O. Box 37
940 644-2435 - *Fax: 644-2076*
Mayor-Colleen Self
Mayor PT-Greta McDaniel
Ald.-Rick Bowling

Ald.-Leah Clark
Ald.-Jimmy Counts
Ald.-Gary Fatheree
City Secy.-Pamela Mils
Atty.-Bill Clary
V.F.D.F.C.-Mike Leal

CHILDRESS 79201
Pop: 6105 (Childress)
P.O. Box 1087
940 937-3684 - *Fax: 937-6420*
cityofchildress.com
Mayor-Brett Parr
Mayor PT-Sharon Blackburn
Ald.-Lee Ann Dean
Ald.-Joshua Johnson
Ald.-Marino Rodriguez
Ald.-Vacant
City Mgr.-Kevin Hodge
Atty.-Steve Bird
C.P.-Otis Garcia
F.C.-Daniel Tyler

CHILLICOTHE 79225
Pop: 707 (Hardeman)
P.O. Box 546
940 852-5211 - *Fax: 852-5797*
Mayor-Cathy Young
Mayor PT-Wallace Clay
Coun.-Rookie Barnett
Coun. Calvin Littlecreek
Coun.-Randy Stidham
Coun.-Michelle Stovall
City Secy.-Marsha Jo Stone
Atty.-Cornell Curtis
F.C.-Henry Perez

CHINA 77613
Pop: 1160 (Jefferson)
P.O. Box 248
409 752-5403 - *Fax: 750-5184*
www.chinatexas.net
Mayor-William T. Sanders
Ald.-Richard Garner
Ald.-Joy Gillim
Ald.-Shirley Hodges
Ald.-Renae McGlashan
Ald.-Kate Osborn
City Secy.-Karan Berman
Clk.-Dawn Lopez
F.C.-Douglas Saunders

CHINA GROVE 78263
Pop: 1250 (Bexar)
2412 FM 1516 South
210 648-4923 - *Fax: 648-6713*
www.cityofchinagrove.org
Mayor-Mary Ann Hajek
Coun.-Gail Beaver
Coun.-Frank Bennett
Coun.-Margie Holisky
Coun.-Larry Keller
Coun.-Dennis Parma
City Admin.-Susan Conaway
Atty.-John Mead
C.P.-Ralph Sramek
F.C.-Mike Winfield

CHIRENO 75937
Pop: 386 (Nacogdoches)
P.O. Box 87
936 362-2312 - *Fax: 362-2188*
www.chireno.com
Mayor-Susan Higginbotham
Mayor PT-Ricky Holloway
Ald.-Mack Grace
Ald.-Ryan Hull
Ald.-William Lane
Ald.-Vacant
City Secy.-Fonda Brewer
City Admin.-Steven Spencer
Atty.-Miles T. Bradshaw
V.F.D.F.C.-Joshua Patton

CHRISTINE 78012
Pop: 390 (Atascosa)
P.O. Box 238
830 784-3320
Mayor-Odel Vasquez
Mayor PT-Patti Bowen
Ald.-Elizabeth Guerra
Ald.-Jackie Jerkins
Ald.-Mary Alice Monse
Ald.-Susan Smith
Clk.-Crystal Preciado

CIBOLO 78108
Pop: 25000 (Guadalupe)
200 S. Main, P.O. Box 826
210 658-9900 - *Fax: 658-1687*
www.cibolotx.gov
Mayor-Stosh Boyle
Coun.-Brian Byrd
Coun.-Verlin "Doug" Garrett
Coun.-Ted Gibbs
Coun.-Jay Hogue
Coun.-Jim Russell
Coun.-Jennifer Schultes
Coun.-Glen Webber
City Mgr.-Robert T. Herrera
City Secy.-Peggy Cimics
Atty.-Habib H. Erkan, Jr.
C.P.-Gary Cox
F.C.-Roger Niemietz

CISCO 76437
Pop: 3899 (Eastland)
P.O. Box 110
254 442-2111 - *Fax: 442-3974*
www.cityofcisco.com
Mayor-James King
Coun.-Randy Boles
Coun.-Dennis Campbell
Coun.-Tammy Douglas
Coun.-Chris Johnson
Coun.-Willard Johnson
Coun.-Jason Weger
City Mgr.-Darwin Archer
City Secy.-Tammy Osborne
P.A.-Peggy Ledbetter
Atty.-W. B. Wright
C.P.-Larry Weikel
F.C.-Walter Fairbanks

CLARENDON 79226
Pop: 2026   (Donley)
P.O. Box 1089
806 874-3438 - *Fax: 874-5136*
Mayor-Sandy Skelton
Coun.-Beverly Burrow
Coun.-Jacob Fangman
Coun.-Nathan Floyd
Coun.-Larry Jeffers
Coun.-John Lockhart
City Secy.-Machiel Covey
City Admin.-David Dockery
Atty.-Slater Elza
F.C.-Jeremy Powell

CLARKSVILLE 75426
Pop: 3285   (Red River)
800 W. Main
903 427-3834 - *Fax: 427-3907*
clarksvilletx.com/
Mayor-Ann Rushing
Coun.-James Ellis
Coun.-W. F. "Babe" Higgins
Coun.-Heath Humphry
Coun.-Charles Malone
Coun.-Juanita Moore
Coun.-Patricia Smith
Coun.-Chrissy Witmer
Coun.-Charlie Wright
City Mgr.-Shannon Barrentine
City Secy.-Tammy Quich
Atty.-Troy Hornsby
C.P.-Larry Whittington
F.C.-Rocky Tolison

CLARKSVILLE CITY
Pop: 865   (Gregg)
P.O. Box 1111
White Oak, TX 75693-6111
903 845-2681 - *Fax: 845-2411*
Mayor-Joe B. Spears
Mayor PT-Carolyn Linder
Ald.-Ronnie Allen
Ald.-Matt Maines
Ald.-Lisa Mitchell
Ald.-Bill Tucker
City Mgr.-John Whitsell
City Secy.-Sandra Thur
Atty.-Blake E. Armstrong
V.F.D.F.C.-Derek Zivney

CLAUDE 79019
Pop: 1196   (Armstrong)
P.O. Box 231
806 226-3261 - *Fax: 226-7019*
cityofclaude.com/
Mayor-Bill Wood
Ald.-Twila Baldwin
Ald.-Joe Minkley
Ald.-Jay Morris
Ald.-Dan Parks
City Secy.-Susan Stockett
Atty.-Angelique Weaver
F.C.-Chris Bowles

CLEAR LAKE SHORES 77565
Pop: 1063   (Galveston)
1006 S. Shore Dr.
281 334-2799 - *Fax: 334-2866*
www.clearlakeshores-tx.gov
Mayor-Michael McNamara
Mayor PT-Amanda Fenwick
Ald.-Jan Bailey
Ald.-Diana Hoerner
Ald.-Christy Lyons
Ald.-Bud Solmonsson
City Secy.-Christy Stroup
City Admin.-George Jones
Atty.-Olson & Olson
C.P.-Kenneth Cook
F.M.-Brent Hahn

CLEBURNE 76033
Pop: 29337   (Johnson)
P.O. Box 677
817 645-0900 - *Fax: 556-8848*
www.cleburne.net
Mayor-Scott Cain
Mayor PT-Robert O. Kelly, D.D.S.
Coun.-Dale Sturgeon
Coun.-John Warren
Coun.-Gayle White
City Mgr.-Steve Polasek
Dir. Fin-Terry Leake
City Secy.-Shelly Doty
C.P.-Robert Severance III
F.C.-Clint Ishmael

CLEVELAND 77327
Pop: 7675   (Liberty)
907 E. Houston
281 592-2667 - *Fax: 592-6624*
www.clevelandtexas.com/
Mayor-Otis Cohn
Mayor PT-Carolyn McWaters
Coun.-Jennifer Bergman
Coun.-Marilyn Clay
Coun.-Danny Lee
Coun.-Mike Penry
City Mgr.-Kelly McDonald
City Secy.-Angela Smith
Atty.-Olson & Olson
C.P.-Darrel Broussard
F.C.-Sean Anderson
Dir. P.W.-Roderick Hainey

CLIFTON 76634
Pop: 3442   (Bosque)
P.O. Box 231
254 675-8337 - *Fax: 675-8358*
www.ci.clifton.tx.us
Mayor-James M. Heid
Mayor PT-J. W. Thiele
Ald.-Chuck Caniford
Ald.-David Neelley
Ald.-Stacey Sadler
Ald.-Mike Schmidt
City Adm./Secy-Pamela K. Harvey
Atty.-Charles Olson

F.C.-Terry Boyle
Dir. P.W.-Brian Baumann

CLINT 79836
Pop: 926   (El Paso)
200 N. San Elizario Rd.
P.O. Box 350
915 851-3146 - *Fax: 851-0040*
Mayor-Charles Gonzalez
Ald.-Patsy Franco
Ald.-Natasha Hernandez
Ald.-Sandra Hernandez
Ald.-Frank Montes
Ald.-Esteban Olivas
Town Clk.-Susana Rodrigues
Atty.-Bertha Ontiveros
C.P.-Pedro Hernandez

CLUTE 77531
Pop: 11211   (Brazoria)
979 265-2541 - *Fax: 265-4551*
www.ci.clute.tx.us
Mayor-Calvin Shiflet
Coun.-Jeff Crisp
Coun.-Don Oakes
Coun.-Chuck Pate
Coun.-Travis Quinn
Coun.-Frances Vaughn
City Mgr.-Gary Beverly
Clk.-Rosie Poitevint
Atty.-Chris Duncan
F.C.-Mike Doucet

CLYDE 79510
Pop: 3713   (Callahan)
P.O. Box 1155
325 893-4234 - *Fax: 893-5010*
clydetexas.us/city
Mayor-Mathew Howard
Mayor PT-Steve Kniffen
Coun.-Anita Chapman
Coun.-J.W. Schlee
Coun.-Richard Sheffield
Coun.-Larry Smedley
City Mgr.-Mike Murray
City Secy.-Connie Thornton
City Admin.-Mike Murray
Atty.-Lois A. Rockefeller
C.P.-Robert Dalton
F.C.-Lonny Broadus

COAHOMA 79511
Pop: 817   (Howard)
P.O. Box 420
432 394-4287 - *Fax: 394-4095*
www.cityofcoahoma.tx.citygovt.org/
Mayor-Warren Wallace
Mayor PT-Jay Holt
Ald.-Cody Ditto
Ald.-Sharon Dodson
Ald.-Brandy Manning
Ald.-Dusty Martin
City Secy.-Tammy Griffith
Atty.-Sterling Burleson

COCKRELL HILL
Pop: 4193 (Dallas)
4125 W. Clarendon
Dallas, TX 75211
214 330-6333 - *Fax: 330-5483*
www.cockrell-hill.tx.us
Mayor-Luis D. Carrera
Ald.-Robert Arredondo
Ald.-Jim Cullar
Ald.-Rene Hudson
Ald.-Miriam Rodriguez
Ald.-Claudia Sandoval
City Admin.-Bret Haney
Atty.-Robert Brown
C.P.-Stephen Barlag
F.C.-Joshua Mosely

COFFEE CITY 75763
Pop: 1750 (Henderson)
7019 Pleasant Ridge Rd.
903 876-3414 - *Fax: 876-2433*
www.coffeecitytx.com/
Mayor-Pam Drost
Mayor PT-Phil Rutledge
Ald.-Terry Cooper
Ald.-David Jenkins
Ald.-Riley Standifer
Ald.-Donald Gary Weaver
City Secy.-Vacant
Atty.-Ronald Stutes
C.P.-Scott Medcalf
F.C.-Chris Moore

COLDSPRING 77331
Pop: 714 (San Jacinto)
P.O. Box 247
936 653-3289
Mayor-Pat Eversole
Mayor PT-Frank McMurrey
Ald.-Charles Altman
Ald.-Kyle Currie
Ald.-Holly Sewell
Ald.-Greg Vore
City Secy.-Suzann Boudreaux
Atty.-Greg Magee

COLEMAN 76834
Pop: 4709 (Coleman)
P.O. Box 592
325 625-5114 - *Fax: 625-5837*
www.cityofcolemantx.us/
Mayor-Tommy Sloan
Mayor PT-Danny Jameson
Coun.-Sharlene Hetzel
Coun.-Bobby McGee
Coun.-Sherman Smith
City Mgr.-Paul Catoe
City Secy.-Karen Langley
Atty.-William "Pat" Chesser
C.P.-Anthony Smith
F.C.-David Martinez

COLLEGE STATION
Pop: 93857 (Brazos)
P.O. Box 9960
College Station, TX 77842-7960
979 764-3541 - *Fax: 764-6377*
www.cstx.gov
Mayor-Karl Mooney
Coun.-James Benham
Coun.-Bob Brick
Coun.-Linda Harvell
Coun.-Barry Moore
Coun.-John Nichols
Coun.-Jerome Rektorik
City Mgr.-Kelly Templin
City Secy.-Tanya D. Smith
Atty.-Carla Robinson
C.P.-Scott McCollum
F.C.-Jonathan McCMahan

COLLEYVILLE 76034
Pop: 22807 (Tarrant)
100 Main Street
817 503-1000 - *Fax: 503-1139*
www.colleyville.com
Mayor-Richard Newton, Ph.D.
Mayor PT-Bobby Lindamood
Coun.-Nancy Coplen
Coun.-George Dodson
Coun.-Tammy Nakamura
Coun.-Mike Taylor
Coun.-Kathy Wheat
City Mgr.-Jerry Ducay
City Secy.-Amy Shelley
Atty.-Whitt Wyatt
C.P.-Vacant
F.C.-Brian Riley

COLLINSVILLE 76233
Pop: 1624 (Grayson)
903 429-6225 - *Fax: 429-3059*
www.collinsvilletexas.org
Mayor-Andy Ray Hammer
Mayor PT-Derek Mark Kays
Ald.-Grady J. Carney
Ald.-Brian K. Radcliff
Ald.-Thomas E. Worsham, Jr.
Ald.-Vacant
City Secy.-Troy Mark Vannoy
Atty.-W.D. Welch, P.C.
C.P.-Randy Winston Roach
F.C.-Benny W. McKee
Dir. P.W.-Mark Duane Patterson

COLMESNEIL 75938
Pop: 596 (Tyler)
P.O. Box 144
409 837-5211 - *Fax: 837-2502*
Mayor-Don Baird
Mayor PT-Duane Crews
Ald.-Gene Allen
Ald.-Billy Andrus
Ald.-Kenneth Davis
Ald.-Elbert Sheffield
City Secy.-Carrie Edwards

COLORADO CITY 79512
Pop: 4146 (Mitchell)
P.O. Box 912
325 728-3464 - *Fax: 728-2597*
www.coloradocitytexas.org/
Mayor-Jim Baum
Mayor PT-Sammy Contreras
Coun.-Marcelo Alvarez, Jr.
Coun.-Tim Boyd
Coun.-Andrew Fuller
Coun.-Keith Hiser
Coun.-Charles Rice
City Mgr.-David Hoover
City Secy.-Donna Madrid
Atty.-Lois A. Rockefeller
C.P.-Vacant
F.C.-Rufino Martinez
Dir. P.W.-Jason Free

COLUMBUS 78934
Pop: 3655 (Colorado)
605 Spring
P.O. Box 87
979 732-2366 - *Fax: 732-8213*
www.columbustexas.net
Mayor-Dwain Dungen
Ald.-Keith Cummings
Ald.-Lori An Gobert
Ald.-Eduardo Hernandez
Ald.-Chuck Rankin
Ald.-Gary Swindle
City Mgr.-Donald Warschak
City Secy.-Bana Schneider
Atty.-Mike Trefny
C.P.-William Lattimore
F.C.-Doyle "Dusty" Dittmar
F.M.-Ford Stein

COMANCHE 76442
Pop: 4335 (Comanche)
200 North Austin
325 356-2616 - *Fax: 356-2137*
www.cityofcomanchetexas.net
Mayor-Ronnie Clifton
Coun.-Kevin Burch
Coun.-Robert Cobb
Coun.-Jerome Hall
Coun.-Jeffrey Jacinto
Coun.-Curtis Stahnke
Int. City Secy.-Jacci Stewart, CCD
Atty.-James H. Dudley
C.P.-Bruce Bradshaw

COMBES, TOWN OF
Pop: 2895   (Cameron)
21626 Hand Road
P.O. Box 280
Combes, TX 78535
956 425-7131 - *Fax: 412-6795*
Mayor-Marco Sanchez
Mayor PT-Silvestre Garcia
Ald.-Jorge Castillo
Ald.-E.G. Cavazos
Ald.-Olga H. Montes
Ald.-Cecil Sorell
Town Secy.-Aida Gutierrez
Town Admin.-Lonnie Bearden
Atty.-Gilberto Hinojosa
C.P.-Patrick M. Quill

COMBINE 75159
Pop: 1942   (Dallas-Kaufman)
123 Davis Road
972 476-1532 - *Fax: 476-2832*
www.combinetx.com
Mayor-Tim Ratcliff
Mayor PT-Sharon Carrier
Coun.-Konni Hughes
Coun.-Brenda Loyd
Coun.-Del MacLaren
Coun.-Patrick Stepp
City Secy.-Robin Price
Atty.-Matthew Boyle
C.P.-Jack Gilbert
F.C.-Larry Settles

COMMERCE 75428
Pop: 8100   (Hunt)
1119 Alamo
903 886-1100 - *Fax: 886-8929*
www.commercetx.org
Mayor-Wyman Williams
Mayor PT-Gene Lockhart
Coun.-Jean Klaus
Coun.-Beckey Thompson
Coun.-John Weatherford
City Mgr.-Darrek Ferrell
Dir. Fin-Brady Olsen
City Secy.-Molly Jacobsen
Atty.-Jay Garrett
C.P.-Kerry Crews
F.C.-Chris Bassham

COMO 75431
Pop: 702   (Hopkins)
P.O. Box 208
903 488-3434 - *Fax: 488-0048*
cityofcomotx.com
Mayor-Darla Henry
Comm.-Sue Jones
Comm.-Jerry Radney
City Secy.-Mary Doss
F.C.-Roy Darby

CONROE 77305
Pop: 71592   (Montgomery)
P.O. Box 3066
936 522-3000
www.cityofconroe.org
Mayor-Toby Powell
Mayor PT-Duke W. Coon
Coun.-Seth M. Gibson
Coun.-Duane Ham
Coun.-Guy Martin
Coun.-Gil Snider
City Secy.-Soco M. Gorjon
City Admin.-Paul Virgadamo
Atty.-Marcus L. Winberry
C.P.-Philip Dupuis
F.C.-Ken Kreger

CONVERSE 78109
Pop: 18198   (Bexar)
210 658-5356 - *Fax: 659-0964*
www.conversetx.net
Mayor-Alfred "Al" Suarez
Coun.-Christopher Boyd
Coun.-Chris L. Clark
Coun.-Deborah James
Coun.-Joan Lindgren
Coun.-Kathy Richel
Coun.-Shawn Russell
City Mgr.-Lanny S. Lambert
Dir. Fin-LeAnn Piatt
City Secy.-Holly Nagy
Atty.-Felix Arambula
C.P.-Fidel A. Villegas
F.C.-Richard Wendt

COOL 76066
Pop: 157   (Parker)
Mayor-Dorothy Hall
Comm.-Gail Godfrey
Comm.-Barbara Rothrock
City Secy.-Laura Watkins
Atty.-Jim Ashby

COOLIDGE 76635
Pop: 955   (Limestone)
P.O. Box 457
254 786-4814 - *Fax: 786-2169*
Mayor-Jesse Ashmore
Mayor PT-Rhonda Ivy
Ald.-Tonia Bruckner
Ald.-Deirdre Erwin
Ald.-Marty Herrera
Ald.-Debbie Nash
City Secy.-Gay Lynn Pranger
Atty.-Charles Buenger
F.C.-Heath Allcorn

COOPER 75432
Pop: 1969   (Delta)
91 North Side Square
903 395-2217 - *Fax: 395-0377*
Mayor-Darren Braddy
Mayor PT-David Phillips
Ald.-E.J. Cates
Ald.-Allen Foster

Ald.-Donna Thomason
Ald.-Willie Bear Wilkins
City Secy.-Emily Howse
P.A.-Darren Braddy
Atty.-Jay Garrett
F.C.-Chuck Toles

COPPELL 75019
Pop: 39880   (Dallas-Denton)
P.O. Box 9478
972 462-0022 - *Fax: 304-3673*
www.coppelltx.gov
Mayor-Karen Hunt
Mayor PT-Nancy Yingling
Coun.-Marvin Franklin
Coun.-Mark Hill
Coun.-Brianna Hinojosa-Flores
Coun.-Cliff Long
Coun.-Wes Mays
Coun.-Gary Roden
City Secy.-Christel Pettinos
Atty.-Robert E. Hager
C.P.-Mac Tristan
F.C.-Kevin Richardson

COPPER CANYON 75077
Pop: 1336   (Denton)
400 Woodland Drive
940 241-2677 - *Fax: 241-2727*
www.coppercanyon-tx.org/
Mayor-Sue Rosson Tejml
Mayor PT-Jeff Mangum
Dep. Mayor PT-Valerie P. Cannaday
Coun.-Bill Castleman
Coun.-Steven Hill
Coun.-Dave Svatik
Town Secy.-Sheila Morales
Town Admin.-Donna Welsh
Atty.-Terry Welch

COPPERAS COVE 76522
Pop: 32032   (Coryell-
                        Lampasas-Bell)
P.O. Drawer 1449
254 547-4221 - *Fax: 547-4301*
www.ci.copperas-cove.tx.us
Mayor-Frank Seffrood
Coun.-Kirby Lack
Coun.-Jay Manning
Coun.-David Morris
Coun.-Marc Payne
Coun.-James Pierce, Jr.
Coun.-Daniel Yancey
Coun.-Charlie Youngs
City Mgr.-Andrea M. Gardner
City Secy.-Lucy Aldrich
P.A.-Tracy Molnes
Atty.-Denton, Navarro, Rocha,
    Bernal, & Zech PC
C.P.-Eddie Wilson
F.C.-Michael Neujahr

CORINTH 76208
Pop: 19935 (Denton)
3300 Corinth Parkway
940 498-3200 - *Fax: 498-7505*
www.cityofcorinth.com/
Mayor-William Heidemann
Mayor PT-Joe R. Harrison
Coun.-Sam Burke
Coun.-Scott Garber
Coun.-Don Glockel
Coun.-Lowell Johnson
City Mgr.-Bob Hart
City Secy.-Kimberly D. Pence
Atty.-Messer, Rockefeller & Ford
C.P.-Debra Walthall
F.C.-Curtis Birt
Dir. P.W.-Cody Collier

CORPUS CHRISTI
Pop: 312574 (Kleberg-Nueces-
San Patricio)
P.O. Box 9277
Corpus Christi, TX 78469
361 826-3000 - *Fax: 826-3113*
www.cctexas.com
Mayor-Joe McComb
Coun.-Rudy Garza Jr.
Coun.-Paulette M. Guajardo
Coun.-Michael Hunter
Coun.-Debbie Lindsey-Opel
Coun.-Ben Molina
Coun.-Lucy Rubio
Coun.-Greg Smith
Coun.-Carolyn Vaughn
City Mgr.-Margie Rose
City Secy.-Rebecca Huerta
P.A.-Michael Barrera
Atty.-Miles Risley
C.P.-Mike Markle
Int. F.C.-Richie Quintero

CORRIGAN 75939
Pop: 1595 (Polk)
101 W. Ben Franklin
936 398-4126 - *Fax: 398-2052*
Mayor-Johnna Gibson
Ald.-Earlie C. Baldwin
Ald.-Johnnie M. Brooks
Ald.-Michael Nobles
Ald.-Bill Safford
Ald.-Irene Thompson
City Mgr.-Darrian Hudman
City Secy.-Carrie Casper
Atty.-Luan Tatum
C.P.-Darrell Gibson
F.C.-John W. Cobb

CORSICANA 75110
Pop: 23770 (Navarro)
200 North 12th St.
903 654-4800 - *Fax: 654-4999*
www.cityofcorsicana.com/
Mayor-Don Denbow
Coun.-Susan Hale
Coun.-John McClung
Coun.-Jeff Smith
Coun.-Ruby Williams
City Mgr.-Connie Standridge
City Secy.-Freddy Thomas
Atty.-Kerri Anderson Donica
C.P.-Robert Johnson
F.C.-Donald McMullan
Dir. P.W.-Terry Franks

COTTONWOOD
Pop: 185 (Kaufman)
P.O. Box 293
Scurry, TX 75158
972 486-4981
Mayor-Jeff Gray
Comm.-Martha Struck
Comm.-Linda Williams
City Secy.-Patty Page
Atty.-Gregory Shumpert

**COTTONWOOD SHORES
78657**
Pop: 1135 (Burnet)
3808 Cottonwood Dr.
830 693-3830 - *Fax: 693-6436*
www.cottonwoodshores.org
Mayor-Donald Orr
Mayor PT-Stephen Sherry
Coun.-Anthony Satsky
Coun.-Brigitte Thomas
Coun.-Cheryl Trinidad
Coun.-Roger L. Wayson
City Admin/Secy-Sheila C. Moore
Atty.-Elliot Barner
C.P.-Greg Palmer

COTULLA 78014
Pop: 3603 (La Salle)
117 N. Front St.
830 879-2367 - *Fax: 879-3285*
Mayor-Jose Javier Garcia
Ald.-Gilbert Ayala
Ald.-Juan A. Garcia
Ald.-Patricia "Trish" Garcia
Ald.-Oralia Koraleski
Ald.-Tanis Lopez
City Secy.-Bianca Malando
City Admin.-Larry Dovalina
Atty.-Steven Pena

COVE 77523
Pop: 510 (Chambers)
7911 Cove Loop
281 573-8309 - *Fax: 573-2457*
Mayor-Judy Leggett
Mayor PT-Wade Clark
Ald.-Charles Joseph
Ald.-Joe A. Presnall
Ald.-Sharon Simmons
Ald.-John T. White
City Secy.-Bobbie Creel
F.C.-Jason Soto

COVINGTON 76636
Pop: 269 (Hill)
P.O. Box 443
254 854-2373 - *Fax: 854-2120*
Mayor-George Burnett
Coun.-Abby Jackson
Coun.-Dean Jones
Coun.-James Milam
Coun.-Edwina Milam
Coun.-Vacant
City Secy.-Brett McVean
F.C.-Kevin Karlicek

COYOTE FLATS 76031
Pop: 312 (Johnson)
Mayor-Doug Peterson
Comm.-Shirley Greene
Comm.-Rob Slough
City Secy. Clara Morton

CRANDALL 75114
Pop: 2858 (Kaufman)
P.O. Box 277
972 427-3771 - *Fax: 472-6601*
www.crandalltexas.com
Mayor-Mike Parker
Mayor PT-Danny Kirbie
Coun.-Tim Atkins
Coun.-Shannon Barnes
Coun.-Ron Lanier
Coun.-David Lindsey
City Mgr.-Jana Shelton
City Secy.-Bobbie Jo Taylor
Atty.-Kent Hofmeister
C.P.-Dean Winters
F.C.-Allen Cousins

CITY SECTION

CRANE 79731
Pop: 3353 (Crane)
115 West 8th St.
432 558-3563 - *Fax: 558-1011*
www.cityofcranetexas.com
Mayor-Mark Pahl
Mayor PT-Sally Dodd
Ald.-Manuel Cadena
Ald.-Berry Jack Ingram
Ald.-Evan Dale Lowery
Ald.-Joe Morrison
Ald.-Norma Pinedo
City Secy.-Latrina Little
City Admin.-Dru Gravens
Atty.-Carlos Rodriguez
C.P.-Jason Little
F.C.-Berry Ingram

CRANFILLS GAP 76637
Pop: 281 (Bosque)
P.O. Box 156
254 597-2756 - *Fax: 597-0669*
www.cranfillsgaptexas.com/
Mayor-David D. Witte
Mayor PT-Larry D. Simmons
Ald.-Owen Carlson
Ald.-Charles Forsyhe
Ald.-Liz Pierce
Ald.-Kenneth Reierson
City Secy.-Joyce Benzenhoefer
Atty.-Natalie Koelher
F.C.-David Witte

CRAWFORD 76638
Pop: 717 (McLennan)
P.O. Box 7
254 486-2125 - *Fax: 486-8922*
Mayor-Marilyn Judy
Mayor PT-Patti Bubel
Coun.-Jamie Burgess
Coun.-Frances Roe
Coun.-Terrence Smith
Coun.-Lewis Snow
City Secy.-Danitta Witty
Atty.-Charles Buenger
C.P.-Clay Bruton
F.C.-Brian Westerfield

CREEDMOOR 78610
Pop: 250 (Travis)
5008 Hartung Lane
512 243-6700 - *Fax: 243-6701*
Mayor-Fran Klestinec
Mayor PT-Jesse Solis
Coun.-Richard Harrison
Coun.-Jeff Jakobeit
Coun.-Sabrina Nelson
Coun.-Leon Smith
City Admin.-Robert Wilhite
Atty.-Donald E. Bird

CRESSON 76035
Pop: 1014 (Parker-Hood-Johnson)
P.O. Box 619
817 396-4729
Mayor-W.R. "Bob" Cornett
Mayor PT-Ronald G. Becker
Ald.-Kenneth Benzenhoefer
Ald.-Jack Farr
Ald.-Pam Manley
Ald.-Ronald Pyles
City Secy.-Rachel Shelly
Atty.-Steve Reid

CROCKETT 75835
Pop: 6950 (Houston)
200 North 5th
936 544-5156 - *Fax: 544-4976*
www.crocketttexas.org
Mayor-Joni K. Clonts
Mayor PT-Muriel Williams
Ald.-Michael Calvert
Ald.-Ernest Jackson
Ald.-Darrell Jones
Ald.-Mike Marsh
City Secy.-Mitzi Thompson
City Admin.-John Angerstein
Atty.-Bill Pemberton
C.P.-David Cross
F.C.-Jason Frizzell

CROSBYTON 79322
Pop: 1741 (Crosby)
221 West Main St.
806 675-2301 - *Fax: 675-7012*
www.cityofcrosbyton.org
Mayor-Dusty Cornelius
Mayor PT-Abel Reyna
Ald.-Heidi Hays
Ald.-Jimmy "J.J." Justus
Ald.-Doyle Parrish
Ald.-Alva Rodriguez
Ald.-Brad Thornhill
City Mgr.-Margot Hardin
City Secy.-Jodie House
Clk.-Diana DeLeon
Atty.-Slater Elza
C.P.-John Wilson
F.C.-Jimmy "J.J." Justus
Dir. P.W.-Leonel Moreno

CROSS PLAINS 76443
Pop: 982 (Callahan)
P.O. Box 129
254 725-6114 - *Fax: 725-6397*
www.crossplains.org/
Mayor-Jerry Cassle
Mayor PT-Colby Walker
Ald.-Don Bryant
Ald.-Gary Moses
Ald.-Randy Strickland
City Mgr.-Debbie Gosnell
City Secy.-Teresa Kennedy
Atty.-Forrest McCray
C.P.-Don Gosnell
F.C.-Ricky Carouth

CROSS ROADS, TOWN OF
Pop: 1100 (Denton)
1401 FM 424
Cross Roads, TX 76227
940 365-9693
Fax: 469 375-5905
/www.crossroadstx.gov/
Mayor-Steve Smith
Coun.-Tom Clark
Coun.-Alan Hauf
Coun.-David Meek
Coun.-Danny Prins
Coun.-Wendy White-Stevens
Town Secy.-Vacant
Atty.-David Berman

CROSS TIMBER 76097
Pop: 268 (Johnson)
P.O. Box 2042
817 295-4543
Mayor-Jerry Schwarzer
Mayor PT-Patti Meier
Ald.-Joe A. Arcos
Ald.-Jim Fowler
Ald.-Tom Jones
Ald.-Vacant
City Secy.-Amy Massey
Atty.-Wayne K. Olson

CROWELL 79227
Pop: 948 (Foard)
P.O. Box 250
940 684-1722 - *Fax: 684-1483*
www.crowelltex.com/
Mayor-Gayle Simpson
Mayor PT-Ronnie Allen
Ald.-Joe Chapman
Ald.-Chris Halsell
Ald.-Charles Henderson
Ald.-Mary Jo Tole
City Secy.-Tonya Hopper
Atty.-Michael Guevara
C.P.-Rusty Moore
F.C.-Perry Shaw

CROWLEY 76036
Pop: 13900 (Johnson-Tarrant)
201 East Main Street
817 297-2201 - *Fax: 297-6178*
www.ci.crowley.tx.us
Mayor-Billy Davis
Mayor PT-Jim Hirth
Coun.-Jerry Beck
Coun.-Christine M. Gilbreath
Coun.-Jesse D. Johnson
Coun.-Tina Pace
Coun.-Johnny Shotwell
City Mgr.-Robert Loftin
Dir. Fin-Lori Watson
City Secy.-Carol Konhauser
Atty.-Robert M. Allibon
Int. C.P.-Kit Long
F.C.-Pleasant Brooks

CRYSTAL CITY 78839
Pop: 7138 (Zavala)
101 E. Dimmit St.
830 374-3477 - *Fax: 374-2123*
cityofcc.org
Mayor-Frank Moreno Jr.
Mayor PT-Joel Barajas
Coun.-Richard Diaz
Coun.-Jaime Isquierdo
Coun.-Michele R. Ruiz
Int. Mgr.-Santos Camarillo
Clk.-Sandra Zavala
Atty.-Javier Villalobos
C.P.-Jesse Lopez
Dir. P.W.-Vacant

CUERO 77954
Pop: 6841 (DeWitt)
P.O. Box 660
361 275-3476 - *Fax: 275-6265*
www.cityofcuero.com/
Mayor-Sara Post Meyer
Mayor PT-William "Bill" Matthys
Coun.-W.T. "Tony" Allen
Coun.-John Fuqua
Coun.-Terry Wayne Glover
Coun.-Brad Hendrick
Coun.-Roy Johnson
City Mgr.-Raymond Zella
City Secy.-Jennifer Zufelt
Atty.-James K. Crain
C.P.-Jay Lewis
F.C.-Keiffer Harwell, Jr.

CUMBY 75433
Pop: 777 (Hopkins)
P.O. Box 349
903 994-2272 - *Fax: 994-2650*
cityofcumby.com
Mayor-Kathy Hall Carter
Mayor PT-David Petty
Ald.-Robert Hines
Ald.-Jackie Holley
Ald.-Doug Simmerman
Ald.-Cody Talley
City Secy.-Kay Lowery
Atty.-Cynthia Humphries
C.P.-Paul Robertson
F.C.-Tommy Faulknor

CUNEY 75759
Pop: 140 (Cherokee)
P.O. Box 68
903 876-2655 - *Fax: 876-4705*
www.cherokeecountytexas.us/
Mayor-Grace Beal
Mayor PT-Keith Slaughter
Ald.-Karen Chilton
Ald.-Vivian Earl
Ald.-Marilyn McClelland
Ald.-Curtis Roberts
Int. City Secy.-Beverly Johnson
C.P.-Gregory Sinkfield

CUSHING 75760
Pop: 612 (Nacogdoches)
P.O. Box 365
936 326-4665 - *Fax: 326-9345*
Mayor-Robert Sides
Comm.-Arthur Joe Clemons
Comm.-Mahesh Desai
City Secy.-Belinda Wade

CUT AND SHOOT
Pop: 1153 (Montgomery)
P.O. Box 7364
Cut And Shoot, TX 77306-0364
936 264-3100 - *Fax: 264-3114*
www.cutandshoot.org
Mayor-Nyla Akin Dalhaus
Ald.-James M. "Mike" Berry
Ald.-Belinda Faulkner
Ald.-Tom Robinson
Ald.-Clifford Todhunter
Ald.-John Winters
City Secy.-Amy L. Wade
Atty.-Larry Foerster
C.P.-Rudy Gomez

DAINGERFIELD 75638
Pop: 2560 (Morris)
108 Coffey St.
903 645-3906 - *Fax: 645-5488*
Mayor-Lou Irvin
Mayor PT-Bob Thorne
Coun.-Martha Campbell
Coun.-Mike Carter
Coun.-Duane Grissett
Coun.-Lonnie Tucker
City Mgr.-Rocky Thomasson
City Secy.-Heide Edmonson
Atty.-Matthew Harris
C.P.-Tracey Climer
F.C.-Jimmy Cornelius

DAISETTA 77533
Pop: 966 (Liberty)
P.O. Box 549
936 536-6761 - *Fax: 536-6329*
Mayor-Debra Kay Fregia
Ald.-Cindy Burchfield
Ald.-Quinn Godwin
Ald.-Don Neyland
Ald.-Kim Retherford
Ald.-Lori Tidwell
City Secy.-Joan Caruthers
C.P.-Mike Parrish

DALHART 79022
Pop: 7930 (Dallam-Hartley)
P.O. Box 2005
806 244-5511 - *Fax: 244-4414*
www.dalharttx.gov
Mayor-Phillip Hass
Coun.-Bryan Brewer
Coun.-Clinton Hale
Coun.-Rusty Hancock
Coun.-Sherrie Haschke
Coun.-Kerry Miller
Coun.-Billy Sisco

Coun.-Brian Walton
Coun.-Tim Yee
City Mgr.-James Stroud
City Secy.-Frances Childers
Atty.-Greg Oelke
C.P.-David Conner
F.M.-Curtis Brown

DALLAS 75201
Pop: 1223804(Collin-Dallas-
    Denton-Kaufman-Rockwall)
City Hall, 1500 Marilla
214 670-3738 - *Fax: 670-5029*
www.dallascityhall.com/
Mayor-Mike Rawlings
Mayor PT-Dwaine Caraway
Dep. Mayor PT-Adam Medrano
Coun.-Tennell Atkins
Coun.-Rickey D. Callahan
Coun.-Mark Clayton
Coun.-Kevin Felder
Coun.-Jennifer S. Gates
Coun.-Sandy Greyson
Coun.-Scott Griggs
Coun.-Philip T. Kingston
Coun.-Lee M. Kleinman
Coun.-Adam McGough
Coun.-Omar Narvaez
Coun.-Casey Thomas II
City Mgr.-T.C. Broadnax
City Secy.-Vacant
Atty.-Larry Casto
C.P.-Rence Hall
F.C.-David Coatney

**DALWORTHINGTON
    GARDENS 76016**
Pop: 2259 (Tarrant)
2600 Roosevelt Drive
817 274-7368 - *Fax: 265-4401*
www.cityofdwg.net
Mayor-Kimberly Fitzpatrick
Mayor PT-Edward Motley
Ald.-Mark McGuire
Ald.-Richard Pell
Ald.-Guy Snodgrass
Ald.-Cathy Stein
City Admin.-Wade Calhoun
Atty.-TOASE Law Firm
C.P.-Aaron Ausmus

DANBURY 77534
Pop: 1715 (Brazoria)
P.O. Box 258
979 922-1551 - *Fax: 922-8143*
Mayor-Richard Stone
Mayor PT-George Phillips
Ald.-Wesley Baldwin
Ald.-Larry Linscombe Jr.
Ald.-Sue Mercado-Powell
Ald.-Bill Turnipseed
City Secy.-Jenny Brogger
Atty.-Laurence E. Boyd
C.P.-Derek Dyson
F.C.-Scott Osburn

DARROUZETT, TOWN OF
Pop: 350   (Lipscomb)
P.O. Box 176
Darrouzett, TX 79024-0176
806 624-2441 - *Fax: 624-2309*
Mayor-Sandra Woods
Mayor PT-William Peil
Ald.-Charlene Duke
Ald.-Haskel Hitt
Ald.-Carley Mercer
Ald.-Mark Peil
Town Mgr.-Kurt Jones
Atty.-Claire Y. Walsh
F.C.-Brandon Meier

DAWSON 76639
Pop: 808   (Navarro)
P.O. Box 400
254 578-1515 - *Fax: 578-1975*
dawsontx.com
Mayor-Stephen Sanders
Mayor PT-Darrell Stevenson
Ald.-Greg Hall
Ald.-Aaron Hogue
Ald.-Tony Mikeska
Ald.-Cameron Shaw
City Secy.-Ronda Franks
Atty.-Terry Jacobson
F.C.-Darryl Rogers

DAYTON 77535
Pop: 7242   (Liberty)
117 Cook St.
936 258-2642 - *Fax: 258-2348*
www.daytontx.org
Mayor-Jeff Lambright
Mayor PT-John S. Johnson
Coun.-Troy Barton
Coun.-Alvin Burress
Coun.-Sherial L. Lawson
Coun.-Josh Townsend
City Mgr.-Vacant
City Secy.-Melinda Soliday
Atty.-Brandon Davis
C.P.-John Headrick
F.C.-Murphy Green

DAYTON LAKES
Pop: 93   (Liberty)
P.O. Box 1476
Dayton, TX 77535-1476
936 257-0177
Mayor-Alicia Charbonneau
Ald.-Terri Andrews
Ald.-Jackie Reeves
Ald.-Jessie Richardson
Ald.-Chris Sullivan
Ald.-Vacant
City Secy.-Dorothy Johnson

DE KALB 75559
Pop: 1699   (Bowie)
110 E. Grizzly Drive
903 667-2410 - *Fax: 667-2689*
www.dekalbtexas.org
Mayor-Dennis Wandrey
Mayor PT-David Meadows
Ald.-Pablo Chinchilla
Ald.-Mike Farris
Ald.-Kolby Holder
Ald.-Bobbie McGee
City Secy.-Abbi M. Capps
Atty.-J. Michael Brock
C.P.-Shawne Walraven
F.C.-Robbie Barrett

DE LEON 76444
Pop: 2246   (Comanche)
P.O. Box 318
254 893-2065 - *Fax: 893-3254*
www.cityofdeleon.org
Mayor-Terry Scott
Coun.-Jon Arbrey
Coun.-James Beck
Coun.-Sarah Childers
Coun.-Jaye Golden
Coun.-Bob Whitney
City Secy.-Melinda Harbour
Aud.-Burl Lowery
Atty.-Eileen Hayman
C.P.-Interim James Dyson
F.C.-Heath Matteson
Dir. P.W.-Rob Duncan

DEAN
Pop: 493   (Clay)
6913 State Highway 79 N
Wichita Falls, TX 76305
940 763-2012
Mayor-Steve L. Sicking
Coun.-Joe Garcia
Coun.-Mike Ward
City Mgr.-Steve Sicking

DECATUR 76234
Pop: 6330   (Wise)
P.O. Box 1299
940 393-0200 - *Fax: 393-0201*
www.decaturtx.org
Mayor-Martin Woodruff
Coun.-Cary Bohn
Coun.-Susan Cocanougher
Coun.-Margaret Doubrava
Coun.-Dr. Carmelina Holloway
Coun.-Mike McQuiston
Coun.-Randy Parker
City Mgr.-Brett Shannon
City Secy.-Diane Cockrell
Atty.-Mason Woodruff
C.P.-Rex Hoskins
Dir. P.W.-Greg Hall

DECORDOVA
Pop: 2683   (Hood)
P.O. Box 5905
Granbury, TX 76049-0905
817 326-2232
Fax: 682 205-3410
www.cityofdecordova.com
Mayor-Pat Revill
Coun.-Judy Goforth
Coun.-Todd Hall
Coun.-Kim Lewis
Coun.-Kathy Murray
Coun.-Blake Thompson
City Secy.-Sylvia Hickey
Atty.-Robert L. Dillard, III

DEER PARK 77536
Pop: 32010   (Harris)
710 E. San Augustine
P.O. Box 700
281 478-7248 - *Fax: 478-7217*
www.deerparktx.gov
Mayor-Jerry L. Mouton, Jr.
Coun.-Sherry Garrison
Coun.-Tommy Ginn
Coun.-Thane Harrison
Coun.-Ron Martin
Coun.-Bill Patterson
Coun.-Rae A. Sinor
City Mgr.-James J. Stokes
City Secy.-Shannon Bennett
Atty.-Jim Fox
C.P.-Greg Grigg
F.C.-Don Davis
F.M.-Buddy Rice

DEL RIO 78840
Pop: 35591   (Val Verde)
109 W. Broadway
830 774-8558 - *Fax: 774-8513*
www.cityofdelrio.com
Mayor-Robert Garza
Mayor PT-Rowland Garza
Coun.-Fred Contreras
Coun.-Elizabeth "Liz" Elizalde
Coun.-Rene "Reno" Luna
Coun.-Diana Salgado
Coun.-John Sheedy
City Mgr.-Henry Arredondo
City Secy.-Alma Levrie
Atty.-Suzanne Jost West
Int. C.P.-Fred Knoll
F.C.-Joe Harrington

DELL CITY 79837
Pop: 365   (Hudspeth)
P.O. Box 125
915 964-2344 - *Fax: 964-2394*
Mayor-Dale Flach
Mayor PT-Eddie Chacon
Ald.-Denny Bergstrom
Ald.-Deborah Berry
Ald.-Joel Muniz
Ald.-Rafael Sanchez
City Secy.-Diana Suarez

DENISON
Pop: 22773 (Grayson)
P.O. Box 347
Denison, TX 75021
903 465-2720 - *Fax: 464-4499*
www.cityofdenison.com
Mayor-Jared Johnson
Coun.-Teresa Adams
Coun.-Michael Baecht
Coun.-JC Doty
Coun.-Janet Gott
Coun.-Wilbert "Bill" Malvern Sr.
Coun.-Kristofor Spiegel
City Mgr.-Judson Rex
Dir. Fin-Renee Waggoner
City Secy.-Christine Wallentine
C.P.-Jay Burch
F.C.-Gregg Loyd

DENTON 76201
Pop: 121123 (Denton)
215 E. McKinney St.
940 349-8200 - *Fax: 349-8596*
www.cityofdenton.com/
Mayor-Chris Watts
Mayor PT-Sara Bagheri
Coun.-Keely G. Briggs
Coun.-Don Duff
Coun.-Dalton Gregory
Coun.-Gerard Hudspeth
Coun.-John Ryan
City Mgr.-Todd Hileman
City Secy.-Jennifer Walters
Atty.-Vacant
C.P.-Lee Howell
F.C.-Robin Paulsgrove

DENVER CITY 79323
Pop: 4479 (Yoakum)
P.O. Box 1539
806 592-5426 - *Fax: 592-9436*
Mayor-Tommy Hicks
Mayor PT-Robert Hanneman
Coun.-Clinton Bowman
Coun.-Joan Breith
Coun.-Keith Mensch
Coun.-Mark Sherman
Coun.-Ronald Weir
City Mgr.-Stan David
City Secy.-Beverly Prather
Atty.-Warren New
C.P.-Jack Miller
F.C.-Cody Freeman

DEPORT 75435
Pop: 578 (Lamar-Red River)
P.O. Box 354 A
903 652-3875 - *Fax: 652-4086*
www.cityofdeport.org
Mayor-John Francis
Mayor PT-Mike Donohue
Ald.-Robert Bailey
Ald.-Jennifer Dorsey
Ald.-Anthonie Hagood
Ald.-Ty Merritt
City Secy.-Jacqueline Dangerfield

DESOTO 75115
Pop: 49047 (Dallas)
211 E. Pleasant Run Rd.
972 230-9660 - *Fax: 230-5793*
www.ci.desoto.tx.us
Mayor-Curtistene S. McCowan
Mayor PT-Rachel Proctor
Coun.-Virgil Helm
Coun.-Deshaundra Lockhart Jones
Coun.-Richard "Dick" North
Coun.-Candice Quarles
Coun.-Vacant
City Mgr.-Tarron Richardson, Ph.D.
City Secy.-Kisha Morris
Atty.-Joseph J. Gorfida, Jr.
C.P.-Joseph Costa
F.C.-Jerry Duffield

DETROIT 75436
Pop: 732 (Red River)
190 East Garner
903 674-4573 - *Fax: 674-6029*
Mayor-Kenneth Snodgrass
Mayor PT-Terrie Shelby
Ald.-Brandon Brown
Ald.-Faye Marshall
Ald.-Lori Melton
Ald.-Vacant
City Secy.-Taylor Blevens
Atty.-Jim D. McLeroy
F.C.-Roger Holderman

DEVERS 77538
Pop: 433 (Liberty)
P.O. Box 338
936 549-7474 - *Fax: 549-7548*
Mayor-Hugh McNeil
Mayor PT-Steven Horelica
Ald.-Mary Clayton
Ald.-Anthony Jones
Ald.-Maria Sanchez
Ald.-Jason Weatherford
City Secy.-Kristi Ayers

DEVINE 78016
Pop: 4350 (Medina)
303 S. Teel
830 663-2804 - *Fax: 663-2208*
www.cityofdevine.com
Mayor-William L. Herring
Mayor PT-Steve A. Lopez
Ald.-David Espinosa
Ald.-Cory Thompson
Ald.-David Valdez
Ald.-Kathy Wilkins
City Adm./Secy-Dora V. Rodriguez
Atty.-Thomas P. Cate
C.P.-Kandy Benavides
F.C.-Jason Johnson

DIBOLL 75941
Pop: 5359 (Angelina)
P.O. Box 340
936 829-4757 - *Fax: 829-1179*
www.cityofdiboll.com/
Mayor-John C. McClain
Mayor PT-Lewis Ivey
Ald.-Tom Farley
Ald.-Don Hendrick
Ald.-Veronica Hernandez
Ald.-Daniel Lopez
Ald.-Charles Moses Sr.
City Mgr.-Gerry Boren
City Secy.-Melissa McCall
Atty.-Jimmy Cassels
C.P.-Steve Baker
F.C.-Gary Jones

DICKENS 79229
Pop: 286 (Dickens)
P.O. Box 118
806 623-5224 - *Fax: 623-5213*
Mayor-David Warren
Mayor PT-Marie Mullins
Ald.-Dillon Hale
Ald.-Stephen Hart
Ald.-Jack Martin
Ald.-Jesus Zarate Jr.
City Secy.-Lillian Atkinson
Dir. P.W.-Jeremy Porter

DICKINSON 77539
Pop: 18680 (Galveston)
4403 Highway 3
281 337-2489 - *Fax: 337-6190*
www.ci.dickinson.tx.us
Mayor-Julie Masters
Mayor PT-Wally Deats
Coun.-Louis Decker
Coun.-Bruce Henderson
Coun.-William H. King, III
Coun.-Charles Suderman
Coun.-Walter Wilson
Int. City Adm.-Ron Morales
City Secy.-Alun Thomas
Atty.-David Olson
C.P.-Ron Morales
Dir. P.W.-Paul Booth

DILLEY 78017
Pop: 3174 (Frio)
P.O. Box 230
830 965-1624 - *Fax: 965-1920*
www.cityofdilleytx.com
Mayor-Mary Ann Obregon
Mayor PT-Ray Aranda
Ald.-Morelsa Aranda
Ald.-Esmeralda Cano
Ald.-Gilbert Eguia
Ald.-Sabino Mena
Dir. Fin-Irma Rodriguez
City Secy.-Juanita V. Gonzalez
City Admin.-Jose Alvarez
Atty.-Robert "Bobby" Maldonado
C.P.-Jerry Reyna
F.C.-Daryl Kallio

DIMMITT 79027
Pop: 4393 (Castro)
P.O. Box 146
806 647-2155 - *Fax: 647-0417*
Mayor-Roger Malone
Mayor PT-Steve Buckley
Coun.-Janie Bugarin
Coun.-Gloria Hernandez
Coun.-Carol Lust
Coun.-John Nino
Coun.-Kenny Paxton
Coun.-Scott Sheffy
City Mgr.-BJ Potts
City Secy.-Karen McGuire
Atty.-Jack Edwards
C.P.-Miguel Ontiveros
F.C.-Randy Griffitt

DISH 76247
Pop: 350 (Denton)
5413 Tim Donald Rd.
940 648-2040 - *Fax: 648-2045*
www.townofdish.com
Mayor-William "Bill" Sciscoe
Comm.-Wester Draper
Comm.-Charles Smith
City Secy.-Dalessa Vardell
Atty.-Bryn Meredith

DODD CITY 75438
Pop: 369 (Fannin)
P.O. Box 129
903 583-7710 - *Fax: 583-2589*
Mayor-Jackie Lackey
Coun.-Tim Davis
Coun.-Casey Fry
Coun.-Cynthia Horton
Coun.-Amber Simpson
Coun.-Dillon Weeks
City Secy.-Cheryl Braden
Atty.-Myles Porter
F.C.-Brandon Horton

DODSON 79230
Pop: 120 (Collingsworth)
P.O. Box 428
806 493-4987
Mayor-Steve Kane
Ald.-Gary Hightower
Ald.-Tommy Hightower
Ald.-Tommy Patterson
Ald.-Vacant
Ald.-Vacant
City Secy.-Keli Ponder

DOMINO 75572
Pop: 93 (Cass)
14555 FM 3129
903 796-2843 - *Fax: 796-1056*
Mayor-Alfred Campbell
Coun.-Thurman Jones
Coun.-Henry McCant
City Secy.-Jean Oliver

DONNA 78537
Pop: 15798 (Hidalgo)
307 S. 12th St.
956 464-3314 - *Fax: 464-9923*
www.cityofdonna.org
Mayor-Irene Munoz
Mayor PT-Sonia Gallegos
Coun.-Cathy Alvarado
Coun.-Joey G. Garza, Jr
Coun.-Simon Sauceda, II
Int. Mgr.-Ernesto Silva
Dir. Fin-David Vasquez
City Secy.-Laura Balderrama
Atty.-Eddy Trevino
C.P.-Ruben De Leon
F.C.-David Simmons

DORCHESTER 75459
Pop: 148 (Grayson)
373 Main St.
903 476-5862 - *Fax: 476-0172*
cityofdorchester.org
Mayor-David Smith
Mayor PT-Willies Ballou
Coun.-Jimmy Aaron
Coun.-Boyd Dunn
Coun.-James Stewart
Coun.-Robert Welch
Clk.-Becky Vincent
Atty.-W.D. Welch, P.C.

**DOUBLE OAK, TOWN OF
75077**
Pop: 2867 (Denton)
320 Waketon Road
972 539-9464 - *Fax: 539-9613*
www.double-oak.com
Mayor-Mike Donnelly
Mayor PT-Ted Gruenloh
Dep. Mayor PT-Andrew Wills
Coun.-Anita Nelson
Coun.-Stacie Stoehner
Coun.-Scott Whisenhunt
Town Secy.-Charlotte Allen
Atty.-David Berman
C.P.-Derrick Watson
F.C.-Scott Whisehunt

DOUGLASSVILLE 75560
Pop: 229 (Cass)
P.O. Box 36
Mayor-Douglass Heath
Mayor PT-Jana Granberry
Ald.-Scott Dupree
Ald.-Kay Gilbert
Ald.-Dewitt McCall
Ald.-Jessica Wylie
City Secy.-Linda Baird

DRAPER, TOWN OF
Pop: 85 (Denton)
14007 Corral City Dr.
Argyle, TX 76226
940 648-3831
Mayor-Mike Collins
Ald.-Frankie Faires
Ald.-Noel Gamblin
Ald.-David Harris
Ald.-Courtney Stark
Ald.-Dr. Jennifer Williams
Town Mgr.-Jamie Harris
Town Secy.-Sara Mosier
Atty.-Terry Welch
C.P.-Robert Crawford
F.C.-Mac Hohenberger

DRIPPING SPRINGS 78620
Pop: 1919 (Hays)
511 Mercer St.
P.O. Box 384
512 858-4725
www.cityofdrippingsprings.com/
Mayor-Todd Purcell
Mayor PT-Bill Foulds
Coun.-William Travis Crow
Coun.-Wade King
Coun.-John Kroll
Coun.-Taline Manassian
City Secy.-Vacant
City Admin.-Michelle Fischer
Atty.-Alan J. Bojorquez

DRISCOLL 78351
Pop: 739 (Nueces)
P.O. Box 178
361 387-3011 - *Fax: 767-4033*
Mayor-Marcos Zavala
Mayor PT-Mark Gonzalez
Comm.-Ariana Maldonado
Atty.-Michael Morris
C.P.-Luther Kim

DUBLIN 76446
Pop: 3654 (Erath)
213 E. Blackjack St.
254 445-3331 - *Fax: 445-3727*
www.ci.dublin.tx.us/
Mayor-David Leatherwood
Mayor PT-Cliff Jackson
Ald.-Darrell Curry
Ald.-Layne Golden
Ald.-John Johnson
Ald.-Lee Jones
Ald.-Fred Lisso
Ald.-Joel Munoz
Ald.-Tammy Sperry
City Mgr.-Nancy Wooldridge
City Secy.-Rhonda Williams
Atty.-Barney Knight
C.P.-Bobby Mendez
F.C.-Paul Warner
Dir. P.W.-Cory James

DUMAS 79029
Pop: 14691   (Moore)
P.O. Box 438
806 935-4101 - *Fax: 935-6104*
www.ci.dumas.tx.us/
Mayor-Pat L. Sims
Comm.-David Bonner
Comm.-Bob Brinkmann
Comm.-Justin Willis
Coun.-Ben Maples
City Mgr.-Arbie Taylor
Dir. Fin-Jay Patel
City Secy.-Kim Rehkopf
Atty.-Jerod Pingelton
C.P.-Jim Nelson
F.C.-Ron Pray

DUNCANVILLE
Pop: 38524   (Dallas)
P.O. Box 380280
Duncanville, TX 75138-0280
972 780-5017 - *Fax: 780-5077*
www.duncanville.com
Mayor-David Green
Mayor PT-Dennis Schwartz
Coun.-Ronald L. Dotson, M.D.
Coun.-Johnette Jameson
Coun.-Patrick LeBlanc
Coun.-Steven Rutherford
Coun.-Leslie Thomas
City Mgr.-Kevin Hugman
City Secy.-Mary Jones
Atty.-Nichols, Jackson, Dillard
    Hager & Smith
C.P.-Robert D. Brown, Jr.
F.C.-Sam Rohde

EAGLE LAKE 77434
Pop: 3639   (Colorado)
P.O. Box 38
979 234-2640 - *Fax: 234-3255*
www.coeltx.net
Mayor-Mary Parr
Ald.-Michael Cooper
Ald.-Carlos Gonzalez
Ald.-Alex Ramirez, Jr.
Ald.-Gaye Lynn Thomas
Ald.-John Young
City Mgr.-Vacant
City Secy.-Lina Ferguson
Atty.-Donald Bendy
C.P.-David Freeman
F.C.-Darrell Stancik
Dir. P.W.-Dan Clark

EAGLE PASS 78852
Pop: 26248   (Maverick)
100 S. Monroe St.
830 773-1111 - *Fax: 773-9170*
www.eaglepasstx.us/
Mayor-Ramsey English Cantu
Mayor PT-Yoland P. Ramon
Coun.-Gloria Hernandez
Coun.-Luis E. Sifuentes
Coun.-Rodolfo E. Villapando

City Mgr.-Vacant
City Secy.-Imelda B. Rodriguez
P.A.-Anna K. De La Garza
Atty.-Heriberto Morales, Jr.
C.P.-Alberto Guajardo
F.C.-Sonny Mello

EARLY 76803
Pop: 2762   (Brown)
P.O. Box 3100
325 643-5451 - *Fax: 643-5452*
www.earlytx.net
Mayor-Robert Mangrum
Mayor PT-Benny Allcorn
Coun.-Travis Eoff
Coun.-Joel Johnson
Coun.-Charles Matlock
Coun.-Bill McCullough
City Secy.-Brenda Kilgo
City Admin.-Tony Aaron
Atty.-Mark Bessent
C.P.-David Mercer
V.F.D.F.C.-Chad Hill

EARTH 79031
Pop: 1065   (Lamb)
P.O. Box 10
806 257-2111 - *Fax: 257-2245*
Mayor-Jerry Carpenter
Ald.-Yvonne Cano
Ald.-Matt Goe
Ald.-Matt Groetken
Ald.-Al Mosqueda
Ald.-David Rodriguez
City Secy.-Lorry Kay Collom

EAST BERNARD 77435
Pop: 2289   (Fort Bend-Wharton)
704 Church St.
979 335-6558 - *Fax: 335-6532*
Mayor-Marvin Holub
Ald.-Karen Haedge
Ald.-John Kopycinski
Ald.-Wes Murrile
Ald.-David Tomchesson
Ald.-Alex Warncke
City Secy.-Audrey Scearce
Atty.-David Olson

EAST MOUNTAIN
Pop: 797   (Gregg-Upshur)
103 Municipal Drive
Gilmer, TX 75645
903 297-6041 - *Fax: 297-4346*
Mayor-Marc Covington
Ald.-John Adams
Ald.-Gari Bellis
Ald.-Lester Glover
Ald.-Charles Medlin
Ald.-Billy Morrow
City Secy.-Tammy Hazel
City Admin.-Ronnie Hill
Atty.-Vacant
V.F.D.F.C.-Dennis Medlin

EAST TAWAKONI 75472
Pop: 883   (Rains)
288 Briggs Blvd.
903 447-2444 - *Fax: 447-5080*
www.cityofeasttawakoni.com
Mayor-Johnnie LaPrade
Mayor PT-Pam Patterson
Coun.-Gary Reeves
Coun.-Chris Roberts
Coun.-D.W. "David" Rose
Coun.-Lynn Wallace
City Secy.-Elinka M. Harper
Atty.-Larry Powers
C.P.-Rick South
V.F.D.F.C.-Joe Bill Jones

EASTLAND 76448
Pop: 3960   (Eastland)
P.O. Box 749
254 629-8321 - *Fax: 629-3171*
www.eastlandtexas.com/
Mayor-Larry Vernon
Mayor PT-John Bird
Comm.-Zac Darr
Comm.-Richard Rossander
Comm.-Frank Saylors
City Mgr.-Ron Duncan
Dir. Fin-Leslie Zander
City Secy.-Shirley Stuart
Atty. Lois A. Rockefeller
C.P.-David Hullum
F.C.-Phillip Arther

EASTON
Pop: 524   (Gregg-Rusk)
P.O. Box 8126
Longview, TX 75607-8126
903 643-7819 - *Fax: 643-2219*
Mayor-Shannon Brown
Mayor PT-Walter Ward
Ald.-Ebbie Lover
Ald.-Janeene Lucas
Ald. Vacant
Ald.-Vacant
City Secy.-Crystal Jenkins
Atty.-Joe Shumate
V.F.D.F.C.-Larry Kellams

ECTOR 75439
Pop: 695   (Fannin)
P.O. Box 188
903 961-2495 - *Fax: 961-2251*
Mayor-Jerry M. Newell
Mayor PT-Donnie Lankford
Ald.-Linda Bohn
Ald.-Kenneth Rhudy
Ald.-Brett J. Stone
Ald.-Colton Whisenhunt
City Secy.-Nelba Baker
Atty.-James Tidwell
C.P.-Greg Garrison
F.C.-J.C. Cobb

EDCOUCH 78538
Pop: 3161 (Hidalgo)
P.O. Box 100
956 262-2140 - *Fax: 262-2920*
https://cityofedcouch.org
Mayor-Virginio Gonzalez Jr.
Mayor PT-Maricela Moreno
Ald.-Esmeralda Cabrera
Ald.-Rene Flores
Ald.-Daniel Guzman
Ald.-Orlando J. Villarreal
Int. Mgr.-Pete De La Cruz
Dir. Fin-Pete De La Cruz
Atty.-Richard Gonzales
C.P.-Eloy Cardenas
F.C.-Ricardo Lopez

EDEN 76837
Pop: 2766 (Concho)
120 Paint Rock Road
325 869-2211 - *Fax: 869-5075*
www.edentexas.com
Mayor-Eddy Markham
Mayor PT-Eugene Spann
Ald.-Wade Ellison
Ald.-Jenifer Gierisch
Ald.-Grover Hall
Ald.-Vacant
City Secy.-Celina Hemmeter
Atty.-E. Dwain Psencik

EDGECLIFF VILLAGE 76134
Pop: 2776 (Tarrant)
1605 Edgecliff Road
817 293-4313 - *Fax: 293-8726*
cour60.wix.com/evgov
Mayor-Mickey Rigney
Mayor PT-Tony Dauphinot
Ald.-Ray Beamer
Ald.-Sy Conley
Ald.-Robert Cross
Ald.-Jackie Luther
City Secy.-Veronica Gamboa
Atty.-Cara White
F.C.-Jeff Ballew

EDGEWOOD 75117
Pop: 1441 (Van Zandt)
P.O. Box 377
903 896-4448 - *Fax: 896-7033*
http://edgewoodtexas.org
Mayor-Stevan Steadham
Mayor PT-Louis Dunn
Coun.-Randy Fitzgerald
Coun.-Brenda J. Pendlton
Coun.-Keith Rogers
Coun.-Ruby Smith
City Secy.-Kathleen Jordan
City Admin.-Petra Marley
Atty.-David S. Mallard
C.P.-David Hammonds
F.C.-Jarred Cooper

EDINBURG
Pop: 77100 (Hidalgo)
P.O. Box 1079
Edinburg, TX 78540-1079
956 388-8204 - *Fax: 383-7111*
www.cityofedinburg.com
Mayor-Richard Molina
Mayor PT-David Torres
Coun.-Gilbert Enriquez
Coun.-Homer Jasso Jr.
Coun.-Jorge Salinas
City Mgr.-Richard M. Hinojosa
Dir. Fin-Ascencion Alonzo
City Secy.-Myra L. Ayala-Garza
P.A.-Lorena Fuentes
C.P.-David White
F.C.-Shawn Snider

EDMONSON 79032
Pop: 111 (Hale)
P.O. Box 58
806 864-3396
Mayor-Sammy Shannon
Ald.-Randy Bain
Ald.-David Block
Ald.-Wendall Edmonson
Ald.-Auerelio Guerreru
Ald.-Mike Stinson
F.C.-Robert Block

EDNA 77957
Pop: 5499 (Jackson)
126 W. Main
361 782-3122 - *Fax: 782-3590*
www.cityofedna.com/
Mayor-Joe D. Hermes
Coun.-Wayne Callis
Coun.-Dustin Muncrieff
Coun.-Maxine Price
Coun.-Lance Smiga
Coun.-Johnny Vasquez
City Mgr.-Don Doering
Dir. Fin-Olga Salomon
City Secy.-Becky Miska
Atty.-Jake Srp
C.P.-Clinton Wooldridge
Dir. P.W.-Brad Ryan

EDOM 75754
Pop: 375 (Van Zandt)
150 VZCR 4800
903 852-2311 - *Fax: 852-6397*
www.edomtexas.com
Mayor-Barbara Crow
Mayor PT-Lee Shults
Coun.-Denise Baskind
Coun.-Lynn Huff
Coun.-Amy Murphy
Coun.-Vacant
V.F.D.F.C.-Eddie Wood

EL CAMPO 77437
Pop: 11602 (Wharton)
315 E. Jackson
979 541-5000 - *Fax: 543-0027*
www.cityofelcampo.org
Mayor-Randy Collins
Mayor PT-Richard Young
Coun.-Jeff Allgayer
Coun.-John Hancock
Coun.-Gloria Harris
Coun.-Tommy Hitzfeld
Coun.-Anisa Vasquez
City Mgr.-Mindi Snyder
City Secy.-Lori Hollingsworth
Atty.-Ronald B. Collins
C.P.-Terry Stanphill
V.F.D.F.C.-Jimmy George

EL CENIZO 78046
Pop: 3500 (Webb)
507 Cadena
956 712-9107 - *Fax: 717-3365*
www.cityofelcenizo.com/
Mayor-Raul L. Reyes
Comm.-San Juanita Valdez
Comm.-Reynaldo Vasquez
City Secy.-Juany Perez
C.P.-Veronica Garcia
F.C.-Chief Vela

EL LAGO 77586
Pop: 2706 (Harris)
411 Tallowood
281 326-1951 - *Fax: 326-2134*
www.ellago-tx.gov
Mayor-Mark Briggs
Coun.-Jim Kelly
Coun.-Jeff Michalak
Coun.-John Skelton
Coun.-Jeff Tave
Coun.-Ann Vernon
City Secy.-William A. Grigsby
Atty.-Arthur Val Perkins
C.P.-Tom Savage
F.C.-Ray Cook

EL PASO 79901
Pop: 671563 (El Paso)
300 N. Campbell
915 212-0023
www.elpasotexas.gov
Mayor-Dee Margo
Rep.-Alexsandra Annello
Rep.-Cassandra Brown
Rep.-Cecilia Lizarraga
Rep.-Sam Morgan
Rep.-Michiel Noe
Rep.-Claudia Ordaz
Rep.-Henry Rivera
Rep.-Peter Svarzbein
City Mgr.-Tommy Gonzalez
Int. City Clk.-Laura Prine
Atty.-Sylvia Borunda Firth
C.P.-Gregory K. Allen
F.C.-Mario D'Agostino

ELDORADO 76936
Pop: 1951   (Schleicher)
325 853-2691 - *Fax: 853-3353*
http://www.eldorado-texas.com
Mayor-John Nikolauk
Mayor PT-George M. Arispe
Coun.-Vicki Farmer
Coun.-Danny Halbert
Coun.-Wayne McGinnes
Coun.-Paul Rebuck
Coun.-Ronnie Sauer
City Secy.-Melissa Truelove
Atty.-Barney Knight
F.C.-Joey Jones

ELECTRA 76360
Pop: 2765   (Wichita)
101 N. Main
940 495-2146 - *Fax: 495-3025*
cityofelectra.com
Mayor-Rickey Foster
Mayor PT-Lynda Lynn
Comm.-Fran Davis
Comm.-Bob Doan
Comm.-James W. Gottfried
City Secy.-Tracey Lowe
City Admin.-Steve Bowlin
Atty.-Brett Hale
C.P.-Michael Dozier
F.M.-Greg Lynn

ELGIN 78621
Pop: 8135   (Bastrop)
P.O. Box 591
512 281-5724 - *Fax: 285-3016*
www.elgintx.com/
Mayor-Chris Cannon
Mayor PT-Juan Gonzalez
Coun.-Susie Arreaga
Coun.-Jessica A. Bega
Coun.-Sue Brashar
Coun.-Keith Joesel
Coun.-Daniel Lopez
Coun.-Mary Penson
Coun.-Phillip Thomas
City Mgr.-Thomas Mattis
Dir. Fin-Buck LaQuey
City Secy.-Amelia Sanchez
Atty.-Charlie Crossfield
C.P.-Patrick South
F.C.-Randy Reyna

ELKHART 75839
Pop: 1371   (Anderson)
110 W. Parker
P.O. Box 944
903 764-5657 - *Fax: 764-2059*
www.andersoncountytexas.us
Mayor-Mike Gordon
Mayor PT-Billy Jack Wright
Ald.-Beverly Anderson
Ald.-Chris Bice
Ald.-Rhonda Brewer
Ald.-Chris Sheridan

City Secy.-Carla Sheridan
Atty.-Blake E. Armstrong

ELMENDORF 78112
Pop: 1488   (Bexar)
P.O. Box 247
210 635-8210 - *Fax: 635-8221*
www.elmendorf-tx.com
Mayor-Michael James Gonzales
Ald.-R.M. "Andy" Anderson
Ald.-Polo Maldonado
Ald.-Linda Pena Ortiz
Ald.-Tracy Riojas
Ald.-Richard B. Rodriguez
City Secy.-Roxanne De Leon
Clk.-Ronda Brewer
City Admin.-Cody Dailey
Atty.-Michael Guevara
C.P.-Marco Pena

ELSA 78543
Pop: 5660   (Hidalgo)
P.O. Box 427
956 262-2127 - *Fax: 262-5002*
cityofelsa.net
Mayor-Alonzo R. "Al" Perez Jr.
Mayor PT-Victor L. Hernandez
Comm.-Robert Escobar
Comm.-Daniel Marichalar Jr.
Comm.-Ricardo Sanchez
City Mgr.-Juan Ybarra
City Secy.-Delmira Yanez
Atty.-Gustavo Acevedo
C.P.-Primitivo Rodriguez
F.C.-Bryan L. Hathorn
Dir. P.W.-Pedro Rivera III

EMHOUSE
Pop: 159   (Navarro)
3825 Joe Johnson Dr.
Corsicana, TX 75110
903 354-6984
Mayor-Johnny Pattison
Mayor PT-Mary Jones
Ald.-Jacob Eldridge
Ald.-Kimberly Eldridge
Ald.-Vacant
Ald.-Vacant
Town Secy.-Kimberly Eldridge

EMORY 75440
Pop: 1239   (Rains)
P.O. Box 100
903 473-2465 - *Fax: 473-2110*
www.cityofemory.com
Mayor-Trey Hill
Mayor PT-Emery Cathey
Coun.-Max Fletcher
Coun.-Howard Garrett
Coun.-Travis Potts
Coun.-Jannie Stephens
City Secy.-Donna Raper
City Admin.-Mike Dunn
Atty.-Phillip Alexander
C.P.-Tracy Rosson
Dir. P.W.-Gary Wallace

ENCHANTED OAKS
Pop: 460   (Henderson)
P.O. Box 5019
Gun Barrel City, TX 75147-5019
903 451-2222 - *Fax: 451-9909*
www.enchantedoaks.org
Mayor-Sam McVay
Mayor PT-Sandi Rando
Coun.-Greg Colley
Coun.-Jerry Cryer
Coun.-Doug Napps
Coun.-Marty Nulf
City Secy.-Pam Foster
Atty.-Jeff Irion
C.P.-Cliff Webster
F.C.-Lyndon Patrick

ENCINAL 78019
Pop: 1288   (La Salle)
P.O. Box 120
956 948-5226 - *Fax: 948-5571*
Mayor-Sylvano Sanchez
Coun.-Roberto Aldaco
Coun.-Irma Arizola
Coun.-Oliver Jordan, Jr.
Coun.-Brianda Lopez
Coun.-Christina Maldonado
City Mgr.-Velma Davila
F.C.-Vacant

ENNIS 75119
Pop: 18513   (Ellis)
115 W. Brown St.
P.O. Box 220
972 875-1234 - *Fax: 875-9086*
www.ennistx.gov
Mayor-Angie W. Juenemann
Mayor PT-Matt Walker
Comm.-Scott Hejny
Comm.-Marco Hernandez
Comm.-Bill Honza
Comm.-Rowdy Pruitt
Comm.-Shirley Watson
City Mgr.-Scott Dixon
City Secy.-Angie Wade
Atty.-Brenda McDonald
C.P.-John Erisman
F.C.-Jeff Aycock

ESCOBARES 78584
Pop: 1954   (Starr)
956 847-1200 - *Fax: 847-1222*
Mayor-Noel Escobar
Mayor PT-Ruperto B. Escobar
Coun.-Gloria E. Alvarez
Coun.-Alfedo Escobar
Coun.-Armando Flores
Coun.-Roberto L. Naranjo
City Secy.-Rosario Rivera
Atty.-Jacqueline R. Salinas

ESTELLINE 79233
Pop: 145 (Hall)
P.O. Box 8
806 888-1212 - *Fax: 888-1040*
Mayor-Jeff Jones
Ald.-Dan Cooper
Ald.-Holly Hall
Ald.-Scott Mahaffey
Ald.-Dawn Shipman
Ald.-Ty Walker
City Secy.-Tresa Sims
C.P.-Scott Burton

EULESS 76039
Pop: 51277 (Tarrant)
201 North Ector Drive
817 685-1419 - *Fax: 685-1416*
www.eulesstx.gov
Mayor-Linda Martin
Mayor PT-Eddie Price
Coun.-Perry Bynum
Coun.-Linda Ellenfeldt
Coun.-Tim Stinneford
Coun.-Jeremy Tompkins
Coun.-Harry Zimmer
City Mgr.-Loretta Getchell
Dir. Fin-Janina Jewell
City Secy.-Kim Sutter
P.M.-Mike Lowry
Atty.-Wayne K. Olson
C.P.-Michael Brown
F.C.-Wes Rhodes

EUREKA
Pop: 307 (Navarro)
1305 FM 2859
Corsicana, TX 75109
903 874-8016
Mayor-Barney Thomas
Mayor PT-Mike Wisdom
Ald.-Jo Ann Bottoms
Ald.-Ginny Folmar
Ald.-Patricia Pritchett
Ald.-Carroll Sigman
City Secy.-Susan Wisdom

EUSTACE 75124
Pop: 991 (Henderson)
P.O. Box 579
903 425-4702 - *Fax: 425-4168*
www.cityofeustace.com
Mayor-Dustin Shelton
Mayor PT-Charles Powers
Coun.-Marlin Chambers
Coun.-Tim Meyer
Coun.-Adrian Parham
Coun.-Daniel Smith
City Secy.-Sandy Lane
Atty.-Blake E. Armstrong
C.P.-Jason Perrini
V.F.D.F.C.-Chris Anthony
Dir. P.W.-Gene Burns

EVANT 76525
Pop: 426 (Coryell-Hamilton)
598 E. Hwy. 84
P.O. Box 10
254 471-3135 - *Fax: 471-5724*
http://www.cityofevant.com/
Mayor-Sterling Manning
Mayor PT-Keith Rainwater
Coun.-Brian Mauney
Coun.-Charles Weeks
Coun.-James Wiedemann
Coun.-Joy Witty
City Secy.-Pat Parr
Atty.-Barney Knight
F.C.-Chuck Weeks

EVERMAN 76140
Pop: 6108 (Tarrant)
212 N. Race St.
817 293-0525 - *Fax: 551-7549*
www.evermantx.net
Mayor-Ray Richardson
Mayor PT-Susan Mackey
Coun.-Johnnie Mae Allen
Coun.-Miriam Davila
Coun.-Kelly Denison
Coun.-Michelle Meyer
Coun.-Judy Sellers
City Mgr.-Michael Box
Dir. Fin-Michael Gunderson
City Secy.-Mindi Parks
Atty.-Bojorquez Law Firm
F.C.-Randy Sanders
Dir. P.W.-Jeff Reed
Chief of Police/PS-Craig Spencer

FAIR OAKS RANCH 78015
Pop: 6084 (Bexar-Comal-Kendall)
7286 Dietz Elkhorn
210 698-0900 - *Fax: 698-3565*
www.fairoaksranchtx.org
Mayor-Garry Manitzas
Mayor PT-Al Schmidt
Ald.-Roy E. Elizondo
Ald.-Steve Hartpence
Ald.-Mary Anne Harvard
Ald.-Snehal R. Patel
City Mgr.-Tobin Maples
Atty.-Charles E. "Charlie" Zech
C.P.-Scott Rubin

FAIRCHILDS, VILLAGE OF
Pop: 763 (Fort Bend)
8713 Fairchilds Road
Richmond, TX 77469
979 793-6676
Mayor-Bob Haenel
Ald.-Lance Bertolino
Ald.-Linda Kaluza
Ald.-Greg Leslie
Ald.-Richard Vacek
Ald.-Debra Zagala
City Secy.-Jan Vacek
Atty.-Lora Lenzsch
F.C.-Josh Shed

FAIRFIELD 75840
Pop: 3091 (Freestone)
222 S. Mount St.
903 389-2633 - *Fax: 389-6327*
fairfieldtexas.com/
Mayor-Roy W. Hill
Mayor PT-Joe Kirgan, Jr.
Ald.-Landis Bayless
Ald.-Keith Daniels
Ald.-Kenneth Hughes
Ald.-Randy Johnson
Int. City Secy.-Misty Richardson
City Admin.-Jeff Looney
Atty.-Alan J. Bojorquez
C.P.-Kenny Bulger
F.C.-Matt Foree

FAIRVIEW, TOWN OF 75069
Pop: 8400 (Collin)
372 Town Place
972 562-0522 - *Fax: 548-0268*
www.fairviewtexas.org
Mayor-Darion Culbertson
Mayor PT-John Adler
Coun.-Paul Hendricks
Coun.-Henry Lessner
Coun.-Pam Little
Coun.-Bill Nicol
Coun.-Renee Powell
Town Mgr.-Julie Couch
Town Secy.-Elizabeth Cappon
Atty.-Clark H. McCoy, Jr.
C.P.-Granver Tolliver
F.C.-Jeff Bell

FALFURRIAS 78355
Pop: 4981 (Brooks)
P.O. Drawer E
361 325-2420 - *Fax: 325-9784*
www.ci.falfurrias.tx.us
Mayor-David G. Longoria
Mayor PT-Frank Nevarez
Ald.-Manuel Perez, Jr.
Ald.-Justo Ramirez
Ald.-Isaac Homer Salinas, Jr.
Clk.-Melinda Garza
City Admin.-L. David Flores
Atty.-Alan Ozuna
C.P.-Alberto Gonzalez

FALLS CITY 78113
Pop: 611 (Karnes)
P.O. Box 250
830 254-3242
Mayor-Brent Houdmann
Mayor PT-Andrews Wiatrek
Coun.-Corey Albert
Coun.-Wes Gisler
Coun.-Steven Swierc
Coun.-Aaron Wiatrek
City Secy.-Lauren Sturm
Atty.-Denton, Navarro, Rocha,
  Bernal, & Zech PC
F.C.-Raymond Dziuk

FARMERS BRANCH
Pop: 28616 (Dallas)
13000 William Dodson Parkway
P.O. Box 819010
Farmers Branch, TX 75381-9010
972 247-3131 - *Fax: 247-5939*
www.farmersbranchtx.gov
Mayor-Robert C. Dye
Mayor PT-John Norwood
Dep. Mayor PT-Mike Bomgardner
Coun.-Bronson Blackson
Coun.-Terry Lynne
Coun.-Ana Reyes
City Mgr.-Charles Cox
City Secy.-Amy Piukana
P.A.-Lee Hammock
Atty.-Peter G. Smith
C.P.-David Hale
F.C.-Steve Parker

FARMERSVILLE 75442
Pop: 3350 (Collin)
205 S. Main St.
972 782-6151 - *Fax: 782-6604*
www.farmersvilletx.com
Mayor-Diane Piwko
Mayor PT-Mike Hurst
Ald.-Michael Hesse
Ald.-Donny Mason
Ald.-Craig Oversteet
Ald.-Todd Rolen
City Mgr.-Ben White
Dir. Fin-Daphne Hamlin
City Secy.-Sandra Green
Atty.-Alan Lathrom
C.P.-Mike Sullivan
F.C.-Kim Morris

FARWELL 79325
Pop: 1363 (Parmer)
P.O. Box 338
806 481-3620 - *Fax: 481-3622*
Mayor-Joe Stanton
Ald.-Ysleta Kittrell
Ald.-Mario Lara
Ald.-Stephen Schilling
Ald.-Tom Taylor
Ald.-Gary White
City Secy.-Sheila Jennings
Atty.-Jeff W. Actkinson
C.P.-Larry Kelsay

FATE 75132
Pop: 11380 (Rockwall)
P.O. Box 159
972 771-4601 - *Fax: 772-3343*
www.cityoffate.com/
Mayor-Lorne Megyesi
Coun.-David Billings
Coun.-Blake Buchanan
Coun.-Joe Burger
Coun.-Steve Herrmann
Coun.-Lance Megyesi
Coun.-Nikki Robinson

City Mgr.-Michael Kovacs
Dir. Fin-Li Jen Lee
City Secy.-Vickey Raduechel
Atty.-Brenda McDonald
Dir. P.S.-Brian Griffeth

FAYETTEVILLE 78940
Pop: 258 (Fayette)
202 West Main
979 378-2559 - *Fax: 378-2313*
http://fayettevillecitytx.com
Mayor-Stephen Cushing
Mayor PT-Liz Fritsch
Ald.-Greg Gillespie
Ald.-Bradley Girndt
Ald.-Amy Nini
Ald.-Steve Pavlicek
City Secy.-Janice Wasut
Atty.-Cary Bovey
F.C.-Randy Noviskie

FERRIS 75125
Pop: 2436 (Ellis)
100 Town Plaza
972 544-2110 - *City Secretary*
  Fax: 842-2609
www.ferristexas.gov
Mayor-Micheal Driggars
Mayor PT-Richard Barrett
Ald.-Clayton Hunter
Ald.-Bobby Lindsey
Ald.-Jim Swafford
Ald.-Carol Wright
Dir. Fin-Melissa Gonzalez
City Secy.-Callie Green
Atty.-Michael B. Halla
C.P.-Eddie Salazar
F.C.-David Petricca

FLATONIA 78941
Pop: 1383 (Fayette)
P.O. Box 329
361 865-3548 - *Fax: 865-2817*
www.destinationflatonia.com
Mayor-Bryan Milson
Mayor PT-Catherine Steinhauser
Coun.-Donna Cockrell
Coun.-Mark Eversole
Coun.-Dennis Geesaman
Coun.-Ginny Sears
City Mgr.-Mark McLaughlin
City Secy.-Melissa Brunner
Atty.-Angela Beck
C.P.-Perry Kram
F.C.-John Burleson

FLORENCE 76527
Pop: 1136 (Williamson)
106 South Patterson
P.O. Box 430
254 793-2490 - *Fax: 793-3766*
www.florencetex.com
Mayor-Mary Condon
Ald.-Debra Bartos Cahill
Ald.-Denise Deichmann

Ald.-Richard Moon
Ald.-Lesa Ragsdale
Ald.-Kory Woolverton
City Secy.-Amy L. Crane
Atty.-Randall C. Stump
C.P.-Adam Marsh
F.C.-Robert Shelton

FLORESVILLE 78114
Pop: 6448 (Wilson)
1120 D St.
830 393-3105 - *Fax: 393-2056*
www.floresvilletx.gov
Mayor-Cecelia G. Gonzalez-Dippel
Coun.-Gloria Cantu
Coun.-Gerard Jimenez
Coun.-David Johns
Coun.-Nick Nissen
Coun.-Juan Ortiz
City Mgr.-Henrietta Turner
City Secy.-Monica Cordova
Atty.-Charles E. "Charlie" Zech
C.P.-Lorenzo Herrera
F.C.-Lorenzo Ortiz

**FLOWER MOUND,
TOWN OF 75028**
Pop: 71253 (Denton-Tarrant)
2121 Cross Timbers Rd.
972 874-6000
www.flower-mound.com
Mayor-Tom Hayden
Mayor PT-Don McDaniel
Dep. Mayor PT-Kevin Bryant
Coun.-Claudio Forest
Coun.-Jason Webb
Coun.-Bryan Webb
Town Mgr.-Jimmy Stathatos
Town Secy.-Theresa Scott
Atty.-Bryn Meredith
C.P.-Andy Kancel
F.C.-Eric Greaser

FLOYDADA 79235
Pop: 3038 (Floyd)
114 W. Virginia
806 983-2834 - *Fax: 983-5542*
Mayor-Bobby Gilliland
Mayor PT-Sam Green
Coun.-Dana Crossland
Coun.-Gail DuBois
Coun.-Bettye King
Coun.-Steve Lloyd
Coun.-Cory Speed
City Mgr.-Jeff Johnston
City Secy.-Selia Arellano
Atty.-Karen Houchin
C.P.-Darrell Gooch
F.C.-Craig DuBois

FOLLETT 79034
Pop: 459 (Lipscomb)
P.O. Box 216
806 653-2601 - *Fax: 653-5911*
Mayor-Kevin Wynn
Mayor PT-Neal Ashpaugh
Ald.-Jerry Helmuth
Ald.-David Howard
Ald.-Michael Howard
Ald.-Orville Robison
City Mgr.-Robert Williamson
City Secy.-Wynona Lusk
Atty.-Matt Bartosiewiez
V.F.D.F.C.-Jayson Winn

FOREST HILL 76119
Pop: 13000 (Tarrant)
3219 California Parkway
817 568-3040 - *Fax: 568-3049*
www.foresthilltx.org
Mayor-Lyndia Thomas
Coun.-Michielle Benson
Coun.-Stephanie Boardingham
Coun.-Clara Faulkner
Coun.-Becky Duncan Hayes
Coun.-Carlie Jones
Coun.-Cameron Wafer
City Mgr.-Sheyi I. Ipaye, CPM
City Secy.-Othel Murphree
Atty.-Warren J. Spencer
C.P.-Dan Dennis
F.C.-Randy Chapman
Dir. P.W.-Roberto Duenes

FORNEY 75126
Pop: 17480 (Kaufman)
101 East Main
P.O. Box 826
972 564-7302 - *Fax: 564-7349*
www.cityofforney.org
Mayor-Rick Wilson
Mayor PT-Mary Penn
Coun.-David Johnson
Coun.-Corey McGee
Coun.-Kevin Moon
Coun.-Shaun Myers
Coun.-Robbie Powers
City Secy.-Dorothy Brooks
Atty.-Jon Thatcher
C.P.-Rob Sherwin
F.C.-Rick Townsend

FORSAN 79733
Pop: 210 (Howard)
P.O. Box 714
432 457-2355 - *Fax: 457-0003*
Mayor-Steve Park
Ald.-Debbie Burton
Ald.-Patrick Carnahan
Ald.-Mary Gressett
Ald.-Ramon Holguin
Ald.-Fred Holguin
City Secy.-Jenny Sayles

FORT STOCKTON 79735
Pop: 8283 (Pecos)
P.O. Box 1000
432 336-8525 - *Fax: 336-6273*
cityoffortstockton.com/
Mayor-Chris Alexander
Mayor PT-Billy Jackson
Coun.-Ruben Falcon
Coun.-Dino Ramirez
Coun.-Mike Ureta, Jr.
Coun.-Vacant
City Mgr.-Frank Rodriguez III
Dir. Fin-Maria Rodriguez Interim
City Secy.-Delma A. Gonzalez
Atty.-Jesse Gonzales, Jr.
Int. C.P.-Salvador Rangel

FORT WORTH 76102
Pop: 781000 (Denton-Tarrant-
Wise)
817 392-2255 - *Fax: 392-6196*
www.fortworthtexas.gov
Mayor-Betsy Price
Mayor PT-Dennis Shingleton
Coun.-Gyna Bivens
Coun.-Brian Byrd
Coun.-Carlos Flores
Coun.-Kelly Allen Gray
Coun.-Jungus Jordan
Coun.-Cary G. Moon
Coun.-Ann Zadeh
City Mgr.-David Cooke
City Secy.-Mary J. Kayser
Atty.-Sarah J. Fullenwider
C.P.-Joel Fitzgerald
F.C.-Rudy Jackson
Purchasing-Jack Dale, J.D.

FRANKLIN 77856
Pop: 1564 (Robertson)
P.O. Box 428
979 828-3257 - *Fax: 828-3390*
http://cityoffranklintx.com
Mayor-Molly Hedrick
Ald.-Kelly Ellison
Ald.-Jana Foreman
Ald.-Raymond Hawkins
Ald.-Rodney McFadden
Ald.-Ferman Richard
City Secy.-Shirley Smith
Atty.-Bryan F. "Rusty" Russ, Jr.
C.P.-Terry Thibodeaux
F.C.-Jimmy Redden

FRANKSTON 75763
Pop: 1229 (Anderson)
P.O. Box 186
903 876-2241 - *Fax: 876-3837*
www.frankstontexas.com
Mayor-Sharyn Harrison
Mayor PT-Eugene Brooks
Coun.-Alfonso Lang
Coun.-Roger McDonald
Coun.-Mark Slaughter
Coun.-Johnny Wheeler

City Secy.-Jan Hamilton
C.P.-Darren Goodman
F.C.-Scottie Rodgers

FREDERICKSBURG 78624
Pop: 10530 (Gillespie)
126 W. Main St.
830 997-7521 - *Fax: 997-1861*
www.fbgtx.org
Mayor-Linda Langerhans
Coun.-Charlie Kiehne
Coun.-Jerry Luckenbach
Coun.-Gary Neffendorf
Coun.-Bobby Watson
City Mgr.-Kent Myers
City Secy.-Shelley Britton
Atty.-Daniel Jones
C.P.-Steve Wetz
F.C.-Lynn Bizzell

FREEPORT 77541
Pop: 12708 (Brazoria)
200 W. 2nd St.
979 233-3526 - *Fax: 233-8867*
www.freeport.tx.us
Mayor-Troy T. Brimage
Coun.-Brooks Bass
Coun.-Larry L. McDonald
Coun.-Nicole Mireles
Coun.-Roy E. Yates
City Mgr.-Jeff Pynes
City Secy.-Delia Munoz
Atty.-Wallace N. Shaw
C.P.-Ray Garivey
F.C.-Chris Motley

FREER 78357
Pop: 2818 (Duval)
P.O. Drawer N
361 394-6612 - *Fax: 394-6689*
freertx.org/
Mayor-Arnoldo Cantu
Mayor PT-Fernando Carballeira
Ald.-Lando Hinojosa
Ald.-Debbie Martinez
Ald.-Martin Martinez Jr.
Ald.-Carlos Salinas
City Secy.-Ana Casares
Atty.-Gilbert N. Saenz
C.P.-John Spillers
Int. F.C.-Arturo Martinez

FRIENDSWOOD 77546
Pop: 39871 (Galveston-Harris)
910 S. Friendswood Drive
281 996-3200 - *Fax: 482-1634*
www.ci.friendswood.tx.us
Mayor-Kevin M. Holland
Mayor PT-Steve Rockey
Coun.-Sally Branson
Coun.-Mike Foreman
Coun.-Carl W. Gustafson
Coun.-Jim Hill
Coun.-John Scott
City Mgr.-Roger C. Roecker

City Secy.-Melinda Welsh
Atty.-Mary Kay Fischer
C.P.-Robert B. Wieners
F.M.-Terry Byrd

FRIONA 79035
Pop: 4123 (Parmer)
623 Main St.
806 250-2761 - *Fax: 250-2893*
Mayor-Ricky White
Ald.-Martha Barker
Ald.-Nancy Davis
Ald.-Bruce Fleming
Ald.-Greg Lewellen
Ald.-Alan Monroe
City Mgr.-Vacant
Atty.-Marcus Norris
C.P.-Isidro Jimenez
F.C.-Jim Taylor
Dir. P.W.-Salvador Garcia

FRISCO 75034
Pop: 140220 (Collin-Denton)
6101 Frisco Square Blvd.
972 292-5000 - *Fax: 292-5122*
www.friscotexas.gov
Mayor-Jeff Cheney
Mayor PT-Will Sowell
Dep. Mayor PT-Tim Nelson
Coun.-Shona Huffman
Coun.-John Keating
Coun.-Brian Livingston
Coun.-Bill Woodard
City Mgr.-George Purefoy
City Secy.-Jenny Page
Atty.-Richard Abernathy
C.P.-John Bruce
F.C.-Mark Piland

FRITCH 79036
Pop: 2117 (Hutchinson)
P.O. Box 758
806 857-3143 - *Fax: 857-3229*
fritchcityhall.com/
Mayor-W. Kelly Henderson
Mayor PT-Richard Hein
Ald.-Arlin Audrain
Ald.-Denise Campbell
Ald.-Dwight Kirksey
Ald.-Thomas Ray
City Mgr.-Drew Brassfield
City Secy.-Cindy Cook
Atty.-Marcus Norris
C.P.-Houston Gass
F.C.-Ed Adamson
Dir. P.W.-Brody Crupe

FROST 76641
Pop: 643 (Navarro)
P.O. Drawer X
903 682-3861 - *Fax: 682-3868*
Mayor-Lance Reed
Mayor PT-J.J. Bratcher
Ald.-Velma Ballew
Ald.-Penny Harris
Ald.-Candi Ratliff

Ald.-Justo Supulveda
City Secry/Court Clk.-Terry McGill
C.P.-Terry Kuhn
F.C.-William Meskimen

FRUITVALE 75127
Pop: 408 (Van Zandt)
P.O. Box 197
903 271-1643
Mayor-Jennifer Johnston
Ald.-George Adams
Ald.-Vicki Ferguson
Ald.-Cindy Lambert
Ald.-Susan Murre
Ald.-Keith Tharp
City Secy.-Susan Murre
Atty.-Vacant
F.C.-Jeremy Barker

FULSHEAR 77441
Pop: 8620 (Fort Bend)
281 346-1796 - *Fax: 346-2556*
www.fulsheartexas.gov
Mayor-Jeff Roberts
Mayor PT-Tricia Thompson Krenek
Ald.-Lauren Ashley
Ald.-Jim Fatheree
Ald.-Stephen Gill
Ald.-Dana Hollingsworth
Ald.-Kaye Kahlich
City Secy.-Diana Gordon Offord
City Admin.-CJ Snipes
Atty.-J. Grady Randle
C.P.-Kenny Seymour

FULTON, TOWN OF
Pop: 1553 (Aransas)
201 N. 7th Street
P.O. Box 1130
Fulton, TX 78358-1130
361 729-5533 - *Fax: 729-7029*
www.fultontexas.org
Mayor-Jimmy Kendrick
Mayor PT-Craig Bohn
Ald.-Les Cole
Ald.-Beverly Garis
Ald.-Larry Pahmiyer
Ald.-Carol Thompson
City Secy.-Jan Hill
Atty.-Hal George
C.P.-Rick McLester
F.C.-Rickey McLester

GAINESVILLE 76240
Pop: 16002 (Cooke)
200 S. Rusk
940 668-4500 - *Fax: 668-4518*
www.gainesville.tx.us
Mayor-Jim Goldsworthy
Mayor PT-Keith Clegg
Coun.-Mary Jo Dollar
Coun.-Steve Gordon
Coun.-Carolyn Hendricks
Coun.-Ken Keeler
Coun.-Tommy Moore
City Mgr.-Barry Sullivan

City Secy.-Caitlyn Huddleston
Atty.-Bill Harris
C.P.-Kevin Phillips
F.C.-Wally Cox

GALENA PARK 77547
Pop: 10887 (Harris)
P.O. Box 46
713 672-2556 - *Fax: 672-1840*
www.cityofgalenapark-tx.gov
Mayor-Esmeralda Moya
Comm.-Eric Broussard
Comm.-Rodney Chersky
Comm.-Barry Ponder
Comm.-Oscar Silva Jr.
City Secy.-Mayra Gonzales
Atty.-Robert Collins
Int. C.P.-Rsses Martin
F.C.-Paul Gregory

GALLATIN 75764
Pop: 419 (Cherokee)
P.O. Box 95
903 683-6000
Mayor-Juanita Cotton
Coun.-Ashley Dethlefs
Coun.-Kathy Dethlefs
Coun.-Mark Scallon
City Secy.-Jane Bolden
Atty.-Steven Guy
F.C. George Bostock, IV

GALVESTON
Pop: 49608 (Galveston)
P.O. Box 779
Galveston, TX 77553-0779
409 797-3500 - *Fax: 797-3511*
www.galvestontx.gov
Mayor-James D. Yarbrough
Mayor PT-Terrilyn
Tarlton-Shannon
Coun.-Amy Carmen Bly
Coun.-Craig Brown
Coun.-Mike Doherty
Coun.-Frank Thomas Maceo
Coun.-Carolyn Sunseri
City Mgr.-Brian Maxwell
City Secy.-Janelle Williams
Atty.-Donald S. Glywasky
C.P.-Vernon "Rick" Hale
F.C.-Mike Wisko

GANADO 77962
Pop: 2003 (Jackson)
P.O. Box 264
361 771-2232 - *Fax: 771-3015*
Mayor-Clinton Tegeler
Mayor PT-Blake Petrash
Coun.-Robin Bauerle
Coun.-Calvin Callies
Coun.-Mike Konarik
Coun.-James Sudik
City Secy.-Kristi Rogers
Atty.-Gary Olson
C.P.-David Merritt
F.C.-Bernard Scott

GARDEN RIDGE 78266
Pop: 3259 (Comal)
9400 Municipal Parkway
210 651-6632 - *Fax: 651-9638*
www.ci.garden-ridge.tx.us
Mayor-Larry Thompson
Mayor PT-John McCaw
Ald.-Todd Arvidson
Ald.-Kay Bower
Ald.-Robb Erickson
Ald.-Bryan Lantzy
City Secy.-Shelley Goodwin
City Admin.-Nancy Cain
Atty.-Charles E. "Charlie" Zech
C.P.-Ron Eberhardt

GARLAND
Pop: 226876 (Collin-
Dallas-Rockwall)
200 N. 5th Street
P.O. Box 469002
Garland, TX 75046-9002
972 205-2404 - *Fax: 205-2504*
www.garlandtx.gov
Mayor-Vacant
Coun.-Richard Aubin
Coun.-David Gibbons
Coun.-Anita Goebel
Coun.-Scott LeMay
Coun.-Jerry A. Nickerson
Coun.-Robert John Smith
Coun.-Robert Vera
Coun.-B.J. Williams
City Mgr.-Bryan Bradford
City Secy.-René Dowl
Atty.-Brad Neighbor
C.P.-Mitch Bates
F.C.-Mark Lee

GARRETT 75119
Pop: 806 (Ellis)
208 N. Ferris
972 8/5-5893 - *Fax: 875-0226*
www.cityofgarrett.com/
Mayor-Matt Newsom
Mayor PT-Jami Rogers
Ald.-Dan Cepak
Ald.-Sheri Payne
Ald.-Becky Rodgers
Ald.-Vacant
City Secy.-Judy Braddock
Atty.-Michael B. Halla
C.P.-Chad Nelson

GARRISON 75946
Pop: 921 (Nacogdoches)
330 South B Avenue
936 347-2201 - *Fax: 347-2200*
cityofgarrison.us
Mayor-Russell Wright
Mayor PT-Tim Burton
Ald.-Hope Hallmark
Ald.-Steve Jones
Ald.-Travis Simon

Ald.-Tim Wright
City Secy.-Terrie Bell
Atty.-Blake Thompson
C.P.-Tim Barton
F.C.-Ricky Colle
Dir. P.S.-Sgt. James Brazil

GARY 75643
Pop: 311 (Panola)
P.O. Drawer 160
903 685-2225 - *Fax: 685-2224*
Mayor-Maxie Lake
Mayor PT-Debra Smith
Ald.-Jerri Bolton
Ald.-Glenda Grimes
Ald.-Mark Thornton
Ald.-Linda Thorson
City Secy.-Pam Woodfin
Atty.-Rick McPherson
V.F.D.F.C.-Mark Dawson

GATESVILLE 76528
Pop: 15985 (Coryell)
110 North 8th
254 865-8951 - *Fax: 865-8320*
www.ci.gatesville.tx.us
Mayor-Gary M. Chumley
Mayor PT-Ronnie Viss
Coun.-Jack Doyle
Coun.-Randy Hitt
Coun.-David Mitchell
Coun.-Meredith Rainer
Coun.-Dwight Suson
City Mgr.-William H. Parry III
City Secy.-Wendy Cole
Atty.-Sandy Gately
C.P.-Nathan Gohlke
F.C.-Billy Vaden

GEORGE WEST 78022
Pop: 2445 (Live Oak)
361 449-1556 - *Fax: 449-3030*
Mayor-Andrew Garza
Mayor PT-Ana Guerrero
Coun.-Patricia Clifton
Coun.-Gerald Hardesty
Coun.-Kitley Wasicek
City Mgr.-Georgia Vines
City Secy.-Debra Myers
Int. City Attorne-Carlos Valdez
C.P.-Suzanne Martin
V.F.D.F.C.-Lloyd Wientjes

GEORGETOWN 78626
Pop: 52303 (Williamson)
113 E. 8th St.
P.O. Box 409
Georgetown, TX 78627-0409
512 930-3652 - *Fax: 930-3659*
www.georgetown.org
Mayor-Dale Ross
Mayor PT-Anna Eby
Coun.-Steve Fought
Coun.-Ty Gipson
Coun.-Tommy Gonzalez

Coun.-John Hesser
Coun.-Rachael Jonrowe
Coun.-Valerie Nicholson
City Mgr.-David Morgan
City Secy.-Shelley Nowling
Atty.-Charlie McNabb
C.P.-Wayne Nero
F.C.-John Sullivan

GHOLSON
Pop: 1061 (McLennan)
155 Wesley Chapel Rd.
Waco, TX 76705
254 829-2084
Mayor-Larry Binnion
Mayor PT-Ron McCartney
Coun.-Tom Buzbee
Coun.-Brandon Heaton
Coun.-Russell S. Smith
Coun.-Tommy Wiley
City Secy.-Mel Priest
Aud.-William B. Sanders
Atty.-Jacob G. Straub

GIDDINGS 78942
Pop: 5113 (Lee)
118 E. Richmond St.
979 540-2710 - *Fax: 542-0950*
www.giddings.net
Mayor-John Dowell
Mayor PT-Fred Jones
Coun.-Alan Casey
Coun.-Frank Castro
Coun.-Joel Lopez
Coun.-Linda Pruitt
City Mgr.-Ricky Jorgensen
City Secy.-Lola Hazel
Atty.-Charlie Crossfield
C.P.-Haril Walpole
F.C.-Jimmy Mitschke

GILMER 75644
Pop: 5187 (Upshur)
P.O. Box 760
903 843-2552 - *Fax: 843-3508*
www.gilmer-tx.com
Mayor-Tim Marshall
Mayor PT-William Hornsby
Coun.-Michael Chevalier
Coun.-Brenda Jeffery
Coun.-Marty Jordan
Coun.-Jarom Tefteller
Coun.-Brian Williams
City Mgr.-Greg Hutson
City Secy.-Kathy D. Hoover
Atty.-Mike Martin
C.P.-Mark Case
F.C.-Jerry Taylor

GLADEWATER 75647
Pop: 6441 (Gregg-Upshur)
P.O. Box 1725
903 845-2196 - *Fax: 845-6891*
www.cityofgladewater.com
Mayor-Harold R. Wells
Mayor PT-J.D. Shipp
Coun.-Elijah Anderson
Coun.-Nick Foster
Coun.-Lana L. Niemann
Coun.-Dennis R. Robertson
Coun.-Leon Watson
City Mgr.-Ricky Tow
City Secy.-Melba Haralson
Atty.-Ronald Stutes
C.P.-Robert Vine

GLEN ROSE 76043
Pop: 2444 (Somervell)
P.O. Box 1949
254 897-2272 - *Fax: 897-7989*
www.glenrosebluegrass.com/
Mayor-Sam Moody
Mayor PT-Sandra Ramsay
Coun.-Mike Jones
Coun.-Robert Marquez
Coun.-Doug Mitchell
Coun.-Dennis Moore
Dir. Fin-Sherry Reeves
City Secy.-Terri Johnson
City Admin.-Chester Nolen
Atty.-Vacant
C.P.-Buck Martin
F.C.-Mark Crawford
Dir. P.W.-Jim Holder

GLENN HEIGHTS 75154
Pop: 11278 (Dallas-Ellis)
1938 S. Hampton Rd.
972 223-1690 - *Fax: 223-9307*
www.glennheightstx.gov
Mayor-Leon Tate
Mayor PT-Tony Bradley
Coun.-Ron Adams
Coun.-Travis Bruton
Coun.-Harry A. Garrett
Coun.-Emma Ipaye
Coun.-Vacant
City Mgr.-Aretha Ferrell-Benavides
Dir. Fin-Lakeita Sutton
City Secy.-Juanita Willman
Atty.-Nichols, Jackson, Dillard,
   Hager and Smith, LLP
C.P.-Phillip Prasifka
F.C.-Eddie Burns

GODLEY 76044
Pop: 1009 (Johnson)
P.O. Box 27
817 389-3539 - *Fax: 886-2557*
www.godleytx.gov
Mayor-David Wallis
Mayor PT-Jan Whitehead
Ald.-Rosemary Fuller
Ald.-David Hamm

Ald.-Mary Ann Matthews
Ald.-Acy McGehee
City Secy.-Stephanie Hodges
Atty.-Cass Callaway
C.P.-Jason Jordan
F.C.-James Woolard

GOLDSMITH 79741
Pop: 257 (Ector)
P.O. Box 629
432 827-3404 - *Fax: 827-3937*
Mayor-Dickie Bradley
Coun.-Robert Clinton
Coun.-Glen Henderson
Coun.-Monty Oglesby
Coun.-Jay Stockton
City Mgr.-Bennie Cope
City Secy.-Shanna Bavousett
F.C.-Monty Oglesby

GOLDTHWAITE 76844
Pop: 1878 (Mills)
P.O. Box 450
325 648-3186 - *Fax: 648-2570*
Mayor-Mike McMahan
Mayor PT-Ramona Flores
Ald.-Lynn Bouse
Ald.-Rich Brown
Ald.-Steve Patrick
Ald.-J Wilson
City Mgr.-Robert E. Lindsey III
City Secy.-Darnelle White
Atty.-Gerald Hale
C.P.-Clint Hammonds
F.C.-David Schwartz

GOLIAD 77963
Pop: 2037 (Goliad)
P.O. Box 939
361 645-3454 - *Fax: 645-8315*
www.goliadtx.net
Mayor-Trudia Preston
Mayor PT-Luis Rodriguez
Coun.-Robin Alaniz
Coun.-Charles Benavides
Coun.-Mary J. Burns
Coun.-Nathan Edward Lill
City Admin/Secy-K. M. Hubert
Atty.-Barbara Boulware-Wells
F.C.-Alonzo Morales, Jr.

GOLINDA 76655
Pop: 559 (Falls-McLennan)
7039 Golinda Dr.
254 881-7333 - *Fax: 881-5782*
Mayor-Doyle Parks
Mayor PT-Joyce Farar
Ald.-Leland Busbee
Ald.-Billy Elkins
Ald.-Shirley Graves
Ald.-Cedric Perdue
City Secy.-Jessica Guerrero
Atty.-Charles Olson
F.C.-Quincy Lee

GONZALES 78629
Pop: 7660 (Gonzales)
P.O. Box 547
830 672-2815 - *Fax: 672-2813*
www.gonzales.texas.gov
Mayor-Connie Kacir
Mayor PT-Dan Blakemore
Coun.-Bobby O'Neal
Coun.-Gary Schroeder
Coun.-Tommy Schurig
City Mgr.-Vacant
Dir. Fin-Laura Zella
City Secy.-Kristina Vega
Atty.-Jackie L. Williamson
C.P.-Tim Crow
F.C.-Keith Schmidt

GOODLOW 75144
Pop: 400 (Navarro)
P.O. Box 248
903 396-7862 - *Fax: 396-7866*
Mayor-Willie Washington
Mayor PT-Earnest Betts
Ald.-Christine Bryant
Ald.-Jackie Copeland
Ald.-Vacant
Ald.-Vacant
City Secy.-Ruthie Washington
Atty.-Kelly R. Myers

GOODRICH 77335
Pop: 264 (Polk)
P.O. Box 277
936 365-2228 - *Fax: 365-4567*
Mayor-Kelly Nelson
Ald.-Louie Hill
Ald.-Mary Orozco
Ald.-Clestel Riffe
Ald.-Bobby Wright
Ald.-Vacant
City Secy.-Sally Yingling
Atty.-Olson & Olson

GORDON 76453
Pop: 478 (Palo Pinto)
105 S. Main
P.O. Box 227
254 693-5676 - *Fax: 693-5859*
Mayor-Jack Coleman
Mayor PT-Albert Dickson Jr.
Ald.-Penny Jones
Ald.-Roger Keck
Ald.-Sherrye Stallings Mills
Ald.-Ricky Speer
City Secy.-Teresa Johnson
Atty.-George Gault
F.C.-Arthur James

GOREE 76363
Pop: 203 (Knox)
P.O. Box 248
940 422-5306 - *Fax: 422-5306*
Mayor-Randy Hibdon
Mayor PT-Vickie Huffman
Coun.-Trey Harlan
Coun.-Arvel Hibdon
Coun.-Mike Hord
Coun.-Jonathan Ramirez
City Secy.-Crystal Graham
Atty.-Michael Guevara
F.C.-Trae Harlin

GORMAN 76454
Pop: 1083 (Eastland)
P.O. Box 236
254 734-2317 - *Fax: 734-2270*
http://www.gormantx.com/
Mayor-Robert Ervin
Comm.-Dylan Cogburn
Comm.-Kenneth Good
Comm.-Justin Johnson
Comm.-David Stanley
City Secy.-Tacy Warren
Atty.-William "Pat" Chesser
C.P.-Steven Anderson
F.C.-Jim Guthery

GRAFORD 76449
Pop: 584 (Palo Pinto)
P.O. Box 97
940 664-2125 - *Fax: 664-3130*
Mayor-Carl S. Walston
Mayor PT-Alice Sain
Coun.-Wesley Bloxham
Coun.-David Carlyle
Coun.-Gregory Dunn
Coun.-Eddie Nowak
City Secy.-Cynthia Perry
Atty.-Phil Garrett

GRAHAM 76450
Pop: 8903 (Young)
P.O. Box 1449
940 549-3324 - *Fax: 549-5030*
www.cityofgrahamtexas.com/
Mayor-Jack Graham
Coun.-Brint Albritton
Coun.-Lee Boyd
Coun.-Darby Brockway
Coun.-Kyle Peavy
City Mgr.-Brandon Anderson
Dir. Fin-Sharon McFadden
City Secy.-Sharon McFadden
P.A.-Janice Snow
Atty.-William A. Myers
C.P.-Tony Widner
F.C.-Jerry David
Dir. P.W.-Jason Cottongame

GRANBURY 76048
Pop: 7978 (Hood)
P.O. Box 969
817 573-1114 - *Fax: 573-7678*
www.granbury.org
Mayor-Nin Hulett
Coun.-Tony Allen
Coun.-Greg Corrigan
Coun.-Gary Couch
Coun.-Tony Mobly
Coun.-Trish Reiner
City Mgr.-Chris Coffman, CPM
City Secy.-Carla Walker
P.A.-Alvin Scott
Atty.-Walter W. Leonard
C.P.-Mitch Galvan
F.C.-Brent Blackmon

GRAND PRAIRIE
Pop: 175396 (Dallas-Ellis-Tarrant)
P.O. Box 534045
Grand Prairie, TX 75053-4045
972 237-8000 - *Fax: 237-8088*
www.gptx.org
Mayor-Ron Jensen
Mayor PT-Jeff Wooldridge
Dep. Mayor PT-Jeff Copeland
Coun.-Mike Del Bosque
Coun.-Jorja Clemson
Coun.-Richard Fregoe
Coun.-Greg Giessner
Coun.-Tony Shotwell
Coun.-Jim Swafford
City Mgr.-Tom Hart
City Secy.-Cathy DiMaggio
P.A.-A. Bryce Davis
Atty.-Don Postell
C.P.-Steve Dye
F.C.-Robert Fite

GRAND SALINE 75140
Pop: 3136 (Van Zandt)
132 E. Frank St.
903 962-3122 - *Fax: 962-3363*
https://grandsaline.org
Mayor-Casey Jordan
Mayor PT-Jaron Cude
Coun.-Nick Haley
Coun.-Mary Jane Hollowell
Coun.-Brian Marshall
Coun.-Gary Milam
City Secy.-Alesia F. Mayne
City Admin.-Tully Davidson
Atty.-Joel Elliott
F.C.-Ethan Joslin

GRANDFALLS 79742
Pop: 360 (Ward)
P.O. Box 327
432 547-2331 - *Fax: 547-2039*
Mayor-Chuck Brandenburg
Ald.-Jim Cahill
Ald.-Jeannie Crawford
Ald.-Paula Francisco
Ald.-Andrea Porras
Ald.-Roberto Vasquez

City Secy.-Courtney Hunt
City Admin.-Geraldine Bookmiller
F.C.-J. D. Stocks

GRANDVIEW 76050
Pop: 1561 (Johnson)
P.O. Box 425
817 866-2699 - *Fax: 866-2961*
www.cityofgrandview.org
Mayor-Chuck McGowen
Coun.-Bat Clark
Coun.-Ray Johnson
Coun.-Zachary Stewart
Coun.-Roy Tackett
Coun.-Meghan York
City Admin.-David Henley
Atty.-Fritz Quast
C.P.-David Henley
F.C.-Jack Baker

GRANGER 76530
Pop: 1419 (Williamson)
P.O. Box 367
512 859-2755 - *Fax: 859-2871*
www.cityofgranger.org
Mayor-Trevor Cheatham
Mayor PT-Jill Cox
Ald.-Monica Schwitzer
Ald.-Monica Stojanik
Ald.-Hugh Tidwell
Ald.-Linda Vrabel
City Admin.-Andrew Bill
Atty.-Hejl & Schroeder, P.C.
C.P.-Robert Shelton
F.C.-James Cervenka

GRANITE SHOALS 78654
Pop: 5087 (Burnet)
2221 N. Phillips Ranch Rd.
830 598-2424 - *Fax: 598-6538*
www.graniteshoals.org
Mayor-Carl Brugger
Mayor PT-Jim Davant
Coun.-Tom Dillard
Coun.-Anita Hisey
Coun.-Todd Holland
Coun.-Shirley King
Coun.-Mark Morren
City Mgr.-Ken Nickel
Dir. Fin-Wendy Gholson
City Secy.-Elaine Simpson
Atty.-Bradley B. Young
C.P.-Gary Boshears
F.C.-Austin Stanphill

GRANJENO 78572
Pop: 298 (Hidalgo)
6603 S. FM 494
Mission, TX 78572
956 519-0032 - *Fax: 519-7662*
Mayor-Yvette Cabrera
Mayor PT-Miguel Cisneros
Comm.-Jennifer Alvarez
City Admin.-Martin Villarreal

GRAPELAND 75844
Pop: 1489 (Houston)
P.O. Box 567
936 687-2115 - *Fax: 687-2799*
Mayor-Balis E. Dailey
Mayor PT-Michael Chapman
Coun.-Justin Lumbreraz
Coun.-Velda Parker
Coun.-George R. Pierson
Coun.-Will Watson
City Secy.-Donna Deal
Atty.-Bill Pemberton
F.C.-Roger Dickey

GRAPEVINE 76051
Pop: 50514 (Dallas-
Tarrant-Denton)
P.O. Box 95104
Grapevine, TX 76099-5104
817 410-3104 - *Fax: 410-3002*
www.grapevinetexas.gov
Mayor-William D. Tate
Mayor PT-Darlene Freed
Coun.-Chris Coy
Coun.-Mike Lease
Coun.-Duff O'Dell
Coun.-Paul Slechta
Coun.-Sharron Spencer
City Mgr.-Bruno Rumbelow
City Secy.-Tara Brooks
P.A.-Bob Smeby, CPM
Atty.-John Boyle
C.P.-Eddie Salame
F.C.-Darrell Brown

GRAYS PRAIRIE
Pop: 337 (Kaufman)
P.O. Box 116
Scurry, TX 75158
972 452-8729
Mayor-Lorenzo Garza, Jr.
Comm. Karen Kolacek
Comm.-Keith Norman
City Secy.-Cathy Garza

GREENVILLE 75403
Pop: 26600 (Hunt)
P.O. Box 1049
903 457-3121 - *Fax: 457-0506*
www.ci.greenville.tx.us
Mayor-David Dreiling
Mayor PT-Jerry Ransom
Coun.-Cedric Dean
Coun.-James Evans
Coun.-Holly Gotcher
Coun.-Brent Money
Coun.-John W. Turner
City Mgr.-Vacant
Int. City Secy.-Carole Kuykendall
P.A.-Traci McDonald
Atty.-Daniel W. Ray
C.P.-Daniel Busken
F.C.-Jeremy Powell

GREGORY 78359
Pop: 2376 (San Patricio)
P.O. Box 297
361 643-6562 - *Fax: 643-1335*
Mayor-Celestino Zambrano
Ald.-Christopher Flores
Ald.-Alvaro Lopez
Ald.-Pablo Martinez
Ald.-Estanislao Parales
Ald.-Kristina Zambrano
City Admin.-Robert Meager
Atty.-Don Kubicek
C.P.-Vacant
F.C.-Dustin Amy

GREY FOREST 78023
Pop: 418 (Bexar)
18502 Scenic Loop Rd.
210 695-3261 - *Fax: 695-9640*
greyforest-tx.gov
Mayor-Ron Reinhard
Coun.-Susan Darst
Coun.-Holly Holleway
Coun.-Phillip A. Howard
Coun.-Jennifer Nottingham
Coun.-Lynn Tiner
City Secy.-Shannan Kinsley
Atty.-Adolph Jacobson
C.P.-David Bejar
F.C.-Shane Reddout

GROESBECK 76642
Pop: 4328 (Limestone)
402 W. Navasota
P.O. Box 227
254 729-3293 - *Fax: 729-3501*
www.cityofgroesbeck.com
Mayor-Ray O'Docharty
Mayor PT-Matthew Dawley
Dep. Mayor PT-Kim Harris
Ald.-Warren Anglin
Ald.-Tamikia Jackson
Ald.-Michael Thompson
City Secy.-Brenda Jackson
City Admin.-Chris Henson
Atty.-Charles Buenger
C.P.-Chris Henson
V.F.D.F.C.-Pat Samuels

GROOM 79039
Pop: 574 (Carson)
P.O. Box 217
806 248-7929
Mayor-Joe Homer
Ald.-Matt Fields
Ald.-Greg Hendricks
Ald.-Melissa Lambert
Ald.-Seth Ritter
Ald.-Nick Weinheimer
City Secy.-Sherry Rocha
Atty.-James T. "Jim" Shelton
F.C.-Gary Don Babcock

GROVES 77619
Pop: 16144 (Jefferson)
3947 Lincoln Avenue
409 962-4471 - *Fax: 963-3388*
www.cigrovestx.com/
Mayor-Brad P. Bailey
Coun.-Sidney Badon, Jr.
Coun.-Cross Coburn
Coun.-Kyle Hollier
Coun.-James Rasa
Coun.-Karen Theis
City Mgr.-D.E. Sosa
Clk.-Kimbra Lowery
Atty.-James Black
Mar.-Norman Reynolds Jr.
F.C.-Dale Jackson

GROVETON 75845
Pop: 1057 (Trinity)
P.O. Box 37
936 642-1122 - *Fax: 642-2211*
http://cityofgroveton.com/
Mayor-Byron Richards
Mayor PT-Ralph Bennett
Coun.-Stephen Casper
Coun.-Joe Don Kennedy
Coun.-Robert Smith
Coun.-Tommy Walton
City Secy.-Donna M. Dial
P.A.-Donna M. Dial
Atty.-Robert Flournoy
C.P.-John Raiford
F.C.-Glenn Hammond

GRUVER 79040
Pop: 1194 (Hansford)
P.O. Box 947
806 733-2424 - *Fax: 733-5038*
www.gruver.net
Mayor-Steven Davis
Comm.-John Holland
Comm.-Chad Logsdon
City Mgr.-Johnnie Williams
City Secy.-Lynn Vela
F.C.-Todd Williams

GUN BARREL CITY 75156
Pop: 5672 (Henderson)
1716 W. Main Street
903 887-1087 - *Fax: 887-6666*
www.gunbarrelcity.net
Mayor-Jim Braswell
Mayor PT-David Skains
Coun.-Anne Mullins
Coun.-Linda Rankin
Coun.-Rob Rea
Coun.-Ron Wyrick
City Mgr.-Bret Bauer
Tres.-Mickie Raney
City Secy.-Janet Dillard
Atty.-Blake E. Armstrong
C.P.-Vacant
F.C.-Joseph Lindaman

GUNTER 75058
Pop: 1498 (Grayson)
105 N. 4th
P. O. Box 349
903 433-5185 - *Fax: 433-8039*
ci.gunter.tx.us
Mayor-Mark Millar
Mayor PT-Larry Peters
Coun.-Jeannie Anderson
Coun.-Frederic Geisendorff
Coun.-Michael Lang
Coun.-Jason White
City Secy.-Dyann Clay
Atty.-Julie Fort
C.P.-Shawn Johnson
F.C.-David Gallagher

GUSTINE 76455
Pop: 457 (Comanche)
P.O. Box 145
325 667-7933 - *Fax: 667-7095*
Mayor-Ken Huey
Ald.-Kelley Adcock
Ald.-Betty Glover
Ald.-William Z. Kirkland
Ald.-Billy F. Knight
Ald.-Alan Luker
City Secy.-Judy Westfall

HACKBERRY
Pop: 900 (Denton)
119 Maxwell B-7
Frisco, TX 75034
972 292-3223 - *Fax: 292-2790*
http://cityofhackberry.net/
Mayor-Ronald Austin
Mayor PT-Beverly Hickerson
Ald.-Bryant Green
Ald.-Geraldine Schultz
Ald.-Debra Waring
Ald.-Vacant
City Admin.-Brenda Lewallen
Atty.-John Rapier

HALE CENTER 79041
Pop: 2252 (Hale)
806 839-2411 - *Fax: 839-9970*
www.cityofhalecenter.com
Mayor-W.H. Johnson
Mayor PT-Karen Boyce
Coun.-Richard Castillo
Coun.-Mario Martinez
Coun.-Janet Peoples
Coun.-Christine Reyna
City Mgr.-Dennis Burton
City Secy.-Patricia Isaguirre
Atty.-Lanny Voss
C.P.-Brandon Richardson
F.C.-Mike Watson

HALLETTSVILLE 77964
Pop: 2598 (Lavaca)
101 N. Main
361 798-3681 - *Fax: 798-5952*
www.cityofhallettsville.org
Mayor-Stephen Hunter
Mayor PT-Dean Madden
Coun.-Audrey Barrera
Coun.-Elmo Grant
Coun.-Cindy Renken
Coun.-Alice Jo Summers
City Admin/Secy-Jason Cozza
P.A.-Cheryl Sommer
Atty.-James A. Evans
C.P.-Vacant
F.M.-Alton Brown
Dir. P.W.-Otto Cervenka

HALLSBURG 76705
Pop: 530 (McLennan)
1115 Wilbanks Drive
254 875-2022 - *Fax: 875-2022*
Mayor-Mike Glockzin
Ald.-Mike Fitch
Ald.-Kathy McNair
Ald.-Larry Thompson
Ald.-Rick Wegwerth
Ald.-Mike Zipperlen
City Secy.-Phyllis Glockzin
Atty.-Charles Buenger
F.C.-Fred Kubitza

HALLSVILLE 75650
Pop: 3577 (Harrison)
P.O. Box 899
903 668-2313 - *Fax: 668-3959*
cityofhallsvilletx.com
Mayor-Jesse Casey
Mayor PT-Dan Herrington
Ald.-Mike Bailey
Ald.-Frankie Dunagan
Ald.-Charlie Hunt
Ald.-Brandon Sheffield
City Secy.-Kimberly Smith
Atty.-Jason Searcy
C.P.-Wesley Freeman

HALTOM CITY 76117
Pop: 42409 (Tarrant)
5024 Broadway Avenue
P.O. Box 14246
817 222-7700 - *Fax: 834-7237*
www.haltomcitytx.com
Mayor-David Averitt
Coun.-Ricky Brown
Coun.-Trae Fowler
Coun.-Walter Grow
Coun.-Jeannine Nunn
Coun.-An Truong
Coun.-Bob Watkins
City Mgr.-Keith Lane
Dir. Fin-Jennifer Fung

City Secy.-Art Camacho
Atty.-Wayne K. Olson
C.P.-Cody Phillips
F.C.-Perry Bynum

HAMILTON 76531
Pop: 3095 (Hamilton)
200 E. Main
254 386-8116 - *Fax: 386-3508*
www.hamiltontexas.com
Mayor-Michael R. Collett
Mayor PT-Beverly Gilstrap
Coun.-Henry DeLeon
Coun.-John Galindo
Coun.-Jack Kindle
Coun.-Ray Riley
City Secy.-Ryan Polster
City Admin.-Pete Kampfer
Atty.-Connie White
C.P.-Robert McGinnis
V.F.D.F.C.-Paul Gomez

HAMLIN 79520
Pop: 2124 (Fisher-Jones)
325 576-2711 - *Fax: 576-3426*
Mayor-EC Ice
Mayor PT-Gary Morgenson
Ald.-Bill Neely
Ald.-James Turner
Ald.-Billy Villanueva
Ald.-Kenneth Williams
City Secy.-Rose Soliz
City Admin.-Bobby Evans
Atty.-Isaac M. Castro
C.P.-Bobby Evans
F.C.-Gary Morgenson
Dir. P.S.-Andres Arce, Jr.

HAPPY 79042
Pop: 647 (Randall-Swisher)
P.O. Box 216
806 558-2121 - *Fax: 558-5009*
Mayor-Sara Tirey
Comm.-Julie Dempsey
Comm.-Casey McBroom
City Secy.-N. Scott Downing
Atty.-Stephen Rohde
C.P.-Joe Bill Dempsey
F.C.-Jerry Sims

HARDIN 77561
Pop: 903 (Liberty)
936 298-2117 - *Fax: 298-3732*
www.hardintexas.com
Mayor-Stephanie Blume
Mayor PT-Anthony Landry
Coun.-Christian Goodwin
Coun.-David Meadows
Coun.-Morris Nelms
Coun.-Art Reilly
City Secy.-Lana Webb
Atty.-Wesley N. Hinch

HARKER HEIGHTS 76548
Pop: 26700 (Bell)
305 Miller's Crossing
254 953-5600 - *Fax: 953-5614*
www.harkerheights.com
Mayor-Spencer H. Smith
Coun.-Steve Carpenter
Coun.-Jackeline Fountain
Coun.-Jody Nicholas
Coun.-John Reider
Coun.-Hal Schiffman
City Mgr.-David Mitchell
Dir. Fin-Alberta Barrett
Atty.-Burk Roberts
C.P.-Michael Gentry
F.C./EMC-Paul Sims

HARLINGEN
Pop: 64849 (Cameron)
118 E. Tyler
P.O. Box 2207
Harlingen, TX 78551-2207
956 216-5000 - *Fax: 216-5012*
www.myharlingen.us
Mayor-Chris Boswell
Comm.-Ruben de la Rosa
Comm.-Victor Leal
Comm.-Michael Mezmar
Comm.-Tudor G. Uhlhorn
Comm.-Richard Uribe
City Mgr. Dan Serna
City Secy.-Amanda C. Elizondo
Atty.-Ricardo Navarro
C.P.-Jeffery Addickes
F.C.-Roy Rubio Sr.

HART 79043
Pop: 1114 (Castro)
P.O. Box 329
806 938-2171 - *Fax: 938-2046*
Mayor-Eliazar Castillo
Mayor PT-Vickie Etheridge
Ald.-Ezekiel Barron
Ald.-Johnny Carrasco
Ald.-George Chapa, Jr.
Ald.-Mary Reyna
City Secy.-Monica Guzman
Atty.-Jack Edwards
F.C.-Paul Ramirez

HASKELL 79521
Pop: 3322 (Haskell)
P.O. Box 1003
940 864-2333 - *Fax: 864-3053*
haskelltexasusa.com/
Mayor-John Gannaway
Mayor PT-Jill Druesedow
Ald.-Johnny Fuentes
Ald.-Steve King
Ald.-JoNell Roberts
Ald.-Tell Stevens
City Mgr.-Janet Moeller
City Secy.-Cindy Walker
Atty.-Lois A. Rockefeller
C.P.-Scott Kennedy
F.C.-Casey Moeller

HASLET 76052
Pop: 1660 (Tarrant-Denton)
817 439-5931 - *Fax: 439-1606*
www.haslet.org
Mayor-Bob Golden
Mayor PT-Warren Robb
Coun.-Patricia Hilborn
Coun.-Mitch Hill
Coun.-Kathy Hopper
Coun.-Harold Williams
Dir. Fin-Marcy Lamb
City Secy.-Dianna Buchanan
City Admin.-Jim Quin
Atty.-Robert M. Allibon
F.C.-Kirt Mays
Dir. P.W.-David Rogers

HAWK COVE 75474
Pop: 483 (Hunt)
903 447-5330 - *Fax: 447-5655*
Mayor-Joseph Kelley
Ald.-Michelle Cagle
Ald.-Mark Collins
Ald.-Darren Evans
Ald.-Judy Fowler
Ald.-Kelly Reeves
City Secy.-Patricia Pendergraft
Atty.-Robert Brown
C.P.-Rhonda McKeehan

HAWKINS 75765
Pop: 1278 (Wood)
P.O. Box 329
903 769-2224 - *Fax: 769-2781*
Mayor-Howard Coquat
Mayor PT-Wayne Kirkpatrick
Ald.-Sherry Davis
Ald.-Clara Kay
Ald.-Norma Oglesby
Ald.-Debbie Rushing
City Secy.-Dona R. Jordan
Atty.-Alvin Flynn
C.P.-Ronald L. Voda
F.C.-Stephen Holmes

HAWLEY 79525
Pop: 634 (Jones)
P.O. Box 649
325 537-9528 - *Fax: 537-9735*
https://www.cityofhawley.com
Mayor-Billy Richardson
Ald.-Rhonda Bearden
Ald.-Jason Dokey
Ald.-Frank Garrard
Ald.-Gregg Riggins
Ald.-Janay William
City Secy.-Surenda Lord
Atty.-James M. Decker
C.P.-Brad Wilson

HAYS 78610
Pop: 217 (Hays)
520 County Lane
512 295-4792 - *Fax: 295-6072*
www.haystexas.com
Mayor-Harvey Davis
Mayor PT-Larry Odom
Ald.-Candace Blake
Ald.-Mark Lantrip
Ald.-Terry Strawn
Ald.-Ruth Wagner
City Secy.-Connie Gibbens
Atty.-Knight and Partners

HEARNE 77859
Pop: 4459 (Robertson)
209 Cedar St.
979 279-3461 - *Fax: 279-2431*
http://cityofhearne.us
Mayor-Ruben Gomez
Mayor PT-Emmett Aguirre
Coun.-Martha Ruiz Castilleja
Coun.-Rodrick Jackson
Coun.-Margaret Salvaggio
Coun.-Lashunda E. White
City Mgr.-John Naron
City Secy.-Linda Pecina
Atty.-Floyd Akers
C.P.-Thomas Williams
F.C.-Mark Hilton

HEATH 75032
Pop: 7490 (Rockwall-Kaufman)
200 Laurence Dr.
972 771-6228 - *Fax: 961-4932*
www.heathtx.com
Mayor-Brian Berry
Coun.-Joe Chamberlain
Coun.-Kelson R. Elam
Coun.-Rich Krause
Coun.-Frank New
Coun.-Paul Ruffo
Coun.-Brent Weaver
City Mgr.-Edward Thatcher
City Secy.-Norma Duncan
Atty.-Andy Messer
Dir. P.W.-David M. Herbert

HEBRON Pop: 426 (Denton)
1639 Parker Road
Carrollton, TX 75010-4718
972 394-0816 - *Fax: 394-1879*
Mayor-Kelly Clem
Comm.-Amy Carrington
Comm.-Jimmy Luman
City Secy.-Cheryl Sparks
Atty.-Robert L. Dillard, III

CITY SECTION

HEDLEY 79237
Pop: 329   (Donley)
109 Main St.
806 856-5241 - *Fax: 854-0018*
Mayor-Carrie Butler
Mayor PT-Ernie Copelin
Ald.-Lynn Kelsey
Ald.-Willie Lewis
Ald.-Tonya Metcalf
Ald.-Vacant
City Secy.-Ginger Burnett
F.C.-Neil Keotting

HEDWIG VILLAGE 77024
Pop: 2556   (Harris)
955 Piney Point Road
713 465-6009 - *Fax: 465-6807*
www.thecityofhedwigvillage.com
Mayor-Brian T. Muecke
Mayor PT-Matt Woodruff
Coun.-Carrol R. McGinnis
Coun.-Barry Putterman
Coun.-Shirley Rouse
Coun.-Robert "Bob" Wiener
City Admin.-Kelly Johnson
Atty.-Alan P. Petrov
C.P.-David Gott
F.C.-David Foster

HELOTES 78023
Pop: 8397   (Bexar)
P.O. Box 507
210 695-8877 - *Fax: 695-2123*
www.helotes-tx.gov/
Mayor-Thomas A. Schoolcraft
Mayor PT-Norbert "Bert" Buys
Coun.-Alex Blue
Coun.-Paul Friedrichs
Coun.-Cynthia Massey
Coun.-Edward Villanueva
City Secy.-Celina Perez
City Admin.-Rick Schroder
Atty.-Frank Garza
C.P.-Robert Hunley

HEMPHILL 75948
Pop: 1198   (Sabine)
P.O. Box 788
409 787-2251 - *Fax: 787-2259*
hemphill.govoffice2.com
Mayor-Robert Hamilton
Mayor PT-Lee M. Dutton, Jr.
Ald.-E. W. Ener, Jr.
Ald.-J. Herbert Rice
Ald.-Ray Tomlinson
Ald.-James A. Westbrook
City Mgr.-Donald P. Iles
City Secy.-Laure A. Morgan
Atty.-Robert G. Neal, Jr.
C.P.-Roger McBride
F.C.-Glen Chance
City Secy.-Laure A. Morgan

HEMPSTEAD 77445
Pop: 6700   (Waller)
1125 Austin St.
979 826-2486 - *Fax: 826-6703*
www.hempsteadcitytx.com
Mayor-Michael S. Wolfe, Sr.
Mayor PT-Patricia Chernosky
Coun.-Lonnie Garfield
Coun.-Katherine Ragston
Coun.-Ben Tibbs
Coun.-Charles Tompkins Jr.
City Secy.-Barbara Haffelfinger
Atty.-Arthur Lee "Art" Pertile, III
C.P.-David Hartley
F.C.-L. J. LeCamu
Dir. P.W.-Rooster Smith

HENDERSON 75652
Pop: 13712   (Rusk)
400 West Main St.
903 657-6551 - *Fax: 657-7327*
www.hendersontx.us
Mayor-Pat Brack
Coun.-Tommy Goode
Coun.-Steve Higginbotham
Coun.-Melissa Morton
Coun.-Thomas Ward
Coun.-Reginald Weatherton
City Mgr.-Tim Kelty
City Secy.-Stephanie Kimbrell
Atty.-Joe Shumate
Int. C.P.-Kenny Byrd
F.C.-Rusty Chote

HENRIETTA 76365
Pop: 3141   (Clay)
P.O. Box 409
940 538-4316 - *Fax: 538-4974*
www.cityofhenrietta.com
Mayor-Howard Raeke
Mayor PT-Robert Lavy
Ald.-Mark Hill
Ald.-Jim Lemons
Ald.-Mike Scott
City Secy.-Cathy Mills
City Admin.-Kelley Bloodworth
Atty.-Tracey Jennings
F.C.-Mike Roberts

HEREFORD 79045
Pop: 15370   (Deaf Smith)
P.O. Box 2277
806 363-7100 - *Fax: 363-7106*
http://www.hereford-tx.com
Mayor-Tom Simons
Mayor PT-Charlie Kerr
Comm.-Angie Alonzo
Comm.-Cathy Bunch
Comm.-Marcos Castro
Comm.-Linda Cumpton
Comm.-Jose A. Garza
City Mgr.-Rick L. Hanna
City Secy.-Suzanne Finch
Atty.-Audie Sciumbato

C.P.-Brent Harrison
F.C.-Robert Murray

HEWITT 76643
Pop: 13549   (McLennan)
200 Patriot Court
254 666-6171 - *Fax: 666-6014*
www.cityofhewitt.com
Mayor-Travis Bailey
Mayor PT-Ed Passalugo
Coun.-Steve Fortenberry
Coun.-Bill Fuller
Coun.-Charles "Alex" Snider
Coun.-James Vidrine
Coun.-Wilbert Wachtendorf
City Mgr.-Adam Miles
City Secy.-Lydia Lopez
Atty.-Charles Buenger
C.P.-James W Devlin
F.C.-Lance Bracco, BS-FS

HICKORY CREEK, TOWN OF
Pop: 3247   (Denton)
1075 Ronald Reagan Avenue
Hickory Creek, TX 75065-0453
940 497-2528 - *Fax: 497-3531*
www.hickorycreek-tx.gov
Mayor-Lynn C. Clark
Mayor PT-Paul Kenney
Coun.-Richard DuPree
Coun.-Tracee Elrod
Coun.-Chris Gordon
Coun.-Ian Theodore
Town Secy.-Kristi K. Rogers
Town Admin.-John M. Smith, Jr.
Atty.-Lance Vanzant
C.P.-Carey Dunn
Dir. P.W.-Jeffrey McSpedden

HICO 76457
Pop: 1379   (Hamilton)
P.O. Box 533
254 796-4620 - *Fax: 796-4512*
http://hico-tx.com
Mayor-Dale Tucker
Mayor PT-Roy Ward
Ald.-Charles Erick
Ald.-Donna McInnis
Ald.-Eddie Needham
Ald.-Pat Ross
City Secy.-Kari' Drueckhammer
City Admin.-Adam Niolet
Atty.-Connie White
F.C.-Brandon Keller

HIDALGO 78557
Pop: 13497   (Hidalgo)
704 East Ramon Ayala Drive
956 843-2286 - *Fax: 843-2317*
www.hidalgotexas.com
Mayor-Martin Cepeda
Mayor PT-Noe Reyes
Coun.-Sergio Coronado
Coun.-Rodolfo Franz
Coun.-Gustavo Sanchez
Coun.-Oziel Trevino

City Mgr.-Julian J. Gonzalez
City Secy.-Denise M. Elliff
P.A.-Virginio Gonzalez
Atty.-Ricardo Perez
C.P.-Rodolfo Espinoza
F.C.-Robert Rojas

HIDEAWAY 75771
Pop: 3184 (Smith)
101-B Hideaway Lane Central
214 384-2053
Mayor-Pat Bonds
Mayor PT-Ray Hutchens
Ald.-Billie Bynum
Ald.-Bernie Demers
Ald.-Jerry Godfrey
Ald.-James Hardage
City Secy.-Jan Morris
Atty.-Robert L. Dillard, III

HIGGINS 79046
Pop: 397 (Lipscomb)
201 N. Main Street
P.O. Box 56
806 852-3131 - *Fax: 852-2098*
Mayor-Clarissa Allen
Mayor PT-Paula Mingus
Ald.-Kevin Arnett
Ald.-Michael Callahan
Ald.-Roger Meller
Ald.-Carol Page
City Mgr.-Randy Immel
City Secy.-Carol Barton
Atty.-Matt Bartosiewiez
F.C.-Randy Immel

HIGHLAND HAVEN 78654
Pop: 431 (Burnet)
510A Highland Dr.
830 265-4366
Fax: 512 366-9721
highlandhaventx.com
Mayor-Olan Kelley
Mayor PT-Lonnie Ball
Ald.-Don Hagans
Ald.-Alvin Kahanek
Ald.-Terry Nuss
Ald.-Bill Passmore
City Secy.-Jeannie Gruetzner
Atty.-Barney Knight

HIGHLAND PARK, TOWN OF
Pop: 8564 (Dallas)
4700 Drexel Drive
Highland Park, TX 75205
214 521-4161
www.hptx.org
Mayor-Joel T. Williams III
Mayor PT-Bob Carter
Coun.-David Dowler
Coun.-Eric Gambrell
Coun.-Margo Goodwin
Coun.-John McKnight
Town Secy.-Gayle Kirby
Town Admin.-Bill Lindley

F.M.-Mike Miller
Dir. P.S.-Rick Pyle
Town Attorney-Matthew Boyle

HIGHLAND VILLAGE 75077
Pop: 15056 (Denton)
1000 Highland Village Rd.
972 317-5558 - *Fax: 317-0237*
www.highlandvillage.org
Mayor-Charlotte Wilcox
Mayor PT-Michelle Schwolert
Dep. Mayor PT-Barbara Fleming
Coun.-Frederick Bushe
Coun.-Daniel Jaworski
Coun.-Mike Lombardo
Coun.-John McGee
City Mgr.-Michael Leavitt
City Secy.-Angela Miller
Atty.-Kevin B. Laughlin
C.P.-Douglas Reim
F.C.-Brad Goudie

HILL COUNTRY VILLAGE
Pop: 985 (Bexar)
116 Aspen Lane
San Antonio, TX 78232
210 494-3671 - *Fax: 490-8645*
www.hcv.org
Mayor-Gabriel Durand-Hollis
Mayor PT-Carl A. Register
Coun.-Matthew T. Acock
Coun.-George F. "Rick" Evans
Coun.-Brett Rowe
Coun.-Bernard Swift
City Admin.-Frank Morales, Jr.
Atty.-Marc Schnall
C.P.-Frank Morales, Jr.

HILLCREST VILLAGE
Pop: 730 (Brazoria)
P.O. Box 1172
Alvin, TX 77512-1172
281 756-0577 - *Fax: 388-2460*
www.cityofhillcrestvillage.org
Mayor-Tom Wilson
Mayor PT-Terrell Franzen
Ald.-Nick Droege
Ald.-Larry Higgins
Ald.-Ramiro Mondragon
Ald.-Mark Patterson
Clk.-Rashelle Casas
Atty.-Paul A. Lamp
Mar.-Patrick Caloway

HILLSBORO 76645
Pop: 8456 (Hill)
P.O. Box 568
254 582-3271 - *Fax: 582-0112*
www.hillsborotx.org
Mayor-Edith Turner Omberg
Mayor PT-Andrew L. Smith
Coun.-Eric Fleming
Coun.-Scott Johnson
Coun.-Dana Robinson
Coun.-David Skelton
Coun.-Frances Zarate

City Mgr.-Frank Johnson
City Secy.-Karen S. Warren
Atty.-Lauralee Vallon
Dir. P.S.-Tony Cain

HILSHIRE VILLAGE
Pop: 746 (Harris)
8301 Westview Drive
Houston, TX 77055-6737
713 973-1779 - *Fax: 973-7793*
www.hilshirevillagetexas.com
Mayor-Russell Herron
Mayor PT-Paul Maddock
Ald.-Mike Gordy
Ald.-David Gunn
Ald.-Robert Swanson
Coun.-Robert Byrne
City Admin/Secy.-Susan Blevins
Atty.-Olson & Olson
C.P.-Loyd Evans
F.C.-David Foster

HITCHCOCK 77563
Pop: 7332 (Galveston)
409 986-5591
www.cityofhitchcock.org
Mayor-Vacant
Comm.-Fard K. Abdullah
Comm.-Monica Cantrell
Comm.-Mark Cook
Comm.-Randy Stricklind
City Secy.-Lucy Dieringer
Atty.-Ron Plackemeier
C.P.-John C. Hamm
F.C.-Charles "Butch" Edwards

HOLIDAY LAKES
Pop: 1107 (Brazoria)
Route 4, Box 747
Angleton, TX 77515
979 849-1136 - *Fax: 849-5225*
www.holidaylakestexas.com/
Mayor-Norman C. Schroeder
Mayor PT-Disa Schulze
Coun.-Alvin Justelien
Coun.-John Pastusek
Coun.-Johnny B. Phelps
Coun.-John "J.T." Trevino
City Secy.-Sunday Strickler
C.P.-Harold E. Douglas

HOLLAND 76534
Pop: 1121 (Bell)
102 W. Travis
P.O. Box 157
254 657-2460 - *Fax: 657-8025*
www.cityofholland.org/
Mayor-Stanley Koonsen
Coun.-Paul Bales
Coun.-A J Hill
Coun.-Johnny Kallus
Coun.-Lori Kinard
Coun.-Oscar Perez
City Secy.-Paula Kreinheder
Atty.-Barbara Boulware-Wells
C.P.-Shawn Newsom
F.C.-Coleman Benner

HOLLIDAY 76366
Pop: 1758   (Archer)
P.O. Box 508
940 586-1313 - *Fax: 586-1107*
www.hollidaytx.org
Mayor-Allen Moore
Mayor PT-Gary Bernal
Coun.-Bradley Lawson
Coun.-Randy Molina
Coun.-Kevin Nichols
Coun.-Don Wadsworth
City Secy.-Marie Balthrop
Atty.-James Rasmussen
C.P.-Joseph Chunn
Dir. P.W.-Danny Addison

HOLLYWOOD PARK, TOWN OF
Pop: 3062   (Bexar)
No. 2 Mecca Drive
Hollywood Park, TX 78232-2298
210 494-2023 - *Fax: 494-7859*
www.hollywoodpark-tx.gov
Mayor-Chris Fails
Coun.-Scott Bailey
Coun.-Michael Howe
Coun.-Chris Murphy
Coun.-Debbie Trueman
Coun.-Oscar Villarreal
Town Secy.-Janice Alamia
Atty.-Michael S. Brenan
C.P.-Shad Prichard
F.C.-John Butrico

HONDO 78861
Pop: 8803   (Medina)
1600 Avenue M
830 426-3378 - *Fax: 426-5189*
www.hondo-tx.org
Mayor-James W. Danner, Sr.
Coun.-Ann-Michelle Long
Coun.-John McAnelly
Coun.-Sammy Nooner
Coun.-Eric Torres
Coun.-John Villa
City Mgr.-Kim Davis
Int. City Secy.-Elsa T. Robles
Atty.-Frank J. Garza
C.P.-Brian Valenzuela
V.F.D.F.C.-Herman Schueling
Dir. P.W.-Albert Lara

HONEY GROVE 75446
Pop: 1668   (Fannin)
633 N. 6th St.
903 378-3033 - *Fax: 378-7890*
www.cityofhoneygrove.org
Mayor-Claude Caffee
Mayor PT-Leigh Dixon
Ald.-Terry Paul Cunningham
Ald.-Kenny Massey
Ald.-Brian Owen
Ald.-Thad Weems

City Secy.-Jaci Garner
Atty.-David Hamilton
C.P.-Joseph Matas
F.C.-Joey Rickman

HOOKS 75561
Pop: 3017   (Bowie)
P.O. Box 37
903 547-2261 - *Fax: 547-1107*
Mayor-Jimmy Cochran
Mayor PT-Mat C. Reiter
Coun.-Nick Graves
Coun.-Dwayne Little
Coun.-Vicki Murchison
Coun.-Sherry Phillips
City Secy.-Donald Buchanan
Atty.-J. Michael Brock
C.P.-Keith Schutte
F.C.-Donald "Buck" Buchanan

HORIZON CITY, TOWN OF 79928
Pop: 16735   (El Paso)
14999 Darrington Rd.
915 852-1046 - *Fax: 852-1005*
www.horizoncity.org
Mayor-Ruben Mendoza
Mayor PT-Johnny "Doc" Duran
Ald.-Samantha S. Corral
Ald.-Jerry Garcia
Ald.-Walter Miller
Ald.-Charlie Ortega
Ald.-Rafael Padilla
Ald.-Andres Renteria
Clk.-Karen Ellefson
Atty.-Elaine S. Hengen
C.P.-Michael McConnell Ph.D.
Dir. P.W.-Guillermo Reyes

HORSESHOE BAY 78657
Pop: 3418   (Llano)
830 598-8741 - *Fax: 598-8744*
www.horseshoe-bay-tx.gov
Mayor-Steve Jordan
Mayor PT-Craig Haydon
Coun.-Cynthia Clinesmith
Coun.-Kent Graham
Coun.-Jerry Gray
Coun.-Reagan Lambert
City Mgr.-Stan R. Farmer
Dir. Fin-Larry O. Anderson
City Secy.-Kerri Craig
C.P.-R.T. Wardlaw
F.C.-Joe Morris

HOUSTON 77251
Pop: 2157096   (Fort Bend-Harris-Montgomery)
P.O. Box 1562
832 393-1000 - *Fax: 393-1084*
www.houstontx.gov
Mayor-Sylvester Turner
Mayor PT-Ellen R. Cohen
Coun.-Dwight Boykins
Coun.-Jack Christie
Coun.-Karla Cisneros
Coun.-Jerry Davis
Coun.-Amanda Edwards
Coun.-Robert Gallegos
Coun.-Larry V. Green
Coun.-Mike Knox
Coun.-Michael Kubosh
Coun.-Mike Laster
Coun.-Steve Le
Coun.-Dave Martin
Coun.-David W. Robinson
Coun.-Brenda Stardig
Coun.-Greg Travis
City Secy.-Anna Russell
P.A.-Calvin Wells
Atty.-Ronald Lewis
C.P.-Art Acevedo
F.C.-Samuel Pena
Controller-Ronald C. Green

HOWARDWICK 79226
Pop: 402   (Donley)
245 Rick Husband Blvd.
806 874-2222 - *Fax: 874-9892*
Mayor-Vacant
Mayor PT-Eric Riddle
Ald.-Sam Grider
Ald.-James Miller
Ald.-Shelly Williamson
City Secy.-Tammy Jordan
Atty.-James T. "Jim" Shelton
F.C.-William Jordan

HOWE 75459
Pop: 2600   (Grayson)
P.O. Box 518
903 532-5571 - *Fax: 532-6320*
http://cityofhowe.org
Mayor-Jeffrey Stanley
Mayor PT-Sam Haigis
Coun.-Jonathan Coleman
Coun.-Darren Foster
Coun.-Bill French
Coun.-Georgia Richardson
City Secy.-Joy Stevens
City Admin.-Joe Shephard
Atty.-James Tidwell
C.P.-Vacant
F.C.-Robert Maniet

HUBBARD 76648
Pop: 1423 (Hill)
118 Magnolia
254 576-2576 - *Fax: 576-2421*
www.hubbardcity.com
Mayor-Mary Alderman
Ald.-Kenneth Baldwin
Ald.-Lynn Hammer
Ald.-Evlyn Hawthorne
Ald.-Audrey Johnson
Ald.-Ashley Peacock
City Mgr.-Jason Patrick
City Secy.-Amber Fuller
Atty.-Niel Pirkle
C.P.-Jason Patrick
F.C.-Danny Stuckley

HUDSON 75904
Pop: 4731 (Angelina)
201 Mt. Carmel Rd.
936 875-2358 - *Fax: 875-2317*
www.hudsontx.com
Mayor-Robert Smith
Ald.-Phil Adkison
Ald.-George Knight
Ald.-Joann Novak
Ald.-Juan R. Ramos
Ald.-Terry Taliaferro
City Secy.-Cheryl Everett
City Admin.-James M. Freeman
Atty.-Jimmy Cassels
C.P.-Jimmy Casper
F.C.-Marcial Foisie
F.M.-Joe Burton

HUDSON OAKS 76087
Pop: 1662 (Parker)
210 Hudson Oaks Drive
682 229-2400 - *Fax: 229-2429*
www.hudsonoaks.com/
Mayor-Pat Deen
Mayor PT-Tom Fitzpatrick
Coun.-Brian Lixey
Coun.-Tom Marquardt
Coun.-Marc Povero
Coun.-Marty Schrantz
City Secy.-Shelley Scazzero
City Admin.-Patrick Lawler
Atty.-Robert M. Allibon
C.P.-Michael Baldwin
F.C.-Pat English

HUGHES SPRINGS 75656
Pop: 1760 (Cass)
P.O. Box 805
903 639-7519 - *Fax: 639-3769*
www.hughesspringstxusa.com
Mayor-James C. Samples
Mayor PT-Lee Newsom
Ald.-Jeremy Ale-Ebrahim
Ald.-Kirk Bradley
Ald.-Genneter Ellison
Ald.-Ryan Watkins
City Mgr.-George K. Fite
Atty.-Rick Shelton
C.P.-Randy Kennedy
F.C.-Jay Cates

HUMBLE 77338
Pop: 15133 (Harris)
114 West Higgins
281 446-3061 - *Fax: 446-7843*
www.cityofhumble.com
Mayor-Merle Aaron, Sr.
Mayor PT-Allan Steagall
Coun.-Ray Calfee
Coun.-Andy Curry
Coun.-Norman Funderburk
Coun.-David Pierce
City Secy.-Jason Stuebe
Atty.-Scott Bounds
C.P.-Delbert Dawes
F.C.-Gary Outlaw

HUNTERS CREEK VILLAGE
Pop: 4374 (Harris)
#1 Hunters Creek Place
Houston, TX 77024
713 465-2150
www.cityofhunterscreek.com
Mayor-Jim Pappas
Coun.-Jay Carlton
Coun.-Chip Cowell
Coun.-Stuart Marks
Coun.-Fidel Sapien
Coun.-Ken Spalding
City Secy.-Crystal R. Dozier
City Admin.-Tom Fullen
Atty.-John Hightower
C.P.-Ray Schultz
F.C.-David Foster

HUNTINGTON 75949
Pop: 2118 (Angelina)
802 State Hwy. 69S
P.O. Box 349
936 422-4195 - *Fax: 876-3327*
www.cityofhuntington.org
Mayor-Frank Harris
Mayor PT-Ted Ivy
Coun.-Gary Litton
Coun.-Keith Mixon
Coun.-Todd Ricks
Coun.-Kim Smith
City Mgr.-Bill Stewart
City Secy/Finance-Julie Davis
Atty.-Jimmy Cassels
C.P.-Bobby Epperly
F.C.-Vacant
Dir. P.W.-Robby Roberts

HUNTSVILLE 77340
Pop: 38548 (Walker)
1212 Avenue M
936 291-5400 - *Fax: 291-5409*
www.huntsvilletx.gov
Mayor-Andy Brauninger
Coun.-Ronald Allen
Coun.-Paul Davidhizar
Coun.-Joe Emmett
Coun.-Tish Humphrey
Coun.-Don H. Johnson
Coun.-Lydia Montgomery

Coun.-Keith D. Olson
Coun.-Joe Rodriquez
Int. City Mgr.-Aron Kulhavy
City Secy.-Lee Woodward
P.A.-Billie Smith
Atty.-Leonard Schneider
C.P.-Kevin Lunsford
F.C.-Tom Grisham

HURST 76054
Pop: 38600 (Tarrant)
1505 Precinct Line Rd.
817 788-7000 - *Fax: 788-7054*
hursttx.gov
Mayor-Richard Ward
Mayor PT-Henry Wilson
Coun.-David G. Booe
Coun.-Trasa Robertson Cobern
Coun.-Larry Kitchens
Coun.-Bill McLendon
Coun.-Nancy Welton
City Mgr.-Clay Caruthers
City Secy.-Rita Frick
P.A.-Jerry Lewandowski
Atty.-John Boyle
C.P.-Steve Moore
F.C.-David Palla

HUTCHINS 75141
Pop: 5338 (Dallas)
972 225-6121 - *Fax: 225-5559*
www.cityofhutchins.org
Mayor-Mario Vasquez
Mayor PT-Raymond Elmore
Ald.-Brenda Campbell
Ald.-Freddie Chism
Ald.-Steve Nichols
Ald.-Demarcus Odom
City Secy.-Janis G. Daniels
Atty.-Joseph J. Gorfida, Jr.
C.P.-Steve Perry
F.C.-Stacey Hickson
Purch/Fin Dir-Tanangelia Beatty

HUTTO 78634
Pop: 21992 (Williamson)
401 W. Front Street
512 759-4033 - *Fax: 846-2653*
www.huttotx.gov
Mayor-Doug Gaul
Mayor PT-Tom Hines
Coun.-Terri Grimm
Coun.-Tim Jordan
Coun.-Nathan Killough
Coun.-Scott Rose
Coun.-Lucio Valdez
City Mgr.-Odis Jones
City Secy.-Seth Gipson
Atty.-Mike Shaunessy
C.P.-Byron Frankland
F.C.-Scott Kerwood

HUXLEY
Pop: 385 (Shelby)
11798 FM 2694
Shelbyville, TX 75973
936 368-2272 - *Fax: 368-2388*
Mayor-Larry Vaughn
Mayor PT-Prentice Hendricks
Ald.-Marsha K. Cooper
Ald.-Craig Hendricks
Ald.-Larry Matthews
Ald.-Bob Vandrovec
City Secy.-Debbie Runnels
Atty.-Tom Deaton
Mar.-Billie Jack Corbell

IDALOU 79329
Pop: 2250 (Lubbock)
301 S Main
806 892-2531 - *Fax: 892-3298*
idaloutx.com
Mayor-David Riley
Mayor PT-Troy Stegemoeller
Coun.-Albert Bravo
Coun.-Darrell Fuller
Coun.-Eric Geiser
Coun.-Joe T. Sisk
City Secy.-Renee Wilbanks
City Admin.-Suzette Williams
Atty.-Nolan Greak
C.P.-David Wilson
F.C.-Russ Perkins

IMPACT 79603
Pop: 35 (Taylor)
2102 Impact Dr.
325 675-5188
Mayor-Jack Sharp
Ald.-Trevor Dickson
Ald.-Angela Dickson
Ald.-Shirley Shank
Ald.-Woody Shank
Ald.-Georgette Sharp
Ald.-Diane Thompson
City Secy.-Georgette Sharp
Atty.-Isaac M. Castro

INDIAN LAKE, TOWN OF
Pop: 640 (Cameron)
62 S. Aztec Cove Dr.
Los Fresnos, TX 78566
956 233-4021 - *Fax: 233-5140*
townofindianlake.com
Mayor-Barbara Collum
Mayor PT-Mary Boss
Coun.-James Chambers
Coun.-Lucinda Gavito
Coun.-Doug Waltman
Coun.-Sheila Yore
Town Secy.-Amy S. Gonzales
Atty.-Ricardo Morado
C.P.-Paul Campbell

INDUSTRY 78944
Pop: 304 (Austin)
P.O. Box 190
979 357-2190 - *Fax: 357-2190*
www.industry-tx.com
Mayor-Mable Meyers
Mayor PT-Garth Griffith
Ald.-Justin Huebner
Ald.-Michael Rudloff
Ald.-Anthonetta Short
Ald.-Debra Taylor
City Secy.-Alicia Eckermann
Atty.-Carl E. Clover, Jr.

INGLESIDE 78362
Pop: 9447 (San Patricio)
361 776-2517 - *Fax: 775-0109*
www.inglesidetx.gov/
Mayor-Luis Lamas
Mayor PT-Oscar Adame
Coun.-Dennis Knippa
Coun.-Ronnie Parker
Coun.-John F. Schack
Coun.-Ben Tucker
Coun.-Bill Underbrink
City Mgr.-Melissa Byrne Vossmer
City Secy.-Kimberly Sampson
Atty.-Michael Morris
C.P.-Vacant
F.C.-Steven Loving

INGLESIDE ON THE BAY 78362
Pop: 615 (San Patricio)
P.O. Box 309
361 776-5451 - *Fax: 776-5283*
www.inglesideonthebay.org
Mayor-JoAnn Ehmann
Mayor PT-Susan Hewitt
Ald.-Larry Gillespie
Ald.-Tom Merrick
Ald.-Leona Robbins
Ald.-Cindy Young
City Secy.-Diane Hosea
Atty.-Hal George
F.C.-Howard Gillespie

INGRAM 78025
Pop: 1804 (Kerr)
230 Hwy 39
830 367-5115 - *Fax: 367-3175*
http://www.cityofingram.com
Mayor-Brandon Rowan
Mayor PT-John St.Clair
Ald.-Claud Jordan Jr.
Ald.-Jim Lopez
Ald.-Nelda Mitchell
Ald.-William "Bill" Warren
City Secy.-Stephanie Breckenridge
Atty.-Patrick O'Fiel
C.P.-Byron Griffin
F.C.-Ray Lynch

IOLA 77861
Pop: 401
P.O. Box 84
Fax: 936 394-2110
Mayor-Christina Stover
Mayor PT-Curtis Darby
Ald.-Blake Arrington
Ald.-Samantha Echols
Ald.-Becky Evans
Ald.-Mark Hooper
City Secy.-Vacant
Atty.-Matthew Bobo

IOWA COLONY
Pop: 1170 (Brazoria)
12003 County Rd. 65
Rosharon, TX 77583
281 369-2471 - *Fax: 369-0005*
www.cityofiowacolony.com
Mayor-Michael Holton
Ald.-Robin Bradbery
Ald.-Michael Byrum-Bratsen
Ald.-Susan Cottrell
Ald.-Kacy Smajstrla
Ald.-Chad Wilsey
City Secy.-Geraldine Kucera Frank
Atty.-Laurence E. Boyd
C.P.-Louis Hearn Jr.
V.F.D.F.C.-Steve Bynum

IOWA PARK 76367
Pop: 6355 (Wichita)
P.O. Box 190
940 592-2131 - *Fax: 592-4793*
www.iowapark.com
Mayor-Ray Schultz
Mayor PT-Sherrie Williams
Coun.-Deborah Dyer
Coun.-Tim Sheppard
Coun.-Lori Shierry
Coun.-Brad Wynn
City Mgr.-Jerry Flemming
Dir. Fin-Becky Ferguson
City Secy.-Janice Newman
Atty.-Tracey Jennings
C.P.-Robert Johnson
F.C.-Andy Payne

IRAAN 79744
Pop: 1229 (Pecos)
P.O. Box 457
432 639-2301 - *Fax: 639-2248*
Mayor-Kevin Allen
Mayor PT-Darren Brown
Ald.-Karina Browning
Ald.-Alan Harris
Ald.-Ken Hartman
Ald.-Leigh Scallorn
City Secy.-Laquetta Harris
Atty.-Chad Elkins
F.C.-Edward Evans

IREDELL 76649
Pop: 339 (Bosque)
P.O. Box 147
254 364-2436 - *Fax: 364-2435*
Mayor-Joel Wellborn
Mayor PT-Bradley Fletcher
Ald.-Sue Dickinson
Ald.-David Kettering
Ald.-Sallie Tomlinson
Ald.-Pam Van Winkle
City Secy.-Marilyn Berry
Atty.-Patricia Coy
F.C.-Bradley Fletcher

IRVING
Pop: 232786 (Dallas)
P.O. Box 152288
Irving, TX 75015-2288
972 721-2600 - *Fax: 721-2384*
www.cityofirving.org
Mayor-Rick Stopfer
Coun.-John Danish
Coun.-Brad LaMorgese
Coun.-Allan E. Meagher
Coun.-David Palmer
Coun.-Phil Riddle
Coun.-Kyle Taylor
Coun.-Oscar Ward
Coun.-Dennis Webb
City Mgr.-Chris Hillman
Dir. Fin-Jeff Litchfield
City Secy.-Shanae Jennings
Atty.-Kuruvilla Oommen
C.P.-Jeff Spivey
F.C.-Victor Conley

ITALY 76651
Pop: 1863 (Ellis)
972 483-7329 - *Fax: 483-2800*
www.ci.italy.tx.us/
Mayor-Jackie D. Cate
Mayor PT-Franky Jackson
Ald.-Carl Cash
Ald.-Troy Kowalsky
Ald.-Stevan Varner
Ald.-Gene Williams
C.P.-Michael Taylor
F.C.-Donald Chambers
Dir. P.W.-Shawn Holden

ITASCA 76055
Pop: 1644 (Hill)
134 N. Hill
254 687-2201 - *Fax: 687-9961*
www.biglittletowntexas.com
Mayor-James Bouldin
Mayor PT-Doug White
Ald.-Susie Davis
Ald.-Kathryn Guy
Ald.-Dora Hernandez
Ald.-Patty Miller
City Secy.-CinDee Garrett
City Admin.-George Bolling
Atty.-Stephanie W. Johnson

C.P.-Winson Brewer
F.C.-Cameron Offutt

IVANHOE 75979
Pop: 1425 (Tyler)
409 283-3299 - *Fax: 283-3299*
www.cityofivanhoetx.com
Mayor-Cathy Bennett
Coun.-David Herrington
Coun.-Tommy Morris
Coun.-Mark Peterson
Coun.-Rowland Priddy
Coun.-Chuck Vonderlin
City Secy.-C.D. Woodrome
Atty.-Timothy R. McDonough

JACINTO CITY 77029
Pop: 10553 (Harris)
1301Mercury Dr.
713 674-8424 - *Fax: 675-8525*
www.jacintocity-tx.gov
Mayor-Ana Diaz
Coun.-Carmela Garcia
Coun.-Mario Gonzales
Coun.-Allen Lee
Coun.-Jimmy "JJ" Rivas
Coun.-Gregg Robinson
City Mgr.-Lon D. Squryes
City Secy.-Joyce Raines
Atty.-Jim L. DeFoyd
C.P.-Joe Ayala
F.C.-Rebecca Meir

JACKSBORO 76458
Pop: 4511 (Jack)
112 W. Belknap
940 567-6321 - *Fax: 567-2590*
www.cityofjacksboro.com/
Mayor-Alton Morris
Ald.-Melanie Belcher
Ald.-Jeff Miller
Ald.-Joe Mitchell
Ald.-Jason Nash
Ald.-Gary Oliver
City Mgr.-Michael Smith
City Secy.-Brenda Tarpley
Atty.-David Spiller
F.C.-Jeremy Jennings

JACKSONVILLE 75766
Pop: 14544 (Cherokee)
P.O. Box 1390
903 586-3510 - *Fax: 586-4609*
http://www.jacksonville-texas.com
Mayor-Dick Stone
Coun.-Randy Gorham
Coun.-Rob Gowin
Coun.-Hubert Robinson
Coun.-Jeff Smith
City Mgr.-Mo Raissi
Dir. Fin-Roxanna Martin
City Secy.-Greg Lowe
Atty.-Joe Angle
C.P.-Andrew Hawkes
F.C.-Keith Fortner

JAMAICA BEACH 77554
Pop: 983 (Galveston)
409 737-1142 - *Fax: 737-5211*
www.ci.jamaicabeach.tx.us
Mayor-Steve Spicer
Mayor PT-Gene Montgomery
Ald.-Sherwood Green
Ald.-Rosemary Lindley
Ald.-David Welch
Coun.-Marci Kurtz
City Secy.-Lupe Rushing
City Admin.-John J. Brick
Atty.-Stephen G. Schulz
C.P.-Brad Heiman
F.C.-Kyle Baden

JARRELL 76537
Pop: 1020 (Williamson)
161 Town Center Blvd.
512 746-4593 - *Fax: 746-2052*
www.cityofjarrell.com
Mayor-Larry Bush
Mayor PT-Troy Bradshaw
Ald.-Rusty Bryson
Ald.-Ruth Dotson
Ald.-Dillon Ischy
Ald.-Roger Wenzel
City Mgr.-Mel Yantis
Atty.-Art Rodriguez
C.P.-Roger Thompson

JASPER 75951
Pop: 7590 (Jasper)
P.O. Box 610
409 384-4651 - *Fax: 384-3790*
www.jaspertx.org
Mayor-Randy Sayers
Mayor PT-Raymond Hopson
Coun.-Hazel Johnson
Coun.-Rashad Lewis
Coun.-Mitch McMillon
Coun.-Tommy Schofield
City Mgr.-Denise Kelley
City Secy.-Karen Pumphrey
P.A.-Kim Fowler
Atty.-Michael Ratcliff
C.P.-Gerald Hall
F.C.-Gary Dougharty

JAYTON 79528
Pop: 300 (Kent)
P.O. Box 46
806 237-3822 - *Fax: 237-2138*
Mayor-Charles Arthur
Mayor PT-Wyvonne Spray
Coun.-George Chisum
Coun.-Ray Hall
Coun.-Kyle Harrison
Coun.-Don Wayne Jones
City Secy.-Michele D. Fager
P.A.-Robert Lowery
Atty.-James M. Decker
F.C.-Nathan Brooks

JEFFERSON 75657
Pop: 2109   (Marion)
102 N. Polk
903 665-3922 - *Fax: 665-1002*
www.jeffersontexas.us/
Mayor-Carey B. Heaster Jr.
Ald.-James P. Finstrom
Ald.-Shawn Humphrey
Ald.-Kay McKinnon
Ald.-Victor Perot
Ald.-Roy Richie
Ald.-Richard Turner
City Mgr.-Kevin Huckabee
City Secy.-Doris Hines
Atty.-Michael Martin
C.P.-Gary Amburn

JERSEY VILLAGE 77040
Pop: 7620   (Harris)
16327 Lakeview Drive
713 466-2100 - *Fax: 466-2177*
www.jerseyvillage.info
Mayor-Justin Ray
Coun.-Greg Holden
Coun.-Andrew Mitcham
Coun.-Sheri Sheppard
Coun.-Bobby Warren
Coun.-Gary Wubbenhorst
City Mgr.-Austin Bleess
City Secy.-Lorri Coody
Atty.-Olson & Olson
C.P.-Eric Foerster
F.C.-Mark Bitz

JEWETT 75846
Pop: 1250   (Leon)
P.O. Box 189
903 626-4416 - *Fax: 626-4422*
Mayor-John Sitton
Mayor PT-Tammy Coulter
Ald.-Carmen Flores
Ald.-Jimmy Mills
Ald.-Bessie Woodall
City Secy.-Sharon D. Weiler
City Admin.-Virginia S.
  Sitton-Powell
Atty.-Charles Olson
C.P.-Sean O'Reilly
F.C.-Mike White

JOAQUIN 75954
Pop: 824   (Shelby)
P.O. Box 237
936 269-3021 - *Fax: 269-9622*
Mayor-Pat Gray
Mayor PT-Frankie Cooper
Coun.-Cathy Atkinson
Coun.-Mike Cummings
Coun.-Jessie Griffith
Coun.-Doug Shook
City Secy.-Amanda Willey
Atty.-Gary Rholes
F.C.-Perry Pugh

JOHNSON CITY 78636
Pop: 1673   (Blanco)
P.O. Box 369
830 868-7111 - *Fax: 868-7718*
www.johnsoncitytx.org
Mayor-Dawn Capra
Mayor PT-Rhonda Stell
Ald.-Shelton Coleman
Ald.-Rosie Danz
Ald.-Pat Dildine
Ald.-Gayla Jo Guthrie
Ald.-Mitchell Liesmann
City Secy.-Anthony Holland
Atty.-Bojorquez Law Firm
C.P.-Randy Holland
F.C.-Roy Burdett

JOLLY
Pop: 172   (Clay)
194 Milton St.
Wichita Falls, TX 76310
940 631-4472
Mayor-D. LeAnn Skinner
Comm.-Clint Lyde
Comm.-Brad Walker
City Secy.-Lisa Murphy
F.C.-Terry Pennington

JONES CREEK, VILLAGE OF
Pop: 2020   (Brazoria)
7207 S.F.A. Road
Jones Creek, TX 77541
979 233-2700 - *Fax: 233-3712*
www.villageofjonescreektexas.com
Mayor-Gordon Schlemmer
Mayor PT-Glenn Jordan
Ald.-Mike Chilcote
Ald.-Terry Jeffers
Ald.-AJ Jinkins
Ald.-Rocky Thomas
City Secy.-Kimberly Morris
Atty.-R.C. "Charlie" Stevenson
Mar.-William Tidwell

JONESTOWN 78645
Pop: 2117   (Travis)
P.O. Box 5023
512 267-3243 - *Fax: 267-4572*
www.jonestown.org
Mayor-Paul Johnson
Ald.-Joe Aaron
Ald.-Tom Buckle
Ald.-Dave Nelsen
Ald.-Desiree Peacock
Dir. Fin-Wendy Kelly
City Secy.-Rachel Austin
City Admin.-Ronald Wilde
Atty.-Akers and Akers
C.P.-Paul Taylor
Fire Chief ESD 1-Donnie Norman

JOSEPHINE 75164
Pop: 1246   (Collin-Hunt)
P.O. Box 99
972 843-8282 - *Fax: 843-8377*
www.cityofjosephinetx.com/
Mayor-Keith Koop
Mayor PT-Joe Holt
Ald.-Doug Ewing
Ald.-Katrina Heifner
Ald.-Cedric D. Powell
Ald.-Jason Turney
City Secy.-Patti Brooks
Atty.-Robert L. Dillard, III
F.C.-Cameron Brooks

JOSHUA 76058
Pop: 5910   (Johnson)
101 S. Main
817 558-7447 - *Fax: 641-7526*
www.cityofjoshuatx.us/
Mayor-Joe Hollarn
Coun.-Sharlotta Connally
Coun.-Brent Gibson
Coun.-Kim Henderson
Coun.-Mike Kidd
Coun.-Scott Kimble
Coun.-Jerry Moore
City Mgr.-Josh Jones
City Secy.-Lisa Dawn Cabrera
Atty.-Terrence Welch
C.P.-Shaun Short
F.C.-Wayne Baker

JOURDANTON 78026
Pop: 3871   (Atascosa)
1640 SH 97 E., Suite A
830 769-3589 - *Fax: 769-2598*
jourdantontexas.org
Mayor-Robert A. "Doc" Williams
Coun.-Johnetta "Johnnie" Goetzel
Coun.-Chester Gonzales
Coun.-Jack R. Harrison
Coun.-Raul A. "Roy" Morales
Coun.-Karen Pesek
City Mgr.-Kendall Schorsch
City Secy.-Debbie G. Molina
Atty.-Daniel Santee
C.P.-Eric Kaiser
F.C.-David Prasifka

JUNCTION 76849
Pop: 2615   (Kimble)
730 Main St.
325 446-2622 - *Fax: 446-3003*
www.cityofjunction.com
Mayor-Russell Hammonds
Ald.-Steve Couey
Ald.-Preston McDonald, Jr.
Ald.-Michael Miller
Ald.-Olan Raley
Ald.-Znobia Wootan
City Secy.-Garvene Adams
Atty.-Alan J. Bojorquez
C.P.-Rudy Supak
F.C.-Cecil M. Conner

JUSTIN 76247
Pop: 3450 (Denton)
415 N. College Ave.
P.O. Box 129
940 648-2541 - *Fax: 648-1191*
www.cityofjustin.com
Mayor-David Wilson
Mayor PT-Eric Priddy
Coun.-Teri Addington
Coun.-Lynn Crites
Coun.-Charlotte Moore
Coun.-Alan Woodall
City Mgr.-Cori Reaume
Dir. Fin-Josh Armstrong
City Secy.-Brittany Andrews
Atty.-Robert L. Dillard, III
Int. C.P.-Jack Ely
F.C.-Bill Mitchell

KARNES CITY 78118
Pop: 3042 (Karnes)
314 E. Calvert
830 780-3422 - *Fax: 780-2227*
Mayor-Leroy Skloss
Mayor PT-Jimmy D. Loya, Sr.
Coun.-Helen Hernandez
Coun.-Lillian Lyssy
Coun.-Raymond Robinson
Coun.-Sherry Sommer
City Mgr.-Vacant
City Secy.-Veronica Butler
Atty.-Frank J. Garza
C.P.-Roel E. Salas
F.C.-Charles K. Malik

KATY 77493
Pop: 14102 (Fort Bend-
Harris-Waller)
901 Avenue C, P.O. Box 617
Katy, TX 77492-0617
281 391-4800 - *Fax: 391-4937*
www.cityofkaty.com
Mayor-Chuck Brawner
Mayor PT-Durran C. Dowdle
Coun.-Ray Boothe
Coun.-J. Gary Jones
Coun.-Jimmy Mendez
Coun.-Steve Pierson
City Secy.-Melissa A. Bunch
City Admin.-Byron J. Hebert
Atty.-Arthur Lee "Art" Pertile, III
C.P.-William M. "Bill" Hastings
F.C.-Russell Wilson

KAUFMAN 75142
Pop: 7000 (Kaufman)
P.O. Box 1168
972 932-2216 - *Fax: 932-0307*
www.kaufmantx.org
Mayor-Jeff Jordan
Mayor PT-Patty Patterson
Coun.-Carole Aga
Coun.-Jeff Council
Coun.-Charles Gillenwater

Coun.-Matt Phillips
Coun.-Barry Ratcliffe
City Mgr.-Mike Slye
Dir. Fin-Mary Wennerstrom
City Secy.-Jo Ann Talbot
Atty.-David Dodd III
C.P.-Dana Whitaker
F.C.-Ronnie Davis

KEENE 76059
Pop: 6106 (Johnson)
100 N. Mockingbird
817 641-3336 - *Fax: 556-2060*
www.keenetx.com/
Mayor-James Chapline
Mayor PT-David Patterson
Coun.-Robert G. Cooper
Coun.-Donny Gore
Coun.-Cheryl Schram
Coun.-Vacant
Coun-Vacant
City Mgr.-Brian LaBorde
City Secy.-Holly Owens
Atty.-Robert Brown
C.P.-Emmitt Jackson
F.C.-Brad Fortune
F.M.-Ed Cheever
Dir. P.W.-Don Martin

KELLER 76244
Pop: 41090 (Tarrant)
P.O. Box 770
817 743-4000 - *Fax: 743-4190*
www.cityofkeller.com
Mayor-Pat McGrail
Coun.-Debbie Bryan
Coun.-Tag Green
Coun.-Armin Mizani
Coun.-Eric Schmidt
Coun.-Ed Speakmon
Coun.-Chris Whatley
City Mgr.-Mark Hafner
City Secy.-Kelly Ballard
Atty.-Stanton Lowry
C.P.-Michael Wilson
F.C.-David Jones

KEMAH 77565
Pop: 1773 (Galveston)
1401 State Hwy. 146
281 334-1611 - *Fax: 334-6583*
www.kemah-tx.gov
Mayor-Carl Joiner
Mayor PT-Teresa Vazquez-Evans
Coun.-Kyle Burks
Coun.-Robin Collins
Coun.-Matt Wiggins
Coun.-Wanda Zimmer
City Secy.-Melissa Chilcote
Atty.-Dick Gregg Jr.
Int. C.P.-Chris Reed
F.C.-Brent Hahn

KEMP 75143
Pop: 1154 (Kaufman)
P.O. Box 449
903 498-3191 - *Fax: 498-3209*
www.cityofkemp.org
Mayor-Laura Peace
Coun.-Leona Bounds
Coun.-Barry Lummus
Coun.-Alvin Miller
Coun.-Christi Neal
Coun.-Jackie Self
City Secy.-Allene Gilmore
City Admin.-Regina Kiser
Atty.-Terrence Welch
C.P.-Bradley Delaughter

KEMPNER 76539
Pop: 1089 (Lampasas)
P.O. Box 660
512 932-2180 - *Fax: 932-3124*
cityofkempner.org
Mayor-Carolyn Crane
Mayor PT-Robert McKinnon
Ald.-Bob Crane
Ald.-Clifton Morse
Ald.-David Richardson
Ald.-Melba Vandeveer
City Secy.-Lisa Campanella
Atty.-Barney Knight
C.P.-Forrest Spence
V.F.D.F.C.-Dan Hause

KENDLETON 77451
Pop: 380 (Fort Bend)
P.O. Box 809
979 532-8240 - *Fax: 282-2055*
www.kendletontx.net/
Mayor-Darryl Humphrey, Sr.
Mayor PT-Lester Aldridge
Coun.-Curtis Goodjoint
Coun.-Carolyn Jenkins
Coun.-Destiny Phllips
Coun.-Rachel White
City Secy.-Veronica Harris
Atty.-Martye M. Kendrick

KENEDY 78119
Pop: 3296 (Karnes)
303 W. Main St.
830 583-2230 - *Fax: 583-2063*
www.cityofkenedy.org
Mayor-Randy Garza
Mayor PT-Felipe Leal
Ald.-Alberto Baldarramos
Ald.-Brandon Briones
Ald.-Walter A. Chance
Ald.-Maggie Gonzales
City Mgr.-Barbara Najvar Shaw
City Secy.-Amanda M. Hines
Atty.-Daniel Santee
C.P.-Duane DuBose
F.C.-Juan M. Bryan

KENEFICK
Pop: 710 (Liberty)
3564 FM 1008
Dayton, TX 77535
936 258-2130 - *Fax: 258-2612*
Mayor-Martin Wells
Ald.-Stacey Brown
Ald.-Daniel Christopher
Ald.-Joel Fingleman
Ald.-Ronald Greer
Ald.-Austin McElroy
City Secy.-Marlene Clanton
Atty.-Timothy Kirwin

KENNARD 75847
Pop: 337 (Houston)
P.O. Box 115
936 655-2248 - *Fax: 655-2248*
Mayor-Jesse Stephens
Ald.-Bobby Calhoun
Ald.-Mary Ann Davis
Ald.-Donald Lamb, Sr.
Ald.-G.M. McClinton
Ald.-Michelle Rowe
City Secy.-Vacant
City Admin.-April Wright
Atty.-Bill Pemberton
F.C.-Don Parrish

KENNEDALE 76060
Pop: 7800 (Tarrant)
405 Municipal Drive
817 985-2100 - *Fax: 478-7169*
www.cityofkennedale.com
Mayor-Brian Johnson
Mayor PT-Kelly Turner
Coun.-Liz Carrington
Coun.-Rockie Gilley
Coun.-Jan Joplin
Coun.-Sandra Lee
City Mgr.-George Campbell
Dir. Fin-Brady Olsen
City Secy.-Leslie Galloway
Atty.-Wayne K. Olson
C.P.-Tommy Williams
F.C.-Mike McMurray
Dir. P.W.-Larry Ledbetter

KERENS 75144
Pop: 1573 (Navarro)
P.O. Box 160
903 396-2971 - *Fax: 396-7265*
www.ci.kerens.tx.us
Mayor-Jeffrey Saunders
Mayor PT-Brandon Blue
Ald.-Greg Allen
Ald.-Ann Fessenden
Ald.-Bryant Jennings
Ald.-Rick Neumayer
City Secy.-Cindy Scott
Atty.-Kerri Anderson Donica
C.P.-Bryan Miers
F.C.-Charles Bush

KERMIT 79745
Pop: 5708 (Winkler)
110 S. Tornillo
432 586-3460 - *Fax: 586-2220*
www.kermittexas.us
Mayor-Jerry L. Phillips
Mayor PT-Country Roark
Ald.-Norma Carrillo
Ald.-Richard Jackson
Ald.-Julio Pena
Ald.-Bobby Slaughter
City Mgr.-Gloria Saenz
Dir. Fin-Frankie Davis
City Secy.-Diana Franco
Atty.-Tommy Duckworth Jr.
C.P.-Jamie Dutton
F.C.-Jerry Wright

KERRVILLE 78028
Pop: 22347 (Kerr)
701 Main St.
830 257-8000 - *Fax: 792-3850*
www.kerrville.org
Mayor-Bonnie White
Coun.-George Baroody
Coun.-C. Warren Ferguson
Coun.-Mary Ellen Summerlin
Coun.-Vincent C. Voelkel
City Mgr.-Mark L. McDaniel
Dir. Fin-Sandra Yarbrough
City Secy.-Brenda Glenn Craig
Atty.-Mike Hayes
C.P.-David Knight
F.C.-Dannie Smith

KILGORE 75662
Pop: 12975 (Gregg-Rusk)
815 N. Kilgore St.
903 984-5081 - *Fax: 988-4132*
www.cityofkilgore.com/
Mayor-Ronnie Spradlin
Mayor PT-Harvey McClendon
Comm.-Neil Barr
Comm.-Victor Boyd
Comm.-Merlyn Holmes
City Mgr.-Josh Selleck
Clk.-Deborah Dane
Atty.-Robert G. Schleier
C.P.-Todd Hunter

KILLEEN 76540
Pop: 137147 (Bell)
101 N. College
P.O. Box 1329
254 501-7600 - *Fax: 634-8399*
www.killeentexas.gov
Mayor-Jose Segarra
Mayor PT-Jim Kilpatrick
Coun.-Shirley A. Fleming
Coun.-Steve Harris
Coun.-Gregory Johnson
Coun.-Debbie Nash-King
Coun.-Jonathan Okray

Coun.-Juan Rivera
City Mgr.-Ron Olson
Dir. Fin-Jonathan Locke
City Secy.-Dianna Barker
Atty.-Kathryn Davis
C.P.-Charles Kimble
F.M.-James Chism

KINGSVILLE 78364
Pop: 26213 (Kleberg)
P.O. Box 1458
361 592-5235 - *Fax: 595-8035*
www.cityofkingsville.com
Mayor-Sam Fugate
Mayor PT-Edna Lopez
Comm.-Al Garcia
Comm.-Arturo Pecos
Comm.-Noel Pena
City Mgr.-Jesus A. Garza
City Secy.-Mary Valenzuela
P.A.-David Mason
Atty.-Courtney Alvarez
C.P.-Ricardo Torres
F.C.-Joey Reed

KIRBY 78219
Pop: 8204 (Bexar)
112 Bauman St.
210 661-3198 - *Fax: 661-4525*
www.kirbytx.org
Mayor-Lisa B. Pierce
Mayor PT-Jerry Lehman
Coun.-Barbara C. Bowie
Coun.-Mike Grant
Coun.-Kimberly McGehee-Aldrich
Coun.-John W. Pierce
Coun.-Debra Wilson
City Mgr.-Monique L. Vernon
City Secy.-Patty Cox
Atty.-Marc Schnall
C.P.-Kevin Bois
F.C.-Carlos M. Alfaro

KIRBYVILLE 75956
Pop: 2142 (Jasper)
107 S. Elizabeth
409 423-6191 - *Fax: 423-3664*
Mayor-Frank George
Mayor PT-Laura Palmer Adams
Coun.-Vondol Bailey
Coun.-Andra Grant
Coun.-Wayne Love
Coun.-Preston Williams
City Secy.-Tonja R. Stockman
Atty.-Germer & Gertz
C.P.-Robert Paul Brister
F.C.-Greg Ellis

KIRVIN 75848
Pop: 129 (Freestone)
P.O. Box 161
903 599-2933
Mayor-Vacant
Coun.-Vacant

KNOLLWOOD
Pop: 400 (Grayson)
100 Collins Dr.
Sherman, TX 75092-3908
903 893-5632 - *Fax: 893-6332*
Mayor-Richard Roelke
Mayor PT-Mark Nagel
Ald.-Rosalie Dunn
Ald.-Lura Moitozo
Ald.-Samantha Null Roelke
Ald.-Debbie Smith
City Secy.-Janis Gaines

KNOX CITY 79529
Pop: 1130 (Knox)
902 E. Main St.
940 658-3313 - *Fax: 658-5135*
Mayor-Nickie Ivie Eckman
Coun.-JR Hodges
Coun.-Fred Ledesma
Coun.-Michael McGaughey
Coun.-Greg Oliver
Coun.-Gary Schnable
City Secy.-Betty Johnston
City Admin.-Sam Watson
Atty. Lois A. Rockefeller
C.P.-Richard Candelaria
F.C.-Bill Stewart
Dir. P.W.-Joe Rodriquez

KOSSE 76653
Pop: 464 (Limestone)
P.O Box 116
254 375-2212 - *Fax: 375-2331*
www.kossetexas.com/
Mayor-Jarrod Eno
Mayor PT-Ronnie Funderburk
Ald.-Harley Leazer
Ald.-L.B. Perry
Ald.-Trish Roy
Ald.-Ricky Wright
City Secy.-Christina Lockhart
Atty.-Mike Dixon
F.C.-Jimmy O'Neal

KOUNTZE 77625
Pop: 2123 (Hardin)
P.O. Box 188
409 246-3463 - *Fax: 246-2319*
Mayor-Fred E. Williams
Mayor PT-Elaine Allums
Ald.-Mary Adams
Ald.-Natosha Brown
Ald.-Glenn E. Matthews
Ald.-Lester Williams
City Mgr.-Roderick Hutto

City Secy.-Kim Haynes
Atty.-Guy N. Goodson
C.P.-James B. Slaughter
F.C.-Jimmy Stoeppleman
Dir. P.S.-Tim Drake

KRESS 79052
Pop: 715 (Swisher)
P.O. Box 236
806 684-2525 - *Fax: 684-2308*
Mayor-Amparo Becerra
Mayor PT-Edward Vuittonet
Ald.-Deelare Buske
Ald.-Galen Owen
Ald.-Dina Trevino
Ald.-Michelle Wheeler
City Secy.-Heidi Tiffin
Atty.-Tom Boyd
C.P.-Kenny Hughes
F.C.-Ben Rojas

KRUGERVILLE 76227
Pop: 1880 (Denton)
5097 Highway 377, S.
940 365-5833 - *Fax: 365-5834*
www.krugerville.org
Mayor-Jeff Parrent
Mayor PT-Kristen Kromer
Coun.-Thurman Bridges
Coun.-Eric Gildersleeve
Coun.-John Nipe
Coun.-George Wilthers
City Secy.-Sandy Frantz
Atty.-Robert Brown
C.P.-James Edland

KRUM 76249
Pop: 4157 (Denton)
940 482-3491 - *Fax: 482-3020*
www.ci.krum.tx.us
Mayor-Ronald G. Harris, Jr.
Coun.-Justin Diviney
Coun.-Rhonda Harrison
Coun.-Toby L. Lawrence
Coun.-Austin Petersen
Coun.-Mike Strand
City Secy.-Andrea Dzioba
Atty.-Lance Vanzant
C.P.-Terry Hargis
F.C.-Ken Swindle
Dir. P.W.-Devon Kennedy

KURTEN 77862
Pop: 398 (Brazos)
P.O. Box 101
979 255-0410
www.kurtentexas.com
Mayor-Ronnie Vitulli
Mayor PT-Melanie Estes
Ald.-Nancy Hranicky
Ald.-Gordon Klintworth
Ald.-Phillip Mundine
Ald.-Mel Sergeant
City Secy.-Joy Ramsey
Atty.-Charles Olsen

KYLE 78640
Pop: 37700 (Hays)
P.O. Box 40
512 262-1010 - *Fax: 262-3987*
www.cityofkyle.com
Mayor-Travis Mitchell
Mayor PT-Damon Fogley
Coun.-Shane Arabie
Coun.-Dex Ellison
Coun.-Tracy Scheel
Coun.-Daphne Tenorio
Coun.-Alex Villalobos
City Mgr.-Scott Sellers
City Secy.-Jennifer Vetrano
C.P.-Jeff Barnett
F.C.-Kyle Taylor

LA COSTE 78039
Pop: 1243 (Medina)
P.O. Box 112
830 985-9494 - *Fax: 762-9431*
Mayor-Andy Keller
Ald.-Dale Ames
Ald.-Karl Lutz
Ald.-Bonnie Mangold
Ald.-Kimberly Stiteler
Ald.-Wade Tschirhart
City Admin.-George Salzman
Atty.-Anna L. Whorton
C.P.-Richard Gonzales
F.C.-Ernest Christilles

LA FERIA 78559
Pop: 7302 (Cameron)
115 E. Commercial Ave.
956 797-2261 - *Fax: 797-1898*
www.cityoflaferia.com
Mayor-Olga Maldonado
Mayor PT-Esmeralda Lozano
Comm.-Donato Garcia
Comm. Julian Guevara Jr.
Comm.-Eric Hoff
Comm.-Jesse Zuniga
City Mgr.-Jaime Sandoval
Dir. Fin-Frank Rios
City Secy.-Amanda Morales
Atty.-Rebecca Hayward
C.P.-Cesar Rene Diaz
V.F.D.F.C.-David Phinney
Dir. P.W.-Alfonso Rodriguez

CITY SECTION

LA GRANGE 78945
Pop: 4641   (Fayette)
155 E. Colorado St.
979 968-5805 - *Fax: 968-5743*
www.cityoflg.com
Mayor-Janet Moerbe
Mayor PT-John Cernosek
Coun.-Deborah Bradley
Coun.-Bonnie Busch
Coun.-John Eilert
Coun.-Pat Janca
Coun.-Ken Taylor
Coun.-Kathy Weishuhn
Coun.-Violet Zbranek
City Mgr.-Shawn Raborn
Dir. Fin-Brett Wolff
City Secy.-Lisa Oltmann
P.A.-Gary Skalka
Atty.-Angela Beck
C.P.-David Gilbreath
F.C.-Frank J. Menefee, Jr.

LA GRULLA 78548
Pop: 1622   (Starr)
P.O. Box 197
956 487-3341 - *Fax: 487-5733*
Mayor-Pedro A. Flores
Mayor PT-Laura P. Solis
Comm.-Mercado Banda
City Secy.-Amy Bush
Atty.-Rene Montalvo
C.P.-Ricardo Trevino

LA JOYA 78560
Pop: 3985   (Hidalgo)
P.O. Drawer H
956 581-7002 - *Fax: 580-7000*
Mayor-Jose A. "Fito" Salinas
Mayor PT-Mary Salinas
Comm.-Anna Lisa Ruiz
Comm.-Victorio Salinas
Comm.-Maria E. Salinas
City Secy.-Julianita Sabala
City Admin.-Mike Alaniz
Atty.-Roberto Jackson Jr.
C.P.-Vacant
F.C.-Leroy Salinas
Dir. P.W.-Elizandro de la Rosa

LA MARQUE 77568
Pop: 14509   (Galveston)
1111 Bayou
409 938-9200 - *Fax: 935-0401*
www.cityoflamarque.org
Mayor-Bobby Hocking
Mayor PT-Keith Bell
Coun.-Chris Lane
Coun.-Casey McAuliffe
Coun.-Robert Michetich
City Mgr.-Carol Jo Buttler
Clk.-Robin Eldridge
Atty.-Ellis J. Ortego
C.P.-Kirk Jackson
F.C.-Gerald Grimm

LA PORTE 77571
Pop: 33880   (Harris)
604 W. Fairmont Pkwy.
281 470-5020 - *Fax: 842-3701*
www.ci.la-porte.tx.us
Mayor-Louis R. Rigby
Coun.-Danny Earp
Coun.-Chuck Engelken
Coun.-Dottie Kaminski
Coun.-Daryl Leonard
Coun.-Jay Martin
Coun.-Kristin Martin
Coun.-Nancy Ojeda
Coun.-John Zemanek
City Mgr.-Corby Alexander
City Secy.-Patrice Fogarty
P.A.-Cherell Daeumer
Atty.-Knox W. and Clark T. Askins
C.P.-Kenith Adcox
F.C.-Mike Boaze

LA VERNIA 78121
Pop: 1034   (Wilson)
102 E. Chihuahua
P.O. Box 225
830 779-4541 - *Fax: 253-1198*
www.lavernia-tx.gov
Mayor-Robert Gregory
Mayor PT-Harold Schott
Ald.-Eloi Cormier
Ald.-Mark Doege
Ald.-Jay Hennette
Ald.-Martin Poore
City Secy.-Brittani Porter
City Admin.-Yvonne Griffin
Atty.-Charles E. "Charlie" Zech
C.P.-Bruce W. Ritchey
V.F.D.F.C.-Jason Scheel

LA VILLA 78562
Pop: 1957   (Hidalgo)
916 S. Mike Chapa
P.O. Box 60
956 262-2122 - *Fax: 262-2516*
Mayor-Alma Moron
Mayor PT-Joe Contreras
Ald.-Manuel Hinojosa
Ald.-Mario Lopez
Ald.-Jorge Lopez Jr.
Ald.-David Palomin Sr.
City Secy.-Lupita Suarez
Atty.-Robert J. Salinas
C.P.-Victor Garcia
F.C.-Dino Perez

LA WARD 77970
Pop: 213   (Jackson)
P.O. Box 178
361 872-2362
Mayor-Richard Koch
Ald.-Mary Gutierres
Ald.-Cleo Sanchez
Ald.-Mike Williams
Ald.-Chris Williams
City Secy.-Phyllis Williams
Atty.-Anne Marie Odefey

LACY LAKEVIEW 76705
Pop: 6489   (McLennan)
254 799-2458 - *Fax: 799-6265*
www.lacylakeview.org
Mayor-Calvin Hodde
Mayor PT-Sharon Clark
Coun.-Patrick Bell
Coun.-Bruce Bundrant
Coun.-Amy Hall
Coun.-Jerry Hall
Coun.-Barbara Seitz
City Mgr.-Keith Bond
Dir. Fin-Betty Jennings
City Secy.-Michelle Hicks
Atty.-David Deaconson
C.P.-John Truehitt
F.C.-Patty Byars-Faulkner
Dir. P.W.-Keith Bond

LADONIA 75449
Pop: 612   (Fannin)
P.O. Box 5
903 367-7011 - *Fax: 367-7339*
www.cityofladonia.com
Mayor-Discha Threlkeld
Mayor PT-Todd Akers
Ald.-Jan Cooper
Ald.-Dana Cuba
Ald.-Patricia Harrod
Ald.-Gary Nichols, Sr.
City Secy.-Debbie Nichols
Atty.-James Tidwell
C.P.-Vacant
F.C.-Kyle Stark

LAGO VISTA 78645
Pop: 6450   (Travis)
P.O. Box 4727
512 267-1155 - *Fax: 267-7070*
www.lagovistatexas.org
Mayor-Ed Tidwell
Coun.-Suzanne Bland
Coun.-Arch Davila
Coun.-Ron Smith
Coun.-Kevin Sullivan
Coun.-Dick Weatherly
Coun.-David Williams
City Mgr.-Joshua Ray
City Secy.-Sandra Barton
Atty.-Barney Knight
C.P.-Danny Smith

LAGUNA VISTA 78578
Pop: 3117   (Cameron)
122 Fernandez
956 943-1793 - *Fax: 943-3111*
www.lvtexas.us
Mayor-Susie Houston
Mayor PT-Mike Carter
Coun.-Frank Davalos
Coun.-Rolando Gonzalez
Coun.-Johvonne Howard
Coun.-Gary Meschi
Coun.-Nadine Smith
City Mgr.-Rolando Vela
City Secy.-Alma Deckard
Atty.-Ricardo Morado
C.P.-Tony David
F.C.-Marcus Smith

LAKE BRIDGEPORT 76426
Pop: 340   (Wise)
301 S. Main St.
940 683-2700 - *Fax: 683-2700*
Mayor-Maudie Smith
Mayor PT-Sherry Pewitt
Coun.-Olivia Casillas
Coun.-Amy Conley
Coun.-Ramon Galvan
Coun.-Manley Gregory
City Secy.-Wanda Vick
F.C.-Willie Garrett

LAKE CITY 78368
Pop: 509   (San Patricio)
P.O. Box 177
361 547-3868
Mayor-Dennis Veit
Mayor PT-Joyce Gauntt
Ald.-Janet Dickerson
Ald.-Douglas Gauntt
Ald.-Jake Hoskins
Ald.-Brad Seachord
Tres.-Mary Lee Laurel
City Secy.-Vacant
C.P.-Jim Long

LAKE DALLAS 75065
Pop: 7240   (Denton)
212 Main Street
940 497-2226 - *Fax: 497-4485*
www.lakedallas.com
Mayor-Michael Barnhart
Coun.-Kathy Brownlee
Coun.-Cheryl McClain
Coun.-Andi Nolan
Coun.-Charlie Price
Coun.-Megan Ray
City Mgr.-John Cabrales
City Secy.-Codi Delcambre
Atty.-Kevin B. Laughlin
C.P.-Daniel Carolla
F.C.-Curtis Burt

LAKE JACKSON 77566
Pop: 27000   (Brazoria)
25 Oak Drive
979 415-2500 - *Fax: 297-8823*
www.lakejackson-tx.gov
Mayor-Joe Rinehart
Mayor PT-Gerald Roznovsky
Coun.-Matthew Broaddus
Coun.-Will Brooks
Coun.-Ralph "Buster" Buell III
Coun.-Timothy J. Scott
City Mgr.-William P. Yenne
City Secy.-Alice A. Rodgers
Atty.-Sherri Russell
C.P.-Rick Park
F.C.-Danny Kang

LAKE TANGLEWOOD
Pop: 796   (Randall)
100 North Shore
Amarillo, TX 79118
806 622-8711 - *Fax: 367-6240*
Mayor-Don Carver
Mayor PT-D.J. Powers
Ald.-James Brown
Ald.-Jim Rogers
Ald.-Charla Rose
Ald.-John Teague
City Secy.-Erin Sprague
Atty.-Angelique Weaver
C.P.-Charlie Johnson
F.C.-Robert Hulsey

LAKE WORTH 76135
Pop: 4584   (Tarrant)
3805 Adam Grubb
817 237-1211 - *Fax: 237-1333*
www.lakeworthtx.org
Mayor-Walter Bowen
Mayor PT-Geoffrey White
Coun.-Gene Ferguson
Coun.-Pat Hill
Coun.-Clint Dewayne Narmore
Coun.-Ronny Parsley
Coun.-Jim Smith
Coun.-Gary Stuard
City Mgr.-Stacey Almond
City Secy.-Monica Solko
Atty.-Drew Larkin
Int. C.P.-Jimmy Womack
F.C.-Mike Christenson

LAKEPORT
Pop: 974   (Gregg)
207 Milam Road
Longview, TX 75603
903 643-2562 - *Fax: 643-9187*
Mayor-Johnny Sammons
Mayor PT-Del Knox
Ald.-Anderson Jones Jr.
Ald.-Charles Newhouse
Ald.-Glen Nobles
Ald.-Ardis Wright
City Secy.-Darlene Shelton
Atty.-Darryl Atkinson
C.P.-Bobby Linder, Jr.

LAKESIDE
Pop: 337   (San Patricio)
P.O. Box 787
Mathis, TX 78368-0787
361 688-7376
Mayor-Jeff Mason
Mayor PT-Dayna B. "Bert" Hill
Ald.-Pat Bishop
Ald.-Christina Coen
Ald.-Linda Kunze
Ald.-Angela Lynn Tibbs
City Secy.-Bonnie Taylor

LAKESIDE CITY
Pop: 997   (Archer)
P.O. Box 4287
Wichita Falls, TX 76308
940 691-6603 - *Fax: 691-6601*
www.lakesidecitytx.org
Mayor-Cory Glassburn
Mayor PT-Eric Stevens
Ald.-Michael Chapman
Ald.-John Pezzans
Ald.-Eric Simpson
Ald.-Donald Stevens
City Secy.-Amy L. Anderson
City Admin.-Sam Bownds
Atty.-Michael Guevara
V.F.D.F.C.-James Sons

LAKESIDE, TOWN OF 76108
Pop: 1630   (Tarrant)
9830 Confederate Park Road
Lakeside, TX 76108
817 237-1234 - *Fax: 238-9187*
www.lakesidetexas.us
Mayor-Patrick Jacob
Mayor PT-Kim Ware
Coun.-Katherine Livingston
Coun.-Bill Mohr
Coun.-Don Pitts
Coun.-Amy Robinson
Town Secy/Admin-Norman
  Craven
Atty.-Kenneth E. East P.C.
C.P.-Lee Pitts

LAKEVIEW 79239
Pop: 107   (Hall)
P.O. Box 60
806 867-2111 - *Fax: 867-2111*
Mayor-Kelly Clark
Mayor PT-Starla Phillips
Coun.-Ava Dell Clark
Coun.-Bob Foard
Coun.-Georgia Watson
City Secy.-Ann Byars
Atty.-John M. Deaver, II

CITY SECTION

LAKEWAY 78734
Pop: 12459 (Travis)
1102 Lohmans Crossing
512 314-7500 - *Fax: 314-7501*
www.cityoflakeway.com
Mayor-Joe Bain
Mayor PT-Ron Massa
Coun.-Bridge Bertram
Coun.-Dwight Haley
Coun.-Jean Hennagin
Coun.-Jim Powell
Coun.-Keith Trecker
City Mgr.-Steve Jones
City Secy.-JoAnn Touchstone
Atty.-Alan J. Bojorquez
C.P.-Todd Radford

LAKEWOOD VILLAGE,
TOWN OF 75068
Pop: 812 (Denton)
100 Highridge Dr.
Lakewood Village, TX 75068
972 294-5555 - *Fax: 292-0812*
www.lakewoodvillagetx.us
Mayor-Dr. Mark E. Vargus
Mayor PT-Ed Reed
Coun.-Clint Bushong
Coun.-Gary Newsome
Coun.-Elizabeth Shields
Coun.-Dan Tantalo
Town Secy/Admin-Linda Asbell
Atty.-Andy Messer

LAMESA 79331
Pop: 9422 (Dawson)
601 S. 1st St.
806 872-2124 - *Fax: 872-4338*
www.ci.lamesa.tx.us
Mayor-Josh Stevens
Coun.-Marie Briseno
Coun.-Bobby G. Gonzales
Coun.-Doug Morris
Coun.-Brant Stewart
Coun.-Fred Vera
Coun.-Vacant
City Mgr.-Shawna Burkhart
Dir. Fin-Wayne Chapman
City Secy.-Betty Conde
Atty.-Russell Casselberry
C.P.-Dale Alwan
F.C.-Larry Duyck

LAMPASAS 76550
Pop: 6681 (Lampasas)
312 E. Third St.
512 556-6831 - *Fax: 556-8083*
www.cityoflampasas.com
Mayor-Misti Talbert
Mayor PT-Chuck Williamson
Coun.-Robert McCauley
Coun.-T.J. Monroe
Coun.-Greg Smith
Coun.-Delana Keele Toups
Coun.-Mike White

City Mgr.-Finley deGraffenried
City Secy.-Christina Marez
Atty.-Jo Christy Brown
C.P.-Sammy Bailey
F.C.-Reece Oestreich

LANCASTER 75146
Pop: 38361 (Dallas)
P.O. Box 940
972 218-1311 - *Fax: 275-0902*
www.lancaster-tx.com
Mayor-Marcus E. Knight
Mayor PT-Clyde C. Hairston
Dep. Mayor PT-Nina Morris
Coun.-Spencer W. Hervey, Jr.
Coun.-Stanley M. Jaglowski
Coun.-Marco Mejia
Coun.-Carol Strain-Burk
City Mgr.-Opal Mauldin-Jones
Dir. Fin-Baron Sauls
City Secy.-Sorangel O. Arenas
P.A.-Alton Dixon
Atty.-David T. Ritter
C.P.-Sam Urbanski
F.C.-Rob Franklin
Dir. P.W.-Jim Brewer

LAREDO 78042
Pop: 248187 (Webb)
P.O. Box 579
956 791-7300 - *Fax: 791-7491*
www.ci.laredo.tx.us/
Mayor-Pete Saenz
Coun.-George J. Altgelt
Coun.-Roberto Balli
Coun.-Rudy Gonzalez Jr.
Coun.-Alejandro "Alex" Perez Jr
Coun.-Vidal Rodriguez
Coun.-Charlie San Miguel
Coun.-Alberto Torres Jr.
Coun.-Nelly Vielma
City Mgr.-Horacio De Leon
Int. City Secy.-Heberto L. Ramirez
P.A.-Miguel Pescador
Atty.-Kristina Laurel Hale, Interim
Int. C.P.-Gabriel E. Martinez, Jr.
F.C.-Steve E. Landin
Dir. P.W.-John Orfila

LATEXO 75849
Pop: 272 (Houston)
P.O. Box 1108
936 544-9363
Mayor-Robert Hernandez
Mayor PT-Larry Melson
Ald.-Dyllis Bobbitt
Ald.-Harvey Bruner
Ald.-Toby Low
Ald.-Juan Noyola
Ald.-Vacant
City Secy.-Natalin Kelley

LAVON 75166
Pop: 2950 (Collin)
P.O. Box 340
972 843-4220 - *Fax: 843-0397*
www.cityoflavon.org
Mayor-Chuck Teske
Coun.-Mike Cook
Coun.-Tim Davis
Coun.-Vickie Sanson
Coun.-Mindi Serkland
Coun.-Kay Wright
City Secy.-Kim Dobbs
Atty.-Andy Messer
C.P.-Mike Jones
Dir. P.W.-Sonny Mancias

LAWN 79530
Pop: 314 (Taylor)
P.O. Box 246
325 583-2510
Mayor-Veronica Burleson
Mayor PT-Jerry Stevens
Ald.-Bettye Garza
Ald.-Donnie Griffith
Ald.-Chad Hanna
Ald.-Roy Mourot
City Secy.-Jana Baxter
Atty.-Lois A. Rockefeller
F.C.-James Burleson

LEAGUE CITY 77573
Pop: 83560 (Galveston-Harris)
300 W. Walker
281 554-1000 - *Fax: 554-1035*
www.ci.league-city.tx.us
Mayor-Pat Hallisey
Mayor PT-Todd Kinsey
Coun.-Dan Becker
Coun.-Hank Dugie
Coun.-Greg Gripon
Coun.-Keith Gross
Coun.-Nick Long
Coun.-Larry Millican
City Mgr.-John Baumgartner
Dir. Fin-Rebecca Underhill CPA
City Secy.-Diana Stapp
Atty.-Nghiem Doan
C.P.-Michael Kramm
F.C.-Gary Warren

LEAKEY 78873
Pop: 389 (Real)
P.O. Box 219
830 232-6757 - *Fax: 232-6775*
Mayor-Harry Schneemann
Ald.-Ken Auld
Ald.-Bob Bowers
Ald.-Frankie DeLeon
Ald.-Roel Gonzalez
Ald.-Carl Jensen
City Secy.-DeeDee Wally

LEANDER
Pop: 49033   (Travis-Williamson)
P.O. Box 319
Leander, TX 78646-0319
512 528-2700 - *Fax: 259-1605*
www.leandertx.gov
Mayor-Christopher Fielder
Mayor PT-Jeff Seiler
Coun.-Ron Abruzzese
Coun.-Troy Hill
Coun.-Andrea Navarrette
Coun.-Shanan Shepherd
Coun.-Michelle Stephenson
City Mgr.-Kent Cagle
City Secy.-Dara Crabtree
Atty.-Paige Saenz
C.P.-Greg Minton
F.C.-Bill Gardner

LEARY
Pop: 495   (Bowie)
P.O. Box 1799
Hooks, TX 75561
903 826-1653
Mayor-Keith Storey
Mayor PT-Kathy Meadows
Ald.-Joyce Hegler
Ald.-Coy Lorance
Ald.-Kent Markham
Ald.-Jesse Mauldin
City Admin.-Randy Mansfield

LEFORS 79054
Pop: 497   (Gray)
P.O. Box 383
806 835-2200 - *Fax: 835-2771*
Mayor-Ken Houston
Mayor PT-Craig Seely
Coun.-Jesse Callaway
Coun.-Morgan McBee
Coun.-Anna Young
Coun.-Vacant
City Secy.-Lindy Forsyth
Atty.-Rick Harris
Mar.-Travis Pittman
F.C.-Sy Brown

LEON VALLEY 78238
Pop: 10808   (Bexar)
6400 El Verde Road
210 684-1391 - *Fax: 684-4476*
www.leonvalleytexas.gov
Mayor-Chris Riley
Mayor PT-Benny Martinez
Coun.-Monica Alcocer
Coun.-Belinda Ealy
Coun.-David Edwards
Coun.-David Jordan
City Mgr.-Kelly Kuenstler
City Secy.-Saundra Passailaigue
Atty.-Vitra Denise Frederick
C.P.-Joseph Salvaggio
F.C.-Luis Valdez

LEONA 75850
Pop: 175   (Leon)
P.O. Box 10
903 344-1081 - *Fax: 344-1024*
Mayor-Ernest "Bubba" Oden
Mayor PT-Stacey Crook
Coun.-Don Crawford
Coun.-Brian Stafford
Coun.-Larry Wilson
Coun.-Vacant
City Secy.-Joyce Stafford
Atty.-Tom Holleman
F.C.-Charles Nash

LEONARD 75452
Pop: 1990   (Fannin)
111 W Collin St
903 587-3334 - *Fax: 587-2580*
www.cityofleonard.net/
Mayor-Steven Bolin
Mayor PT-Leonard Phillips
Coun.-Jane Blackerby
Coun.-David Norman
Coun.-Bob Pannkuk Sr.
Coun.-Dion Pontius
City Secy.-Shelly Griffin
City Admin.-William Linn
Atty.-Christina Tillett
C.P.-Brian Meserole
F.C.-Roby Watson

LEROY 76654
Pop: 337   (McLennan)
P.O. Box 38
Mayor-Ernest Moravec
Mayor PT-Charles Garrison
Ald.-Roy Davis
Ald.-David Dresner
Ald.-Gail Ondrej
Ald.-David Williams
City Secy.-Tina Veselka
Atty.-Charles Olson

LEVELLAND 79336
Pop: 13542   (Hockley)
P.O. Box 1010
806 894-0113 - *Fax: 894-0119*
www.levellandtexas.org
Mayor-Barbra Pinner
Mayor PT-Max Ledesma
Coun.-Jim Myatt
Coun.-Joe Bill Vardeman
Coun.-Billy Youngblood
City Mgr.-Rick Osburn
City Secy.-Beth A. Walls
Atty.-Matt Wade
C.P.-Albert Garcia
F.C.-Bill Durham

LEWISVILLE 75057
Pop: 95290   (Dallas-Denton)
972 219-3400 - *Fax: 219-3414*
www.cityoflewisville.com
Mayor-Rudy Durham
Mayor PT-Brent Daniels

Dep. Mayor PT-Brandon Jones
Coun.-R Neil Ferguson
Coun.-TJ Gilmore
Coun.-Bob Troyer
City Mgr.-Donna Barron
City Secy.-Julie Heinze
P.A.-Todd White
Atty.-Lizabeth Plaster
C.P.-Russ Kerbow
F.C.-Tim Tittle

LEXINGTON 78947
Pop: 1177   (Lee)
P.O. Box 56
979 773-2221 - *Fax: 773-3649*
www.lexingtontexas.com
Mayor-Alan Milligan
Mayor PT-Bobby W. Wesner
Ald.-Robert Hasselbush
Ald.-Garland Moffett
Ald.-Melinda Muhl
Ald.-Chris Wornell
City Secy.-Tina Biehle
Atty.-Cary Bovey
Int. C.P.-Ted Walton
F.C.-Don Milburn

LIBERTY 77575
Pop: 8397   (Liberty)
1829 Sam Houston
936 336-3684   *Fax: 336 9846*
www.cityofliberty.org
Mayor-Carl Pickett
Mayor PT-Diane Huddleston
Coun.-David Arnold
Coun.-Dennis Beasley
Coun.-Paul Glazener
Coun.-Louie Potetz
Coun.-Libby Simonson
City Mgr.-Gary Broz
Dir. Fin-Naomi Herrington
City Secy.-Dianne Tidwell
Atty.-Brandon Davis
C.P.-Thomas Claunch
F.C.-Brian Hurst

LIBERTY HILL 78642
Pop: 967   (Williamson)
P.O. Box 1920
512 778-5449 - *Fax: 778-5418*
www.libertyhilltx.gov/
Mayor-Connie Fuller
Mayor PT-Liz Rundzieher
Ald.-Jon Branigan
Ald.-Wendell W. McLeod
Ald.-Ron Rhea
Ald.-Troy Whitehead
City Secy.-Barbara Zwernemann
City Admin.-Greg Boatright
Atty.-Alan J. Bojorquez
C.P.-Maverick Campbell, Sr.
Dir. P.W.-Wayne Bonnet

LINDALE 75771
Pop: 5558 (Smith)
P.O. Box 130
903 882-3422 - *Fax: 882-1054*
www.lindaletx.gov/
Mayor-Jeff Daugherty
Coun.-Clyde Harper
Coun.-Ginger Sims
Coun.-Bryan Summerville
Coun.-Bob Tardiff
Coun.-Rick Thelen
City Mgr.-Carolyn Caldwell
City Secy.-Michelle Phillips
Atty.-Glen Patrick
C.P.-Dan Somes

LINDEN 75563
Pop: 1988 (Cass)
P.O. Box 419
903 756-7502 - *Fax: 756-7980*
www.lindentexas.org
Mayor-Clarence Burns
Ald.-Mike Berry
Ald.-Ruth Halleck
Ald.-Kenny Hamilton
Ald.-Sue Lazara
Ald.-Jeanie Stevens
City Admin.-Bob Swisher
Atty.-Gary Albertson
C.P.-Alton D. McWaters
F.C.-Robert Luzio

LINDSAY 76250
Pop: 1018 (Cooke)
P.O. Box 153
940 665-4455 - *Fax: 665-4910*
Mayor-Donald Metzler
Mayor PT-Danny Nortman
Ald.-Glenn "Tic" Block
Ald.-Jeff Neu
Ald.-Robert Sharp
Ald.-Sam Sparkman
City Secy.-Betsy Fleitman
P.A.-Betsy Fleitman
Atty.-Art Rodriguez
C.P.-Ricky Crow
F.C.-Marcus Dennis

LIPAN 76462
Pop: 430 (Hood)
P.O. Box 129
254 646-3345 - *Fax: 646-3000*
Mayor-Mike Stowe
Mayor PT-Jackie Shockley
Ald.-Kevin Andrews
Ald.-Anita Brian
Ald.-Priscilla Smalley
Ald.-Chris Tarpley
City Mgr.-Mike Stowe
City Secy.-Robin Viducic
P.A.-Robin Viducic
Atty.-Brad Boyd
Mar.-James A. Carter
F.C.-Kevin Andrews

LITTLE ELM 75068
Pop: 33125 (Denton)
214 975-0404
Fax: 972 377-5540
www.littleelm.org
Mayor-David Hillock
Mayor PT-Neil Blais
Coun.-Curtis J. Cornelious
Coun.-James Dominy
Coun.-Nick Musteen
Coun.-Chip Norman
Coun.-Stephanie Shoemaker
Town Mgr.-Matt Mueller
Town Secy.-Kathy Phillips
Atty.-Robert Brown
C.P.-Rodney Harrison
F.C.-Brian Roach
Dir. P.W.-Kevin Mattingly

LITTLE RIVER-ACADEMY 76554
Pop: 1961 (Bell)
P.O. Box 521
254 982-4248 - *Fax: 982-4248*
Mayor-Drew Lanham
Mayor PT-Elmer Williams
Coun.-Jack Bennett
Coun.-Domingo Montalbo
Coun.-David Newsome
Coun.-Bill Wilson
City Secy.-Lynona Tomastik
Atty.-Dan Kacir
C.P.-Frankie Poole
F.C.-David Borders

LITTLEFIELD 79339
Pop: 6372 (Lamb)
301 XIT Drive
P.O. Box 1267
806 385-5161 - *Fax: 385-0014*
littlefieldtexas.net/
Mayor-Eric Turpen
Coun.-Rene Duran
Coun.-Michael Rangel
Coun.-Lottie Spencer
Coun.-Johnny Williamson
City Mgr.-Mitch Grant
City Secy.-Janine Butler
Atty.-Slater Elza
C.P.-Vacant
F.C.-Jamie Grey

LIVE OAK 78233
Pop: 13131 (Bexar)
8001 Shin Oak Drive
210 653-9140 - *Fax: 653-2766*
www.liveoaktx.net
Mayor-Mary M. Dennis
Mayor PT-Aaron Dahl
Coun.-Anthony A. Brooks
Coun.-Ed Cimics
Coun.-Mendell D. Morgan, Jr.
Coun.-Robert "Bob" Tullgren
City Mgr.-Scott Wayman
Dir. Fin-Leroy Kowalik
City Secy.-Deborah L. Goza

Atty.-Clarissa Rodriguez
C.P.-Dan Pue
F.C.-Charles M. Foster
Dir. P.W.-Mark Wagster

LIVERPOOL 77577
Pop: 482 (Brazoria)
P.O. Box 68
281 581-2342 - *Fax: 581-2071*
www.cityofliverpooltexas.com/
Mayor-Bill Strickland
Mayor PT-Ric Bogue
Coun.-Arthur Fuhrmann
Coun.-Craig Kartye
Coun.-Brenda Noel
Coun.-Gay Prevost
City Secy.-Catherine Long
Atty.-Greg Hill
C.P.-Ronnie Nance

LIVINGSTON 77351
Pop: 5335 (Polk)
200 West Church
936 327-4311 - *Fax: 327-7608*
www.cityoflivingston-tx.com
Mayor-Clarke Evans
Mayor PT-Judy B. Cochran
Ald.-Alan Cook
Ald.-Elgin Davis
Ald.-Ray Luna
Ald.-Marion "Bid" Smith
City Mgr.-Billy S. Wiggins
City Secy.-Ellie Monteaux
P.A.-Dennis Clifton
Atty.-Jim Wright
C.P.-Dennis Clifton
F.C.-C. L. Cochran

LLANO 78643
Pop: 3232 (Llano)
301 West Main
325 247-4158 - *Fax: 247-4150*
www.cityofllano.com
Mayor-Gail Lang
Mayor PT-Sammy Leverett
Coun.-Craig Bauman
Coun.-Bryan Miller
Coun.-Kathryn Stephenson
Coun.-Kelli Tudyk
City Mgr.-Scott Edmonson
Dir. Fin-Lynda Kuder
City Secy.-Toni Milam
Atty.-Cary Bovey
C.P.-Kevin Ratliff
F.C.-Jason Hackworth

LOCKHART 78644
Pop: 12698 (Caldwell)
P.O. Box 239
512 398-3461 - *Fax: 398-5103*
www.lockhart-tx.org
Mayor-Lew White
Mayor PT-Angie Gonzales-Sanchez
Coun.-John Castillo
Coun.-Kara McGregor
Coun.-Juan Mendoza
Coun.-Jeffry Michelson
Coun.-Brad Westmoreland
City Mgr.-Vance Rodgers
Dir. Fin-Jeff Hinson
City Secy.-Connie Constancio
Atty.-Peter Gruning
C.P.-Ernest Pedraza
F.C.-Randy Jenkins

LOCKNEY 79241
Pop: 1842 (Floyd)
P.O. Box 387
806 652-2355 - *Fax: 652-2052*
Mayor-Archie Jones
Ald.-Tyler Dunivan
Ald.-Rosie Rendon
Ald.-Jorge Villarreal
Ald.-Matt Williams
City Mgr.-G.A. "Buster" Poling
City Mgr.-G.A. "Buster" Poling
Atty.-Lanny Voss
F.C.-Donnie McCloughlin

LOG CABIN 75148
Pop: 714 (Henderson)
14387 Alamo Rd.
903 489-2195 - *Fax: 489-0240*
Mayor-Lawrence P. "Larry" Nolan
Coun.-Judy Bearden
Coun.-David Campos
Coun.-Tom Garrett
City Secy.-Clasina Watson
Atty.-Blake E. Armstrong
C.P.-Todd Tucker
F.C.-Cory Abbe

LOMETA 76853
Pop: 856 (Lampasas)
P.O. Box 280
512 752-3331 - *Fax: 752-4033*
www.lometatx.com/
Mayor-Cynthia Kirby
Mayor PT-Shane Laughlin
Coun.-David Fair
Coun.-Shad Hill
Coun.-Susan Hines
Coun.-Sara Salinas
City Secy.-Vicki Taylor
Atty.-Law offices of Shahan,
  Guevara, Decker, Arrot
C.P.-Robert Montgomery
F.C.-Bobby Odom

LONE OAK 75453
Pop: 598 (Hunt)
P.O. Box 127
903 662-5116 - *Fax: 662-5334*
Mayor-Doug E. Williams
Mayor PT-Wes Owen
Ald.-Christene Barrow
Ald.-Gordon Galloway
Ald.-Nikki Lovett
Ald.-Sandra Williams
City Secy.-Kathy Voss
Atty.-Andy Messer
C.P.-Joe Sterner

LONE STAR 75668
Pop: 1581 (Morris)
P.O. Box 0218
903 656-2311 - *Fax: 656-3355*
Mayor-Randy Hodges
Mayor PT-Jerri Chism
Ald.-Mona Brown
Ald.-Lynn Cox
Ald.-Ryan Harte
Ald.-Keith Reiter
City Secy.-Devon Whatley
Atty.-Rick Shelton
C.P.-Larry Fleet
F.C.-Jerry Stoermer

LONGVIEW 75606
Pop: 81443 (Gregg-Harrison)
P.O. Box 1952
903 237-1080 - *Fax: 237-1092*
www.longviewtexas.gov/
Mayor-Andy Mack
Coun.-Kristen Ishihara
Coun.-Ed Moore
Coun.-Steve Pirtle
Coun.-Nona Snoddy
Coun.-Kasha Williams
Coun.-David Wright
City Mgr.-Keith Bonds
City Secy.-Angie Shepard
P.A.-Jaye Latch
Atty.-Jim Finley
C.P.-Mike Bishop
F.C.-J.P. Steelman

LORAINE 79532
Pop: 602 (Mitchell)
111 S. Main
P.O. Box 7
325 737-2222 - *Fax: 737-2452*
Mayor-Irene Graham
Mayor PT-Eddie Galvan
Ald.-Miguel Acevido
Ald.-Joann Hutchins
Ald.-Billy Kelly
Ald.-Jeff Woodell
City Secy.-Tina McKinney
Atty.-Jeanie Fuller
C.P.-Vacant
F.C.-Ricky Bailey

LORENA 76655
Pop: 1691 (McLennan)
254 857-4641 - *Fax: 857-4118*
www.ci.lorena.tx.us
Mayor-Chuck Roper
Mayor PT-Bill Coleman
Ald.-J Fagner
Ald.-Jennifer Grimm
Ald.-Jeff Linnstaedter
Ald.-Kelly Yarbrough
City Mgr.-Joseph Pace
City Secy.-Monica Hendrix
Atty.-Barney Knight
C.P.-Tom Dickson
F.C.-Jim Menefee

LORENZO 79343
Pop: 1147 (Crosby)
P.O. Box 430
806 634-5596 - *Fax: 634-5597*
www.cityoflorenzo.org
Mayor-Lester Bownds
Mayor PT-Cheryl Birdwell
Coun.-Charles Cate
Coun.-Rhonda Cypert
Coun.-Felix Martinez
Coun.-Karla Tiner
City Secy.-Monica Longoria
City Admin.-Rusty Forbes
Atty.-Todd Hurd

LOS FRESNOS 78566
Pop: 5542 (Cameron)
200 N. Brazil
956 233-5768 - *Fax: 233-9879*
Mayor-Polo Narvaez
Mayor PT-Javier Mendez
Coun.-Yolanda Cruz
Coun.-Belinda Garza
Coun.-Juan Munoz
Coun.-Swain Real
City Mgr.-Mark W. Milum
City Secy.-Pam Denny
Atty.-Enrique Juarez
C.P.-Hector Gonzalez
F.M.-Geronimo Sheldon

LOS INDIOS 78567
Pop: 1083 (Cameron)
P.O. Box 369
956 399-4255 - *Fax: 399-4582*
Mayor-Rick Cavazos
Mayor PT-Herminia Quintanilla
Ald.-Rita Flores
Ald.-Jaime Gonzalez
Ald.-Andres Guajardo
Ald.-Gualberto Weaver
City Secy.-Yolanda Ysasi
Atty.-Dan Sanchez

CITY SECTION

LOS YBANEZ 79331
Pop: 19   (Dawson)
1919 County Rd. M, Box 52A
806 872-5017
Mayor-Mary A. Ybanez
Ald.-Renee Estraca
Ald.-Ramiro Estraca
Ald.-Vacant
City Mgr.-John Castillo
City Secy.-Judy Hernandez

LOTT 76656
Pop: 759   (Falls)
P.O. Box 398
254 584-2681 - *Fax: 584-2109*
Mayor-Annita Tindle
Mayor PT-Edward Sliva
Coun.-David Hennig
Coun.-Dorothy P. Kohl
Coun.-Shirley Melton
Coun.-Roy Lynn Sehon
City Secy.-Lynne Greger
Atty.-Charles Olsen
F.C.-Walter "Red" Carson

LOVELADY 75851
Pop: 649   (Houston)
P.O. Box 83
936 636-7313 - *Fax: 636-7087*
Mayor-William B. Shoemaker
Mayor PT-Kevin Fritze
Ald.-Lisa Allen
Ald.-Martin Boedekor
Ald.-Michael Sessions
Ald.-Jo Doris Speer
City Secy.-Debbie Wells
Atty.-Bill Pemberton
F.C.-Michael Sessions

LOWRY CROSSING
Pop: 1725   (Collin)
1405 S. Bridgefarmer Rd.
McKinney, TX 75069
972 542-8678 - *Fax: 542-2052*
www.lowrycrossingtexas.org
Mayor-Derek Stephens
Mayor PT-Lee Van Lanen
Coun.-Cindy Cash
Coun.-Greg Griser
Coun.-Julia Phillips
Coun.-Cynthia Sandlin
City Secy.-Janis Cable
Atty.-Regina Edwards
F.C.-Paul Wood

LUBBOCK 79457
Pop: 229573   (Lubbock)
P.O. Box 2000
806 775-2025 - *Fax: 775-3983*
www.ci.lubbock.tx.us
Mayor-Dan Pope
Coun.-Juan A. Chadis
Coun.-Karen Gibson
Coun.-Jeff Griffith
Coun.-Shelia Patterson Harris
Coun.-Latrelle Joy

Coun.-Steve Massengale
City Mgr.-Jarrett Atkinson
City Secy.-Rebecca Garza
Atty.-Chad Weaver
C.P.-Greg Stevens
F.C.-Lance Phelps

LUCAS 75002
Pop: 6300   (Collin)
665 Country Club Rd.
972 727-8999 - *Fax: 727-0091*
www.lucastexas.us
Mayor-Jim Olk
Mayor PT-Kathleen Peele
Coun.-Tim Baney
Coun.-Steve Duke
Coun.-Debbie Fisher
Coun.-Phillip Lawrence
Coun.-Wayne Millsap
City Mgr.-Joni Clarke
City Secy.-Stacy Henderson
Atty.-Joseph J. Gorfida, Jr.
F.C.-Ted Stephens

LUEDERS 79533
Pop: 346   (Jones-Shackelford)
P.O. Box 277
325 228-4522 - *Fax: 228-4701*
Mayor-Benny Jarvis
Mayor PT-Kimberly Neal
Coun.-Alyssa Kimbrough
Coun.-Valen Lopez
Coun.-Daina Moore
Coun.-Misty Stevens
City Secy.-Jennifer Schedule
Atty.-James M. Decker
F.C.-Cody Roberts

LUFKIN 75902
Pop: 35067   (Angelina)
P.O. Drawer 190
936 633-0244 - *Fax: 639-9843*
www.cityoflufkin.com
Mayor-Bob Brown
Mayor PT-Mark Hicks
Coun.-Guessipina Bonner
Coun.-Sarah Murray
Coun.-Robert Shankle
Coun.-Rocky Thigpen
Coun.-Lynn Torres
City Mgr.-Keith N. Wright
Dir. Fin-Belinda Melancon
City Secy.-Kara Atwood
P.A.-Diana Russell
Atty.-Bruce Green
C.P.-Gerald Williamson
F.C.-Ted Lovett

LULING 78648
Pop: 5411   (Caldwell)
509 E. Crockett St.
830 875-2481 - *Fax: 875-2038*
www.cityofluling.net/
Mayor-Mike Hendricks
Mayor PT-John A. Wells
Coun.-Jackie Campbell

Coun.-James Nickells
Coun.-Alton Opiela
Coun.-Wayne Tresner
City Secy.-Martha C. Velasquez
Atty.-Peter Gruning
C.P.-Bill Sala
F.C.-Tom Harmon

LUMBERTON 77657
Pop: 13000   (Hardin)
836 N. Main St.
409 755-3700 - *Fax: 755-0032*
www.cityoflumberton.com/
Mayor-Don Surratt
Coun.-Lynette Barks
Coun.-Dan Bell
Coun.-David Maniscalco
Coun.-Sharon Spears
Coun.-Steve Templeton
Coun.-Kenneth Wahl
City Mgr.-Steve Clark
City Secy.-Susan Collins
Atty.-Curtis Soileau
C.P.-Danny Sullins

LYFORD 78569
Pop: 2611   (Willacy)
13550 Main Avenue
P.O. Box 310
956 347-3512 - *Fax: 347-5434*
Mayor-Wally Solis
Mayor PT-Tony Chavez
Comm.-Albert Cavazos
Comm.-Pablo Morales
Comm.-Maggie Quilantan
Comm.-Rick Salinas
City Secy.-Lydia C. Moreno
Atty.-Rick Hoffman
C.P.-Andres Maldonado
V.F.D.F.C.-Ben Sanchez
Dir. P.W.-Gilbert Vela

LYTLE 78052
Pop: 2492(Atascosa-Bexar-
Medina)
830 709-3692
www.lytletx.org
Mayor-Mark L. Bowen
Ald.-Sam Cortez
Ald.-Jamie Dahler
Ald.-Ruble P. Farmer Jr.
Ald.-Ruben Gonzalez
Ald.-Jerry T. Stone
City Admin/Secy-Josie M. Campa
Atty.-Thomas P. Cate
C.P.-Richard L. Priest
F.C.-Matthew Dear
Dir. P.W.-James J. McGrath, Jr.

MABANK 75147
Pop: 3035   (Kaufman-Henderson)
903 887-3241 - *Fax: 887-0175*
www.cityofmabanktx.org
Mayor-Jeff Norman
Mayor PT-Dennis Terry
Ald.-Tyson Adams

Ald.-John Chappell
Ald.-Midge Odom
Ald.-Larry Teague
City Secy.-Laurie Neustupa
Atty.-R. Michael Groom
C.P.-Keith Bradshaw
F.C.-Richard Myrick
Dir. P.S.-Keith Bradshaw

MADISONVILLE 77864
Pop: 4396 (Madison)
210 W. Cottonwood
936 348-2748 - *Fax: 348-3815*
madisonvilletexas.us/
Mayor-William "Bill" Parten
Mayor PT-Russell Bailey
Coun.-Lois M. Brown
Coun.-Jerry Harper
Coun.-Dale Kovacs
Coun.-Chris McGilbra
City Mgr.-Camilla Viator
Dir. Fin-Doug Holly
City Secy.-Rosa R. Barrera
Atty.-John Bankhead
C.P.-Herbert Gilbert
F.C.-Thom Jones

MAGNOLIA
Pop: 1600 (Montgomery)
18111 Buddy Riley Blvd.
Magnolia, TX 77354
281 356-2266 - *Fax: 259-7811*
www.cityofmagnolia.com
Mayor-Todd Kana
Mayor PT-Richard Carby
Coun.-John W. Bramlett
Coun.-Matthew "Doc" Dantzer
Coun.-Brenda Hoppe
Coun.-Jonny Williams
City Secy.-Lynne George
City Admin.-Paul Mendes
Atty.-Leonard Schneider
C.P.-Terry Enloe
F.C.-Gary M. Vincent

MALAKOFF 75148
Pop: 2324 (Henderson)
P.O. Box 1177
903 489-0699 - *Fax: 489-2517*
cityofmalakoff.net
Mayor-Delois Pagitt
Mayor PT-Tim Trimble
Coun.-Vincent Bailey Jr.
Coun.-Kevin Kilman
Coun.-Jeanette King
Coun.-Jerrilyn Tarver
City Admin.-Ann Barker
Atty.-Hank Skelton
C.P.-Floyd Thomas
F.C.-Eddie Maehlstein

MALONE 76660
Pop: 269 (Hill)
222 N. Pecan St.
254 533-2261 - *Fax: 533-2380*

Mayor-James Lucko
Mayor PT-Veresa Ingrum
Ald.-Bob Degner
Ald.-Elmer Maass
Ald.-Barbara Standfast
City Secy.-Molly Hopson
Atty.-Stephanie W. Johnson
F.C.-Eddy Lehman

MANOR 78653
Pop: 5037 (Travis)
P.O. Box 387
512 272-5555 - *Fax: 272-8792*
www.cityofmanor.org
Mayor-Rita G. Jonse
Coun.-Maria D. Amezcua
Coun.-Deja Hill
Coun.-Gene Kruppa
Coun.-Zindia Pierson
Coun.-Todd Shaner
Coun.-Anne R. Weir
City Mgr.-Thomas M. Bolt
City Secy.-Lluvia Tijerina
Atty.-Paige Saenz
C.P.-Ryan Phipps
F.C.-Ryan Smith

MANSFIELD 76063
Pop: 59954 (Ellis-Johnson-Tarrant)
1200 E. Broad St.
817 276-4200 - *Fax: 473-2925*
www.mansfield-tx.gov
Mayor-David L. Cook
Mayor PT-Larry Broseh
Coun.-Darryl W. Haynes
Coun.-Cory Hoffman
Coun.-Stephen Lindsey
Coun.-Terry M. Moore
Coun.-Brent Newsom
City Mgr.-Clayton W. Chandler
City Secy.-Jeanne Heard
P.A.-Gary Cardinale
Atty.-Allen Taylor
C.P.-Tracy Aaron
F.C.-Barry Bondurant

MANVEL 77578
Pop: 5179 (Brazoria)
20025 HWY 6
P.O. Box 187
281 489-0630 - *Fax: 489-0634*
www.cityofmanvel.com
Mayor-Debra Davison
Mayor PT-Lorraine R. Hehn
Coun.-Jason Albert
Coun.-Adrian Gaspar
Coun.-Jerome Hudson
Coun.-Melissa Sifuentes
Coun.-Brian Wilmer
City Mgr.-Kyle Jung
Dir. Fin-Michael Higgins
City Secy.-Tammy Bell
Atty.-Bobby Gervais
C.P.-Thomas Keith Traylor
F.M.-Micheal Dumas

MARBLE FALLS 78654
Pop: 6128 (Burnet)
606 Ave N
830 693-3615 - *Fax: 693-6737*
www.ci.marble-falls.tx.us
Mayor-John Packer
Mayor PT-Richard Westerman
Coun.-William D. Haddock
Coun.-Megan Klaeger
Coun.-Craig Magerkurth
Coun.-Reed Norman
Coun.-Dave Rhodes
City Mgr.-Mike Hodge
City Secy.-Christina McDonald
Atty.-Patty Akers
C.P.-Mark Whitacre
F.C.-Russell Sander

MARFA 79843
Pop: 1981 (Presidio)
P.O. Box 787
432 729-4315 - *Fax: 729-3158*
Mayor-Ann Marie Nafziger
Mayor PT-Manuel V. Baeza
Coun.-Geneviev Bassham
Coun.-Irma Salgado
Coun.-Mark Scott
Coun.-Brit Webb
City Admin.-James R. Mustard, Jr.
Atty.-Teresa Todd
C.P.-Esteban Marquez
F.C.-Gary Mitschki

MARIETTA 75566
Pop: 134 (Cass)
P.O. Box 247
903 835-5596 - *Fax: 835-2042*
Mayor-Frances Elliott
Coun.-Betty Barnes
Coun.-Kirk Brigance
Coun.-Audrey Crook
Coun.-Lois Shaddix
Coun.-Kathleen Wellborn
City Secy.-Pansy Ham

MARION 78124
Pop: 1066 (Guadalupe)
P.O. Box 158
830 914-2391 - *Fax: 420-4460*
www.cityofmariontx.org
Mayor-William E. Seiler
Ald.-Mark Engstrom
Ald.-Alex Gonzalez
Ald.-Kerry Gutierrez
Ald.-Melba Knight
Ald.-Belinda Reasor
City Secy.-Christina Averill
Atty.-Peter Gruning
C.P.-Donald R. Crane
F.C.-Jeremy Davenport
Dir. P.W.-Micaela Bandel

MARLIN 76661
Pop: 5967   (Falls)
101 Fortune Street
254 883-1450 - *Fax: 883-1456*
www.marlintx.net
Mayor-John Keefer
Mayor PT-Douglas Porter
Coun.-Susan Byrd
Coun.-Scottie R. Henderson
Coun.-Terence McDavid
Coun.-Rose Morin
Coun.-Curtis T. Smith Jr.
City Mgr.-Alan Grindstaff
City Secy.-Sandra Herring
Atty.-Mike Dixon
C.P.-Michael Pesses
Int. F.C.-Donald Pruitt

MARQUEZ 77865
Pop: 263   (Leon)
P.O. Box 85
903 529-3020
Mayor-Stynette Clary
Mayor PT-Diane Bates
Ald.-Nancy Hernandez
Ald.-Valerie Johnson
Ald.-Karen Jones
Ald.-Vacant
City Mgr.-Lauren Powers
F.C.-T.J. Foley

MARSHALL 75671
Pop: 23523   (Harrison)
P.O. Box 698
903 935-4421
www.marshalltexas.net
Chair-Larry Hurta
Comm.-Gail Beil
Comm.-Terri Brown
Comm.-Vernia Calhoun
Comm.-William "Doc" Halliday
Comm.-Doug Lewis
Comm.-Gloria Moon
City Mgr.-Lisa Agnor
Atty.-Todd Fitts
Int. C.P.-Cliff Carruth
F.C.-Reggie Cooper

MART 76664
Pop: 2553   (McLennan)
P.O. Box 360
254 876-2462 - *Fax: 876-3807*
www.cityofmart.net
Mayor-Len Williams
Mayor PT-Henry Witt III
Ald.-Zachary Bird
Ald.-Willie Hurth, Jr.
Ald.-Tommy Roberson
Ald.-Kevin Schaffer
City Secy.-Carol Couch
Atty.-Charles Buenger
C.P.-Paul Cardenas
F.C.-Bud Pavelka

MARTINDALE 78655
Pop: 1116   (Caldwell)
512 357-2639 - *Fax: 357-5826*
www.martindaletexas.org
Mayor-Kim Smith
Coun.-Lisa Shell Allan
Coun.-Latreese Cooke
Coun.-Robert Deviney
Coun.-Mary Alice Paul
Coun.-Sonja Gonzales Villalobos
Clk.-Sylvia Gomez
Atty.-Floyd Akers
C.P.-Harry Juergens
F.C.-Chris Germer

MASON 76856
Pop: 2114   (Mason)
P.O. Box 68
325 347-6449 - *Fax: 347-5955*
www.mason.tx.citygovt.org
Mayor-Brent Hinckley
Comm.-Bonnie Beam
Comm.-Vicki Enrigue
Comm.-Sabin Nelson
Comm.-Sue J. Pledger
City Secy.-Pattie Grote
City Admin.-John Palacio
Atty.-David Young

MATADOR 79244
Pop: 607   (Motley)
P.O. Box 367
806 347-2255 - *Fax: 347-2062*
Mayor-Alvin Alexander
Ald.-Brad Baxter
Ald.-Douglas Campbell
Ald.-Dvonna Grundy
Ald.-Jeromy Jameson
Ald.-Pat Smith
City Secy.-Debra Scott
Atty.-Tom Hamilton
F.C.-Lee Jones

MATHIS 78368
Pop: 4942   (San Patricio)
411 E. San Patricio
361 547-3343 - *Fax: 547-3838*
www.cityofmathis.com
Mayor-Ciri Villarreal
Mayor PT-Abel Trejo
Coun.-David Garcia
Coun.-Eufemia M. Nieto
Coun.-Rosalinda Pena
Coun.-Sandra Quinones
City Mgr.-Michael Barrera
City Secy.-Mary A. Gonzales
Atty.-Lucinda Garcia
C.P.-Pedro Saenz
F.C.-Adrian Ramirez
Dir. P.W.-J. David Vasquez

MAUD 75567
Pop: 1056   (Bowie)
P.O. Box 100
903 585-2294 - *Fax: 585-2752*
Mayor-David Gipson
Mayor PT-Jimmy Clary
Ald.-Joan Brown
Ald.-Debbie Mathis
Ald.-Dawna Montanelli
Ald.-Mickey Williams
City Secy.-Pollyanna Moore
Atty.-J. Michael Brock
C.P.-Kevin Restelle
F.C.-John Nichols

MAYPEARL 76064
Pop: 934   (Ellis)
P.O. Box 400
972 435-2380 - *Fax: 435-2082*
ci.maypearl.tx.us/
Mayor-Kelly Jacobson
Ald.-Jake Brewster
Ald.-Mike Harris
Ald.-Mark Partin
Ald.-John Wayne Pruitt
Ald.-Kathy Wiggins
City Secy.-Jeannie Evans
Atty.-Cara White
C.P.-Boyd Norton
F.C.-Trey Moon

MCALLEN
Pop: 138808   (Hidalgo)
P.O. Box 220
Mc Allen, TX 78505-0220
956 681-1000 - *Fax: 681-1010*
www.mcallen.net
Mayor-James E. Darling
Mayor PT-Aida Ramirez
Comm.-Richard Cortez
Comm.-John Ingram
Comm.-J. Omar Quintanilla
Comm.-Veronica V. Whitacre
Comm.-Joaquin "J.J." Zamora
City Mgr.-Roel "Roy" Rodriguez
City Secy.-Perla Lara
Atty.-Kevin Pagan
C.P.-Victor Rodriguez
F.C.-Rafael Balderas

MCCAMEY 79752
Pop: 1887   (Upton)
P.O. Drawer 1409
432 652-3333 - *Fax: 652-3225*
www.mccameycity.com
Mayor-Patty Jones
Mayor PT-Pedro Rosales
Ald.-Grace Enciso
Ald.-Yolanda Gomez
Ald.-Noe Marquez
Ald.-Gerard Renteria
Ald.-Vilma Rodriguez
City Secy.-Alma Acosta
Atty.-Melanie Spratt-Anderson

MCGREGOR 76657
Pop: 4987 (McLennan)
P.O. Box 192
254 840-2806 - *Fax: 840-2950*
www.mcgregor-texas.com
Mayor-James S. Hering
Mayor PT-Andrew Henderson, Sr.
Coun.-Paul Allison
Coun.-Joe Leos
Coun.-Tony Ocampo
Coun.-David Taylor
City Mgr.-Kevin P. Evans
City Secy.-Angelia D. Sloan
Atty.-Charles Olson
C.P.-James Burson
F.C.-Marty Dominguez
Dir. P.W.-Paul Kilpatrick

MCKINNEY 75070
Pop: 131117 (Collin)
P.O. Box 517
972 547-7500 - *Fax: 547-2607*
www.mckinneytexas.org
Mayor-Brian Loughmiller
Coun.-Chuck Branch
Coun.-Scott Elliott
Coun.-Charlie Philips
Coun.-Tracy Rath
Coun.-Rainey Rogers
Coun.-La'Shadion Anthony
  Shemwell
City Mgr.-Paul Grimes
Dir. Fin-Vacant
City Secy.-Sandy Hart
P.M.-Lisa Littrell
Atty.-Mark S. Houser
C.P.-Greg Conley

MCLEAN 79057
Pop: 778 (Gray)
P.O. Box 9
806 779-2481 - *Fax: 779-2226*
Mayor-Tanner Hess
Ald.-Jimmy Armbrister
Ald.-Andy Eck
Ald.-Woodrow Morton Jr.
Ald.-Clay Reynolds
Ald.-Zane Richardson
City Secy.-Toni Bohlar
Atty.-Mark N. Buzzard
F.C.-David Tolleson

MCLENDON-CHISHOLM 75032
Pop: 2450 (Rockwall-Kaufman)
1371 West FM 550
972 524-2077 - *Fax: 524-9128*
www.mclendon-chisholm.com
Mayor-Robert Steinhagen
Mayor PT-Wayne Orchard
Coun.-Adrienne Balkum
Coun.-Jim Herren
Coun.-Scott L. Turnbull
Coun.-Sim Woodham

City Secy.-Lisa Palomba
City Admin.-David Butler
Atty.-David Paschall
F.C.-Robert Jones

MEADOW 79345
Pop: 593 (Terry)
906 First-Sonny Curtis St
806 539-2377 - *Fax: 539-1207*
Mayor-Natalie Howard
Mayor PT-Kandace Keese-Welch
Ald.-Alan Bayer
Ald.-Jerry Liles
Ald.-Everett McArthur
Ald.-Nacho Sanchez
City Admin.-Terri McClanahan
Atty.-Michael Guevara
F.C.-Jon Williams

MEADOWLAKES 78654
Pop: 2104 (Burnet)
177 Broadmoor
830 693-6840 - *Fax: 693-2124*
www.meadowlakestexas.org
Mayor-Mary Ann Raesener
Coun.-David Baker
Coun.-Mike Barry
Coun.-Bobby Brown
Coun.-Jerry Drummond
Coun.-Edwin O'Hayre
City Mgr.-Johnnie Thompson
City Secy.-Loren Meiner
Atty.-Katherine McAnally

MEADOWS PLACE 77477
Pop: 4660 (Fort Bend)
One Troyan Dr.
281 983-2950 - *Fax: 983-2940*
www.cityofmeadowsplace.org
Mayor-Charles D. Jessup, IV
Mayor PT-Terry Henley
Ald.-Steven H. Bezner
Ald.-John F. Isbell
Ald.-Kelle K. Mills
Ald.-Rick J. Staigle
City Secy.-Courtney Rutherford
Atty.-J. Grady Randle
C.P.-J. Gary Stewart

MEGARGEL 76370
Pop: 203 (Archer)
P.O. Box 31
940 562-2341 - *Fax: 562-2023*
Mayor-Paul McQueen
Mayor PT-Jessica Gleghorn
Coun.-Sherri Bardwell
Coun.-Tonya Desautel
Coun.-Glen Tatum
Coun.-David Wilk
City Secy.-Regina Kellar
F.C.-Kelly Desautel

MELISSA 75454
Pop: 10000 (Collin)
972 838-2338 - *Fax: 837-2452*
www.cityofmelissa.com
Mayor-Reed Greer
Mayor PT-Jay Northcut
Coun.-Craig Ackerman
Coun.-Anthony Figueroa
Coun.-Stacy Jackson
Coun.-Chad Taylor
Coun.-Nicco Warren
City Mgr.-Jason Little
Dir. Fin-Gail Dansby
City Secy.-Linda Bannister
Atty.-Rebecca Brewer
C.P.-Duane Smith
F.C.-Harold Watkins

MELVIN 76858
Pop: 178 (McCulloch)
P.O. Box 777
325 286-4222 - *Fax: 286-4222*
Mayor-Rogelio Torres Castanuela
Coun.-Michael Brown
Coun.-Marlena Brown
Coun.-Linda Pennington
Coun.-Sylvia Silva
Coun.-Stanley Sparks
City Secy.-Claudia Brown
F.C.-Cole Holubec

MEMPHIS 79245
Pop: 2290 (Hall)
721 Robertson
806 259-3001 - *Fax: 259-3852*
Mayor-Robert C. Maddox
Mayor PT-Jim Stewart
Ald.-Ed Bailey
Ald.-Alicia Berry
Ald.-Dell Graham
Ald.-Richard Hutcherson
Ald.-Jo Ella Pate
Ald.-Kitsy Pepper
Ald.-Woodrow Richardson
City Secy.-Nelwyn Ward
Atty.-James T. "Jim" Shelton
C.P.-Chris Jolly
F.C.-Terry Altman

MENARD 76859
Pop: 1471 (Menard)
P.O. Box 145
325 396-4706 - *Fax: 396-2015*
Mayor-Barbara Hooten
Ald.-Robert Brown
Ald.-Genevieve Hough
Ald.-Rocky Saucedo
Ald.-Gay L. Simmons
Ald.-Tyler Wagner
City Secy.-Irma R. Hernandez
City Admin.-Don Kerns
F.C.-Tyler Wagner

MERCEDES 78570
Pop: 15570 (Hidalgo)
P.O. Drawer 837
956 565-3114 - *Fax: 565-8592*
www.cityofmercedes.com
Mayor-Henry Hinojosa
Mayor PT-Ruben Guajardo
Comm.-Cristella De Leon
  Hernandez
Comm.-Leo Villarreal
Comm.-James Howard Wade, Jr.
City Mgr.-Vacant
City Secy.-Arcelia L. Felix
Atty.-Juan R. Molina
C.P.-Olga Maldonado
F.C.-Tommy Ureste

MERIDIAN 76665
Pop: 1493 (Bosque)
P.O. Box 306
254 435-2381 - *Fax: 435-2904*
Mayor-Daniel Yguerabide
Ald.-Angie Buck
Ald.-Elizabeth Davis
Ald.-Ryan Nieuwenhuis
Ald.-Shawn Stauffer
Ald.-Cindy Wallace
City Secy.-Kristina Taylor
City Admin.-Marie Garland
Atty.-Charles Olson
C.P.-Chris Blanton
F.C.-Jeff White
Dir. P.W.-Mike Walker

MERKEL 79536
Pop: 2590 (Taylor)
100 Kent St.
325 928-4911 - *Fax: 928-3171*
www.merkeltexas.com
Mayor-Mary Schrampfer
Mayor PT-Larry Bland
Ald.-Jason Beaird
Ald.-James Grimes
Ald.-Joel Owens
Ald.-Brady Rutledge
City Mgr.-Steve Campbell
City Secy.-Evelyn Morse
Atty.-Claudia Clinton
C.P.-Chris Ortiz
F.C.-Eddy Harris

MERTENS 76666
Pop: 125 (Hill)
P.O. Box 26
903 682-2143 - *Fax: 682-2143*
Mayor-Barbara Crass
Comm.-Mary Anne Brennan
Coun.-Joey Watson
City Secy.-Nanette Wyatt
Atty.-Stephanie W. Johnson
F.C.-Travis Kaddatz

MERTZON 76941
Pop: 781 (Irion)
P.O. Box 456
325 835-5791 - *Fax: 835-7570*
Mayor-Lisa Hight
Mayor PT-Melissa Matthews
Coun.-Celica Belcher
Coun.-Danny Crutchfield
Coun.-Charlene Holland
Coun.-Bill Taylor
City Admin/Secy-Sheri Benson

MESQUITE
Pop: 142950 (Dallas-Kaufman)
P.O. Box 850137
Mesquite, TX 75185-0137
972 216-6244 - *Fax: 216-6469*
www.cityofmesquite.com
Mayor-Stan Pickett
Mayor PT-Jeff Casper
Dep. Mayor PT-Dan Aleman
Coun.-Bruce Archer
Coun.-Tandy Boroughs
Coun.-Robert Miklos
Coun.-Greg Noschese
City Mgr.-Cliff Keheley
City Secy.-Sonja Land
P.A.-Ryan Williams
Atty.-B. J. Smith
C.P.-Charles Cato
F.C.-Mark Kerby

MEXIA 76667
Pop: 7459 (Limestone)
101 N. McKinney
P.O. Box 207
254 562-4100 - *Fax: 562-0828*
www.cityofmexia.com
Mayor-Richard Duncan
Mayor PT-Judy Chambers
Coun.-Arthur Busby
Coun.-Scott Condon
Coun.-Butch Newhouse
Coun.-Blanca Rivera
Coun.-Geary Smith
City Mgr.-Eric Garrity
City Secy.-Christi Shivers
Atty.-Charles Buenger
C.P.-Vacant
F.C.-Robert LaFoy

MIAMI 79059
Pop: 597 (Roberts)
P.O. Box 217
806 868-4791 - *Fax: 868-4391*
www.miamitexas.org
Mayor-Chad Breeding
Mayor PT-Sharmayne Miller
Ald.-Brad Guthrie
Ald.-Bradley Hale
Ald.-Nancy Manley
Ald.-James Morse
City Secy.-Kathy Thompson
Atty.-William P. Weiman
F.C.-Paul Sublett

MIDLAND 79701
Pop: 111147 (Midland)
300 N. Loraine
P.O. Box 1152
Midland, TX 79702
432 685-7100 - *Fax: 685-7433*
www.midlandtexas.gov
Mayor-Jerry Morales
Coun.-Scott Dufford
Coun.-Sharla Hotchkiss
Coun.-J.Ross Lacy
Coun.-John B. Love III
Coun.-Spencer Robnett
Coun.-Jeff Sparks
City Mgr.-Courtney Sharp
City Secy.-Amy Turner
P.A.-Regina Stephensen
Atty.-John Ohnemiller
C.P.-Steve Henry
Int. F.C.-Chuck Blumenauer

MIDLOTHIAN 76065
Pop: 22000 (Ellis)
104 W. Avenue E
972 775-3481 - *Fax: 775-7122*
www.midlothian.tx.us
Mayor-Bill Houston
Mayor PT-T.J. Henley
Coun.-Joe Frizzell
Coun.-Jimmie L. McClure
Coun.-Ted Miller
Coun.-Mike Rodgers
Coun.-Wayne Sibley
City Mgr.-Chris Dick
City Secy.-Tammy Varner
P.A.-Cheryl Allison
Atty.-Joseph J. Gorfida, Jr.
C.P.-Carl Smith
F.C.-Dale McCaskill

MIDWAY 75852
Pop: 228 (Madison)
P.O. Box 227
936 348-6800 - *Fax: 348-6678*
Mayor-Tony Leago
Mayor PT-Jimmy Cook
Ald.-Ed Faw
Ald.-Brenda Ford
Ald.-Gus Kangos
Ald.-Steve Parrish
City Secy.-Debra Newkirk
Atty.-John Bankhead

MILANO 76556
Pop: 420 (Milam)
P.O. Box 52
979 224-0227
Mayor-Rodney D. Gage, Sr.
Mayor PT-David Gunnels, Jr.
Ald.-Edward Lenz
Ald.-Connie Seelke
City Secy.-Carolyn Vinton
Atty.-Barney Knight

MILDRED
Pop: 400   (Navarro)
5415 FM 637
Corsicana, TX 75109
903 872-6110 - *Fax: 874-6468*
Mayor-Kyle Carrigan
Ald.-Wayne McGuire
Ald.-Latriece Richter
Ald.-Bryan Roach
Ald.-Chris Simmons
Ald.-Brandon Tackett
City Secy.-Angela Montfort
Atty.-Sarah Keathley

MILES 76861
Pop: 829   (Runnels)
P.O. Box 398
325 468-3151 - *Fax: 468-3016*
Mayor-Sylvester Schwertner
Mayor PT-Jane Jeschke
Ald.-Tony Dillon
Ald.-Bobby Joe Kasberg
Ald.-Juan Ornelas
Ald.-Paul Sklenarik
City Secy.-Amy Fischer
Atty.-Michael B. Halla
F.C.-Mark Sklenarik

MILFORD 76670
Pop: 728   (Ellis)
100 S. Main St.
P.O. Box 538
972 493-3161 - *Fax: 493-5981*
Mayor-Bruce Perryman
Mayor PT-Ercel Thomas Evans
Ald.-Earnestine Byrd
Ald.-Judy Finch
Ald.-Fadys Gates
Ald.-Alan Singleton
City Secy.-Carlos Phoenix
Atty.-Bill Scott
C.P.-Carlos Phoenix
F.C.-Mark Jackson

MILLER'S COVE
Pop: 149   (Titus)
P.O. Box 300
Winfield, TX 75493
903 305-4327
Mayor-Willie B. Garrett
Comm.-Nancy Yepec Diaz
Comm.-Javiar Ramirez
City Secy.-Araceli Martinez
Atty.-Bird Old

MILLSAP 76066
Pop: 403   (Parker)
P.O. Box 57
940 682-7446 - *Fax: 682-2037*
Mayor-Jamie French
Mayor PT-Michael Kinman
Ald.-Teresa Howard
Ald.-Yolanda Malloux
Ald.-Christopher Schofield
Ald.-Sally Uribe
City Mgr.-Mark Barnes
Atty.-Vacant

MINEOLA 75773
Pop: 4515   (Wood)
P.O. Box 179
903 569-6183 - *Fax: 569-6551*
www.mineola.com
Mayor-Kevin White
Mayor PT-Novada Bigham
Ald.-Sue Jones
Ald.-Polly Jones
Ald.-Jayne Lankford
Ald.-Mitchell Tuck
Coun.-Jack Newman
City Admin.-Mercy L. Rushing
Atty.-Blake E. Armstrong
C.P.-Charles Bittner
F.M.-David Madsen

MINERAL WELLS
Pop: 16800   (Palo Pinto-Parker)
P.O. Box 460
Mineral Wells, TX 76068-0460
940 328-7700 - *Fax: 328-7704*
mineralwellstx.gov
Mayor-Mike Allen
Mayor PT-Tammy Underwood
Coun.-Reagan Johnson
Coun.-Doyle Light
Coun.-Brian Shoemaker
Coun.-Jerrel Tomlin
Coun.-John Upham
City Mgr.-Lance Howerton
Clk.-Peggy Clifton
Atty.-Messer, Rockefeller & Fort
C.P.-Dean Sullivan
F.C.-Michael Pool

MINGUS 76463
Pop: 235   (Palo Pinto)
P.O. Box 115
254 672-5995 - *Fax: 672-5995*
Mayor-Milo Moffit
Mayor PT-Janet Lynn
Ald.-Ricky Andreatta
Ald.-Judy Hansford
Ald.-Michael Mackey
Ald.-Debbie Parker
City Secy.-Mindy Scrivner
Atty.-Phil Garrett

MISSION 78572
Pop: 77058   (Hidalgo)
1201 E. 8th Street
956 580-8650 - *Fax: 580-8669*
www.missiontexas.us/
Mayor-Norberto Salinas
Mayor PT-Norie Garza
Coun.-Armando O'Cana
Coun.-Jessica Ortega-Ochoa
Coun.-Ruben Plata
City Mgr.-Martin Garza
City Secy.-Anna Carrillo
P.A.-Eduardo Belmarez
Atty.-Abiel Flores
C.P.-Roberto Dominguez
F.C.-Gilbert Sanchez

MISSOURI CITY 77489
Pop: 67358   (Fort Bend-Harris)
1522 Texas Parkway
281 403-8500 - *Fax: 208-5591*
www.missouricitytx.gov
Mayor-Allen Owen
Mayor PT-Yolanda Ford
Coun.-Jeffrey L. Boney
Coun.-Floyd Emery
Coun.-Anthony Maroulis
Coun.-Chris Preston
Coun.-Jerry Wyatt
City Mgr.-Anthony Snipes
City Secy.-Maria Jackson
P.M.-Sheila Smith, Interim
Atty.-E. Joyce Iyamu
C.P.-Mike Berezin
F.M.-Eugene Campbell

MOBEETIE 79061
Pop: 101   (Wheeler)
P.O. Box 56
806 845-3581 - *Fax: 845-3581*
Mayor-Bobbie Walker
Mayor PT-Patricia Kephart
Ald.-Carl Bowman
Ald.-Robert Briggs
Ald.-Virginia Ridgway
Ald.-Emily Woodfin
City Secy.-Debbie White
F.C.-Jackie Don May

MOBILE CITY
Pop: 188   (Rockwall)
824 Lilac Lane
Rockwall, TX 75087
972 771-3978 - *Fax: 771-3978*
Mayor-Dana Lawson
Comm.-Juan Garcia
Comm.-Pedro Garcia
City Secy.-Lynn Phario

MONAHANS 79756
Pop: 6953 (Ward-Winkler)
112 W. 2nd St.
432 943-4343 - *Fax: 943-7300*
www.cityofmonahans.org
Mayor-David B. Cutbirth
Mayor PT-Ted Ward
Coun.-Ken Benad
Coun.-Richard Hawkins
Coun.-Rudy M. Hernandez
Coun.-Jeppie Wilson
City Mgr.-David Mills
City Secy.-Lorena Marquez
Atty.-Hal Upchurch
C.P.-William Riley
F.C.-Eddie Nelms

MONT BELVIEU 77580
Pop: 6510 (Chambers-Liberty)
P.O. Box 1048
281 576-2213 - *Fax: 385-0121*
www.montbelvieu.net
Mayor-Nick Dixon
Mayor PT-Joey McWilliams
Coun.-Charlotte Carley
Coun.-Tim Duree
Coun.-Arnold Peters
Coun.-Mike Pomykal
Coun.-Ricky Shelton
City Mgr.-Nathan Watkins
Dir. Fin-John Iles
City Secy.-Kori Schweinle
Atty.-J. Grady Randle
C.P.-Virgil Blasdel
F.C.-Kenny Baumbach

MONTGOMERY 77356
Pop: 621 (Montgomery)
P.O. Box 708
936 597-6434 - *Fax: 597-6437*
www.montgomerytexas.gov
Mayor-Kirk Jones
Coun.-Jon Bickford
Coun.-John Champagne
Coun.-Rebecca Huss
Coun.-Dave McCorquodale
Coun.-TJ Wilkerson
City Secy.-Susan Hensley
City Admin.-Jack Yates
Atty.-Larry Foerster
C.P.-James Napolitano

MOODY 76557
Pop: 1371 (McLennan)
P.O. Box 68
254 853-2314 - *Fax: 853-2164*
www.cityofmoody.net/
Mayor-Kenneth Brown
Mayor PT-John Carpenter
Coun.-Charleen Dowell
Coun.-Tina Eaton
Coun.-Delores Inge
Coun.-Robert C. Siler
City Admin.-William Sterling

Atty.-Denny Lessman
C.P.-Roger Kennedy
V.F.D.F.C.-Mike Alton

MOORE STATION
Pop: 198 (Henderson)
4720 County Road 4319
LaRue, TX 75770-3153
903 681-2767 - *Fax: 852-7298*
Mayor-Charles Anderson
Ald.-Lee Bell
Ald.-Carl McKenzie, Sr.
Ald.-Samual McKenzie
Ald.-Eve Smith
C.P.-Jessie McKenzie Jr.

MORAN 76464
Pop: 270 (Shackelford)
340 Fisher Ave.
P.O. Box 97
325 945-3441 - *Fax: 945-2084*
Mayor-Steven W. Taggart
Mayor PT-Stanley Reeves
Coun.-Shirley Babin
Coun.-Lisa McFerrin
Coun.-James Power
Coun.-Alaine Sanders
City Secy.-Jackie Wallace
F.C.-Chris Robinson

MORGAN 76671
Pop: 490 (Bosque)
P.O. Box 381
254 635-2106 - *Fax: 635-2112*
Mayor-Jon Croom, II
Mayor PT-Joann Rodriguez
Ald.-Anthony Alonzo
Ald.-Marisol Alvarez
Ald.-Maricela Aviles
Ald.-Mary Johns
City Secy.-Lori Smith
Atty.-Charles Olson
F.C.-Brian Moore

MORGAN'S POINT 77571
Pop: 352 (Harris)
1415 E. Main Street
281 471-2171 - *Fax: 471-7473*
www.morganspoint-tx.com
Mayor-Michel J. Bechtel
Mayor PT-Mike Fowler
Coun.-Craig Bland
Coun.-Tim Harris
Coun.-Richard Helmle
Coun.-Thomas Sheffield
City Secy.-Megan Mayes
City Admin.-Brian Schneider
Atty.-Olson & Olson
C.P.-Sherri Ditrich
F.C.-Mike Boaz

MORGAN'S POINT RESORT 76513
Pop: 4170 (Bell)
8 Morgan's Point Blvd.
254 780-1334 - *Fax: 780-9287*
Mayor-Dwayne Gossett
Coun.-Keith Dyer
Coun.-Dennis Green
Coun.-Donna Hartman
Coun.-Michael Siegfried
Coun.-Ronald Snow
City Mgr.-David Huseman
City Secy.-Althea Wall
Atty.-Neale Potts
F.C.-John Phillips

MORTON 79346
Pop: 2006 (Cochran)
201 E. Wilson
806 266-8850 - *Fax: 266-5028*
Mayor-Kim Silhan
Mayor PT-Cynthia Casarez
Coun.-Frank Castillo
Coun.-Buckie Dobson
Coun.-Rusty Trull
Coun.-Trina Williams
City Secy.-Brenda Shaw
Atty.-Slater Elza
F.C.-Bill Sutton

MOULTON 77975
Pop: 886 (Lavaca)
P.O. Box 369
361 596-4621 - *Fax: 596-7075*
Mayor-Mark H. Zimmerman
Mayor PT-Kelley Moeller
Coun.-Nathan Beyer
Coun.-Darryl Helfer
Coun.-Michael Ramirez
Coun.-Donald R. Wagner
City Secy.-LuAnn D. Rogers
Atty.-Ken Kvinta
C.P.-Mark Pritchard
F.C.-Tim Koncaba

MOUNT CALM 76673
Pop: 320 (Hill)
P.O. Box 85
254 993-4211 - *Fax: 994-1047*
Mayor-Jimmy Tucker
Mayor PT-Marvin Bailey
Ald.-L. C. Cornish
Ald.-Steven Haught
Ald.-Margaret Hawkins
Ald.-Don Laseter
City Secy.-Maggie Martinez
F.C.-Milton Stuckly

MOUNT ENTERPRISE 75681
Pop: 447 (Rusk)
103 W. Gregg St.
903 822-3269
Mayor-Harvey Graves
Coun.-Mary Jo Baird
Coun.-Richard Chapman
Coun.-Judy Cox
Coun.-Johnny Fryman
Coun.-Kay Wagnan
CityAdm..-Rosena J. Becker-Ross
Atty.-Norman Law Firm
Mar.-Cody Runels

MOUNT PLEASANT 75455
Pop: 16113 (Titus)
501 N. Madison
903 575-4000 - *Fax: 577-1828*
www.mpcity.net
Mayor-Paul O. Meriwether, M.D.
Mayor PT-Robert Nance
Coun.-Tim Dale
Coun.-Brian Heavner
Coun.-Erman Hensel
Coun.-Michael McGahee
City Mgr.-Michael Ahrens
City Secy.-Darleen D. Denman
Atty.-Kerry Wooten
C.P.-Wayne Isbell
F.C.-Larry McRae

MOUNT VERNON 75457
Pop: 2662 (Franklin)
P.O. Drawer 597
903 537-2252 - *Fax: 537-2634*
www.comvtx.com/
Mayor-Margaret Sears
Mayor PT-Ralph Robertson
Coun.-Jeff Briscoe
Coun.-Steve Hammons
Coun.-Stephanie Hyman
Coun.-Kenneth Shelton
City Admin/Secy-Tina Rose
Atty.-Boyles & Lowry
F.C.-Jeremy Cox

MOUNTAIN CITY 78610
Pop: 648 (Hays)
101 Mountain City Drive
512 262-0028
www.mountaincitytx.com
Mayor-Phillip Taylor
Mayor PT-Ralph McClendon Jr.
Coun.-Suzanne Hallam
Coun.-Cyndie Holmes
Coun.-Ray Patterson
Coun.-Lee Taylor
City Mgr.-Vacant
Tres.-Vicki Senefeld
City Secy.-Ellis Craig
Atty.-George E. Hyde

MUENSTER 76252
Pop: 1544 (Cooke)
P.O. Box 208
940 759-2236 - *Fax: 759-2250*
www.ci.muenster.tx.us/
Mayor-Tim Felderhoff
Mayor PT-Jewel Otto
Ald.-Jack Flusche
Ald.-Cliff Sicking
Ald.-Steve Taylor
Ald.-Nick Walterscheid
City Secy.-Ammie J. Hennigan
City Admin.-Stan Endres
Atty.-Chuck Bartush
C.P.-Tom Barr
F.C.-Mitch Creed

MULESHOE 79347
Pop: 5158 (Bailey)
215 S. First St.
806 272-4528 - *Fax: 272-5260*
www.city-of-muleshoe.com
Mayor-Cliff Black
Coun.-Austin Bamert
Coun.-Earl Behrends
Coun.-Colt Ellis
Coun.-Gary Parker
City Mgr.-LeAnn Gallman
City Secy.-Zanea Carpenter
Atty.-Slater Elza
C.P.-Roy Rice
F.C.-Tom Tadd

MULLIN 76864
Pop: 179 (Mills)
P.O. Box 96
325 985-3448
www.cityofmullintexas.com
Mayor-Jean Smith
Mayor PT-Kristi Mickelson
Ald.-Linda Barnum
Ald.-Dorothy Dailey
Ald.-Joe Phelps
Ald.-Chris Willett
City Secy.-Alisha Sieders
F.C.-Bud West

MUNDAY 76371
Pop: 1300 (Knox)
P.O. Drawer 39
940 422-4331 - *Fax: 422-5197*
www.mundaytexas.com/
Mayor-Robert Bowen
Mayor PT-Ryan Cottingham
Ald.-Billy Carden
Ald.-Karen Longan
Ald.-Trey Singleton
Ald.-Exa Lee Smith
City Mgr.-Frank D. Trevino
Clk.-Bianca Harrimon
Atty.-Lina L Reyes-Trevino
C.P.-Chris Mendoza
F.C.-Kyle Bibb

MURCHISON 75778
Pop: 594 (Henderson)
P.O. Box 33
903 469-3710 - *Fax: 469-3386*
Mayor-Greg Smith
Coun.-Layton Gibson
Coun.-Richard Jones
Coun.-Adam Jordan
Coun.-John Placyk
Coun.-Cheryl Smith
City Secy.-Pam Tedford
F.C.-Brandon Irby

MURPHY 75094
Pop: 17708 (Collin)
206 N. Murphy Rd.
972 468-4000 - *Fax: 468-4012*
www.murphytx.org
Mayor-Scott Barna
Mayor PT-Jennifer Berthiaume
Dep. Mayor PT-Sarah Fincanon
Coun.-Chris George
Coun.-Don Reilly
Coun.-Owais Siddiqui
Coun.-Betty Nichols Spraggins
City Mgr.-Mike Castro
City Secy.-Susie Quinn
Atty.-Andy Messer
C.P.-Arthur Cotten
F.C.-Del Albright

MUSTANG RIDGE 78610
Pop: 985 (Caldwell-Travis)
12800 US Hwy. 183 S.
512 243-1775 - *Fax: 243-1048*
Mayor-Alisandro "Joe" Flores
Mayor PT-Charles Laws
Ald.-David Bunn
Ald.-Gregory Dailey
Ald.-Dennis Dorsett
Ald.-David Vela
City Secy.-Sheri Mack
Clk.-Carolyn Vallejo
Atty.-Wes Ritchie
C.P.-Leonard Cantu

NACOGDOCHES 75963
Pop: 32996 (Nacogdoches)
P.O. Box 635030
936 559-2502 - *Fax: 559-2912*
www.ci.nacogdoches.tx.us
Mayor-Shelley Brophy
Mayor PT-Roy Boldon
Coun.-Garth Hinze
Coun.-Matt Moore
Coun.-David Norton
City Mgr.-James P. Jeffers
City Secy.-Jan Vinson
Atty.-Jefferson B. Davis
C.P.-Jim Sevey
F.C.-Keith Kiplinger

NAPLES 75568
Pop: 1378 (Morris)
P.O. Box 340
903 897-2271 - *Fax: 897-2913*
Mayor-Dennis Chartier
Mayor PT-Jacob Wilson
Ald.-Sally Buford
Ald.-Jimmie Byrd
Ald.-Denise Fulcher
Ald.-John Kirkland
City Secy.-Alyssa Browning
Atty.-James L. Clark
C.P.-Tommy Hunt
F.C.-Larry Betts

NASH 75569
Pop: 3450 (Bowie)
P.O. Box 520
903 838-0751 - *Fax: 831-3411*
nashtx.org
Mayor-Robert Bunch
Mayor PT-Cranford Graves
Ald.-Danica Porter
Ald.-Charles Underwood
Ald.-Dale Vickers
Ald.-John Watwood
City Secy.-Jennifer Studdard
City Admin.-Doug Bowers
Atty.-Troy Hornsby
C.P.-Kelly Dial
F.C.-Steven Rogers

NASSAU BAY 77058
Pop: 4002 (Harris)
1800 Space Park #200
281 333-4211 - *Fax: 333-2301*
www.nassaubay.com
Mayor-Mark A. Denman
Coun.-Jonathan Amdur
Coun.-Bryce Klug
Coun.-John Mahon
Coun.-Don Matter
Coun.-Sandra Mossman
Coun.-Bob Warters
City Mgr.-Jason E. Reynolds
City Secy.-Sandra Ham
Atty.-Dick Gregg Jr.
F.M.-Tony Russo

NATALIA 78059
Pop: 1800 (Medina)
P.O. Box 270
830 663-2926 - *Fax: 663-3806*
cityofnatalia.com
Mayor-Tommy F. Ortiz
Mayor PT-Sam Smith
Ald.-Sam "Chip" Bluemel, Jr.
Ald.-Mike Fernandez
Ald.-Darin Frazier
Ald.-Vacant
City Admin.-Lisa S. Hernandez
Atty.-Charles E. "Charlie" Zech
C.P.-Gilberto Rodriguez

NAVARRO 75109
Pop: 229 (Navarro)
903 874-7617
Mayor-Pam Chapman
Ald.-Vickie Lynn Farmer
Ald.-Annie Loper
Ald.-Ricky Owen
Ald.-Ostein Reamy
City Secy.-Lisa Owen
Atty.-Terry Jacobson
F.C.-Jim Coker

NAVASOTA 77868
Pop: 7049 (Grimes)
200 E. McAlpine St.
P.O. Box 910
936 825-6475
www.navasotatx.gov/
Mayor-Bert Miller
Mayor PT-Grant E. Holt
Coun.-Josh M. Fultz
Coun.-Bernie Gessner
Coun.-Geoff Horn
City Mgr.-Brad Stafford
Dir. Fin-Lance Hall
City Secy.-Susie M. Homeyer
Atty.-Cary Bovey
C.P.-Justin Leeth
F.C.-Jason Katkoski

NAZARETH 79063
Pop: 311 (Castro)
P.O. Box 7
806 945-2285 - *Fax: 945-2547*
Mayor-Marlin Durbin
Comm.-Virgil Huseman
Comm.-Felix Mote
City Secy.-Lacey Farris
Atty.-Jack Edwards
F.C.-Dennis Kern

NEDERLAND 77627
Pop: 17547 (Jefferson)
P.O. Box 967
409 723-1505 - *Fax: 723-1550*
www.ci.nederland.tx.us
Mayor-R.A. "Dick" Nugent
Coun.-Don Albanese
Coun.-Talmadge Austin
Coun.-Craig J. Belaire
Coun.-Billy Neal
City Mgr.-Christopher Duque
Clk.-Gay Ferguson
Atty.-Jesse Branick
C.P.-Darrell Bush
F.C.-Gary Collins

NEEDVILLE 77461
Pop: 2823 (Fort Bend)
9022 Main St.
P.O. Box 527
979 793-4253 - *Fax: 793-6055*
www.cityofneedville.com
Mayor-Ernie Stuart
Ald.-Andrew Bohac
Ald.-William "Brady" Kubenka

Ald.-Scott McElrath
Ald.-Chad Nesvadba
Ald.-Rick Sinclair
City Secy.-Brenda Teykl
Atty.-Lora Lenzsch
C.P.-Michael Dickerson
F.C.-Keith Thumann

NEVADA 75173
Pop: 822 (Collin)
424 E. FM 6
972 853-0027 - *Fax: 853-0027*
www.cityofnevadatx.org
Mayor-Trace Kinnard
Ald.-Stephen Allen
Ald.-Gwen Garlington
Ald.-Kenneth Pfannstiel
Ald.-Rudy Vester
City Secy.-Judy Hill
Atty.-James E. Shepherd
F.C.-Chuck Pulvino

NEW BERLIN 78155
Pop: 511 (Guadalupe)
275 FM 2538
830 914-2455
Mayor-Nick Milanovich
Mayor PT-Joyce Wolfe
Ald.-Barbara Gerhart
Ald.-Gilbert R. Merkle
Ald.-Ron Rohde
Ald.-Claire Walters
Tres.-Joan Milanovich
City Secy.-Gil Offer
Atty.-Amy Lea S.J. Akers
Mar.-Wayne Zwicke

NEW BOSTON 75570
Pop: 4550 (Bowie)
P.O. Box 5
903 628-5596 - *Fax: 628-6034*
Mayor-Johnny L. Branson
Mayor PT-David K. Turner
Ald.-Joe II. Dike
Ald.-Richard C Ellis
Ald.-Greg Harmon
Ald.-Jackie L Laney
City Secy.-Darla Faulknor
Atty.-J. Michael Brock
C.P.-Tony King
F.C.-Rodney Williams

NEW BRAUNFELS 78130
Pop: 62998 (Comal-Guadalupe)
550 Landa Street
830 221-4000 - *Fax: 608-2109*
www.nbtexas.org
Mayor-Barron Casteel
Mayor PT-Wayne Peters
Coun.-Leah Garcia
Coun.-Justin Meadows
Coun.-Chris Monceballez
Coun.-Ron Reaves
Coun.-Vacant

City Mgr.-Robert Camareno
City Secy.-Patrick Aten
Atty.-Valeria M. Acevedo
C.P.-Tom Wibert
F.C.-Kenneth Jacks

NEW CHAPEL HILL
Pop: 594 (Smith)
P.O. Box 132717
Tyler, TX 75713
903 283-0700
Mayor-Riley Harris
Ald.-Kenneth Carnes
Ald.-Henry Falgoust
Ald.-Nicole Mathis
Ald.-Rita Turner
Ald.-Mary Lou Tyer
City Secy.-Marvin Harman, Jr.
Atty.-William Sheehy

NEW DEAL 79350
Pop: 794 (Lubbock)
P.O. Box 126
806 746-6399 - *Fax: 746-6505*
Mayor-Leta Owens-Maxfield
Mayor PT-Gayla Teeter
Coun.-Marcos Blanco
Coun.-Todd Smith
Coun.-Wade Smith
Coun.-Gina Stockman
City Secy. Sharon Trumble
Atty.-Todd Hurd
C.P.-Michael Hobson
F.C. Randy Teeter

NEW FAIRVIEW 76078
Pop: 1258 (Wise)
999 Illinois Lane
817 638-5366 - *Fax: 638-5369*
www.ci.new-fairview.tx.us
Mayor-Joe Max Wilson
Mayor PT-Louis "Lou" Moran
Ald.-Mike Georgia
Ald.-Scott Johnson
Ald.-Curtis Kent
Ald.-Rick White
City Adm./Secy-Monica Rodriguez
Aud.-Pete Chaney
Atty.-Bradley Anderle

NEW HOME 79383
Pop: 334 (Lynn)
P.O. Box 278
806 924-7514 - *Fax: 924-7514*
Mayor-David Gandy
Ald.-Evan Clem
Ald.-Brady Gass
Ald.-Jim Olsen
Ald.-Alex Redelsky
City Secy.-Jammie Clem
Atty.-W. Calloway "Cal" Huffaker
F.C.-Dale Clem

NEW HOPE, TOWN OF 75070
Pop: 614 (Collin)
972 548-2489
newhopetx.gov
Mayor-Jeff Herbst
Mayor PT-Bob Parmelee
Coun.-Kimberly Barrow
Coun.-Kelly Huges
Coun.-Carol King
Coun.-Omar Nunez
Town Secy.-Rita Petty
Atty.-John Rapier

NEW LONDON 75682
Pop: 998 (Rusk)
P.O. Box 428
903 895-4466 - *Fax: 895-4668*
Mayor-Dale McNeel
Ald.-Jean Bradshaw
Ald.-Michael Cline
Ald.-Glenda Fleming
Ald.-Stephanie Hawkins
Ald.-Cindy Mitchell
City Secy.-Vicki Gerhardt
Atty.-David Brown
C.P.-Michael Smith
F.C.-Curtis Riley
Dir. P.W.-James Boggus

NEW SUMMERFIELD 75780
Pop: 1111 (Cherokee)
903 726-3651 - *Fax: 726-3544*
Mayor-Jane Barrow
Mayor PT-Brandon Bannister
Ald.-Tammy Byrom
Ald.-Donna Cameron
Ald.-Tim Tipton
Ald.-Don Williams
City Mgr.-Vacant
City Secy.-Casey Davis
Atty.-Dallas Tharpe
C.P.-Dan Finkelstein
F.C.-Scott Bragg

NEW WAVERLY 77358
Pop: 1032 (Walker)
P.O. Box 753
936 344-6621 - *Fax: 344-2346*
Mayor-Dan Underwood
Ald.-Nathaniel James
Ald.-Lisa Koonce
Ald.-Joe Mayrant
Ald.-Vincent Paulsel
Ald.-Ignatius Slott
City Secy.-Rosemary Bartee
Atty.-Larry Foerster
F.C.-Jacob Slott

NEWARK 76071
Pop: 1005 (Wise-Tarrant)
P.O. Box 156
817 489-2201 - *Fax: 489-5202*
www.newarktexas.com
Mayor-Gary L. VanWagner
Mayor PT-Mark Wondolowski
Coun.-Eric Fleischer

Coun.-Chris Raines
Coun.-Vacant
Coun.-Vacant
City Admin.-Diane Rasor
Atty.-Andy Messer
F.C.-James Edgemon

NEWCASTLE 76372
Pop: 585 (Young)
P.O. Box 66
940 846-3547 - *Fax: 846-3200*
Mayor-Gina Maxwell
Mayor PT-Mike Peterson
Ald.-Kim Dodson
Ald.-Adrian Ontiveroz
Ald.-Lynn Robinson
Ald.-Shelly Shields
City Secy.-Cory Spurlin
V.F.D.F.C.-Gary Bohannan

NEWTON 75966
Pop: 2478 (Newton)
101 North St.
409 379-5061 - *Fax: 379-5065*
www.newtontexas.org
Mayor-Mark Bean
Ald.-Mike Adams
Ald.-James Bean
Ald.-Joni Miller
Ald.-John Pollock
Ald.-Tommy Westbrook
City Secy.-Molly Will
City Admin.-Donald H. Meek
Atty.-Guy N. Goodson
C.P.-Will Jackson
F.C.-Herb Kelley

NEYLANDVILLE 75401
Pop: 97 (Hunt)
2469 County Road 4311
Greenville, TX 75401
Mayor-Kathy Wilson
Ald.-Hudson McMurray
Ald.-Carl McMurray
Ald.-Billy Pannell
Ald.-Patricia Wilson
City Secy.-Stephanie Johnson
Atty.-Smith E. Gilley

NIEDERWALD 78640
Pop: 565 (Caldwell-Hays)
8807 Niederwald Strasse
512 398-6338 - *Fax: 376-9966*
Mayor-Reynell Smith
Mayor PT-Monique Boitnott
Ald.-Charles Bisson
Ald.-Kristie Brady
Ald.-Rick Riel
Ald.-Diane Shirey
City Adm./Secy-Richard L. Crandal Jr.
Atty.-Cary Bovey

NIXON 78140
Pop: 2465   (Gonzales-Wilson)
100 W. Third St.
830 582-1924 - *Fax: 582-1136*
www.cityofnixon.org
Mayor-Gladyne Finch
Mayor PT-Patricia Dingler
Ald.-Joseph Bjorgaard
Ald.-Mary Ann Fatheree
Ald.-Doug Koenig
Ald.-Justin B. LaFleur
Int. Mgr.-Harold Rice
City Secy.-Gina Trotter
Atty.-Eduardo "Eddie" Escobar
Int. C.P.-Floyd Toliver
F.C.-Mark Mendez

NOCONA 76255
Pop: 3033   (Montague)
100 Cooke St.
940 825-3282 - *Fax: 825-6240*
Mayor-Robert Fenoglio
Mayor PT-Tracy O'Neal
Coun.-Don C. Davis
Coun.-Robert G. Ferguson
Coun.-Tom Horn
Coun.-Steve Tettleton
City Mgr.-Lynn Henley
City Secy.-Revell Hardison
Atty.-Tracey Jennings
C.P.-Gerald Kent Holcomb
F.C.-Rusty Henley
F.M.-Gerald Kent Holcomb

NOLANVILLE 76559
Pop: 4259   (Bell)
101 North 5th Street
254 698-6335 - *Fax: 698-2540*
ci.nolanville.tx.us/
Mayor-Christina Rosenthal
Mayor PT-George French III
Coun.-James Lynn Bilberry
Coun.-Joan Hinshaw
Coun.-Lawrence "Butch" Reis
Coun.-David Williams
City Mgr.-Kara Escajeda
City Secy.-Crystal Biggs
Atty.-Alan J. Bojorquez
C.P.-Dan Porter
F.C.-Jason Worsdale
Dir. P.W.-Mr. Chris Atkinson

NOME 77629
Pop: 588   (Jefferson)
P.O. Box D
409 253-2391 - *Fax: 253-2533*
Mayor-Kerry Abney
Ald.-Rob Brooks
Ald.-Sean Guillory
Ald.-Cindy Hood
Ald.-Becky Lewis
Ald.-Hob Warren
City Secy.-Vacant
Clk.-Mary Ray
Atty.-Susan Oliver

NOONDAY
Pop: 777   (Smith)
P.O. Box 6425
Tyler, TX 75711-6425
903 561-3351 - *Fax: 561-5371*
Mayor-J. Mike Turman
Mayor PT-Bobby Smith
Coun.-Karl Artmire
Coun.-David Minick
Coun.-Susan Robertson
Coun.-Vivian Turman
City Secy.-Tina Adams

NORDHEIM 78141
Pop: 307   (DeWitt)
P.O. Box 266
361 938-5223 - *Fax: 938-7101*
Mayor-Katherine Payne
Mayor PT-René M. Garcia
Ald.-Larry C. Baucum
Ald.-Patricia Garcia
Ald.-Jose Gonzales, Jr.
Ald.-Roberta Hale
City Secy.-Peggy Johnson
Atty.-James K. Crain
V.F.D.F.C.-Ronald Pfeifer

NORMANGEE 77871
Pop: 778   (Leon-Madison)
P.O. Box 37
936 396-3691 - *Fax: 396-5100*
Mayor-Gary Dawkins
Mayor PT-Troy Noey
Coun.-Timothy Hemphill
Coun.-Melanie Lee
Coun.-Denis Noey
Coun.-William B. Wagner
City Secy.-Sunny Reichert
C.P.-Vacant

NORTH CLEVELAND 77328
Pop: 247   (Liberty)
P.O. Box 1266
281 592-5542 - *Fax: 592-0288*
Mayor-Bob Bartlett
Mayor PT-Joseph Bartlett
Coun.-Robert Bartlett
Coun.-Sue Chapman
Coun.-Jamie Crawford
City Secy.-Vicki Bartlett
C.P.-Frank Chapman

NORTH RICHLAND HILLS
Pop: 63780   (Tarrant)
4301 City Point Dr.
P.O. Box 820609
N.Richland Hills, TX 76182-0609
817 427-6100 - *Fax: 427-6101*
www.nrhtx.com
Mayor-Oscar Trevino
Mayor PT-Scott Turnage
Coun.-Tim Barth
Coun.-Mike Benton
Coun.-Tom Lombard
Coun.-Rita Wright Oujesky

Coun.-Tito Rodriguez
Coun.-Tim Welch
City Mgr.-Mark Hindman
City Secy.-Alicia Richardson
Atty.-Maleshia McGinnis
C.P.-Jimmy Perdue
F.C.-Stan Tinney

NORTHLAKE 76247
Pop: 2650   (Denton)
940 648-3290 - *Fax: 648-0363*
www.town.northlake.tx.us
Mayor-Peter Dewing
Mayor PT-Mike McBride
Coun.-Michael Ganz
Coun.-Roger Sessions
Coun.-Danny Simpson
Coun.-Jean Young
Town Secy.-Shirley Rogers
Town Admin.-Drew Corn
Atty.-Ashley D. Dierker
C.P.-Robert Crawford

NOVICE 79538
Pop: 139   (Coleman)
268 6th Street
P.O. Box 3
325 864-2036
Mayor-Bobby Green
Mayor PT-Wanda Motley
Ald.-Katherine Hollis
Ald.-Ouieda Morris
Ald.-Deanna Whitlock
Ald.-Letica Wilson
City Secy.-Jason Walker
F.C.-Jason Walker

O'BRIEN 79539
Pop: 106   (Haskell)
P.O. Box 38
Mayor-Chris Casillas
Ald.-Joe Banner
Ald.-Jan Frost
Ald.-Jimmy Johnston
Ald.-C.H. Underwood
Ald.-Cathy Watson
City Secy.-Isabel Diaz

O'DONNELL 79351
Pop: 831   (Dawson-Lynn)
P.O. Box 236
806 428-3239 - *Fax: 428-3440*
Mayor-Scott Martinez
Ald.-John David Belasquez
Ald.-Toby Mires
Ald.-Kim Parker
Ald.-Jessie Perez
Ald.-Mark Roye
City Secy.-Esther Smith
Atty.-Cal Huffacker
C.P.-Bill Achey
F.C.-Spencer Pyron

OAK GROVE 75142
Pop: 603 (Kaufman)
214 460-7513
Mayor-Jeff Davis
Mayor PT-Jordan Chambers
Coun.-Edgar Cotton
Coun.-John Dean
Coun.-John Moore, Sr.
Coun.-Don Stoy
City Secy.-Joyce Moore
Atty.-Wade Gent

OAK LEAF 75154
Pop: 1298 (Ellis)
301 Locust Dr.
972 617-2660 - *Fax: 617-7108*
www.oakleaftexas.org
Mayor-Bob Rader
Mayor PT-James Pierce
Coun.-Susanne Ellis
Coun.-Christy Godwin
Coun.-Jimmie Lamb
Coun.-Joyce Liptak
City Secy.-Ronda Quintana
Atty.-J. Michael Weston

OAK POINT 75068
Pop: 2786 (Denton)
100 Naylor Rd.
972 294-2312 - *Fax: 294-1619*
www.oakpointtexas.com
Mayor-Keith Palmer
Mayor PT-Lynn Harpold
Dep. Mayor PT-Judith Camp
Coun.-Jim Almond
Coun.-Donald Lindemann
Coun.-John Lusk
City Mgr.-Luke Olson
City Secy.-Amy Bockes
Atty.-Jeffrey Moore
C.P.-Michael Shackleford

OAK RIDGE
Pop: 495 (Kaufman)
P.O. Box 458
Kaufman, TX 75142
972 551-0343 - *Fax: 551-0345*
www.cityofoakridgetx.com
Mayor-Al Rudin
Mayor PT-Scherri Holmes
Coun.-Janelle Davis
Coun.-Rolando Guzman
Coun.-Nena Langford
Coun.-Jimmy Quick Jr.
City Secy.-Donna Sprague
Atty.-Robert Brown

OAK RIDGE NORTH 77385
Pop: 3049 (Montgomery)
27424 Robinson Rd.
281 292-4648 - *Fax: 367-7729*
www.oakridgenorth.com
Mayor-Jim Kuykendall
Mayor PT-Clint McClaren
Coun.-Paul Bond
Coun.-Michelle Cassio

Coun.-Alex Jones
Coun.-Frances Planchard
City Mgr.-Vicky Rudy
City Secy.-Laura Calcote
Atty.-Christopher L. Nichols
C.P.-A. T. Walters

OAK RIDGE, TOWN OF
Pop: 141 (Cooke)
129 Oak Ridge Dr.
Gainesville, TX 76240
940 665-8474 - *Fax: 665-0232*
Mayor-Chad A. Ramsey
Mayor PT-Denise Langston
Town Secy.-Darlene Nelson
Atty.-Lee Tatum
C.P.-Janet Van Patten
F.C.-Nick Tiller

OAK VALLEY
Pop: 368 (Navarro)
2211 Oak Valley Lane
Corsicana, TX 75110
903 872-3168
Mayor-Linda Bennett
Mayor PT-Neal Silvers
Coun.-Jim Barrington
Coun.-Bill Castner
Coun.-Glenda Robinson
Coun.-Ronnie Spence
City Secy.-Connie Silvers

OAKWOOD 75855
Pop: 471 (Leon)
P.O. Box 96
903 545-2131 - *Fax: 545-2172*
cityofoakwood.tx.citygovt.org
Mayor-Vicki Stroud
Mayor PT-Dorothy Bell
Ald.-Bobbye Bullock
Ald.-Jacquelyn Morrow
Ald.-Mark Neel
Ald.-Barry Olive
City Secy.-Sherry Smith
C.P.-James Hommel
F.C.-Greg Smith
Dir. P.W.-Steve Butler

ODEM 78370
Pop: 2389 (San Patricio)
P.O. Box 754
361 368-2831 - *Fax: 368-4100*
Mayor-Billy Huerta
Mayor PT-Olga Martinez Kiefer
Ald.-Yolanda Roblez Alvaro
Ald.-Virginia Garza
Ald.-Martin Huerta
Ald.-Lynnette Tidwell
City Secy.-Vacant
Atty.-Epimenio Ysassi
F.C.-John Redgate

ODESSA 79760
Pop: 99940 (Ector-Midland)
P.O. Box 4398
432 335-3200 - *Fax: 335-4160*
www.odessa-tx.gov
Mayor-David R. Turner
Coun.-Dewey Bryant
Coun.-Michael Gardner
Coun.-Filiberto Gonzales
Coun.-Barbara Graff
Coun.-Malcolm Hamilton
Int. Mgr.-Michael Marrero
City Secy.-Norma Aguilar-
  Grimaldo
P.A.-Phillip Urrutia
Atty.-Larry Long
C.P.-Michael Gerke
F.C.-John Alvarez
Dir. P.W.-Tom Kerr

OGLESBY 76561
Pop: 484 (Coryell)
P.O. Box 185
254 470-2944 - *Fax: 470-2944*
Mayor-Bruce Pomerenke
Mayor PT-Melissa Leos-Wells
Ald.-Mike Homan
Ald.-Ray McEnroe
Ald.-Tommy Norwood
Ald.-Brenda Williams
City Secy.-Jennifer Thompson
Atty.-Vacant
F.C.-Mark Luckie

OLD RIVER-WINFREE Pop:
1245 (Chambers-Liberty)
P.O. Box 1169
Mont Belvieu, TX 77580-1169
281 385-1735 - *Fax: 385-5465*
Mayor-Joe Landry
Mayor PT-Amber Creel
Ald.-Kenneth Epperson
Ald.-Kathy Franssen
Ald.-Jackie Johnson
Ald.-Judy F. Steadham
City Secy.-Linda Murphy
Atty.-Dane Listi

OLMOS PARK
Pop: 2237 (Bexar)
120 W. El Prado Drive
San Antonio, TX 78212
210 824-3281 - *Fax: 826-5008*
www.olmospark.org
Mayor-Ronald Hornberger
Coun.-Juliana Dusek
Coun.-Casey Fry
Coun.-Kenyon McDonald
Coun.-Enzo Pellegrino
Coun.-Sharon Plant
City Mgr.-Celia DeLeon
City Secy.-Diane Gonzales
Atty.-Frank J. Garza
C.P.-Rene Valenciano
F.C.-John Surber

OLNEY 76374
Pop: 3285 (Young)
P.O. Box 546
940 564-2102 - *Fax: 564-5496*
www.olney.tx.citygovt.org
Mayor-Phil B. Jeske II
Mayor PT-Tom Parker
Coun.-Tommy Kimbro
Coun.-Andrew McPhie
Coun.-Rue Rogers
Coun.-Chuck Stennett
City Secy.-Tim Houston
Clk.-Lydia Greenway
City Admin.-Vacant
Atty.-William A. Myers
C.P.-Barry Louis Roberts
F.C.-Ronnie Keeter

OLTON 79064
Pop: 2215 (Lamb)
P.O. Box 1087
806 285-2611 - *Fax: 285-2139*
Mayor-Mark McFadden
Mayor PT-Allan Williams
Ald.-Ronnie Digby
Ald.-Lupe Ruiz
Ald.-Vacant
Ald.-Vacant
City Secy.-Lynette DeBerry
City Admin.-Keeley Adams
Atty.-Lanny Voss
C.P.-Reginald Holmes Jr.
F.C.-Hector Galvan

OMAHA 75571
Pop: 1021 (Morris)
305 White Oak Avenue
P.O. Box 937
903 884-2302 - *Fax: 884-2746*
Mayor-Ernest Pewitt
Mayor PT-Bettie Roberson
Ald.-Odis Cline
Ald.-William Pope
Ald.-Linda Sibley
Ald.-Junetta Whitecotton
City Secy.-Debbie Lafollett
P.A.-Carl Minton
Atty.-James L. Clark
C.P.-Billy Weatherford
F.C.-Bud McCollum

ONALASKA 77360
Pop: 1764 (Polk)
P.O. Box 880
936 646-5376 - *Fax: 646-2833*
cityofonalaska.us/
Mayor-Roy Newport
Mayor PT-Shirley Gilmore
Coun.-James Arnett
Coun.-Chip Choate
Coun.-Carl Cruse
Coun.-Patsy Goins
City Secy.-Angela Stutts
Atty.-David Moorman
C.P.-Ronald Gilbert
F.C.-J. C. Stutts

OPDYKE WEST
Pop: 174 (Hockley)
301 Drew Drive
Levelland, TX 79336-1179
806 894-1518
Mayor-Wayne Riggins
Ald.-Russell Allen
Ald.-Vicente Cisneros
Ald.-Ginger Mulloy
Ald.-Vacant
Ald.-Vacant
City Secy.-Kelly Dunn

ORANGE 77631
Pop: 18595 (Orange)
P.O. Box 520
409 886-3611 - *Fax: 883-1096*
www.orangetexas.net
Mayor-Jimmy Sims
Mayor PT-Larry Spears Jr.
Coun.-Brad Childs
Coun.-Bill Mello
Coun.-Annette Parnell
Coun.-Patrick A. Pullen
Coun.-Terrie T. Salter
City Mgr.-Shawn Oubre, Ph.D.
City Secy.-Patricia Anderson
P.A.-Kay Gragg
Atty.-John Smith
C.P.-Lane Martin
F.C.-David Frenzel

ORANGE GROVE 78372
Pop: 1318 (Jim Wells)
P.O. Box 1350
361 384-2322 - *Fax: 384-2390*
Mayor-Carl Srp
Mayor PT-Natalie David
Ald.-Noe Aguilar
Ald.-Norma Cornejo
Ald.-Lynn Kichoff
Ald.-Lonnie Wostal
City Secy.-Glena Hackfeld
City Admin.-Rick Lopez
Atty.-Lucinda Garcia
Int. C.P.-Roy Guerrero
F.C.-Lynn Kirchoff

ORCHARD 77464
Pop: 352 (Fort Bend)
P.O. Box 59
979 478-6893
Fax: 888 216-8503
www.orchardtexas.org
Mayor-Rodney Pavlock
Mayor PT-Matt Perreault
Comm.-Joe Supak
City Secy.-Merry Sue Hajdik
Atty.-David Olson

ORE CITY 75683
Pop: 1144 (Upshur)
302 E. Main St.
903 968-2511 - *Fax: 968-6996*
Mayor-Gail Weir
Ald.-Cory Coleman
Ald.-Lee Fuller
Ald.-Kelvin Gunnells
Ald.-Steve Heim
Ald.-Lisa Hobbs
City Secy.-Kristan Kahler
Atty.-Stanton Lowry
C.P.-Dave Morris
F.C.-Gaston DeBerry, III

OVERTON 75684
Pop: 2554 (Rusk-Smith)
P.O. Drawer D
903 834-3171 - *Fax: 834-3174*
www.ci.overton.tx.us
Mayor-C.R. Evans
Mayor PT-Philip Cox
Coun.-Jerry Clark
Coun.-Lawrence Davis
Coun.-John C. Posey, Jr.
Coun.-Michael Paul Williams
Int. Mgr.-Clyde Carter
City Secy.-Rachel Gafford
Atty.-Blake Thompson
C.P.-Clyde Carter
F.C.-Jim White
F.M.-Michael Vinson

OVILLA 75154
Pop: 3998 (Dallas-Ellis)
105 S. Cockrell Hill Road
972 617-7262 - *Fax: 515-3221*
Mayor-Richard A. Dormier
Mayor PT-David Griffin
Coun.-Rachel Huber
Coun. Douglas W. "Doug" Hunt
Coun.-J Michael Myers
Coun.-Dean Oberg
City Mgr.-John R. Dean, Jr.
City Secy.-Pam Higgs Woodall
Atty.-Ron G. MacFarlane Jr.
C.P.-Brian Windham
F.C.-Brandon Kennedy
F.M.-Kevin Lindsey
Dir. P.W.-Brad Piland

OYSTER CREEK 77541
Pop: 1111 (Brazoria)
3210 FM 523
979 233-0243 - *Fax: 233-1568*
Mayor-Clifford Louis Guidry
Mayor PT-Justin Mills
Ald.-Lonnie Carr Jr.
Ald.-Erik Chitwood
Ald.-Darrell Raska
Ald.-Harold Vandergrifft
City Secy.-Andrea Ford
Atty.-Laurence E. Boyd
C.P.-Tim Bradberry
F.C.-Mark Westmoreland

PADUCAH 79248
Pop: 1186 (Cottle)
P.O. Box 759
806 492-3713 - *Fax: 492-2066*
Mayor-Richard Cranford
Coun.-Rodger Brannen
Coun.-Richard Gregory
Coun.-Zach Osburn
Coun.-Andre Patterson
Coun.-Jim Slover
City Secy.-Traci Beck
Clk.-Janice Nash
Atty.-Michael Guevara
C.P.-Roy Lee Rodriquez
F.C.-Chris Wiley

PAINT ROCK 76866
Pop: 273 (Concho)
P.O. Box 157
325 732-4330 - *Fax: 732-4330*
Mayor-Ricky Donalvson
Mayor PT-Paul Thorpe
Ald.-Andrew Archipolo
Ald.-Delton Bailey
Ald.-Brad Dannheim
Ald.-Wesley Evans
City Secy.-Crystal Ellis

PALACIOS 77465
Pop: 4718 (Matagorda)
311 Henderson
361 972-3605 - *Fax: 972-6555*
www.cityofpalacios.org
Mayor-Glen Smith
Ald.-Judy Chavez
Ald.-Mary Crocker
Ald.-Andy Erdelt
Ald.-Troy Lewis
Ald.-Stephen McGovern
Ald.-Johnny Tran
City Mgr.-David Kocurek
City Secy.-Angela Flores
Atty.-Randall B. "Randy" Strong
C.P.-David T. Miles
F.C.-Mike Hooper
Dir. P.W.-David Kauffman

PALESTINE 75801
Pop: 18712 (Anderson)
504 N. Queen St.
903 731-8400 - *Fax: 731-8486*
www.cityofpalestinetx.com
Mayor-Steve Presley
Mayor PT-Doug Smith
Coun.-Joe Baxter
Coun.-Will Brule
Coun.-Vickey L. Chivers
Coun.-Ann Connor
Coun.-Mitchell Jordan
City Mgr.-Mike Hornes
Dir. Fin-Steve Groom
City Secy.-Teresa Herrera
Atty.-Ronald Stutes

F.C.-Shannon Davis
F.M.-Kelly Hughes
Dir. P.W.-Tim Perry

PALISADES
Pop: 325 (Randall)
115 Brentwood
Amarillo, TX 79118
806 622-3165
Mayor-Nate Green
Mayor PT-Amelia Salazar
Ald.-Dale Conner
Ald.-Sherry Fleming
Ald.-Charlie Johnson
Ald.-Viki Massey
Tres.-Phil Boothe
City Secy.-JoAnne Short
Atty.-Angelique Weaver
C.P.-Ronnie Rogers
F.C.-Dennis Massey

PALM VALLEY 78552
Pop: 1304 (Cameron)
1313 Stuart Place Rd.
956 423-8384 - *Fax: 423-6324*
palmvalleytx.com/
Mayor-George Rivera
Mayor PT-John Widger
Coun.-Julie C. Martin
Coun.-Paul Powers
Coun.-Cynthia Thompson
Coun.-Debe Wright
City Secy.-Sylvia R. Trevino
Atty.-Jason R. Mann
C.P.-Alvaro Garcia

PALMER 75152
Pop: 2000 (Ellis)
113 W. Jefferson
P.O. Box 489
972 449-3160 - *Fax: 449-3417*
www.ci.palmer.tx.us/
Mayor-Kenneth Bateman
Mayor PT-Lance Anglin
Ald.-Shannon Conger
Ald.-Jeffery Greenlee
Ald.-Wallace Hughey Jr.
Ald.-Jeff Vick
City Secy.-Alicia Baran
City Admin.-Doug Young
Atty.-Larry Jackson
C.P.-John Zaidle
F.C.-Kevin Rhoades

PALMHURST 78573
Pop: 2607 (Hidalgo)
4417 N. Shary Rd.
956 583-8697 - *Fax: 581-4630*
www.cityofpalmhursttx.com
Mayor-Ramiro J. Rodriguez, Jr.
Mayor PT-Robert A. Salinas
Coun.-James "Jaime" Aranda
Coun.-Ruben DeLeon
Coun.-Ofelia Pena-Perez
Coun.-Israel Silva

City Mgr.-Lori A. Lopez
City Secy.-Richard Garcia
Atty.-Darrell Davis
C.P.-Michael A. Vela

PALMVIEW 78572
Pop: 5460 (Hidalgo)
400 W. Veterans Blvd.
956 432-0300 - *Fax: 581-7494*
cityofpalmview.com
Mayor-Gerardo Perez
Mayor PT-Joseliot Hernandez
Coun.-Joel Garcia
Coun.-Javier Ramirez
Coun.-Linda Sarabia
Coun.-Ricardo Villarreal
City Mgr.-Leonardo Olivares
City Secy.-Bertha Garza
Atty.-Ricardo Perez
C.P.-C. Robert Barrera
F.C.-Jerry Alaniz

PAMPA
Pop: 17994 (Gray)
P.O. Box 2499
Pampa, TX 79065-2499
806 669-5750 - *Fax: 669-5767*
cityofpampa.org
Mayor-Brad Pingel
Comm.-Robert Dixon
Comm.-Karen McLain
Comm.-Chris Porter
Comm.-Gary L. Winton
City Mgr.-Shane Stokes
City Secy.-Karen L. Price
Atty.-Lee Waters
C.P.-Lance Richburg
F.C.-Greg Lee

PANHANDLE 79068
Pop: 2452 (Carson)
P.O. Box 129
806 537-3517 - *Fax: 537-5049*
Mayor-Doyle Robinson
Mayor PT-Brady Shadid
Coun.-Phillip Lacy
Coun.-Bill McLeod
Coun.-Tim Roberts
Coun.-Dusty Sloan
City Mgr.-Terry Coffee
City Secy.-Veronica Willburn
Atty.-Angelique Weaver
C.P.-Sace Hardman
F.C.-Terry Chavez

CITY SECTION

PANORAMA VILLAGE 77304
Pop: 2170 (Montgomery)
99 Hiwon Drive
936 856-2821 - *Fax: 856-2547*
www.panoramavillagetx.gov
Mayor-Lynn Scott
Mayor PT-John Langley
Ald.-Dean Bishop
Ald.-Clint Fowler
Ald.-Doug McEntire
Ald.-Ted Nichols
City Secy.-Lisa F. Evans
Atty.-Larry Foerster
C.P.-Joseph L. Scarboroug
F.C.-Jason Oliphant

PANTEGO, TOWN OF 76013
Pop: 2394 (Tarrant)
1614 S. Bowen Road
817 617-3700 - *Fax: 617-3726*
www.townofpantego.com
Mayor-Doug Davis
Mayor PT-Russell Brewster
Coun.-Fred Adair
Coun.-Jane Barrett
Coun.-Don Funderlic
Coun.-Don Surratt
City Mgr.-Matt Fielder
City Secy.-Jessie Hanks
Atty.-Jim Jeffrey
Dir. P.W.-Scott Williams
Dir. P.S.-Thomas Griffith

PARADISE 76073
Pop: 441 (Wise)
P.O. Box 314
940 969-2114 - *Fax: 969-2205*
Mayor-Roy Steel
Ald.-Amanda Black
Ald.-Brad Largent
Ald.-Sandy Onks
Ald.-Robert Owensby
Ald.-John Ward
City Secy.-Teresa Moody
Atty.-Walter W. Leonard
F.C.-John Neal

PARIS 75461
Pop: 25171 (Lamar)
903 785-7511 - *Fax: 784-1798*
www.paristexas.gov
Mayor-Steve Clifford
Coun.-Cleonne Drake
Coun.-Aaron Jenkins
Coun.-Linda Su Knox
Coun.-Billie Sue Lancaster
Coun.-Paula Portugal
Coun.-Bill Trenado
City Mgr.-John Godwin
Dir. Fin-Gene Anderson
Clk.-Janice Ellis
Atty.-Stephanie Harris
C.P.-Bob Hundley
F.C.-Larry Wright

PARKER 75002
Pop: 4200 (Collin)
5700 East Parker Rd.
972 442-6811 - *Fax: 442-2894*
www.parkertexas.us
Mayor-Z Marshall
Mayor PT-Scott Levine
Coun.-Cindy Meyer
Coun.-Lee Pettle
Coun.-Cleburne Raney
Coun.-Ed Standridge
City Secy.-Patti Scott Grey
City Admin.-Jeff Flanigan
Atty.-Brandon Shelby
C.P.-Richard Brooks
F.C.-Mike Sheff

PASADENA 77501
Pop: 149043 (Harris)
1211 Southmore
P.O. Box 672
713 475-5533 - *Fax: 475-7883*
www.ci.pasadena.tx.us
Mayor-Jeff Wagner
Coun.-Thomas Schoenbein
Coun.-Felipe Villarreal
Coun.-Cody Ray Wheeler
Coun.-Don Harrison
Coun.-Bruce Leamon
Coun.-Sammy Casados
Coun.-Cary Bass
Coun.-Phil Cayten
City Secy.-Linda Rorick
Atty.-Lee Clark
C.P.-Al Espinoza
F.C.-Lanny Armstrong

PATTISON 77466
Pop: 472 (Waller)
P.O. Box 223
281 934-3715
Mayor-Joe Garcia
Mayor PT-Frank Cobio
Coun.-Fred Branch
Coun.-Mikel Leff
Coun.-Robert MacCallum
Coun.-Seth Stokes
City Secy.-Lynda L. Fairchild
Atty.-Monte Akers

PATTON VILLAGE 77372
Pop: 1557 (Montgomery)
16940 Main
281 689-9511 - *Fax: 689-1039*
www.pattonvillage.us/
Mayor-Leah Tarrant
Mayor PT-Randy Lefevre
Coun.-Dave Fields
Coun.-Clyde Reeves
Coun.-Theresa White
Coun.-John Whitworth
City Secy.-Joy Dawson
Atty.-Alan P. Petrov
C.P.-Shannon Sharp

PAYNE SPRINGS
Pop: 767 (Henderson)
19601 CR 2529
Mabank, TX 75156
903 451-9229 - *Fax: 451-0137*
Mayor-Rondney Renberg
Mayor PT-Dick Hoffman
Ald.-Dutch Antonisse
Ald.-Michael Juica
Ald.-Chris Reed
Ald.-Vacant
City Secy.-Karen Juica
Atty.-Blake E. Armstrong

PEARLAND 77581
Pop: 91252 (Brazoria-Fort Bend-Harris)
3519 Liberty Dr.
281 652-1662 - *Fax: 652-1708*
www.pearlandtx.gov
Mayor-Tom Reid
Mayor PT-Derrick Reed
Coun.-Tony Carbone
Coun.-David Little
Coun.-Gary Moore
Coun.-Keith Ordeneaux
Coun.-Woody Owens
Coun.-Trent Perez
City Mgr.-Clay Pearson
City Secy.-Young Lorfing
P.A.-Bob Pearce
Atty.-Darrin Coker
C.P.-Johnny Spires
F.C.-Vance Riley

PEARSALL 78061
Pop: 9146 (Frio)
215 S. Ash St.
830 334-3676 - *Fax: 334-4750*
www.cityofpearsall.org
Mayor-Mary Moore
Mayor PT-Julian Hernandez
Coun.-Ben Briscoe
Coun.-Toby Lopez Jr.
Coun.-Mando Martinez
Coun.-Chris Valadez
Coun.-Robert Villarreal
Coun.-Vacant
City Mgr.-Charles Jackson
Clk.-Krystal Garcia
Atty.-Robert "Bobby" Maldonado
C.P.-Henry Martinez
F.C.-Placido Aguilar

PECAN GAP 75469
Pop: 203 (Delta-Fannin)
P.O. Box 37
903 359-6484
Mayor-Warner Cheney
Mayor PT-Ed Pickard
Ald.-Jack Kiley
Ald.-Raymond Miller
Ald.-Jerry Park
City Secy.-Carol Billingsley
F.C.-Jack Kiley

PECAN HILL 75154
Pop: 626   (Ellis)
1094 S. Lowrance Road
972 617-6274 - *Fax: 576-3174*
www.pecanhill.com
Mayor-Stephanie Starrett
Mayor PT-Don Schmerse
Ald.-Mackey Boone
Ald.-Ellen Hardin
Ald.-Richard Parker
Ald.-Will Rogers
City Secy.-Shelley Martinez
Atty.-Ron G. MacFarlane Jr.
Mar.-Charles Kellis

PECOS 79772
Pop: 8780   (Reeves)
P.O. Box 929
432 445-2421 - *Fax: 445-6670*
www.townofpecoscitytx.com/
Mayor-Venetta Seals
Mayor PT-Gerald Tellez
Ald.-Veronica Baca
Ald.-Wally Moon
Ald.-Oscar Ornelas
Ald.-Arthur Orona
City Mgr.-Seth Sorensen
City Secy.-Syra Nichols
Atty.-Rod Ponton
C.P.-Clay D. McKinney
F.M.-Jack Brookshire

PELICAN BAY 76020
Pop: 1547   (Tarrant)
1300 Pelican Cir.
817 444-1234 - *Fax: 444-2725*
cityofpelicanbay.com/
Mayor-Bill Morley
Mayor PT-Glen Oberg
Ald.-Kevin Crawford
Ald.-Ben Long
Ald.-Linda Sellers
Ald.-Nick Stephenson
City Secy.-Teri Anthony
Atty.-Warren J. Spencer
C.P.-Robert Porter

PENELOPE 76676
Pop: 198   (Hill)
P.O. Box 125
Mayor-Ben Neal
Comm.-Kyle Kucera
Comm.-Vincent Sinkule
City Secy.-Sharon Howard

PENITAS 78576
Pop: 4403   (Hidalgo)
P.O. Box 204
956 581-3345 - *Fax: 581-3346*
www.cityofpenitas.com
Mayor-Rodrigo "Rigo" Lopez
Mayor PT-J.R. Flores
Coun.-Alex Guajardo
Coun.-Ramiro Loya
Coun.-Felipe Quintanilla

City Mgr.-Omar X. Romero
City Secy.-Ana Valdez
Atty.-Rep. Oscar Longoria
C.P.-Roel Bermea

PERRYTON 79070
Pop: 8802   (Ochiltree)
P.O. Box 849
806 435-4014 - *Fax: 435-2490*
Mayor-Charles Kelly
Mayor PT-Kerry Symons
Coun.-Shae Cunningham
Coun.-Zak Felts
Coun.-Greg Good
Coun.-Marcia Hale
City Mgr.-David Landis
City Secy.-Kim Fowler
P.A.-Teressa Creswell
Atty.-Angelique Weaver
C.P.-William Anthony "Tony" Hill
F.C.-Paul Dutcher

PETERSBURG 79250
Pop: 1202   (Hale)
P.O. Box 326
806 667-3461 - *Fax: 667-3678*
www.petersburgtx.com
Mayor-Susie Martinez
Mayor PT-Gilbert Gonzales
Coun.-Nancy Horn
Coun.-Carroll Leon
Coun.-Rosa Marroquin
Coun.-Kim Porter
City Mgr.-Ronald Heggemeier
City Secy.-Kayla Monroe
Atty.-Audie Sciumbato
C.P.-Brandon Thurman
F.C.-Tommy J. Marquez

PETROLIA 76377
Pop: 782   (Clay)
940 524-3315 - *Fax: 524-3657*
Mayor-Buddy Alexander
Mayor PT-Mark Ivey
Ald.-Robert Clemens
Ald.-Everett England
Ald.-DL Lundy
Ald.-Mike McDonld
City Secy.-Belinda Branigan
Atty.-Vacant
F.C.-Buddy Alexander

PETRONILA
Pop: 113   (Nueces)
P.O. Box 1227
Robstown, TX 78380
361 688-5026
Mayor-Todd Wright
Ald.-Robert Beasley
Ald.-Melvin Burch
Ald.-Luis Elizando
Ald.-Diana Sanchez
City Secy.-Sydonia Wright
Atty.-John D. Bell

PFLUGERVILLE 78691
Pop: 56831   (Travis-Williamson)
512 990-6101 - *Fax: 990-4364*
www.pflugervilletx.gov
Mayor-Victor Gonzales
Mayor PT-Omar Pena
Coun.-Mike Heath
Coun.-Jeff Marsh
Coun.-Jim McDonald
Coun.-Rudy Metayer
City Secy.-Karen Thompson
Atty.-Charles Zech
C.P.-Jessica Robledo

PHARR 78577
Pop: 70400   (Hidalgo)
118 S. Cage
P.O. Box 1729
956 402-4100
www.pharr-tx.gov
Mayor-Ambrosio Hernandez
Mayor PT-Roberto Carrillo
Comm.-Mario Bracamontes
Comm.-Ramiro Caballero
Comm.-Daniel Chavez
Comm.-Eleazar Guajardo
Comm.-Ricardo Medina
City Mgr.-Juan C. Guerra,
Dir. Fin-Karla Moya
Clk.-Hilda Pedraza
P.A.-Veronica Gutierrez
Atty.-Patricia Rigney
C.P.-Ruben Villescas
F.C.-Leonardo Perez

PILOT POINT 76258
Pop: 5047   (Denton)
940 686-2165 - *Fax: 686-4338*
www.cityofpilotpoint.org
Mayor-Shea Dane-Patterson
Coun.-Elisa Carrasco
Coun.-Dean Cordell
Coun.-Whitney Delcourt
Coun.-CJ Hilliard
Coun.-Jim Porter
Coun.-John White
Coun.-Vacant
City Mgr.-Alan Guard
City Secy.-Alice Holloway
Atty.-Andy Messer
Int. C.P.-Barry Pennell
F.C.-Heath Hudson

PINE FOREST
Pop: 487   (Orange)
305 Nagel Drive
Vidor, TX 77662
409 786-4100
Mayor-Cathy Nagel
Mayor PT-Kevin Singleton
Coun.-Wesley Brown
Coun.-Jason Dunwoody
Coun.-Brian Elliott
Coun.-Mike Lea
City Secy.-Kimberly Craig
Atty.-Rodney Price

PINE ISLAND, TOWN OF
Pop: 988   (Waller)
36722 Brumlow Rd.
Hempstead, TX 77445
281 433-2529
Fax: 979 826-9727
Mayor-Steve Nagy
Comm.-Clay Cole
Comm.-Mike Garrett
City Secy.-Linda Cole
Atty.-Debra Mergel

PINEHURST
Pop: 2097   (Orange)
2497 Martin Luther King Jr. Drive
Orange, TX 77630
409 886-3873 - *Fax: 886-7660*
www.cityofpinehurst.com
Mayor-Joseph L. "Pete" Runnels
Ald.-Sarah McClendon
Ald.-Dan Mohon
Ald.-T. W. Permenter
Ald.-John Zerko
City Secy.-Debbie Cormier
City Admin.-Robbie L. Hood
Atty.-Tommy Gunn
C.P.-Fred Hanauer, III
F.C.-Shon Branham

PINELAND 75968
Pop: 850   (Sabine)
P.O. Box 6
409 584-2390 - *Fax: 584-2846*
Mayor-Randy Burch
Coun.-Patsy Kilcrease
Coun.-Joe Lane
Coun.-Tracy Lane
Coun.-Don Tate
Coun.-Lisa Welch
City Secy.-Gail Welch
Atty.-Robert G. Neal, Jr.
C.P.-Jeff Richardson
F.C.-Joe Lane

PINEY POINT VILLAGE 77063
Pop: 3125   (Harris)
713 782-0271 - *Fax: 782-0281*
www.pineypt.org
Mayor-Mark Kobelan
Mayor PT-John L. Ebeling
Ald.-Joel Bender
Ald.-Dale Dodds
Ald.-Henry Kollenberg
Ald.-Brian Thompson
City Secy.-Maggie Carty
City Admin.-Roger Nelson
Atty.-David Olson
C.P.-Raymond D. Schultz
F.C.-David Foster

PITTSBURG 75686
Pop: 4497   (Camp)
200 Rusk St.
903 856-3621 - *Fax: 856-0544*
www.pittsburgtexas.com
Mayor-Shawn Kennington
Mayor PT-David Abernathy
Ald.-Kendal Burns
Ald.-Fred Cook
Ald.-John Livingston
Ald.-Rico Willis
City Mgr.-Clint Hardeman
City Secy.-Victoria Janway
Atty.-Michael Setty
C.P.-Richard Penn

PLAINS 79355
Pop: 1481   (Yoakum)
1015 Avenue F
P.O. Box 550
806 456-2288 - *Fax: 456-4341*
Mayor-Pamela K. Redman
Mayor PT-Debbie J. Smith
Coun.-Neal Bearden
Coun.-Christy Martin
Coun.-Alfred Martinez
Coun.-Shane McKinzie
City Secy.-Pamela K. Rowe
City Admin.-Terry B. Howard
Atty.-Richard Husen
F.C.-Peter Redekop

PLAINVIEW 79072
Pop: 22194   (Hale)
901 Broadway
806 296-1100 - *Fax: 296-1125*
www.plainviewtx.org
Mayor-Wendell Dunlap
Mayor PT-Charles N. Starnes
Coun.-Oliver Aldape
Coun.-Susan Blackerby
Coun.-John Gatica
Coun.-Norma Galvan Juarez
Coun.-Teressa King
Coun.-Larry A. Williams
City Mgr.-Jeffrey Snyder
City Secy.-Belinda Hinojosa
Atty.-Vacant
C.P.-Ken Coughlin
F.C.-Mr. Rusty Powers

PLANO 75086
Pop: 277720   (Collin-Denton)
P.O. Box 860358
972 941-7000 - *Fax: 423-9587*
www.plano.gov
Mayor-Harry LaRosiliere
Mayor PT-Rick Grady
Dep. Mayor PT-Ron Kelley
Coun.-Tom Harrison
Coun.-Angela Miner
Coun.-Kayci Prince
Coun.-Anthony Ricciardelli
Coun.-Rick Smith

City Mgr.-Bruce D. Glasscock
City Secy.-Lisa Henderson
Atty.-Paige Mims
C.P.-Gregory W. Rushin
F.C.-Sam Greif

PLEAK VILLAGE
Pop: 1044   (Fort Bend)
6621 FM 2218 S.
Richmond, TX 77469
281 239-8504 - *Fax: 239-8504*
villageofpleak.com
Mayor-Larry J. Bittner
Mayor PT-Michael A. John
Ald.-Wade A. Goates
Ald.-Brenda Jaynes
Ald.-Damon Kuhn
Ald.-Al Warnasch
City Secy.-Nancy Walker
Atty.-Lora Lenzsch
F.C.-Jordan Blegen

PLEASANT VALLEY
Pop: 336   (Wichita)
4006 Bus. 287 J
Iowa Park, TX 76367
940 851-8518 - *Fax: 851-8513*
Mayor-J. D. Gholson
Ald.-Phil Bess
Ald.-Randy Brown
Ald.-Merla Rogers
Ald.-Joe Slack
Ald.-Ronnie Waters
City Secy.-Joann Moer
City Admin.-Norm Hodges
P.A.-Norm Hodges
Atty.-Jay Cantrell

PLEASANTON 78064
Pop: 8934   (Atascosa)
P.O. Box 209
830 569-3867 - *Fax: 569-5974*
www.pleasantontx.org
Mayor-Clinton J. Powell
Mayor PT-Travis Hall
Coun.-Eliseo Flores
Coun.-Kenneth A. Hernandez
Coun.-Robert Lionhardt
Coun.-Diana K. Prasifka
Coun.-Robert Earl Wood
Int. Mgr.-Johnny Huizar
City Secy.-Andres Aguirre
Atty.-Robert "Bobby" Maldonado
C.P.-Ronald Sanchez
F.C.-Chuck Garris

PLUM GROVE
Pop: 600 (Liberty)
P.O. Box 1358
Splendora, TX 77372
281 659-4300
Mayor-LeeAnn Walker
Ald.-Calvin Lee
Ald.-Barbara Norris
Ald.-Melissa Pouncey
Ald.-Sharon Reed
Ald.-Marilyn Willis
City Secy.-Vacant
F.C.-Joe Johnson, II

POINT 75472
Pop: 820 (Rains)
365 Locust
903 598-3296 - *Fax: 598-3371*
Mayor-Johnny Northcutt
Mayor PT-Drew Roberts
Coun.-John Ellsworth
Coun.-Kurt Fischer
Coun.-Judy Luckett
Coun.-Mary Oler
City Secy.-Angelia Good
Atty.-Jim D. McLeroy
C.P.-Tony Ingram
F.C.-Richie Schillinger
Dir. P.W.-Charles Lilley

POINT BLANK 77364
Pop: 688 (San Jacinto)
P.O Box 479
936 377-2899 - *Fax: 377-2900*
Mayor-Mark T. Wood
Ald.-Mel Basham
Ald.-Larry Gumpert
Ald.-Chuck King
Ald.-Paul Singleton
Ald.-Roy Tipton
City Secy.-Kelly Hoot

POINT COMFORT 77978
Pop: 737 (Calhoun)
P.O. Box 497
361 987-266 - *Fax: 987-2798*
Mayor-Leslie Machicek
Mayor PT-Linda Brush
Coun.-George Hernandez
Coun.-Kelli Hischer Hynes
Coun.-Stephen Lambden
Coun.-Wesley McKelvy
City Secy.-Rhonda Wilkins
Atty.-Carly Wall
C.P.-Roger Free
F.C.-Steve Lambden

POINT VENTURE 78645
Pop: 800 (Travis)
18606 Venture Drive
512 267-5511 - *Fax: 267-0818*
www.vopv.org
Mayor-Jeffrey Warneke
Mayor PT-Roy Ables
Coun.-Kris Arrieta
Coun.-Donald Conyer
Coun.-Matthew Meyer
Coun.-Stacey Worsham
City Secy.-Vacant
Atty.-Monte Akers

PONDER, TOWN OF 76259
Pop: 1395 (Denton)
405 Shaffner St.
940 479-2396 - *Fax: 479-2100*
www.pondertx.com
Mayor-John Bassler
Mayor PT-Alan Gorman
Coun.-Dan Cockburn
Coun.-Ben Crowell
Coun.-Robert M. Mann
Coun.-Matthew Poole
Town Secy.-Sheri Clearman
Atty.-John Boyle
C.P.-Robert Genova
F.C.-Charlie Williams

PORT ARANSAS 78373
Pop: 3480 (Nueces)
710 W. Avenue A
361 749-4111 - *Fax: 749-4723*
www.cityofportaransas.org
Mayor-Charles R. Bujan
Mayor PT-Wendy Moore
Coun.-Beverly Bolner
Coun.-Bruce Clark
Coun.-Charles Crawford, Jr.
Coun.-Joan Holt
Coun.-Beth Owens
City Mgr.-David Parsons
Dir. Fin-Darla Honea
City Secy.-Irma Parker
Atty.-Michael Morris
C.P.-Scott Burroughs
F.C.-Chris Shanklin

PORT ARTHUR 77641
Pop: 53818 (Jefferson)
P.O. Box 1089
409 983-8115 - *Fax: 983-8128*
www.portarthur.net
Mayor-Derrick Freeman
Mayor PT-Cal J. Jones
Coun.-Harold Doucet
Coun.-Kaprina Frank
Coun.-Thomas J. Kinlaw III
Coun.-Willie "Bae" Lewis Jr.
Coun.-Charlotte Moses
Coun.-Raymond Scott Jr.
Coun.-Osman Swati
City Mgr.-Vacant
Dir. Fin-Andrew Vasquez

City Secy.-Sherri Bellard
P.A.-Clifton Williams
Atty.-Valencia "Val" Tizeno
C.P.-Patrick Melvin
F.C.-Larry Richard

PORT ISABEL 78578
Pop: 5006 (Cameron)
305 East Maxan St.
956 943-2682 - *Fax: 943-2029*
www.portisabel-texas.com/cityhall
Mayor-Juan Jose "JJ" Zamora
Comm.-Martin Cantu, Jr.
Comm.-Martin C. Cantu
Comm.-Jeffery David Martinez
Comm.-Carmen Rios
City Mgr.-Jared Hockema
City Secy.-Susie Alcocer
Atty.-Gilberto Hinojosa
C.P.-Robert Lopez
F.M.-John Sandoval

PORT LAVACA 77979
Pop: 12248 (Calhoun)
202 N. Virginia
361 552-7933 - *Fax: 552-7933*
www.portlavaca.org
Mayor-Jack Whitlow
Mayor PT-Ken Barr
Coun.-Tim Dent
Coun.-Rosie Padron
Coun.-Jan Regan
Coun.-Jerry Smith
Coun.-Jim Ward
City Mgr.-Vacant
City Secy.-Mandy Grant
Atty.-Anne Marie Odefey
C.P.-Colin Rangnow
F.C.-Joe Reyes

PORT NECHES 77651
Pop: 13040 (Jefferson)
P.O. Box 758
409 719-4208 - *Fax: 719-4302*
www.ci.port-neches.tx.us
Mayor-Glenn Johnson
Mayor PT-Julie Gauthier
Coun.-Adam Anders
Coun.-Robert Arnold
Coun.-John Davenport
Coun.-Chris McMahon
City Mgr.-Andre' Wimer
City Secy.-Jamie Mendoza
Atty.-Pete Steele
C.P.-Paul Lemoine
F.C.-Steve Curran
Dir. P.W.-Taylor Shelton

PORTLAND 78374
Pop: 15099 (Nueces-San Patricio)
1900 Billy G Webb Drive
361 777-4500 - *Fax: 777-4501*
portlandtx.com
Mayor-David Krebs
Mayor PT-Ron Jorgensen
Coun.-John Green
Coun.-Gary Moore, Sr.
Coun.-Cathy Skurow
Coun.-John G. Sutton, Jr.
Coun.-Bill T. Wilson II
City Mgr.-Randy L. Wright
Dir. Fin-Katie Griffin
City Secy.-Annette Hall
Atty.-Hal George
C.P.-Mark Cory
F.C.-Lyle Lombard

POST 79356
Pop: 5376 (Garza)
105 E. Main St.
806 495-2811 - *Fax: 990-3724*
Mayor-Archie Gill
Mayor PT-Anita Morris
Ald.-Melba Cimental
Ald.-Pixie Grisham
Ald.-Les Looney
Ald.-Mark Short
City Secy.-Deana Smith
Atty.-Slater Elza
F.C.-Les Looney

POST OAK BEND CITY
Pop: 600 (Kaufman)
1175 County Road 278
Kaufman, TX 75142
214 686-8887
Mayor-Raymond Bedrick
Mayor PT-Billy McMahan, Jr.
Ald.-Judith Ball
Ald.-Jonathan Hicks
Ald.-Jimmy Lambeth
Ald.-Stephen McMahon
City Secy.-Barbara Bedrick

POTEET 78065
Pop: 3260 (Atascosa)
P.O. Box 378
830 742-3574 - *Fax: 742-8747*
Mayor-Albert Trevino
Ald.-Reynaldo Anzaldva
Ald.-Susanna Perez
Ald.-Estella Rocha
Ald.-Nicholas Sanchez
Ald.-Richard Tuttle
City Secy.-Abigayle Frautschi
City Admin.-Eric Jiminez
Atty.-Robert "Bobby" Maldonado
C.P.-Bruce Hickman
F.C.-Curtis Adams
Dir. P.W.-Robert Buentello

POTH 78147
Pop: 1908 (Wilson)
P.O. Box 579
830 484-2111 - *Fax: 484-2374*
www.cityofpoth.org
Mayor-Anthony Smolka
Mayor PT-Chrystal Eckel
Ald.-Chuck Morris
Ald.-Keith Rogers
Ald.-Ronald Weimer
Ald.-Steven Wiatrek
City Secy.-Rose Huizar
Atty.-Vacant
C.P.-Gerald Sanchez
F.C.-Lawrence Jansky
Dir. P.S.-Kenneth Griffin

POTTSBORO 75076
Pop: 2160 (Grayson)
P.O. Box 1089
903 786-2281 - *Fax: 786-6393*
www.pottsboro.govoffice2.com
Mayor-Frank Budra
Mayor PT-David Waller
Ald.-Bruce Barnett
Ald.-Landon Goin
Ald.-Summer Holbrook
Ald.-Gary Watkins
City Mgr.-Kevin M. Farley
City Secy.-Denise Smith
Atty.-Peter K. Munson
C.P.-Shone Nix
F.C.-Donnie Glenn

POWELL 75153
Pop: 136 (Navarro)
P.O. Box 426
Mayor-Clay Jackson
Coun.-Wayne Cotten
Coun.-Mike Hestand
City Secy.-Vacant
F.C.-Tony Kuta

POYNOR 75782
Pop: 305 (Henderson)
P.O. Box 191
903 876-2673
Mayor-Dannie Smith
Mayor PT-Mickye Bristow
Ald.-Lloyd Hanks
Ald.-Bobby Holcomb
Ald.-Bonnie Stringfield
Ald.-Randy Williams
City Secy.-Charlotte Ethridge
Atty.-Blake E. Armstrong
F.C.-Mark Craig

PRAIRIE VIEW 77446
Pop: 5576 (Waller)
P.O. Box 817
936 857-3711 - *Fax: 857-5836*
www.prairieviewtexas.gov
Mayor-David Allen
Coun.-Kendric D. Jones
Coun.-Paulette Matthews-Barnett
Coun.-Jonathan Randle
Coun.-Brian Rowland
Coun.-Wendy Williams
City Admin/Secy-Vacant
Atty.-Olson & Olson
C.P.-Anthony Solomon
F.C.-Frank D. Jackson

PREMONT 78375
Pop: 2653 (Jim Wells)
P.O. Drawer 340
361 348-2022 - *Fax: 348-3247*
Mayor-Mario A. Rodriguez
Mayor PT-Idolina Perez
Coun.-Richard Belasquez
Coun.-Raul R. Garcia
Coun.-Andres Garza
Coun.-Irma C. Martinez
City Secy.-Iris Flores
Atty.-Terry Canales
C.P.-Bill Hack
F.C.-Jerry LaRue

PRESIDIO 79845
Pop: 4426 (Presidio)
507 W. O'Reilly St.
P.O. Box 1899
432 229-3517 - *Fax: 229-3505*
presidiotx.us/
Mayor-John Ferguson
Mayor PT-Alcee Manuel Tavarez
Ald.-Samuel Carrasco
Ald.-Victor Hernandez
Ald.-Antonio Manriquez
Ald.-Isela Nunez
City Admin.-Joe Tortillo
Atty.-Rod Ponton
C.P.-Marco Baeza
V.F.D.F.C.-Saul Pardo

PRIMERA 78552
Pop: 4070 (Cameron)
22893 Stuart Place Road
956 423-9654 - *Fax: 423-2166*
Mayor-Dave Kusch
Mayor PT-Hilda Siller
Ald.-Rudy Garza Jr.
Ald.-Chuck Navarro
Ald.-Diana Ramirez
Ald.-Felix Siller
City Secy.-Javier Mendez
Atty.-Gustavo Ruiz
C.P.-Manuel Trevino

PRINCETON 75407
Pop: 10000   (Collin)
123 W. Princeton Dr.
972 734-2416 - *Fax: 734-2548*
www.princetontx.gov
Mayor-John Mark Caldwell
Ald.-Nathan P. Council
Ald.-Mike Guillen
Ald.-Rich Hooper
Ald.-David Kleiber
Coun.-Steven Deffibaugh
City Mgr.-Derek Borg
City Secy.-Lesia Gronemeier
Atty.-Wolf, Tidwell & McCoy, LLP
C.P.-James Waters
F.C.-Thomas Harvey

PROGRESO 78579
Pop: 5507   (Hidalgo)
300 N. FM 1015
956 565-0241 - *Fax: 565-1332*
Mayor-Arturo Aleman
Mayor PT-Ruben Abundiz
Ald.-Gerardo Alanis
Ald.-Armendo Cavazos
Ald.-Eric Chaidez
Ald.-Blas Medrano
City Secy.-Frank Alaniz
Clk.-Raul Garcia
City Admin.-Alfredo Espinosa
Atty.-Javier Villalobos
C.P.-David Hernandez

PROGRESO LAKES 78579
Pop: 250   (Hidalgo)
P.O. Box 760
956 565-3602 - *Fax: 565-3602*
Mayor-O. D. "Butch" Emery
Mayor PT-Harold Seiver
Ald.-Benton Beckwith
Ald.-Karen Evans
Ald.-David Martin
Ald.-James Payne
City Secy.-Maria V. Valdez
Atty.-Ivan Perez

PROSPER, TOWN OF 75078
Pop: 14710   (Collin-Denton)
P.O. Box 307
972 569-1011 - *Fax: 346-9335*
www.prospertx.gov
Mayor-Ray Smith
Mayor PT-Curry Vogelsang Jr.
Dep. Mayor PT-Jason Dixon
Coun.-Kenneth Dugger
Coun.-Jeff Hodges
Coun.-Mike Korbuly
Coun.-Meigs Miller
Town Mgr.-Harlan Jefferson
Town Secy.-Robyn Battle
C.P.-Doug Kowalski
F.C.-Ronnie Tucker
Town Attorney-Terrence Welch

PROVIDENCE VILLAGE, TOWN OF 76227
Pop: 6310   (Denton)
940 365-9333 - *Fax: 365-9373*
townofprovidencevillage.com
Mayor-Michael Jordan
Mayor PT-J. Eric Newton
Ald.-Chris Blue
Ald.-James T. Connor III
Ald.-Linda Inman
Ald.-Steve Miller
Town Mayor-Brian D. Roberson
Town Secy.-Connie Hansen
Town Clk.-Jenny Sawyers
Atty.-Julie Fort

PUTNAM 76469
Pop: 94   (Callahan)
P.O. Box 1064
325 662-3601 - *Fax: 662-3552*
Mayor-Hubert Donaway
Mayor PT-Marty Smith
Ald.-Gayle Isenhower
Ald.-Ken Newman
Ald.-Darlene Reed
Ald.-Sheri Whitehead
City Secy.-Mary Green
F.C.-Marty Smith

PYOTE 79777
Pop: 114   (Ward)
P.O. Box 137
432 389-5845 - *Fax: 389-5845*
Mayor PT-Abigail Pritchard
Ald.-Sharon Coughran
Ald.-Jerry Tefertiller
Ald.-Vacant
City Mgr.-Lloyd F. Collins
City Secy.-Schasta Carter
V.F.D.F.C.-Harol Don Creech

QUANAH 79252
Pop: 2641   (Hardeman)
P.O. Box 629
940 663-5336 - *Fax: 663-6241*
Mayor-Dale Eaton
Ald.-Susie Bagby
Ald.-Neita Brandon
Ald.-Ricky Deel
Ald.-Nell Looper
Ald.-Jason Poole
Ald.-Michael Woods
City Mgr.-Paula Wilson
Atty.-David Brinkerhoff
F.C.-Alan Whitaker

QUEEN CITY 75572
Pop: 1476   (Cass)
P.O. Box 301
903 796-7986 - *Fax: 855 330-1186*
Mayor-Harold Martin
Mayor PT-William Quarrels
Ald.-A.M. Benefield
Ald.-Jean Cothren
Ald.-Jackie Gilliam

Ald.-Charles Mathus
City Secy.-Vickie Ray
Atty.-Butch Dunbar
C.P.-Robert W. McGee

QUINLAN 75474
Pop: 1394   (Hunt)
P.O. Box 2740
903 356-3306 - *Fax: 356-4267*
Mayor-Jacky Goleman
Mayor PT-Brandon Frazier
Ald.-Tim McDaniel
Ald.-R.W. Oliver
Ald.-Miguel Serrano
Ald.-Tommy Underwood
City Secy.-Laura Kennemer
City Admin.-John Adel
Atty.-Jeffrey L. Moore
C.P.-Johnny Thornburg

QUINTANA, TOWN OF 77541
Pop: 56   (Brazoria)
814 N. Lamar
979 233-0848 - *Fax: 239-1815*
www.quintanatx.org
Mayor-Stephen Alongis
Ald.-Debbie Alongis
Ald.-Mike Cassata
Ald.-Mike Fletcher
Ald.-Macedonio Salinas
Ald. Shari Wright
Town Admin.-Tammi Cimiotta
Atty.-Alan P. Petrov

QUITAQUE 79255
Pop: 411   (Briscoe)
P.O. Box 427
806 455-1456 - *Fax: 455-1225*
Mayor-Janice Henson
Mayor PT-Phil Barefield
Ald.-Arnold Castillo
Ald.-Dennis Farley
Ald.-Ruth Proctor
Ald.-Brandei Taylor
City Mgr.-Maria Cruz Merrell
F.C.-Jake Gass

QUITMAN 75783
Pop: 1809   (Wood)
401 E. Goode
P.O. Box 1855
903 763-2223 - *Fax: 763-5631*
www.quitmantx.org
Mayor-David Dobbs
Mayor PT-Randy C. Dunn
Ald.-Kevin Gilbreath
Ald.-Brad Medlin
Ald.-Susan Resnik
Ald.-Vacant
City Admin/Secy-Gregory D. Hollen
Atty.-Jim D. McLeroy
C.P.-Kelly Cole
V.F.D.F.C.-Scott Wheeler

CITY SECTION

RALLS 79357
Pop: 1944 (Crosby)
800 Ave. I
806 253-2558 - *Fax: 253-2550*
Mayor-Heath Verett
Mayor PT-Don Hamilton
Ald.-Ricky Arthur
Ald.-Giselle Brock
Ald.-Bruce K. Harris
Ald.-Gail Johnson
Ald.-Johnny Zuniga
City Secy.-Kimberly Perez
City Admin.-Gloria Velasquez
Atty.-Matt Wade
F.C.-William R. Tidwell
Dir. P.S.-Aunie Sellers

RANCHO VIEJO 78575
Pop: 2437 (Cameron)
3301 Carmen Ave.
956 350-4093 - *Fax: 350-4156*
www.ranchoviejotexas.com
Mayor-Cyndie Rathbun
Mayor PT-Bitty Truan
Ald.-Maribel Guerrero
Ald.-Erick Lucio
Ald.-Grace Salinas
Ald.-Javier Vera
Town Admin.-Fred Blanco
Atty.-Daniel Rentfro
C.P.-Manuel Cruz, Jr.
F.C.-Volunteer Fire Dept.

RANGER 76470
Pop: 2468 (Eastland)
400 W. Main St.
254 647-3522 - *Fax: 647-1407*
Mayor-Joe Pilgrim
Comm.-John Casey
Comm.-Vicki Gerdes
Comm.-Esther Pierce
Comm.-Vacant
City Mgr. Chad Roberts
City Secy.-Savannah Fortenberry
Atty.-Barney Knight
C.P.-Vacant
F.C.-Darrell Fox

RANGERVILLE
Pop: 289 (Cameron)
31850 Rangerville Rd.
San Benito, TX 78586
956 873-2816 - *Fax: 423-4671*
Mayor-Wayne Halbert
Comm.-Chris Allen
Comm.-Rene de los Santos
City Secy.-Vacant
Atty.-William Wepfer

RANKIN 79778
Pop: 778 (Upton)
P.O. Box 61
432 693-2474 - *Fax: 693-2471*
Mayor-Brandon Brown
Mayor PT-Tammy Gomez
Ald.-Murry Brooks

Ald.-Vonda Garner
Ald.-JoJo Guerra
Ald.-Timothy Potter
City Secy.-Miriam Watson
Atty.-Chad Elkins
V.F.D.F.C.-Jesus Lopez

RANSOM CANYON 79366
Pop: 1096 (Lubbock)
24 Lee Kitchens Dr.
806 829-2470 - *Fax: 829-2680*
Mayor-Billy Williams
Mayor PT-Jana Trew
Ald.-Michael Brooks
Ald.-Brandt Underwood
Ald.-Dr. Terry Waldren
Ald.-Lyle Way
City Admin.-Maria Elena
 Quintanilla
Atty.-John Sims
C.P.-James Hill
F.C.-Rand McPherson

RAVENNA 75476
Pop: 209 (Fannin)
103 N. Main
P.O. Box 88
903 486-6687
Mayor-Claude L. Lewis
Mayor PT-Ronnie Bruce
Comm.-Joseph Passanisi
City Secy.-David E. Jones
V.F.D.F.C.-Kenny Sewell

RAYMONDVILLE 78580
Pop: 11284 (Willacy)
142 S. 7th Street
956 689-2443 - *Fax: 689-0981*
raymondvilletx.us/
Mayor-Gilbert Gonzales
Mayor PT-Clifton Smith
Comm.-Yolanda Alexandre
Comm.-Zeke Cavazos
Comm.-Chris Tamez
City Mgr.-Eleazar Garcia, Jr.
Atty.-William Wepfer
C.P.-Uvaldo Zamora
F.C.-Oscar Gutierrez
Dir. P.W.-Joel Soto

RED LICK
Pop: 1008 (Bowie)
3193 Old Redlick Road
Texarkana, TX 75503
903 831-3691 - *Fax: 831-3691*
Mayor-Ronald Higgins
Mayor PT-Bob Akin
Ald.-Wendell Boozer
Ald.-Lila Murray
Ald.-Jerry Norton
Ald.-Vacant
City Secy.-Linda Lowe

RED OAK 75154
Pop: 11560 (Ellis)
P.O. Box 393
972 617-3638
www.redoaktx.org
Mayor-Alan Hugley
Mayor PT-Gordon Toney
Coun.-William L. Drake
Coun.-Timothy Lightfoot
Coun.-L. Scott Lindsey
Coun.-Ron Wilson
City Mgr.-Todd Fuller
Dir. Fin-Virginia Richardson
City Secy.-Dana Argumaniz
Atty.-Robert E. Hager
C.P.-Garland Wolf
F.C.-Eric Thompson

REDWATER 75573
Pop: 1057 (Bowie)
P.O. Box 209
903 671-2775 - *Fax: 671-2625*
www.redwatertexas.com
Mayor-Robert Lorance
Mayor PT-Leo Whelchel
Coun.-Charles "Chuck" Bradford
Coun.-Paula Coggin
Coun.-Tammy Cowdery
Coun.-Ronnie Starkey
Dir. Fin-Webb Stanley
City Secy.-Dessie Whelchel
Atty.-Cary Rochelle
V.F.D.F.C.-Alton Wheat

REFUGIO 78377
Pop: 2890 (Refugio)
P.O. Box 1020
361 526-5361 - *Fax: 526-5614*
Mayor-Wanda Dukes
Ald.-Leonard Anzaldua
Ald.-Frank Hosey
Ald.-Michael Rocha
Ald.-Dale Skrobarcek
Ald.-Karen A. Watts
City Secy.-Callie Shreckengost
Atty.-Michael Morris
C.P.-Enrigue Diaz
F.C.-Don Pullin

REKLAW 75784
Pop: 379 (Cherokee-Rusk)
P.O. Box 250
936 369-4368 - *Fax: 369-4228*
Mayor-Harlan Crawford
Mayor PT-Jenelle Laughlin
Ald.-Larry Irwin
Ald.-Betty Jackson
Ald.-Johnnie Miller
Ald.-Bob Parrott
City Secy.-Judy Ritter
Atty.-Steven Guy
F.C.-Francisco Hernandez

RENO
Pop: 2494 (Parker)
195 W. Reno Rd.
Azle, TX 76020-6001
817 221-2500 - *Fax: 221-3650*
www.cityofrenotx.com
Mayor-Eric Hunter
Mayor PT-Bonnie Black
Coun.-John Basham
Coun.-Ken Parnell
Coun.-Billie Steele
Coun.-Larry Trammell
City Secy.-Ramah Burns
City Admin.-Joe Polino
Atty.-Walter W. Leonard
C.P.-Timothy C. Holzschuh
V.F.D.F.C.-Shannon Smithers
Dir. P.W.-Scott Passmore

RENO 75462
Pop: 3166 (Lamar)
160 Blackburn St.
903 785-6581 - *Fax: 785-0453*
www.renotexas.us
Mayor-Bart Jetton
Mayor PT-Joey McCarthy
Ald.-Rick Jordan
Ald.-Stacey Nichols
Ald.-Brandon Thomas
Ald.-Amanda Willows
Int, City Secy.-Tricia Smith
Atty.-David Hamilton
C.P.-Matt Birch
F.C.-Chad Graves

RETREAT
Pop: 377 (Navarro)
621 N. Spikes Road
Corsicana, TX 75110
903 654-8348
Mayor-Janice Barfknecht
Mayor PT-Norman L. Gorzynski
Ald.-Justin Barham
Ald.-Terry Barrett
Ald.-Danny Hudson
Ald.-John Robinson
City Secy.-Diana Robinson
F.C.-Hunter Smith

RHOME 76078
Pop: 1573 (Wise)
P.O. Box 228
817 636-2462 - *Fax: 636-2465*
www.cityofrhome.com
Mayor-Michelle Pittman Di Credico
Mayor PT-Sam Eason
Coun.-Kenny Crenshaw
Coun.-Colton Lorance
Coun.-Leeanne Mackowski
Coun.-Charles Pennington
City Secy.-Shannon Montgomery
Atty.-Carvan Adkins
C.P.-Sam Love
F.C.-Darrell Fitch
Dir. P.W.-Lance Petty

RICE 75155
Pop: 923 (Navarro)
P.O. Box 97
903 326-7500 - *Fax: 326-7106*
Mayor-Vickie Young
Ald.-Jessica Chatman
Ald.-John Perry
Ald.-Doug Soffell
Ald.-Garry Teague
Ald.-Robby Valdez
City Admin.-Tonya Roberts
Atty.-Robert E. Hager
C.P.-Charles Parson

RICHARDSON 75083
Pop: 102430 (Collin-Dallas)
411 W. Arapaho Road
P.O. Box 830309
972 744-4203 - *Fax: 744-5803*
www.cor.net
Mayor-Paul Voelker
Mayor PT-Mark Solomon
Coun.-Bob Dubey
Coun.-Scott Dunn
Coun.-Marta Gomez Frey
Coun.-Steve Mitchell
Coun.-Mabel Simpson
City Mgr.-Dan Johnson
City Secy.-Aimee Nemer
P.M.-Todd Gastorf
Atty.-Peter G. Smith
C.P.-Jim Spivey
F.C.-Curtis Poovey

RICHLAND 76681
Pop: 264 (Navarro)
P.O. Box 179
903 362-3707 - *Fax: 362-1953*
Mayor-Kenneth Guard
Mayor PT-Shirley Thomas
Coun.-Caren Brown-Smith
Coun.-Jodie Farmer
Coun.-Jay Tidwell
Coun.-Vacant
City Secy.-Sharon Settlemyer
Atty.-Vacant
V.F.D.F.C.-Kenneth Guard

RICHLAND HILLS 76118
Pop: 7801 (Tarrant)
3200 Diana Drive
817 616-3810 - *Fax: 616-3803*
www.richlandhills.com
Mayor-Bill Agan
Mayor PT-Allison Barger
Coun.-Curtis A Bergthold
Coun.-Athena Campbell
Coun.-Travis Malone
Coun.-Vacant
City Mgr.-Eric Strong
Dir. Fin-Ariel Carmona
City Secy.-Cathy Bourg
Atty.-Betsy Elam
C.P.-Barbara Childress
F.C.-Russell Shelley

RICHLAND SPRINGS 76871
Pop: 338 (San Saba)
P.O. Box 27
325 452-3409 - *Fax: 452-3553*
Mayor-Veronica Muncy
Mayor PT-Frank Pearce
Ald.-Marty Moats
Ald.-Marilyn Suber
Ald.-Vacant
City Secy.-Veronica Muncy
F.C.-Jeffrey Bates

RICHMOND 77469
Pop: 11679 (Fort Bend)
402 Morton
281 342-5456 - *Fax: 232-8626*
www.richmondtx.gov
Mayor-Evalyn W. Moore
Comm.-Barry C. Beard
Comm.-Carl Drozd
Comm.-Josh Lockhart
Comm.-Jesse Torres
City Mgr.-Terri Vela
City Secy.-Laura Scarlato
Atty.-Gary W. Smith
C.P.-Gary Adams
F.C.-Michael Youngblood

RICHWOOD 77531
Pop: 3510 (Brazoria)
1800 N. Brazosport Blvd.
979 265-2082 - *Fax: 265-7345*
richwoodtx.gov
Mayor-Mark Guthrie
Mayor PT-Lauren LaCount
Coun.-Frank Blanks
Coun.-Chris Hardison
Coun.-Paul C. Raymond
Coun.-Sarah Reed
City Mgr.-Michael Coon
City Secy.-Giani Cantu
Atty.-Jason Cordoba
C.P.-Bryan Corb
F.C.-Clint Kocurek

RIESEL 76682
Pop: 1007 (McLennan)
P.O. Box 249
254 896-6501 - *Fax: 896-2404*
www.cityofriesel.org
Mayor-Roger Fitzpatrick
Mayor PT-Jeanne Lehrmann
Coun.-Brandon Blasingame
Coun.-Bobby Dieterich
Coun.-Kevin S. Hogg
Tres.-Phyllis Koester
City Secy.-Alisha Flanary
Atty.-Mike Dixon
C.P.-Danny Krumnow
F.C.-David Minter

RIO BRAVO 78046
Pop: 4794 (Webb)
1701 Centeno Lane
956 790-9500 - *Fax: 790-9503*
Mayor-Francisco I Pena, M.D.
Comm.-Eusebio "Billy" Gomez
Comm.-Deborah L. Serrano
City Secy.-Megel Berry
City Admin.-Miguel Berry
F.C.-Juan Gonzalez

RIO GRANDE CITY 78582
Pop: 13834 (Starr)
5332 E. U.S. Highway 83
956 487-0672 - *Fax: 716-8899*
www.cityofrgc.com/
Mayor-Joel Villarreal
Mayor PT-Hernan R. Garza, III
Comm.-Dave Jones
Comm.-Rey Ramirez
Comm.-Arcadio J. Salinas, III
City Mgr.-Alberto Perez
Deputy CM-Elisa Y. Beas
City Secy.-Holly D. Guerrero
Atty.-Calixtro Villarreal
C.P.-Noe Castillo
F.C.-Ricardo Reyes

RIO HONDO 78583
Pop: 2356 (Cameron)
P.O. Box 389
956 748-2102 - *Fax: 748-4394*
www.riohondo.us
Mayor-Gustavo "Gus" Olivares
Comm.-Tony David
Comm.-Juan D. Garza
Comm.-Alonzo Garza
Comm.-Gerald Hartzog
Comm.-Joseph Lopez
City Admin.-Ben Medina
Atty.-Rep. Eddie Lucio III
Dir. P.S.-William Bilokury

RIO VISTA 76093
Pop: 873 (Johnson)
P.O. Box 129
817 373-2588 - *Fax: 373-2988*
Mayor-Keith Hutchison
Mayor PT-Ruth Hardin
Ald.-Brenda Hall
Ald.-Adriana Mock
Ald.-J.L. Stiles
City Secy.-Connie Coppock
Atty.-Bill Conover
C.P.-David Niederhaus
F.C.-Dale Hutchison

RISING STAR 76471
Pop: 835 (Eastland)
P.O. Box 35
254 643-4261 - *Fax: 643-1212*
Mayor-Phil Mitchell
Mayor PT-Jim Carpenter
Ald.-Ben Childers
Ald.-Johnny Jack Hubbard

Ald.-Larry McIntire
Ald.-Tricia Nall
City Admin.-Jan Clark
Atty.-William "Pat" Chesser
C.P.-Randal Davis
F.C.-Josh Constancio

RIVER OAKS 76114
Pop: 7427 (Tarrant)
4900 River Oaks Blvd.
817 626-5421 - *Fax: 624-2154*
www.riveroakstx.com
Mayor-Herman Earwood
Mayor PT-Joe Ashton
Coun.-JoAnn Butler
Coun.-Dan Chisholm
Coun.-Steve Holland
Coun.-Bruce Scott
City Admin.-Marvin Gregory
Atty.-Betsy Elam
C.P.-Christopher Spieldenner
F.C.-Russell Shelley
Dir. P.W.-Gordon Smith

RIVERSIDE 77367
Pop: 510 (Walker)
P.O. Box 623
936 594-2520 - *Fax: 594-3101*
Mayor-John LeMaire
Mayor PT-Billy Philio
Ald.-Jimmy Brummett
Ald.-G.F. Rich
Ald.-Bill Tutor
Ald.-Monty Zunker
City Secy.-Joan Harvey
City Secy.-Stormy Perez
Atty.-Victor Schneider
F.C.-Gabe Johnson

ROANOKE 76262
Pop: 8000 (Denton-Tarrant)
108 S. Oak St.
817 491-2411 - *Fax: 491-2242*
www.roanoketexas.com
Mayor-Carl "Scooter" Gierisch, Jr.
Mayor PT-Holly Gray-McPherson
Coun.-Brian Darby
Coun.-Angie Grimm
Coun.-Steve Heath
Coun.-Dion M. Jones
Coun.-Kirby Smith
City Mgr.-Scott Campbell
City Secy.-April S. Hill
Atty.-Jeff Moore
C.P.-Gary Johnson
F.C.-Mike Duncan

ROARING SPRINGS 79256
Pop: 234 (Motley)
P.O. Box 247
806 348-7231 - *Fax: 348-7334*
Mayor-Corky Marshall
Mayor PT-Jeff Thacker
Coun.-Timmy Brooks
Coun.-Kelly Keltz
Coun.-James McCleskey

Coun.-James Sanders
City Secy.-Tina Brooks

ROBERT LEE 76945
Pop: 1049 (Coke)
P.O. Box 26
325 453-2831 - *Fax: 453-4531*
Mayor-Leroy Casey
Ald.-Roger Alexander
Ald.-Shaunna Grantham
Ald.-Joe Longoria
Ald.-Janie Munoz
Ald.-Toni Rainwater
City Secy.-Kay Torres
Atty.-Vacant
F.C.-Ross Torres

ROBINSON 76706
Pop: 10509 (McLennan)
111 W. Lyndale
254 662-1415 - *Fax: 662-1035*
www.robinsontexas.org
Mayor-Bert Echterling
Mayor PT-James Mastergeorge
Coun.-Steve Janics
Coun.-Brenton Lane
Coun.-Jimmy Rogers
Coun.-Jeremy Stivener
Coun.-Steven Tindell
City Mgr.-Craig Lemin
City Secy.-Jana Lewellen
Atty.-Mike Dixon
F.C.-Gerald Groppe

ROBSTOWN 78380
Pop: 11487 (Nueces)
101 E. Main
361 387-4589 - *Fax: 387-3646*
Mayor-Mandy Barrera
Mayor PT-Joey Rodriguez
Coun.-Larry Cantu Jr.
Coun.-Roland R. Flores
Coun.-Juan Padilla
Coun.-Sybil D. Tipton
Coun.-Elias R. Vasquez
City Secy.-Herman Rodriguez
Atty.-Patrick L. Beam
C.P.-Albert Stout
F.C.-Ricardo Gonzalez

ROBY 79543
Pop: 643 (Fisher)
P.O. Box 170
325 776-2271 - *Fax: 776-2404*
Mayor-Eli Sepeda
Comm.-Laura Carrion
Comm.-Roy Rivas
City Mgr.-Jack Brown
City Secy.-Brandy Buckner
F.C.-Kevin Rivers

ROCHESTER 79544
Pop: 324 (Haskell)
P.O. Box 186
940 742-3411 - *Fax: 742-3711*
Mayor-Lonnetta Farrar
Mayor PT-Basilio Andrada
Ald.-Greg Addington
Ald.-John Hicks
Ald.-Edie Strickland
Ald.-Robert Yates
City Admin/Secy-Gail Nunn
F.C.-Greg Addington

ROCKDALE 76567
Pop: 5595 (Milam)
P.O. Box 586
512 446-2511 - *Fax: 446-6258*
Mayor-John King
Mayor PT-Joyce Dalley
Coun.-Nathan Bland
Coun.-Doug Calame
Coun.-Colby Fisher
Coun.-Willie Phillips, Sr.
Coun.-Denise Wallace
City Mgr.-Chris Whittaker
City Secy.-Terry Blanchard
Atty.-Michelle Lehmkuhl
C.P.-Thomas Harris
F.C.-Ward Roddam

ROCKPORT 78382
Pop: 8766 (Aransas)
622 E. Market St.
361 729-2213 - *Fax: 790-5966*
www.cityofrockport.com
Mayor-Charles J. "C.J." Wax
Mayor PT-Patrick Rios
Coun.-J. Russell "Rusty" Day Jr.
Coun.-Barbara Gurtner
Coun.-Joe David "J.D." Villa
City Mgr.-Kevin Carruth
Dir. Fin-Patty Howard
City Secy.-Teresa Valdez
Atty.-Terry E. Baiamonte
C.P.-Tim Jayroe

ROCKSPRINGS 78880
Pop: 1182 (Edwards)
P.O. Box 796
830 683-3181 - *Fax: 683-3182*
Mayor-Pauline Gonzales
Mayor PT-Vicenta Ramirez
Coun.-Emma Barnebey
Coun.-Christine Chapa
Coun.-Melinda Ortiz
Coun.-Christina Reyes
City Admin/Secy-Robin Clanton
Atty.-Leslie C. Kassahn

ROCKWALL 75087
Pop: 41370 (Rockwall)
385 S. Goliad
972 771-7700 - *Fax: 771-7727*
www.rockwall.com
Mayor-Jim Pruitt
Mayor PT-John Hohenshelt
Coun.-Bennie Daniels
Coun.-Kevin Fowler
Coun.-Dennis Lewis
Coun.-Dana Macalik
Coun.-Mike Townsend
City Mgr.-Rick Crowley
City Secy.-Kristy Cole
Atty.-Frank J. Garza
C.P.-Kirk Riggs
F.C.-Kenneth Cullins

ROCKY MOUND
Pop: 75 (Camp)
P.O. Box 795
Pittsburg, TX 75686-0795
903 856-7889 - *Fax: 856-6644*
Mayor-Noble T. Smith
Mayor PT-Norris E. Smith
Ald.-Sandra D. Carrington
Ald.-Russell Hill
Ald.-Tillard A. Smith
City Secy.-Sandra D. Carrington
Atty.-Matthew Patton
Mar.-Noble T. Smith
F.C.-Noble T. Smith

ROGERS 76569
Pop: 1218 (Bell)
2 W Mesquite St.
P.O. Box 250
254 642-3312 - *Fax: 642-3102*
cityofrogers.us/
Mayor-Tammy Cockrum
Mayor PT-Thomas Williams
Ald.-Billy Crow
Ald.-Terry Mejia
Ald.-Matthew Salladay
Ald.-Brandon Skrhak
City Admin.-Chris Hill
Atty.-James Parker
C.P.-Robert Wireman
F.C.-Ernest Stroud

ROLLINGWOOD 78746
Pop: 1412 (Travis)
403 Nixon Drive
512 327-1838 - *Fax: 327-1869*
www.cityofrollingwood.com
Mayor-Roxanne McKee
Ald.-Joe Basham
Ald.-Bobby Dillard
Ald.-Michael Dyson
Ald.-Sara Hutson
Ald.-Gavin Massingill
Dir. Fin-Abel Campos
City Secy.-Robyn Ryan
City Admin.-Vacant
Atty.-Doug Young
Dir. P.W.-Jackie Bob Wright

ROMA 78584
Pop: 9765 (Starr)
P.O. Box 947
956 849-1411 - *Fax: 849-3963*
www.cityofroma.net
Mayor-Roberto A. Salinas
Coun.-Mary Lou G. Cruz
Coun.-Carlos M. Gonzalez Jr.
Coun.-Gilberto Ramirez, Jr.
Coun.-Ramiro Sarabia
City Mgr.-Crisanto Salinas
City Secy.-Liliana "Lily" Sandoval
Atty.-Bradley B. Young
C.P.-Jose H. Garcia
F.C.-Alfredo Garza

ROMAN FOREST 77357
Pop: 1782 (Montgomery)
2430 Roman Forest Blvd.
281 399-2660 - *Fax: 306-1024*
www.cityofromanforest.org
Mayor-Chris Parr
Mayor PT-Jill Carlson
Coun.-Tony Garza
Coun.-David Mullane
Coun.-Gregory Partin
Coun.-Conley Wallace
City Secy.-Sheryl Muro
City Admin.-Liz Mullane
Atty.-Larry Foerster
C.P.-Steve Carlisle
F.C.-Jeff Taylor

ROPESVILLE 79358
Pop: 434 (Hockley)
P.O. Box 96
806 562-3531 - *Fax: 562-4026*
Mayor-Brenda Rabel
Ald.-Miles Evans
Ald.-Brannon Greenlee
Ald.-Fred Melton
Ald.-David Vasquez
City Secy.-Ofelia Corral
City Secy.-Deann Villegas
Atty.-Allen J. Hammons

ROSCOE 79545
Pop: 1322 (Nolan)
P.O. Box 340
325 766-3871 - *Fax: 766-2313*
www.roscoetx.com
Mayor-Frank S. "Pete" Porter
Mayor PT-Billy Joe Jay
Ald.-Susie Alford
Ald.-Edwin Duncan
Ald.-KC Hope
Ald.-Robert McBride
City Secy.-Donna Parker
City Admin.-Cody Thompson
Atty.-Zollie Steakley
C.P.-Felix Pantoja
F.C.-Gary Armstrong

ROSE CITY 77662
Pop: 502   (Orange)
370 S. Rose City Dr.
409 769-6809 - *Fax: 769-6199*
Mayor-Bonnie Stephenson
Mayor PT-Hernando Ramos
Coun.-Jayme McGlothlin
Coun.-Robert Nolan
Coun.-Melinda Reese
Coun.-Richard Travis
City Secy.-Tonya Veazey
Atty.-Rodney Price
Mar.-Jeffery Sasar

ROSE HILL ACRES 77657
Pop: 466   (Hardin)
100 Jordan Road
409 454-6593
Mayor-Rick L. Thomisee
Mayor PT-Donna Kountz
Ald.-Tina Bosch
Ald.-Ann O'Bannion
Ald.-Claude Webb
Ald.-Terrell Woolsey
City Secy.-Karen R. Granato
Atty.-Derrick Fowler
Mar.-Eric Vogel

ROSEBUD 76570
Pop: 1412   (Falls)
402 W. Main
P.O. Box 657
254 583-7926 - *Fax: 583-2157*
rosebudtexas.us
Mayor-Roy L Spivey
Ald.-Sam Carey
Ald.-Debra Kimble
Ald.-Joe Marek
Ald.-Sharon Skupin
Ald.-Katrina Whitfield
Ald.-Andrea "Andy" Wright
City Secy.-Molly Trezise Wilson
City Admin.-Keith Whitfield
Atty.-James Parker
C.P.-Vacant
V.F.D.F.C.-Donald Zipperlin

ROSENBERG 77471
Pop: 34127   (Fort Bend)
P.O. Box 32
832 595-3310 - *Fax: 595-3333*
www.rosenbergtx.gov
Mayor-William "Bill" Benton
Mayor PT-Jimmie J. Pena
Coun.-Jacob E. Balderas
Coun.-Amanda J. Barta
Coun.-Susan Kroll Euton
Coun.-Alice S. Jozwiak
Coun.-Lynn Moses
City Mgr.-John Maresh
Dir. Fin-Joyce Vasut
City Secy.-Linda Cernosek
Atty.-George E. Hyde
C.P.-Dallis Warren
F.C.-Darrell Himly

ROSS 76684
Pop: 283   (McLennan)
P.O. Box 40
254 495-0737
Mayor-Jim Jaska
Mayor PT-Rick Maddox
Ald.-Craig Jameson Andrle
Ald.-John Curtis
Ald.-David Filer
Ald.-Cecilia Kukles
City Secy.-David Filer
Atty.-Frank Beard

ROSSER 75157
Pop: 332   (Kaufman)
P.O. Box 31
Mayor-Shannon R. Corder
Mayor PT-Jeff Wells
Coun.-Rick Avery
Coun.-Fred Cochran
Coun.-Frances Myles
Coun.-Vacant
City Secy.-Pam Corder
Atty.-Wade Gent
F.C.-Kenneth Orman

ROTAN 79546
Pop: 1508   (Fisher)
302 W. Sammy Baugh
325 735-2251 - *Fax: 735-2229*
Mayor-Marisa Nowlin
Mayor PT-Donny Mullins
Ald.-Larry Messick
Ald.-Frank Miranda
Ald.-Scott Toliver
Ald.-Patrick Zambrano
City Mgr.-Carla Thornton
Atty.-James M. Decker
F.C.-Robert Hoffmann

ROUND MOUNTAIN 78663
Pop: 181   (Blanco)
P.O. Box 40
830 825-3233 - *Fax: 825-3276*
Mayor-Alvin Gutierrez
Mayor PT-Julian Gutierrez
Ald.-George Birck
Ald.-Robert Gott
Ald.-Mary Gutierrez
Ald.-Eddie Holt
City Secy.-Ingrid Moursund
Atty.-Will S. Moursund

ROUND ROCK 78664
Pop: 106573   (Travis-Williamson)
221 E. Main St.
512 218-5410 - *Fax: 218-7097*
www.roundrocktexas.gov
Mayor-Craig Morgan
Mayor PT-Tammy Young
Coun.-Writ Baese
Coun.-Rene Flores
Coun.-Frank Leffingwell
Coun.-Hilda Montgomery
Coun.-Will Peckham
City Mgr.-Laurie Hadley

Clk.-Sara White
Atty.-Steve Sheets
C.P.-Allen Banks
F.C.-Robert Isbell

ROUND TOP 78954
Pop: 90   (Fayette)
P.O. Box 215
979 249-5885 - *Fax: 249-2085*
townofroundtop.com
Mayor-Barnell Albers
Mayor PT-Ronny Sacks
Ald.-Stephen Ditzler
Ald.-Frank Hillbolt
Ald.-Jerry Hinkel
Ald.-Louis Sellers
Town Secy.-Dwight Nittsche
F.C.-Calvin Krause

ROWLETT 75030
Pop: 58043   (Dallas-Rockwall)
972 412-6100 - *Fax: 412-6118*
www.ci.rowlett.tx.us
Mayor-Tammy Dana-Bashian
Dep. Mayor PT-Debby Bobbitt
Coun.-Pamela Bell
Coun.-Martha Brown
Coun.-Brownie Sherill
Coun.-Bruce Hargrave
Coun.-Matt Grubisich
City Mgr.-Brian Funderburk
Dir. Fin-Alan Guard
City Secy.-Laura Hallmark
P.A.-Allyson Wilson
Atty.-David Berman
C.P.-Mike Brodnax
F.C.-Neil Howard
F.M.-Bryan Beckner

ROXTON 75477
Pop: 650   (Lamar)
P.O. Box 176
903 346-3535 - *Fax: 346-3759*
Mayor-Phillip Rutherford
Mayor PT-Jo Marie Bush
Ald.-Shirley Cooper
Ald.-Paul Helms
Ald.-Cody Jones
Ald.-Timothey Walsworth
City Secy.-Janet Wheeler
Atty.-Brady Fisher

ROYSE CITY 75189
Pop: 10349(Collin-Rockwall-
Hunt)
P.O. Box 638
972 636-2250 - *Fax: 635-2434*
www.roysecity.com
Mayor-Janet Nichol
Mayor PT-Clay Ellis
Coun.-Bruce Bradley
Coun.-James Branch
Coun.-Tom Crowley
Coun.-Charles Houk
Coun.-Matt Wheatly
City Mgr.-Carl Alsabrook

City Secy.-Deborah Sorensen
Atty.-Jason Day
C.P.-Jeff Stapleton
F.C.-Richard "Rickey" Bell
Dir. P.W.-Dario Lopez
CFO-Shannon Raymond

RULE 79547
Pop: 636   (Haskell)
P.O. Box 607
940 996-2214 - *Fax: 996-2159*
Mayor-Jerry Cannon
Mayor PT-Bobby Robinson
Coun.-Alan Beard
Coun.-Jim Kowalski
Coun.-Gilbert Navarrette
Coun.-Delle Davis Watkins
City Secy.-Teresa Sorrells
P.A.-Teresa Sorrells
Atty.-Michael Guevara
C.P.-Justin Stewart
F.C.-Caleb Sorrells

RUNAWAY BAY 76426
Pop: 1286   (Wise)
101 Runaway Bay Drive
940 575-4745 - *Fax: 575-2563*
www.runawaybaytexas.com
Mayor-John W. Boyd
Mayor PT-Jerry St.John
Coun.-Deborah Lewis
Coun.-Roland Ray
Coun.-Janice Sivley
Coun.-Berry White
City Secy.-Vacant
Atty.-Robert Brown
F.C.-JD Haselden
Dir. P.S.-Doug Angell

RUNGE 78151
Pop: 1031   (Karnes)
P.O. Box 206
830 239-4121 - *Fax: 239-4970*
Mayor-Homer Lott Jr.
Comm.-Christine Ramirez
Coun.-Felix Zapata
City Secy.-Esmeralda B. Castro
Atty.-Cary Bovey

RUSK 75785
Pop: 5551   (Cherokee)
205 S. Main St.
903 683-2213 - *Fax: 683-5964*
www.rusktx.org
Mayor-Angela Raiborn
Coun.-Sam Florian
Coun.-Don Jones
Coun.-Ben Middlebrooks
Coun.-Walter Session
Coun.-Donald Woodard
City Mgr.-Jim Dunaway
City Secy.-Cinda Etheridge
Atty.-Brett Brewer
C.P.-Joe Williams
F.C.-Donald Lankford
Dir. P.W.-Thomas Thompson

SABINAL 78881
Pop: 1695   (Uvalde)
P.O. Box 838
830 988-2218 - *Fax: 988-2217*
Mayor-Charles D. Story
Mayor PT-Javier R. Flores
Ald.-Ali Alejandro
Ald.-Danny Dean
Ald.-Louis A. Landedos
Ald.-Mike Nuckles
Ald.-Andy Schaefer
City Secy.-Betty Jo Harris
Atty.-Molly Solis
C.P.-Jesus C. Rayes
F.C.-Andy Schaefer

SACHSE 75048
Pop: 23950   (Collin-Dallas)
3815 Sachse Road, Building B
972 495-1212 - *Fax: 530-0426*
www.cityofsachse.com
Mayor-Mike Felix
Mayor PT-Paul Watkins
Coun.-Bill Adams
Coun.-Jeff Bickerstaff
Coun.-Brett Franks
Coun.-Cullen King
Coun.-Charlie Ross
City Mgr.-Gina Nash
Dir. Fin-Teresa Savage
City Secy.-Michelle Lewis Sirianni
Atty.-Peter G. Smith
C.P.-Bryan Sylvester
F.C.-Martin Wade

SADLER 76264
Pop: 343   (Grayson)
P.O. Box 543
903 564-9607 - *Fax: 564-9607*
www.cityofsadler.org
Mayor-Jaime Vannoy
Mayor PT-Jackie Moss
Coun.-Sandi Freeman
Coun.-Gary Knight
Coun.-Kathy Richardson
Coun.-Vacant
City Secy.-Linda Gann
Atty.-Wolfe Tidwell and McCoy
F.C.-Corgey Fisher

SAGINAW 76179
Pop: 20370   (Tarrant)
817 232-4640 - *Fax: 232-4644*
www.ci.saginaw.tx.us
Mayor-Todd Flippo
Mayor PT-David Flory
Coun.-Sheri A. Adams
Coun.-Cindy Bighorse
Coun.-Mary Copeland
Coun.-Patrick Farr
Coun.-Valcrie Tankersley
Int. Mgr.-Dan O'leary
Dir. Fin-Dolph Johnson
City Secy.-Janice England

Atty.-Bryn Meredith
C.P.-Roger Macon
F.C.-Doug Spears

SAINT HEDWIG 78152
Pop: 2094   (Bexar)
P.O. Box 40
210 667-9568 - *Fax: 667-1448*
Mayor-Dee Grimm
Mayor PT-Dwayne Padalecki
Coun.-Susann Baker
Coun.-John Hafner
Coun.-Deborah McInerney
Coun.-Doug Thomas
City Secy.-Barbara Pawelek
Atty.-Jameene Williams

SAINT JO 76265
Pop: 1043   (Montague)
P.O. Box 186
940 995-2337 - *Fax: 995-2018*
Mayor-Lucas Thompson
Ald.-Brad Bugg
Ald.-Randall Flusche
Ald.-Paul Mouring
Ald.-Stephanie West
Ald.-Bryan Wolf
City Secy.-Melinda Robeson
Atty.-Andy Messer
C.P.-Tyler Roy
F.C.-Scott Thomas

SALADO, VILLAGE OF 76571
Pop: 2126   (Bell)
P.O. Box 219
254 947-5060 - *Fax: 947-5061*
www.saladotx.gov/
Mayor-Skip Blancett
Ald.-Fred Brown
Ald.-Frank Coachman
Ald.-Amber P. Dankert
Ald.-Andy Jackson
Ald.-Michael McDougal
City Secy.-Cara McPartland
City Admin.-Don Ferguson
Atty.-Alan J. Bojorquez
C.P.-Rick Ashe

SAN ANGELO 76903
Pop: 95887   (Tom Green)
72 W. College Ave.
325 657-4241 - *Fax: 657-4335*
www.cosatx.us
Mayor-Brenda Gunter
Coun.-Lane Carter
Coun.-Billie DeWitt
Coun.-Lucy Gonzales
Coun.-Tommy Hiebert
Coun.-Harry Thomas
Coun.-Tom Thompson
City Mgr.-Daniel Valenzuela
Clk.-Bryan Kendrick
P.A.-Julia Antilley
Atty.-Theresa James
C.P.-Frank Carter
F.C.-Brian Dunn

SAN ANTONIO 78205
Pop: 1410000   (Bexar)
210 207-7253 - *Fax: 207-7032*
www.sanantonio.gov
Mayor-Ron Nirenberg
Coun.-Greg Brockhouse
Coun.-John Courage
Coun.-Shirley Gonzales
Coun.-Manny Pelaez
Coun.-Clayton Perry
Coun.-Rey Saldaña
Coun.-Ana E. Sandoval
Coun.-William "Cruz" Shaw
Coun.-Roberto C. Treviño
Coun.-Rebecca Viagran
City Mgr.-Sheryl L. Sculley
Clk.-Leticia M. Vacek
Aud.-Kevin Barthold
Atty.-Andy Segovia
C.P.-William McManus
F.C.-Charles N. Hood
CFO-Ben Gorzell, Jr.

SAN AUGUSTINE 75972
Pop: 2108   (San Augustine)
301 S. Harrison St.
936 275-2121 - *Fax: 275-9146*
Mayor-Leroy Hughes
Mayor PT-Michael Malone
Ald.-Claudia Cabriales
Ald.-Dan Fussell
Ald.-Valencia Price
Ald.-Pamela N. Teel
City Mgr.-Randy Whiteman
City Secy.-Cinda Garner
Atty.-Wade Flasowski
C.P.-Gary Fountain
F.C.-Steven Hayes

SAN BENITO 78586
Pop: 24250   (Cameron)
401 N. Sam Houston
956 361-3800 - *Fax: 361-3805*
www.cityofsanbenito.com/
Mayor-Benjamin Gomez
Mayor PT-Carol Lynn Sanchez
Mayor PT-Antonio Gonzales
Comm.-Esteban S. Rodriguez
Comm.-Rene Villafranco
City Mgr.-Manuel De La Rosa
City Secy.-Lupita Passement
Atty.-Ricardo Morado
C.P.-Michael Galvan
F.C.-Raul Zuniga

SAN DIEGO 78384
Pop: 4488   (Duval-Jim Wells)
404 S. Mier
361 279-3341 - *Fax: 279-3401*
Mayor-Sally Lichtenberger
Mayor PT-Araceli Gaitan
Ald.-Rolando T. Guerrero
Ald.-Janie Lopez
Ald.-Margarito Maldonado III
Ald.-Ricky Munoz
City Mgr.-Aleida L. Luera
City Secy.-Elma Martinez
Atty.-Rumaldo Solis Jr.
C.P.-Richard R. Nava, II
F.C.-Matthew Valdez

SAN ELIZARIO 78949
Pop: 9700   (El Paso)
915 974-7037
Mayor-Maya Sanchez
Ald.-George Almanzar
Ald.-David Cantu
Ald.-Leticia Hurtado-Miranda
Ald.-Rebecca Martinez-Juarez
Ald.-Miguel Najera Jr.
City Admin.-Vacant
Atty.-Alan J. Bojorquez

SAN FELIPE, TOWN OF 77473
Pop: 747   (Austin)
P.O. Box 129
San Felipe, TX 77473-0129
979 885-7035 - *Fax: 885-0747*
Mayor-Bobby Byars
Mayor PT-Alfred Hall
Ald.-Louis T. Bonner Jr.
Ald.-Derrick Dabney
Ald.-Brenda Newsome
Ald.-Jeff Zeigler
Town Secy.-Sue Foley
Atty.-Ross Fischer
C.P.-D. Randle

SAN JUAN 78589
Pop: 33856   (Hidalgo)
709 S. Nebraska
956 223-2200 - *Fax: 787-5978*
www.cityofsanjuantexas.com/
Mayor-Mario Garza
Mayor PT-Jesse Ramirez
Comm.-Pete Garcia
Comm.-Raudel Maldonado
Coun.-Ernesto "Neto" Guajardo
City Mgr.-Benjamin Arjona
Int. City Secy.-Palmira Cepeda
P.A.-Rene Jaime
Atty.-Ricardo Palacios
C.P.-Juan Gonzalez
F.C.-Tirso Garza

SAN LEANNA, VILLAGE OF
Pop: 497   (Travis)
P.O. Box 1107
Manchaca, TX 78652-1107
512 280-3898 - *Fax: 280-3898*
www.sanleannatx.com
Mayor-Elizabeth A. Korts
Mayor PT-Charlie Burks
Ald.-Fred Helmerichs
Ald.-Barbara Quarles
Ald.-Molly Quirk
Ald.-Elaine Voeltz
City Admin.-Rebecca Howe
Atty.-Monte Akers

SAN MARCOS 78666
Pop: 50000   (Hays)
630 E. Hopkins
512 393-8000
Fax: 855 246-9100
www.sanmarcostx.gov
Mayor-John Thomaides
Coun.-Melissa Derrick
Coun.-Saul Gonzales
Coun.-Scott Gregson
Coun.-Jane Hughson
Coun.-Ed Mihalkanin
Coun.-Lisa Prewitt
City Mgr.-Bert Lumbreras
Dir. Fin-Heather Hurlbert
Clk.-Jamie Lee Case
P.M.-Cheryl Pantermuehl
Atty.-Michael Cosentino
C.P.-Chase Stapp
F.C.-Les Stephens

SAN PATRICIO
Pop: 395   (San Patricio)
4615 Main Street
Mathis, TX 78368-9216
361 547-2256
Mayor-Lonnie Glasscock, III
Mayor PT-Robert Miller
Ald.-Margot Byerley
Ald.-Jackie Hale
Ald.-Joyce Newlin
Ald.-Skip Rohrer

Tres.-Dolly Gibson
City Secy.-Donna Ingram
Atty.-William Burnett

SAN PERLITA 78590
Pop: 573   (Willacy)
14168 7th Street
P.O. Box 121
956 248-5725 - *Fax: 248-5348*
Mayor-Aurora de Luna
Comm.-George Guadiana
Comm.-Frances C. Salazar
City Secy.-Joyi Rodriguez

SAN SABA 76877
Pop: 3099   (San Saba)
303 S. Clear St.
P.O. Box 788
325 372-5144 - *Fax: 372-3989*
www.sansabatexas.com
Mayor-Ken Jordan
Ald.-Mark Amthor
Ald.-Oleta Reyes Behrens
Ald.-Shawn Oliver
Ald.-Charles L. Peeler
Ald.-Robert M. Whitten
City Mgr.-Stan Weik
City Secy.-Sabrina Maultsby
Atty.-Barney Knight
C.P.-Ray Riggs
F.C.-Chris Stewart

SANCTUARY 76098
Pop: 329   (Parker)
Fax: 817 221-6016
Mayor-Cliff Scallan
Mayor PT-Megs Elliott
Ald.-Nancy Cozad
Ald.-Michelle McCoy
Ald.-Paul Reeves
Ald.-Carissa Wagner
City Secy.-Chris Stewart
Atty.-Walter W. Leonard

SANDY OAKS 78112
Pop: 200   (Bexar)
210 300-6405
www.cityofsandyoaks.com/
Mayor-Karen M. Tanguma
Ald.-Charles Fillinger
Ald.-Anthony Garcia
Ald.-Tom Repino
Ald.-Brandon P. Smith
Ald.-Douglas Tomasini

SANDY POINT 77583
Pop: 250   (Brazoria)
P.O. Box 1098
281 798-9808
Mayor-Curt Mowery
Comm.-John Caldwell
Comm.-Kurt Quinn
City Secy.-Frances Underwood
Atty.-Laurence E. Boyd

SANFORD 79078
Pop: 164   (Hutchinson)
P.O. Box 220
806 865-3612 - *Fax: 865-0049*
Mayor-Bernard Pacheco
Mayor PT-Stephanie Trammel
Ald.-Charlotte Beedle
Ald.-Melinda Danford
Ald.-Carolyn Davis
Ald.-James Lewis
City Secy.-Terrie Bechtel
Atty.-Angelique Weaver
F.C.-Jim Williams

SANGER 76266
Pop: 6916   (Denton)
502 Elm
P.O. Box 1729
940 458-7930 - *Fax: 458-4180*
www.sangertexas.org
Mayor-Thomas Muir
Coun.-Lee Allison
Coun.-Gary Bilyeu
Coun.-William Boutwell
Coun.-Allen Chick
Coun.-David Clark
City Mgr.-Mike Brice
Dir. Fin-Clayton Gray
City Secy.-Cheryl Price
Atty.-Nichols, Jackson, etal
C.P. Curtis Amyx
F.C.-David Pennington
Dir. P.W.-Neal Welch

SANSOM PARK
Pop: 4686   (Tarrant)
5705 Azle Ave.
Fort Worth, TX 76114
817 626-3791 - *Fax: 626-0023*
www.sansompark.org
Mayor-Jim Barnett, Jr.
Mayor PT-Crystal Harris
Coun.-Jim Barnett, Sr.
Coun. Donna Bell
Coun.-Tanya Easterling Gregory
Coun.-Jerry Sewall
City Secy.-Wendy Blocker
City Admin.-Angela Winkle
Atty.-Lee Thomas
C.P.-Will Wilkerson
F.C.-Allen Richards
Dir. P.W.-Ronald Douglas

SANTA ANNA 76878
Pop: 1081   (Coleman)
709 Wallis
325 348-3403 - *Fax: 348-3406*
Mayor-Harold Fahrlender
Ald.-Earl Ellis
Ald.-Richard Horner
Ald.-Jeanne Johnston
Ald.-Todd McMillan
Ald.-Marie Silvias
City Secy.-Shirley Rankin
Atty.-Barney Knight

C.P.-Carlos M. Torres
F.C.-David Huggins

SANTA CLARA
Pop: 725   (Guadalupe)
1535 N. Santa Clara Rd
P.O. Box 429
Marion, TX 78124
830 914-4443
www.cisantaclaratx.us
Mayor-Jeff Hunt
Mayor PT-Marian Carty
Ald.-Jim Folbre
Ald.-Ernest Schoenefeldt
Ald.-Lynette Sierer
Ald.-Danny Trammell
City Secy.-Donna White
Atty.-Amy Akers

SANTA FE 77510
Pop: 12222   (Galveston)
P.O. Box 950
409 925-6412 - *Fax: 316-1941*
www.ci.santa-fe.tx.us
Mayor-Jeff Tambrella
Mayor PT-Corey Jannett
Coun.-Joe Carothers
Coun.-Charles Coleman
Coun.-Ronald "Bubba" Jannett
Coun.-Bill Pittman
City Mgr. Joe Dickson
City Secy.-Janet L. Davis
Atty.-Ellis J. Ortego
C.P.-Jeffrey M. Powell
F.M.-Tony Dauphine

SANTA ROSA 78593
Pop: 2873   (Cameron)
411 S. 6th St.
P.O. Box 326
956 636-1113 - *Fax: 636-2044*
Mayor-Andres Contreras
Mayor PT-Javier Florencia
Ald.-Raul Hinojosa
Ald.-Jose Luis Perez Jr.
Ald.-Jaime Quiroga
Ald.-Ruben Vela Jr.
City Secy.-Rachel Flores
Atty.-Gustavo Ruiz
F.C.-Danny Theys

SAVOY 75479
Pop: 831   (Fannin)
405 E. Hayes St.
903 965-7706 - *Fax: 965-4023*
www.cityofsavoy.org
Mayor-Denise Pugh
Mayor PT-Robert Goodwin
Coun.-Katherine Cornwell
Coun.-Charles Downs
Coun.-Mike Stone
Coun.-David Warlick
City Secy.-Melissa Rickman
Atty.-James Tidwell
F.C.-Billy Burks

SCHERTZ 78154
Pop: 31788(Bexar-Comal-
  Guadalupe)
1400 Schertz Parkway
210 619-1000 - *Fax: 619-1039*
www.schertz.com
Mayor-Michael R. Carpenter
Coun.-Bert Crawford
Coun.-Mark Davis
Coun.-Cedric Edwards
Coun.-Ralph Gutierrez
Coun.-Angelina Kiser
Coun.-Scott Larson
Coun.-David Scagliola
City Mgr.-John Kessel
City Secy.-Brenda Dennis
Atty.-Charles E. "Charlie" Zech
C.P.-Michael Hansen
F.C.-Kade Long

SCHULENBURG 78956
Pop: 2852   (Fayette)
979 743-4126 - *Fax: 743-4760*
schulenburgtx.org
Mayor-Otto Kocian
Mayor PT-Harvey Hercik
Ald.-Chip Bubela
Ald.-Wendy Fietsam
Ald.-Arnold Stoever
Ald.-Larry Veselka
City Admin/Secy-Tami
  Blaschke-Walker
P.A.-Megan Bartos
Atty.-Monte Akers
C.P.-Troy Brenek
F.C.-Jeff Proske

SCOTLAND 76379
Pop: 501   (Archer)
P.O. Box 32
940 541-2360 - *Fax: 541-2360*
Mayor-Brian Vieth
Mayor PT-Grady Schenk Jr.
Ald.-Louis Garrett
Ald.-Sean Hoff
Ald.-Matthew Lindemann
Ald.-Carolyn Smith
City Secy.-Kim Hemmi
V.F.D.F.C.-Kenneth Nichols

SCOTTSVILLE 75688
Pop: 376   (Harrison)
P.O. Box 453
903 930-1313
Mayor-Kerry L. Cade
Mayor PT-Alvin Patterson
Ald.-Elroy Cade
Ald.-Dennis Engdahl
Ald.-Eddie Haggerty
Ald.-Lena Mae Singleton
City Secy.-Elaine Adair
Atty.-Dean Searles
F.C.-Alvin Patterson

SCURRY 75158
Pop: 681   (Kaufman)
Mayor-Johnny Blazek
Mayor PT-Rodney Richman
Coun.-Butch Conner
Coun.-Kevin Jones
Coun.-Linda McWhorter
Coun.-Andy Sloan
City Secy.-Holly Adkison
Atty.-Whitt Wyatt
V.F.D.F.C.-Jody Hatcher

SEABROOK 77586
Pop: 11952(Chambers-Galveston-
  Harris)
1700 First St.
281 291-5600 - *Fax: 291-5690*
www.seabrooktx.gov
Mayor-Thomas G. Kolupski
Mayor PT-Gary Johnson
Coun.-Glenna Adovasio
Coun.-Laura Davis
Coun.-Robert J. Llorente
Coun.-Natalie Picha
Coun.-Vacant
City Mgr.-Gayle Cook
City Secy.-Robin Hicks
P.A.-Vacant
Atty.-Steven Weathered
C.P.-Sean Wright
F.C.-Andrew Gutaker

SEADRIFT 77983
Pop: 1364   (Calhoun)
P.O. Box 159
361 785-2251 - *Fax: 785-2208*
Mayor-Elmer DeForest
Mayor PT-June Cantrell
Ald.-Ranier Brigham
Ald.-Peggy Gaines
Ald.-Geoffrey Hunt
Ald.-Kenneth Reese
City Secy.-Gabriela Torres
Clk.-Mary Alice Romero
Atty.-John Griffin
C.P.-Leonard Bermea Jr.
F.C.-Peter DeForest

SEAGOVILLE 75159
Pop: 15130   (Dallas-Kaufman)
972 287-2050 - *Fax: 287-3891*
www.seagoville.us
Mayor-Dennis K. Childress
Mayor PT-Jon Epps
Coun.-Mike Fruin
Coun.-Jose Hernandez
Coun.-Rick Howard
Coun.-Harold Magill
City Mgr.-Patrick "Pat" Stallings
City Secy.-Kandi Jackson
Atty.-Bob Hager
C.P.-Raymond Calverley
F.C.-Todd Gilcrease

SEAGRAVES 79359
Pop: 2417   (Gaines)
P.O. Box 37
806 387-2593 - *Fax: 387-2595*
http://seagravestx.us/contact/
Mayor-Vacant
Mayor PT-Charles Evans
Ald.-Cindy Durham
Ald.-Debra Middleton
Ald.-Kendra Sellers
Ald.-Ruben Valles
City Secy.-Dan Grife
Atty.-Monty Akers
C.P.-Brent Grundstrom
F.C.-Ruben Valles

SEALY 77474
Pop: 6019   (Austin)
P.O. Box 517
979 885-3511 - *Fax: 885-3513*
www.ci.sealy.tx.us
Mayor-Janice Whitehead
Mayor PT-Sandra Vrablec
Coun.-John Hinze
Coun.-Larry W. Koy
Coun.-Dee Anne Lerma
Coun.-Jennifer Sullivan
Coun.-Vacant
Int. Mgr.-Warren Escovy
Dir. Fin-Steven Kutra
City Secy.-Dayl Cooksey
Atty.-Lora Lenzsch
C.P.-Chris Noble

SEGUIN 78155
Pop: 25175   (Guadalupe)
P.O. Box 591
830 379-3212 - *Fax: 401-2499*
www.seguintexas.gov
Mayor-Don Keil
Coun.-Tomas V Castellon, Jr.
Coun.-Jeannette "Jet" Crabb
Coun.-Donna Dodgen
Coun.-Mark Herbold
Coun.-Ernest Leal
Coun.-Fonda Mathis
Coun.-Carlos Medrano
City Mgr.-Douglas G. Faseler
Dir. Fin-Susan Caddell
City Secy.-Naomi Manski
Atty.-Andy Quittner
C.P.-Kevin K. Kelso
Fire Chief/EMS-Dale Skinner

SELMA 78154
Pop: 5540(Bexar-Comal-
  Guadalupe)
9375 Corporate Drive
210 651-6661 - *Fax: 651-0385*
www.ci.selma.tx.us
Mayor-Tom Daly
Mayor PT-Ken Polasek
Coun.-Harry Green
Coun.-Kevin Hadas
Coun.-Ken Harris
Coun.-Jim Parma

City Admin.-Johnny Casias
Atty.-Marc Schnall
C.P.-David Padula
F.C.-Ric Braun

SEMINOLE 79360

Pop: 7206 (Gaines)
302 S. Main St.
432 758-3676 - *Fax: 758-6639*
Mayor-Wayne Mixon
Mayor PT-Rey Saldana
Coun.-Chet Clark
Coun.-Whitney Concotelli
Coun.-Anna Friessen
Coun.-Michel Powers
City Secy.-Debbie Gressett
City Admin.-Tommy Phillips
Atty.-Joe Nagy
C.P.-Bernie Kraft
F.C.-Richard Alvarado
Dir. P.W.-Jeff Rose

SEVEN OAKS

Pop: 111 (Polk)
12642 Hwy. 59 N
P.O. Box 334
Leggett, TX 77350
936 707-3440
Mayor-Centa Evans
Mayor PT-Dina Dickerson
Ald.-Christine Hansen
Ald. Elaine Hardy
City Secy.-Gloria English

SEVEN POINTS 75143

Pop: 1455 (Henderson-Kaufman)
P.O. Box 43233
903 432-4610 - *Fax: 432-2400*
www.sevenpointstexas.com
Mayor-Bill Hash
Mayor PT-Andy Perdue
Coun.-Louis Beaver
Coun.-Cheryl Jones
Coun.-Tommy Taylor
Coun.-Skippy Waters
City Secy.-Shirley Kirksey
Atty.-Blake E. Armstrong
C.P.-Raymond Wennerstrom
F.C.-Bobby Conn

SEYMOUR 76380

Pop: 2740 (Baylor)
P.O. Box 31
940 889-3148 - *Fax: 889-8882*
www.cityofseymour.org
Mayor-Josh Sosolik
Mayor PT-Jon Hrncirik
Coun.-Mary K. Fair
Coun.-Monty Glass
Coun.-Les Hons
Coun.-Paula K. Vaden
Dir. Fin-Mary Griffin
City Secy.-Conchita Torrez
City Admin.-Steve Biedermann
Atty.-Jonathan Whitsitt
C.P.-Mike Griffin
F.C.-Les Hons

SHADY SHORES

Pop: 2612 (Denton)
101 S. Shady Shores Rd
Shady Shore, TX 76208
940 498-0044 - *Fax: 497-2597*
www.shady-shores.com/
Mayor-Cindy Aughinbaugh
Mayor PT-Paula Woolworth
Ald.-Charles Grimes
Ald.-Matthew Haines
Ald.-Jack Nelson
Ald.-Tom Newell
Town Secy.-Wendy Withers
Atty.-James E. Shepherd
C.P.-Debra Walthall

SHALLOWATER 79363

Pop: 2555 (Lubbock)
P.O. Box 246
806 832-4521 - *Fax: 832-4495*
www.shallowatertx.us
Mayor-Robert Olmsted
Mayor PT-Keny Arnold
Ald.-Chris Cody
Ald.-Silas Jones
Ald.-Tory McAuley
Ald.-Brant Sebastian
City Secy.-Amanda Cummings
Atty.-Will Griffis
C.P.-Bart Hurst
F.C.-Cory Buck

SHAMROCK 79079

Pop: 1910 (Wheeler)
116 W. Second St.
806 256-3281 - *Fax: 256-5137*
Mayor-H. Frank "Buc" Weatherby
Ald.-Belinda Beck
Ald.-Jamie Daberry
Ald.-Mary Garner
Ald.-Sherry Palmer
Ald.-Michael Throckmorton
City Mgr.-David Rushing
City Secy. Annette Walden
Atty.-Leslie Standefer
C.P.-Joe Daniels
F.C.-Randy Tallant

SHAVANO PARK 78231

Pop: 3035 (Bexar)
900 Saddletree Court
210 493-3478 - *Fax: 492-3816*
www.shavanopark.org
Mayor-Bob Werner
Mayor PT-Michele B. Ross
Ald.-Mike Colemere
Ald.-Bob Heintzelman
Ald.-Mary Ann Hisel
Ald.-Mike Simpson
City Mgr.-Bill Hill
City Secy.-Zina Tedford
Atty.-Charles E. "Charlie" Zech
C.P.-Ray Lacy
F.C.-Michael Naughton

SHENANDOAH 77381

Pop: 2134 (Montgomery)
29955 I-45 N
281 298-5522 - *Fax: 367-2225*
www.shenandoahtx.us
Mayor-M. Ritchey Wheeler
Mayor PT-Charlie Bradt
Coun.-Byron Bevers
Coun.-Ted Fletcher
Coun.-Michael McLeod
Coun.-Ron Raymaker
City Secy.-Kathie Reyer
Int. City Adm.-Kathie Reyer
Atty.-William C. Ferebee
C.P.-Raymond M. Shaw

SHEPHERD 77371

Pop: 2319 (San Jacinto)
11020 Hwy. 150
936 628-3305 - *Fax: 628-6491*
www.shepherdtx.org
Mayor-Earl Brown
Ald.-Shannon Bailey
Ald.-Charles Minton
Ald.-C. Mark Porter
Ald.-Yvonne Ryba
City Secy.-Debra Hagler
Atty.-Larry Foerster
F.C.-Wayne Jenkins

SHERMAN

Pop: 39943 (Grayson)
P.O. Box 1106
Sherman, TX 75092
903 892-7206 - *Fax: 892-7394*
www.ci.sherman.tx.us
Mayor-David Plyler
Dep. Mayor PT-Jason Sofey
Coun.-Daron Holland
Coun.-Pamela L. Howeth
Coun.-Willie Steele
Coun.-Josh Stevenson
Coun.-Shawn C. Teamann
City Mgr.-Robby Hefton CPM
Clk.-Linda Ashby
Atty.-Brandon Shelby
C.P.-Zachary Flores
F.C.-Danny Jones

SHINER 77984

Pop: 2069 (Lavaca)
P.O. Box 308
361 594-3362 - *Fax: 594-3566*
Mayor-Fred Henry Hilscher
Mayor PT-David Schroeder
Ald.-Frankie Bates
Ald.-Alvin Robert Boehm
Ald.-Alois Louis Herman
Ald.-Gregory Murrile
City Secy.-Susan Nollkamper
Atty.-William J. Natho
C.P.-Ronald Leck
F.C.-Tim Kalich

SHOREACRES 77571
Pop: 1493   (Harris-Chambers)
601 Shore Acres Blvd.
281 471-2244 - *Fax: 471-8955*
www.cityofshoreacres.us
Mayor-Kim Sanford
Ald.-Ricky Bowles
Ald.-Ron Hoskins
Ald.-David Jennings
Ald.-Jerome McKown
Ald.-Felicia Ramos
City Admin.-David K. Stall
Atty.-Christopher A. Gregg
C.P.-Troy Harrison
Dir. P.W.-Erick Ingram

SILSBEE 77656
Pop: 6611   (Hardin)
105 S. 3rd St.
409 385-2863
www.cityofsilsbee.com
Mayor-Herbert Muckleroy
Mayor PT-Jim Willis
Coun.-Adalaide Balaban
Coun.-Sue Bard
Coun.-Chris Barnes
Coun.-Gary Strahan
Coun.-Thomas Tyler
City Mgr.-DeeAnn Zimmerman
Secy/Finance-DeeAnn Zimmerman
Atty.-Harry Wright
C.P.-Waylan Rhodes
F.C.-Robin Jones
Dir. P.W.-Joe Moreno

SILVERTON 79257
Pop: 731   (Briscoe)
P.O. Box 250
806 823-2125 - *Fax: 823-2125*
Mayor-Lane B. Garvin
Mayor PT-Kyle Fuston
Ald.-Eloy Beltran
Ald.-Kraig Cox
Ald.-Anthony Kingery
Ald.-Delane Smith
City Secy.-Julie Gamble
City Admin.-Wade Willson
Atty.-Stephen Rohde
F.C.-JoDee Robison

SIMONTON 77476
Pop: 814   (Fort Bend)
P.O. Box 7
281 533-9809
www.simontontexas.org
Mayor-Louis J. Boudreaux
Mayor PT-Jeff Young
Ald.-Sandy Bohannon
Ald.-Laurie Boudreaux
Ald.-Jake Davis
Ald.-Todd Lippincott
City Secy.-Erica Molina
City Admin.-Shelly Elliott
Atty.-David Olson

SINTON 78387
Pop: 5665   (San Patricio)
301 E. Market
P.O. Box 1395
361 364-2381 - *Fax: 364-3781*
www.sintontexas.org
Mayor-Edward Adams
Mayor PT-Patricia G. Vargas
Coun.-Danny Davila
Coun.-Nathan Lindeman
Coun.-Cherl Rigotti
City Mgr.-John Hobson
City Secy.-Cathy Duhart
Atty.-Desireé Voth
C.P.-Eugene DeLeon
F.C.-Thomas Sanchez
Dir. P.W.-Hilario Chavez

SKELLYTOWN 79080
Pop: 473   (Carson)
500 Chamberlain St.
P.O. Box 129
806 848-2477 - *Fax: 848-2599*
www.skellytowntexas.com
Mayor-Wanda Rogers
Mayor PT-Suzie Wilson
Ald.-Bob Epperson
Ald.-Jim Fox
Ald.-Caren Garrard
Ald.-Mark Ruth
City Secy.-Kara Tice
Atty.-Bryan Denham
F.C.-Jacob Clifton

SLATON 79364
Pop: 6121   (Lubbock)
130 S. 9th
806 828-2000 - *Fax: 828-2002*
cityofslaton.com/
Mayor-D.W. Englund
Mayor PT-Lynn Buxkemper
Comm.-Benny Lopez
Comm.-Weldon Self
Comm.-James Tucker
City Secy.-Toni Chrestman
City Admin.-Mike Lamberson
Atty.-Harvey Morton
C.P.-Trevor Barnes
F.C.-Ethan Johnson

SMILEY 78159
Pop: 549   (Gonzales)
P.O. Box 189
830 587-6220 - *Fax: 587-6231*
www.smileytx.com
Mayor-Ellis Villasana
Mayor PT-Kathy Whitehead
Ald.-Willie Ann Canion
Ald.-Elisa Douglas
Ald.-Robert "Bob" Peck
Ald.-H. Wayne South
City Secy.-Rebecca Mejia
Atty.-Eduardo "Eddie" Escobar
F.C.-Billy Egger
F.M.-Donald Janicek

SMITHVILLE 78957
Pop: 3927   (Bastrop)
P.O. Box 449
512 237-3282 - *Fax: 237-4549*
www.ci.smithville.tx.us
Mayor-Scott Saunders
Mayor PT-Joanna Morgan
Coun.-Bill Gordon
Coun.-Rhonda Janak
Coun.-Bennie Rooks
Coun.-Troy Streuer
City Mgr.-Robert Tamble
Dir. Fin-Cynthia White
City Secy.-Brenda C. Page
Atty.-Sheets & Crossfield, P.C.
C.P.-Michael Maugere
F.C.-John Summarell
F.M.-Jack Page, Jr.
Dir. P.W.-Jack Page, Jr.

SMYER 79367
Pop: 474   (Hockley)
P.O. Box 203
806 234-3861 - *Fax: 234-3071*
smyertx.com
Mayor-Mary Beth Sims
Ald.-Chris Bradberry
Ald.-Kathy Price
Ald.-Joe Riddle
Ald.-Jeff Riedel
Ald.-Patrick Riedel
City Secy.-Jo Ann Beard
Atty.-Richard Husen
F.C.-Chris Bradberry
Dir. P.W.-Jaime Torres

SNOOK 77878
Pop: 511   (Burleson)
P.O. Box 10
979 272-3021 - *Fax: 272-6301*
Mayor-John W. See, III
Mayor PT-David Kovar
Ald.-Edward Green
Ald. Craig Kovar
Ald.-Marilyn Rubach
Ald.-Bob Schubert
City Secy.-Tammi Bryan
Atty.-Cary Bovey
Mar.-Michael Burkhalter
F.C.-Jon Collins

SNYDER
Pop: 11400   (Scurry)
P.O. Box 1341
Snyder, TX 79550
325 573-4957 - *Fax: 573-7505*
www.ci.snyder.tx.us/
Mayor-Tony Wofford
Mayor PT-Steve Highfield
Coun.-Luann Burleson
Coun.-Vernon Clay
Coun.-Ben Martin
Coun.-Steve Rich
Coun.-Thomas Strayhorn
City Mgr.-Merle Taylor, Jr.

Dir. Fin-Patricia Warren
City Secy.-Shai Green
Atty.-Bryan Guymon
C.P.-Terry Luecke
F.C./EMC-Perry Westmoreland

SOCORRO 79927
Pop: 32013 (El Paso)
124 S. Horizon Blvd.
915 858-2915 - *Fax: 858-9288*
www.ci.socorro.tx.us
Mayor-Vacant
Coun.-Yvonne Colon-Villalobos
Coun.-Ralph Duran
Coun.-Cesar Nevarez
Coun.-Victor Perez
Coun.-Rene Rodriguez
City Mgr.-Adriana Rodarte
Clk.-Olivia Navarro
Atty.-James A. Martinez
C.P.-Carlos Maldonado

SOMERSET 78069
Pop: 1631 (Bexar)
7360 E. 6th St.
830 701-4100 - *Fax: 429-3781*
www.cityofsomersettx.com
Mayor-Lydia Hernandez
Mayor PT-Jesse Vidales
Ald.-Ricardo Abundes
Ald.-Jonathan Gutierrez
Ald.-Harold Orosco
Ald.-Y. H. Perez III
Clk.-Veronica Lopez
City Admin.-Miguel Cantu
Atty.-Robert "Bobby" Maldonado
C.P.-Maria Dominguez

SOMERVILLE 77879
Pop: 1376 (Burleson)
P.O. Box 159
979 596-1122 - *Fax: 596-1931*
www.somervilletx.us.com/
Mayor Ken Tharp, Jr.
Ald.-Angelia Clark Beene
Ald.-Joel Brock
Ald.-Kimberly Camarillo
Ald.-Don "Skipper" Murray
Ald.-Jeff Schoppe
City Secy.-Rose Rosser
Atty.-Barney Knight
C.P.-Nic Malmstrom
Dir. P.W.-Dennis Moehlmann

SONORA 76950
Pop: 3027 (Sutton)
201 E. Main Street
325 387-2558 - *Fax: 387-5923*
www.sonora-texas.com
Mayor-Wanda Shurley
Coun.-Juanita Barrera
Coun.-Cody Gann
Coun.-Manuel Martinez
Coun.-Norm Rousselot

City Mgr.-Edward Carrasco
City Secy.-Belia Fay
Atty.-James A. Kosub
C.P.-William Dudley
F.C.-Rick Cearley

SOUR LAKE 77659
Pop: 1813 (Hardin)
625 Hwy. 105 W
409 287-3573 - *Fax: 287-2800*
www.cityofsourlake.com
Mayor-Bruce Robinson
Mayor PT-Shannon McDonald
Ald.-Marcus Dickerson
Ald.-Robin Powell
Ald.-Shane Rich
Ald.-Johnathan Williams
City Mgr.-Jack Provost
City Secy.-Debbie Morgan
Atty.-Richard Ferguson and
  Richard Baker
C.P.-Larry Saurage

SOUTH HOUSTON 77587
Pop: 16983 (Harris)
1018 Dallas
P.O. Box 238
713 947-7700 - *Fax: 947-3563*
www.southhoustontx.org
Mayor-Joe Soto
Mayor PT-Guillermo Rios
Ald.-Mary Castillo
Ald.-Louis Martinez
Ald.-Cynthia Pina
Ald.-Irene Tamayo
City Secy.-Lance Avant
Atty.-Dick Gregg Jr.
C.P.-Enrique Guzman

SOUTH MOUNTAIN
Pop: 384 (Coryell)
2005 E. Main, Ste. 221
Gatesville, TX 76528
254 865-5140
Mayor-Donald Smart
Mayor PT-Ronald Paul
Ald.-Nate Bird
Ald.-A. J. Weaver
Ald.-Vacant
City Secy.-Vernon Jones

SOUTH PADRE ISLAND 78597
Pop: 5704 (Cameron)
4601 Padre Blvd.
956 761-6456 - *Fax: 761-3888*
www.myspi.org
Mayor-Dennis Stahl
Mayor PT-Paul Munarriz
Coun.-Alita Bagley
Coun.-Ken Medders, Jr.
Coun.-Theresa Metty
Coun.-Ron Pitcock
City Mgr.-Susan Guthrie

City Secy.-Susan Hill
C.P.-Randy Smith
F.C.-William Douglas Fowler

SOUTHLAKE 76092
Pop: 27080 (Denton-Tarrant)
1400 Main St., Suite 270
817 748-8016 - *Fax: 748-8270*
www.ci.southlake.tx.us
Mayor-Laura Hill
Mayor PT-Randy Williamson
Dep. Mayor PT-Shawn McCaskill
Coun.-John R. Huffman
Coun.-Chad M. Patton
Coun.-Shahid Shafi
Coun.-Vacant
City Mgr.-Shana Yelverton
City Secy.-Lori Payne
Atty.-Taylor Olson Adkins Sralla &
  Elam, LLP
C.P.-James Brandon
F.C.-Mike Starr

SOUTHMAYD 76268
Pop: 1016 (Grayson)
4525 Elementary Drive
P.O. Box 88
903 868-9420 - *Fax: 813-1029*
www.southmaydtx.com
Mayor-Tom Byler
Mayor PT-Debra Thompson
Ald.-Michael Horstman
Ald.-Teresa Miller
Ald.-Robert Thompson
Ald.-David Turner
City Secy.-Lisa Stricklin
Atty.-Kent Hofmeister
C.P.-Chad McKee
F.C.-Andy Brazie

SOUTHSIDE PLACE
Pop: 1808 (Harris)
6309 Edloe Ave.
Houston, TX 77005
713 668-2341 - *Fax: 668-3305*
www.thecityofsouthsideplace.com
Mayor-Glenn "Pat" Patterson
Mayor PT-Andy Chan
Coun.-Jennifer W. Anderson
Coun.-Melissa Byers
Coun.-Doug Corbett
Coun.-Dr. Melissa Knop
City Mgr.-David N. Moss
City Secy.-Olga Garza
Atty.-Richard Rothfelder
C.P.-Don McCall
F.C.-Michael Pack

CITY SECTION

SPEARMAN 79081
Pop: 3368   (Hansford)
P.O. Box 37
806 659-2524 - *Fax: 659-3859*
Mayor-Tobe Shields
Ald.-Ole Bergan
Ald.-Annette Bynum
Ald.-Tim Cooper
Ald.-Jeremy Frost
Ald.-Bob Pearson
City Mgr.-Suzanne Bellsnyder
City Secy.-Cheryl Gibson-Salgado
Atty.-Barney Knight
C.P.-Lance Swan
F.C.-Roger Close

SPLENDORA 77372
Pop: 1615   (Montgomery)
P.O. Drawer 1087
281 689-3197 - *Fax: 689-3249*
www.cityofsplendora.org
Mayor-Dorothy Welch
Mayor PT-Buck Clendennen
Ald.-David Aden
Ald.-Lisa Carr
Ald.-Alton DuLaney
Ald.-Evelyn Meyers
City Secy.-Danna Welter
Atty.-Leonard Schneider
C.P.-Wally Wieghat

SPOFFORD
Pop: 95   (Kinney)
P.O. Box 1541
Brackettville, TX 78832
830 563-7244 - *Fax: 563-2312*
Mayor-Pablo Resendez
Ald.-Robert Hearne
Ald.-Antonia "Toni" Pena
Ald.-Leticia Vela
Ald.-Brad Whitaker
Ald.-Ronald Winburn
City Secy. Donna Winburn

SPRING VALLEY VILLAGE
Pop: 4013   (Harris)
1025 Campbell Road
Houston, TX 77055
713 465-8308 - *Fax: 461-7969*
www.springvalleytx.com
Mayor-Tom Ramsey
Coun.-Bo Bothe
Coun.-Allen Carpenter
Coun.-Tom Donaho
Coun.-Aaron Stai
Coun.-Marcus Vajdos
Tres.-Michelle Yi
City Secy.-Roxanne Benitez
City Admin.-Julie Robinson
Atty.-Loren B. Smith
C.P.-Loyd Evans
F.C.-David Foster

SPRINGLAKE 79082
Pop: 108   (Lamb)
P.O. Box 249
806 986-4211 - *Fax: 986-4225*
Mayor-Gaylon Conner
Mayor PT-Mike Ritchie
Ald.-Keith Clayton
Ald.-Chuck Conner
Ald.-Johnny Landrum
Ald.-Jake Loudder
City Secy.-Melinda Lewis
F.C.-Keith Clayton

SPRINGTOWN 76082
Pop: 2658   (Parker)
P.O. Box 444
817 220-4834 - *Fax: 523-3179*
www.cityofspringtown.com
Mayor-Tom W. Clayton
Mayor PT-Dennie Harms
Ald.-Annette Burk
Ald.-Greg Hood
Ald.-Richelle Pruitt
City Secy.-Jhanna L. Bogan
Int. City Adm.-Jhanna L. Bogan
Atty.-George Staples
C.P.-A. Motley

SPUR 79370
Pop: 1318   (Dickens)
402 N. Burlington
806 271-3316 - *Fax: 271-4378*
Mayor-Louise Jones
Mayor PT-Glenda White
Ald.-Crystal Leary
Ald.-Rhea Melton
Ald.-Margaret Morris
Ald.-Robert Vasquez
Ald.-Kenneth Wright
City Secy.-Laura Adams
Atty.-W. Calloway "Cal" Huffaker
C.P.-Kara Wilson
F.C.-Rick Paschall

ST PAUL, TOWN OF 75098
Pop: 1066   (Collin)
2505 Butscher's Block
972 442-7212 - *Fax: 905-7406*
www.stpaultexas.us
Mayor-Opie Walter
Mayor PT-Robert Simmons
Coun.-Bruce Dunn
Coun.-David Gensler
Coun.-Robert Kellow
Town Secy.-Bob A. London
Town Clk.-Liz Tamez
Atty.-Robert L. Dillard, III

STAFFORD 77477
Pop: 19560   (Fort Bend-Harris)
2610 S. Main St.
281 261-3900 - *Fax: 261-3994*
www.staffordtx.gov/
Mayor-Leonard Scarcella

Mayor PT-Cecil Willis, Jr.
Coun.-Wen Guerra
Coun.-Arthur J. Honore
Coun.-Donald A. Jones
Coun.-Ken Mathew
Coun.-Virginia Rosas
Dir. Fin-Vacant
City Secy.-Tomika R. Lewis
Atty.-Arthur Lee "Art" Pertile, III
C.P.-Richard Ramirez
F.C.-Larry Di Camillo

STAGECOACH 77355
Pop: 538   (Montgomery)
16930 Boot Hill Road
281 259-0224 - *Fax: 259-4963*
www.stagecoachtx.us
Mayor-Galen Mansee
Ald.-Jim Cooley
Ald.-Sharon McClure
Ald.-Bill McGahen
Ald.-Mark McGill
Ald.-James Osteen
City Secy.-Brenda Rutt
Atty.-Janice Baldwin
C.P.-Michael C. Wethington

STAMFORD 79553
Pop: 3124   (Haskell-Jones)
201 E. McHarg
P.O. Drawer 191
325 773-2591 - *Fax: 773-2145*
Mayor-Johnny Anders
Mayor PT-Leldon Clifton
Coun.-Dennis Braden
Coun.-James Decker
Coun.-Pam Reither
Coun.-Melinda Smith
City Mgr.-Alan Plumlee
City Secy.-Kim Kelley
Atty.-Raymond Hollabaugh
C.P.-Darwin Huston
Int. F.C.-Alan Plumlee

STANTON 79782
Pop: 2492   (Martin)
P.O. Box 370
432 756-3301 - *Fax: 756-2083*
www.cityofstantontx.com
Mayor-Jim Smith
Mayor PT-James Jenkins
Ald.-Danny Fryar
Ald.-Brian McHenry
Ald.-Steven Villa
Ald.-Gib Wheeler
City Admin.-Jessie Montez
Atty.-Bill Clifton
C.P.-Fred Schroyer
F.C.-Lonnie Long

STAPLES 78670
Pop: 267 (Guadalupe)
512 357-9981 - *Fax: 357-9981*
www.cityofstaples.com
Mayor-Eddie Daffern
Mayor PT-Carol Wester
Ald.-Ronnie Clark
Ald.-Ann Huebner
Ald.-James Rector
Coun.-Lynda Lowman Henson
City Secy.-Marilyn DeVere
Atty.-Paige Saenz
C.P.-Andrew Chavez
F.C.-Andrew Munk

STAR HARBOR
Pop: 444 (Henderson)
P.O. Box 949
Malakoff, TX 75148-0949
903 489-0091 - *Fax: 489-2105*
Mayor-Warren Claxton
Ald.-Ray Batten
Ald.-Tommy Clark
Ald.-David Morris
Ald.-Marion Morrison
Ald.-Jackie Robinson
City Secy.-Adabeth Routt-Shumate
Atty.-Vacant
C.P.-Todd Tucker

STEPHENVILLE 76401
Pop: 19560 (Erath)
298 W. Washington
254 918-1212 - *Fax: 918-1207*
www.stephenvilletx.gov
Mayor-Kenny Weldon
Coun.-Rhett Harrison
Coun.-Mark McClinton
Coun.-Alan Nix
Coun.-Brady Pendleton
Coun.-Doug Svien
Coun.-Carla Trussell
Coun.-Jerry Warren
Coun.-Sherry Zachery
City Secy.-Staci King
City Admin.-Allen L. Barnes
P.A.-Tricia Wortley
Atty.-Randy Thomas
C.P.-Jason King
F.C.-Jimmy Chew

STERLING CITY 76951
Pop: 888 (Sterling)
P.O. Box 1022
325 378-2811 - *Fax: 378-2334*
www.sterlingcitytexas.com/
Mayor-Lane Horwood
Mayor PT-Randy Guetersloh
Coun.-Andrea Davis
Coun.-Brook Dickison
Coun.-Mike Havlak
Coun.-George Rodriguez
Coun.-Charles Stevens
City Secy.-Marla Arizola

STINNETT 79083
Pop: 1881 (Hutchinson)
P.O. Drawer 909
806 878-2422 - *Fax: 878-2540*
www.cityofstinnett.com
Mayor-Colin Locke
Ald.-Ralph Batenhorst
Ald.-Justin Hart
Ald.-Jeff Irvin
Ald.-Char Kerr
Ald.-Andrew Trahan
City Mgr.-Durk Downs
City Secy.-Lynette Sloan
Atty.-Angelique Weaver
C.P.-Wiley Wagner
F.C.-Alan Wells

STOCKDALE 78160
Pop: 1442 (Wilson)
700 W. Main
P.O. Box 446
830 996-3128 - *Fax: 996-3130*
stockdaletx.org
Mayor-Ray Wolff
Mayor PT-Scott Soden
Coun.-Becky Adams
Coun.-Neal Bennett
Coun.-Saul Bosquez
Coun.-Sherry D. Lambeck
City Mgr.-Banks Akin
City Secy.-Thania Santos
Clk.-Margaret Hastings
Atty.-Charles E. "Charlie" Zech
F.C.-Edwin Baker

STOCKTON BEND 76048
Pop: 305 (Hood)
817 403-0053
Mayor-Vern Oechsle
Mayor PT-Dean White
Ald.-John Adcock
Ald.-Rex Becham
Ald.-Ken Knieper
Ald.-Edward Reiter
City Secy.-Donald Walton
Atty.-Monte Akers

STRATFORD 79084
Pop: 2017 (Sherman)
P.O. Box 188
806 366-5581 - *Fax: 366-2254*
stratfordtx.com/
Mayor-Ricky Reed
Mayor PT-Joe Zak
Ald.-Ann Johnson
Ald.-Kyle Sandvig
Ald.-Greg Wright
Ald.-Vacant
City Secy.-Kathy Rendon
City Admin.-Tommy R. Bogart
Atty.-Robert L. Elliott, III
C.P.-Randy Hooks
F.C.-Danny Davis

STRAWN 76475
Pop: 739 (Palo Pinto)
P.O. Box 581
254 672-5311 - *Fax: 672-5250*
www.strawntx.com/
Mayor-Tye Jackson
Mayor PT-Omar Mallory
Ald.-Delane Abbott
Ald.-Alan Alison
Ald.-Regina Baker
Ald.-Brenda Orsini
City Secy.-Danny Miller
Atty.-Phil Garrett
F.C.-Jimmy A. Dixon

STREETMAN 75859
Pop: 247 (Freestone-Navarro)
Mayor-Johnny A. Robinson
Comm.-Heather Davis
Comm.-Barbara Polk
Clk.-Heather Marfell
F.C.-Brian Davis

SUDAN 79371
Pop: 958 (Lamb)
111 E. First Ave.
P.O. Box 59
806 227-2112 - *Fax: 227-2164*
www.cityofsudantx.com/
Mayor-Sam Miller
Mayor PT-Sam Merryman
Ald.-Rosendo Alcaraz
Ald.-Celia Garza
Ald.-Stacy Smith
Ald.-Michael Williamson
City Secy.-Mechele Edwards
Clk.-Gwenna Gore
Atty.-Slater Elza
C.P.-Vacant
F.C.-Mike Hill
Dir. P.W.-Richard Salazar

SUGAR LAND 77478
Pop: 87773 (Fort Bend)
2700 Town Center Blvd. N.
Sugar Land, TX 77479
281 275-2730 - *Fax: 275-2293*
www.sugarlandtx.gov
Mayor-Joe R. Zimmerman
Coun.-Harish Jajoo
Coun.-Mary Joyce
Coun.-Carol K. McCutcheon
Coun.-Amy Mitchell
Coun.-Steve Porter
Coun.-Bridget Yeung
City Mgr.-Allen Bogard
City Secy.-Glenda Gundermann
Atty.-Meredith Riede
C.P.-Douglas Brinkley
F.C.-Juan J. Adame

CITY SECTION

SULLIVAN CITY 78595
Pop: 4002 (Hidalgo)
P.O. Box 249
956 485-2828 - *Fax: 485-9551*
www.sullivancity.org
Mayor-Leonel Garcia
Mayor PT-Adriana Rodriguez
Coun.-Sylvia Castillo
Coun.-Daniel Flores
Coun.-Gabriel Salinas
City Mgr.-Juan Cedillo
City Secy.-Veronica Gutierrez
Atty.-Ricardo "Ric" Gonzalez
C.P.-Richard Ozuna
F.C.-Ricardo Pena

SULPHUR SPRINGS 75482
Pop: 15449 (Hopkins)
201 N. Davis St.
903 885-7541 - *Fax: 439-2092*
www.sulphurspringstx.org
Mayor-John Sellers
Mayor PT-Oscar Aguilar
Coun.-Dan Froneberger
Coun.-Emily Glass
Coun.-Craig Johnson
Coun.-Freddie Taylor
Coun.-Clay Walker
City Mgr.-Marc Maxwell
City Secy.-Gale Roberts
Atty.-Jim D. McLeroy
C.P.-James Sanders
F.C.-Eric Hill

SUN VALLEY
Pop: 69 (Lamar)
800 Shady Grove Road
Paris, TX 75462
903 982-6111 - *Fax: 982-6113*
Mayor-Tom Wagnon
Ald.-Francis Brewer
Ald.-Tammy Mancille
Ald.-Tamala Noble
Ald.-Sharron Young
Ald.-Vacant
City Secy.-Shaunee Wagnon
Atty.-Ed Ellis

SUNDOWN 79372
Pop: 1500 (Hockley)
P.O. Box 600
806 229-3131 - *Fax: 229-2161*
Mayor-Jim Winn
Mayor PT-Dewane Fryar
Ald.-Doug Barry
Ald.-Lonnie Geisler
Ald.-Randy Hart
Ald.-Dennis Heatherly
City Secy.-Lora Dockery
City Admin.-Billy Hernandez
Atty.-Cary Bovey
C.P.-Carey James
F.C.-Cole Mulloy

SUNNYVALE, TOWN OF 75182
Pop: 5130 (Dallas)
127 N. Collins Road
972 226-7177 - *Fax: 226-1804*
www.townofsunnyvale.org
Mayor-Jim Phaup
Mayor PT-Saji George
Coun.-Mark Egan
Coun.-Karen Hill
Coun.-Chris McNeill
Coun.-Kara Ranta
Coun.-Jim Wade
Town Mgr.-Sean Fox
Town Secy.-Rachel Ramsey
Atty.-David Dodd
F.C.-Doug Kendrick

SUNRAY 79086
Pop: 1926 (Moore)
P.O. Box 250
806 948-4111 - *Fax: 948-4485*
www.cityofsunray.com
Mayor-Bruce Broxson
Mayor PT-Brenda Emmert
Ald.-Mike Raymond
Ald.-James Walker
Ald.-Melvin Weatherford
Ald.-Mark Wisdom
City Mgr.-Rob Roach
Atty.-Robert L. Elliott, III
C.P.-Tim Dean
F.C.-Rocky Rexrode

SUNRISE BEACH VILLAGE 78643
Pop: 713 (Llano)
124 Sunrise Drive
325 388-6438 - *Fax: 388-6973*
www.cityofsunrisebeach.org
Mayor-Tommy Martin
Mayor PT-Fred Butler
Comm.-Mike Byrd
Comm.-Hank Gath
Comm.-Dan Gower
Coun.-Ruth Stanley
City Secy.-Linda Wendling
Atty.-Paige Saenz
C.P.-Laurie Brock

SUNSET VALLEY 78745
Pop: 749 (Travis)
3205 Jones Road
512 892-1383 - *Fax: 892-6108*
www.sunsetvalley.org
Mayor-Rose Cardona
Coun.-Marc Bruner
Coun.-Walter Jenkins
Coun.-Ketan U. Kharod
Coun.-Mickie Powers
Coun.-Rudi Rosengarten
City Secy.-Rae Gene Greenough
City Admin.-Clay Collins
Atty.-Doug Young
C.P.-Sean Ford

SURFSIDE BEACH 77541
Pop: 482 (Brazoria)
1304 Monument Dr.
979 233-1531 - *Fax: 373-0699*
www.surfsidetx.org
Mayor-Larry Davidson
Mayor PT-Troy McMinn
Ald.-Toni Capretta
Ald.-Dave Guzman
Ald.-Peggy P. Llewellyn
Ald.-Marissa McMinn
City Secy.-Amanda Davenport
Atty.-Vacant
C.P.-Gary Phillips
F.C.-Pete David

SWEENY 77480
Pop: 3684 (Brazoria)
P.O. Box 248
979 548-3321 - *Fax: 548-7745*
www.ci.sweeny.tx.us/
Mayor-Dale Lemon
Ald.-Sandra K. Blaine
Ald.-Brian Brooks
Ald.-Jeff Farley
Ald.-Tim Pettigrew
Ald.-Kay Roe
City Mgr.-Cindy King
City Secy.-Reatta Minshew
Clk.-Laurie Martinez
Atty.-R.C. "Charlie" Stevenson
C.P.-John Barnard
F.C.-Roger Barton

SWEETWATER 79556
Pop: 10906 (Nolan)
P.O. Box 450
325 236-6313 - *Fax: 235-1850*
www.cityofsweetwatertx.com
Mayor-Jim McKenzie
Mayor PT-Jerod Peek
Comm.-Ricky Castro
Comm.-Jim Lee
Comm.-Larry May
City Mgr.-David Vela
City Secy.-Patty Torres
P.A.-Russell Jones
Atty.-Peter Sheridan
C.P.-Brian Frieda

TAFT 78390
Pop: 3048 (San Patricio)
P.O. Box 416
361 528-3512 - *Fax: 528-3515*
www.cityoftaft.us
Mayor-Pete Lopez
Mayor PT-Denise L. Hitt
Ald.-Donnie Riojas
Ald.-Ronnie Rodriguez
Int. Mgr.-Ray De Los Santos
City Secy.-Jennifer Peniola
Atty.-Roxann Cotroneo
C.P.-Vacant
F.C.-Dan Gibson

TAHOKA 79373
Pop: 2673   (Lynn)
P.O. Box 300
806 561-4211 - *Fax: 561-4444*
www.tahoka-texas.com
Mayor-John B. Baker
Mayor PT-Ray D. Box
Coun.-Tyler Hawthorne
Coun.-Ronny Jolly
Coun.-Jeff Martin
Coun.-Johnny Rosas
City Mgr.-Jerry W. Webster
City Secy.-Retha Pittman
Atty.-W. Calloway Huffaker
C.P.-Miguel Reyna
V.F.D.F.C.-Steve Sanders
Dir. P.W.-Raymond Vega

TALCO 75487
Pop: 516   (Titus)
P.O. Box 365
903 379-3731 - *Fax: 379-3311*
Mayor-K. M. Sloan
Comm.-Michael Mars
Comm.-Keith Thompson
City Secy.-Jackie Moore
Atty.-Billy W. Flanagan
F.C.-Randy Carroll

TALTY
Pop: 1770   (Kaufman)
9550 Helms Trail, Ste. 500
Forney, TX 75126-8041
972 552-9592
www.taltytexas.com
Mayor-Larry Farthing
Mayor PT-Frank Garrison
Coun.-Bobby Crowley
Coun.-Brad Davis
Coun.-Courtney McGrath
Coun.-Al Werning
Town Secy.-Sherry Bagby
Town Admin.-James Stroman
Atty.-David Berman
C.P.-Michael Hoskins

TATUM 75691
Pop: 1385   (Panola-Rusk)
P.O. Box 1105
903 947-2260 - *Fax: 947-2680*
Mayor-Phil Cory
Mayor PT-E. W. Nelson
Ald.-Dana Budducke
Ald.-Jeff Keller
Ald.-Kim R. Smith
Ald.-Jack York
City Secy.-Rhonda Ross
Atty.-Joe Shumate
C.P.-April Rains
F.C.-Rayford Gibson

TAYLOR 76574
Pop: 18291   (Williamson)
512 352-3676 - *Fax: 352-8255*
www.ci.taylor.tx.us
Mayor PT-Brandt Rydell
Coun.-Dwayne Ariola
Coun.-Robert Garcia
Coun.-Christopher Gonzales
Coun.-Christine Lopez
City Mgr.-Isaac Turner
Dir. Fin-Rosemarie Dennis
Clk.-Susan Brock
Atty.-Ted Hejl
C.P.-Henry Fluck
F.C./EMC-Pat L. Ekiss

TAYLOR LAKE VILLAGE 77586
Pop: 3500   (Harris)
500 Kirby Blvd
281 326-2843 - *Fax: 326-5456*
www.taylorlakevillage.us
Mayor-Jon Keeney
Mayor PT-Einar Goerland
Coun.-Doug Blanchard
Coun.-Bob Davee
Coun.-Tony Galt
Coun.-Douglas W. Shows
City Secy.-Stacey Fields
Atty.-Olson & Olson
C.P.-Tom Savage

TAYLOR LANDING 77627
Pop: 228   (Jefferson)
409 527-3349
Mayor-John Durkay
Comm.-Phil Owens
Comm.-Lauren Rahe
Clk.-Tina Burks

TEAGUE 75860
Pop: 3560   (Freestone)
105 S. 4th Ave.
254 739-2547 - *Fax: 739-2433*
www.cityofteaguetx.com/
Mayor-Earnest Pack
Mayor PT-Marilyn Michaud
Ald.-Marie Hetenberger
Ald.-Melvin Mims
Ald.-Chris Nickleberry
Ald.-Ron Rasbeary
City Admin/Secy-Theresa Prasil
Atty.-Alan J. Bojorquez
C.P.-Daniel Ramsey
F.C.-Jody Bodine

TEHUACANA 76686
Pop: 283   (Limestone)
P.O. Box 67
254 395-4408 - *Fax: 395-4064*
Mayor-Roy Cholopisa
Mayor PT-Bill Kuehn
Coun.-Brooke Anderson
Coun.-Bill Ferris

Coun.-Chuck "Clutch" Henry
Coun.-Tommy Platt
City Secy.-Norma Fielder
Atty.-Charles Olson
F.C.-Richard Johnson

TEMPLE 76501
Pop: 70190   (Bell)
2 North Main
254 298-5302 - *Fax: 298-5637*
www.ci.temple.tx.us
Mayor-Danny Dunn
Mayor PT-Tim Davis
Coun.-Susan Long
Coun.-Judy Morales
Coun.-Mike Pilkington
Int. Mgr.-Brynn Myers
City Secy.-Lacy Borgeson
P.A.-Belinda Mattke
Atty.-Kayla Landeros
C.P.-Floyd O. Mitchell
F.C.-Mitch Randles

TENAHA 75974
Pop: 1160   (Shelby)
258 N. George Bowers Drive
936 248-3841 - *Fax: 248-5942*
Mayor-Carl W. Jernigan
Mayor PT-Natalie Harris
Ald.-Stephanie Glenn
Ald.-Craig Gray
Ald.-Cliff Lloyd
Ald.-Durand Steadman
City Secy.-Sheryl R. Clark
Atty.-Miles T. Bradshaw
Mar.-Jimmy Wagstaff
F.C.-Mark Odom
Dir. P.W.-Matt Barton

TERRELL 75160
Pop: 15816   (Kaufman)
P.O. Box 310
972 551-6600 - *Fax: 551-6682*
www.cityofterrell.org
Mayor-D.J. Ory
Mayor PT-Sandra Wilson
Dep. Mayor PT-Charles Whitaker
Coun.-Tim Royse
Coun.-Tommy Spencer
City Mgr.-Torry Edwards
City Secy.-John Rounsavall
Atty.-Mary Gayle Ramsey
Int. C.P.-Ken McKeown
F.C.-Jim Harper

CITY SECTION

TERRELL HILLS
Pop: 4878 (Bexar)
5100 N. New Braunfels Ave.
San Antonio, TX 78209
210 824-7401 - *Fax: 822-2297*
www.terrell-hills.com
Mayor-Anne M. Ballantyne
Mayor PT-Marilyn Eldridge
Coun.-John Low
Coun.-William W. Ochse
Coun.-Charles W. Parish, Jr.
City Mgr.-Greg Whitlock
Atty.-Frank J. Garza
C.P.-Bill Foley
F.C.-William Knupp

TEXARKANA 75504
Pop: 36411 (Bowie)
P.O. Box 1967
903 798-3900 - *Fax: 798-3448*
www.ci.texarkana.tx.us
Mayor-Bob Bruggeman
Coun.-Christie Alcorn
Coun.-Josh Davis
Coun.-Bill Harp
Coun.-Mary Hart
Coun.-Jean Matlock
Coun.-Betty Williams
City Mgr.-Shirley Jaster
City Secy.-Jennifer Evans
C.P.-Daniel L. Shiner

TEXAS CITY 77592
Pop: 45099 (Galveston)
P.O. Box 2608
409 948-3111 - *Fax: 942-1073*
www.texas-city-tx.org
Mayor-Matthew T. Doyle
Mayor PT-Phil Roberts
Comm.-Thelma Bowie
Comm.-Jami Clark
Comm.-Bruce Clawson
Comm.-Dee Ann Haney
Comm.-Dorthea Jones
Dir. Fin-Laura Boyd
City Secy.-Nicholas J. Finan
Atty.-Ron Plackemeier
C.P.-Robert J. Burby
F.C.-David Zacherl

TEXHOMA 73960
Pop: 346 (Sherman)
P.O. Box 10123
806 827-7411 - *Fax: 827-7411*
Mayor-Missy Cartwright
Mayor PT-Ismael Hernandez
Coun.-Chris Beattie
Coun.-Shaun Crawford
Coun.-Shaun Crawford
Coun.-Diane Murphey
City Secy.-Jennifer Johnson
Atty.-Robert L. Elliott, III

TEXLINE 79087
Pop: 507 (Dallam)
517 S. 2nd St.
P.O. Box 150
806 362-4849 - *Fax: 362-4226*
Mayor-Billy Allen Davis
Coun.-Ricky Arnold
Coun.-Charlene Newlon
Coun.-Brett Poling
Coun.-Stan Sanner
Coun.-Greg Ward
City Secy.-Marcia French
Atty.-Slater Elza
F.C.-Brad Riley

THE COLONY 75056
Pop: 36328 (Denton)
6800 Main St.
972 625-1756 - *Fax: 624-2316*
www.thecolonytx.gov
Mayor-Joe McCourry
Dep. Mayor PT-Perry Schrag
Coun.-Richard Boyer
Coun.-Joel Marks
Coun.-Kirk Mikulec
Coun.-David Terre
Coun.-Brian R. Wade
City Mgr.-Troy C. Powell
Dir. Fin-David Cranford
City Secy.-Tina Stewart
P.A.-Alice Pitts
Atty.-Jeff Moore
C.P.-David Coulon
F.C.-Scott Thompson

THOMPSONS 77481
Pop: 236 (Fort Bend)
P.O. Box 29
281 343-9929 - *Fax: 343-7786*
Mayor-Freddie Newsome
Mayor PT-Carol Gubbles
Ald.-Deborah Brown
Ald.-Linda Garcia
Ald.-Edward Taylor
Ald.-Gina S. Treadgold
City Secy.-Mary Ann Manna
Atty.-Olson & Olson
C.P.-James H. Pirie
F.C.-Ray Freshour

THORNDALE 76577
Pop: 1336 (Milam)
P.O. Box 308
512 898-2523 - *Fax: 898-5459*
www.thorndaletx.com
Mayor-Mara McDowell, Interim
Mayor PT-Stephanie Churchman
Coun.-Larry Drakek
Coun.-Rickey Melde
Coun.-Sam Pickett
City Secy.-Stacy Irwin
City Admin.-Keith Kiesling
Atty.-Ted Hejl
C.P.-Martin L. Jackson
F.C.-Eric Melde

THORNTON 76687
Pop: 526 (Limestone)
205 E. 11th Street
254 385-6438 - *Fax: 385-6204*
Mayor-Kenneth Capps
Mayor PT-Jud Hughes
Ald.-Traci Cordova
Ald.-Carla Robison
Ald.-Troy Waddle
Ald.-Devin Wilson
City Secy.-Victoria Winstead
Atty.-Brian Gibson
C.P.-Timothy Brewer
F.C.-Paul Miller

THORNTONVILLE
Pop: 476 (Ward)
2414 West. 2nd St.
Monahans, TX 79756
432 943-3752
www.thorntonville.org
Mayor-David Mitchell
Mayor PT-Danny W. Greenwood
Coun.-Chad Eubanks
Coun.-Chris Hall
Coun.-Beverly Huey
Coun.-Bryan Mann
Coun.-Vacant
City Secy.-Tara Williams

THRALL 76578
Pop: 839 (Williamson)
P.O. Box 346
512 898-5306 - *Fax: 898-4126*
Mayor-Troy Marx
Comm.-J. "Scooter" Dubec
Comm.-Nicole Walla
City Secy.-Ginger Gross
Atty.-Ted Hejl
C.P.-Whitney Whitworth
F.C.-Mark Muellenberg

THREE RIVERS 78071
Pop: 1848 (Live Oak)
P.O. Box 398
361 786-2528 - *Fax: 786-3281*
www.threeriverstx.org
Mayor-Sam Garcia
Mayor PT-Sally Rodriguez
Ald.-Tommy House
Ald.-Patsy Roberts
Ald.-Tim Stroleny
Ald.-Reynaldo Trevino
City Admin.-Arnold Saenz
Atty.-Roxann Pais Cotroneo
C.P.-Vance Roberts
F.C.-Henry Pullin

THROCKMORTON 76483
Pop: 828 (Throckmorton)
P.O. Box 640
940 849-4411 - *Fax: 849-3163*
www.throckmortontx.org
Mayor-Will Carroll
Mayor PT-Judy Jackson

Ald.-Brad Bellah
Ald.-Ricky Escalon
Ald.-Corey Keeter
Ald.-Susie Oliver
City Secy.-Melanie Gober
F.C.-Rob Rankin

TIKI ISLAND 77554
Pop: 968 (Galveston)
802 Tiki Drive
409 935-1427 - *Fax: 935-4670*
www.villageoftikiisland.org
Mayor-Vernon "Goldie" Teltschick
Mayor PT-Ron Simons
Ald.-Freddie Carmichael
Ald.-Wayne Crozier
Ald.-Tom Fisher
Ald.-Karen Hearring
City Secy.-Brandee Lawther
Atty.-Ellis J. Ortego
C.P.-Adren Sustaita
F.C.-Micah Simons

**TIMBERCREEK CANYON,
 VILLAGE OF**
Pop: 418 (Randall)
101-A N. Timbercreek Dr.
Amarillo, TX 79118
806 622-9336 - *Fax: 373-9365*
Mayor-Bill Young
Mayor PT-Brian Giffin
Ald.-Mike Fuller
Ald.-Dickie Haney
Ald.-Tara Murrell
Ald.-Sarah Wilson
City Mgr.-Joe Price
Tres.-Elaine Dollar
City Secy.-Betty M. Howe
Atty.-Angelique Weaver
C.P.-Jeremy Hoffman
F.C.-Eddie Wood

TIMPSON 75975
Pop: 1155 (Shelby)
P.O. Box 369
936 254-2421 - *Fax: 254-2933*
www.cityoftimpson.com
Mayor-Debra P. Smith
Mayor PT-Kyle Allen
Coun.-Tiffany Collins
Coun.-Charleston Johnson
Coun.-Yvonne Ramsey
Coun.-Al Skinner
City Secy.-Leslie Leathers
Atty.-Cary Bovey
C.P.-Kent Graham
F.C.-Tuffy Green

TIOGA 76271
Pop: 795 (Grayson)
P.O. Box 206
940 437-2351 - *Fax: 437-2432*
www.tiogatx.gov/
Mayor-Craig Jezek
Ald.-Kurt A. Hall

Ald.-Tommy Hunter
Ald.-Mead McGee
Ald.-Jeff Moncrief
Ald.-Heather Nesmith
City Secy.-Donna Carney
Atty.-Lance Vanzant
C.P.-Curtis Macomb
F.C.-Paul Rodarmer

TIRA 75482
Pop: 297 (Hopkins)
903 945-2190
Mayor-Powell Vickery
Ald.-Joyce Dodd
Ald.-Tami Joslin
Ald.-Janie Lewis
Ald.-Sherry Smiddy
Ald.-Yvonne Weir
City Secy.-Jan Vaughn
Atty.-Joel Sheffield
F.C.-John Martin

TOCO
Pop: 75 (Lamar)
2105 Chestnut
Brookston, TX 75421
Mayor-J. Jason Waller
Ald.-Larry Ellis
Ald.-Sharon Frazier
Ald.-Flordia Johnson
Ald.-Mary Ladell
Ald.-Ronnie Manjane
City Secy.-Kim Hanley

TODD MISSION
Pop: 107 (Grimes)
21718 FM 1774
Plantersville, TX 77363
936 894-3001 - *Fax: 894-3002*
www.cityoftoddmission.org
Mayor-George Coulam
Coun.-Brett Bratcher
Coun.-Heather Moon
Coun.-Kristy Pendley
Coun.-Vacant
City Mgr.-Terre Albert
City Secy.-Julie Lunsford
Atty.-Arthur Lee "Art" Pertile, III
C.P.-Johnny Martinez

TOLAR 76476
Pop: 681 (Hood)
P.O. Box 100
254 835-4390 - *Fax: 835-4392*
www.tolartexas.com
Mayor-Terry Johnson
Mayor PT-Matt Hutsell
Coun.-Chip Foster
Coun.-Kevin Fron
Coun.-Barbara Gilliam
Coun.-Sally Grimes
City Secy.-Joyce Johnson
Atty.-David Dodd
V.F.D.F.C.-Matt Hutsell
Dir. P.W.-J.R. Higgins

TOM BEAN 75489
Pop: 1045 (Grayson)
P.O. Box 659
903 546-6321 - *Fax: 546-4878*
www.tombean.net
Mayor-Sherry E. Howard
Mayor PT-Ben Vincent
Ald.-Daniel Harrison
Ald.-Lonnie Jones
Ald.-Brittany Melton
Ald.-Dawson Nitcholas
City Secy.-Cathy Pugh
Atty.-W.D. Welch, P.C.
C.P.-Tim Green
F.C.-Jason Lankford

TOMBALL 77375
Pop: 11124 (Harris)
401 Market St.
281 290-1002 - *Fax: 351-6256*
www.ci.tomball.tx.us
Mayor-Getchen B. Fagan
Coun.-Chad Degges
Coun.-John F. Ford
Coun.-Lori Klein Quinn
Coun.-Mark Stoll
Coun.-Derek Townsend Sr.
City Mgr.-George Shackelford
Dir. Fin-Glenn Windsor
City Secy.-Doris Speer
Atty.-Loren B. Smith
C.P.-Billy Tidwell
F.C.-Randall Parr
Dir. P.W.-David Esquivel

TOOL 75143
Pop: 2240 (Henderson)
701 N. Tool Drive
903 432-3522 - *Fax: 432-3867*
www.tooltexas.org
Mayor-Donny Daniel
Mayor PT-Roland Napoles
Coun.-Tawnya Austin
Coun.-Michael Fladmark
Coun.-Randy Whitehurst
Coun.-Barbara Whitfill
City Secy.-Makenzie D Lyons
Clk.-Debbie Arender
Atty.-Blake E. Armstrong
C.P.-Vacant

TOYAH 79785
Pop: 90 (Reeves)
P.O. Box 144
432 259-3908
Mayor-Vacant
Mayor PT-Naomi Machuca
Coun.-Misty Begay
Coun.-Loretta Campos
Coun.-David Domeny
Coun.-Adrianna Machuca
Int. City Secy.-Marilou Martin
Atty.-Adolfo Ruiz
F.C.-Vacant

TRENT 79561
Pop: 337   (Taylor)
P.O. Box 67
325 862-6281 - *Fax: 862-0241*
Mayor-Leanna West
Mayor PT-Robert Reed
Ald.-Jerry Patterson
Ald.-Orville Patterson
Ald.-Wayne Robertson
Ald.-Tina Stephens
City Secy.-Debbie Boles
Atty.-Claudia Clinton
F.C.-Carlton King

TRENTON 75490
Pop: 635   (Fannin)
P.O. Box 44
903 989-2237 - *Fax: 989-2315*
Mayor-Rodney Alexander
Mayor PT-Lew Donaghey
Coun.-Laurie Alexander
Coun.-Glenda Hackney
Coun.-Scott Shoemaker
Coun.-Terri Jo Vasquez
City Secy.-Jamie Davis
Atty.-John H. Skotnik
C.P.-William Robertson
V.F.D.F.C.-C.J. Fillingham

TRINIDAD 75163
Pop: 886   (Henderson)
P.O. Box 345
903 778-2525 - *Fax: 778-2754*
trinidadtexas.com
Mayor-Vacant
Mayor PT-Kay Hernandez
Ald.-Mary Beth Parker
Ald.-Chris Quinn
Ald.-Roy Stanfield
Ald.-Velma Womack
City Admin.-Terri R. Newhouse
Atty.-Barney Knight
C.P.-Richard Smith
F.C.-Arthur Arnold

TRINITY 75862
Pop: 2697   (Trinity)
P.O. Box 431
936 594-2507 - *Fax: 594-8364*
www.cityoftrinity.com/
Mayor-Billy Slaughter
Mayor PT-Wayne Huffman
Ald.-Chris Dennis
Ald.-Clegg Dewalt
Ald.-Billy Goodin
Ald.-Phillip Morrison
City Secy.-Jennifer Priddy
City Admin.-Jo Bitner
Atty.-Robert Flournoy
C.P.-Steven Jones
F.C.-Hayne Huffman

TROPHY CLUB, TOWN OF 76262
Pop: 12000   (Denton-Tarrant)
1 Trophy Wood Drive
682 237-2900 - *Fax: 237-2996*
www.trophyclub.org
Mayor-Nick Sanders
Mayor PT-Rhylan Rowe
Coun.-Alicia L. Fleury
Coun.-Eric Jensen
Coun.-Timothy Kurtz
Coun.-Greg Lamont
Coun.-Philip Shoffner
Town Mgr.-Thomas M. Class, Sr.
Dir. Fin-Amber Karkauskas
Town Secy.-Holly Fimbres
Atty.-David Dodd III
C.P.-Patrick Arata
F.C.-Wade Carroll

TROUP 75789
Pop: 1869   (Cherokee-Smith)
106 East Duval St.
P.O. Box 637
903 842-3128 - *Fax: 842-2964*
www.trouptexas.org
Mayor-Joe Carlyle
Mayor PT-Carole Wilson
Coun.-Nelson Darden
Coun.-Jeff Hale
Coun.-Chip Richardson
Coun.-Gary Salyer
City Mgr.-Gene Cottle
City Secy.-Buffie Deason
Atty.-Blake E. Armstrong
C.P.-Pat Hendrix
F.C.-Tim Mager

TROY 76579
Pop: 1645   (Bell)
P.O. Box 389
254 938-2505 - *Fax: 938-0440*
troytexas.us
Mayor-Michael Morgan
Mayor PT-Laurie Bailey
Ald.-Calvin Creech
Ald.-James Hicks
Ald.-Paul Ramirez
Ald.-Jason Sheffler
City Admin.-Jeff Straub
Atty.-Alan J. Bojorquez
C.P.-Gary O. Smith
F.C.-Justin Jackson

TULIA 79088
Pop: 4967   (Swisher)
P.O. Box 847
806 995-3547 - *Fax: 995-2331*
tuliatexas.org
Mayor-Russell Proctor
Coun.-Jason Jack
Coun.-Israel Ramirez
Coun.-Jimmy Thomas, Jr.
Coun.-Kathy Vestal
City Mgr.-Dion Miller
Dir. Fin-James Davis

City Secy.-Kristina Solomon
Atty.-Stephen Rohde
C.P.-Steven Brush
F.C.-Johnny Daniels

TURKEY 79261
Pop: 421   (Hall)
P.O. Box 415
806 423-1033 - *Fax: 423-1221*
Mayor-Pat Carson
Mayor PT-Doyle Proctor
Coun.-Amanda Barclay
Coun.-Mary Fierro
Coun.-Rex Fuston
Coun.-Christy Yates
City Mgr.-Lynn Gray
City Admin.-DeVonna Gray
CFO-DeVonna Gray

TUSCOLA 79562
Pop: 742   (Taylor)
P.O. Box 34
325 554-7766 - *Fax: 554-7145*
www.cityoftuscolatx.com
Mayor-Robert Elkins
Ald.-John Bryant
Ald.-Brenda Ford
Ald.-Donna Jernigan
Ald.-Steve Neeley
Ald.-Sam Stanaland
City Secy.-Genny Abercrombie
Atty.-Kenneth H. Slimp
F.C.-Brad Karr

TYE 79563
Pop: 1242   (Taylor)
P.O. Box 369
205 North St.
325 692-8588 - *Fax: 692-9322*
www.cityoftye.org
Mayor-Roy Votaw
Mayor PT-Chuck Downs
Coun.-Vada Childers
Coun.-Sherry Lyle
Coun.-Nancy Moore
Coun.-Linda Parsons
City Secy.-Belinda Hohhertz
Atty.-Matt Wade
C.P.-Jay Strong
F.C.-Shawn Hicks

TYLER 75702
Pop: 96900   (Smith)
P.O. Box 2039
Tyler, TX 75710
903 531-1250 - *Fax: 531-1166*
www.cityoftyler.org
Mayor-Martin Heines
Mayor PT-Don Warren
Coun.-Darryl Bowdre
Coun.-Edward Moore
Coun.-John Nix
Coun.-Linda Sellers
Coun.-Bob Westbrook
City Mgr.-Edward A. Broussard
Clk.-Cassandra Brager

Atty.-Deborah Pullum
C.P.-Jimmy Toler
F.C.-David Coble

UHLAND 78640
Pop: 1014   (Caldwell-Hays)
15 North Old Spanish Trail
512 398-7399
www.cityofuhland.com/
Mayor-Bryan Geiger
Mayor PT-Vicki Hunter
Ald.-Brian Heideman
Ald.-Daniel Heideman
Ald.-Jessica Hodge
Ald.-Russell Schultz
City Admin.-Karen Gallaher
Atty.-Alan J. Bojorquez

UNCERTAIN 75661
Pop: 150   (Harrison)
P.O. Box 277
903 789-3443
www.cityofuncertain.com
Mayor-Mike Fox
Mayor PT-Greg Jones
Ald.-Martha Brown
Ald.-Sue Campbell
Ald.-Dale Renkenberger
Ald.-Zach Warren
City Secy.-Judy VanDeventer
V.F.D.F.C.-Jeff Shaw

UNION GROVE
Pop: 357   (Upshur)
10648 US Highway 271 S
Gladewater, TX 75647
903 845-3837 - *Fax: 845-4659*
Mayor-Randy Lee Simcox

UNION VALLEY 75189
Pop: 307   (Hunt)
7967 FM 1565
972 635-6655
Mayor-Craig Waskow
Mayor PT-John Oznick
Ald.-John Abram Jr.
City Secy.-Angela Smith
Atty.-Andy Messer
F.C.-Mark Plemmons

UNIVERSAL CITY 78148
Pop: 18530   (Bexar)
2150 Universal City Blvd.
210 659-0333 - *Fax: 659-7062*
www.universalcitytexas.com
Mayor-John Williams
Mayor PT-Richard "Dick" Neville
Coun.-Thomas England
Coun.-S.Bear Goolsby
Coun.-Tom Maxwell
Coun.-William Shelby
Coun.-Beverly Volle
City Mgr.-Ken Taylor
Clk.-Kristin Mueller
Atty.-Jameene Williams
C.P.-Gary Speer

F.C.-Manuel Casarez
Dir. P.W.-Randy Luensmann

UNIVERSITY PARK 75205
Pop: 23068   (Dallas)
3800 University Blvd.
214 363-1644 - *Fax: 987-5399*
www.uptexas.org
Mayor-Olin Lane Jr.
Mayor PT-Dawn E. Moore
Coun.-Taylor Armstrong
Coun.-Randy Biddle
Coun.-Gage Prichard
City Mgr.-Robbie Corder
City Secy.-Christine Green
P.A.-Elizabeth Anderson
Atty.-Robert L. Dillard, III
C.P.-Greg Spradlin
F.C.-Randy Howell

UVALDE 78802
Pop: 15751   (Uvalde)
P.O. Box 799
830 278-3315 - *Fax: 278-2234*
www.uvaldetx.com
Mayor-Don McLaughlin Jr.
Mayor PT-Rogelio M. Munoz
Coun.-Stephen Balke
Coun.-John H. Flores, Jr.
Coun.-Ernest W. "Chip" King III
Coun.-Margaret Palermo
City Mgr.-Vince DiPazza
Dir. Fin Phillip Conner
City Secy.-Sorayda Sanchez
Atty.-Tarski Law Offices
C.P.-Eric Herrera
F.C.-Gene Ayala

VALENTINE 79854
Pop: 134   (Jeff Davis)
P.O. Box 6
432 467-2601 - *Fax: 467-2039*
Mayor-Jesus Calderon
Comm.-Danny Garcia
Comm.-Andrew White
Clk.-Albert Miller
Atty.-Teresa Todd

VALLEY MILLS 76689
Pop: 1203   (Bosque-McLennan)
P.O. Box 641
254 932-6146 - *Fax: 932-5608*
www.vmtx.us
Mayor-Jerry Wittmer
Mayor PT-Rodney Nichols
Ald.-Bill Lancaster
Ald.-Bill McKain
Ald.-Larry Turner
Ald.-Curtis Wiethorn
City Secy.-Robin Skinner
City Admin.-William Linn
Atty.-Bojorquez Law Firm
C.P.-Robert Summers
F.C.-David Fisk

VALLEY VIEW 76272
Pop: 757   (Cooke)
P.O. Box 268
940 726-3740 - *Fax: 726-6253*
cityofvv.com
Mayor-Joshua Brinkley
Mayor PT-William Shelburne
Ald.-Janson Bewley
Ald.-Cody Cartwright
Ald.-Jason Grands
Ald.-Nathan Sandmann
City Secy.-Cynthia Ritchie
Atty.-W.D. Welch, P.C.
C.P.-Vacant
F.C.-Zack Kupper

VAN 75790
Pop: 2632   (Van Zandt)
903 963-7216 - *Fax: 963-5643*
vantexas.org
Mayor-Don Smith
Mayor PT-Amanda Davis
Coun.-Paul Bullington
Coun.-Ernie Burns
Coun.-Pete Lucas
Coun.-Linzy Neal
City Secy.-Sereca Huff-Huggins
City Admin.-Charles West
Atty.-Jay Mills
C.P.-John Brown
F.C.-Bobby Hynes
Dir. P.S.-John Beall

VAN ALSTYNE 75495
Pop: 3046   (Grayson)
P.O. Box 247
903 482-5426 - *Fax: 482-5122*
www.cityofvanalstyne.us
Mayor-Larry Cooper
Mayor PT-Teddie Ann Salmon
Ald.-Brad Clough
Ald.-Suzon Crowell
Ald.-Robert Jaska
Ald.-Lee Thomas
City Mgr.-Vacant
Clk.-Jennifer Gould
Atty.-Julie Fort
C.P.-Tim Barnes
F.C.-Vacant
Dir. P.W.-Steve White

VAN HORN 79855
Pop: 2063   (Culberson)
P.O. Box 517
432 283-2050 - *Fax: 283-2839*
Mayor-Glenn Humphries
Ald.-Rudy Hinojos
Ald.-Ryan Martinez
Ald.-Lynn McDonald
Ald.-Nuny Morriss
Ald.-Pam Young
Dir. Fin-Jodi Corrales
City Admin.-Fran Malafronte
Atty.-Stephen L. Mitchell

CITY SECTION

VEGA 79092
Pop: 884 (Oldham)
P.O. Box 470
806 267-2144 - *Fax: 267-0504*
Mayor-Mark Groneman
Mayor PT-David Newkirk
Ald.-Roudy Blasingame
Ald.-Gavin Ellis
Ald.-Russell Jarnagin
Ald.-Clay Taylor
City Secy.-Tammy Hubbart
Clk.-Peggy Tretow
Atty.-The Honorable Kent Birdsong
F.C.-David Newkirk
Mar.-Zane Price

VENUS 76084
Pop: 2960 (Johnson-Ellis)
P.O. Box 380
972 366-3348 - *Fax: 366-3824*
http://www.cityofvenus.org
Mayor-James Burgess
Mayor PT-Jeanie Scott
Ald.-Wesley Dady
Ald.-Laurna M. Guidry-Shaw
Ald.-Geronimo Hernandez Jr.
Ald.-Jeannie Prazak
City Secy.-Rana Gamel
City Admin.-Michael Boese
Atty.-Cass Callaway
C.P.-Michael Boese
F.C.-Richard Allen

VERNON 76384
Pop: 11002 (Wilbarger)
1725 Wilbarger St.
940 552-2581 - *Fax: 552-0569*
www.vernontx.gov
Mayor-Joe Rogers
Comm.-Don Aydelott
Comm.-Britt Ferguson
Comm.-Ruben Hinojosa
Comm.-Guy Spears
City Mgr.-Martin Mangum
City Secy.-Christy Carness Bradshaw
Atty.-John Whitsitt
C.P.-Tom Wilson
F.C.-J.J. Oznick
Dir. P.W.-Darrell Kennon

VICTORIA 77902
Pop: 62592 (Victoria)
P.O. Box 1758
361 485-3000 - *Fax: 485-3045*
www.victoriatx.org
Mayor-Paul Polasek
Mayor PT-Jeff Bauknight
Coun.-Rafael DeLaGarza, III
Coun.-Tom Halepaska
Coun.-Jan Scott
Coun.-Josephine E. Soliz
Coun.-Dr. Andrew Young
City Mgr.-Charmelle Garrett
City Secy.-April Hilbrich
P.A.-Lana Schultz

Atty.-Thomas Gwosdz
C.P.-Jeff Craig
F.C.-Taner Drake
Dir. P.W.-Donald Reese

VIDOR 77662
Pop: 10579 (Orange)
1395 N. Main
409 769-5473 - *Fax: 769-8853*
www.cityofvidor.com
Mayor-Robert Viator Jr.
Mayor PT-Kelly Carder
Coun.-Keith Buesing
Coun.-Gary Herrera
Coun.-Angela Jordan
Coun.-Ted David Slaughter
Coun.-Misty Songe
City Mgr.-Mike Kunst
City Secy.-Vicki Watson
Atty.-Guy N. Goodson
C.P.-Rod Carroll

VILLAGE OF THE HILLS 78738
Pop: 2472 (Travis)
102 Trophy Drive
512 261-6281 - *Fax: 261-4810*
www.villageofthehills.org
Mayor-Eric Ovlen
Mayor PT-J. R. Smith
Ald.-Jim Nelson
Ald.-Hilda Potsavich
Ald.-Robert Smith
Ald.-George Spencer
City Mgr.-Wendy L. Smith
City Secy.-Linda Lunney
Atty.-Barney Knight

VINTON, VILLAGE OF 79821
Pop: 1981 (El Paso)
436 E. Vinton Road
Vinton, TX 79821
915 886-5104 - *Fax: 886-4120*
www.vintontx.govoffice2.com
Mayor-Manuel "Manny" Leos
Ald.-Sonia Arceo
Ald.-Victor A. Carrejo
Ald.-Lulu Cloud
Ald.-Santos Lucero
Ald.-Yolanda Lucero
City Admin.-Jessica Garza
Atty.-Shane English
Dir. P.W.-Perfecto Valdez

VOLENTE 78641
Pop: 520 (Travis)
16100 Wharf Cove
512 250-2075 - *Fax: 436-8014*
villageofvolente-tx.gov
Mayor-Ken Beck
Mayor PT-Chris Wilder
Coun.-Bill Connors
Coun.-Robert Mokry
Coun.-Sean Ryan
Coun.-Jan Yenawine

City Secy.-Nicole Vicuna
Atty.-Tom Buckle

VON ORMY 78073
Pop: 1085 (Bexar)
210 622-9935 - *Fax: 622-9941*
www.vonormytexas.com
Mayor-Trina Reyes
Mayor PT-Sally Martinez
Coun.-Alejandro Quintanilla
Clk.-Juanita De Anda
Atty.-Robert "Woody" Wilson

WACO 76702
Pop: 124805 (McLennan)
P.O. Box 2570
254 750-5600 - *Fax: 750-5748*
www.waco-texas.com
Mayor-Kyle Deaver
Mayor PT-Jim Holmes
Coun.-Noah Jackson Jr.
Coun.-John Kinnaird
Coun.-Dillon Meek
Coun.-Alice Rodriguez
City Mgr.-Wiley Stem III
City Secy.-Esmeralda Hudson
P.A.-Kelly Holecek
Atty.-Jennifer Richie
C.P.-Ryan Holt
F.M.-Kevin Vranich

WAELDER 78959
Pop: 1065 (Gonzales)
P.O. Box 427
830 788-7331 - *Fax: 788-7432*
cityofwaelder.org
Mayor-Roy Tovar
Mayor PT-Valentino Hernandez
Ald.-Michael Harris
Ald.-Oscar Melchor
Ald.-Samuel Quintero
Ald.-Robert Tovar
City Secy.-Melinda Caballero
Atty.-Richard L. Crozier
C.P.-Rudy Hille
F.C.-Adan Ibarra

WAKE VILLAGE 75501
Pop: 5492 (Bowie)
P.O. Box 3776
903 838-0515 - *Fax: 831-4327*
Mayor-Jim Roberts
Coun.-Sheryl Collum
Coun.-Bill Parker
Coun.-Brad Pearson
Coun.-Steven Shelley
Coun.-Dexter Summers Jr.
City Admin.-Mike Burke
Atty.-J. Michael Brock
C.P.-Ronny Sharp
F.C.-James Guyton

WALLER 77484
Pop: 2396   (Harris-Waller)
P.O. Box 239
936 372-3880 - *Fax: 372-3477*
www.wallertexas.com
Mayor-Danny Marburger
Mayor PT-Edna Eaton
Coun.-Nancy Arnold
Coun.-Dwayne Hajek
Coun.-Mike McCormick
Coun.-Jason Tones
City Secy.-Cynthia Ward
Atty.-Olson & Olson
C.P.-Mike Williams
Dir. P.W.-Gene Schmidt

WALLIS 77485
Pop: 1252   (Austin)
P.O. Box 190
979 478-6712 - *Fax: 478-7537*
wallistexas.org
Mayor-Steven Bockel
Ald.-Felix Galvan, Jr.
Ald.-Belinda Halfin
Ald.-James King
Ald.-Clark Main, Jr.
Ald.-Barnadette Parr
Clk.-Sheila Moseley
Atty.-Arthur Lee "Art" Pertile, III
C.P.-David Moseley

WALNUT SPRINGS 76690
Pop: 827   (Bosque)
P.O. Box 272
254 797-3721 - *Fax: 797-7210*
Mayor-Larry Stafford
Mayor PT-Beverly Huffman
Ald.-Elizabeth Moore
Ald.-Whitleigh Oliver
Ald.-Sammy Ortega
Ald.-Ray Uloth
City Secy.-Cheri Buccino
Atty.-Vacant
F.C.-Gary Anderson

WARREN CITY
Pop: 298   (Gregg-Upshur)
3004 George Richey Rd.
Gladewater, TX 75647
903 845-3917 - *Fax: 845-6915*
Mayor-Ricky Wallace
Mayor PT-Rusty Shofner
Coun.-Marjorie Barrow
Coun.-David Berryhill
Coun.-Gary Oneal Wallace
Coun.-David Wilson
City Secy.-Tammy Hazel
Atty.-Brad Echols
V.F.D.F.C.-Derek Zivney

WASKOM 75692
Pop: 2160   (Harrison)
P.O. Box 730
903 687-3374 - *Fax: 687-2574*
cityofwaskom.com/
Mayor-Jesse Moore
Mayor PT-James King
Ald.-Russell Allbritton
Ald.-Jimmy Moore
Ald.-Michael Phillips
Ald.-Tommy L. Philpot, Sr.
City Secy.-Tammy Lofton
Atty.-Kurt Truelove
C.P.-Charles Meisenheimer
F.C.-James King

WATAUGA 76148
Pop: 23497   (Tarrant)
7105 Whitley Road
817 514-5800 - *Fax: 514-3625*
www.cowtx.org
Mayor-Hector F. Garcia
Mayor PT-Patrick Shelbourne
Coun.-Melva Clark
Coun.-Robert L. "Bob" Davis
Coun.-Hal Gerhardt
Coun.-Lee Griffin
Coun.-Brandon Krausse
Coun.-James Wright
City Mgr.-Greg Vick
City Secy.-Zolaina R. Parker
Atty.-Mark Daniel
C.P.-Glen Fowler
F.C.-Shawn Fannan

WAXAHACHIE
Pop: 30233   (Ellis)
P.O. Box 757
Waxahachie, TX 75168
469 309-4005 - *Fax: 309-4003*
www.waxahachie.com
Mayor-Kevin Strength
Mayor PT-Mark Singleton
Coun.-Chuck Beatty
Coun.-David Hill
Coun.-Mary Lou Shipley
City Mgr.-Michael Scott
City Secy.-Lori Saunders
Atty.-Brown & Hofmeister, LLP
C.P.-Wade Goolsby
F.C.-Ricky Boyd

WEATHERFORD 76086
Pop: 26200   (Parker)
P.O. Box 255
817 598-4201 - *Fax: 598-4294*
www.weatherfordtx.gov
Mayor-Craig Swancy
Mayor PT-Jeff Robinson
Coun.-Kevin Cleveland
Coun.-Dale Fleeger
Coun.-Heidi Wilder
City Mgr.-Sharon Hayes

City Secy.-Malinda Nowell
Atty.-Ed Zellers
C.P.-Lance Arnold
F.C.-Paul Rust

WEBBERVILLE, VILLAGE OF 78621
Pop: 392   (Travis)
512 276-1865
www.webberville.org
Mayor-Hector Gonzales
Comm.-Sean McMahon
Comm.-Ronnie Tidwell
Clk.-Carissa Cannaday
Atty.-Alan J. Bojorquez

WEBSTER 77598
Pop: 10400   (Harris)
101 Pennsylvania
281 332-1826 - *Fax: 332-5834*
www.cityofwebster.com
Mayor-Donna Rogers
Coun.-Beverly Gaines
Coun.-Martin Graves
Coun.-Jennifer Heidt
Coun.-Edward Lapeyre
Coun.-Larry Tosto
Coun. Andrea Wilson
City Mgr.-Wayne J. Sabo
City Secy.-Crystal N. Roan
Atty.-Dick Gregg Jr
C.P.-Daniel Presley
F.C.-Patrick Shipp

WEIMAR 78962
Pop: 2151   (Colorado)
P.O. Box 67
979 725-8554 - *Fax: 725-8488*
www.weimartexas.org
Mayor-Milton Koller
Mayor PT-Roy Ulrich
Ald.-Kevin Janecka
Ald.-Rex Kloesel
Ald.-Becky Roberts
Ald.-Ronell Wilson
City Mgr.-Mike Barrow
City Secy.-Dolores Stoever
Atty.-Carl "Bo" Dawson
C.P.-Patrick Todd Jacobs
V.F.D.F.C.-Roy Christen

WEINERT 76388
Pop: 149   (Haskell)
P.O. Box 248
940 673-8223 - *Fax: 673-8223*
Mayor-Ed Murphy
Mayor PT-Caron Yates
Ald.-Cherie Dutton
Ald.-Stanley Hager
Ald.-Mary Murphy
Ald.-Bill Walker
Dir. Fin-Patricia A. Horan
City Secy.-Patricia A. Horan
F.C.-Pete Trevino

WEIR 78674
Pop: 450 (Williamson)
P.O. Box 264
512 863-7984 - *Fax: 863-2021*
Mayor-Mervin Walker
Mayor PT-Alber G. Walther
Ald.-Paul Bohanan
Ald.-Ron Foster
Ald.-Steve King
Ald.-Ken Neans
City Secy.-Julia E. Navarrette
Atty.-Randall C. Stump
F.C.-Charlie Frymire

WELLINGTON 79095
Pop: 2189 (Collingsworth)
P.O. Box 949
806 447-2544 - *Fax: 447-5755*
wellingtontx.com/
Mayor-J.D. Hamby
Mayor PT-Brent Martin
Ald.-Larry Adams
Ald.-Carroll Daves
Ald.-Tammy Riley
Ald.-Kenneth Warren
City Mgr.-Jon Sessions
City Secy.-Sherrie Dunlap
F.C.-Kevin Hamby

WELLMAN 79378
Pop: 203 (Terry)
P.O. Box 124
806 637-4063 - *Fax: 637-8823*
Mayor-Karl Spuhler
Coun.-Lynn Delong
Coun.-Naomi Garnsey
Coun.-Cody Griffiths
Coun.-Gary Parker
Coun.-Sally Rodriguez
City Secy.-Donna DeBusk
Atty.-Matt Wade

WELLS 75976
Pop: 790 (Cherokee)
P.O. Box 20
936 867-4615 - *Fax: 867-5060*
Mayor-C. W. Williams
Mayor PT-Dorothy McMillion
Ald.-Eva Alexander
Ald.-Robert Kalka
Ald.-Richard Myer
Coun.-Billie Petty
City Secy.-Melanie Williamson
Atty.-Robert Flournoy
C.P.-Vacant
F.C.-Robert Kalka

WESLACO 78596
Pop: 35670 (Hidalgo)
255 South Kansas Avenue
956 968-3181 - *Fax: 968-6717*
www.weslacotx.gov/
Mayor-David Suarez
Mayor PT-Gerardo "Jerry" Tafolla
Comm.-Greg Kerr

Comm.-Letty Lopez
Comm.-Leo Munoz
Comm.-Josh Pedraza
Comm.-J.P. Rodriguez
City Mgr.-Mike Perez
City Secy.-Elizabeth M. Walker
Atty.-Juan E. Gonzalez
C.P.-Stephen Scot Mayer
F.C.-Tony Lopez

WEST 76691
Pop: 2807 (McLennan)
P.O. Box 97
254 826-5351 - *Fax: 826-5969*
www.cityofwest.com
Mayor-Tommy Muska
Mayor PT-Steve Vanek
Ald.-Karla Dulock
Ald.-Cheryl Marak
Ald.-David Pratka
Ald.-Joe Pustejovsky
City Admin/Secy-Shelly Nors
Clk.-Shannon Cox
Atty.-Walter Reaves, Jr.
C.P.-Darryl Barton
F.C.-George Nors
Dir. P.W.-CJ Gillaspie

WEST COLUMBIA 77486
Pop: 3905 (Brazoria)
512 E. Brazos
P.O. Box 487
979 345-3123 - *Fax: 345-3178*
www.westcolumbiatx.org
Mayor-Laurie Kincannon
Mayor PT-Jamie Walker
Ald.-Roy E. Maynor
Ald.-Robert Thomas
Ald.-Charley Tindol
Ald.-Dietrich von Biedenfeld
City Mgr.-Debbie A. Sutherland
City Secy.-Kelli Kuban
Atty.-David Olson
C.P.-Paul Odin
F.M.-Michael Eulenfeld

WEST LAKE HILLS 78746
Pop: 3116 (Travis)
911 Westlake Dr.
512 327-3628 - *Fax: 327-1863*
www.westlakehills.org
Mayor-Linda Anthony
Mayor PT-Jim O'Connor
Coun.-Rhonda McCollough
Coun.-Brian Plunkett
Coun.-Beth South
Coun.-Darin Walker
City Secy.-Lacie Hale
City Admin.-Robert Wood
Atty.-Alan J. Bojorquez
C.P.-Scott Gerdes

WEST ORANGE 77630
Pop: 3443 (Orange)
2700 Western Avenue
409 883-3468 - *Fax: 882-0652*
www.cityofwestorange.com
Mayor-Roy McDonald
Mayor PT-Shirley Bonnin
Coun.-Dale Dardeau
Coun.-Frances Droddy-Lopez PhD
Coun.-Mike Shugart, Sr.
Coun.-Carl K. Thibodeaux R.Ph.
City Secy.-Theresa Van Meter
Atty.-Rex Peveto
C.P.-Michael Stelly
F.C.-Terry Veitch
Dir. P.W.-Michael Stelly

WEST TAWAKONI 75474
Pop: 1576 (Hunt)
1533 E. Hwy. 276
903 447-2285 - *Fax: 447-4935*
www.cityofwesttawakoni.com/
Mayor-Calvin Travers
Mayor PT-Linda Kattner
Ald.-Keith Goodson
Ald.-Donna Milburn Ph.D.
Ald.-Alan Shoemake
Ald.-Lyle Varnes
City Secy.-Anette Lemons
City Admin.-Susan Roberts
Atty.-Jim D. McLeroy
C.P.-Brandon Kilpatrick
F.C.-Jeff Felts

**WEST UNIVERSITY PLACE
77005**
Pop: 14787 (Harris)
3800 University Blvd.
713 662-5813 - *Fax: 662-5305*
www.westutx.gov
Mayor-Susan Sample
Mayor PT-Wayne J. Franklin, MD
Coun.-Kelle Burke
Coun.-Bob Higley
Coun.-Mardi Turner
City Mgr.-Chris Peifer
City Secy.-Thelma A. Gilliam
Atty.-Alan P. Petrov
C.P.-Ken Walker
F.C.-Aaron Taylor

WESTBROOK 79565
Pop: 253 (Mitchell)
P.O. Box 124
325 644-3131 - *Fax: 644-5363*
Mayor-Lynn Gaston
Coun.-David Bray
Coun.-Darlene Moore
City Secy.-Pansy Fernandez
F.C.-Brandon Hale

WESTLAKE, TOWN OF 76262
Pop: 1040   (Denton-Tarrant)
817 430-0941 - *Fax: 430-1812*
www.westlake-tx.org
Mayor-Laura Wheat
Mayor PT-Carol Langdon
Coun.-Michael Barrett
Coun.-Alesa Belvedere
Coun.-Rick Rennhack
Coun.-Wayne Stoltenberg
Town Mgr.-Thomas Brymer
Town Secy.-Kelly Edwards
Atty.-Stanton Lowry
C.P.-Michael Wilson
F.C.-Richard Whitten

WESTON 75097
Pop: 563   (Collin)
P.O. Box 248
972 382-1001 - *Fax: 382-8409*
www.westontexas.com
Mayor-Patti Harrington
Ald.-Kevin Deal
Ald.-Carol Decker
Ald.-Randall Hales
Ald.-Tralyn Molinar
Ald.-John D. Tingle
City Secy.-Susan Coffer
Atty.-Bryn Meredith

WESTON LAKES 77441
Pop: 3500   (Fort Bend)
281 533-0907 - *Fax: 533-0907*
www.cityofwestonlakes-tx.gov
Mayor-Mary Rose Zdunkewicz
Mayor PT-Denis De Luca
Ald.-Ted Case
Ald.-Linda Harnist
Ald.-Bill Ragle
Ald.-Trent Thomas
City Secy.-Jenni McJunkin
Atty.-David Olson

WESTOVER HILLS, TOWN OF
Pop: 703   (Tarrant)
5824 Merrymount Rd.
Fort Worth, TX 76107
817 735-8027 - *Fax: 423-6054*
www.westoverhills.us
Mayor-Steven Tatum
Mayor PT-Kelly Thompson
Ald.-Elliot Goldman
Ald.-Jack Koslow
Ald.-Marcus Snyder
Ald.-John Thompson III
City Secy.-Penny Spikes
Town Admin.-Joseph S. Portugal
Atty.-Stanton Lowry
C.P.-David Burgus

WESTWORTH VILLAGE 76114
Pop: 3100   (Tarrant)
311 Burton Hill Road
817 710-2500 - *Fax: 710-2501*
www.cityofwestworth.com
Mayor-Michael R. Coleman
Coun.-Tiffany Aller
Coun.-Steve Beckman
Coun.-Nick Encke
Coun.-Dan Novak
Coun.-Carlos Zavala
City Secy.-Brandy Barrett
City Admin.-Sterling Naron
Atty.-Ashley D. Dierker
C.P.-Kevin Reaves
F.C.-FD of Fort Worth

WHARTON 77488
Pop: 8832   (Wharton)
120 East Caney
979 532-2491 - *Fax: 532-0181*
www.cityofwharton.com
Mayor-Tim Barker
Mayor PT-Donald Mueller
Coun.-Al Bryant
Coun.-Terry Freese
Coun.-Vincent Huerta
Coun.-Russell Machann
Coun.-Steven Schneider
City Mgr.-Andres Garza Jr.
City Secy.-Paula Favors
Atty.-Paul Webb
C.P.-Terry David Lynch
F.C.-Anthony Abbott

WHEELER 79096
Pop: 1592   (Wheeler)
P.O. Box 98
806 826-3222 - *Fax: 826-5601*
Mayor-Bob McCain
Mayor PT-Kendall Hefley
Ald.-Britt McCarter
Ald.-Stacy McQueen
Ald.-Carol Porton
Ald.-Don Rose
City Secy.-Kristi Petit
P.A.-Paul Arganbright
Atty.-Bryan Guymon
F.C.-Robert Ford

WHITE DEER 79097
Pop: 1000   (Carson)
P.O. Box 98
806 883-4191 - *Fax: 883-3601*
Mayor-Kent Kelp
Mayor PT-Lyn Luster
Ald.-Randel Barrett
Ald.-Summer Kelly
Ald.-Wade Petty
Ald.-Alan Warminski
City Secy.-Katrina Warminski
Atty.-Daren Brown
C.P.-Darell Luster
F.C.-Troy D. Fulton

WHITE OAK 75693
Pop: 6469   (Gregg)
903 759-3936 - *Fax: 297-3452*
www.cityofwhiteoak.com
Mayor-Kyle Kutch
Mayor PT-Greg Hulett
Coun.-Thomas Cash
Coun.-Kevin Hood
Coun.-Lance Noll
Coun.-Barbara Ray
City Mgr.-Charles Smith
Atty.-Brad Echols
C.P.-Terry Roach
V.F.D.F.C.-Bill McBride
Dir. P.W.-Tracey Fears

WHITE SETTLEMENT 76108
Pop: 16116   (Tarrant)
214 Meadow Park Drive
817 246-4971 - *Fax: 246-4164*
www.wstx.us
Mayor-Ronald A. White
Coun.-Danny Anderson
Coun.-Gregg Geesa
Coun.-David Mann
Coun.-Paul Moore
Coun.-Evelyn Spurlock
City Mgr.-Jim Ryan
City Secy.-Amy Arnold
Atty.-Warren J. Spencer
C.P.-J.P. Beverlng
F.C.-Brian Thompson

WHITEFACE 79379
Pop: 449   (Cochran)
P.O. Box 248
806 287-1111 - *Fax: 287-1120*
Mayor-Jack Seay
Mayor PT-Durward Stockman
Ald.-Joe Ketcherside
Ald.-Stacy Kirkendall
Ald.-Stephanie Nunn
Ald.-Bonnie Purcell
City Secy.-Belinda Terrell
Atty.-Matt Wade
F.C.-Bruce Heflin

WHITEHOUSE 75791
Pop: 7660   (Smith)
P.O. Box 776
903 839-4914 - *Fax: 839-4915*
www.whitehousetx.org
Mayor-Charles Parker
Coun.-Chad Cleckler
Coun.-Paul Hickey
Coun.-Dick Jackson
Coun.-David Roquemore
Coun.-Vacant
City Mgr.-Aaron Smith
City Secy.-Susan Hargis
Atty.-Blake E. Armstrong
C.P.-Ed Morris
F.C.-Madison Johnson

WHITESBORO 76273
Pop: 3793 (Grayson)
P.O. Box 340
903 564-3311 - *Fax: 564-6105*
www.whitesborotexas.com
Mayor-W.D. "Dee" Welch
Mayor PT-Jim Keller
Ald.-Cole Braun
Ald.-Chuck Cox
Ald.-Barry Keller
Ald.-Colby Meals
City Secy.-Teresa Nino
City Admin.-Michael Marter
P.A.-Kyle Maynard
Atty.-Brock Benson
C.P.-Scott Taylor
F.C.-Kevin Walton

WHITEWRIGHT 75491
Pop: 1604 (Grayson-Fannin)
206 West Grand Ave.
P.O. Box 966
903 364-2219 - *Fax: 364-3001*
www.whitewright.com
Mayor-Jeremiah Looney
Mayor PT-Russell Ponder
Ald.-Bart Bodine
Ald.-Sarah Beth Owen
Ald.-Gregory Owens
Ald.-John Simon
City Secy.-Tona Shiplet
Atty.-James Tidwell
F.C.-Dwayne Henderson
Dir. P.W.-Brandon Latimer

WHITNEY 76692
Pop: 2087 (Hill)
P.O. Box 2050
254 694-2261 - *Fax: 694-5332*
www.cityofwhitneytx.com
Mayor-Kristen Sims-Miller
Ald.-Wendy Dove
Ald.-Richard "Chip" Hundley
Ald.-Mary Rae
Ald.-Robin Sliva
Ald.-Vacant
City Secy.-Kristi Woellert
City Admin.-Christopher Bentley
Atty.-Monte Akers
C.P.-Christopher Bentley
F.C.-Wayland Price

WICHITA FALLS 76307
Pop: 104553 (Wichita)
P.O. Box 1431
940 761-7404 - *Fax: 761-8833*
www.wichitafallstx.gov
Mayor-Stephen Santellana
Coun.-Jesse Brown
Coun.-DeAndra Chenault
Coun.-Brian Hooker
Coun.-Tom Quintero
Coun.-Bobby Whiteley
Coun.-Bobby Whitely
City Mgr.-Darron Leiker

Clk.-Tracy Norr
P.A.-Jennifer Babineaux
Atty.-Kinley Hegglund
C.P.-Manuel Borrego
F.C.-Jon Reese

WICKETT 79788
Pop: 498 (Ward)
P.O. Box 185
432 943-6765 - *Fax: 943-6472*
Mayor-Scott Lindsey
Mayor PT-Xavier Estrada
Ald.-Christian Deanda
Ald.-Roy Schoolcraft
Ald.-Richard Sellars
Ald.-Chad White
City Secy.-Mayra Jimenez
Atty.-Vacant
F.C.-Billy Thackerson

WILLIS 77378
Pop: 6677 (Montgomery)
936 856-4611 - *Fax: 890-1246*
www.ci.willis.tx.us
Mayor-Leonard Reed
Mayor PT-Tamara Young-Hector
Coun.-Thomas Belinoski
Coun.-Tom Luster
Coun.-Johnnie B. Stone
Coun.-Bill Van Alstyne
City Mgr.-Hector Forestier
City Secy.-Marissa Quintanilla
Atty.-Larry Foerster
C.P.-James Nowak
Dir. P.W.-Pat Riley

WILLOW PARK 76087
Pop: 3982 (Parker)
516 Ranch House Road
817 441-7108 - *Fax: 441-6900*
www.willowpark.org
Mayor-Doyle Moss
Mayor PT-John Gohlson
Coun.-Amy Fennell
Coun.-Norman Hogue
Coun.-Greg Runnebaum
Coun.-Bruce Williams
Int. City Secy.-Candice Scott
City Admin.-Bryan Grimes
Atty.-David Dodd III
C.P.-Carrie West
F.C.-Mike LeNoir

WILLS POINT 75169
Pop: 3524 (Van Zandt)
P.O. Box 505
903 873-2578 - *Fax: 873-5512*
www.cityofwillspoint.com
Mayor-Mark Turner
Mayor PT-Mike Jones
Coun.-Kyle Anderson
Coun.-Wade Emerson
Coun.-Lance Lybrand
Coun.-Oscar Rogers
City Secy.-Carla Oldacre

City Admin.-Pam Pearson
Atty.-Tracy Lowe
C.P.-Lonnie Carroll
F.C.-Ed Liepply

WILMER 75172
Pop: 3682 (Dallas)
128 N. Dallas Ave.
972 441-6373 - *Fax: 441-3061*
cityofwilmer.net
Mayor-Casey Burgess
Mayor PT-Sheila Petta
Coun.-Sergio Campos
Coun.-John Eggen
Coun.-Candy Madrigal
Coun.-Melissa Ramirez
Int. City Adm.-Denny Wheat
City Secy.-Vacant
Atty.-Michael B. Halla
C.P.-Victor Kemp
F.C.-Mark Hamilton
Dir. P.W.-Douglas Jistel

WILSON 79381
Pop: 489 (Lynn)
806 628-6221 - *Fax: 628-6223*
Mayor-Donald Klaus
Mayor PT-Helen Stephenson
Ald.-Pat Cates
Ald.-Randy Dunn
Ald.-David Maldonado
Ald.-Clyde Wilke
City Secy.-Susann Follis
F.C.-Craig Wilke

WIMBERLEY 78676
Pop: 2626 (Hays)
221 Stillwater
P.O. Box 2027
512 847-0025 - *Fax: 847-0422*
www.cityofwimberley.com
Mayor Herschel McCullough
Mayor PT-Steve Thurber
Coun.-Gary Barchfeld
Coun.-Allison Davis
Coun.-Craig Fore
Coun.-Roberta Holland
City Secy.-Cara McPartland
Int. City Adm.-Cara McPartland
F.C.-Chief Czichos
Dir. P.W.-Aaron Reed

WINDCREST 78239
Pop: 5364 (Bexar)
8601 Midcrown
210 655-0022 - *Fax: 655-8776*
www.windcrest-tx.gov
Mayor-Dan Reese
Ald.-Frank Archuleta
Ald.-Gerd "Jake" Jacobi
Ald.-James M. McFall
Ald.-Joan Pedrotti
Ald.-Jim Shelton
City Mgr.-Rafael Castillo Jr.

City Secy.-Kelly Rodriguez
Atty.-Michael S. Brenan
C.P.-A. O. "Al" Ballew
Int. F.C.-Josh Brown
Dir. P.W.-Thomas Garcia

WINDOM 75492
Pop: 199 (Fannin)
510 Maple
P.O. Box 1027
903 623-3425 - *Fax: 623-4067*
Mayor-Donny Cobb
Mayor PT-Doris Pendleton
Ald.-Louise Knight
Ald.-Joe Pate
Ald.-Ronnie Payne
Ald.-Bob Simpson
City Secy.-Liena Fox
Atty.-W.D. Welch, P.C.

WINDTHORST 76389
Pop: 409 (Archer-Clay)
P.O. Box 128
940 423-6682
Mayor-Greg P. Vieth
Mayor PT-Justin Keener
Ald.-James Roffan Jr.
Ald.-Leon Schneider
Ald.-Dennis Schroeder
Ald.-Brittany Wolf
City Secy.-Debbie Schroeder
F.C.-Dale Scheffe
Dir. P.W.-Jerry Ostermann

WINFIELD 75493
Pop: 524 (Titus)
P.O. Box 98
903 524-2020 - *Fax: 524-2098*
Mayor-Hoyt Scogin
Ald.-Rosemary Banda
Ald.-Arlon Leon Garretson
Ald.-Susan Grubbs
Ald.-Esiquio Ramirez
Ald.-Bret Webster
City Secy. Marla White
Atty.-Jodi Cox
V.F.D.F.C.-Jerry Ward

WINK 79789
Pop: 940 (Winkler)
213 E. Hendricks Blvd.
432 527-3441 - *Fax: 527-3303*
Mayor-Eric Hawkins
Mayor PT-Linda Plunkett
Ald.-Eddie Boggess
Ald.-Coby Purcell
Ald.-Stacy Richardson
Ald.-Billy Voyles
City Secy.-Tonya Todd
Atty.-Cassandra Moholt-Cheek
C.P.-James Swanson
F.C.-Robbie Wolf

WINNSBORO 75494
Pop: 3434 (Franklin-Wood)
501 S. Main St.
903 342-3654 - *Fax: 342-5708*
www.cityofwinnsboro.org
Mayor-Richard R. Parrish
Mayor PT-Brenda Shirley
Coun.-Jim Hollowell
Coun.-Michael Jaynes
Coun.-Joan Morris
Coun.-Katy Perez
City Secy.-Jondra Hixon
City Admin.-Craig Lindholm
Atty.-Stanton Lowry
C.P.-Andy Chester
F.M.-Tully Davidson

WINONA 75792
Pop: 576 (Smith)
110 Dallas St.
P O Box 97
903 877-3381 - *Fax: 877-2370*
www.winonatexas.com/
Mayor-Pat Schlau
Mayor PT-Michael Jones
Ald.-Candy Folley
Ald.-Ray McFarland
Ald.-Karl L. Rutledge
Ald.-Dede Stroud
City Secy.-Deana Powell
Atty.-Blake E. Armstrong

WINTERS 79567
Pop: 2562 (Runnels)
310 S. Main
325 754-4424 - *Fax: 754-4284*
www.cityofwinters.net
Mayor-Lisa Yates
Ald.-Jessia Ahrens
Ald.-Sandee Schneider
Ald.-Sidney Tucker
Ald.-Clayton Woffenden
City Secy.-Virginia Ochoa
Atty.-Kenneth H. Slimp
C.P.-Paula Geyer
F.C.-Mark Bridgeman

WIXON VALLEY
Pop: 254 (Brazos)
9500 East State Hwy 21
Bryan, TX 77808
979 589-1688 - *Fax: 589-1688*
Mayor-James "Jim" Soefje
Mayor PT-Myra Gott
Coun.-Danny Harvell
Coun.-Debbie Perez
Coun.-Marianne Welch
City Secy.-Barbara Riley
Atty.-Bill Younkin

WOLFE CITY 75496
Pop: 1412 (Hunt)
P.O. Box 106
903 496-2251 - *Fax: 496-2335*
wolfecitytx.org
Mayor-Sharion Scott
Coun.-Rita Dodson
Coun.-Betty Teel Malone
Coun.-Chad Mashburn
Coun.-Jamie Moore
Coun.-Richard Owens
City Secy.-Sondra LaFavers
Atty.-Daniel W. Ray
C.P.-Jeff Honea
F.C.-Gene Dawson

WOLFFORTH 79382
Pop: 4000 (Lubbock)
P.O. Box 36
806 855-4120 - *Fax: 855-4121*
www.wolfforthtx.us
Mayor-Charles Addington II
Mayor PT-Randy Gross
Coun.-Mike Bickle
Coun.-David Cooper
Coun.-Julie Merrill
Coun.-Brandon Tyler
City Mgr.-Darrell Newsom
City Secy.-Debra Perkey
Atty.-Michael Guevara
C.P.-Rick Scott
F.C.-Charles Addington II
Dir. P.W.-Doug Hutcheson

WOODBRANCH VILLAGE
Pop: 1282 (Montgomery)
58-A Woodbranch
New Caney, TX 77357
281 399-3979 - *Fax: 399-8300*
www.woodbranchtx.us/
Mayor-Vera Craig
Ald.-Scott Essmeier
Ald.-Joe Krispinsky
Ald.-Mark Kroll
Ald.-Debbie Lawson
Ald.-TJ Mulhern
City Secy.-Charlotte Smith
Atty.-Leonard Schneider
C.P.-Rene Silva

WOODCREEK 78676
Pop: 1457 (Hays)
41 Champions Circle
512 847-9390 - *Fax: 847-6661*
www.cityofwoodcreek.com
Mayor-William Scheel
Mayor PT-Nancye Britner
Coun.-Judy Brizendine
Coun.-Aurora LeBrun
Coun.-Jerry T. Moore
Coun.-Ray Don Tilley
City Mgr.-Brenton B. Lewis
Clk.-Barbara Grant
Atty.-Bojorquez Law Firm
Dir. P.W.-Frank Wood

CITY SECTION

WOODLANDS, THE 77381
Pop: 93847   (Harris-Montgomery)
281 210-3800
thewoodlandstownship-tx.gov/
Chairman-Ed Robb
Vice Chairman-Mike Bass
Director-John Anthony Brown
Director-John P. McMullan
Director-Ann Snyder
Tres.-Laura Fillault
City Secy.-Gordy Bunch
F.C.-Alan Benson

WOODLOCH
Pop: 207   (Montgomery)
P.O. Box 1379
Conroe, TX 77305-1379
936 321-3700 - *Fax: 321-9199*
www.woodlochtx.org
Mayor-Diane L. Lincoln
Ald.-Andy Brown
Ald.-Courtney Brown
Ald.-Ralph Leino
Ald.-Robert Ray
Atty.-Oscar Sommers

WOODSBORO 78393
Pop: 1512   (Refugio)
P.O. Box 632
361 543-4505 - *Fax: 543-4187*
Mayor-Kay Roach
Coun.-Tony Abila
Coun.-Freddie Arriaga
Coun.-Ralph Cisneros
Coun.-Johnny Cisneros
Coun.-Richard Sanchez
City Secy.-Ruby H. DeLaGarza
Atty.-Don Kubicek
C.P.-Martin De Leon

WOODSON 76491
Pop: 264   (Throckmorton)
P.O. Box 251
940 345-6536 - *Fax: 345-7171*
Mayor-Bobby Mathiews
Mayor PT-Edalia Oliver
Ald.-Martha Brown
Ald.-Ricky Clark
Ald.-Jason Lester
Ald.-Jon Webb
City Secy.-Joy Bryant

WOODVILLE 75979
Pop: 2586   (Tyler)
400 W. Bluff St.
409 283-2234 - *Fax: 283-8412*
www.woodville-tx.gov
Mayor-Russ Nalley
Mayor PT-Joyce Wilson
Ald.-Amy Bythewood
Ald.-Lee P. Mann
Ald.-Byron L. Stowe
Ald.-Janice Weatherford

City Secy.-Terri Bible
City Admin.-Mandy K. Risinger
Atty.-Brad Elrod
C.P.-Scott Yosko
F.C.-Tommy Shane
Dir. P.W.-Charles H. Maclin

WOODWAY 76712
Pop: 8452   (McLennan)
922 Estates Drive
254 772-4480 - *Fax: 772-0695*
www.woodway-texas.com
Mayor-Donald J. Baker
Mayor PT-Jane Kittner
Coun.-Scott A. Giddings
Coun.-Barbara Grandy
Coun.-Bob Howard
Coun.-Gil Lillard
Coun.-Mike Tamberella
City Mgr.-Yousry Zakhary
City Secy.-Donna Barkley
Atty.-David E. Cherry
C.P.-Yousry Zakhary
F.M.-Justin Zang

WORTHAM 76693
Pop: 1073   (Freestone)
P.O. Box 186
254 765-3319 - *Fax: 765-3310*
www.worthamtx.com
Mayor-Rodney Price
Mayor PT-Cliff NeSmith
Ald.-Jeff Carr
Ald.-Frank McClellan
Ald.-Mindy McGlone
Ald.-John Tacker
City Secy.-Kasi Wright
Atty.-Zachary Evans
C.P.-Kelly Butler

WYLIE 75098
Pop: 41427   (Collin-
Dallas-Rockwall)
300 Country Club Road
972 516-6010 - *Fax: 516-6026*
www.wylietexas.gov
Mayor-Eric Hogue
Mayor PT-Keith Stephens
Coun.-Candy Arrington
Coun.-Diane Culver
Coun.-David Dahl
Coun.-Jeff Forrester
Coun.-Timothy T. Wallis
City Mgr.-Mindy Manson
Asst. City Mgr.-Chris Holsted
Dir. Fin-Linda Bantz
City Secy.-Carole Ehrlich
P.A.-Glenna Hayes
Atty.-Richard Abernathy
C.P.-Anthony Henderson
F.C.-Brent Parke

YANTIS 75497
Pop: 388   (Wood)
P.O. Box 245
903 383-2610 - *Fax: 383-7982*
Mayor-Jerry E. Miller
Mayor PT-John D. Norris, III
Ald.-Reed Gambline
Ald.-Betty Jenkins
Ald.-Kenneth Kincaid
Ald.-Bruce Summer
City Secy.-Tonya Norris
F.C.-Wesley Crist

YOAKUM 77995
Pop: 5815   (DeWitt-Lavaca)
P.O. Box 738
361 293-6321 - *Fax: 293-3318*
www.cityofyoakum.org
Mayor-Anita R. Rodriguez
Mayor PT-Elorine Sitka
Coun.-Rodney Jahn
Coun.-Tim McCoy
Coun.-Carl O'Neill
City Mgr.-Kevin M Coleman
Dir. Fin-Sandra Jacob
Clk.-Theresa A. Bowe TRMC
P.A.-Joe Bennett
Atty.-Ken Kvinta
C.P.-Karl VanSlooten
F.C.-Mark Herchek
Dir. P.W.-Michael Bennett

YORKTOWN 78164
Pop: 2092   (DeWitt)
P.O. Box 605
361 564-2611 - *Fax: 564-2787*
www.yorktowntx.com
Mayor-Rene Hernandez
Mayor PT-Ruben "B.B." Garcia
Coun.-William "Bill" Baker
Coun.-Rene Hernandez
Coun.-Travis Peyton
Coun.-Manuel Serrano
Coun.-Vacant
Dir. Fin-Michele Warwas
City Admin.-John Barth
Atty.-Cary Bovey
F.C.-William Potchinske

ZAVALLA 75980
Pop: 713   (Angelina)
936 897-3311 - *Fax: 897-8032*
www.cityofzavalla.com/
Mayor-Carlos Guzman
Mayor PT-Pam Hooks
Ald.-Brenda Cox
Ald.-Kelly Dickinson
Ald.-Randall Dykes
Ald.-Denita Ross
City Secy.-Waunesa Herrington
Atty.-Jimmy Cassels
C.P.-Chris Wade
F.C.-Chris Wade
Dir. P.W.-Jess Williams

FEDERAL

SECTION

FEDERAL SECTION

The Federal Section of the TEXAS STATE DIRECTORY includes the names, addresses and telephone numbers of Texas' Congressional delegation, federal law enforcement officials, and members of the federal judiciary in Texas. The material is organized in the following way:

> United States Senators
> Members of the United States House of Representatives
> 115th Congress Texas Delegation Committees
> Congressional District Map
> United States Court of Appeals, Fifth Circuit
> Federal District Judges (including their areas of jurisdiction)

Bill Status: 202/225-1772

Web Site: U.S. Senate   www.senate.gov
                 U.S. House of Representatives   www.house.gov

UNITED STATES SENATORS

JOHN CORNYN (Sandy), R-San Antonio
Attorney. Trinity University-1973; Saint Mary's University School of Law-1977; Masters of Law, Univ. of Virginia Law School-1995.
2-2-1952. U.S. Senate-2002-present, 114th Congress Majority Whip
Room 517 Hart Senate Office Bldg., Washington, DC 20510-4305
 202/224-2934; *Fax: 202/228-2856*
221 West Sixth Street, Suite 1530, Austin 78701 • 512/469-6034
Fax: 512/469-6020
5300 Memorial Drive Suite 980, Houston 77007 • 713/572-3337
Fax: 713/572-3777
Finance; Judiciary; Select Committee on Intelligence

TED CRUZ (Heidi), R-Houston
Attorney. BA-Princeton University; JD-Harvard Law School.
 12-22-1970. U.S. Senate-2013-present.
Room 404 Russell Senate Office Building, Washington, DC 20510
 202/224-5922; *Fax: 202/228-0755*
808 Travis St., Suite 1420, Houston 77002 • 713/718-3057
9901 IH-10 W., Suite 950, San Antonio 78230 • 210/340-2885
3626 N. Hall St., Suite 410, Dallas 75219 • 214/599-8749
300 E. 8th St., Suite 961, Austin 78701 • 512/916-5834

**Armed Services; Commerce, Science, and Transportation;
Judiciary; Rules and Administration**

( )Spouse

FEDERAL SECTION

U.S. HOUSE OF REPRESENTATIVES
Bill Status: 202/225-1772 • clerk.house.gov

JODEY C. ARRINGTON (Anne), R-Lubbock
President of Scott Laboratories, Inc. Texas Tech University -
  BA, Political Science; MPA. 3-9-1972. C-2017-present.
Room 1029 Longworth HOB, Washington, DC 20515 • 202/225-4005
  Fax: 202/225-9615
500 Chestnut, Suite 819, Abilene 79602 • 325/675-9779
  Fax: 325/675-5038

Nineteenth District - Bailey, Borden, Castro, Cochran, Crosby, Fisher,
  Floyd (59%) Gaines, Garza, Hale, Haskell, Hockley, Howard, Jones,
  Kent, Lamb, Lubbock, Lynn, Nolan, Parmer, Scurry, Shackelford,
  Stephens (24%), Stonewall, Taylor, Terry, Throckmorton, Yoakum,
  Young

Agriculture; Budget; Veterans' Affairs

BRIAN BABIN, D.D.S. (Roxanne), R-Woodville
Dentist. BS, Lamar University; DS, The University of Texas Dental
  Branch-Houston. 3-23-1948. C-2015-present
Room 316 Cannon HOB, Washington, DC 20515 202/225-1555
  Fax: 202/226-0396
1201 Childers Road, Orange 77630 • 409/883-8075
  Fax: 409/886-9918

Thirty-Sixth District - Chambers, Hardin, Harris (8%), Jasper,
  Liberty, Newton, Orange, Polk, Tyler

Science, Space & Technology; Transportation & Infrastructure

JOE L. BARTON, R-Ennis
Engineer. BS-Texas A&M University, MA-Purdue University.
  9-15-1949. C-1985-present.
Room 2107 Rayburn HOB, Washington, DC 20515 • 202/225-2002
  Fax: 202/225-3052
6001 W. Ronald Reagan Memorial Highway, #200, Arlington 76017
  817/543-1000; *Fax: 817/548-7029*; 2106-A West Ennis Avenue,
  Ennis 75119 • 972/875-8488; *Fax: 972/875-1907*

Sixth District - Ellis, Navarro, Tarrant (28%)

Energy & Commerce

KEVIN BRADY (Cathy), R-The Woodlands
Chamber of Commerce Executive. BS-University of South Dakota.
  4-11-1955. THR-1991-97; C-1997-present.
Room 1011 Longworth HOB, Washington, DC 20515 • 202/225-4901
  Fax: 202/225-5524
200 River Pointe Dr., Suite 304, Conroe 77304 • 936/441-5700
  Fax: 936/441-5757; 1300 11th Street, Suite 400, Huntsville 77340
  936/439-9532; *Fax: 936/439-9546*

Eighth District - Grimes, Harris (2%), Houston, Leon (41%),
  Madison, Montgomery, San Jacinto, Trinity, Walker

Ways & Means-Chairman

( )Spouse

U.S. HOUSE OF REPRESENTATIVES
Bill Status: 202/225-1772 • clerk.house.gov

MICHAEL C. BURGESS, M.D. (Laura), R-Flower Mound
Physician-Obstetrics and Gynecology. BS, Biology;
  MA, Physiology-North Texas State University (UNT);
  MD-UT Medical Center in Houston; MA-Medical Management,
  UT Dallas. 12-23-1950. C-2003-present.
Room 2336 Rayburn HOB, Washington, DC 20515
  202/225-7772; *Fax: 202/225-2919*
2000 S. Stemmons Frwy., Suite 200, Lake Dallas 75065
  940/497-5031; *Fax: 940/497-5067*

Twenty-Sixth District - Dallas (1%), Denton (83%), Tarrant (8%)

Energy & Commerce, Rules

JOHN R. CARTER (Erika), R-Georgetown
State District Judge, Retired. 11-6-1941. C-2003-present.
Room 2110 Rayburn HOB, Washington, DC 20515 • 202/225-3864
1717 N. IH 35, Suite 303, Round Rock 78664 • 512/246-1600
6544B So. General Bruce Drive, Temple 76502 • 254/933-1392

Thirty-First District - Bell (89%), Williamson

Appropriations

JOAQUIN CASTRO (Anna), D-San Antonio
Attorney. BA-Stanford University; JD-Harvard Law School.
  9-16-1964. THR-2003-2013; C-2013-present.
Room 1221 Longworth HOB, Washington, DC 20515
  202/225-3236; *Fax: 202/225-1915*
727 E. Cesar Chavez Blvd., Ste. B128, San Antionio 78206
  210/348-8216; *Fax: 210/979-0737*

Twentieth District - Bexar (41%)

Foreign Affairs; Intelligence

K. MICHAEL CONAWAY (Suzanne), R-Midland
CPA. BBA-Texas A&M Commerce. 6-11-1948. C-2005-present.
Room 2430 Rayburn HOB, Washington, DC 20515 • 202/225-3605
  Fax: 202/225-1783
6 Desta Drive, Ste. 2000, Midland 79705 • 432/687-2390
  Fax: 432/687-0277

Eleventh District - Andrews, Brown, Callahan, Coke, Coleman,
  Comanche, Concho, Dawson, Eastland, Ector, Erath (54%), Glasscock,
  Hood, Irion, Kimble, Llano, Martin, Mason, McCulloch, Menard,
  Midland, Mills, Mitchell, Palo Pinto, Runnels, San Saba,
  Stephens (76%), Sterling, Tom Green

Agriculture-C; Armed Services; Intelligence

( )Spouse

U.S. HOUSE OF REPRESENTATIVES
Bill Status: 202/225-1772 • clerk.house.gov

HENRY R. CUELLAR (Imelda), D-Laredo
Attorney & Businessman. AA-Laredo CC, 1976; BSFS-Georgetown
  Univ., 1978; Masters in International Trade-Texas A&M International
  University, 1980; JD-Univ. of Texas, 1981; Ph.D.-Govt.-UT-Austin,
  1998. 9-19-1955. C-2005-present.
Room 2209 Rayburn HOB, Washington, DC 20515 • 202/225-1640
  Fax: 202/225-1641
602 E. Calton Road, Suite 2, Laredo 78041 • 956/725-0639
  Fax: 956/725-2647
615 E. Houston St., Suite 563, San Antonio 78205 • 210/271-2851
  Fax: 210/277-6671

Twenty-Eighth District - Atascosa, Bexar (9%), Hidalgo (17%),
  LaSalle (26%), McMullen, Starr, Webb, Wilson (90%), Zapata

Appropriations

JOHN CULBERSON (Belinda), R-Houston
Civil Defense Attorney. BA-Southern Methodist University;
  JD-South Texas College of Law. 8-24-1956. THR-1987-2001;
  C-2001-present.
Room 2161 Rayburn HOB, Washington, DC 20515 • 202/225-2571
  Fax: 202/225-4381
10000 Memorial Drive, #620, Houston 77024 • 713/682-8828

Seventh District - Harris (17%)

Appropriations

LLOYD DOGGETT (Libby), D-Austin
Attorney. BBA, JD-The University of Texas at Austin. 10-06-1946.
  TS-1973-85; C-1994-present.
Room 2307 Rayburn HOB, Washington, DC 20515 • 202/225-4865
300 East 8th St., Ste. 763, Austin 78701 • 512/916-5921
217 W. Travis St., San Antonio 78205 • 210/704-1080

Thirty-Fifth District - Bexar (19%), Caldwell (47%), Comal (29%),
  Guadalupe (17%), Hays (52%), Travis (21%)

Ways & Means

( )Spouse

U.S. HOUSE OF REPRESENTATIVES
Bill Status: 202/225-1772 • clerk.house.gov

R. BLAKE FARENTHOLD (Debbie), R-Corpus Christi
Computer Consultant/Radio talk show host. BS, RTF-UT Austin;
 JD-St. Mary's School of Law. 12-12-1961. C-2011-present.
Room 2331 Rayburn HOB, Washington, DC 20515 • 202/225-7742
 Fax: 202/226-1134
101 N. Shoreline Blvd., Suite 300, Corpus Christi 78401
 361/884-2222; *Fax: 361/884-2223*

Twenty-Seventh District - Aransas, Bastrop (40%), Caldwell (53%),
 Calhoun, Gonzales (69%), Jackson, Lavaca, Matagorda, Nueces,
 Refugio, San Patricio (68%), Victoria, Wharton

**Oversight and Government Reform; Judiciary;
 Transportation & Infrastructure**

BILL FLORES (Gina), R-Waco
Retired from Energy Business. BBA Accounting-Texas A&M Univ.;
 MBA- Houston Baptist University. 2-25-1954. C-2011-present.
Room 2440 Rayburn HOB, Washington, DC 20515
 202/225-6105; *Fax: 202/225-0350*
400 Austin Avenue, Suite 302, Waco 76701 • 254/732-0748
 Fax: 254/732-1755

Seventeenth District - Bastrop (1%), Brazos, Burleson, Falls,
 Freestone, Lee (29%), Leon (59%), Limestone, McLennan, Milam,
 Robertson, Travis (13%)

Energy and Commerce

LOUIE GOHMERT (Kathy), R-Tyler
Attorney. Texas A&M University; JD-Baylor Law School. 8-18-1953.
 C-2005-present.
Room 2243 Rayburn HOB, Washington, DC 20515
 202/225-3035; *Fax: 202/226-1230*
1121 ESE Loop 323, Suite 206, Tyler 75701 • 903/561-6349
 Fax: 903/561-7110

First District - Angelina, Gregg, Harrison, Nacogdoches, Panola,
 Rusk, Sabine, San Augustine, Shelby, Smith, Upshur (31%),
 Wood (38%)

Judiciary; Natural Resources

VICENTE GONZALEZ (Lorena), D-McAllen
Attorney. B.S.-Embry Riddle Aeronautical University, Corpus Christi
 Naval Air Station. JD-Texas A&M School of Law.
 9-4-1967. C-2017-present.
Room 113 Cannon HOB, Washington, DC 20515 • 202/225-2531
2864 West Trenton Road, Edinburg 78539 • 956/682-5545

Fifteenth District - Brooks, Duval, Guadalupe (83%), Hidalgo (69%),
 Jim Hogg, Karnes, Live Oak, Wilson (10%)

Financial Services

FEDERAL SECTION

( )Spouse

U.S. HOUSE OF REPRESENTATIVES
Bill Status: 202/225-1772 • clerk.house.gov

KAY GRANGER, R-Fort Worth
Businesswoman, Insurance Agent, Teacher. BS-Texas Wesleyan
 University. 1-18-1943. C-1997-present.
Room 1026 Longworth HOB, Washington, DC 20515 • 202/225-5071
 Fax: 202/225-5683
1701 River Run Road, Suite 407, Fort Worth 76107 • 817/338-0909
 Fax: 817/335-5852

Twelfth District - Parker, Tarrant (31%), Wise (39%)

Appropriations

AL GREEN, D-Houston
Attorney. JD-Texas Southern University. 9-01-1947. C-2005-present.
Room 2347 Rayburn HOB, Washington, DC 20515 • 202/225-7508
 Fax: 202/225-2947
3003 So. Loop West, Suite 460, Houston 77054 • 713/383-9234
 Fax: 713/383-9202

Ninth District - Fort Bend (25%), Harris (14%)

Financial Services

GENE GREEN (Helen), D-Houston
Businessman. BBA-University of Houston. 10-17-1947.
 THR-1973-85; TS-1985-93; C-1993-2019.
Room 2470 Rayburn HOB, Washington, DC 20515 • 202/225-1688
 Fax: 202/225-9903
256 N. Sam Houston Parkway East, Suite 29, Houston 77060
 281/999-5879; *Fax: 281/999-5716*

Twenty-Ninth District - Harris (17%)

Energy & Commerce

JEB HENSARLING (Melissa), R-Dallas
Businessman. BA-Texas A&M University, 1979; JD-University
 of Texas at Austin, 1982. 5-29-1957. C-2003-2019.
Room 2228 Rayburn HOB, Washington, DC 20515 • 202/225-3484
 Fax: 202/226-4888
6510 Abrams Road, Suite 243, Dallas 75231-7217 • 214/349-9996
 Fax: 214/349-0738

Fifth District - Anderson, Cherokee, Dallas (14%), Henderson,
 Kaufman, Van Zandt, Wood (62%)

Financial Services-Chairman

( )Spouse

U.S. HOUSE OF REPRESENTATIVES
Bill Status: 202/225-1772 • http://clerkweb.house.gov

WILL HURD, R-Helotes
Cybersecurity expert. BS Computer Science-Texas A&M Univ., 2000.
  8-19-1977. C-2015-present.
Room 317 Cannon HOB, Washington, DC 20515 • 202/225-4511
  Fax: 202/225-2237
17721 Rogers Ranch Parkway, Suite 120, San Antonio 78258
  210/921-3130; *Fax: 210/927-4903*

Twenty-Third District - Bexar (16%), Brewster, Crane, Crockett, Culberson,
  Dimmit, Edwards, El Paso (13%), Frio, Hudspeth, Jeff Davis, Kinney, La Salle
  (74%), Loving, Maverick, Medina, Pecos, Presidio, Reagan, Reeves,
  Schleicher, Sutton, Terrell, Upton, Uvalde, Val Verde, Ward, Winkler, Zavala

Oversight and Government Reform; Intelligence; Homeland Security

SHEILA JACKSON-LEE (Elwyn), D-Houston
Attorney. Political Science Degree-Yale; JD-University of Virginia
  School of Law. 1-12-1950. C-1995-present.
Room 2187 Rayburn HOB, Washington, DC 20515 • 202/225-3816
  Fax: 202/225-3317
1919 Smith Street, Suite 1180, Houston 77002 • 713/655-0050
  Fax: 713/655-1612

Eighteenth District - Harris (17%)

Budget; Homeland Security; Judiciary

EDDIE BERNICE JOHNSON, D-Dallas
Member of U.S. Congress. BS-Texas Christian University;
MPA-Southern Methodist University. 12-3-1935. THR-1972-77;
  TS-1986-93; C-1993-present.
Room 2468 Rayburn HOB, Washington, DC 20515 • 202/225-8885
  Fax: 202/226-1477
1825 Market Center Blvd., Suite 440, Dallas 75207 • 214/922-8885
  Fax: 214/922-7028

Thirtieth District - Dallas (29%)

Science, Space & Technology; Transportation & Infrastructure

SAM JOHNSON (Shirley), R-Plano
Retired Air Force (Col.). BBA-Southern Methodist University;
  MSIA-George Washington University. 10-11-1930.
  THR-1985-91; C-1991-2019.
Room 2304 Rayburn HOB, Washington, DC 20515 • 202/225-4201
1255 W. 15th Street, Suite 170, Plano 75075 • 469/304-0382
  Fax: 469/304-0392

Third District - Collin (89%)

Ways & Means

( )Spouse

U.S. HOUSE OF REPRESENTATIVES
Bill Status: 202/225-1772 • clerk.house.gov

KENNY MARCHANT (Donna), R-Coppell
Investor. BA-Southern Nazarene University; Honorary Doctorate,
  Southern Nazarene University, 1999. 2-23-1951.
  THR-1987-2005; C-2005-present.
Room 2369 Rayburn HOB, Washington, DC 20515 • 202/225-6605
  Fax: 202/225-0074
9901 E. Valley Ranch Parkway, Suite 2060, Irving 75063
  972/556-0162; *Fax: 972/409-9704*
Twenty-Fourth District - Dallas (14%), Denton (17%), Tarrant (14%)
Ethics; Ways & Means

MICHAEL MCCAUL (Linda), R-Austin
Former Federal and State Prosecutor. BS-Trinity University;
  JD-St. Mary's Univ. School of Law; JFK School of Government,
  Harvard University. 1-14-1962. C-2005-present.
Room 2001 Rayburn HOB, Washington, DC 20515 • 202/225-2401
  Fax: 202/225-5955
9009 Mountain Ridge Drive, Austin Building, Suite 230, Austin 78759
  512/473-2357; *Fax: 512/473-0514*
Tenth District - Austin, Bastrop (59%), Colorado, Fayette, Harris (6%),
  Lee (71%), Travis (24%), Waller, Washington
Homeland Security-Chairman; **Foreign Affairs**

ROBERT F. "BETO" O'ROURKE (Amy), D-El Paso
Businessman. BA-English, Columbia University, 1995.
  9-26-1972. C-2013-present.
Room 1330 Longworth HOB, Washington, DC 20515 • 202/225-4831
303 N. Oregon, Suite 210, El Paso 79901 • 915/541-1400
Fax: 915/541-1407
Sixteenth District - El Paso (87%)
Armed Services; Veterans' Affairs

( )Spouse

U.S. HOUSE OF REPRESENTATIVES
Bill Status: 202/225-1772 • clerk.house.gov

PETE OLSON (Nancy), R-Sugar Land
Attorney. BA-Rice University, 1985; JD-University of Texas
  School of Law, 1988. 12-9-1962. C-2009 to present.
Room 2133 Rayburn HOB, Washington, DC 20515 • 202/225-5951
  Fax: 202/225-5241
1650 Highway 6, Suite 150, Sugar Land 77478 • 281/494-2690
  Fax: 281/494-2649

Twenty-Second District - Brazoria (51%), Fort Bend (75%),
  Harris (2%)

Energy & Commerce

TED POE (Carol), R-Humble
Felony Court Judge. BA-Abilene Christian University;
    JD-University of Houston Law School. 9-10-1948. C-2005-2019.
Room 2132 Rayburn HOB, Washington, DC 20515 • 202/225-6565
  Fax: 202/225-5547
1801 Kingwood Dr., Suite 240, Kingwood 77339 • 281/446-0242
  Fax: 281/446-0252

Second District - Harris (17%)

Foreign Affairs; Judiciary

JOHN RATCLIFFE (Michele), R-Heath
Attorney. J.D.- Southern Methodist Law School. 10-20-1965.
  C-2015-present.
Room 325 Cannon HOB, Washington, DC 20515 • 202/225-6673
  Fax: 202/225-3332
6531 Horizon Road, Ste. A, Rockwall 75032 • 972/771-0100
  Fax: 972/771-1222

Fourth District - Bowie, Camp, Cass, Collin (5%), Delta, Fannin,
  Franklin, Grayson, Hopkins, Hunt, Lamar, Marion, Morris, Rains,
  Red River, Rockwall, Titus, Upshur (69%)

Homeland Security; Judiciary

PETE SESSIONS (Karen), R-Dallas
Member of Congress. BS-Southwestern University. 3-22-1955.
  C-1997-present.
Room 2233 Rayburn HOB, Washington, DC 20515 • 202/225-2231
  Fax: 202/225-5878
Lakeside Square, 12377 Merit Dr., Ste. 750, Dallas 75251
  972/392-0505; *Fax: 972/392-0615*

Thirty-Second District - Collin (6%), Dallas (27%)

Rules-Chairman

( )Spouse

U.S. HOUSE OF REPRESENTATIVES
Bill Status: 202/225-1772 • clerk.house.gov

LAMAR SMITH (Beth), R-San Antonio
Rancher, Attorney. BA-Yale College; JD-Southern Methodist
University. 11-19-1947. THR-1981-82; C-1987-2019.
Room 2409 Rayburn HOB, Washington, DC 20515
202/225-4236; *Fax: 202/225-8628*
1100 NE Loop 410, Suite 640, San Antonio 78209
210/821-5024; *Fax: 210/821-5947*
2211 S. IH-35, Suite 106, Austin 78741 • 512/912-7508
Fax: 512/912-7519

Twenty-First District - Bandera, Bexar (15%), Blanco, Comal
(71%), Gillespie, Hays (23%), Kendall, Kerr, Real, Travis (18%)

**Science, Space & Technology-Chairman; Homeland Security;
Judiciary**

WILLIAM M. "MAC" THORNBERRY (Sally), R-Clarendon
Rancher/Attorney. BA-Texas Tech University, JD-University of Texas.
7-15-1958. C-1995-present.
Room 2208 Rayburn HOB, Washington, DC 20515 • 202/225-3706
Fax: 202/225-3486
620 S. Taylor, Ste. 200, Amarillo 79101 • 806/371-8844
Fax: 806/371-7044

Thirteenth District - Archer, Armstrong, Baylor, Briscoe, Carson,
Childress, Clay, Collingsworth, Cooke, Cottle, Dallam, Deaf Smith,
Dickens, Donley, Floyd (41%), Foard, Gray, Hall, Hansford,
Hardeman, Hartley, Hemphill, Hutchinson, Jack, King, Knox,
Lipscomb, Montague, Moore, Motley, Ochiltree, Oldham, Potter,
Randall, Roberts, Sherman, Swisher, Wheeler, Wichita, Wilbarger,
Wise (61%)

Armed Services-Chairman

MARC VEASEY (Tonya), D-Fort Worth
Real Estate. BS-Texas Wesleyan University. 01-03-1971.
THR-2005-2013; C-2013-present.
Room 1519 Longworth HOB, Washington, DC 20515 • 202/225-9897
Fax: 202/225-9702
6707 Brentwood Stair Rd., Suite 200, Fort Worth 76112
817/920-9086; *Fax: 817/920-9324*

Thirty-Third District - Dallas (15%), Tarrant (19%)

Armed Services; Science, Space & Technology

TEXAS HOUSE OF REPRESENTATIVES

Bill Status: 202/225-1772 • clerk.house.gov

FILEMON VELA, JR. (Rose), D-Brownsville
Attorney. BA-Georgetown University, 1985; JD-University of Texas at
   Austin, 1987. 2-13-1963. C-2013-present.
Room 437 Cannon HOB, Washington, DC 20515 • 202/225-9901
   Fax: 202/225-9770
333 Ebony Avenue, Brownsville 78520 • 956/544-8352
   Fax: 956/280-5114

Thirty-Fourth District - Bee, Cameron, De Witt, Goliad,
   Gonzales (31%), Hidalgo (14%), Jim Wells, Kenedy, Kleberg,
   San Patricio (32%), Willacy

Agriculture; Homeland Security

RANDY WEBER (Brenda), R-Friendswood
Small Business Owner. Alvin Community College;
BS-University of Houston at Clear Lake. 7-2-1953. THR-2009-2013;
   C-2013-present.
Room 1708 Longworth HOB, Washington, DC 20515 • 202/225-2831
   Fax: 202/225-0271
505 Orleans Street, Ste. 103, Beaumont 77701 • 409/835-0108
   Fax: 409/835-0578

Fourteenth District - Brazoria (49%), Galveston, Jefferson

Science, Space & Technology, Transportation and Infrastructure

ROGER WILLIAMS (Patty), R-Weatherford
Automobile Dealer. Texas Christian University. 9-13-1949.
   C-2013-present.
Room 1323 Longworth HOB, Washington, DC 20515 • 202/225-9896
   Fax: 202/225-2919
1005 Congress Ave., Suite 925, Austin 78701 • 512/473-8910
   Fax: 512/473-8946

Twenty-Fifth District: Bell (11%), Bosque, Burnet, Coryell,
   Erath (46%), Hamilton, Hays (25%), Hill, Johnson, Lampasas,
   Somervell, Travis (24%)

Financial Services

( )Spouse

115th CONGRESS
TEXAS DELEGATION STANDING COMMITTEES

Bill Status: 202/225-1772 • http://clerk.house.gov

The Honorable Jodey C. Arrington
Committee on Agriculture
Committee on the Budget
Committee on Veterans' Affairs

The Honorable Brian Babin, D.D.S
Committee on Science, Space & Technology
Committee on Transportation & Infrastructure

The Honorable Joe L. Barton
Committee on Energy & Commerce

The Honorable Kevin Brady
Committee on Ways & Means-**Chair**

The Honorable Michael C. Burgess, M.D.
Committee on Energy & Commerce
Committee on Rules

The Honorable John R. Carter
Committee on Appropriations

The Honorable Joaquin Castro
Committee on Foreign Affairs
Select Committee on Intelligence

The Honorable K. Michael Conaway
Committee on Agriculture-**Chair**
Committee on Armed Services
Select Committee on Intelligence

The Honorable Henry R. Cuellar
Committee on Appropriations

The Honorable John Culberson
Committee on Appropriations

The Honorable Lloyd Doggett
Committee on Ways & Means

The Honorable R. Blake Farenthold
Committee on Oversight & Govt. Reform
Committee on Judiciary
Committee on Transportation & Infrastructure

The Honorable Bill Flores
Committee on Energy & Commerce

The Honorable Louie Gohmert
Committee on Judiciary
Committee on Natural Resources

The Honorable Vicente Gonzalez
Committee on Financial Services

The Honorable Kay Granger
Committee on Appropriations

The Honorable Al Green
Committee on Financial Services

The Honorable Gene Green
Committee on Energy & Commerce

The Honorable Jeb Hensarling
Committee on Financial Services-**Chair**

The Honorable Will Hurd
Committee on Oversight & Govt. Reform
Committee on Homeland Security

The Honorable Sheila Jackson-Lee
Committee on the Budget
Committee on Homeland Security
Committee on Judiciary

The Honorable Eddie Bernice Johnson
Committee on Transportation & Infrastructure
Committee on Science, Space & Technology

The Honorable Sam Johnson
Committee on Ways & Means

The Honorable Kenny Marchant
Committee on Ethics
Committee on Ways & Means

The Honorable Michael McCaul
Committee on Homeland Security-**Chair**
Committee on Foreign Affairs

The Honorable Robert Francis O'Rourke
Committee on Armed Services
Committee on Veterans' Affairs

The Honorable Pete Olson
Committee on Energy & Commerce

The Honorable Ted Poe
Committee on Foreign Affairs
Committee on Judiciary

The Honorable John Ratcliffe
Committee on Homeland Security
Committee on Judiciary

The Honorable Pete Sessions
Committee on Rules-**Chair**

The Honorable Lamar Smith
Committee on Science, Space &
  Technology-**Chair**
Committee on Homeland Security
Committee on Judiciary

115th CONGRESSIONAL COMMITTEES Cont.

The Honorable William M. "Mac" Thornberry
Committee on Armed Services-**Chair**

The Honorable Marc Veasey
Committee on Armed Services
Committee on Science, Space & Technology

The Honorable Filemon Vela Jr.
Committee on Agriculture
Committee on Homeland Security

The Honorable Randy Weber
Committee on Science, Space & Technology
Committee on Transportation & Infrastructure

The Honorable Roger Williams
Committee on Financial Services

CONGRESSIONAL DISTRICT MAP

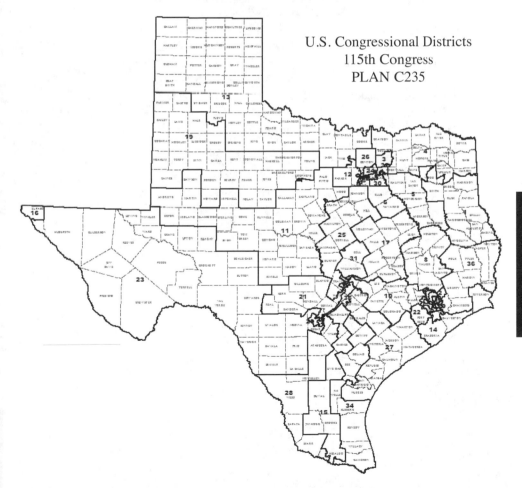

U.S. Congressional Districts
115th Congress
PLAN C235

UNITED STATES COURT OF APPEALS
· FIFTH CIRCUIT

Courthouse: 600 Camp Street, New Orleans LA 70130
Clerk: 600 S. Maestri Place, New Orleans, LA 70130 • 504/310-7700
www.ca5.uscourts.gov

The Fifth Circuit is composed of Mississippi, Louisiana, and Texas. Sessions of court shall be held in each of the states constituting the circuit at least once a year. Sessions may be scheduled at any location having adequate facilities.

CHIEF JUDGE:

The Hon. Carl E. Stewart
1994-Present

300 Fannin, Suite 5226
Shreveport, LA 71101-3074

318/676-3765

CIRCUIT JUDGES:

The Hon. Edith H. Jones
1985-Present

515 Rusk Avenue, Room 12505
Houston, TX 77002-2655

713/250-5484

The Hon. Jerry E. Smith
1987-Present

515 Rusk Avenue, Room 12621
Houston, TX 77002-2698

713/250-5101

The Hon. James L. Dennis
1995-Present

600 Camp Street, Room 219
New Orleans, LA 70130-3425

504/310-8000

The Hon. Edith Brown Clement
2001-Present

600 Camp Street, Room 200
New Orleans, LA 70130-3425

504/310-8068

The Hon. Edward C. Prado
2003-Present

755 E. Mulberry Avenue, Suite 350
San Antonio, TX 78212-3186

210/472-4060

The Hon. Priscilla R. Owen
2005-Present

903 San Jacinto Blvd., Room 434
Austin, TX 78701-2450

512/916-5167

The Hon. Jennifer Walker Elrod
2007-Present

515 Rusk Avenue, Room 12014
Houston, TX 77002-2603

713/250-7590

The Hon. Leslie H. Southwick
2007-Present

501 E. Court St., Suite 3.750
Jackson, MS 39201

601/608-4760

The Hon. Catharina Haynes
2008-Present

1100 Commerce Street, Room 1452
Dallas, TX 75242

214/753-2750

The Hon. James E. Graves, Jr.
2011-Present

501 E. Court St., Suite 3.550
Jackson, MS 39201

601/608-4775

The Hon. Stephen A. Higginson
2011-Present

600 Camp Street, Room 300
New Orleans, LA 70130-3425

504/310-8228

The Hon. Gregg J. Costa
2014-Present

515 Rusk Avenue, Room 4627
Houston, TX 77002

713/250-5030

The Hon. James Chiun-Yue Ho
2017-Present

The Hon. Don R. Willett
2011-Present

SENIOR JUDGES:

The Hon. Carolyn Dineen King 1979-Present	515 Rusk Avenue, Room 11020 Houston, TX 77002-2694	7131250-5750
The Hon. Thomas M. Reavley 1979-Present	515 Rusk Avenue, Room 11009 Houston, TX 77002-2605	713/250-5185
The Hon. Patrick E. Higginbotham 1982-Present	903 San Jacinto Blvd., Room 400 Austin, TX 78701-2450	512/916-5723
The Hon. E. Grady Jolly 1982-Present	501 E. Court Street, Suite 3.850 Jackson, MS 39201	601/608-4745
The Hon. W. Eugene Davis 1983-Present	600 Camp Street, Room 210 New Orleans, LA 70501-6883	504/310-8036
The Hon. John Malcolm, Duhe, Jr. 1988-Present		
The Hon. Rhesa H. Barksdale 1990-Present	501 E. Court Street, Suite 3.800 Jackson, MS 39201	601/608-4730
The Hon. Jacques L. Wiener, Jr. 1990-Present	600 Camp Street, Room 244 New Orleans, LA 70130-3425	504/310-8098
The Hon. Fortunato P. Benavides 1994-Present	903 San Jacinto Blvd., Room 450 Austin, TX 78701-2450	512/916-5796
Clerk of the Court	Lyle W. Cayce	504/310-7700

UNITED STATES DISTRICT COURTS

NORTHERN DISTRICT
www.txnd.uscourts.gov

EASTERN DISTRICT
www.txed.uscourts.gov

WESTERN DISTRICT
www.txwd.uscourts.gov

SOUTHERN DISTRICT
www.txs.uscourts.gov

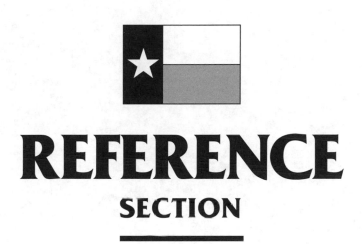

REFERENCE
SECTION

TEXAS DEMOCRATIC PARTY
STATE HEADQUARTERS STAFF
4818 E. Ben White Blvd., Suite 104, Austin 78741 • 512/478-9800 • *FAX: 512/480-2500*
www.txdemocrats.org • @txdems

Chairman	Gilberto Hinojosa	ghinojosa@txdemocrats.org
Executive Director	Crystal Kay Perkins	crystal@txdemocrats.org
Deputy Executive Director	Manny Garcia	manny@txdemocrats.org
Vice Chair	Fredericka Phillips	512/478-9800
Financial Chair	Mike Collier	512/478-9800
Secretary	Lee Forbes	512/478-9800
Treasurer	Michael Apodaca	512/478-9800
Parliamentarian	George Nassar	512/478-9800
	Rick Cofer	512/478-9800
Sergeant-At-Arms	Donna Beth McCormick	512/478-9800
Legislative Affairs Director	Glen Maxey	gmaxey@txdemocrats.org

REPUBLICAN PARTY OF TEXAS
STATE HEADQUARTERS STAFF
1108 Lavaca, Suite 500, Austin 78701 • 512/477-9821; *FAX: 512-480-0709*
www.texasgop.org • @texasgop

Chairman	Tom Mechler	512/477-9821
Executive Director	Kyle Whatley	kwhatley@texasgop.org
State Vice-Chairman	Amy Clark	vicechair@texasgop.org
Sergeant At Arms	Nelda Eppesr	512/477-9821
Treasurer	Tom Washington	512/477-9821
Parliamentarian	Butch Davis	512/477-9821
Communications Coordinator	Michael Joyce	mjoyce@texasgop.org
Finance Coordinator	Jared Campbell	jcampbell@texasgop.org
Director of Party Organization and Training	Mikenley Heller	mheller@texasgop.org

TEXAS PUBLIC EMPLOYEES ASSOCIATION
512 East 11th Street, Suite 100, Austin 78701
512/476-2691 • 1-888-FOR-TPEA • *FAX: 512/476-1338*
www.tpea.org • mail@tpea.org (staff)

OFFICERS:

Gilbert Jordan	President, El Paso
Stephanie DeWitt	President-elect, San Angelo
Wanda Carter-Dyer	Vice-President, Victoria
Richard Babcock	Secretary, Angleton
Jim Zukowski	Treasurer, Austin

DIRECTORS:

Ben Coker	Wichita Falls
Jose Gaytan	Corpus Christi
Kysha Holland	Fort Worth
Julia Johnson	Austin
Jim McDonnell	Marble Falls
Kelly Medders	Mount Vernon
Alan Moreau	New Caney
Shirley Reynolds	Lufkin
Russell Smith	Lubbock

STAFF:

Gary W. Anderson	Executive Director	512/476-2691
	ganderson@tpea.org	
Charlotte Wilsan	Director of Financial Affairs	512/476-2691
	cwilsan@tpea.org	
Sarah Smock	Director of Marketing and Commmunications	512/476-2691
	ssmock@tpea.org	
Sonta Henderson	State Agency Liaison	512/476-2691
	shenderson@tpea.org	
Jennifer Paz	Administrative Assistant	512/476-2691
	membership@tpea.org	

BASIC STEPS IN THE LEGISLATIVE PROCESS

This diagram displays the sequential flow of a bill from the time it is introduced in the House of Representatives to final passage and transmittal to the Governor. A bill introduced in the Senate would follow the same procedure in reverse.

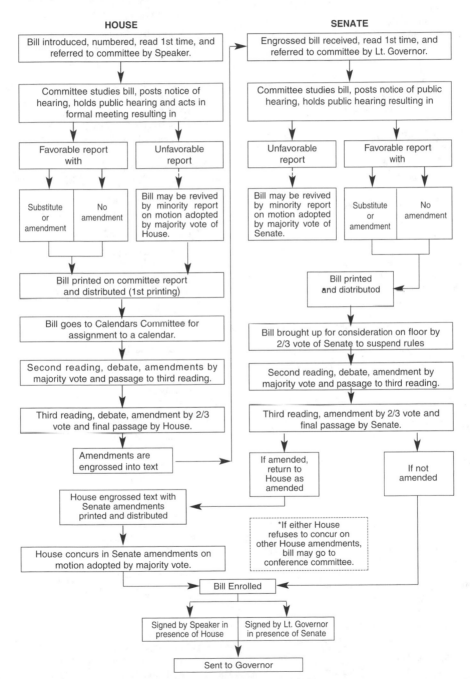

HOUSE

Bill introduced, numbered, read 1st time, and referred to committee by Speaker.

Committee studies bill, posts notice of hearing, holds public hearing and acts in formal meeting resulting in

Favorable report with

Unfavorable report

Substitute or amendment

No amendment

Bill may be revived by minority report on motion adopted by majority vote of House.

Bill printed on committee report and distributed (1st printing)

Bill goes to Calendars Committee for assignment to a calendar.

Second reading, debate, amendments by majority vote and passage to third reading.

Third reading, debate, amendment by 2/3 vote and final passage by House.

Amendments are engrossed into text

House engrossed text with Senate amendments printed and distributed

House concurs in Senate amendments on motion adopted by majority vote.

SENATE

Engrossed bill received, read 1st time, and referred to committee by Lt. Governor.

Committee studies bill, posts notice of public hearing, holds public hearing resulting in

Unfavorable report

Favorable report with

Bill may be revived by minority report on motion adopted by majority vote of Senate.

Substitute or amendment

No amendment

Bill printed and distributed

Bill brought up for consideration on floor by 2/3 vote of Senate to suspend rules

Second reading, debate, amendment by majority vote and passage to third reading.

Third reading, amendment by 2/3 vote and final passage by Senate.

If amended, return to House as amended

If not amended

*If either House refuses to concur on other House amendments, bill may go to conference committee.

Bill Enrolled

Signed by Speaker in presence of House

Signed by Lt. Governor in presence of Senate

Sent to Governor

ADDRESSING PROCEDURES

NATIONAL

President:

The Honorable (full name)
President of the United States
The White House
1600 Pennsylvania Avenue, NW
Washington, D.C. 20500

Dear Mr. President:
Speaking: Mr. President
          President (last name)

Vice President:

The Honorable (full name)
Vice President of the United States
Old Executive Office Building
17th & Pennsylvania Avenue
Washington, D.C. 20501

Dear Mr. Vice President:
Speaking: Mr. Vice President
          Vice President (last name)
Closing: Very respectfully yours,

Cabinet Member:

The Honorable (full name)
Secretary of (cabinet post)
Washington, D.C. 20520

Dear Mr./Madam Secretary:
Speaking: Mr./Madam Secretary
          Secretary (last name)

Attorney General:

The Honorable (full name)
Attorney General

Dear Attorney General (lastname):
Speaking: General (lastname)

U.S. Senator:

The Honorable (full name)
United States Senate
Washington, D.C. 20510

Dear Senator (last name):
Speaking: Senator (last name)

Speaker of the House of Representatives:

The Honorable (full name)
Speaker of the House
U.S. House of Representatives
Washington, D.C. 20515

Dear Mr. Speaker:
Speaking: Mr./Madam Speaker

U.S. Representative:

The Honorable (full name)
U. S. House of Representatives
Washington, D.C. 20515

Dear Mr./Mrs. (last name):
Speaking: Representative (last name)
          Mr./Ms. (last name)

STATE OFFICIALS

Governor:

The Honorable (full name)
Governor of Texas
State Capitol
P.O. Box 12428
Austin, TX 78711

Dear Governor (last name):
Speaking: Governor (last name)

Lieutenant Governor:

The Honorable (full name)
Lt. Governor of Texas
P.O. Box 12068
Austin, TX 78711-2068

Dear Governor (last name):
Speaking: Governor (last name)

Speaker of the House:

The Honorable (full name)
Texas House of Representatives
P.O. Box 2910
Austin, TX 78768-2910

Dear Mr./Ms. (last name):
Speaking: Mr./Madam Speaker

State Senator:

The Honorable (full name)
Texas Senate
P.O. Box 12068
Austin, TX 78711-2068

Dear Senator (last name):
Speaking: Senator (last name)

State Representative:

The Honorable (full name)
Texas House of Representatives
P.O. Box 2910
Austin, TX 78768-2910

Dear Mr./Ms. (last name):
Speaking: Representative (last name)
          Mr./Ms. (last name)

CITY AND COUNTY OFFICIALS

Mayor:
The Honorable (full name)
Mayor
City of (city)
City Hall
Address, if known
City, State and zip code

Dear Mayor (last name):
Speaking: Mayor (last name)

City Council:
The Honorable (full name)
Council Member
City Council
City of (city)
City Hall (and address, if known)
City, State and zip code

Dear Councilman/Councilwoman (last name):
Speaking: Councilman/Councilwoman (last name)

County Judge:
The Honorable (full name)
County Judge
County Courthouse
Address, if known
City, State and zip code

Dear Judge (last name):
Speaking: Judge (last name)

County Commissioner
The Honorable (full name)
County Commissioner
Precinct Number
County Courthouse (and address, if known)
City, State and zip code

Dear Commissioner (last name):
Speaking: Commissioner (last name)

Note: The correct closing for all the above letters is: Sincerely yours,

THE LEGISLATURE OF THE STATE OF TEXAS

In Texas, all legislative power is vested by the state's Constitution in a bicameral body styled The Legislature of the State of Texas. The Legislature is required by the Constitution to meet every two years for a regular session that may not exceed 140 days. By statute, (Article 5422), the Legislature convenes in regular session on the second Tuesday of each odd-numbered year. The Constitution also establishes the general order of business for the regular session; however, the Legislature is allowed, by affirmative vote of four-fifths of the membership of each house, to establish its own order of business. Special legislative sessions (30 day limit) may only be called by the Governor and may only consider matters submitted by him.

Both the Senate and the House of Representatives operate their day-to-day business through committee systems. The rules of each house govern the organization and membership of committees. Both houses are required to have a quorum of two-thirds of its membership present to conduct business. However, each house may, with less than a quorum, compel absent members to attend. Each house is also required to publish a journal of its proceedings and votes.

SENATE

The Texas Senate is composed of thirty-one members, each elected for a four-year term. One-half of the Senate is elected every two years. A member of the Senate must be a citizen of the United States, a qualified elector of the state, and have attained the age of twenty-six. He must have been a resident of Texas for five years immediately preceding his election, and the last year thereof a resident of the district from which he was chosen.

Except for the Lieutenant Governor who is designated by the Constitution as President of the Senate, the Senate elects its own officers, creates and enforces its own rules, and judges the qualifications and election of its own members.

The Senate is required to advise and consent on virtually all of the Governor's appointments to state commissions, boards, and offices. It is only during such nomination proceedings that the Senate is allowed to conduct a closed or executive session. All other business of the Legislature must be conducted in open session. The Senate also sits as a court of impeachment to try persons impeached by the House of Representatives; two-thirds vote of the Senators present are required for conviction.

The Lieutenant Governor presides over the Senate and makes Committee assignments. He is not a member of the Senate and votes only in case of a tie.

HOUSE OF REPRESENTATIVES

The House of Representatives is composed of 150 members, each elected for a two-year term. A member of the House must be a citizen of the United States, a qualified elector of the state, and have attained the age of twenty-one. He must have been a resident of the state for two years immediately preceding election, the last year thereof a resident of the district from which he was chosen.

The House of Representatives elects its own presiding officer, the Speaker of the House, and all other officers. Like the Senate, the House creates and enforces its own rules and judges the qualifications and elections of its members. The House has maintained traditionally a larger number of standing committees than the Senate due to the larger number of members involved.

All revenue bills considered by the Legislature must originate in the House of Representatives. Although the Senate may not consider revenue measures until they have been passed on the by House, the Senate may accept, amend, or reject in total such measures as it sees fit. Also, the House alone can bring impeachment charges which must be tried by the Senate.

The Speaker presides over the House and makes Committee assignments. He is a member of the House and may vote at any time.

FORMS OF LEGISLATION

There are two major classes of measures considered by the legislature resolutions and bills. Bills are introduced and may be passed. Resolutions are proposed and adopted.

While bills comprise by far the greater portion of the legislative work load, resolutions can sometimes be of equal or greater importance. The three types of resolutions are joint resolutions, concurrent resolutions and simple resolutions.

Joint Resolutions—These measures are reserved for matters of great importance to the legislature or the state. They are used primarily for proposing amendments to the state constitution. Other uses are: to memorialize Congress, to ratify amendments to the United States Constitution, to authorize the expenditure of legislative funds and to form joint legislative committees. They must be passed by both houses. If it is an amendment to the state constitution, it requires a two-thirds vote of each house and must be approved by the voters before it becomes law.

Concurrent Resolutions—This type of resolution is used for matters of concurrent interest to the two houses: fixing the time of final adjournment of a session, requesting information from state agencies or action by Congress, adopting or changing joint rules and for calling joint sessions of the legislature. Concurrent resolutions must be adopted by both houses and enrolled. They are then sent to committee. Other than in matters of adjournment they are submitted to the Governor.

Simple Resolutions—House simple or Senate resolutions are measures comprising independent action of the house of origin and pertain to matters involving that house only. They are used for such purposes as adoption of rules, appointment of officers and employees, requesting opinions from the attorney general and house organization, including assignment of desks to members at the beginning of a session. These measures may be referred to committee or acted on without such consideration. Adoption requires a simple majority vote.

Bills and resolutions are numbered consecutively in separate series.

S.B. 1 means Senate Bill 1
H.B. 1 means House Bill 1
S.J.R. 1 means Senate Joint Resolution 1
H.J.R. 1 means House Joint Resolution 1
S.C.R. 1 means Senate Concurrent Resolution 1
H.C.R. 1 means House Concurrent Resolution 1
S.R. 1 means Senate Resolution 1
H.S.R. 1 means House Simple Resolution 1

REFERENCES

STATE OF TEXAS FACTS

Bird	Mockingbird, adopted in 1927
Fish	Guadalupe Bass, adopted in 1989
Flag	Lone Star Flag, adopted 1839
Flower	Bluebonnet, adopted in 1901
Fruit	Red Grapefruit, adopted in 1993
Insect	Monarch Butterfly, adopted in 1995
Nickname	The Lone Star State
Mammal	Texas Longhorn
Motto	Friendship, adopted in 1930
Tree	Pecan, adopted in 1919
Song	Texas, Our Texas, adopted in 1929
	written by William J. Marsh
Gem	Blue Topaz
Dish	Chili, adopted in 1919
Entered the Union, 28th State	December 29, 1845
Land Area	261,797
Rank in Nation	2nd
Population	27,725,192
	(2016 projected population)
Rank in Nation	2nd
Density per square mile	106 (approx.)
Number of U.S. Senators	2
Number of Representatives in Congress	36
Number of State Senators	31
Number of State Representatives	150
Capital City	Austin
Population (2016 census est.)	949,587
Ranked in State	4th
Largest City	Houston
Population (2016 census est.)	2,157,096
Incorporated Cities in Texas	1,215

TOP TEN TEXAS CITIES BY POPULATION

Houston 2,157,096	Austin 949,587	Arlington 373,050
San Antonio 1,371,208	Fort Worth 764,105	Corpus Christi . . .312,574
Dallas 1,223,804	El Paso 671,563	Plano 270,227
		Laredo 248,187

REQUIREMENTS FOR VOTING IN TEXAS

REQUIRED IDENTIFICATION FOR VOTING IN PERSON

List of the acceptable forms of photo ID:

Texas driver license issued by the Texas Department of Public Safety (DPS)
Texas Election Identification Certificate issued by DPS
Texas personal identification card issued by DPS
Texas license to carry a handgun issued by DPS
United States military identification card containing the person's photograph
United States citizenship certificate containing the person's photograph
United States passport

With the exception of the U.S. citizenship certificate, the identification must be current or have expired no more than 4 years before being presented for voter qualification at the polling place.

Election Identification Certificates are available from DPS driver license offices during regular business hours.

Supporting forms of ID that can be presented if the voter does not possess one of the forms of acceptable photo ID and cannot obtain one due to a reasonable impediment:

Valid voter registration certificate
Certified birth certificate (must be an original)
Copy of or original current utility bill
Copy of or original bank statement
Copy of or original government check
Copy of or original paycheck
Copy of or original government document with your name and an address
(original required if it contains a photograph)

After presenting a supporting form of ID, the voter must execute a Reasonable Impediment Declaration.

REFERENCES

QUALIFICATIONS FOR OFFICE

	U.S. Citizen	Texas Resident	District Resident	Registered to Vote Area Elected From Age	Practicing Lawyer or Judge	Source	Term of Office
United States Senator	9 yrs	Yes[2]	not req'd	30	–	I§3	6 yrs.
United States Representative	7 yrs	Yes[2]	not req'd	25	–	I§2	2 yrs.
Governor	Yes	5 yrs.[3]	–	30	–	IV§4	4 yrs.
Lieutenant Governor	Yes	5 yrs.[3]	–	30	–	IV§16	4 yrs.
Attorney General	Yes	12 mo.[4]	–	18	not req'd	IV§22	4 yrs.
Comptroller of Public Accounts	Yes	12 mo.[4]	–	–	18	–	IV§23	4 yrs.
Commissioner of General Land Office	Yes	12 mo.[4]	–	–	18	–	IV§23	4 yrs.
Commissioner of Agriculture	Yes	12 mo.[4]	–	–	18	–	IV§23	4 yrs.
Railroad Commissioner	Yes	Yes[2]	–	25	no RR intrsts	art. 6447	6 yrs.
Justice, Supreme Court	Yes	Yes[2]	–	–	35	10 yrs[3]	V§2	6 yrs.
Judge, Court of Criminal Appeals	Yes	Yes[2]	–	–	35	10 yrs[3]	V§4	6 yrs.
Member, State Board of Education	Yes	1 yr.[3]	1 yr.[3]	26	–	§7.103	4 yrs.
State Senator	Yes	5 yrs.[3]	1 yr.[3]	No–	26[3]	–	III§6	4 yrs.
State Representative	Yes	2 yrs.[3]	1 yr.[3]	No–	21[3]	–	III§7	2 yrs.
Chief Justice, Court of Appeals	Yes	Yes[2]	–	–	35	10 yrs.[3]	V§6	6 yrs.
Justice, Court of Appeals	Yes	Yes[2]	–	–	35	10 yrs.[3]	V§6	6 yrs.
District Judge	Yes	2 yrs.[3]	2 yrs.[3]	–	18	4 yrs.[3]	V§7	4 yrs.
Criminal District Judge	Yes	2 yrs.[3]	2 yrs.[3]	–	18	4 yrs.[3]	V§7	4 yrs.
Family District Judge	Yes	2 yrs.[3]	2 yrs.[3]	–	18	4 yrs.[3]	V§7	4 yrs.
Criminal District Attorney	Yes	Yes[5]	Yes[5]	–	18	Yes[5]	V§30	4 yrs.

	U.S. Citizen	Texas Resident	District Resident	Registered to Vote in Texas	Age	Practicing Lawyer or Judge	Source	Term of Office
County Judge	Yes	12 mo.[4]	6 mo.[4]	–	18	not req'd	V§15	4 yrs.
Judge, County Criminal Court	Yes	Yes[5]	Yes[5]	–	18	Yes[5]	V§30	4 yrs.
Judge, County Probate Court	Yes	Yes[5]	Yes[5]	–	18	Yes[5]	V§30	4 yrs.
County Atorney	Yes	12 mo.[4]	6 mo.[4]		18	Yes[5]	V§21/41.001	4 yrs.
Sheriff[6]	Yes	12 mo.[4]	6 mo.[4]		18		V§23	4 yrs.
District Clerk	Yes	12 mo.[4]	6 mo.[4]	–	18	–	V§9	4 yrs.
District & County Clerk	Yes	12 mo.[4]	6 mo.[4]	–	18	–	V§20	4 yrs.
County Clerk	Yes	12 mo.[4]	6 mo.[4]	–	18	–	V§20	4 yrs.
County Treasurer	Yes	12 mo.[4]	6 mo.[4]	–	18	–	XVI§44	4 yrs.
County Surveyor	Yes	12 mo.[4]	6 mo.[4]	–	18	–	XVI§44	4 yrs.
Inspector of Hides & Animals	Yes	12 mo.[4]	6 mo.[4]	–	18	–	XVI§64	4 yrs.
County Commissioner	Yes	12 mo.[4]	6 mo.[4]	–	18	–	V§18	4 yrs.
Constable[6]	Yes	12 mo.[4]	6 mo.[4]	–	18	–	V§18	4 yrs.
Justice of the Peace	Yes	12 mo.[4]	6 mo.[4]	–	18	–	V§18	4 yrs.
Public Weigher	Yes	12 mo.[4]	6 mo.[4]	–	18	–	XVI§65	4 yrs.

[1] *Citations Refer to article and section number of the U.S. Constitution For U.S. Sen. And U.S. Rep.; section number of the Texas Election Code for Member, State Board of Education; section number of the civil statutes for Railroad Commissioner; and article and section number of the Tex. Const. For all others. Also see §141.001 of the Texas Election Code.*

[2] *No duration specified.*

[3] *Before date of general election.*

[4] *Before January 2, 2004 if candidate for Democratic or Republican Party Nomination. Before March 13, 2004 if other party nominee for precinct, county, or single-county district office. Before March 20, 2004 if other party nominee for multi-county district office. Before June 12, 2004 if other party nominee for statewide office. Before May 13, 2004 if independent candidate.[5]*

[5] *Statutory qualifications may vary, contact your local party or the Secretary of State.*

[6] *Additional qualifications for constable/sheriff: must have a high school diploma or high school equivalency degree and be eligible to be licensed under sections 1701.309, 1701.312 and 1701.502 of the tex. Occupation Code.*

OFFICES UP FOR ELECTION IN 2018

Offices	Term
U.S. Senator	4 yr. term
All 36 United States Representatives	2 yr. term
Governor	4 yr. term
Lieutenant Governor	4 yr. term
Attorney General	4 yr. term
Comptroller of Public Accounts	4 yr. term
Commissioner of General Land Office	4 yr. term
Commissioner of Agriculture	4 yr. term
Railroad Commissioners	6 yr. term

> Christi Craddick

3 Members of the Supreme Court — 6 yr. term

> Jimmy Blacklock, Place 2
>
> John Devine, Place 4
>
> Jeff Brown, Place 6

3 Members of the Court of Criminal Appeals — 6 yr. term

> Sharon Keller, Presiding Judge, Place 1
>
> Barbara Parker Hervey, Place 7
>
> Elsa Alcala, Place 8

7 Members, State Board of Education — 4 yr. term

> Ruben Cortez Jr., District 2
>
> Marisa Perez, District 3
>
> Lawrence A. Allen Jr., District 4
>
> David Bradley, District 7
>
> Patricia "Pat" Hardy, District 11
>
> Geraldine "Tincy" Miller, District 12
>
> Erika Beltran, District 13

15 State Senators — 4 yr. term

> Bob Hall, District 2
>
> Robert Nichols, District 3
>
> Charles Schwertner, District 5
>
> Paul Bettencourt, District 7
>
> Van Taylor, District 8
>
> Kelly Hancock, District 9
>
> Konni Burton, District 10
>
> Kirk Watson, District 14

John Whitmire, District 15

Don Huffines, District 16

Joan Huffman, District 17

Royce West, District 23

Donna Campbell, District 25

Craig Estes, District 30

Kel Seliger, District 31

All 150 State Representatives   2 yr. term

5 Chief Justice of Court of Appeals   6 yr. term

Bonnie Sudderth, 2nd Court of Appeals

Carolyn Wright, 5th Court of Appeals

Tom Gray, 10th Court of Appeals

Jim R. Wright, 11th Court of Appeals

Roy Valdez, 13th Court of Appeals

Various Court of Appeals Justices	6 yr. term
Various District Judges, Criminal District Judges	4 yr. term
Various Family District Judges	4 yr. term
District Attorneys	4 yr. term
Criminal District Attorney	4 yr. term
County Judge	
County Court at Law	4 yr. term
Judge County Court at Law	4 yr. term
Judge, County Criminal Ct.	4 yr. term
Judge, County Probate Ct.	4 yr. term
District Clerk	4 yr. term
District and County Clerk	4 yr. term
County Clerk	4 yr. term
County Treasurer	4 yr. term
County Surveyor	4 yr. term
County Commissioners, Precincts 2 & 4	4 yr. term
Justices of the Peace	4 yr. term
Constable	4 yr. term

ADVERTISERS' INDEX

INDEX

REFERENCES

REFERENCES

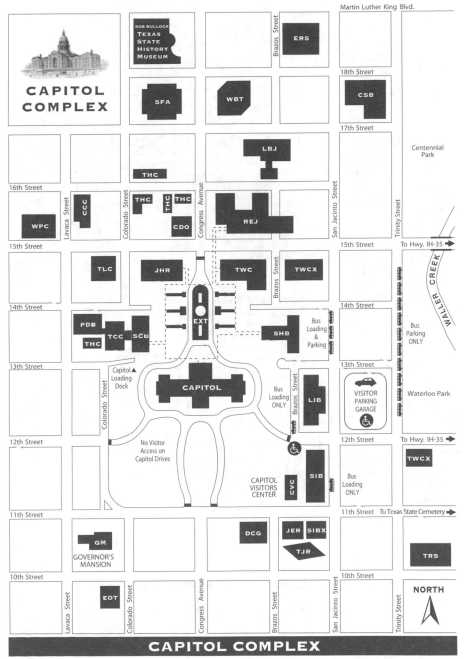

CAPITOL COMPLEX

REFERENCES

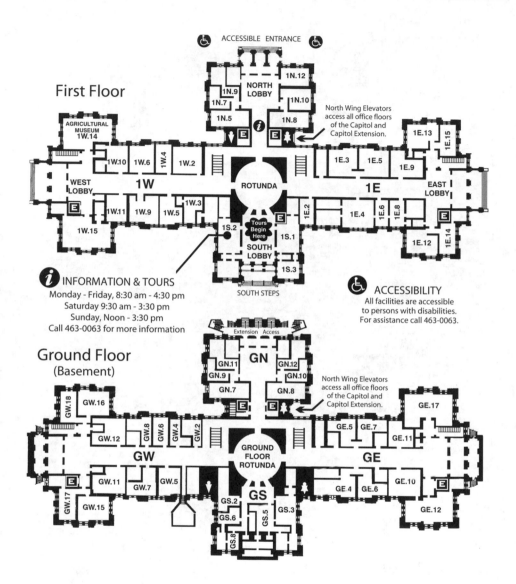

ACCESSIBLE ENTRANCE

First Floor

North Wing Elevators access all office floors of the Capitol and Capitol Extension.

INFORMATION & TOURS
Monday - Friday, 8:30 am - 4:30 pm
Saturday 9:30 am - 3:30 pm
Sunday, Noon - 3:30 pm
Call 463-0063 for more information

ACCESSIBILITY
All facilities are accessible to persons with disabilities. For assistance call 463-0063.

Ground Floor
(Basement)

North Wing Elevators access all office floors of the Capitol and Capitol Extension.

CAPITOL BUILDING GUIDE
FLOORS 1 & GROUND

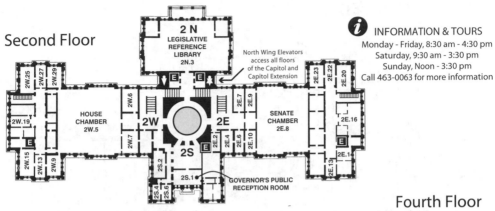

Second Floor

2 N
LEGISLATIVE
REFERENCE
LIBRARY
2N.3

North Wing Elevators
access all floors
of the Capitol and
Capitol Extension

HOUSE
CHAMBER
2W.5

2W

2E

SENATE
CHAMBER
2E.8

2S

GOVERNOR'S PUBLIC
RECEPTION ROOM

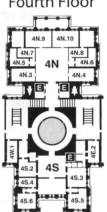

INFORMATION & TOURS
Monday - Friday, 8:30 am - 4:30 pm
Saturday, 9:30 am - 3:30 pm
Sunday, Noon - 3:30 pm
Call 463-0063 for more information

Capitol Extension Access: Take the North Wing elevators to Floor E1 or E2 of the underground Capitol Extension. Please visit the Capitol Giftshop on Floor E1 for Texas and Capitol mementos and books, as well as mints, medicines, and other sundries. Also located on level E1 are a public cafeteria, an Automatic Teller Machine (ATM) and vending machines.

Fourth Floor

4N

4S

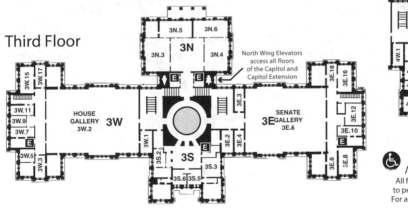

Third Floor

3N.5   3N.6

3N

3N.3   3N.4

North Wing Elevators
access all floors
of the Capitol and
Capitol Extension

HOUSE
GALLERY
3W.2

3W

SENATE
GALLERY
3E.6

3E

3S

ACCESSIBILITY
All facilities are accessible
to persons with disabilities.
For assistance call 463-0063.

CAPITOL BUILDING GUIDE
FLOORS 2, 3, & 4

Extension
First Floor (E1)

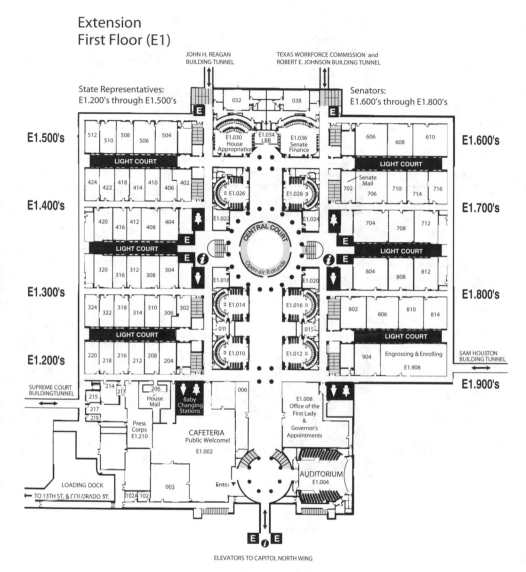

Capitol Extension Guide
Floor E1

Extension
Second Floor (E2)

State Representatives Offices
E2.200 through E2.900's

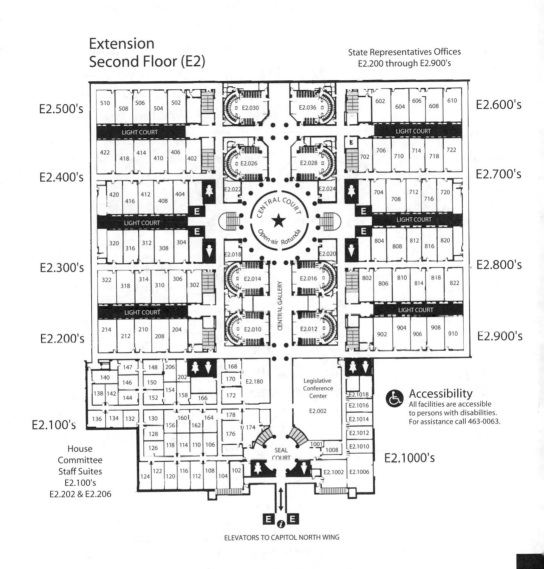

E2.500's
E2.400's
E2.300's
E2.200's
E2.100's

E2.600's
E2.700's
E2.800's
E2.900's
E2.1000's

House
Committee
Staff Suites
E2.100's
E2.202 & E2.206

Accessibility
All facilities are accessible
to persons with disabilities.
For assistance call 463-0063.

ELEVATORS TO CAPITOL NORTH WING

Capitol Extension Guide
Floor E2

2018 LEGAL HOLIDAYS

Monday	January 1, 2018	New Year's Day*
Monday	January 15, 2018	Martin Luther King, Jr. Day*
Friday	January 19, 2018	Confederate Heroes' Day†
Monday	February 19, 2018	President's Day*
Friday	March 2, 2018	Texas Independence Day†
Friday	March 30, 2018	Good Friday**
Saturday	March 31, 2018	Cesar Chavez Day**
Saturday	April 21, 2018	San Jacinto Day†
Monday	May 28, 2018	Memorial Day*
Tuesday	June 19, 2018	Emancipation Day†
Wednesday	July 4, 2018	Independence Day*
Monday	August 27, 2018	LBJ's Birthday†
Monday	September 3, 2018	Labor Day*
Monday	September 10, 2018	Rosh Hashanah**
Tuesday	September 11, 2018	Rosh Hashanah**
Tuesday	September 18, 2018	Yom Kippur
Sunday	November 11, 2018	Veterans' Day*
Thursday	November 22, 2018	Thanksgiving Day*
Friday	November 23, 2018	Day After Thanksgiving*
Monday	December 24, 2018	Christmas Eve*
Tuesday	December 25, 2018	Christmas Day*

Weekend Holidays: Offices will not be closed on another day when designated holidays fall on a Saturday or Sunday. Such holidays will not be observed.

† **Skeleton Crew Holidays:** Office must have enough employees to conduct business.

* **National Holidays**: All offices closed.

** **Optional Holidays:** Employee is entitled to observe Rosh Hashanah, Yom Kippur, Good Friday, and Cesar Chavez Day in lieu of any state holiday where a skeleton crew is required.